A Textbook of

HISTOLOGY

by

ALEXANDER A. MAXIMOW

LATE PROFESSOR OF ANATOMY, UNIVERSITY OF CHICAGO

and

WILLIAM BLOOM

PROFESSOR OF ANATOMY, UNIVERSITY OF CHICAGO

SEVENTH EDITION

With 1082 Illustrations, 265 in Color, on 631 Figures

W. B. Saunders Company

Philadelphia and London   1957

Preface to the Seventh Edition

IN THE nearly 300 years that the microscope has been used for the study of biological materials, no period has seen the knowledge of minute structure advance so greatly as the last decade. Vistas of the submicroscopic world have come into view and an exciting chapter is beginning with the fusion of some aspects of biochemistry and biophysics with histology. Some of the old histological problems have been solved and many new ones have arisen as the power of analytical methods has increased enormously through development of new techniques, and as new points of view and improved insight have vied with advances in instrumentation. It is thus necessary to present medical students with an orienting text which not only describes the structure of the human body as seen with the optical microscope but which also considers relevant submicroscopic analysis and discusses function. As in previous revisions, I have sought to balance inclusion of new material with deletion of old. I have added many electron micrographs with the realization that some of them may have to be replaced in a few years because of rapid advances in knowledge.

For this revision I have been helped by a number of people. Professor W. L. Doyle rewrote and enlarged Chapter 1 with particular emphasis on submicroscopic structure and Professor R. E. Zirkle revised the description of mitosis. Professor E. A. Boyden condensed his discussion of the biliary passages and Professor E. M. K. Geiling helped with new data on some of the hormones. Professor H. Kaplan wrote a discussion of leukemia in mice for the chapter on the thymus. Professor F. C. McLean, with the aid of Drs. A. Budy and J. Jowsey, made some of the changes in the chapter on bone. The description of the ear has benefited by the criticism of Professor H. Perlman. The revision of the chapter on nervous tissue is, in large part, due to Professor Ruth Rhines. The chapter on the skin has been revised by Professors R. Rothman and R. Stoughton. Professor I. Schour reviewed the chapter on teeth and Professor W. H. Taliaferro helped with some of the cellular aspects of immunity. My wife revised the chapter on cartilage and helped liberally with changes in many parts of the book. I am indebted to Professor Berta Scharrer and Drs. J. Gross and D. Spiro for many helpful suggestions. Three new figures in color and twelve in black and white were drawn by Mrs. E. Bohlman Patterson.

It is a pleasure to acknowledge once more the help of those who contributed importantly to previous editions. Above all, I am indebted to Professor C. Judson Herrick, for I would not have tried to complete Professor Maximow's unfinished book if he had not written the chapters on the nervous tissue, basing them in part on Maximow's writings. I shall always be thankful to the late Professor R. R. Bensley for the help I received from him. Professor G. W. Bartelmez revised the chapter on the female generative system for several editions and contributed a description of the early stages of human placentation. The late Professor S. Polyak rewrote the chapters on the nervous tissue and sense organs for the third and fourth editions. Professor C. G. Loosli revised the chapter on the lung for several editions. For the last edition Professor I. Gersh enlarged the chapters on glands and the endocrine organs. Professor P. De Bruyn revised and condensed the discussion of the connective and blood forming tissues and organs. Many helpful suggestions were made by Professors S. W. Becker, M. Block, E. R. Clark, D. Bodian, R. W. Gerard, J. Markee, R. G. Murray and J. Walter Wilson for several of the earlier editions.

Throughout its existence the book has been improved by the help of the many histologists who have generously offered illustrations and tendered corrections and constructive criticism.

WILLIAM BLOOM

Chicago, Illinois
April, 1957

Contents

CHAPTER 1

Protoplasm and the Cell

HISTOLOGY is concerned with the constitution and organization of the tissues of the organism. Two aspects of the subject are distinguished; *special histology* deals with the arrangement and special adaptations of tissues in the various organs whereas *general histology* deals with the components of the individual tissues. *Tissues* are composed of cells of given degrees of differentiation, i.e., specialization, and characteristic intercellular substances. Although in some tissues the intercellular substances may comprise the major portion of the volume, the tissues are primarily classified according to the predominating types of cells which they contain. The *cell* is the biological unit of the living substance which has been termed *protoplasm*. Within the cell, it is customary to distinguish between protoplasm of the *nucleus* and the surrounding *cytoplasm*.

Microscopy. In the higher animals most cells have dimensions of a few hundredths of a millimeter. Accordingly most of the basic information comprising histology has been obtained by direct observation of living or preserved specimens with a microscope using visible light.

Although such light microscopes have been used for about 300 years for the study of minute anatomy, modern histology began with an outburst of investigation in the third and fourth decades of the nineteenth century and received its greatest impetus from Schwann's conclusion that nucleated cells are the basis of the formation of all animals and plants. His idea was received with great en-

thusiasm because, as Henle (1841) said, it gave the key to a multitude of known facts and the direction for new, planned investigations.

The succeeding century of intensive histological investigation may be divided into several fairly distinct periods, each with different immediate aims and philosophies. But the entire history has been characterized by the desire for further knowledge of the origin and function of the parts of animals and plants as evidenced by minute structure.

As most tissues and organs are too thick to be examined directly with the microscope, the histologists of a hundred years ago examined thin membranes and scrapings and teasings of thick organs. These teasings disrupted topographic relations, and the cells soon died. With their imperfect microscopes and with the aid of only a few reagents, such as acetic acid, it seems remarkable that they saw as much as they did.

The study of living and surviving cells was replaced to a large extent during the next fifty years by the investigation of details made visible in dead cells through the introduction of methods for the preservation of tissues, cutting them in thin slices and staining them with a variety of dyes. Such studies were made possible by great improvements in microscopes and microtomes and a host of "fixing" and staining methods. During this period there was accumulated a great mass of descriptive embryological, histological and histopathological data. Basic processes in the life history of the unicellular and multicellular organisms were recognized, such as their modes of reproduction, and the occurrence of growth, multiplication, differentiation and death of cells.

About the turn of the century a new period began, characterized by attempts at interpretation of structure in terms of function and by renewed interest in correlating living and dead appearances. As one of the results, a number of investigators began to look on all sectioned material as artefact and to accept as true only what could be seen directly in living cells. This view was rapidly modified as the more constant components of living cells were distinguished from the artefacts by means of refined techniques. Of course, constancy of occurrence or consistency in interpretation might mean merely that anatomists have accepted a specified group of procedures and it does not necessarily follow that the images obtained are valid representations in all respects. Today, midway in the twentieth century, the availability and use of increasing numbers of electron microscopes have rather suddenly shifted emphasis to protoplasmic structures at dimensions almost 100 diameters smaller than were observable during the preceding 300 years.

With the aid of an optical microscope one can visually distinguish objects as individual particles if they are not less than 0.2 micron

apart. The resolving power of a microscope is dependent on the wavelength of the light and the light-gathering capacity (numerical aperture) of the objective. The best oil immersion objects have a numerical aperture of 1.4, but most histological work is done with lenses of numerical aperture 1.0 or less. By using shorter wavelengths it is possible to increase the resolving power of the microscope to 0.1 micron with ultraviolet light. Particles smaller than the limit of resolution can be seen by the light reflected from them in dark-field illumination of the ultramicroscope, but it is not possible to determine their dimensions or shape precisely. From Figure 1–1 it can be seen that it should be possible to distinguish individual molecules, provided one uses wavelengths which are sufficiently short and if lenses are available with sufficiently high numerical apertures. Electron beams have much shorter wavelengths than light and magnetic lenses have been developed so that the practical limit of resolution currently achievable is about 20 angstrom units (A). With this resolving power the morphology of viruses and the structure of some protein molecules can be viewed directly on the fluorescent screen of the electron microscope or photographed. This extension of limits of microscopic resolution has revived the necessity for reexamining the effects of our investigative procedures

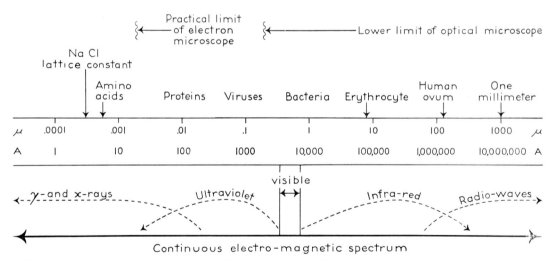

Fig. 1–1. Comparison of dimensions of molecules and cells with wavelengths of the electromagnetic spectrum. Logarithmic scale. The different names given to overlapping regions of the spectrum do not represent different kinds of radiation. These names were determined historically by the range of sensitivity of the human eye and the varying approaches of investigation and instrumentation centering around different regions of what is actually a single continuous spectrum. (From data supplied by A. B. Hastings, T. F. Young and R. Uretz.)

on the inherent structure of protoplasm. At the same time new interpretations are being provided for the appearances of objects as they are viewed directly. Other major advances in microscopy, more suited to examination of fresh material, involve phase contrast, interference, and polarization phenomena and the adaptation of spectrophotometry to the microscope.

CELL STRUCTURE

Protoplasm. Although special techniques of tissue culture and microdissection permit the study of living tissue, the great mass of work done in both normal and pathological histology is based on preserved material which has been appropriately stained. Figure 1–5 demonstrates that much of the structural appearance of the living cell can be preserved by appropriate treatment. At this level of magnification the more stable cell structures seem to be well preserved by a variety of procedures, and the stains hematoxylin and eosin reveal them in a manner which is easily reproducible in any laboratory. Accordingly, these procedures have become standardized for most medical teaching and pathological studies.

To appreciate the action of preservatives and stains on biological material, it is necessary to have some understanding of the nature of the living substance—protoplasm. This involves a consideration of its appearance, its physical constitution and its underlying chemistry. By *structure of protoplasm* we refer to the spatial configuration of all the materials present in cells. *Fine structure* refers to configurations which approach the dimensions of molecules. In this sense structure and chemical composition become synonymous. Since many of the constituents of protoplasm exist naturally as aqueous solutions, the dehydrated images discernible in fixed preparations must be interpreted as residues of these solutions. In so doing we must also be aware of the dynamic nature of the cell, as an operating system. To begin we will examine the appearance of the cell as viewed directly under the microscope. It must be realized that most colorless structures embedded in colorless protoplasm, unless they are highly refractile, are seen indistinctly, if at all. If these structures are of different re-

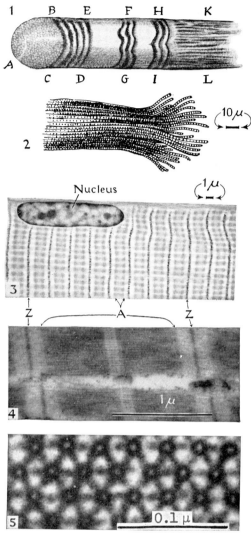

Fig. 1–2. Stages in the resolution of the structure of striated muscle:

1. Leeuwenhoek (1682) depicted muscle fibers as composed of long fibrils shown in cross section (*A*) and in longitudinal section (*KL*). It is uncertain whether he realized the cross striations of the fibers extend through the fibrils (*BCDE; FG; HI*).

2. Bowman (1840) showed the dissociation of a muscle fiber into fibrils and of these into smaller units comparable to sarcomeres.

3. Striated muscle fiber of rat, showing differentiated regions within the sarcomeres. Iron-hematoxylin stain.

4. Electron micrograph of Amblystoma muscle indicating more precisely the regions within the sarcomere (*Z-Z*) and the continuity of fine fibrous structure through successive sarcomeres. (Courtesy of K. Porter.)

5. Very high power electron micrograph of cross section of insect flight muscle showing "tubular" appearance of myofilaments and hexagonal system of cross bridges. See Fig. 8–17. (Courtesy of A. Hodge.)

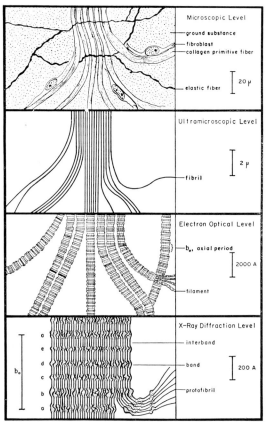

Fig. 1–3. This diagram indicates some of the major structural elements in connective tissue and the correspondence between them and the methods of study. (After Bear, 1952.)

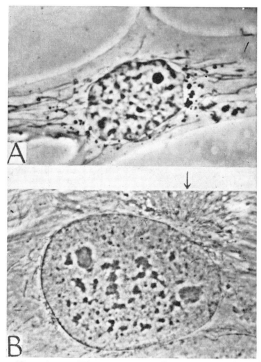

Fig. 1–4. Phase-contrast photomicrographs of newt cells in living culture. A, outstretched macrophage; the largest nuclear body is the nucleolus; long mitochondria are prominent in the cytoplasm. B, portion of fibroblast, showing nucleoli and chromatin particles in the nucleus. The arrow points to the concentration of mitochondria about the clearer cytocentrum adjacent to the nucleus. 900 ×. (Courtesy of L. Wang.)

fractive index from that of protoplasm, the phase-contrast device provides differences in light intensity which reveal them.

As a unit the cell is partially isolated from its environment by its limiting surface, and materials are continually being exchanged between the environment and the protoplasm across this boundary—the so-called *plasma membrane* or *cell membrane*. Under the microscope the nucleus is seen to be set off from the cytoplasm by a delicate but clearly defined *nuclear membrane*. Although the constituents of the nucleus play a dominant role in reproductive and hereditary processes of the cell they are also intimately involved in maintenance of the more immediate metabolism of the nondividing cell. In the *cytoplasm* near the nuclear membrane there is a relatively small *centrosome* (cytocentrum of Fig. 1–4) which has a prominent role in the process of cell division. The cytoplasm of living cells has

the appearance under the microscope of a clear or hyaline substance in which various droplets, vacuoles, granules and filaments may be suspended. Certain of these discrete bodies are essential components of the cell, for example the filamentous or spherical *mitochondria* (Fig. 1–10). Some of the major chemical transformations in the combustion of food and in the capture of energy for synthetic purposes take place in mitochondria. Some bodies, such as fat droplets, may be considered as reserve food while others are difficult to identify and classify. These various structures seen in the living cytoplasm range downward in size to the limits of resolution (0.2 micron) of the microscope. *Throughout this book, unless otherwise indicated, "microscope" refers to the optical microscope using visible light.*

The submicroscopic or fine structure of cytoplasm can be studied with other instru-

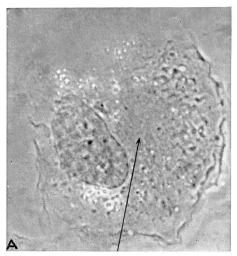
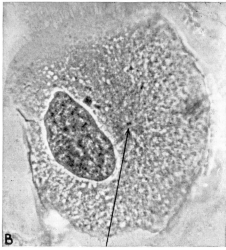

Fig. 1–5. Photomicrograph by phase-difference microscopy of a macrophage of newt in tissue culture. *A*, before fixation; *B*, same cell in 95 per cent alcohol thirty-four minutes after fixation in Zenker-formol. The arrows point to the centrioles. 800 ×. (After Buchsbaum.)

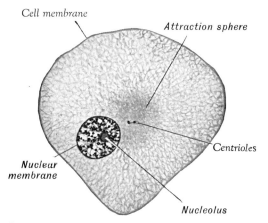

Cell membrane

Attraction sphere

Centrioles

Nuclear membrane

Nucleolus

Fig. 1–6. Interstitial cell from the ovary of a rabbit. Iron-hematoxylin stain. 1300 ×. (A.A.M.)

ments including electron microscopes having resolving powers of 20 angstrom units (0.002 micron). Unfortunately, the examination of materials with the electron microscope requires that the specimen be introduced into a vacuum so that only the structure of the dried substance is revealed. The use of preserved or fixed specimens is however common practice in histology so that to some degree histologists are aware of the structural differences between living and preserved specimens. As long as the structures observed in preserved specimens are of a size suitable for direct observation in the living condition the investigator has available a measure of control of their validity. To obtain such control at the submicroscopic level the investigator must rely on interpretations of physical and chemical evidence other than direct visualization. Neglecting for the moment the dynamic organization essential to the living state, certain structural characteristics of protoplasm may be deduced by analogy with simpler systems.

Chemical Composition. Description of the detailed composition of protoplasm is properly the domain of biochemistry, but certain aspects are essential to a consideration of structure. As the cell may be considered to be an organized set of systems in dynamic equilibrium with their environments, it is not surprising that many of the more abundant chemical elements are to be found in protoplasm. The human body has the following percentage composition on a fresh weight basis: oxygen, 65; carbon, 18; hydrogen, 10; nitrogen, 3; calcium, 2; phosphorus, 1.1; potassium, 0.35; sulfur, 0.25; sodium, 0.15; chlorine, 0.15; magnesium, 0.05; iron, 0.004. In addition to these, traces of two dozen or so other elements normally found in living organisms are vital to life. However, on the basis of the number of molecules and ions present, a table of the composition of the body would have a different aspect; thus there are 1.7 times more hydrogen atoms in the body than all the other atoms put together.

An analysis of protoplasm reveals the presence of water, inorganic ions and innumerable naturally occurring organic compounds,

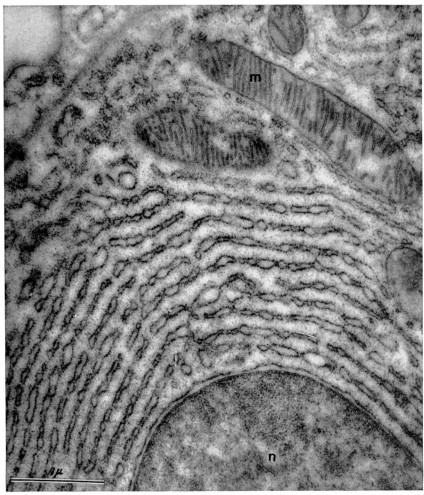

Fig. 1–7.   Electron micrograph of section through acinar cell of guinea pig pancreas. Near the nucleus (*n*) are paired cytoplasmic membranes (endoplasmic reticulum) and tiny dense granules, seen more clearly in the higher magnification of Fig. 1–16. Much finer lamellae are seen in the mitochondria (*m*). Many of the dense granules in the upper portion of the figure are not closely associated with the cytomembranes. Buffered osmic acid fixation. (Courtesy of G. Palade.)

some of which may be broadly classed as proteins, carbohydrates, lipid substances, their combinations, their constituents and their precursors. Preëminent in the architecture of cells are the proteins. Some of them vary from one cell type to another and are specific for organ and species. Other proteins seem to be of common occurrence. Important constituents of nucleus and cytoplasm are the nucleoproteins. Carbohydrates occur in animal cells as glycogen and its hydrolytic products and also in combination with proteins and lipids. Intracellular fats vary from minute droplets of neutral fats in many types of cells to large accumulations in the fat cells which

are specialized for the storage of these substances. Although more complex lipids such as sterols and phosphatides are widely dispersed in cells, they are demonstrable only by special procedures.

Protoplasm contains much potassium, little sodium, small amounts of magnesium, and even less calcium; the heavy metals are present in traces. Of the anions, bicarbonate and phosphate predominate; chloride is present in small amounts if at all, except in red blood cells. This contrasts strongly with the intercellular fluids, in which sodium salts, especially the chloride, predominate (Fig. 1–8).

The *nucleic acids* are of primary signifi-

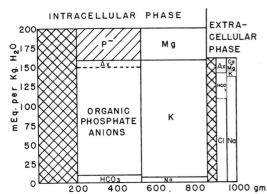

Fig. 1–8. Diagram of constitution of skeletal muscle. Concentrations in milliequivalents per kilogram of water are plotted vertically; amounts of intracellular and extracellular solids and fluids are plotted horizontally. The solids are represented as cross-hatched areas and the fluids as clear ones. For details, see text (p. 22). (Courtesy of A. B. Hastings.)

cance in the cell; they fall into two major categories: (1) Desoxyribonucleic acid (DNA) contains four nucleotides, each of which contains phosphoric acid, desoxyribose and one of the four bases—thymine, adenine, cytosine, or guanine. The proportions of nucleotides may vary, depending on the species and tissue from which the nucleic acid is derived. (2) Ribonucleic acid (RNA) is similarly constituted with ribose as the sugar and with uracil replacing thymine. These types of nucleic acids occur naturally combined with basic proteins in the form of nucleoprotein. Despite marked variation in appearance and size of nuclei in the various cell types in mammalian species, it would seem that for nondividing cells the DNA content of all diploid nuclei is essentially constant for the species. Values for a variety of mammalian species are similar, being of the order of 5×10^{-6} micrograms per nucleus (Vendrely). The amount is doubled prior to cell division.

Ultraviolet microscopic absorption spectroscopy, as developed by Caspersson, has provided a useful device for analysis of the distribution of nucleic acids in the nucleus and cytoplasm. Studies by this method, coupled with analytical fractionation procedures and the use of specific enzymes such as ribonuclease (Brachet), have gone hand in hand with advances in microbiology and genetics to indicate the chemical constitution and biochemical role of nucleoproteins in the nucleus and in the cytoplasm.

The demonstration of variations in the concentration of nucleoproteins in nucleus and cytoplasm has resulted in theories relating nucleoproteins to the synthesis of proteins. Some features of these hypotheses are presented under "organelles" and under "dynamics of the cell" in this chapter.

Structural Aspects of Solutions. It was noted above that the physical dimensions of light impose a lower limit on the dimensions of objects which can be directly observed and that in practice this limit is approximately 2000 angstrom units. Above these limits of resolution of the microscope one may observe the features of cellular components which constitute the classical concepts of cytology and histology. The basic structure of protoplasm is, however, not to be discerned within such fixed dimensional limits. The natural lower limits of size of biological structure are at the dimensions of molecular configurations in aqueous solutions. Quantitatively *water* is the most abundant substance in protoplasm. Even in the simplest solution structure appears in the form of orientation of ions and molecules to one another.

Protein molecules in solution acquire an "atmosphere" of ions and water molecules. Hydrated molecules thus acquire fields of force which can affect the orientation of other molecules. Solutions of molecules as small as common soaps, which are quite fluid when freshly prepared, readily demonstrate the orientation of molecules and the subsequent association of molecules to the extent that the solutions may set to form gels. Not only can a fairly uniform structure of oriented and cross-connected molecules arise in such simple solutions, but more complex structures are characteristic of solutions of substances of very high molecular weight, i.e., *macromolecules*. When the dissolved substance acquires colloidal dimensions either by aggregation of smaller particles or by virtue of a high molecular weight, the rate of diffusion of the particles is diminished. Thus at these dimensions the dispersive forces of diffusion may be balanced by forces of attraction which exist between molecules so that there may occur a separation of the originally homogeneous solution into local regions of higher concentrations of solute surrounding less concentrated areas or vice versa. These local regions which develop in solutions of very large molecules may be primarily linear (*nematic*) in shape, or two dimensional (*smectic*) or subspherical (*tactoid* or *coacervate*). Since these paracrystalline states arise spontaneously as a balance between dispersive and associative forces it is to be expected that they are structures of extreme delicacy which can be disrupted by slight changes in temperature, ionic concentration or even by simple mixing.

It is found however that, once established, the associations of molecules in these so-called mesmomorphic states between liquid and solid tend to become stabilized by the development of linkages between molecules. In protoplasm the complexity of substances present makes it probable that a variety of phases, or variations in concentration of substances might be expected to develop within cells. It is probable, too, that the surfaces of these phases, once established, will tend to become more complex. The principle is well established that substances tending to lower surface energy will tend to become concentrated at surfaces. Under some circumstances such surfaces arising as variations in concentrations may acquire some of the properties of membranes.

Protoplasm contains a variety of substances which collectively are dissolved or hydrated in a complex and fairly concentrated solution. In addition to considering the properties of the dispersed or suspended elements in such solutions it is necessary to consider the continuous phase in which these elements are suspended. It may be noted here that protoplasm exhibits viscosity properties characteristic of the gels formed by solutions of proteins and nucleic acids. Evidence of the development of structure is not confined to the internal phases and surfaces of cells but is also to be observed in the intercellular substance. Thus fibers (of *collagen*) found in the intercellular substance are typically formed in the proximity of cells called fibroblasts. It is doubtful that these fibers arise as such within the cells, although the cells are probably involved in the initial formation of the protein. The collagen fibers may be brought into molecular solution and subsequently reprecipitated as fibers showing a fine structure whose similarity to the original depends on the chemical treatment (see Chapter 4).

To sum up we may state that, structurally, protoplasm has many of the properties of a colloidal system of many phases. This system has some of the properties of an emulsion with various types of localized areas suspended in a continuous phase which has some of the fibrous properties of a gel. Such a definition, while elucidating structure by analogy, tends to minimize those fundamental dynamic aspects of the organization of protoplasm which distinguish it from the static, non-living model. The structural aspects of the solutions described above have dimensions between the upper limits of molecular size and the lower limits of microscopic resolution.

It is important to recognize the dimensional ranges of the forces involved, lest relations which are highly significant between molecules a few angstrom units apart are erroneously used in considering the behavior of structures as large as mitochondria. For example, the electrostatic forces between individual ions act at distances of 1.1 A and decrease with the square of the distance between the charges. The hydrogen bond distance in water is 2.8 A and the interaction force between the ion and the magnetic dipole decreases with the cube of the distance. The more general Van der Waals forces effective between molecules at distances of a few angstrom units decrease with the fifth to seventh power of the distance between molecules.

Water is the predominating compound in protoplasm and to some extent the cell behaves as a solution of salts and organic compounds separated from a watery environment by a semipermeable membrane. This aspect of the cell has undoubtedly been overemphasized and has led to exaggeration of the significance of diffusion processes in the cell. The production of homogeneity in solutions by the thermal agitation of molecules is more probable in true solutions than in protoplasm. The properties of the substances present in protoplasm are such that aggregations, surface formation and structure development occur at least to some degree with a conservation rather than expenditure of energy. Embryologists have sought for measures of the "energy of organization" with the conclusion that such a quantity must be very small. While this concept embraces dynamic as well as structural aspects it should be noted that some of the development of embryonic structure may conserve energy.

The foregoing account of some aspects of colloidal solutions similar to protoplasm has been included in order to emphasize the effects of fixation on living cells. Our knowledge of colloidal solutions is inadequate and in much that follows the examples given are elementary and crude. Much of the thinking on biological organization "will at every phase of development assume the form of physical or technical analogies stimulated by the status of those subjects at the time of writing" (Granit). With the extension of observations on structure to the limits of resolution of the electron microscope the need for more information on the structure of solutions is urgently required.

Fixation. For a variety of practical purposes it is desirable to use preserved rather than living protoplasm. For microscopic examination semipermanent preparations are useful if they provide reasonably faithful representation of the major features of the tissues and cells and if these preparations are sufficiently reproducible in all laboratories so that description based on standardized procedures may be interpreted in some common language. Special procedures for the demonstration of particular constituents of the cell attain value as they represent more faithfully the living configuration or as they demonstrate some attribute of the chemical composition or biochemical organization of the cell.

The first requirement for preservation of protoplasmic structure is to interrupt the dynamic processes of the cell as promptly as possible and to fix the structure with a minimum of change. In effect we wish to render or maintain as much as possible of the structure in an insoluble form with a minimum of distortion.

In view of the discussion presented above on the submicroscopic structure of colloidal solutions, it is interesting to consider some of the observations made by Hardy in 1899. "In the formation of an insoluble modification of a colloid from a soluble form, there is a separation of the solid from the liquid so that the particles of the former adhere to form a framework which holds the liquid in its interstices." . . . "The figure which the framework offers depends primarily upon the concentration of the initial stage, i.e., the proportion of solid to liquid, and upon the nature of the fixing agent which is used, and upon the particular colloid employed, and to a less extent upon the temperature during and subsequent to fixation, and the nature and concentration of the crystalloid bodies not immediately concerned in fixation which may be present during the process." Thus, the very essence of the process of fixation is the separation of solid from liquid and the formation thereby of a structure which may have had no counterpart whatever before fixation occurred. In solutions with three components, gelatin, water and alcohol, he found that the effect of cooling upon the structure depended on the rate. With slow cooling only two phases appeared, but if cooling was more rapid an additional system of small droplets appeared. In all the mixtures he examined these were formed in the continuous phase. "When the hydrogel is exposed to a rapid fall in temperature the phase which lies on the convex side of the surface of separation undergoes division into two secondary phases." The formation of the secondary phases therefore occurs in that one of the primary phases which is under the lower hydrostatic pressure. "Once formed the phases have considerable stability. If the droplets are composed of a solid solution one may, by the addition of water, cause them to increase to relatively vast dimensions without their being destroyed . . ."

These observations demonstrate the need for comparison of uncoagulated protoplasm with the images obtained after fixation.

Hardy's statements were based on visual observations of models assumed to resemble protoplasm. They emphasize that considerations which apply primarily to the submicroscopic organization of colloids may in particular circumstances affect visible structure. There are dimensional limits to the known forces acting between molecules as has been noted above. There is, however, no reason to assume that an entirely new set of physical considerations arises just at the dimensions where direct visual observation becomes relatively simple.

Fixation implies the dehydration or coagulation of protoplasmic substances to give insoluble material. With dehydrated specimens we must be particularly aware of the actual structural significance of water in the existence of paracrystalline, coacervate or other colloidal entities. The many unique properties of water render it particularly difficult to replace it without distortion, or destruction of the natural configuration of protoplasmic substances. On the other hand, some of the biostructures, such as collagen fibers of the connective tissue, are naturally sufficiently dehydrated and so strongly linked internally that they retain characteristic configurations in submicroscopic and essentially molecular detail (Fig. 4–2).

That histology has developed to its present state largely on the basis of the study of preserved materials is thus dependent on the presence in protoplasm of substances in the macromolecular state and primarily on the properties of proteins, nucleic acid-protein complexes, other compound protein substances and mucopolysaccharides. Upon fixation with a variety of methods these substances may remain in the form of brush heaps and tangled skeins, as a spongy network or with granules interspersed in fibrous structures. All sorts of reagents have been applied to tissues to preserve them; notably acids, ions of heavy metals, formalin, heat and sudden freezing. These reagents transform the semifluid gel into a rigid, more or less insoluble, framework from which the water is separated. The shape and character of the non-watery and undissolved remains depend on the reagent used. The early histologists considered that the fibrillar appearance of protoplasm produced by their fixatives represented the fundamental structure of protoplasm. As summarized by Wilson "fibrillar conceptions of protoplasm grouped themselves into two general views, which may be designated as the reticular and filar theories of protoplasm." Advocates of the reticular theory assumed that the fibrillae formed "a fine continuous network or reticulum extending throughout the cell and even from cell to cell. On the other hand, Flemming and later Heidenhain believed the fibrillae to be in general unbranched and discontinuous."

Against this background Bütschli, Hardy and Fischer stressed the danger of confusing coagulation artefacts with normal structural elements. Hardy also noted as "one of the most remarkable facts in the history of biological science that the urgency and priority of this question should have appealed to so few minds." Bütschli, who stressed the alveolar nature of protoplasm as observed in living cells and artificial emulsions, distinguished between a "true or primary" alveolar structure and coarser secondary vesiculation. Altmann was primarily responsible for stressing the essentially granular structure of protoplasm to the extent of considering the granules as elementary organisms or bioblasts.

Although Altmann overextended his interpretations of the significance of the granular patterns he observed, he was also the first to use drying in the frozen state to obtain fixation. This method was finally developed in more usable form by Gersh. Many structural differences are observable between frozen-dried preparations and those obtained with the older methods. In this procedure the method of dehydration does not render the proteins insoluble so that additional reagents are required if the specimens are to remain "fixed" in watery reagents.

The common methods reveal cells with their nuclei. Within the cytoplasm, initially existing structures are retained to various degrees by the different methods. Distortion of the cytoplasm between structures results in a variety of appearances. Under the low power of the microscope (100 diameters magnification) these differences are minimized; under the higher powers (1000 ×) they become increasingly important. When one uses the electron microscope with a resolving power of 20 A the distortion produced by the different methods may reveal differences which exceed the similarities. Thus boundaries which are readily observable in the living, such as nuclear and cell membranes, may no longer be revealed as sharp interfaces. Vacuoles and structures such as mitochondria appear with outlines of variable distinctness and containing new features. New structures smaller than those resolvable by the optical microscope are revealed for which we have no criteria of preexistence. Establishing the validity of these newly discovered structures is a major problem of current research. Validity of an entity must refer more to its existence as a functional unit or its representation of some structural differentiation in the living state than to an exact configuration of living structure.

At the present time, the degree of magnification required for these observations is attainable only in vacuum and therefore in dehydrated protoplasm. Accordingly, it is with increasing uncertainty that one may describe the precise morphological reality represented by what is revealed at the higher powers of the electron microscope. However, by suitable cytochemical procedures cells may be fractionated and if not living at least partially functional units may be separated which can then be examined for structural characteristics by means other than microscopic. With some reservations there is every reason to accept the existence of structurally differentiated elements of the cytoplasm all the way down to molecular dimensions. Most of the electron micrographs which have been published in recent years are of material which has been fixed in some mixture of osmic acid, passed through organic solvents and embedded in plastic for sectioning at about 0.1 μ thickness (in contrast to 2 to 10 μ for light microscopy). In such preparations, in addition to the structures normally visible under the optical microscope, there regularly appears a variety of heretofore unsuspected granules and images of interfaces suggesting differentiations within the material which in the living appears as homogeneous, glass-like cytoplasm. Some of these internal interfaces appear to arise by invagination of the surface membrane of the cell as is the case in kidney tubule cells and myelin sheaths of nerves (Figs. 28–13; 9–19); others appear to come from extensions of polymorphic vacuoles. These interfaces may take the form of roughly equidistant lamellae in some areas of the cytoplasm and characteristic small granules may be found associated with them.

The status of the evaluation of these minute structures has been well stated by De Robertis and Bennett (1955). "Moreover, exploration of cytoplasmic detail with the electron microscope is still in its infancy, and a satisfactory classification or understanding of all the cell components encountered is not yet at hand. With the limited experience at our disposal, interpretation of such matters as extent or limits of cell borders and cell membranes, the nature of particulate components, the 'granular' or 'vesicular' character of bodies encountered, the recognition of many of the profiles revealed in the mi-

crography, and the distinction of artefact from true image, present many hazards and uncertainties which are not likely to be solved definitively without many years of further study and experience on the part of cytologists throughout the world."

If living cells are disrupted in suitable media it is possible to centrifuge the resulting suspensions and to isolate various fractions. In such preparations the nuclei sediment first and then the mitochondria. From these preparations mitochondria can be recovered which exhibit certain of the biochemical properties of living protoplasm. Some of these properties have been shown to depend upon maintenance of the structural integrity of the mitochondria. From the suspension of cell fragments remaining after removal of nuclei and mitochondria, certain other particulates can be obtained by application of increased centrifugal force. Since the particles are small and the medium somewhat viscous, forces of approximately 100,000 times gravity are commonly employed. The particles so obtained have been variously termed *microsomes,* small granules and *ultramicroscopic particles.* They are not homogeneous but include a variety of different bodies. This fraction contains about half of the RNA of the cell. One of the smaller granules seems to be particularly rich in RNA. As the preparation is made the first fraction of these components to sediment in the centrifuge is found to have less RNA than the later sediments of smaller particles. These small RNA containing particles often appear to be associated with some larger particles in a functional as well as in a morphological relation. These small "RNA-rich" granules from centrifuged preparations have approximately the dimensions of the electron-dense particles which are observed under the electron microscope in sectioned cells to be associated with certain vesicles which have been termed "endoplasmic reticulum." The particles are particularly prominent in cells or regions of cells which under the light microscope exhibit a strong affinity for basic dyes. In the classical cytological literature substances with such affinity for particular dyes were termed *ergastoplasm* and *chromophile substance* (see p. 18). Thus the visible microscopic appearance of a so-called "substance" may be found to be represented by a multicomponent structure when examined under the electron microscope.

Without in any way detracting from the tremendous significance of the advances being made with the electron microscope, the fact that the specimens which are observed represent precipitated, dehydrated and solvent-extracted residues of protoplasm requires that students of structure must seek and consider carefully other evidence to be obtained with methods avoiding these disadvantages.

One of the more powerful tools for the examination of structure in protoplasm depends on the polarization of light produced by molecular orientation. The results of investigations with this method emphasize (1) the linear or fibril-like orientation of some structures in protoplasm, such as the spindle fibers of dividing cells (Fig. *1–22*), (2) the orientation and dimensions of membranes, and (3) configurations of intercellular substances (Fig. *7–11*).

Although the fibrous components of the tissue appear to reach their greatest dimensions in the intercellular substance, there are readily visible fibrils inside muscle cells and good evidence for smaller elements of similar nature in epidermal, nerve and smooth muscle cells. The appearance of fresh muscle in polarized light permitted the deduction of some aspects of its fine structure before it was delineated by electron microscopy. It is in fact in the fibrous aspects of protoplasmic structure that there is the greatest correspondence between classical and modern concepts (Fig. *1–2*).

Fixed and Stained Preparations. The different fixatives in common usage precipitate proteins of protoplasm in aggregates having various physical patterns and chemical properties; some of them leave the lipids in place but most of them remove the carbohydrates and a large part of the salts. Accordingly, to study all these constituents of a cell, various methods must be used. Some are better than others with respect to (a) preservation of the cells and their constituents with a minimum of visible distortion, (b) speed of penetration, and (c) subsequent application of various stains. In general, the more acid the fixative, the more the nuclear material will be clumped; as this clumping becomes prominent after staining, there results the common belief

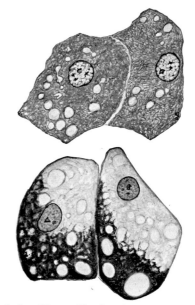

Fig. *1–9.* Liver cells of amblystoma fixed by the Altmann-Gersh method (above) and by Zenker-formol (below) and stained with hematoxylin and Best's carmine for glycogen. The glycogen is evenly distributed in the former and clumped in the latter. 400 ×. (Courtesy of I. Gersh.) (W. B.)

that fixatives with picric acid, acetic or trichloracetic acid are "good" fixatives. Actually, the various fixing solutions containing neutral formalin, osmic acid and mercuric chloride, singly or in combination, are among the best for visual observation. Histochemical analysis of cells usually requires special fixatives.

In the Altmann-Gersh freezing-drying technique, tissues are made available for study with a minimum of chemical alteration. The movement of crystalloids and some organic substances that takes place during the application of the usual fixatives is also minimized if freezing is sufficiently rapid (Fig. *1–9*).

The next step in the preparation of fixed tissues for study consists in slicing them into thin layers. This is accomplished by infiltrating them with a solution of gelatin, paraffin, celloidin or other plastics which are later solidified so that the tissue and the embedding matrix may be sectioned together. The use of paraffin or celloidin requires that the tissue be dehydrated in solvents which remove most of the lipids. Tissues embedded in paraffin may be sectioned relatively rapidly in thin slices. Celloidin, on the other hand, disturbs the arrangement of the cells less and causes less shrinkage than does the paraffin method. Sections may be prepared rapidly with a freezing microtome.

These thin slices may be stained to demonstrate the various parts of the cell and the intercellular substance. Many staining methods have been devised; a few are indispensable, but a great many are of questionable value. Although many staining reactions are primarily physical processes (see Conn), others appear to be due to chemical interactions between cellular constituents and certain dyes. The interpretations of some of these reactions are discussed by Dempsey and Wislocki and by Pearse.

The most commonly used staining method —hematoxylin and eosin—stains the nuclear structures dark purple or blue and practically all other structures, cells and intercellular substances varying shades of red. An important exception is the blue-to-purple color of the interstitial substance of cartilage. After Zenker-formol fixation, smooth muscle stains lavender. **Special staining methods are necessary to demonstrate certain cellular constituents present in the dead cell body which are not made visible by hematoxylin and eosin.** Figures 1–10, 1–11 and 1–12 show that a single staining method does not suffice.

The Mallory aniline blue and Mallory-azan methods stain the collagenous and reticular fibers a bright blue, most nuclei orange or deep red, and various cell bodies red, blue, orange or purple. With hematoxylin-eosin-azure II, nuclei are blue, collagen is pink, muscle various shades of purple, and cell bodies vary from deep blue to red, depending on the cell type. After iron hematoxylin (Heidenhain), cell structures range through shades of gray to jet black, although intercellular substance is sometimes a pale yellow. Orcein and resorcin-fuchsin stain elastic fibers an orange-brown or deep purple against a pale background. In silver impregnations (Bielschowsky) reticular fibers are black and collagen fibers purple-brown. Another type of silver impregnation (Golgi) is useful for the demonstration of entire nerve cells with their processes.

Some of the striking differences in the effects of a few of the commonly used fixing and staining agents are shown in Figure 1–10, of cells from the small intestine of the guinea pig. It is seen that the nuclei consist of a sharp membrane, a prominent body called the nucleolus, and darkly staining granules (chromatin) embedded in pale material, the nuclear sap. The cells fixed in neutral formalin and Zenker-formol show much the same structures, although the latter shows more chromatin material. Absolute alcohol and the two distinctly acid fixatives (Bouin and Zenker-acetic) show nuclei with heavily clumped, prominent chromatin. This figure also shows the differences in the effect of these fixatives on mitochondria (see p. 17). These cellular constituents are seen with difficulty in the living cell; they are obvious as blue rods and granules after supravital staining with Janus green, and are black in the cells stained with Heidenhain's iron-hematoxylin after neutral formalin and Zenker-formol fixation. But they are not visible with this stain after Bouin or Zenker-acetic fixation nor are they visible after any of these fixatives followed by staining with hematoxylin and eosin.

In Figure 1–10 three cells were dehydrated in the frozen state and sectioned. The sections were then treated with alcohol and stained either by periodate leucofuchsin method for insoluble carbohydrates, or by leucofuchsin after appropriate treatment with mercuric salts for plasmal, or stained with H and E. As the striated border and the Golgi apparatus (see p. 19) are stained with periodate leucofuchsin, mucopolysaccharides may be present in them. The plasmal reaction is believed to indicate long chain lipid aldehydes.

As the cells of the intestine change their shape greatly with the extensive movements of this organ, conclusions should not be drawn from the differences in size and shape of these cells as seen in Figure 1–10 after the various fixing agents used. However, the impression that the cells and their nuclei are larger in the living than after histological preparation is correct.

Some of the features to be seen in fixed liver cells with special staining reactions are illustrated in Figure 1–11. Here the usual appearance in hematoxylin and eosin preparations after Zenker-formol fixation is shown; by addition of azure II additional basophilic regions of nucleus and cytoplasm are revealed. A frozen-dried Altmann-Gersh preparation treated with alcohol and hematoxylin-

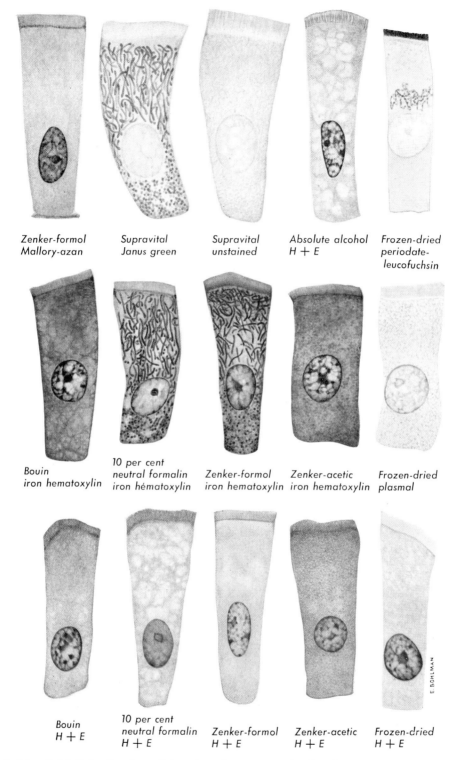

Zenker-formol
Mallory-azan

Supravital
Janus green

Supravital
unstained

Absolute alcohol
H + E

Frozen-dried
periodate-
leucofuchsin

Bouin
iron hematoxylin

10 per cent
neutral formalin
iron hématoxylin

Zenker-formol
iron hematoxylin

Zenker-acetic
iron hematoxylin

Frozen-dried
plasmal

Bouin
H + E

10 per cent
neutral formalin
H + E

Zenker-formol
H + E

Zenker-acetic
H + E

Frozen-dried
H + E

Fig. 1–10. Epithelial cells of small intestine of guinea pig fixed and stained in a variety of ways to emphasize the extreme importance of choice of method for the preservation, demonstration and study of cytoplasmic and nuclear structures. For explanation, see text. 1620 ×.

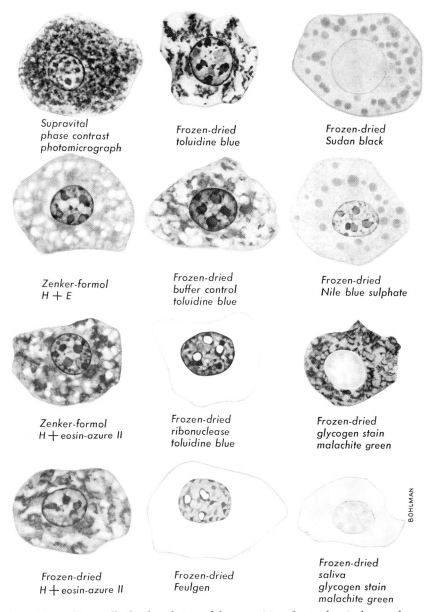

Supravital phase contrast photomicrograph

Frozen-dried toluidine blue

Frozen-dried Sudan black

Zenker-formol H + E

Frozen-dried buffer control toluidine blue

Frozen-dried Nile blue sulphate

Zenker-formol H + eosin-azure II

Frozen-dried ribonuclease toluidine blue

Frozen-dried glycogen stain malachite green

Frozen-dried H + eosin-azure II

Frozen-dried Feulgen

Frozen-dried saliva glycogen stain malachite green

BOHLMAN

Fig. 1–11. Mouse liver cells fixed and stained by a variety of cytochemical procedures to show distribution of desoxyribonucleic acid, ribonucleic acid, glycogen and lipid droplets. As these tests were all done on material fixed by freezing and drying, some of the sections are compared with similarly stained ones fixed by Zenker-formol. For further orientation, the fixed cell stained by hematoxylin and eosin and the unfixed cell photographed by phase contrast are also included. For interpretation of the tests, see page 13. 1500 ×.

eosin-azure II should be compared with Zenker-formol and hematoxylin-eosin-azure II, since the remaining figures were fixed by this method. Toluidine blue is frequently substituted for hematoxylin-eosin-azure II to demonstrate basophile components. Those containing desoxyribonucleic acid are stained by

the Feulgen method. That these are not dissolved by treatment with ribonuclease is also shown. The effect of ribonuclease is largely due to the removal of ribonucleic acid-containing elements from both nucleus and cytoplasm. Cells stained by the Feulgen method closely resemble those treated with ribonu-

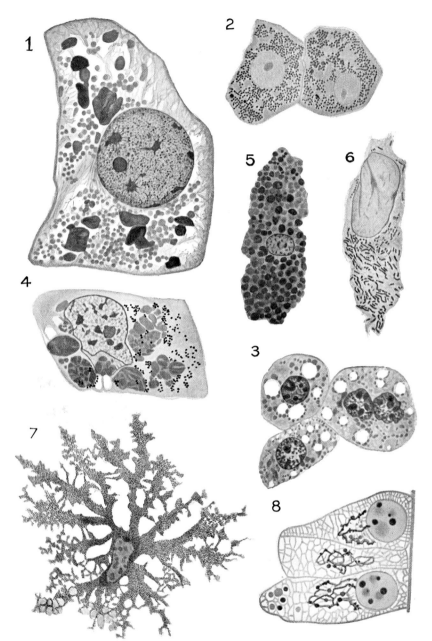

Fig. 1–12. Cells with various organelles and inclusions. *1*, liver cell of axolotl, containing red-stained mitochondria and purple-stained protein inclusions (chromophil substance). The nucleus contains an acidophil (red) nucleolus. Hematoxylin-eosin-azure. 1100 ×.

2, liver cells of rabbit: dark green-stained protein inclusions and mitochondria (stained red). Altmann stain. 750 ×.

3, liver cells of rat: one cell is binucleate; the clear spaces are vacuoles resulting from dissolving the fat; the red granules are glycogen. Fixed in alcohol and stained with Best's carmine. 800 ×.

4, epithelial cell, from mouth of an axolotl embryo, containing dark pigment granules and red-stained yolk inclusions. Eosin-azure. 1200 ×.

5, macrophage of a rat, stained intravitally with isamine blue. 1200 ×.

6, a fibroblast with rod-shaped mitochondria from a rat. 1200 ×.

7, chromatophore from an axolotl embryo, with pigment granules and pink-stained yolk granules. Eosin-azure. 600 ×.

8, first stage in elaboration of secretion granules (red) in the pelvic gland of *Triton taeniatus*. The granules first appear near the Golgi net (stained gray). The few granules near the free border of the lowest cell are from the preceding secretory cycle. Fixation Champy, stained with the Altmann method and aurantia. (5 and 6 are from Tschaschin, and 8 is from Nassonow.) (A.A.M.)

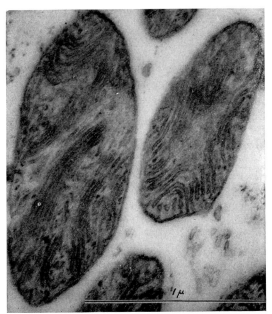

Fig. 1–13. Electron micrograph of section of mitochondria in the muscle of a rat diaphragm. Note the densely packed, paired lamellae running in several directions within the mitochondria. Compare with Figure 1–14 of mitochondria from rat liver. Buffered osmic acid fixation. (Courtesy of G. Palade.)

clease and then stained for basophilic substances. Since treatment with the ribonuclease solution may have other solvent action than that due to the enzyme, a better comparison may be made with a section treated with buffer solution.

The glycogen and other carbohydrate content of such cells is shown by the periodate leucofuchsin reaction, and the effect of treatment with saliva on such preparations is also shown, the loss of red staining being due to removal of glycogen by amylase in the saliva. Fatty components can be demonstrated, if fat solvents are avoided; they are colored with Sudan black and Nile blue. In the cell stained with Nile blue sulfate the blue component is nonspecific, but the salmon-pink staining occurs in fat droplets.

By the various fixation and staining methods, many structures have been described within the cell; these are artificial to the extent that the structures in fixed material are not the same as those in the living cell, nor are all the structures of the living cell still present in any given preparation. However, with constant fixation and staining methods, there are constant factors of artificiality. With improved methods of studying living cells, evidence has been found for the presence in the living cell of most of the important structures which had been described on the basis of fixed and stained preparations. The study of some of these relations is facilitated by phase microscopy and vital and supravital staining. In *vital staining,* certain dyes, when introduced into the living organism, will accumulate in definite parts of it, as in macrophages (Fig. 1–12). *Supravital staining* results from the addition of a dye to surviving tissues, as the staining of mitochondria with Janus green B (Fig. 1–10).

Organelles. The basis of the cytoplasm is frequently spoken of as the ground substance. Embedded in it are the microscopically visible formed constituents of the cytoplasm. From studies with the optical microscope, these structures were divided into organelles (*organoids*) and inclusions. The organelles, present in practically all cells, were generally believed to be specific particles of living substance in contrast to the *inclusions,* which were thought of as lifeless, temporary constituents of the cell. The organelles comprise the *mitochondria,* the *Golgi apparatus,* the *centrioles* and *fibrils;* the inclusions are accumulations of *proteins, fats, carbohydrates, pigments, secretory granules* and *crystals.* The position of *chromophile substance* and of the *submicroscopic microsomes* in this classification must be revised to place them among the organelles because of their role in cell dynamics. With advancing knowledge of the chemistry and submicroscopic structure of protoplasm, the complete separation of all cellular constituents into either "living" or "non-living" no longer appears as apposite as it once did. Whereas it may seem clear that a fat droplet is lifeless in the organization of the cell, it is impossible to say at what point an individual molecule of any substance becomes caught up in the organization as part of the vital machinery.

Mitochondria. These are small structures found in all animal cells. They vary from tiny spheres to short rods or filaments. They may be distinguished in unstained living cells, although their identification becomes much easier through the aid of Janus green B, applied supravitally (Fig. 1–10). They are prominent in living cells studied by dark-field illumination and by phase microscopy (Fig.

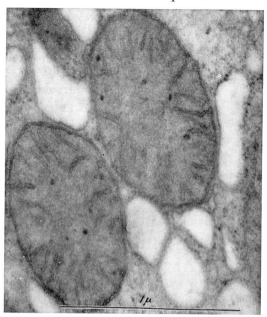

Fig. 1–14. Electron micrograph of section of two mitochondria in rat liver showing thin, paired lamellae apparently arising from the external double membrane of the organelle. These membranes, also called crests, are much fewer than in the mitochondria of rat diaphragm shown in Figure 1–13. Dense granules, apparently not connected with the crests, can also be seen. Buffered osmic acid fixation. (Courtesy of G. Palade.)

1–4). In properly fixed preparations they may be stained more or less electively (Fig. 1–12, 2 and 6). They vary from a few to several hundred in a given cell.

Studies on mitochondria separated from suspensions of disrupted cells have revealed the fundamental role of these organelles in the metabolism of the cell. They have been found to contain the entire cell complement of certain enzymes (page 25). Isolated mitochondria possess a semipermeable membrane as indicated by their active accumulation (secretion) of certain substances. However, they are probably not transformed into secretion granules. In composition mitochondria are approximately 65 per cent protein and most of the balance is lipid substances. Earlier views that they contained ribose nucleic acid appear to have been due to contamination of the samples with microsomal components. Mitochondria, by their distribution and changes in form and number, undoubtedly reflect the activity of the cell. In

some cases they bear a definite relationship to the polarity of the cell (Fig. 2–10).

The internal structure observed in electron microscope preparations of mitochondria depends in part upon the fixation and preparative procedures employed. With buffered osmic acid fixation, internal lamellae (cristae) have been commonly observed; they have not been found in frozen dried preparations. The complexity of internal structure observed in mitochondria has been found to vary with the species and with differences in rate of oxygen utilization in different organs, being highly developed in muscle and kidney cortex. Small granules also appear within mitochondria. Functional aspects of mitochondria are discussed under the section on cell dynamics in this chapter.

Chromophil Substance (Ergastoplasm, Microsmal Components, Intracellular Membranes, Endoplasmic Reticulum). In many cells, diffuse or discrete masses of a material which stains with the same basic dyes as does the nuclear chromatin may be found in the cytoplasm. This material was accordingly called chromophil substance; the most prominent examples are the Nissl substance in nerve cells and the basophil substance in the salivary and pancreatic glands. Similarly, ergastoplasm was described in earlier work and much of these ergastic substances, which were considered as reserves of food, would now be designated as chromophil substance. This material, containing ribose nucleoprotein, changes greatly during the activity of the cell.

With the development of electron microscopy, interest has been focussed on the basophilic components of cytoplasm. With this tool, regions of the cytoplasm which are basophilic in the usual microscopic preparations are found to exhibit, after osmic acid fixation, two primary structures: the first, "electron-dense," "RNA-rich" small granules about 140 A in diameter (Fig. 1–16) which are often but not always associated with a second structure, currently termed "endoplasmic reticulum" or "lamellae" or ergastoplasm. Functional aspects of the "electron-dense" particles are discussed in the section on cell dynamics in relation to the so-called microsomes isolated from disrupted cells.

The endoplasmic reticulum was described

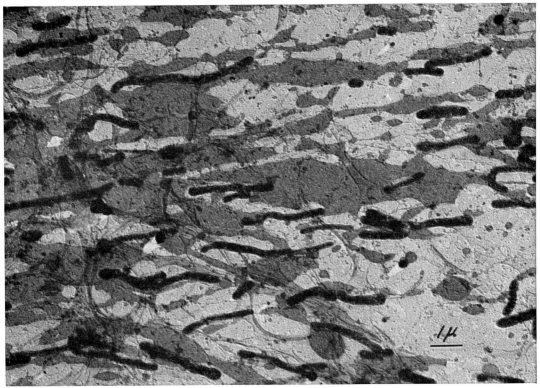

Fig. 1–15. Electron micrograph through whole mount of thin cytoplasmic membrane of a cultured endothelial cell from the heart of a rabbit. The irregular, slightly curving dark rods are mitochondria. The medium dark structures of exceedingly irregular sizes and shapes forming a network constitute the endoplasmic reticulum. This structure when seen in cross section appears as the closely packed membranes and vesicles of the cytoplasmic lamellae (endoplasmic reticulum). Osmic acid fixation. (Courtesy of G. Palade and K. Porter.)

by Porter and co-workers in electron micrographs of whole mounts of cells in tissue culture, as a network of irregularly shaped and sized tubes and vesicles (Fig. 1–15). In sections (Palade and Porter) it appears as dense or loose aggregates of double membranes often with sac-like dilatations and frequently with RNA-rich granules attached to or between the membranes (Fig. 1–16). Sjöstrand prefers to classify the several types of double membrane systems within cells as *α-cytomembranes* for those just mentioned as constituting much of the chromophil substance; *β-cytomembranes* for the infoldings of the plasma membrane (Fig. 28–13); and *γ-cytomembranes* (Fig. 1–18) for those in the *Golgi apparatus* (to be described in the next paragraph). The investigation of these structures with the electron microscope has just started, and as it is too early for agreement on their nature, and hence on their terminology, several of these names will be used interchangeably.

Internal Reticular Apparatus of Golgi. This structure consists of an irregularly arranged, interlacing network of fibrils, as seen in fixed preparations (Fig. 1–12, 8). The network may be extensive or may be localized in a small part of the cell. At times it may be broken up into a large number of scattered threads. In general, it is said to be of a more or less constant type in a given kind of cell, and is usually localized about the cell center.

This network (often called the Golgi network or apparatus or material or complex) has been thought by many to play an important role in cellular activities, particularly those dealing with secretion. It is quite improbable, however, that the Golgi net is transformed directly into secretory vacuoles. The network is thought to contain lipids and mucoproteins and probably varies in composition

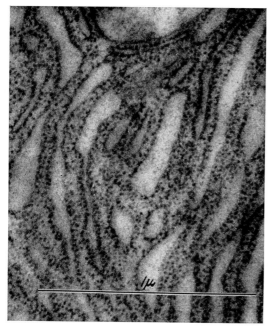

Fig. 1–16. Electron micrograph of acinar cell of rat pancreas showing cross sections of flattened vesicles and the dark, RNA-rich granules (chromophil substance, ergastoplasm, endoplasmic reticulum). Buffered osmic acid fixation. (Courtesy of G. Palade.)

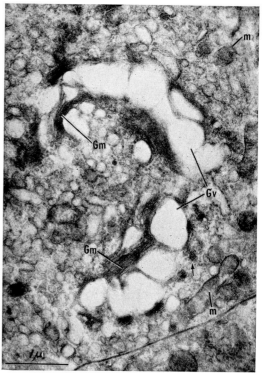

Fig. 1–17. Electron micrograph through the Golgi zone of epithelial cell in head of epididymis of mouse. *Gv,* Golgi vesicles; *Gm,* closely packed thin Golgi membranes; *m,* mitochondria. The arrows point to granules characteristically associated with the Golgi apparatus; they are larger than the dense RNA rich granules. Buffered osmic acid fixation. (Courtesy of J. Dalton and M. Felix.)

from cell to cell. Experiments with the ultracentrifuge have shown that the apparatus in some cells is lighter and the mitochondria heavier than the rest of the cytoplasm. In certain living cells, as in the islets of Langerhans, clear, canal-like structures can be seen which are identical with the Golgi apparatus seen in fixed preparations. When living cells are stained with a solution of neutral red, vacuoles of dye may be seen in many of them. The canalicular apparatus in mammals does not stain with neutral red. Kirkman and Severinghaus, and Dalton and Felix review the literature on this organelle.

In electron micrographs the region of the Golgi apparatus was found by Dalton and Felix and by others to have a variable appearance and to consist of a few pairs of double membranes, a small number of vesicles and some granules larger than the dense RNA granules mentioned in the previous section on chromophile substance. Some of the variations in the appearance of the Golgi apparatus are seen in Figures *1–17* and *1–18.*

Cell Center. In most cells, usually close to the nucleus, is a condensed portion of protoplasm, called the *cell center,* or *attraction sphere.* It contains two or more small spheres which can be seen in favorable living specimens with phase microscopy (Fig. *1–5*) and in the fixed state after staining with iron hematoxylin. They are usually close together and are called the *centrioles* or the *diplosome* (Fig. *1–6*). With the electron microscope, the centriole in some cells appears as a ring (Fig. *1–19*). The Golgi apparatus is generally located around the cell center.

The cell center and its centrioles are prominent during mitosis. Occasionally, cells are found with two nuclei; these usually contain one cell center and two or more distinct diplosomes. In the relatively rare, multinucleated cells in mammals, the cell center may be large and may contain several isolated groups of centrioles. Certain cells, as those of the nervous system, do not divide; they are seldom provided with centrioles.

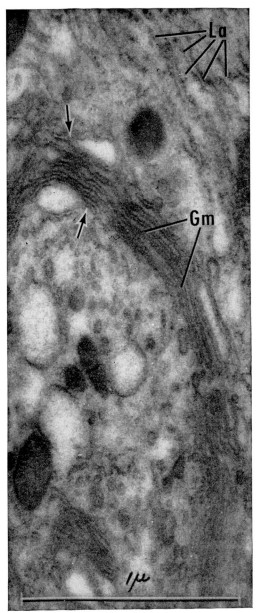

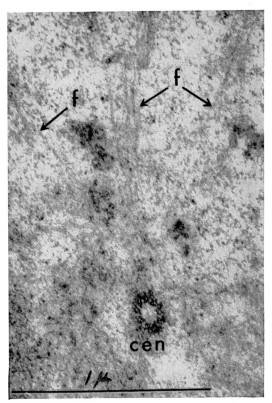

Fig. 1–19. Electron micrograph of centriole (*cen*) of dividing spermatocyte of cat. Delicate filaments (*f*) of the spindle apparatus converge upon the centriole. Buffered osmic acid fixation. (Courtesy of D. Fawcett.)

Fig. 1–18. Electron micrograph through the Golgi zone of a plasma cell in duodenum of a mouse. The Golgi membranes (*Gm*) seem to be dilating into vesicles at the arrows. Cytoplasmic lamellae with dense granules (endoplasmic reticulum) are indicated at *La*. Buffered osmic fixation. (Courtesy of J. Dalton and M. Felix.)

Fibrils. Fine fibrils develop in many cells. Some of them have been assumed to offer stability to the cell. They have been called *tonofibrils* and are characteristic in certain epithelial cells. They disappear from a cell during mitosis and reappear in the daughter cells.

Very prominent are the fibrils found in nerve and muscle cells. They are one of the most characteristic features of the various types of muscle fibers. The nerve fibrils have been studied in tissue stained supravitally with methylene blue and in fixed and stained preparations. Microdissection studies suggest that they are present in the living nerve fiber, and they have been seen in living embryonic chick ganglion cells in tissue culture. They may be displaced to one side of the cell by the ultracentrifuge.

Inclusions. ***Proteins, Fats and Carbohydrates.*** The inclusions of the cell may be granules of protein material, such as the dark purple-stained granules of Figure *1–12, 1,* or the dark green-stained masses in *2* of the same figure. They may be of lipoid nature, as the red-stained yolk inclusions in *4* of Figure *1–12.* In the usual histological preparations, however, the free fatty materials which were present in the cell are dissolved during the preparation of the section and thus appear as holes in the cells (Fig. *1–12, 3*). Much of the fat in the cell cannot be demonstrated microscopically, although it can be extracted chemically; this is called masked or bound fat.

Carbohydrates in the form of glycogen may be demonstrated in many cells. Most watery fixatives must be avoided to prevent solution of the granules (Fig. *1–12, 3*).

Crystals. Peculiar crystals, probably arising from proteins, are found in several types of cells (see Figs. *29–7* and *29–21*). Their function is unknown.

Secretory Granules. In many epithelial cells various secretory granules occur. These change cyclically in the same type of cell, depending on the stage of secretory activity of the cell. In some cases the nature of these granules has been correlated with the chemical composition of the secretion, but in most cases their exact nature is not known. The secretory granules in certain cells contain antecedents of enzymes (pro-enzymes or zymogen granules); after they have left the cell, they become active enzymes. These small granules gradually progress toward the free border of the cell, where, it is claimed, they imbibe water and become vacuoles, after which they are discharged from the cell. The origin of the secretory granules is unknown.

Pigment Granules. Many cells scattered throughout the body in characteristic positions, particularly in Amphibia, contain large amounts of pigment granules, usually a melanin (Fig. *1–12, 7*). These cells are now usually called *melanocytes.*

Submicroscopic Particles. By differential centrifugation and by electron micrographic study, submicroscopic particles have been isolated as cellular constituents. They vary in size from 50 to 250 angstrom units and undoubtedly comprise a variety of materials. In the liver, some of them contain glycogen, while others are rich in ribonucleic acid.

THE CELL MEMBRANE AND CELL DYNAMICS

The *plasma membrane* at the cell surface regulates the interchange of materials between the cell and its environment. The nature of the surface membrane of the cell is still in doubt. This membrane, estimated as 100 to 200 angstrom units thick, is usually described as differentially permeable; that is, the membrane acts selectively, in unknown fashion, to permit the accumulation within the cell of some solutes and not of others. The extensive body of knowledge dealing with this topic has been thoroughly reviewed by Davson and Danielli, by Höber and by Clarke.

By microdissection it has been determined that the cell membrane is somewhat resistant and highly elastic and that, when it is destroyed at one point on a cell, a new membrane is soon formed from the cytoplasm.

Extracellular and Intracellular Phases of Tissue. The distribution of constituents of the tissues between the intra- and extracellular locations has been studied for several tissues. The over-all chemical composition of different tissues from the same animal or of the same tissue from different animals varies widely. For a relatively homogeneous tissue, such as muscle, heart or liver, it is possible to calculate: (1) The proportions of the tissue that constitute the composition of the extracellular and intracellular phases, (2) the ionic composition of the extracellular fluid and (3) the concentration of certain constituents of intracellular fluid. These calculations are made by expressing analytical results on a fat-free, blood-free basis and by assuming that chloride is extracellular and that its concentration is almost equal to that of blood plasma. (See Fig. *1–8.*)

In the tissues the cells are surrounded by intercellular substance or are exposed at organ surfaces to body fluids. Under the microscope the cells appear to be bounded by a distinct but delicate membrane. (Surface specializations, such as those of intestinal and kidney cells and thicker cuticles will be discussed subsequently and in the next chapter.)

It should be borne in mind that a droplet of pure water suspended in pure paraffin oil will also be seen to be bounded by a distinct dark line. Visualization of this interface between the oil and water depends on the differences of refractive index between the two substances and not on the existence of a differentiated surface of measurable thickness. Similarly the dimensions of the cell surface are below the limits of resolution of the light microscope and our evidence for the existence of a membrane somewhat thicker than 100 A, at the surface of the cell is based on other considerations.

It has been noted that many substances in solution tend to accumulate at interfaces of the solution and the wide variety of substances in protoplasm makes possible highly complex associations of molecules at the cell surface.

From studies on the exchange of substances between the cell and its environment across cell boundaries certain concepts have been derived concerning the cell surface. One early theory assumed a sieve-like structure to account for the passage of small molecules and the exclusion of large ones. Another, taking account of the differences in passage of lipid soluble and water soluble compounds into the cell assumed that at least some patches on the sieve framework were lipids in which some substances might dissolve. More recent formulations stress the orientation and association of lipid and protein molecules in the membrane and they incorporate provision for dynamic factors under the term "active transport" to distinguish some features of permeability from simple diffusion.

To meet the requirements of consistency with physiological observations, our present concepts of the structure of the cell surface have become more varied and more complex than the older models. For example, some of the classical evidence which has been used to deduce the nature of the cell membrane can now, in the light of our knowledge of ion exchange phenomena, be explained without postulating the existence of a membrane. On the other hand newer evidence on enzymatic processes has indicated that certain enzymes function to regulate the penetration of substances into cells.

Most of the calculations on rates of penetration of substances into cells have assumed smooth surfaces on the cells in calculating the area of the cell membrane. Although this assumption may be valid for the cells used in the particular experiments, increasing examples of specializations of the cell surface are being discovered in electron microscope studies on tissue cells. The free surfaces of cells specialized for the absorption of substances are characterized by thousands of processes which collectively have the appearances called brush border and striated border (Fig. 2–17). These processes enormously increase the area of the cell surface but they are so tightly packed together that the effective surface area is difficult to calculate and the surface characteristics may be quite changed. Transport of substances into the cell may also occur by engulfment of substances in solution by a process called *pinocytosis*.

Current theories of structure of the cell membrane remain obligated to explain such classic phenomena as the effects of lipid soluble anesthetics and of calcium ions on penetration of substances into the cell and must account for the maintenance of electrical potentials across natural membranes. Observations in polarized light reveal considerable changes in surface and sub-surface orientation of substances in relation to fertilization of ova. They also provide estimates of the thickness of the plasma membrane (perhaps 120 A). Direct observations on the thickness of the differentiated surface are still very approximate. It must also be kept in mind that lipids as well as proteins are required as components of the surface to account for many observations and that in the fixed preparations used for optical and electron microscopy some of the lipid components have been extracted.

The study of microscopic preparations and the analysis of the chemical composition of cells may lead to a false impression that the prominent constituents of the cell are relatively inert. But it has been estimated that half of the total proteins in liver are replaced after only ten days in man and within five days in the rat. This estimate includes some of the more stable nuclear components and is thus not an adequate index of the maximal rate of synthesis. Studies with labelled amino acids indicate a high degree of formation of proteins in microsomal granules of the liver in twenty minutes. Other of the more constant features of the morphology of the cell must also be continually undergoing reconstitution at quite rapid rates.

Enzymes. Food substances provide the materials and the necessary energy for the synthesis of protoplasm. The intermediate processes of metabolism involve many complex chemical reactions. These reactions occur with great rapidity at body temperatures because of the presence of enzymes for each of the transformations. Enzymes are biological catalysts which accelerate the attainment of equilibrium in the chemical reactions. The number of enzymes present in an organism must be extremely large. Various estimates have been made by geneticists of the numbers of genes in organisms and the minimum figure for man must exceed 100,000. It is generally accepted that each of these genes requires one enzyme for its expression. Although it is not to be expected that all genes, and hence all enzymes, are functional at a given time in all cells, it is evident that the number of different enzymatic proteins required by a cell is impressively large. The variety of processes carried out within the limited confines of the cell not only remains to be enumerated but also requires an organization which is yet to be formulated. The number of metabolic reactions which operate simultaneously within a single cell is large compared to the number of morphological entities which have been distinguished. Accordingly, it is necessary to postulate a highly organized and structurally compartmentalized machinery. This living machinery uniquely reconstitutes itself as it operates and in the ordinary sense it does not show signs of wear. It does show signs of age in nondividing cells and this seems to be a result of accumulation of faulty replacements.

The enzymes are typically specific for different kinds of reactions or even for particular compounds. Among the more important groups are those catalyzing oxidations, reductions, hydrolyses and phosphorylations; esters are split by esterases and peptide bonds by peptidases, and so on. Since the syntheses of many constituents of protoplasm require energy, there must be mechanisms for coupling the reactions which produce energy to those which require it. This coupling implies a structural organization or cyto-architecture within the cytoplasm and its formed components. The compartmentalization of certain constellations of enzymes within mitochondria is discussed below.

Owing to the remarkable specificity of enzymes, it is not always necessary that there be a compartment for each reaction. A sequence of reactions may be brought about without benefit of structural organization if there are enzymes present which bring about the subsequent reaction as soon as the products of the preceding are formed. This has been termed organization by specificity.

Numerous syntheses take place within cells. To a certain degree, as in the elaboration of proteins for the protoplasm of the individual cell, these syntheses are common to all cells, but there is also a high degree of specialization in the synthetic processes carried on within cells. The degree to which the organism as a whole can provide for its complex needs is indicated by the facts that animals can be kept alive and in excellent health with all dietary nitrogen furnished in the form of pure amino acids, and that many of the amino acids themselves can be synthesized in the body. There is evidence that protein synthesis requires the simultaneous presence of all the constituent amino acids before a specific protein is formed. This implies some sort of template in the synthetic mechanism. The animal organism can make certain transformations between proteins, fats and carbohydrates; indeed, it can utilize carbon dioxide in synthesis of carbohydrate.

The end products of metabolism are chiefly carbon dioxide, water and urea. These substances diffuse readily through cell membranes, and no other process is necessary for the individual cell to rid itself of these end products. In the higher animals, however, many cells are specialized for the removal of waste products from the body.

In multicellular animals, and more particularly in the higher forms, many cells are specialized for the execution of particular functions. These may be classified as dealing primarily with (1) vegetative existence, (2) growth and reproduction, and (3) special functions. The vegetative activities of the cell, defined as the minimum of activities necessary for its continued existence, are concerned chiefly with its energy metabolism (or respiration), with the assimilation of food and the elimination of waste materials.

In the body the energetic requirements for the specific synthesis of secretions, for doing osmotic work, for mechanical work, etc., over and above the requirements for self-maintenance vary considerably among the various specialized cells as indicated by their different requirements for oxygen. Some investigators have applied special (histochemical) techniques to the detection of qualitative and quantitative differences in the enzymatic constitution of specialized cells and tissues. It is, however, difficult to deduce the physiological role of the enzymes merely from their localization or relatively high concentration. The enzymes are characteristically composed of proteins plus certain minerals or vitamins which function as coenzymes in the metabolic machinery of the cell. In the various transformations of chemical substances during metabolism there is no real distinction between fuel and machinery. At one moment an amino acid may be incorporated in a protein of the organized machinery and at another moment it may be found in a reserve "intracellular pool" of metabolites.

Whereas laboratory and industrial chemical processes are usually considered as unidirectional for the production of a given product, the processes of living systems exhibit mechanisms for the cyclic reconstitution of intermediate products. These cycles have been likened to continuous belt carrier systems. The cytochrome system, for example, is an electron transport system which provides the means for the reduction of oxygen. The oxygen consumption of a tissue is a direct measure of the activity of the cytochrome oxidase system. In other systems the unit transported is of molecular size, e.g., urea formation in the ornithine cycle. One of the major cyclic systems of the cell is the citric acid system or the Krebs cycle. In aerobic metabolism, products of the breakdown of carbohydrates, proteins and fats reach a stage where molecular fragments consisting of two-carbon units are coupled to a four-carbon compound (oxaloacetic acid) to produce the six-carbon citric acid. By a series of transformations, two molecules of carbon dioxide are eliminated, and the energy provided by the oxidation is captured by a coupling mechanism in the form of specific phosphate compounds. Eventually, the original four-carbon compound (oxaloacetic acid) is regenerated to pass through the cycle again. Nine major enzymatically catalyzed reactions are commonly recognized in the direct pathway of one such cycle but this cycle is geared into other cycles for the reconstitution of the intermediaries and to the cytochrome cycle for the utilization of oxygen. The student is referred to textbooks of biochemistry for details of this process and interrelated cycles.

Mitochondrial Systems. By differential centrifugation of suspensions of disrupted cells, fractions can be obtained which consist almost entirely of mitochondria. Such mitochondria vary somewhat in enzymatic composition according to the cell type from which they are obtained. Mitochondria from a variety of tissues contain the entire cell complement of (1) the enzymes of the citric acid cycle, (2) fatty acid oxidase and (3) the cytochrome oxidase system. Such isolated mitochondria are also capable of carrying out coupled oxidative-phosphorylation reactions. Upon disruption of the mitochondria, various segments of its biochemical systems may be lost depending on the procedures employed. The isolated mitochondrial preparations have been reported to contain a score or more of other enzymes which are not exclusively lodged in them. That so many reactions occur in the limited confines of single mitochondria argues for an intimate structural ordering of at least some of the enzymes in a sequential manner corresponding to the order of the chemical reactions in the cyclic systems.

Biochemical Systems in Microsomal Components. Although the mitochondria are not very large they are usually identifiable visually with the ordinary microscope and small mitochondria can be identified in electron microscopy. Also present in the cytoplasm are a variety of smaller bodies, mostly below the limit of microscopic visibility but which can be seen under the electron microscope and some of these can be separated from suspensions of cytoplasm by use of the centrifuge. There are a number of uncertainties in the identification of particles found in suspensions of disrupted cells. To begin with, we have no diluting or washing medium known to be appropriate for maintaining the natural structures without forming new ones. Solutions of sucrose are commonly considered to be sufficiently inert for the isolation of mitochondria and they have been used on the other suspended elements. The rate of separation of particles in suspensions by centrifuging depends upon the density of the particles in relation to the density of the medium and upon the size of the particles. If the force applied is sufficiently great, it is possible to achieve centrifugal separation of molecules from solution and this is one method used for determination of the molecular weights of large biomolecules.

In laboratories equipped with current

models of superspeed centrifuges, forces of the order of 100,000 times gravity are employed in the separation of those protoplasmic particles which remain suspended after separation of the mitochondria. The larger or denser particles are progressively sedimented. Those classes of particles which have a wide range of sizes or are subject to variations in density will be difficult or impossible to separate by this method.

The supernatant suspension remaining after sedimentation of mitochondria consists of crystalloids and small organic molecules in solution and large organic molecules in solution or in suspension in particulate form. Those particles which are removed by centrifuging at forces up to 100,000 $\times$ gravity for several hours are collectively called the "microsomes," "small granules" or "submicroscopic particles." After separation of this sediment from the supernatant suspension of finer particles and molecules it is observed that some enzymes are present in the supernatant and other in the sediment. Some enzymes arrive in the sediment before others, being incorporated in the larger or denser elements. There are interesting differences in chemical composition between the supernatant and the sediment. The granules which are sedimented soonest have a smaller ribonucleic acid content than certain particles which sediment later. Glycogen particles also appear in the sediment from liver cells.

If the sedimented glycogen is separated from the fraction containing ribonucleic acid, the latter may be refractionated. It has been found that as the fractions show increased content of ribonucleic acid they show increased activity in some aspects of the enzymatic synthesis of proteins. In order to identify the particles in the microsome fraction of centrifuged preparations, electron micrographs have been made of the particles. These particles with the high content of ribonucleic acid appear to correspond to certain dark (electron dense) particles found in electron micrographs. For lack of a better name these are called "RNA-rich" particles (Fig. *1–16*).

The microsomal fraction also shows the ability to synthesize cholesterol. This system can be dissociated from the protein synthesizing one and there is some evidence that it is associated with the vesicular or lamellar portions of the microsome fraction.

At the centrifugal forces so far employed in these studies some enzymes, notably certain ones hydrolyzing peptides (dipeptidase), remain in the supernate whereas others acting on other peptides are found among the sedimented particles. Some esterases are obviously located on very small particles or dissolved in the supernate. Some phosphatases are found in mitochondria, other in smaller particulates and others appear to be in solution.

Assuming that the "RNA-rich" particles are the site of appreciable protein synthesis in the cell, they meet the classical requirements for classification as organelles of the cell. It is not logical to set dimensional barriers around what we consider to be organelles so that the question may be raised as to whether single enzyme molecules in solution are not also organelles.

The particles found in centrifuged preparations may not all exist as discrete particles in living protoplasm. It would be reasonable to expect that some of the more continuous phases of the protoplasmic colloid would appear after disruption as particles although some other phases might dissolve in the suspending medium. The extent to which these events occur is yet to be resolved.

Nucleus. The nucleus is bounded by the *nuclear membrane* which appears in the light microscope as a thin line. There are contradictory reports on the constitution of this structure when studied with the electron microscope, some even claiming that the membrane is discontinuous. As the conflicting opinions may be based on differences in the techniques used, it does not seem profitable to discuss them at this time.

Within the nuclear membrane are strands or granules of material which stains deeply with basic dyes (chromatin), often connected by paler staining strands, and more or less associated spheroidal or angular *nucleoli* all surrounded by nuclear fluid. During cellular division the chromatin is condensed into readily visible discrete *chromosomes,* and the nucleoli disappear (page 28). The prominence of these elements during interphase is dependent on the synthetic activities of the cell. Chromosomes, the chromatin granules of resting cells, and the nucleoli consist of nucleic acids, basic proteins and acidic proteins in variable proportions. In a given interphase nucleus, however, the total content of desoxyribonucleic acid seems to be constant until it is doubled just prior to mitosis.

On the basis of x-ray scattering data and chemical composition, Watson and Crick have proposed a structure for DNA. In this structure two complementary strands are wound about each other to form a double helix, each strand being tied to the other by hydrogen bonding between a purine (or pyrimidine) on one strand and a pyrimidine (or purine) on the other. The purine adenine is always bonded with the pyrimidine thymine, and guanine and cytosine are likewise paired, thus explaining the chemically observed ratio of adenine/thymine = 1 and guanine/cytosine = 1. Duplication consists in the separation by some unknown means of the two strands and the synthesis of new complementary strands to each of the two original strands, thus producing two new double helices identical with the original. The manner in which proteins such as the histones might be bound to such a structure is still not clear.

The usual staining properties following basic and acid dyes or natural dyestuffs are profoundly altered by the changing proportions of acidic basic components of these nucleic acids, diamino acids, histones and acidic proteins. Consequently the basophilia to be expected of elements containing nucleic acids may not always occur; in fact, a structure rich in ribose nucleic acid—as most nucleoli are—may be quite acidophilic in the presence of adequate amounts of appropriate proteins. The morphological changes during condensation and swelling of the chromosomes also have corresponding effects on their tinctorial and optical properties. Many of the early investigators considered that differences in staining reaction indicated structures of different origins, but in his summary of 1925 Wilson concluded that oxyphilic and basophilic reactions in both chromatin and nucleoli were due to different phases varying according to the "ratios between nucleic acid and protein components."

In growing cells there are numerous examples of marked hypertrophy of nucleoli, and Heidenhain in 1907 pointed out that there was an obvious relationship between nucleolar growth and the growth of nucleus and cell body, but none with the formation of secretion granules. For the next few decades, the role of the nucleolus was largely ignored, as a result of preoccupation of cytologists with cytogenetic and mitotic phenomena.

The development of a microscope with quartz optics permitting the use of ultraviolet light revealed that certain nuclear structures absorbed ultraviolet light strongly and these properties have been interpreted in quantitative terms. The nucleic acid content of chromatin and of nucleoli has been found in some cases to vary in relation to cell division and to cellular synthetic processes. The presence of nucleic acids is demonstrable histologically by means of their ultraviolet absorption (as measured at 2600 angstrom units) and by their basophilia. The ribose nucleic acids are differentiated from the desoxyribonucleic acids by means of the Feulgen reaction, which is positive only for the latter. The basophilia, however, as already noted, is dependent in large part on the amount and nature of the associated proteins, so that in the presence of large amounts of basic protein, such stains (other than the Feulgen reaction) will not demonstrate nucleic acids. These studies have clarified our knowledge of the way in which some morphological components may undergo changes in chemical constitution. The detailed quantitative work on the nucleic acid and protein content of chromosomes, nucleoli and cytoplasm has revived interest in the significance of such changes for the physiology of the cell.

Barr and his associates have found that in a variety of species, including man, the sex of an individual can be determined by a sex difference in the nuclei of many types of resting cells, e.g., neurons or squamous epithelium. In females, but not in males, there is a small chromatin particle which they believe to be the sex chromosome.

CELL DIVISION

Many organs of the mature mammal show relatively few cells in division, and the central nervous system shows none. In many tissues the average period between divisions (*interphase*) is measured in years. However, frequent divisions occur in blood-cell-forming tissues, male germinal epithelium, female

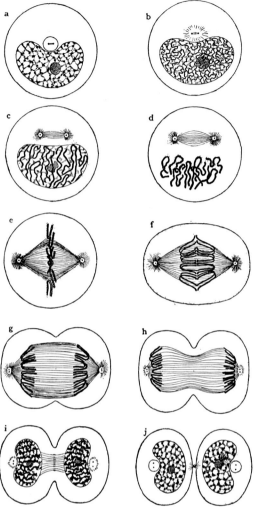

Fig. 1–20.   Diagram of various stages of mitosis in a newt cell. See text.

Mitotic Division. Mitosis is a complex of various processes, as a result of which the two daughter nuclei receive identical chromosome complements. The sequence of changes that occur in the various cell parts is divided for convenience into several *phases* (Fig. *1*–20). During *prophase* (*b, c*) the cell center of the resting (nondividing) cell (*a*) divides, and the two resulting centers move apart, the mitotic spindle forming between them. The nucleolus and the nuclear membrane begin to disappear. The chromatin granules disappear and concomitantly the rod-shaped chromosomes appear. During *prometaphase* (*d*) the chromosomes move onto the equatorial plane of the spindle, thus producing the *metaphase* configuration shown in side view at (*e*). At metaphase one usually sees for the first time that each chromosome consists of two identical rods (*chromatids*). During *anaphase* (*f, g, h*) one of each pair of chromatids (now called *daughter chromosomes*) moves to each pole of the spindle. The single centriole (*f*) in the cell center divides (*g*), preparatory to the next mitosis. The spindle elongates (*f, g*) and constriction of the cell body (cytokinesis) begins (*g, h*). Each group of daughter chromosomes forms a fused mass (not diagrammed) which during *telophase* (*i*) becomes surrounded by a nuclear membrane. Nucleoli appear in the nuclei. The individual chromosomes become indistinguishable and progressively less chromatic until the typical resting condition of the nucleus (*j*) is reached. Cytokinesis advances during telophase until the cell body is constricted into two daughter cells that in some cases remain connected for some time by the *intermediate body* of Flemming.

The story described by Figure *1*–20 was obtained during the late 1800's largely by means of fixed and stained material. As a rule, the details of living cells are not clearly revealed, although some can be distinguished, by ordinary microscopy. By phase-contrast microscopy many parts of both resting (Figs. *1*–4, *1*–5) and mitotic (Fig. *1*–21) cells are clearly visualized, particularly nucleoli, chromatin granules, mitochondria, various membranes, chromosomes and cell centers, but other parts—notably the spindle—are not regularly revealed so well. In some cells the spindle is clearly seen with the polarization microscope (Fig. *1*–22).

generative organs in cyclic changes, gastrointestinal epithelium and epidermis. Since, in mammalian cells, the small size and large number of the chromosomes make detailed observations difficult, most studies of cell division have been made on cells of lower forms.

A typical cell division consists of a division of nuclear material (*karyokinesis*) followed by a division of the cell body (*cytokinesis*), each of the two daughter cells receiving one of the two daughter nuclei. In certain cells karyokinesis occurs normally without cytokinesis, and in certain others cytokinesis can be induced without karyokinesis. Karyokinesis is accomplished in most cells by *mitosis* (*indirect division*) in contrast to *amitosis* (*direct division*).

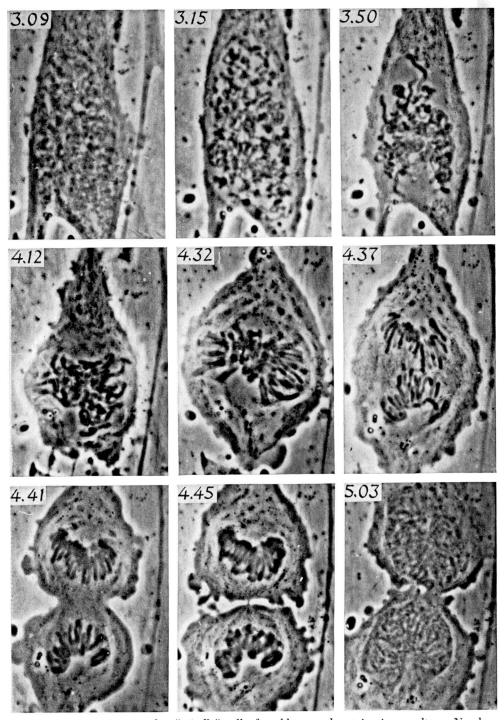

Fig. 1–21. Stages in mitosis of a "spindle" cell of amblystoma heart in tissue culture. Numbers are clock readings. Phase contrast. 785 ×. (Courtesy of L. Wang.)

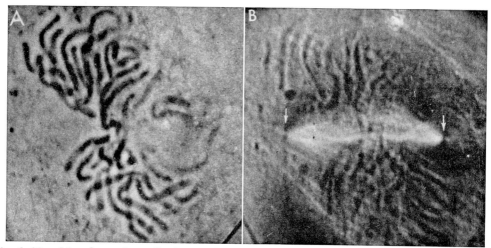

Fig. 1–22. Metaphase of a cell of newt heart in tissue culture: *A,* by phase-contrast microscopy; *B,* by polarization microscopy, which demonstrates the oriented structure of the spindle. The arrows point to the centrioles. (Courtesy of R. Uretz.)

Although the individual chromosomes cannot be distinguished microscopically during interphase, the science of genetics furnishes convincing evidence that each chromosome maintains its individuality throughout this period. Moreover, it appears that chromosome replication occurs during interphase, since cytochemical studies show that DNA doubles during this period and cytogenetic analysis of breakage of chromatids proves that each chromosome is composed of two (sometimes four) chromatids before prophase begins. Thus, although the chromosome's double nature is not seen microscopically until metaphase, it is evident that the mitotic process has nothing to do with chromosome replication but has the sole function of distributing to each daughter nucleus one chromatid of each chromosome in the mother nucleus. Since genetic evidence shows that, unless chromosome replication is interfered with, two sister chromatids contain identical linear arrays of genes, which are generally regarded as the primary hereditary factors of the cell and of the organism, the genetic apparatus is identical in the two daughter nuclei. This equal chromosome distribution achieved by mitosis is of preëminent importance because genic imbalance, brought about by misdistribution of whole chromosomes or of parts of chromosomes, may cause abnormality or even death of the organism. Some general ways in which such misdistribution can be

brought about are: *multipolar mitosis,* in which more than two cell centers are present, more than one spindle forms, and the chromosomes of the mother nucleus are distributed to more than two daughter nuclei; *nondisjunction* of sister chromatids, so that both go to one daughter nucleus, giving it an excess of the pertinent set of genes and leaving the other daughter nucleus correspondingly deficient; production of certain chromosomes or segments of chromosomes that cannot join the metaphase plate or participate in a normal anaphase, so that they are distributed at random to the two daughter nuclei or may even form small accessory nuclei by themselves, thus leaving the main daughter nuclei deficient.

None of the movement of cell parts involved in mitosis (Figs. *1–20, 1–21*) has been satisfactorily explained, although many theories have been advanced to account for the forces evidently at work. Also, the mechanism of chromosome doubling in interphase is not understood. *A priori* two general possibilities are recognized: (a) each chromosome "splits" longitudinally into two, each gene being divided in the process; (b) each chromosome acts as a template for the formation of another like it, each gene being replicated in the process. Some experiments with radioactive tracers indicate that the template mechanism is the one actually involved.

A special type of nuclear division (meio-

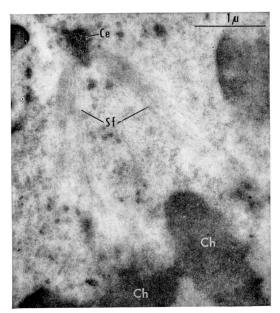

Fig. 1–23. Electron micrograph of section of mitotic cell in rat spleen. Dense body (*Ce*) is a centriole. Connected with it are bundles of delicate spindle filaments (*Sf*) which extend toward the chromosomes (*Ch*). Buffered osmic acid fixation. (Courtesy of E. Yamada.)

sis) that occurs during the formation of the sex cells is discussed in the chapters on the genital organs.

Cytokinesis. In mitotic animal cells the cell body is typically divided by a constriction that, beginning in late anaphase or early telophase (Figs. 1–20, 1–21) and advancing in a plane perpendicular to the spindle axis and between the two groups of anaphase chromosomes, provides that each daughter cell shall have one nucleus. Since there is no mechanism to insure similar equal distribution of cytoplasmic organelles, inclusions and genetic factors (plasmagenes), these are apportioned more or less equally between the two daughter cells, depending on the degree of randomness of their distribution in the mother cell and on the location of the spindle in the mother cell. The forces producing the constriction are not understood.

Amitosis. In sharp contrast to the precisely operating mechanism of mitosis is the mode of karyokinesis called amitosis or indirect division. In this case the nucleus is reported as merely constricting until it finally divides into two more or less equal daughter nuclei. There has been much controversy as

to whether this process actually occurs under normal conditions. There seems to be no well authenticated instance in which a complete cytokinesis has been observed to follow an amitotic karyokinesis in the same individual cell. In any event, since there is no mechanism for equal distribution of chromosomes, the daughter nuclei must practically always be grossly imbalanced. The whole question of amitosis needs more investigation.

REFERENCES

The first group of references are important source books in the fields of cytology and histology; those in the second group deal with histological techniques; while those in the third group are concerned with some of the special fields of current interest and investigation.

In searching for more information on a particular topic, the student would do well to start with the handbooks edited by von Möllendorff-Bargmann and by Cowdry and the manuals of Kölliker-von Ebner and of Prenant, Bouin and Maillard.

I.

von Bardeleben, K., and von Eggeling, H.: Handbuch der Anatomie des Menschen. 1896–1926.

Bolk, L., Goppert, E., Kallius, E., and Lubosch, W.: Handbuch der vergleichenden Anatomie der Wirbeltiere. Berlin, 1931.

Brachet, J.: Chemical Embryology. New York, Interscience, 1950.

Braus, H.: Anatomie des Menschen. Berlin, 1955 et seq.

Cowdry, E. V. (editor): General Cytology. Chicago, 1924. Special Cytology, New York, 1932.

Heidenhain, M.: Plasma und Zelle. Jena, 1907–11.

von Herrath and Abramow: Atlas der normalen Histologie und mikroskopischen Anatomie des Menschen. Stuttgart, Georg Thieme Verlag, 1950.

Kölliker, T. A., and von Ebner, V.: Handbuch der Gewebelehre des Menschen. 6th ed., Leipzig, 1889–1902.

Levi, G.: Trattato di istologia. 4 ed., Torino, 1955.

von Möllendorff-Bargmann: Handbuch der mikroskopischen Anatomie des Menschen. Berlin, 1927 et seq.

Needham, J.: Biochemistry and Morphogenesis. Cambridge University Press, 1942.

Oppel, A.: Lehrbuch der vergleichenden mikroskopischen Anatomie der Wirbeltiere. Jena, 1896.

Policard, A.: Précis d'histologie physiologique. 5th ed., Paris, 1950.

Prenant, A., Bouin, P., and Maillard, L.: Traité d'histologie. Paris, 1910, 1911.

Willier, B. H., Weiss, P. A., and Hamburger, V. (editors): Analysis of Development. Philadelphia, W. B. Saunders Co., 1955.

Wilson, E. B.: The Cell in Development and Heredity. The Macmillan Co., New York, 1925.

Winterstein, H.: Handbuch der vergleichenden Physiologie. Jena, 1913–1924.

II.

Boyd, G. A.: Autoradiography in Biology and Medicine. New York, Academic Press, Inc., 1955.

Clark, E. R., and Clark, E. L.: Further observations on living lymphatic vessels in the transparent chamber in the rabbit's ear—their relation to the tissue spaces. Am. J. Anat., 52:273, 1933.

Conn, H. J.: Biological Stains: A Handbook on the Nature and Uses of the Dyes Employed in the Biological

Laboratory. 5th ed., Geneva, N. Y., Biotech. Publications, 1946.

Gersh, I.: Application in pathology of the method of fixation by freezing and drying of tissues. Bull. Int. Ass. Med. Museums, *28:*179, 1948.

Gomori, G.: Microscopic Histochemistry. Chicago, Univ. of Chicago Press, 1952.

Knisely, M. H.: A method of illuminating living structures for microscopic study. Anat. Rec., *64:*499, 1936.

Kopac, M.: Recent developments in cellular micrurgy. Trans. New York Acad. Sci., *17:*257, 1955.

Krause, R. P., Ehrlich, et al.: Encyklopädie der mikroskopischen Technik. Berlin and Vienna, 1926.

Lee, A. B.: Microtomists Vade-Mecum. 11th ed. (Gattenby and Cowdry). Philadelphia, 1950.

Lewis, W. H., and Lewis, M. R.: Behavior of Cells in Tissue Cultures in Cowdry: General Cytology. Chicago, 1924, p. 385.

Lison, L.: Histochimie et cytochemie animale. Paris, 2nd ed., 1952.

Mellors, R. C. (editor): Analytical Cytology. New York, McGraw-Hill Book Co., 1955.

Oster, G., and Pollister, A. W. (editors): Physical Techniques in Biological Research. Academic Press Inc., New York, 1955.

Parker, R. C.: Methods of Tissue Culture, 2d ed., New York, Paul B. Hoeber, Inc., 1950.

Pearse, A. G.: Histochemistry. London, 1953.

Romeis, B.: Taschenbuch der mikroskopischen Technik. 15th ed., Munich, 1948.

III.

Allfrey, V. G., Mirsky, A. E., and Stern, H.: Chemistry of the cell nucleus. Advances in Enzymology, *16:*411, 1955.

Barr, M. L., Bertram, L. F., and Lindsay, H. A.: Morphology of nerve cell nucleus according to sex. Anat. Rec., *107:*283, 1950.

Bensley, R. R., and Gersh, I.: Studies on cell structure by the freezing-drying method. I. Introduction. II. Mitochondria. III. Nissl substance. Anat. Rec., *57:* 205, 369, 1933.

Bensley, R. R., and Hoerr, N. L.: Studies on cell structure by the freezing-drying method. VI. The preparation and properties of mitochondria. Anat. Rec., *60:*449, 1934.

Bucher, N. L. R., and McGarrahan, K.: Biosynthesis of cholesterol from acetate–1–C^{14} by cellular fractions of rat liver. J. Biol. Chem. *222:*1, 1956.

Caspersson, T. O.: Cell Growth and Cell Function. A Cytochemical Study. New York, W. W. Norton and Co. Inc., 1950.

Clarke, H. T.: Ed. Ion Transport Across Membranes. Academic Press, New York, 1954.

Dalton, A. J., and Felix, Marie D.: Cytologic and cytochemical characteristics of the Golgi substance of epithelial cells of the epididymis—in situ, in homogenates and after isolation. Am. J. Anat., *94:*171, 1954.

De Bruyn, P. P. H., Robertson, R. C., and Farr, R. S.: In vivo affinity of diaminoacridines for nuclei. Anat. Rec., *108:*279, 1950.

De Robertis, E. D. P., and Bennett, H. S.: Some features of the submicroscopic morphology of synapses in frog and earthworm. J. Biophys. Biochem. Cytol., *1:*47, 1955.

Doyle, W. L.: Quantitative histochemistry of phosphatases. Int. Rev. of Cytology, *2:*249, 1953.

Gaebler, O. H. (editor): Symposium on Enzymes: Units of Biological Structure and Function. New York, 1956.

Gersh, I.: The Altmann technique for fixation by drying while freezing. Anat. Rec., *53:*309, 1932. Recent developments in histochemistry. Physiol. Rev., *21:*242, 1941.

Hardy, W. B.: On the structure of cell protoplasm. J. Physiol., *24:*158, 1899. On the mechanism of gelation in reversible colloidal systems. Proc. Roy. Soc., *66:*95, 1900.

Höber, R., and others: Physical Chemistry of Cells and Tissues. Philadelphia, Blakiston Co., 1945.

Hughes, A.: The Mitotic Cycle. London and New York, 1952.

Kirkman, H., and Severinghaus, A. E.: A review of the Golgi apparatus. Anat. Rec., *70:*413, 557; *71:*79, 1938.

Kuff, E. L., Hogeboom, G. H., and Dalton, A. J.: Centrifugal, biochemical, and electron microscopic analysis of cytoplasmic particulates in liver homogenates. J. Biophys. Biochem. Cytol., *2:*33, 1956.

Lindberg, O., and Ernster, L.: Chemistry and Physiology of Mitochondria and Microsomes. Protoplasmatologica, III A 4, 1954.

Moog, F.: The physiological significance of the phosphomonoesterases. Biol. Rev., *21:*41, 1946.

Novikoff, A. B.: Electron microscopy: cytology of cell fractions. Science, *124:*969–972, 1956.

Painter, T. S.: A comparative study of the chromosomes of mammals. Am. Nat., *59:*385, 1925.

Palade, G. E.: A small particulate component of the cytoplasm. J. Biophys. Biochem. Cytol., *1:*59, 1955. Studies on the endoplasmic reticulum. II. Simple dispositions in cells *in situ.* Ibid. *1:*567, 1955.

Palade, G. E., and Porter, K. R.: Studies on the endoplasmic reticulum. I. Its identification in cells *in situ.* J. Exper. Med., *100:*641, 1954.

Porter, K. R.: The fine structure of cells. Fed. Proc., *14:* 673, 1955. Observations on a submicroscopic basophilic component of cytoplasm. J. Exper. Med., *97:* 727, 1953.

Schmitt, F. O.: Cell Constitution. Section III, Chapter I in Analysis of Development, edited by Willier, Weiss and Hamburger. Philadelphia, W. B. Saunders Co., 1955.

Schrader, F.: Mitosis. 2d ed., Columbia, New York, 1953.

Sjöstrand, F.: The Ultrastructure of Cells as Revealed by the Electron Microscope. Int. Rev. Cytol., *5:*455–533, 1956.

Symposium: Basophilic components of cytoplasm. J. Histochem. and Cytochem., *2:*317–406, 1954.

Symposium: Biochemistry of nucleic acids. J. Cell and Comp. Physiol., *38:* Suppl I., 1951.

Symposium: Fine Structure of Cells. New York, Interscience Publishers, Inc., 1956.

Symposium: Frontiers in Cytochemistry. Biol. Symposia. X. Lancaster, J. Cattell Press, 1943.

Symposium: Structure and biochemistry of mitochondria. J. Histochem. and Cytochem., *1:*199–276, 1953.

Symposium: Tissue fine structure. J. Biophys. and Biochem. Cytol., *2:* No. 4, Suppl., 1956.

Wilson, J. W.: Cellular tissue and the dawn of the cell theory. Isis, *35:*168, 1944.

CHAPTER 2

Epithelium

IN THE FOREGOING pages some of the most important visible and submicroscopic constituents of cells have been discussed. This emphasis on cells may be misleading unless it is realized that isolated cells do not occur in complex multicellular animals, except in the blood. Cells are bound together with varying amounts of intercellular substances to form *tissues* and *organs*. This applies also to the blood, the plasma of which constitutes the intercellular substance. Even in the earliest stages, when the fertilized egg divides repeatedly, the resulting cells stick together and pass through a series of complex developmental processes which take place in an orderly sequence. There is a transient phase when the early embryo consists only of simple epithelial layers (Fig. 2–1). Later, the *three primitive germ layers* give rise to *four primary tissues:* (1) epithelium—the cells are generally applied closely to one another with little cementing substance. The sheets of cells may develop into the covering of the outer and inner surfaces of the body and the glands and other structures derived from them. (2) Connective tissues—the cells are generally separated from one another to a greater or less degree by a rather rich amount of intercellular substance. From these cells are derived the blood cells and the blood cell-forming tissues, the connective tissue in its manifold varieties, cartilage and bone. These derivatives differ not only in their cell populations, but also in the nature and amount of the intercellular substance. (3) Muscle—the cells are of several varieties which are associated with move-

ment of the skeleton and contractility in many organs, including those of the vascular system. (4) Nerve tissue—the cells are concerned primarily with rapid conduction of impulses in the integration of numerous functions. The details of these tissues will be considered in the next few chapters.

As cells are aggregated to form tissues, so these are combined and integrated in different manners to form functional structures, the organs of the body. A variety of influences come to bear on the interrelations of the tissues composing an organ—neural, endocrine,

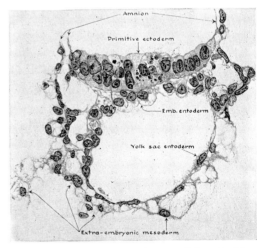

Fig. 2–1. Section of embryonic disk and yolk sac of human embryo of about thirteen days (Brewer). At this state there is no mesoderm between the primitive ectoderm and entoderm. (After Bloom and Bartelmez.)

Page 33

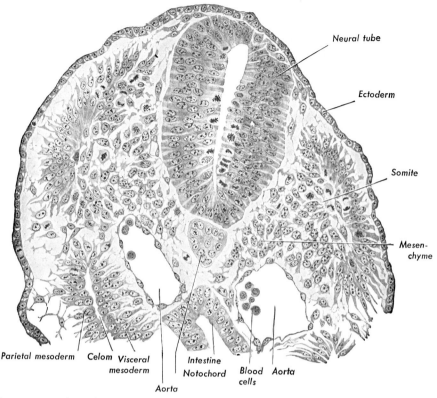

Neural tube

Ectoderm

Somite

Mesen-
chyme

Parietal mesoderm   Celom   Visceral   Intestine   Blood   Aorta
                              mesoderm   Notochord   cells

Aorta

Fig. 2–2.   Cross section through the dorsal part of a guinea pig embryo of twelve somites. Development
of mesenchyme from the medial wall of a somite. 165 ×. (A.A.M.)

metabolic, physical and circulatory. A great part of the book is devoted to the organization of the tissues which go to form organs.

Epithelium forms the outer protecting surface of the body and all the glands, furnishes important parts of the sense organs, and lines the walls of the internal cavities, except those which develop exclusively in and from the mesenchyme, the lining epithelium of which is called *endothelium* or *mesothelium* (p. 47). The most important and general function of the epithelial tissue is its participation in the metabolism of the body through the absorption of substances from the outside medium, their modification in the body, and the elimination of other substances to the outside. All substances normally received and given off by the body must pass through the epithelium. For the performance of the secretory function, the epithelial tissue produces special structures called glands.

Histogenesis of Epithelium. Early histologists described epithelium as a layer of closely connected cells lining the cavities of

the body. The term was later extended to the similar layers covering the body, and was further broadened when it was shown that the vertebrate (and most invertebrate) embryos pass through a stage during which they consist of three simple layers of cells—the embryonic germ layers called *ectoderm, mesoderm* and *entoderm.* While this concept has been fruitful, the derivatives of the three germ layers are no longer considered to be completely separated from one another. For it has been shown by experiment that some cells from parts of each germ layer can be made to become integral parts of the other layers. However, in adult vertebrates, epithelial elements, especially of ectodermal and entodermal origin, and those of the connective tissues are morphologically independent, and transformations between them are rare. As the embryo develops, these germ layers form the organs and tissues of the body. In some parts they persist as epithelial layers; in other parts they lose their epithelial arrangement permanently; while in still others the

Parietal cell   Vessels   Cells of lamina propria

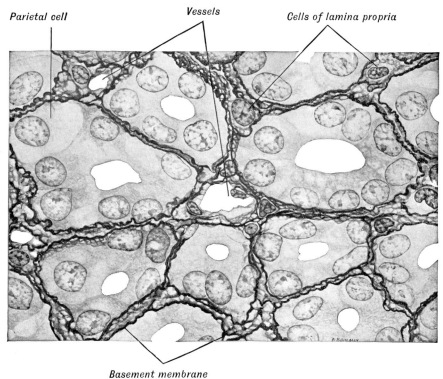

Basement membrane

Fig. 2–3.   Basement membranes surrounding cross sections of fundic glands of human stomach. Bielschowsky stain for reticular fibers and hematoxylin. 1500 ×.

epithelial arrangement seems to be completely lost, but may become apparent in inflammation, tissue culture, or tumor. If the term "epithelium" is used in a purely descriptive sense, the student will often find it difficult to understand how the cells of many glands can be called epithelium. Accordingly, it might be advisable in many cases to distinguish between covering epithelium and glandular epithelium.

It is the unequal growth of these epithelial layers which produces the various organs. Some folds grow outward as evaginations, usually with a core of *mesenchyme,* the embryonic connective tissue; others grow inward as invaginations into the mesenchyme. An invagination may fuse at its mouth, severing its connection with the epithelium from which it developed, and so give rise to isolated epithelial organs surrounded by mesenchyme.

Part of the outer germ layer, or *ectoderm,* curves inward to form the *neural tube,* from which develop the elements of the brain and spinal cord. The rest of the ectoderm keeps its epithelial form and gives rise to the epider-

mis, the lining of the oral cavity, and parts of the sense organs.

The inner layer, the *entoderm,* furnishes the epithelial lining and the glands of the intestinal and respiratory systems.

The middle layer, or *mesoderm,* keeps its epithelial character in the epithelium of the urinary and genital systems. The part of the mesoderm which lines the *celom*—the *peritoneal, pleural* and *pericardial cavities*—is an epithelium of special type and is called *mesothelium.* A considerable part of the mesoderm is transformed into the striated muscular tissue and into the heart muscle, while another large part of it becomes the mesenchyme, which gives rise to smooth muscle and the various types of connective tissue, cartilage, bone and blood.

The *notochord,* the axial supporting structure of the embryo, probably arises from the totipotent tissue of the blastopore and behaves like a mesodermal derivative.

Experimental studies of vertebrate development, especially as carried out on amphibians and to a lesser extent on birds, show that

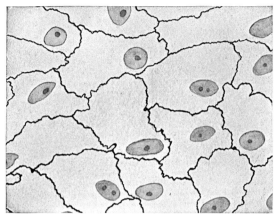

Fig. 2–4.   Surface view of the simple squamous mesothelium of a frog's mesentery; the cell limits are stained black with silver nitrate; the nuclei are stained with picrocarmine. 390 ×.

Some types of epithelium seem to lack a basement membrane (thyroid gland in young animals). In the sulcus spiralis externus and in the stria vascularis of the cochlea, the epithelial cells send processes deep into the connective tissue. The original, simple, anatomical relations between epithelium and connective tissue are also completely altered in most of the endocrine glands and in the liver.

Types of Epithelial Tissue.   As different types of epithelium may arise from the same germ layer, as different germ layers may produce similar epithelial types, and as the physiological role of certain epithelia has not been determined, the various types of epithelial tissue are best classified in terms of (*a*) the shape of the epithelial cells and (*b*) their arrangement in the epithelial sheet.

Shape of Epithelial Cells. Epithelial cells in the living condition change considerably

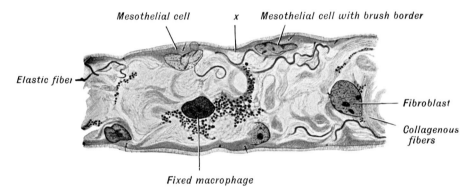

Mesothelial cell   x   Mesothelial cell with brush border

Elastic fiber

Fibroblast

Collagenous fibers

Fixed macrophage

Fig. 2–5.   Cross section of a rabbit's mesentery; *x*, cross section of cell limits. Iron-hematoxylin stain. 750 ×. (A.A.M.)

many of the cells in these embryonic germ layers have no inherent specificity during early developmental stages. That is, if they are moved from one place to another, they will often proceed to develop in conformity with their new surroundings. These and similar interesting problems of development are discussed at length by numerous authors in the "Analysis of Development" edited by Willier, Weiss and Hamburger.

Basement Membrane. Between the epithelium and the underlying connective tissue there is usually a basement membrane, a condensation of the intercellular substance of the connective tissue at the surface of its contact with the epithelium. In hematoxylin and eosin preparations the basement membrane often is hard to see, but special techniques help to demonstrate it.

in shape if the surface they cover is subject to stretching and contraction. Stretching flattens them; contraction permits them to gain in height. In the healing of wounds, in other pathological conditions, and in tissue cultures, the form of an epithelial cell may change with its movement.

Squamous, cuboidal and columnar epithelial cells may be distinguished.

1. *Squamous Cells.* The height of the cell body is negligible in comparison with the other dimensions; the cell is a thin plate. In profile it looks like a slender rod which is usually slightly thickened in the vicinity of the nucleus (Figs. 2–4, 2–5).

2. *Cuboidal Cells.* The height is about equal to the width. When seen from the free surface, the cells appear as small polygons; in a section perpendicular to the surface they

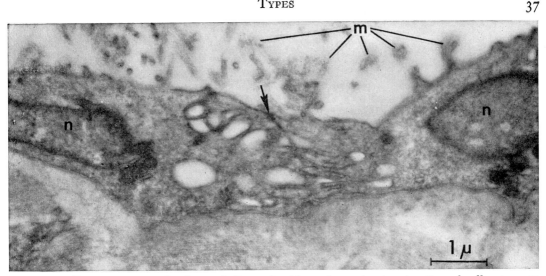

Fig. 2–6. Electron micrograph of mesothelium of oviduct of rat showing junction of cells at arrow. *m*, microvilli; *n*, nuclei of the two cells. Buffered osmic acid fixation. (Courtesy of L. Odor.)

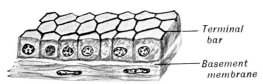

Fig. 2–7. Diagram of simple cuboidal epithelium. (Redrawn and slightly modified after Stöhr-von Möllendorff.)

appear square. They are short prisms (Fig. 2–7).

3. **Columnar Cells.** The height greatly exceeds the width. In a section parallel to the surface the cells appear as small polygons (Figs. 2–8, 2–10, 2–11); in a perpendicular section, as rectangles. They are irregular tall prisms. The end directed toward the underlying tissue is often tapering and pointed, or irregularly angular and branched. Cells of a fairly regular cylindrical shape are found in the epithelium of the higher sense organs. On curved surfaces the columnar and cuboidal cells assume the shape of truncated pyramids whose thin ends are directed to either the free or the fixed surface.

Transitional forms between these three types also occur. All three forms may be provided on their free surface with motile, hair-like outgrowths called *cilia* or with a *brush border* (p. 42).

Arrangement of the Cells in Epithelial Sheets. Epithelial sheets may be classified on morphological grounds into several categories, depending on whether they consist of one or more layers and on the shapes of the cells. In the stratified epithelia only the cells of the

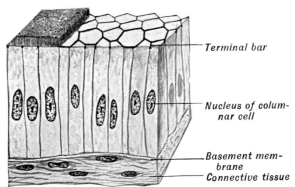

Fig. 2–8. Diagram of the columnar epithelium of the small intestine. The striated border has been removed in the right half to show the terminal bars. (Redrawn and slightly modified after Stöhr-von Möllendorff.)

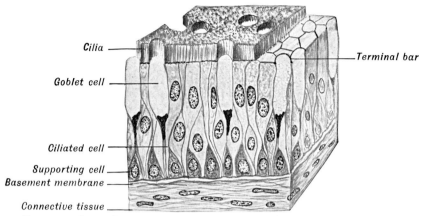

Fig. 2–9.   Diagram of pseudostratified ciliated columnar epithelium. (Redrawn and slightly modified after Stöhr-von Möllendorff.)

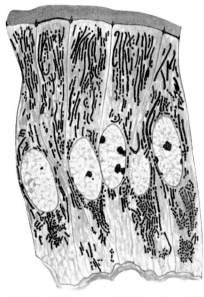

Fig. 2–10.   Columnar epithelium from the intestine of a rat, showing striated border, terminal bars, and filamentous supranuclear, and granular infranuclear mitochondria. Iron-hematoxylin stain. 1000 ×. (A.A.M.)

lowest layer touch the underlying tissue. In the *pseudostratified columnar epithelium* the cells seem to be arranged in more than one layer, but all of them touch the underlying tissue (see Fig. 2–9).

1. *Simple Squamous Epithelium.* Thin, platelike cells are arranged in one layer on the surface of the connective tissue and adhere closely to one another by their edges. On examination from the surface, especially after the cell limits are stained with silver nitrate, a typical mosaic pattern is seen. The individual cells have regular (usually hexagonal) or irregular wavy outlines, and each contains a nucleus

(Fig. 2–4). In perpendicular sections a thin stripe is seen, subdivided into small parts which correspond to the single cells. A given section will not pass through the nuclei of all the cells. In profile the cell may appear as a plump spindle.

An epithelium of this variety is found in the human body on the inner surface of the wall of the membranous labyrinth and on the inner surface of the tympanic membrane of the ear; on the parietal layer of the capsule of Bowman and in the descending limb of the loop of Henle in the kidney; in the rete testis, and in the smallest excretory ducts of many glands.

The *mesothelium* lining the serous cavities, the *mesenchymal epithelium* lining cavities in the connective tissue, and the *endothelial* cells lining the walls of the blood and lymph vessels—all three groups being squamous cells—are also considered by many authorities to be true epithelium. However, despite the structural similarity, these elements differ in origin and developmental potencies from true epithelium (p. 47).

2. *Simple Cuboidal Epithelium.* The low prismatic cell bodies adhere to one another by their lateral surfaces. On the free surface this epithelium appears as a mosaic of small, usually hexagonal polygons; the ribbon-like cross section of the sheet is subdivided into squares (Fig. 2–7).

This epithelium is found in many glands, as in the thyroid, on the free surface of the ovary, on the choroid plexus, on the inner surface of the capsule of the lens, in some areas of the labyrinth, in the excretory ducts of many glands and as the pigmented epithelium of the retina. The secreting epithelium in the terminal portions of many glands can often be placed in this class, although the cells here usually have the form of truncated pyramids.

3. *Simple Columnar Epithelium.* The tall prismatic cells adhere to one another by their lateral surfaces. In sections parallel to the surface is seen a mosaic much like that in other simple epithelia (Fig. 2–8). In sections perpendicular to the surface the tall rectangles stand upright like fence palings. In many cases the oval nuclei are at approximately the same level.

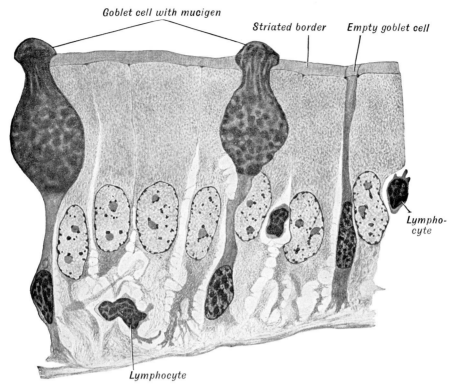

Goblet cell with mucigen   Striated border   Empty goblet cell

Lympho-
cyte

Lymphocyte

Fig. 2–11. Perpendicular section of the simple columnar epithelium of the intestine of the axolotl. The lateral surfaces of the epithelial cells are slightly detached from each other, and in the intercellular spaces protoplasmic bridges are seen. 750 ×. (A.A.M.)

Such an epithelium lines the surface of the digestive tract from the cardia to the anus and is also common in the excretory ducts of many glands.

4. *Simple Columnar Ciliated Epithelium.* This is like 3, except that the free surface of the cells is provided with cilia. It is found in the uterus and oviducts, in the small bronchi, in some of the nasal sinuses, and in the central canal of the spinal cord.

5. *Stratified Squamous Epithelium.* The epithelial sheet is thick, and a perpendicular section shows the cells to be unequal in form (Fig. 20–2). The layer next to the underlying tissue consists of cuboidal or even columnar cells, sometimes with rounded upper ends, as in the cornea. Then follow a varying number of layers of more or less irregular polyhedral cells, often provided with excavations which fit the convex surfaces of their neighbors, or with long stalks attached to the basement membrane. The nearer to the free surface, the more the cells are flattened. The superficial layers consist of thin, squamous cells (Fig. 2–12).

This epithelium is found in the epidermis, the mouth, esophagus, a part of the epiglottis, a part of the conjunctiva, the cornea, the vagina and a part of the female urethra.

6. *Stratified Columnar Epithelium.* The deeper layer or layers consist of small, irregularly polyhedral or fusiform cells which do not reach the free surface. The superficial cells are tall and prismatic and are not connected with the underlying tissue (Fig. 28–

21). This epithelium is rare and covers small surfaces. It is found in the fornix of the conjunctiva, in the cavernous part of the urethra, in some places in the anal mucous membrane, in the pharynx, on the epiglottis, and in the large excretory ducts of some glands. Some authors place the epithelium of the enamel organ in this group.

7. *Stratified Columnar Ciliated Epithelium.* The cells are arranged as in the preceding type, but the free surface of the superficial columnar cells is provided with cilia (Fig. 2–13). It is found on the upper (nasal) surface of the soft palate, in the larynx and, transiently, in the fetal esophagus.

8. *Pseudostratified Columnar Epithelium.* In the pseudostratified epithelium the nuclei are at different levels and the cells lack uniformity (Fig. 2–9). Some of the cells, while attached to the underlying connective tissue, may lose their connection with the free surface. These supporting cells are covered by the tall, superficial cells. In a perpendicular section the nuclei form several rows. Owing to mutual pressure, the cells may become irregular in shape and the tissue may appear to be stratified. Such an epithelium occurs in the large excretory ducts of several glands (parotid) and in the male urethra.

9. *Pseudostratified Columnar Ciliated Epithelium.* This is exactly as in 8, except that the free surface of the cells is provided with motile or nonmotile cilia (Fig. 2–9). It is found on the greater part of the mucous membrane of the respiratory passages, in

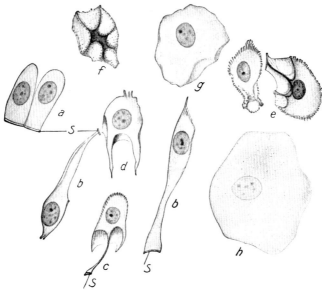

Fig. 2–12. Isolated cells from the stratified squamous epithelium of the cornea of the ox. *a,* Basal cells; *s,* cuticular border; *b,* club-shaped cells; *c,* cell with wing-shaped processes and with a thin stalk attached to the basement membrane; *d,* similar cell from one of the more superficial cell layers; *e,* prickle cells in profile; *f,* same in surface view; *g,* squamous cell; *h,* superficial flattened cell. 740 ×. (After Schaffer.)

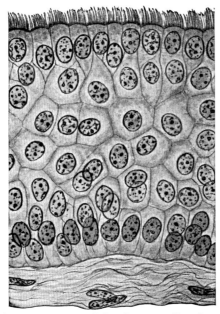

Fig. 2–13. Stratified columnar ciliated epithelium from the laryngeal surface of the epiglottis of a thirty-one-week human embryo. 795 ×. (After V. Patzelt, from Schaffer.)

the eustachian tube, in a part of the tympanic cavity, in the lacrimal sac and in the excretory passages of the male sexual system.

10. *Transitional Epithelium.* This was originally supposed to represent a transition between the strati-

fied squamous and the columnar epithelia. As it is found on the walls of hollow organs which are subject to great mechanical changes by contraction and stretching, its appearance varies greatly. In the contracted condition it consists of many cell layers. The deepest elements have a cuboidal or even columnar shape, then follow several layers of irregularly polyhedral cells, while the superficial layer consists of large cells with a convex free surface. In the stretched condition, usually only two layers can be distinguished: a superficial layer of large squamous elements over a layer of irregular cuboidal cells. This epithelium is characteristic of the mucous membrane of the excretory passages of the urinary system from the renal calices to the urethra.

This classification applies only to the epithelia of the higher vertebrates. In chronic inflammatory irritations or in some neoplasms, one type of epithelium may change into another through the process of *metaplasia.* Thus the columnar bronchial epithelium may change into the stratified squamous.

Inner Structure of Epithelial Cells. The nucleus is generally single and of simple shape. In the squamous cells it is an oval disk; in the cuboidal cells it is spherical; in columnar cells it extends along the cell axis and may appear cylindrical. Epithelial cells with several nuclei sometimes occur (liver cells, parietal cells). The *cell center,* represented by a diplosome, is usually located above the nu-

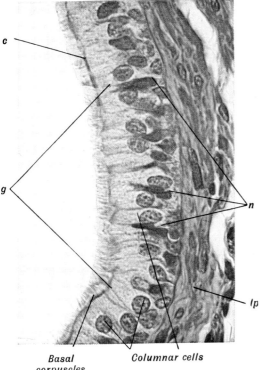

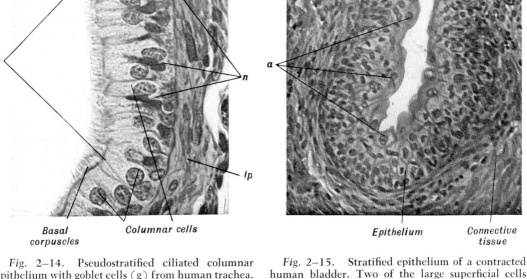

Basal   Columnar cells
corpuscles

Epithelium   Connective
tissue

Fig. 2–14. Pseudostratified ciliated columnar epithelium with goblet cells (*g*) from human trachea. *c,* cilia; *n,* nuclei of goblet cells; *lp,* lamina propria. Mallory-azan stain. 400 ×. (After von Herrath and Abramow.)

Fig. 2–15. Stratified epithelium of a contracted human bladder. Two of the large superficial cells (*a*) are binucleate. Photomicrograph. H + E, 240 ×. (After von Herrath and Abramow.)

cleus and in columnar cells may occupy a position directly under the free surface.

Mitochondria are usually abundant. In squamous cells they surround the nucleus; in columnar cells they are arranged mainly above and below it. The longer mitochondria are usually parallel to the axis of the cell body. A *Golgi net* is always present, typically above the nucleus.

Tonofibrils are fairly common in epithelial cells. They are supposed by some to give the soft cell body a supporting framework, while others believe them to be only tension striae in the cytoplasm. They reach an especially high development in the stratified squamous epithelium, where they form parallel or wavy bundles. Submicroscopic filaments aggregate into the tonofibrils visible with the optical microscope.

Polarity of Epithelial Cells. A peculiarity of all epithelial cells is their *polarity*—the fact that the "proximal" side of the cell attached to the underlying tissue differs from

the "distal" side, directed toward the free surface. The *cell axis,* an imaginary line connecting these two sides of the cell, is usually perpendicular to the surface of the epithelial sheet.

The polarity of epithelial cells results from their arrangement in sheets, for the two surfaces of a sheet of cells cannot have the same conditions of existence. The polarity manifests itself by the arrangement and the shape of the mitochondria at the base and at the top of glandular cells, by the unilateral position of the cytocentrum and the Golgi net, and so on. Generally, the proximal end of an epithelial cell is less differentiated and therefore more similar in the various types of epithelium, reflecting the fact that the proximal end is mainly instrumental in the reception of the nutritive material, which must always be similar. The distal part, on the contrary, is subject to manifold external influences, and in its protoplasm, above the nucleus, appear the different products of metab-

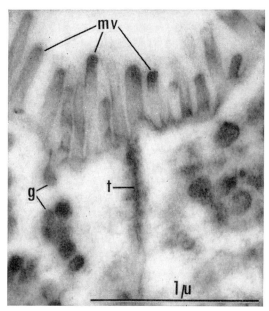

Fig. 2–16. Electron micrograph of section through surface of gallbladder epithelium of mouse. Microvilli (*mv*) project from the cell. The granules (*g*) perhaps indicate absorption of materials. The darkened area (*t*) along the intercellular membrane is a terminal bar. Buffered osmic acid fixation. (Courtesy of E. Yamada.)

olism which are specific for each kind of epithelium—the secretory inclusions, the cuticular formations, and so forth.

The general structure of the epithelial elements just described presents innumerable variations due both to the special type of epithelium and to changing functional conditions. The details of these variations are described with the structure of the various organs in the chapters on special histology. All the types of inclusions mentioned in Chapter 1 may occur in and profoundly modify the structure of epithelial cells.

Free Surface of Epithelial Cells. Structures may develop on the free surface of epithelial cells by (1) specific modification of the superficial layer of protoplasm and (2) formation of membrane-like products of secretion (cuticles).

1. Specialization of the Superficial Protoplasm. The simplest of these structures is a thin layer of condensed cytoplasm on the free surface, as on the superficial cells of the transitional epithelium of the urinary bladder. This is not a true membrane which can be isolated. In a perpendicular section it appears on the free edge as a thin, refringent line.

In many epithelia the free surface of the cells is provided with numerous very thin, hairlike, protoplasmic projections. These vary from exceedingly fine filaments not visible with the light microscope to relatively large structures which have long been known. The very tiny ones made visible by the electron microscope have been called *microvilli.* (See Figs. 2–16; 2–6.) Closely packed, larger, rodlike structures of this general type have long been known on the intestinal epithelium, of all vertebrates, where they were called "striated border" (Figs. 24–5 and 24–7) and on the free surface of the cells of the proximal convolution in the renal tubule where they form a "brush border" (Fig. 2–17). The projections on the intestinal and renal epithelial cells are supposed to aid in the absorption of materials from the intestinal cavity and the lumen of the renal tubules respectively. The microvilli and the projections forming the striated and brush borders with their relatively simple structure are quite different from the motile processes called *cilia* and *flagella.*

The highest structural differentiation of the free surface of the epithelium is reached in the *ciliated cells* (Fig. 2–13). These carry on their free surface a large number of cilia, i.e., thin, usually motile, processes. The length of the cilia in different types of epithelium varies considerably. Their substance appears homogeneous under the optical microscope, although an axial filament or a cross striation has sometimes been described. As a rule, at the base of each cilium, in the superficial layer of protoplasm is a small thickening, the *basal corpuscle.* It has a high refractive index and stains black with iron hematoxylin.

With the electron microscope it is seen that in practically all plant and animal forms, the cilia—and flagella—contain nine pairs of peripherally arranged longitudinal fibrils and two central pairs. These are best seen in cross sections (Fig. 2–19). The cilia have slightly different constitutions at different levels along their length. The electron microscope has also shown that the basal corpuscle and its connection with the cilium form very complex structures.

The movement of the cilia, which propels a constant stream of mucus or other liquid

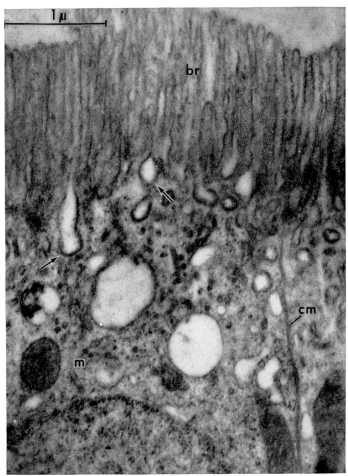

Fig. 2–17. Electron micrograph of section through free surface of epithelium of proximal convolution of kidney of a rat. *br*, Brush border; *m*, mitochondria; *cm*, intercellular membrane. The arrows point to vesicles connecting with the lumen at the base of the microvilli forming the brush border. Buffered osmic acid fixation. (Courtesy of D. C. Pease.)

secretory material, consists in a rapid effective beat and a slower recovery stroke, always in one direction. The beat of each cilium begins slightly later than the beat of the one which precedes it in the direction from which movement proceeds, so that the beating moves across the ciliated surface in rapid and regular waves. If the connection between the cells in the path of the movement is severed, the waves in the separated areas become independent. The basis of the ciliary movement is not known.

In the respiratory passages the ciliary movement drives the mucus toward the mouth, and with it are eliminated the particles of inhaled dust which stick to the mucous membrane. In the ductuli efferentes of the testis the ciliary movement probably helps to forward the spermia from the rete testis to the duct of the epididymis.

In the epididymis the epithelium carries long, nonmotile cilia which are supposed to help in the elimination of the secretion from the cells.

The nonmotile hairs of the epithelium of the maculae and the cristae in the inner ear serve as receptors of vibratory stimuli and transmit them to the cell body. The retinal rods, according to studies with the electron microscope, are also modified cilia.

In the same category of structures are the *central flagella*, which have been found in many epithelial cells, especially in glandular ducts (Fig. 2–20) and in the mesothelial cells in the serous membranes. At its free surface the cytoplasm contains a diplosome, with its axis standing perpendicularly. From the distal centriole an extremely thin, apparently nonmotile filament extends beyond the cell body.

2. *Cuticles.* Cuticle is generally a layer of a more or less solid substance which is secreted

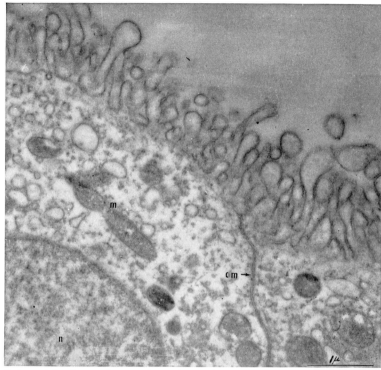

Fig. 2–18. Polypoid border on free surface of ependymal epithelium of rat. *cm,* Intercellular membrane; *m,* mitochondria; *n,* nucleus. Buffered osmic acid fixation. (Courtesy of D. C. Pease and D. Maxwell.)

by and covers the free surface of an epithelial sheet. Unlike the protoplasmic crust, the cuticle is sharply delimited from the cell surface and can be detached from it. The cuticle often becomes impregnated with lime salts, chitin, and the like, and may consist of separate areas, each corresponding to one cell (tooth enamel), or it may become continuous through fusion of contiguous areas.

In the mammals the cuticles are infrequent; examples are the enamel of the teeth; the capsule of the lens; and the tectorial membrane, the lamina reticularis, and the otolithic membrane in the internal ear.

Connections between the Cells in an Epithelial Sheet. Adjacent epithelial cells cohere so tightly that relatively strong mechanical forces are necessary to separate them. This cohesion is particularly striking in the epithelium of the oral cavity and of the intestinal tract, where the movement of hard masses is unable to separate the cells from one another. It is probable that the small amount of interstitial substance acts as a plastic cement. Microdissection studies have shown that in

most types of epithelium the superficial cytoplasm of the living cells contains an adhesive substance which keeps the cells together.

Certain epithelial cells, as in the epidermis, are kept together by many small protoplasmic processes, running from one cell body to another and forming "intercellular bridges" with prominent *desmosomes* or *bridge corpuscles.* Investigation with the electron microscope shows that the tonofibrils stop at the bridge corpuscle and do not pass from cell to cell (Fig. 2–21).

In those epithelia which have no intercellular spaces, the lateral surfaces of the cells adhere tightly to one another and intercellular bridges cannot be seen. In the simple columnar epithelium the cells sometimes separate, and then bridges are distinct. Because this separation can be produced by the use of fixing reagents which cause shrinkage, these bridges are believed by some to be artefacts.

After the action of silver nitrate, especially in the simple squamous epithelium (or mesothelium and endothelium), the cell limits are outlined by black contours. What look to be

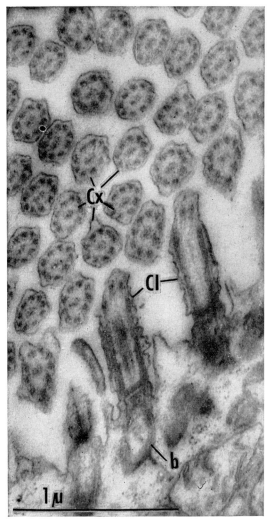

Fig. 2–19. Electron micrograph of cilia from the gill of a clam (Mya). *Cx,* cilia in cross section and *Cl,* in longitudinal section. At lower right— junction of a cilium with its basal body, *b,* in longitudinal section. Buffered osmic acid fixation. (Courtesy of D. Fawcett.)

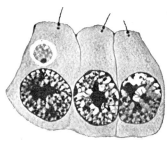

Fig. 2–20. Three epithelial cells with central flagella from a urinary tubule of the mesonephros of a rabbit embryo of 9.5 mm. 1500 ×. (A.A.M.)

large openings in such preparations, the "stomata" which the old histologists thought were present between the edges of the simple squamous epithelial (mesothelial or endothelial) cells, are artefacts. They are sometimes prominent as black dots along the intercellular lines.

Epithelial cells sometimes cohere intimately by means of special structures. Thus, in the convoluted uriniferous tubules the lateral surfaces of the cells are provided with alternating ridges and grooves which interdigitate with those of neighboring cells. (See also Fig. 9–59 of the choroid plexus and Fig. 25–8 of a mortice and tenon-like structure joining hepatic cells.)

When the limits between the cells cannot be detected, the epithelial sheet is called a *syncytium.* This is found, for instance, in the epithelium of the uterine mucous membrane at the beginning of pregnancy and in some areas of the ectoderm of the embryo (trophoblast).

Terminal Bars. In various kinds of epithelium stained with iron hematoxylin, the free surfaces of the single cells are outlined by black lines different from those appearing after the action of silver nitrate. They are smoothly outlined rods of a dense cement substance which solders the edges of the cell surfaces, and are called *terminal bars* because they are supposed to close the intercellular spaces on the free surface (Figs. 2–22 and 2–23).

The terminal bars, when stained with iron hematoxylin, appear as dots if they are seen in cross section, or as short black lines if they happen to lie in the plane of the section. If the free surface of the cells is provided with a cuticle, a striated or brush border, or with cilia, the bars are always located beneath these structures.

Blood Vessels and Nerve Fibers. As a rule, epithelial tissue lacks blood vessels. The nutritive liquid from the blood vessels of the underlying connective tissue reaches the epithelial elements after passing through the basement membrane and through the thin intercellular spaces between the epithelial cells. If the epithelium forms a thick layer, as in the skin, the surface of the connective tissue is usually provided with outgrowths, *papillae,* which carry blood capillaries, bulge deeply into the epithelium and probably facilitate nutrition. In a few cases (stria vascularis of the cochlea) loops of blood capillaries with thin strands of connective tissue may penetrate the epithelium. Nearly everywhere the epithelium is

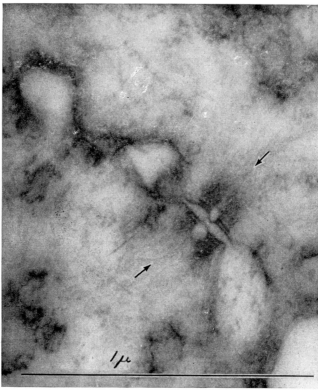

Fig. 2–21. Electron micrograph of "intercellular bridges" in the epidermis of amblystoma. The delicate filaments (arrows) stop at the bridge corpuscle. They do not cross from one cell into the next. Buffered osmic acid fixation. (Courtesy of K. Porter.)

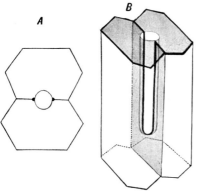

Fig. 2–22. Diagram of two adjacent glandular cells with a secretory capillary between them and with terminal bars: *A*, view in cross section; *B*, side view. (Redrawn after Zimmermann.)

provided with numerous terminal branchings of nerve fibers which pierce the basement membrane and run between and even into the epithelial cells.

Extraneous Cells. Foreign cells may enter the epithelium from the connective tissue. The epithelium of the intestine is always infiltrated in special areas by a multitude of lymphocytes; these may even push aside and disfigure the epithelial cells. After they have left, the latter regain their usual form and resume their former relations. Such an infiltration reaches its highest degree in the thymus.

Regeneration of Epithelium. The epithelial layers, especially those which cover the outer surface of the body and the intestinal tract, are subject to constant mechanical and other injuries. Under physiologic conditions their cells perish continuously and are shed. This is especially manifest in the epidermis, where the superficial cells are continuously undergoing a peculiar degeneration, called *cornification.* The cornified cells are constantly desquamated and are replaced by new ones which arise through the transformation of the cells of the deeper layers. In the respiratory passages, in the inner cavities of the body, and especially in most of the glands, degeneration of the epithelium is rare.

The physiologic loss of cells in the epithelium is balanced by a corresponding regeneration. In vertebrates this is always effected through mitotic proliferation of indifferent epithelial elements. In the stratified squa-

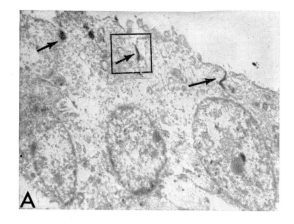

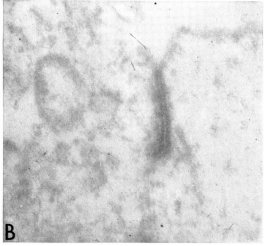

Fig. 2–23. Electron micrograph through ependyma of the posterior pituitary of chicken. The terminal bars between three cells are shown at arrows in Figure *A* at 2800 ×. The area outlined is shown in *B* at a magnification of 17,000 ×. The terminal bar appears as a dark double membrane with a pale central longitudinal cleft. Buffered osmic acid fixation. (Courtesy of D. Duncan.)

mous epithelium the mitoses are found mainly in the deeper columnar and polyhedral cell layers (stratum germinativum). The simple columnar epithelium of the stomach and the intestine is regenerated from special areas of proliferating undifferentiated epithelium in the base of the gastric foveolae or in the crypts of Lieberkühn. In the pseudostratified and stratified columnar epithelium, dividing cells are occasionally found between the resting ones. Their round, contracted bodies usually move toward the surface.

In pathological conditions, as after local injuries, almost every type of epithelium in the human organism may display a considerable ability for regenerative proliferation, although the process may produce new, abnormal cell types. In tissue cultures several types of epithelium (thyroid, iris and liver) were observed to proliferate and to grow in "pure cultures" of thin sheets of flattened cells which did not change for some months. The various types of epithelium, especially those of ectodermal and entodermal origin, seem to keep their specific character even after a prolonged series of transplantations. Although some workers have claimed that epithelial cells in tissue culture develop into fibroblasts, the evidence to date indicates that this is not true.

The proliferation in epithelial regeneration occurs only by mitotic division. Amitosis has been found in the transitional epithelium of the urinary bladder, in the mesothelium of the serous membranes and especially in tissue cultures, but it seems to result only in the formation of multinucleated cells.

In the body, excluding ciliated cells, the epithelial elements are not motile, as a rule. In the healing of wounds and in tissue cultures, however, they flatten and rapidly cover large denuded areas of connective tissue before regenerative division sets in. Occasionally, epithelial cells form ameboid pseudopodia. Wolbach and collaborators have shown that a deficiency of vitamin A in the diet of guinea pigs and rats results in atrophy of most of the epithelia of the body; in their place appears "a stratified keratinizing epithelium, identical in appearance in all locations, and arising from focal proliferation of basal cells." When the vitamin is supplied, the original type of epithelium appears in a few days.

Endothelium, Mesothelium and Mesenchymal Epithelium. The name *endothelium* is reserved for the simple layer of squamous cells which lines the inner surface of the wall of the blood and lymph vessels and of the heart (p. 228). In the early stages of embryonic development the endothelium arises through the flattening of mesenchymal cells (p. 107). In the later ontogenetic stages and in the adult it grows only through proliferation of its own elements. On the other hand, endothelial cells can transform into fibroblasts.

The *mesothelium* is a simple, squamous cell layer which covers the surface of all the serous membranes (peritoneum, pericardium, pleura). Its elements are squamous epithelial cells provided with a more or less distinct brush border; there is a diplosome with a typical central flagellum protruding into the serous cavity (Fig. 2–5).

The prospective potencies of these elements are of

double nature—epithelial and fibroblastic. In tissue cultures the mesothelium of mammals may show for a time a purely epithelial type of growth in islands and sheets of polyhedral, flattened cells. Tumors of epithelial character may develop from the mesothelium and, possibly, structures similar to uterine glands. On the other hand, in inflammation and in some tissue cultures, mesothelial cells may give rise to typical fibroblasts but they do not become macrophages.

Mesenchymal epithelium is the simple layer of squamous cells which lines the subdural and subarachnoid spaces, the perilymphatic spaces in the inner ear and the chambers of the eyeball. These elements originate through flattening of common fibroblasts. The relations between the mesenchymal epithelium and the mesothelium have not been sufficiently elucidated.

The cavities of joints are *not* lined by mesenchymal epithelium. See page 155.

REFERENCES

Arey, L. B.: Wound healing. Physiol. Rev., *16:*327, 1936.

Chambers, R., and de Renyi, G. S.: The structure of the cells in tissues as revealed by microdissection. I. The physical relationships of the cells in epithelia. Am. J. Anat., *35:*385, 1925.

Fawcett, D. W., and Porter, K. R.: A study of the fine structure of ciliated epithelia. J. Morph., *94:*221, 1954.

Lucas, A. M.: Ciliated Epithelium, in Cowdry's Special Cytology. 2d ed., P. Hoeber, New York, (1), 407, 1932.

Reid, M. E.: Interrelations of calcium and ascorbic acid to cell surfaces and intercellular substances and to physiological action. Physiol. Rev., *23:*76, 1943.

Schaffer, J.: Das Epithelgewebe, Handb. d. mikr. Anat. (v. Möllendorff). Berlin, (2), Part I, 1927.

Wilbur, K. M., and Chambers, R.: Cell movements in the healing of micro-wounds in vitro. J. Exper. Zool., *91:*287, 1942.

Wolbach, S. B.: The pathologic changes resulting from vitamin deficiency. J.A.M.A., *108:*7, 1937.

Wolbach, S. B., and Howe, P. R.: Epithelial repair in recovery from vitamin A deficiency. An experimental study. J. Exper. Med., *57:*511, 1933.

Worley, L. G.: Microdissection studies of the ciliated epithelial cell. J. Cell. & Comp. Physiol., *18:*187, 1941.

Worley, L. G., Fischbein, E., and Shapiro, J. E.: The structure of ciliated epithelial cells as revealed by the electron microscope and in phase-contrast. J. Morph., *92:*545, 1953.

CHAPTER 3

Blood

THE EMBRYONIC connective tissue, the *mesenchyme,* gives rise to the blood, the blood vessels and the various types of connective tissue. The mesenchyme develops from the mesoderm immediately after the formation of the germ layers and soon accumulates in masses between them. The mesenchymal cells at first are irregularly stellate and connected by their processes, and their cell bodies are separated by a jellylike, intercellular substance (Fig. 2–2). The cells undergo many changes to form the various blood and connective tissue cells.

There are four main types of connective tissue, all characterized by an abundant intercellular substance: (1) blood and lymph, (2) connective tissue proper, (3) cartilage and (4) bone. In the blood and lymph the intercellular substance is liquid. In the connective tissue proper, of which there are many types, the intercellular substance always contains fibers and varies from a soft jelly to a tough fibrous mass. In cartilage the intercellular substance contains masked fibers and has a rubbery consistency. In bone the fibrous intercellular substance is impregnated with lime salts.

In the adult organism the various tissues of the connective substance cannot be sharply separated from one another in all respects. The fibers of the connective tissue proper continue into both cartilage and bone, and certain characteristic chemical substances are common to the intercellular substance in the connective tissue proper, cartilage and bone. Similarly, the cells of the blood cannot be separated from those of the connective tissue proper, since there is a constant exchange of cells between them. Certain cells of the blood and the other connective tissues may display marked differences in form and function when their environment is changed. Thus a leukocyte which seems to be inactive while in the blood may previously have been active while in the connective tissue proper and may become active again on reentering this tissue from the blood.

In the earliest stages of development the endothelial cells of the blood vessels and the blood cells arise simultaneously from the same mesenchymal elements. Moreover, the embryonic endothelium occasionally turns into blood cells. In the later stages, however, the endothelium becomes more differentiated and independent, and new vessels arise only through sprouting of preëxisting ones. Thus all the vessels, including the heart, become a comprehensive specialized system, described in Chapter 10. The blood vessels are always accompanied by connective tissue. However, as we shall see, some cells with the potencies of development of mesenchymal cells persist in the adult organism around the blood vessels and in the blood-cell-forming organs.

FORMED ELEMENTS OF THE BLOOD

The blood of adult vertebrates is a red liquid which circulates in a closed system of tubes, the blood vessels. Its quantity in man is estimated as about 7 per cent of the body weight. The liquid menstruum of the blood, the *plasma,* appears colorless in a thin film examined under the microscope, but varies from gray to yellow, according to species, when seen in large amounts with the naked eye. Suspended in the plasma are several kinds of formed elements: the *red corpuscles* (*erythrocytes*), *colorless corpuscles* (*white blood corpuscles* or *leukocytes*) and, in mammals, the *blood platelets.**

RED BLOOD CORPUSCLES

In the mammals the red blood corpuscles are nonmotile, highly differentiated cells which have lost their nucleus, Golgi net, mitochondria and centrioles during maturation. In the other vertebrates they retain the nucleus.

A normal adult man has about five and a woman about four and a half million erythrocytes in 1 cu. mm. of blood. Sojourn in high altitudes causes a marked increase in their number. The changes in pathological conditions are still more prominent. The erythrocytes are not always evenly distributed over the circulatory system.

The size of the erythrocytes, under normal conditions, is remarkably uniform; in man the diameter averages 7.74 microns, the thickness at the edge, 1.9 microns. According to some estimates, the erythrocytes of man have a diameter well over 8 microns, and the smaller figure given here is due to dehydration during preparation. The total surface area of all the red blood corpuscles in the human body is computed as about 3500 square meters. The specific gravity of the erythrocytes is higher than that of the plasma; the estimates vary from 1.02 to 1.08.

The red blood corpuscles are a pale, greenish yellow. This is especially marked at the periphery of the corpuscle, where the layer of the colored substance is thickest. In dense masses of erythrocytes the yellow color turns into a distinct red.

The pigment which gives the erythrocytes their color can be easily separated from the corpuscles. It then dissolves in the plasma

* In an attempt to eliminate some of the hematological confusion connected with many of the names of cells now in use, a new nomenclature has been introduced in this country for the various blood cells and their precursors. For instance, in this new terminology it is proposed to supplant *erythrocyte* by *rubricyte.* Until this or another new terminology has been accepted by scientists of all nations, we shall continue to use the conventional names.

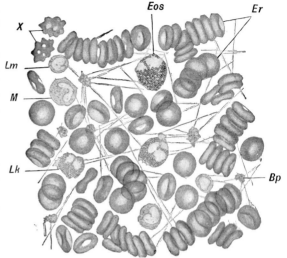

Fig. 3–1.   Fresh preparation of human blood. *Bp,* platelets; *Er,* erythrocytes; *Eos,* eosinophile leukocyte; *Lk,* neutrophile leukocyte; *Lm,* lymphocyte; *M,* monocyte; *X,* crenated erythrocytes. Note the strands of fibrin and rouleaux of erythrocytes. High magnification. (A.A.M.)

and gives it a distinct color, while the corpuscles become colorless, although they more or less keep their form. This process is called *hemolysis.* The pigment is *hemoglobin;* the colorless part which remains after the hemoglobin leaves is called the *stroma.* Hemoglobin and the colorless substances are present in the erythrocytes as a colloidal mixture, of which hemoglobin forms about 95 per cent of the dried weight.

The erythrocytes of the mammals are biconcave disks. In profile they have elongated bodies with rounded ends and a constricted middle part, more marked on one side than on the other.

Some investigators claim that they are shallow cups and that the biconcave form is the result of shrinkage due to an increase in the osmotic pressure of the plasma during examination. It is possible that, in the normal blood, both forms, as well as all transitions between them, are present at the same time. In the camel and the llama the erythrocytes are biconcave ovals devoid of nuclei.

The erythrocytes are extremely soft and flexible. The slightest mechanical influences distort them, but the usual form is restored as soon as the mechanical factor ceases to act. This can be seen easily during the observation of the circulating blood in living capillaries. When an erythrocyte is forced through a blood vessel of small caliber, it becomes considerably drawn out, but resumes the disk shape as soon as it enters a larger vessel. In living condition their substance appears homogeneous even with dark-field illumination. Ultracentrifuged erythrocytes are stratified into two or three layers; this indicates that they are composed of at least three substances.

Under physiological conditions the interior of the erythrocytes and the plasma are in a state of osmotic equilibrium. If the molecular concentration of the plasma is lowered through addition of water, water enters the erythrocyte. If the osmotic pressure of the plasma increases, the interior of the erythrocyte gives up water to the plasma (*crenation,* Figs. 3–1,*x;* 3–3). A solution of 0.9 per cent sodium chloride is isotonic with normal human plasma and therefore does not alter the size or form of the erythrocytes; it is called physiologic salt solution.

In spite of the fact that the red cells and the plasma are in a state of osmotic equilibrium, there are peculiarities of distribution of ions between them (Fig. 3–2). The distribution of the anions Cl^- and HCO_3^- is understood as a consequence of the difference in concentration of nondiffusible protein ions (Donnan equilibrium). The mechanism by which the gradients in concentration of sodium and potassium are maintained is not fully understood.

Erythrocytes have a marked tendency to adhere to one another by their broad surfaces and to assemble in long, curved columns resembling piles of coins (Fig. 3–1). This can be observed in a drop of fresh, undiluted blood. The piles or *rouleaux* arise at once; a slight pressure on the coverslip breaks them up. They also are formed in the living body while circulating in the blood vessels. The adhesion is so strong that, if the motion of the blood stream in the vessel is not too swift, the piles are seen gliding, serpent-like, through the smaller vessels. The cause of the rouleau formation is not known. Some believe that it is a display of surface tension forces which cause bodies suspended in a fluid to apply to one another by their greatest surfaces.

Irregular, persisting clumps of erythrocytes occur in the circulating blood in a variety of

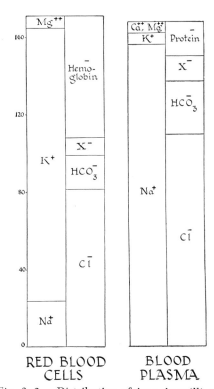

Fig. 3–2. Distribution of ions, in milli-equivalents per kilogram of water between red blood corpuscles and plasma. Modified after Peters and Van Slyke. (Courtesy of A. B. Hastings.)

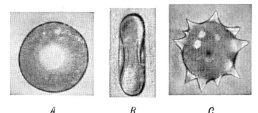

A   *B*   *C*

Fig. 3–3. Red blood corpuscle in 0.9 per cent sodium chloride solution, seen from the broad surface (*A*), in profile (*B*) and crenated (*C*). (After Broderson.)

pathological conditions; these masses of erythrocytes, called *sludges,* have been studied extensively by Knisely and co-workers. They may cause severe local or generalized damage.

Agglutination. Various reagents, such as acid salt solutions or solutions of glucose, may cause agglutination of erythrocytes. They attract one another and assemble in small, dense groups. Agglutination of erythrocytes under the influence of *agglutinins* can occur in the circulatory system of the living organism; the resulting clusters of erythrocytes obstruct the small blood vessels and may lead to severe injuries of the tissues involved.

Abnormal Erythrocyte Forms. A detailed description of abnormal forms of erythrocytes belongs to the textbooks of pathology. Sometimes they occur in the blood of an apparently normal person, or are a manifestation of an accelerated formation of blood.

The erythrocyte may be unusually large or small. This phenomenon is called *anisocytosis.* The largest corpuscles are called *macrocytes;* the smallest ones, *microcytes.* If the erythrocytes acquire irregular contours, *poikilocytosis* is present. This occurs when there is a grave disturbance of hemopoiesis, as in pernicious anemia. In a special type of anemia the erythrocytes are *sickle-* or *crescent-shaped.*

The hemoglobin content may show great variations; in chlorosis each corpuscle contains an abnormally small quantity of this pigment and consequently appears paler than usual (*hypochromic*). In pernicious anemia the individual erythrocytes are abnormally rich in hemoglobin (*hyperchromic*).

is a poor one because of the frequent confusion with "reticular cells."

In the *basophile granulated* or *"stippled" erythrocytes,* with the Romanowsky stain, the substance of the erythrocytes is mottled with numerous, fine, blue granules. Stippled erythrocytes occur in the blood of embryos and of adult mammals, including man. They are found in various types of anemia, especially those of toxic nature, as in lead poisoning. In the hemopoietic organs of the adult they do not occur under physiological conditions. It is possible that the stippled condition is also a manifestation of immaturity in much the same way as the polychromia, but of an immaturity which is physiological only in the embryo; while in the adult it is an indication of an abnormal return to an embryonic type of development. The origin of the basophile granules is traced to either the nucleus of the erythroblast or to its basophile cytoplasm. It is possible that their substance is similar to

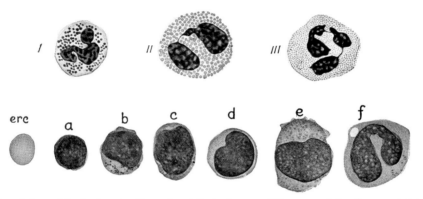

Fig. 3–4. *I,* basophile leukocyte; *II,* eosinophile leukocyte; *III,* neutrophile (heterophile) leukocyte; *erc,* erythrocyte; *a, b, c, d,* lymphocytes; *e, f,* monocytes; from Romanowsky-stained, dry smears of human blood, except *I,* which is stained with thionine. (A.A.M.)

The normal, mature erythrocytes in a dry smear are *acidophile;* that is, in a mixture of an acid (eosin) and a basic dye (methylene blue), such as in the Romanowsky mixture, they are stained electively with the acid dye and appear red (Fig. 3–4). In some cases, however, their substance will stain purple or bluish with this mixture. This condition is called *polychromia.* Polychromatic erythrocytes may occur in the human blood in various anemias. Under physiological conditions they are rarely found in the circulating blood, but are common in the bone marrow. The young forms of the erythrocytes (*erythroblasts*) also have a polychromatic protoplasm. Thus polychromia is a manifestation of immaturity of the red blood corpuscle, although it may also be found in degenerating erythrocytes. The polychromatic erythrocyte always shows a "reticulated substance" on supravital staining. It is possible that this stained network is the result of an artificial clumping of the diffused substance which causes the polychromatophilia seen with the Romanowsky stain. Protoporphyrin has been found in the blood and occurs only in the *reticulocytes* and is possibly the substance which is stained with brilliant cresyl blue in these almost mature erythrocytes. The term "reticulocytes"

the basophile substance in the polychromatic erythrocyte and differs from it only by its granular instead of diffuse distribution in the corpuscle. From this point of view the granules would be a manifestation of a degenerative change of the young erythrocytes.

Quite different from the basophile granules of the mottled erythrocytes are the peculiar granular *Howell-Jolly bodies.* These are undoubtedly remnants of the nuclear chromatin. They often occur in seemingly quite normal erythrocytes of adult and especially of embryonic mammals. They are small, sharply outlined, round or angular bodies which stain intensely with nuclear dyes, and especially with methyl green, which never stains the basophile granulation. Their number is limited to one or two in an erythrocyte.

In some pathological cases the erythrocytes contain the *rings of Cabot.* Although some believe them to be the membrane of the dissolved or extruded nucleus, Schleicher holds that they are artefacts which represent aggregated and denatured proteins of erythrocytes exposed to hemolytic agents.

Certain toxins cause the appearance of peculiar granules in the erythrocytes of the circulating blood —the *granules of Ehrlich-Heinz.* They can be stained with acid dyes in fixed smears and are products of the disintegration of hemoglobin.

Function of the Erythrocytes. The erythrocytes are carriers of oxygen. In the blood vessels of the lungs (or gills) their hemoglobin combines with oxygen and is transformed into oxyhemoglobin. In the tissues of the body where the oxygen tension is much less than in the respiratory organs, oxyhemoglobin is reduced and its oxygen is used in the metabolic processes of the cells. Hemoglobin plays an equally important part in the transport of carbon dioxide from the tissues to the lungs. As it loses oxygen it becomes a weaker acid, the diminution in its acid strength being nearly sufficient to compensate for the carbonic acid formed from the oxygen it delivers to the tissues. In the lungs, as oxygen is taken up and carbon dioxide is lost, it again becomes a stronger acid. In addition, part of the carbon dioxide carried from the tissues to the lungs is combined directly with hemoglobin in the form of hemoglobin carbamate.

COLORLESS CORPUSCLES: LEUKOCYTES, OR WHITE BLOOD CORPUSCLES

The blood of all animals contains a number of colorless corpuscles. Although the origin and morphology of these leukocytes have been studied intensively, little is known of their physiological functions.

The white blood corpuscles are more resistant to change in the surrounding medium than are the erythrocytes. In a drop of fresh blood, if desiccation is prevented, they remain alive for a considerable time and can be studied easily. Their number is far smaller than that of the erythrocytes, averaging in the normal human blood 5000 to 9000 in a cu. mm. In children the figures are higher. The number of leukocytes in the circulating blood varies at different times of the day, during digestion, in the various parts of the circulatory system and, in addition, may change rapidly under the influence of numerous conditions which are hard to control. Consequently, many of the leukocyte counts frequently have only a relative value.

The leukocytes are true cells with a nucleus and cytoplasm; they are all more or less ameboid. In fresh human blood several types can be distinguished: (1) small cells, about the size of an erythrocyte or slightly larger, with a scanty, clear, homogeneous cytoplasm and a faintly outlined, relatively large round, or indented, or irregular nucleus (*lymphocytes*); these merge by a series of transition forms into (2) slightly larger cells with an oval or indented nucleus and somewhat greater amounts of cytoplasm (*monocytes*); these cells are easily distinguishable from (3) cells with a cytoplasm filled with fine granules and a lobated nucleus (*heterophile granular leukocytes* [*neutrophile* in man]). (4) There are also a few cells with coarse, round, yellowish, brilliant granules and usually two clear spots representing the nucleus (*eosinophile granular leukocytes*). (5) Another type of leukocyte, the *basophile granular leukocyte,* is hard to identify when unstained. Thus the white blood corpuscles may be separated into two groups: (1) nongranular leukocytes, and (2) granular leukocytes. It must be emphasized that the cells, as seen in the living or in sections, are quite different from the same cells seen in dry smears, which flatten a sphere to a relatively large, thin disk. In this process many structural details are greatly changed and often distorted. For instance, the obvious nucleolus of the smaller lymphocytes is obscured in dry smears.

Nongranular or Lymphoid Leukocytes; Agranulocytes. This group contains the lymphocytes and the monocytes. As we shall see in the section on the lymphatic tissue, the largest lymphocytes do not gain access to the blood stream under normal conditions, and the large lymphocyte of the blood is the same as the medium-sized lymphocyte of the lymphatic tissue. Under abnormal conditions, large lymphocytes of lymphatic tissue appear in the blood; they are usually called *lymphoblasts.*

Lymphocytes. In human blood the lymphocytes are spherical cells 6 to 8 microns in diameter, although a few of them may be even a little larger. On the average, they are slightly larger than erythrocytes.

Fig. 3–5. Lymphocyte of human blood, showing mitochondria stained supravitally with Janus green. (After Cowdry.)

The characteristic feature of a small lymphocyte is a relatively large nucleus surrounded by a thin layer of cytoplasm. The nucleus is spherical; on one side it always has a more or less marked indentation. In stained preparations the chromatin forms a thick layer at the membrane and several darkly staining particles in the interior. The nucleus accordingly appears dark. The large nucleolus is invisible in stained dry smears. The cytoplasm forms a slightly larger accumulation on the indented side of the nucleus. It is homogeneous and basophile; in dry smears it stains pale blue with the Romanowsky eosin-methylene-azure mixture.

In human blood the lymphocytes form 20 to 25 per cent of the total number of colorless corpuscles.

The larger cells among the lymphocytes (Fig. 3–4, *b, c, d*) are relatively scarce. Their larger size is due to a slightly greater amount of cytoplasm, while the nucleus remains unchanged or is less compact.

The cytocentrum is represented by a pair of centrioles at the indentation of the nucleus (Fig. 3–6); it is surrounded by a small Golgi net. The mitochondria are scarce and small and have the form of small dots or short rods. They are easily stained supravitally with Janus green. Supravital staining with neutral red seldom reveals more than three to five inclusions in man. In many lymphocytes in some animals, such as the rat, a sometimes considerable number of small red vacuoles can be seen around the cytocentrum. Except for occasional small lipoid droplets, no other inclusions are found in the living, unchanged lymphocytes.

Although the lymphocytes are nongranular leukocytes, Romanowsky-stained, dry smears occasionally reveal a few round granules of different sizes and of a bright purple color in their cytoplasm. These are called *azurophile granules.* Unlike the granules of the granu-

locytes, they are not a constant feature of this cell type.

In the guinea pig many lymphocytes and monocytes contain a large spherical inclusion, the *Kurloff body.* In dry smears it stains in the same way as do the azurophile granules and is probably also an accumulation of a substance elaborated by the protoplasm, although it has other staining reactions which differentiate it from the azurophile granules. In living cells the Kurloff body is a homogeneous, yellowish-green body.

Monocytes. There is much confusion as to just what a monocyte is, since the delimitation of this cell type has been obscured by the contradictory opinions of the proponents of the various theories of blood formation. When preparations of blood are examined objectively, the nongranular leukocytes are seen to consist of a series of transition forms which begins with the smaller lymphocytes and ends with larger cells of quite different appearance, the monocytes, which will be described shortly. But in the midportion of this series of transitions is a group of cells which cannot be classified as either typical lymphocytes or typical monocytes. The following description refers to the typical monocytes of the blood; a discussion of their origin is found on page 113.

The typical monocytes measure 9 to 12 microns in diameter. In dry smears, in which they are flattened and stretched, their diameter may reach 20 microns. They constitute 3 to 8 per cent of the leukocytes of the circulating blood. Their enumeration is especially difficult, because, as mentioned before, they cannot always be sharply differentiated from the larger lymphocytes of the blood.

In the typical monocytes the cytoplasm is far more abundant than in the lymphocytes, while the nucleus is relatively small. In the older monocytes the nucleus has an eccentric position, and is oval or kidney-shaped. A few monocytes have a horseshoe-shaped or deeply constricted nucleus—these are the oldest ones. The nuclear membrane is much thinner and the chromatin granules finer and more numerous than in the lymphocytes. Therefore the nucleus stains paler, especially in dry smears. One or several small nucleoli are always present, although not seen in dry smears.

Fig. 3–6. Lymphocytes of human blood, showing cytocentrum. Iron-hemotoxylin stain. (After Weidenreich.)

The abundant cytoplasm has a pale, grayish-blue color in dry smears stained with eosin-methylene-azure. Special methods show that it contains the usual diplosome and a considerable number of mitochondria. At the periphery, near the indentation of the nucleus, is a Golgi net. Supravital staining with Janus green and neutral red reveals a spherical group of fine red vacuoles, the rosette, which surrounds the cytocentrum; its position corresponds with that of the Golgi net. The bluish-green stained mitochondria are arranged in a wreath around the rosette. The claim that this rosette is specific for monocytes is incorrect, for closely allied cell types may have neutral red rosettes (lymphocytes in the rat, plasma cells, some macrophages, some of the septal cells of the lung). The number of circulating monocytes may be increased experimentally in rabbits by infection with *L. monocytogenes,* or by injections of the phospholipids of the tubercle bacillus.

Monocytes are often erroneously identified with macrophages, especially in some inflammatory processes in which all the mononuclear exudate cells have been loosely spoken of as constituting a "monocytic reaction" (see p. 76).

Granular Leukocytes, or Granulocytes. In contrast to the lymphocytes and monocytes, the granulocytes always contain specific granules. These are of the same form in any given cell, but are distinctly different in various classes of granulocytes in a given species and in the homologous cells of different species.

They may be relatively large or small, spherules or ovoids, or may be irregular in outline, filamentous or rod-shaped. Another general characteristic of the mature granular leukocytes is the shape of their nucleus. Instead of being spherical and slightly indented or kidney-shaped, as in the majority of the nongranular leukocytes, the nucleus of the granulocytes is constricted into a varying number of lobes. The lobated nucleus of the mature cells gradually develops from the compact, spherical nucleus of the young forms (see Fig. 5–3). Although different classes of granulocytes may be identified on the basis of their nuclear form and the morphology of the cytoplasmic granules, the most convenient classification is based upon a combination of the morphology and staining reactions of the granules.

In such a classification the granulocytes fall into three general groups designated as (1) acidophile, (2) basophile, and (3) heterophile leukocytes (neutrophile in man). In the first, the granules in the cytoplasm are most often spherical or oval and are electively stained with acid dyes; in the second they are of similar form, but stain electively with basic dyes; while in the third group the granules, although constant in a particular species, differ as to form, size and staining reaction according to species (Fig. 3–7). Systematic studies with the electron microscope of the fine structure of the various granules in the leukocytes of many animal species have not been made. The granules of the eosinophile

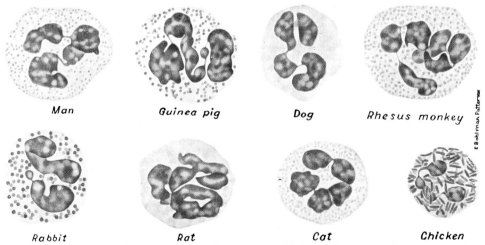

Man   Guinea pig   Dog   Rhesus monkey

Rabbit   Rat   Cat   Chicken

Fig. 3–7. Heterophile leukocytes of several species. Note the variations in size and staining of the granules in those species in which they are present. Wright's stain. (Courtesy of M. Block.)

leukocytes are reported to have a long, barlike structure made up of many parallel lamellae.

Acidophile or Eosinophile Leukocytes. The diameter of these cells, which are spherical in the fresh condition, is about 9 microns. In dry smears the size of the flattened cells is about 12 microns. Their number in the normal adult blood varies from 2 to 5 per cent of the total leukocyte count.

The nucleus usually has two oval lobes connected by a thin chromatin thread. In fixed and stained preparations, the lobes of the nucleus show a fairly dense chromatin network, but no nucleoli. A similar nucleus is found in the eosinophile leukocytes of the other mammals. In the rat and mouse it is a thick, irregular ring.

The cytoplasm forms a thin layer at the periphery of the cell. It is more distinct in moving cells, in which it sends out pseudopodia. In the interior of the cell body the cytoplasm is reduced to thin partitions between the granules and stains faintly with basic dyes. In the middle of the cell body a small area free of granules is occupied by the cytocentrum with its diplosome.

The coarse granules, in man, are spherical and are stained with acid dyes; after Romanowsky type stains they are red. Supravital staining with Janus green reveals a few mitochondria between the eosinophile granules. With the exception of some fishes, all vertebrates have typical eosinophile leukocytes in their blood.

Basophile Leukocytes. These cells are difficult to find in human blood, because they form only about one half of 1 per cent of the total number of leukocytes. Their size is about the same as that of the heterophile leukocytes. In a dry smear they measure 10 microns in diameter. The nucleus is elongated, often bent in the form of an **S**, and provided with two or more constrictions. The chromatin network is looser and paler than in the eosinophile leukocytes, and does not contain any nucleoli. The granules in the cytoplasm of the living cells have a low refractive index. Their substance, in man, is soluble in water; therefore, in preparations stained with the usual watery dye solutions, the granules are partly dissolved and disfigured. In dry smears or in sections of alcohol-fixed material, the cytoplasm contains round granules of different sizes, which stain a metachro-matic purple with alcoholic thionine or toluidin blue. Supravital application of neutral red gives the granules a dark red color.

The solubility of the basophile granules has created considerable confusion in regard to the nature of these cells, but the use of suitable methods leaves no doubt as to their specific nature. In the guinea pig, their granules are large, oval, insoluble in water, and stain but faintly. In the dog, the granules are fine and are assembled in a small, compact group. In the cat, rat and mouse, the basophile leukocytes seem to be absent from the blood normally. In the lower vertebrates the variations are still greater.

Heterophile Leukocytes (Neutrophile in Man). This type of leukocyte is the most numerous in the blood of all vertebrates. In fresh human blood these cells can be recognized easily by their fine granulation, which is seen especially well when the cells move (Fig. 3–1, *Lk*). The size of the spherical cells in fresh condition is from 7 to 9 microns. In a dry smear they measure from 10 to 12 microns, and constitute 65 to 75 per cent of the total number of leukocytes.

The nucleus is highly polymorphous. It is an elongated, bent or twisted body consisting of several irregularly oval or angular lobes connected by thin chromatin threads. During ameboid motion the nucleus undergoes passive changes of its form, but the constrictions and the thickenings are constant. The number of the lobes varies from three to five and increases with the age of the cell. Under physiological conditions the majority of the cells have a three-lobed nucleus. In pathological cases these relations may change considerably. A dark chromatin network is seen in the lobes in stained sections; nucleoli are absent.

The cytoplasm has a peripheral, homogeneous layer which forms the pseudopodia. The inner, slightly acidophile mass is full of fine granules, except for a small, clear area in the center of the cell body which contains the diplosome. In man the granules are stained with neutral dyes, and are, therefore, called neutrophile. The Romanowsky mixture gives them a purple hue. They can also be stained with acid dyes such as eosin. Supravital staining with Janus green reveals the presence of a few mitochondria. Neutral red applied supravitally gives the granules an indistinct, pale yellowish hue. Occasionally, small vacuoles and inclusions of fat or glycogen can be found between the granules.

In other mammals the granules have a variable size and staining reaction which are more or less typical for the species. In the guinea pig and rabbit the granules are stainable with either acid or basic dyes, although they show a predilection for acid dyes and, therefore, were called *pseudoeosinophils*. In some species the granules are so small that they are hardly seen with the highest powers of the microscope (see Fig. 3–7).

Abnormal Forms of Leukocytes. In some diseases the blood may contain degenerating leukocytes. Vacuoles, droplets of fat or lipids may appear in the protoplasm. These are well shown by the use of supravital stains. In the granular leukocytes the nucleus may undergo fragmentation into separate parts (*rhexis*) or shrinkage (*pyknosis*). Atypical and immature leukocytes enter the blood in certain diseases.

Free Macrophages of the Blood. Many investigators have described macrophages in the blood. They have a large, eccentric nucleus and a vacuolated, ameboid cytoplasm which often contains phagocytosed inclusions. In animals which have had intravenous injections of vital dyes or corpuscular matter, large quantities of these substances accumulate in the free macrophages (see p. 78). They originate in the spleen, liver and bone marrow from fixed macrophages through contraction and isolation. They are found especially in the blood of the veins and of the right heart, and the major part of them is filtered off in the capillaries of the lungs, but some may occasionally enter the general circulation.

The free macrophages appear in the blood in certain diseases, especially in those of septic nature. Their presence in the normal blood, as claimed by some authors, is doubtful, and their presence in the blood even in pathological cases is considered by some to be merely an agonal phenomenon. Confusion has been caused because many authors did not distinguish the blood macrophages from the monocytes. The cells described by some authors in leukemias and other diseases under the name of hemohistioblasts are for the most part the same free macrophages. In some cases, artificially damaged hemocytoblasts or myelocytes in dry smears have been mistaken for free macrophages or hemohistioblasts.

Functions of the Leukocytes. Little is known of the functions of the leukocytes while in the blood stream. Occasionally some of them phagocytose particulate material, such as bacteria or carbon particles. However, the function of the leukocytes is apparent when they are outside the vascular system, where they show active movement and phagocytosis; some turn into other cell types.

Movement. All leukocytes are capable of active movement, provided they have a solid substrate to move on. The movement can be observed in a drop of fresh blood protected from desiccation and kept at body temperature or, better, in tissue cultures. The movement of the leukocytes is identical in essential details with that of an ameba. The factors concerned in the movement of leukocytes are discussed by DeBruyn.

The ability of the leukocytes to move explains why they are not confined to the system of blood or lymph vessels, but may be found everywhere in the connective tissue and occasionally even in other tissues. Under physiological conditions, single leukocytes, especially lymphocytes, migrate out of the vessels into the tissue, and may return again into the blood or lymph channels. In inflammation—the reaction of a tissue to local injury—the leukocytes assemble rapidly in the blood vessels of the region and migrate in enormous numbers through the vessel walls into the tissue (see p. 76).

Chemotaxis. The migration of the leukocytes into the tissue toward the site of a local injury is believed to be caused by their chemotactic properties. In *in vitro* studies it is primarily the granulocytes which show chemotaxis when tested with bacterial products, products of damaged tissue and a number of carbohydrates. Although the lymphocytes do not react chemotactically to any of these substances, they as well as the monocytes also accumulate in great numbers in injured tissues.

Phagocytosis. The heterophile granulocytes display a marked capacity for ingesting small, discrete particles, such as cinnabar, carbon and bacteria. This action may occur within the circulating blood stream, but is distinctly more extensive in extravascular locations. Phagocytosis can be watched outside the body when living leukocytes and bacteria are brought together under suitable conditions. The phagocytosis and digestion of bacteria by the heterophile granulocytes is one of the means by which the host destroys bacteria, and the issue of some infections may depend upon the extent of phagocytosis.

The eosinophile leukocytes display phagocytosis rarely, if ever. The agranulocytes in the blood stream are seldom phagocytic, although, under suitable extravascular conditions, the monocytes, in contrast to the small lymphocytes, engulf particulate matter.

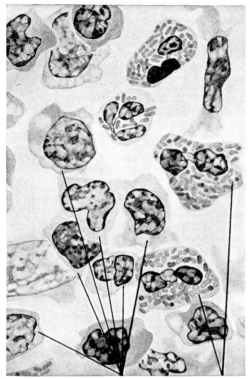

*Polyblasts   Basophile
leukocytes*

Fig. 3–8.   Basophile granular leukocytes in the local reaction of the connective tissue of a guinea pig to the injection of ventriculin 10 days previously. Hematoxylin-eosin-azure II. 2240 ×. (Courtesy of N. Plimpton; drawn by Miss E. Bohlman.)

Other Properties of the Leukocytes. A positive oxidase reaction occurs in the granulocytes and in most of the monocytes. The lymphocytes do not give this reaction. Some investigators believe that lymphocytes are a source of antibodies (p. 79). The number of leukocytes in the peripheral blood can undergo variations as a result of certain pathological conditions. Certain stimuli affect one cell type more than the others. The number of eosinophils increases greatly when certain animal parasites are in the body and also during various allergic disorders. Administration of adrenocorticotropic hormone or cortisone causes a disappearance of the eosinophils from the blood, and this is used as a guide during clinical administration of these hormones. This cell type may accumulate in enormous numbers in local tissue areas, as in the mucous membranes of the respiratory passages in bronchial asthma, or about animal parasites.

The basophils increase in number in the blood stream of guinea pigs infected with *L. monocytogenes.* They appear in great numbers in the inflamed area caused by the local injection of egg albumen or ventriculin in guinea pigs (Fig. 3–8).

Lymphocytes accumulate in small numbers about autogenous tissue grafts and in greater numbers about homoplastic tissue grafts. Heteroplastic grafts are surrounded by a large number of heterophile leukocytes and lymphocytes (Loeb).

BLOOD PLATELETS

In the circulating blood the platelets of all mammals are small, colorless corpuscles. They are round or oval, biconvex disks; when seen in profile, they look like small, plump spindles or rods (Fig. 3–9). Their spindle shape and their content of granules are clearly shown in electron micrographs (Fig. 3–10). Their size is not quite uniform, the average being 3 microns. Their number varies considerably and is usually given as 250,000 in 1 cu. mm. of blood, although some authors give much higher figures. It is extremely diffi-

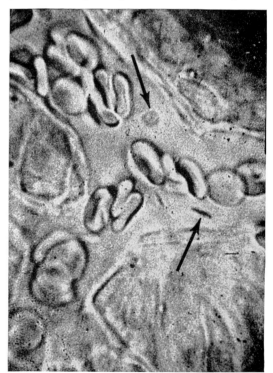

Fig. 3–9.   Blood vessel of chamber in skin of a mouse showing blood platelets in profile and surface view (arrows). From a frame of a 16 mm. motion picture film. (Courtesy of G. Algire.)

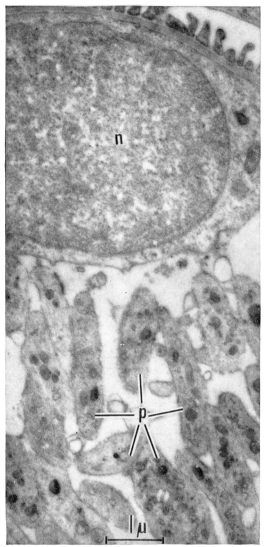

Fig. 3–10. Electron micrograph of thrombus in glomerular capillary of rat showing densely packed, spindle-shaped platelets (*p*). *n*, nucleus of endothelial cell. Buffered osmic acid fixation. (Courtesy of D. Pease.)

taneously, around and radiating from them, fibrils of fibrin appear in the plasma (Fig. 3–1).

They may be preserved for observation by rendering the blood incoagulable through the addition of sodium citrate or heparin. Of all fixing reagents, solutions of osmic acid preserve them best. In rapidly prepared dry smears, the platelets are preserved as round corpuscles.

In dry smears stained with the Romanowsky mixture, each platelet is seen to consist of two parts. One is highly refractile and contains purple granules. This is the *chromomere.* The other is pale and homogeneous, and stains a pale blue—the *hyalomere.* The chromomere occupies a central or peripheral position. The hyalomere is often seen to send out pointed processes (Fig. 3–11). Sometimes the platelets contain small vacuoles.

At present the dominant opinion connects the origin of the platelets with peculiar giant cells, the *megakaryocytes,* which are found in the bone marrow of all mammals. It is believed that excrescences become pinched off the surface of the megakaryocytes and enter the blood stream as platelets.

The changes of the platelets in a fresh drop of blood make it probable that they play a part in the coagulation of the blood. It is believed by some that they are the source of the enzymes which are necessary at least to initiate this process of clotting. However, they cannot be the only source of such en-

cult to determine the real number, because, as soon as the blood leaves the vessel, the platelets adhere to one another and to all surfaces with which they come in contact (Fig. 3–1).

In a fresh drop of blood the platelets at once agglutinate into small and large clusters and stick to the glass. They are the lightest elements of the blood, so that in centrifuged blood they form the uppermost white layer, lose their smooth outlines, and finally disintegrate into small groups of granules. Simul-

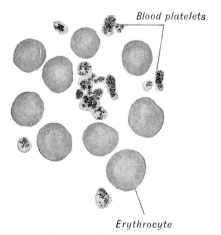

Blood platelets

Erythrocyte

Fig. 3–11. From a dry, Romanowsky-stained smear of human blood, showing platelets with their hyalomere and the dark, punctiform chromomere.

zymes, because blood plasma freed of platelets clots nevertheless. Platelets are absent from the blood of the inframammalian vertebrates. These animals have, instead, nucleated spindle cells which play a role in blood clotting, and the term "thrombocytes" should be reserved for them.

Blood Clotting. Blood, as it circulates normally in the vascular system, is a fluid tissue. Upon cessation of the circulation or upon removal of blood from the vessels, the fluidity is rapidly lost, the blood becoming a jellylike mass. This change is termed "blood clotting" or "blood coagulation."

The physical factor involved in this change is the aggregation of a protein of the normal plasma into threads which form an interlacing network, in the small meshes of which are entangled the blood corpuscles and the aqueous menstruum.

The dispersed protein of normal plasma which contributes to the formation of the network is *fibrinogen*. This, when modified physically and chemically to form the network, is known as *fibrin*. With the electron microscope it can be seen that the fibrin fibers formed from bovine fibrinogen are "cross striated." The width of these bands is about 250 angstrom units. The liquid fraction of the plasma which remains after the subtraction of fibrin is called *serum*.

Although many factors are known which modify the speed and extent of fibrin formation, and hence of blood clotting, no ultimate analysis of the phenomenon has been reached. Methods have been developed by which fibrin formation may be greatly delayed.

For the details of clotting and the chemical composition of the blood, reference should be made to a text on physiological chemistry.

LYMPH

The lymph, the liquid which fills the lymphatic vessels, is collected from all over the body and returned to the blood. The composition of the lymph arising in different organs varies markedly. There are no cells in the smallest lymph vessels, the lymph capillaries. As it passes through the lymph nodes, however, more and more cells are added to the lymph. In the thoracic duct it is a more or less opaque, sometimes pinkish liquid which contains large numbers of cells. The lymph here is similar to the plasma of the blood; it also clots, although the clot is much looser and softer. The number of cells in the lymph varies within wide limits, although their character is uniform. As a rule, besides some few erythrocytes and occasional eosinophile leukocytes, about 99 per cent of the cells are lymphocytes, of which the small lymphocytes form 80 to 85 per cent. Medium-sized and, especially, large lymphocytes are relatively rare. Cells of monocytic character occur but rarely under physiological conditions; the same is true of larger cells of the macrophage type. Under pathological or experimental conditions, including tissue cultures of lymph, the cellular aspect of the lymph changes rapidly, and numerous macrophages develop from the lymphocytes.

Fig. 3–12. Electron micrograph of fibrin, showing the periodic cross striation. 55,000 ×. (After Porter and Hawn.)

REFERENCES

The student will find detailed discussions of the cells of the blood in Downey's Handbook of Hematology. New York, Hoeber, 1938.

Beams, H. W., and Hines, E. B.: Stratification of the rat erythrocyte by ultracentrifuging. Anat. Rec., *90:*155, 1944.

Bunting, C. H.: The Granular Leukocytes, in Cowdry's Special Cytology. 2d ed. New York, (2), 683, 1932.

Conference on leukocytic functions. Ann. New York Acad. Sci., *59:*665, 1955.

Conway, E. A.: Reaction of lymphatic tissue in early

stages of *B. monocytogenes* infection. Arch. Path., *25:* 200, 1938.

DeBruyn, P. P. H.: Theories of ameboid motion. Quart. Rev. Biol., *22:*1, 1947.

Hawn, C. van Z., and Porter, K. R.: The fine structure of clots formed from purified bovine fibrinogen and thrombin: A study with the electron microscope. J. Exper. Med., *86:*285, 1947.

Jordan, H. E.: The origin and significance of the megakaryocytes of the lungs. Anat. Rec., *77:*91, 1940.

Knisely, M. H., Bloch, E. H., Eliot, T. S., and Warner, L.: Sludged blood. Science, *106:*431, 1947.

Maximow, A.: The Lymphocytes and Plasma Cells, in Cowdry's Special Cytology. 2d ed. New York, (2), 601, 1932.

McCutcheon, M.: Chemotaxis in leukocytes. Physiol. Rev., *26:*319, 1946.

Merrell, M., Gellhorn, A., and Flexner, L. B.: Studies on rates of exchange of substances between the blood and extravascular fluid. II. The exchange of sodium in the guinea pig. J. Biol. Chem., *153:*83, 1944.

Pappenheim, A.: Morphologische Hämatologie (1 and 2). Leipzig, 1919.

Porter, K. R., and Hawn, C. van Z.: Sequences in the formation of clots from purified bovine fibrinogen and thrombin: A study with the electron microscope. J. Exper. Med., *90:*225, 1949.

Quick, A. J.: The anticoagulants effective in vivo with special reference to heparin and Dicumarol. Physiol. Rev., *24:*297, 1944.

Rebuck, J. W., and Woods, Helen L.: Electron microscope studies of blood cells. Blood, J. Hematol., *3:* 175, 1948.

Sabin, F. R., Smithburn, K. C., and Thomas, R. M.: Cellular reactions to wax-like materials from acid-fast bacteria. J. Exper. Med., *62:*751, 1935.

Schleicher, E. M.: The origin and nature of the Cabot ring bodies of erythrocytes. J. Lab. & Clin. Med., *27:* 983, 1942.

Speirs, R. S.: Physiological approaches to an understanding of the function of eosinophils and basophils. Ann. New York Acad. Sci., *59:*706, 1955.

Sturgis, C. C., and Bethell, F. H.: Quantitative and qualitative variations in normal leukocytes. Physiol. Rev., *23:*279, 1943.

Waugh, D. F.: The ultrastructure of the envelope of mammalian erythrocytes. Ann. New York Acad. Sci., *50:*835, 1950.

Weidenreich, F.: Die Leucocyten und verwandte Zellformen. Wiesbaden, 1911.

CHAPTER 4

The Connective Tissue Proper

THE CONNECTIVE tissue proper always contains fibers in its intercellular substance. As this substance and the cells present numerous variations, this type of tissue may be subdivided into numerous categories. The classification is difficult and inexact, for the different categories are linked by transitional forms. Even in the adult organism one type of connective tissue may be directly transformed into another.

The fibrous components of the connective tissue of the body are in general irregularly arranged. Depending on whether the fibers are loosely woven or densely packed, we speak of *loose connective tissue* or *dense connective tissue*. The fibers have a regular arrangement in tendons, fibrous membranes and in the connective tissue lamellae of some organs; these are therefore called *regular connective tissues*. In addition, there are a number of types of connective tissues with special properties: *mucous connective tissue, elastic tissue, reticular tissue, adipose tissue, pigment tissue,* the specialized connective tissue (lamina propria) of the intestinal and uterine mucous membranes, and the interstitial connective tissue of lung, testis and ovary. All are modifications of the basic loose connective tissue.

LOOSE CONNECTIVE TISSUE

The loose connective tissue develops from the mesenchyme which remains after all the other types of the connective tissue have been formed. It contains almost all the cellular and intercellular elements (or their precursors) which occur in the other kinds of connective tissue, and serves as a prototype of the connective tissue in general. It is a whitish, sticky mass, which fills out the spaces between the organs and penetrates with the blood vessels into the interior of the organs. Where the organs are separated from one another it is stretched between them in thin membranes and threads, and is easily torn during dissection. Like a collapsed sponge, it contains innumerable potential cavities which can be easily filled artificially with liquids or air. These are the "cells" of the old anatomists, who are responsible for the name "areolar tissue" sometimes used.

Intercellular Substance. The intercellular substance forms the main mass of the tissue; three parts can be distinguished in it: (1) the collagenous or white fibers, (2) the elastic or yellow fibers, and (3) the ground substance. In addition, there are reticular fibers which occur at the boundary of the connective tissue and other structures.

Collagenous Fibers. All types of connective tissue show collagenous fibers as their most characteristic element. In the loose tissue these are long, straight or wavy threads or ribbons of 1 to 12 microns in thickness. They run in all directions (Fig. 4–7), and their ends cannot be found. They are colorless and show longitudinal striation, while in cross section they seem granular. This microscopic appearance results from the fact that the fibers consist of parallel fibrils, 0.3 to 0.5 micron in thickness, held together by a cementing substance, presumably a protein, since it is digested by trypsin. On the surface of the fiber the cement substance forms a thin membrane. The fibrils are thought not to branch, but the fibers branch in many places.

The collagenous fibers are flexible, but offer a great resistance to a pulling force. The breaking point of human collagenous fibers (tendon) is reached with a force of several hundred kg./cm.², and their elongation at this point is only a few per cent. In polarized light, collagenous fibers show positive uniaxial form and also crystalline birefringence. The *form birefringence* indicates the presence of submicroscopic, elongate structures oriented in the direction of the fiber axis and made visible as fibrils by the electron microscope. The presence of *crystalline birefringence* reflects the fact that inside these fibrils a finer structure is present of molecular dimensions and with a regular periodic pattern. This is in accordance with the findings based on x-ray diffraction methods, according to which the fibrils consist of long polypeptide chains running predominantly in the direction of the fiber axis. In the electron microscope the fibrils are cross striated; the distance between the bands is 640 A on the average. When stained with phosphotungstic acid, each striation is resolved in a series of smaller bands.

Tropocollagen, the fundamental building block or molecule of collagen, is a rodlike particle of the order of 2600-3000 A long and 15 wide. Its existence and properties were deduced from electron microscope studies of the highly ordered fibrils and crystallites precipitated from collagen solutions. Nearly all the collagen in solution can be precipitated as native fibrils with the typical 640 A axial period (Fig. 4–2, A), or as "long spacing" fibrils (FLS) with periods of about 2400 A (Fig. 4–2, B), or as short segments (SLS) of varying width, and about 2400 A long (Figs. 4–2, C). Each form can be readily dissolved and precipitated in either of the other forms. The tropocollagen hypothesis rests on the observation that: (1) collagen can be precipitated quantitatively in any of these three states, (2) that one of them, SLS, is composed of long thin particles the length of the segment, and (3) that FLS is formed by lateral and lengthwise aggrega-

tion of similar particles. Physical chemical studies on solutions of collagen have confirmed the existence of the tropocollagen particle. The native collagen fibril is believed to result from the arraying of tropocollagen particles in an orderly but staggered fashion thus giving rise to the appearance of 640 A subperiods of the major repeating unit of about 2600 A.

The concept of extracellular fiber formation is supported by the observation that a form of collagen, extractible from fresh connective tissue by neutral salt solutions, can be precipitated as a mass of fibrils identical with those in the native tissue simply by warming the solution to 37° C.

In boiling water the collagenous substance dissolves and yields a solution of animal glue or gelatin. In weak acids and alkalis the collagenous fibers swell. Pepsin in acid solution digests the collagenous bundles, but they resist alkaline trypsin solution.

A typical reaction is obtained with dilute formic acid (Fig. 4–1). This causes the bundles to swell considerably, lose their longitudinal striation, and become transparent; in many places these swollen bundles are constricted transversely or obliquely. No satisfactory explanation of this phenomenon has been given. Concentrated acids and alkalies destroy collagenous fibers. Collagen gives an insoluble product with salts of heavy metals and with tannic acid. Collagenous fibers have no specific staining reactions; however, acid aniline dyes, as, for instance, the acid fuchsin of van Gieson's stain or the aniline blue in Mallory's mixture, stain the bundles sharply, especially after mordants. Collagen may present physical and chemical differences in vari-

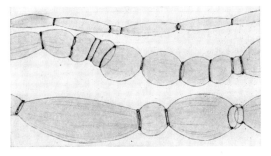

Fig. 4–1. Swelling of collagenous fibers, from the loose connective tissue of a rabbit, on the addition of 0.5 per cent formic acid. 185 ×. (A.A.M.)

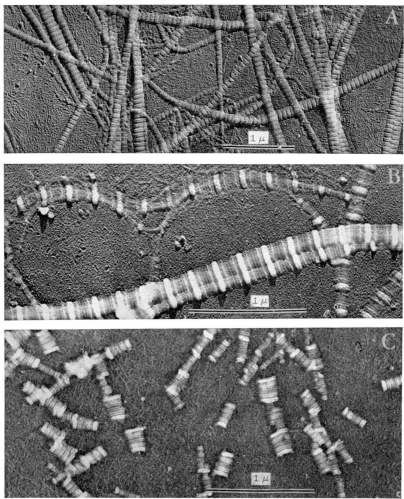

Fig. 4–2. Electron micrographs of collagen. *A,* fibrils with typical collagen period (640 A.). Precipitated from collagen solution by dialysis against 1% NaCl. Chromium shadowed. *B,* fibrous long spacing (FLS). Produced by dialysis against water of a mixture of α_1 acid glycoprotein of serum and collagen solution. Stained with phosphotungstic acid hematoxylin. *C,* segment long spacing (SLS). Precipitation from acid solution of collagen by addition of ATP. Chromium shadowed. (Courtesy of J. Gross, F. O. Schmitt and J. H. Highberger.)

ous parts of the body and in different species of animals.

Elastic Fibers. In the loose connective tissue, elastic fibers are scarce. They are long and run in various directions; they appear as brilliant, highly refractive cylindrical threads or flat ribbons, much thinner than the collagenous fibers. In contrast to the latter, the elastic fibers are not fibrillar, but are usually homogeneous, although the larger fibers may stain more deeply at their periphery; they branch and anastomose freely and form a loose network (Fig. 4–7). If the tissue is fixed in its natural position, the elastic fibers are straight, while in teased preparations they often appear wavy or spiral. When assembled in large numbers, they have a yellowish color on macroscopic examination.

Elastic fibers yields easily to stretching. The breaking point occurs when they are stretched to about 150 per cent of their original length. For this a force of only 20 to 30 kg./cm.² is necessary. When released after stretching, elastic fibers return practically entirely to their former length. Elastic fibers at most show only weak positive birefringence, but become strongly birefringent on stretching. This is caused by an orientation

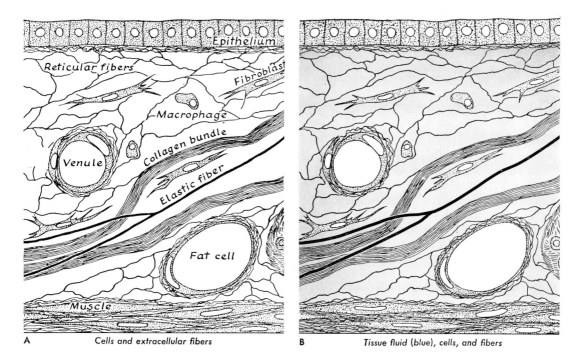

A   *Cells and extracellular fibers*

B   *Tissue fluid (blue), cells, and fibers*

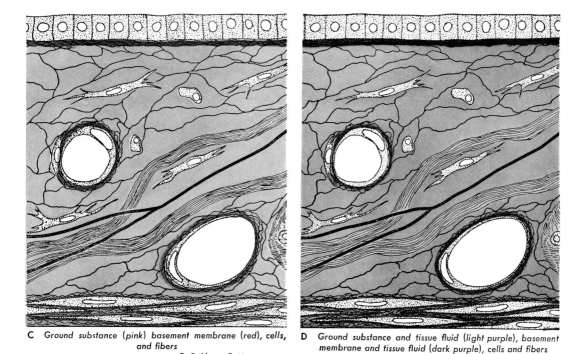

C   *Ground substance (pink) basement membrane (red), cells, and fibers*

E. Bohlman Patterson

D   *Ground substance and tissue fluid (light purple), basement membrane and tissue fluid (dark purple), cells and fibers*

Fig. 4–3. Diagram of relations of cells, tissue fluid, ground substance and connective tissue fibers. *A,* cells and extracellular fibers. *B,* tissue fluid (blue), cells and fibers. *C,* ground substance (pink), basement membrane (red), cells and fibers. *D,* ground substance and tissue fluid (light purple), basement membrane and tissue fluid (dark purple), cells and fibers. (Drawn by E. Bohlman Patterson; after Gersh.)

of the submicroscopic components in the direction of the fiber axis.

The characteristic constituent of the elastic fiber, *elastin,* is an albuminoid and may vary slightly in its qualities according to its origin. It is highly resistant to boiling water, acids and alkalies, and through the action of alkalies it can be isolated from the other constituents of the tissue. Unlike the collagenous fibers, elastic fibers can be stained fairly electively (orcein or resorcin fuchsin). Elastic fibers do not show an ordered structure in electron micrographs.

Ground Substance. Collagenous, reticular and elastic fibers and the cells of connective tissue are embedded in a homogeneous material, the ground substance which stains metachromatically (purple with toluidine blue). It is believed to be derived from connective tissue cells and is a complex mixture of proteins—including collagen in molecular dispersion and glycoproteins—carbohydrates, lipids and water. Closely associated with it is the *tissue fluid* which originates from the blood plasma and is the medium for the exchange of metabolites between circulating blood and tissue cells. The viscosity varies from fluid to gel-like and is markedly affected by *spreading factors,* of which the most notable is *hyaluronidase.* When the ground substance surrounds certain structures (muscle, capillaries), or is at the base of certain epithelial structures, it is so modified that, together with the enclosed reticular fibers, it

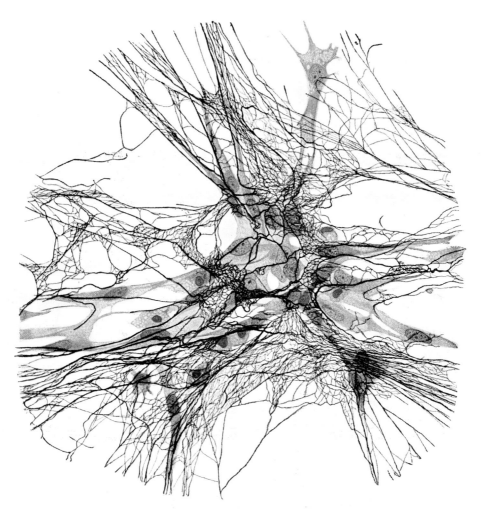

Fig. 4–4.   Development of reticular fibers in a twenty-day culture of adult rabbit thymus. The reticular fibers stain black. Bielschowsky-Foot and Mallory-Azan stains. 900 ×. (A.A.M.)

forms the basement membrane. Alterations in the ground substance have been described with age, activity, and in certain pathological conditions. It is presumably the ground substance which appears to be affected by hormones such as *relaxin, adrenocorticotropic hormone* and *cortisone.* The whole range of activities influenced by the state of the ground substance is not yet known, but it appears to be implicated in diffusion of nutrients in extracellular spaces, capillary permeability, growth of certain organs and tumors, cartilage, bone formation and resorption, and calcification.

Reticular Fibers. In certain places in the loose connective tissue are networks of highly branched, reticular fibers. Most stains do not demonstrate them as they are very thin. They are, however, electively impregnated with silver by modified Bielschowsky methods, after which they appear as black, sharply drawn nets.

They occur where connective tissue is adjacent to other tissues. In the basement membrane they form a dense network separating the epithelium from the connective tissue (Figs. 2–3; 24–13). Similar networks are formed around blood vessels, particularly capillaries, muscle fibers, nerve fibers, fat cells and in the respiratory portions of the lung. Reticular fibers are continuous with collagenous fibers, and there is a gradual transition of one into the other. Microdissection studies have shown reticular fibers to be inelastic. Like the collagenous fibers, they resist digestion by trypsin in an alkaline medium, but, unlike them, do not swell on the addition of dilute organic acids. Their submicroscopic structure is like that of the collagenous fibers. Some consider the reticular fibers to be immature collagenous fibers and call them "precollagenous" fibers. The idea of the immature nature of the reticular fibers agrees well with the fact that they are usually found in those places in the connective tissue where undifferentiated cells of mesenchymal nature are assembled (see Chap. 5).

Origin of Fibers. Practically all investigators believe that connective tissue fibers arise between the cells through a condensation or crystallization of an intercellular substance secreted by the cells.

The process of collagen formation is identical in principle in the body of an embryo, in young scar tissue and in a tissue culture; the silver impregnation methods give a clear insight into the morphology of this process. Delicate networks of branching and anastomosing fibrils appear on the surface and between the fibroblasts (Fig. 4–4). The fibrils may follow the outlines of the cell bodies and their processes, but they also extend far into the intercellular substance. The finest of the developing fibrils are shown by the electron microscope to have the characteristic cross striation of collagen and to be apparently extracellular (Fig. 4–5). The first networks increase in number and thickness, and then are rearranged into parallel, wavy bundles which continue into the argyrophile networks. The bundles of fibrils increase in thickness and finally lose the ability to be impregnated with silver (Fig. 4–6). Instead, they begin to stain with the methods for collagenous fibers (Mallory, van Gieson) and, like them, resist digestion by pancreatin in an alkaline medium. The final arrangement and direction of the collagenous bundles are probably influenced by mechanical forces. Connective tissue fibers do not develop in scorbutic guinea pigs, and they appear rapidly when such animals are given vitamin C. Extracellular phosphatase is present in large amounts in the developing collagen of a scar.

The elastic fibers appear in the embryo much later. Their histogenesis has not been adequately studied.

Cellular Elements. The loose connective tissue contains the following cell types: fibroblasts, undifferentiated cells, macrophages (histiocytes) and a varying, but much smaller, number of lymphoid wandering cells, mast cells, eosinophils, plasma cells, pigment cells and fat cells.

Fibroblasts. These common connective tissue cells are generally believed to be instrumental in the elaboration of the intercellular fibers. The fibroblasts are long, flat elements which in profile appear as slender spindles. Their elongated or star-shaped body sends out several spear-shaped processes which end with one or several points. These cell bodies are easily demonstrable with iron hematoxylin, but are hard to see in hematoxylin and

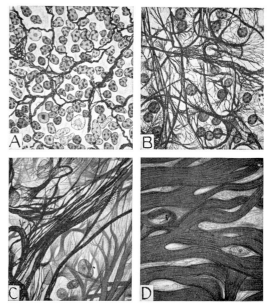

Fig. 4–6. Four stages in development in tissue culture of collagenous fibers from reticular tissue of rabbit lymph node: *A*, section of normal lymph node showing cells and reticular fibers (black); *B*, the reticular fibers are branching and much more numerous after four days in vitro; *C*, after five days in vitro the reticular fibers (black) contrast with newly formed collagenous fibers (gray); *D*, after six days in culture there are only thick bundles of collagenous fibers. Bielschowsky-Foot and Mallory-Azan stains. About 500 ×. (After McKinney.)

Fig. 4–5. Electron micrograph of a formation of collagen fibers which developed from an explant of chick embryo skin during nine days in culture. Only broader compound strands would be visible with the light microscope. Compare with Figure 4–6. 19,600 ×. (After Porter and Vanamee.)

eosin preparations (Fig. 4–7). The cells are usually adjacent to the surface of the collagenous bundles. The large, oval nucleus has a delicate, sometimes slightly folded, outline and contains dustlike chromatin particles and one or more large nucleoli. Near the nucleus are a diplosome and a Golgi net. The mitochondria appear as slender rods which are scarce in the processes, but more numerous near the nucleus and around the cytocentrum. Tonofibrils (fibroglia fibers) run along the inner surface of the cell.

The cytoplasm of the fibroblast rarely contains inclusions except occasional, small, fat droplets and usually remains colorless when neutral red is applied supravitally (Fig. 4–8). In inflammation and tissue cultures, however, it contains a number of small neu-

tral red vacuoles. Granules which stain with the periodate-leucofuchsin method become numerous at times in the cytoplasm.

The majority opinion holds that fibroblasts are differentiated cells which do not give rise to other types of free cells of the connective substance. There is good evidence, however, that they can develop into bone cells and some indication that they become slightly phagocytic on intense stimulation. Not all the relations of fibroblasts to mesenchymal and reticular cells have been determined.

Each fibroblast is an independent cellular element. In inflamed tissue and in tissue cultures it moves with a gliding motion which does not affect the outer form of the cell body. Ameboid pseudopodia are never observed.

Undifferentiated (Mesenchymal) Cells. Many investigators believe with Marchand

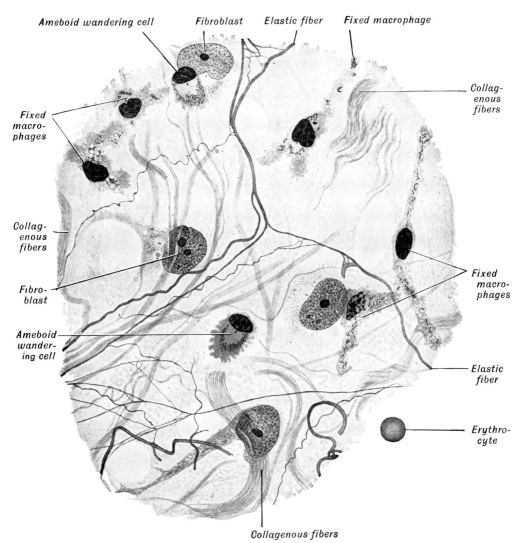

Ameboid wandering cell   *Fibroblast*   *Elastic fiber*   *Fixed macrophage*

*Collag-
enous
fibers*

*Fixed
macro-
phages*

*Collag-
enous
fibers*

*Fibro-
blast*

*Fixed
macro-
phages*

*Ameboid
wander-
ing cell*

*Elastic
fiber*

*Erythro-
cyte*

Collagenous fibers

Fig. 4–7.   Section through slightly edematous, subcutaneous, loose connective tissue from the thigh of a
man. Iron-hematoxylin stain. 950 ×. (A.A.M.)

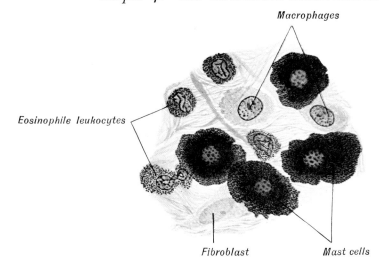

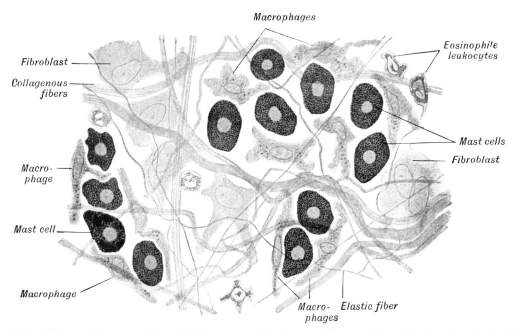

Fig. 4–8.   The two figures are from the loose connective tissue of the rat. *Above:* fixed and stained with hematoxylin-eosin-azure. 600 ×. *Below:* stained supravitally with neutral red. 800 ×. (A.A.M.)

that some outstretched connective tissue cells persist in the adult organism with the potencies of mesenchymal cells. They are often smaller than the fibroblasts, but have the same general appearance; in the loose connective tissue they are usually arranged along the blood vessels, particularly along the capillaries (Fig. 4–10). The conviction that they are not common fibroblasts, but are undifferentiated cells is gathered from numerous observations which show that, under the influence of certain stimuli—as in tissue cultures, inflammation, and the effects of injection of blood toxins—they may develop into new cell types. They probably have much the same properties as the *primitive reticular* cells of the blood-forming tissues and of the free lymphoid stem cells. (See p. 89; Fig. 5–23).

Macrophages (Histiocytes). In the loose connective tissue the number of macrophages

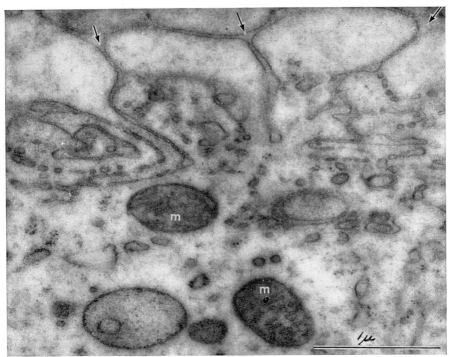

Fig. 4–9. Electron micrograph of macrophage in rat spleen with three infoldings of the surface indicated by arrows. At the right and at the left these infoldings suggest that they are giving rise to rows of tiny vesicles. *m*, mitochondria. Buffered osmic acid fixation. (Courtesy of G. Palade.)

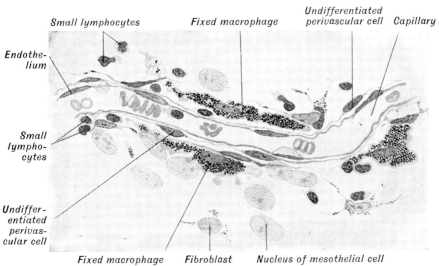

Fig. 4–10. Stretch preparation of omentum of a rabbit vitally stained with lithium carmine. Hematoxylin stain. 500 ×. (A.A.M.)

varies according to the region of the body and the animal species. On the average they seem to be almost as numerous as the fibroblasts, which they outnumber in the richly vascular areas. They are scattered singly among the fibroblasts or are assembled in small groups.

The macrophages in the normal loose connective tissue are usually outstretched resting cells, but in inflammation they round up and become actively motile, *free macrophages.*

In form the outstretched macrophages vary from flat, rounded or oval cells to elongated, spindle-shaped elements which sometimes have branched processes. Ameboid movements are not seen under physiological conditions. The nucleus is smaller than that of the fibroblast, has a heavy, slightly folded membrane, and is irregular, oval or kidney-shaped. It contains no large nucleoli; the chromatin particles are coarser and stain darker than in the fibroblasts. The cytoplasm has distinct, ragged outlines and stains darkly (Fig. 4–7). Near the nucleus there is a distinct diplosome and a Golgi net; the mitochondria are short rods or granules and are assembled mainly around the cytocentrum. The cytoplasm usually contains a number of small vacuoles which stain supravitally with neutral red (Fig. 4–8). These cells are able to ingest many types of particulate matter and store electively certain electronegative, acid aniline dyes in colloidal solution, such as trypan blue and lithium carmine. After repeated injections, the dye inclusions become numerous and large, and the tissue develops a distinct, macroscopic color. As the fibroblasts store little or none of the dye, this method allows a precise identification of the macrophages. The most intense storage is obtained where the concentrated dye solution has immediate access to the cells, as in a subcutaneous injection. The vital storage of acid dyes has been looked upon as a phagocytosis of ultramicroscopic particles.

In the loose connective tissue of mammals, under physiological conditions, transitional forms between macrophages and fibroblasts and between lymphoid wandering cells and macrophages are rare. But in inflamed tissue the sharp limits between the cells are effaced in certain stages (p. 78). The distinction between these different cell types may also be difficult in the lower vertebrates.

The macrophages of the loose connective tissue have also been called *clasmatocytes, rhagiocrine cells, histiocytes, resting wandering cells,* and many other names. The macrophages along the blood vessels, together with the perivascular undifferentiated cells, have also been called *adventitial cells.*

Lymphoid Wandering Cells. These cells present marked variations in size and shape (Fig. 4–7), and are so irregularly distributed that large stretches of loose connective tissue may be devoid of them. The smallest have a round, large, darkly-staining nucleus and a scanty, basophile cytoplasm which contains few or no inclusions after supravital staining with neutral red. Such cells resemble the lymphocytes of the blood in every respect.

Many of the wandering cells appear to be monocytes and, among other properties, display a neutral red rosette. The largest cells, which normally are rare, may be 12 microns or more in diameter and have an eccentric, kidney-shaped nucleus and a highly ameboid cytoplasm containing various inclusions when stained supravitally with neutral red (p. 54). Such elements are structurally identical with the small *polyblasts* of inflammation, in which a continuous series of gradual transitions can be found between all these cell types (p. 78).

Although the lymphoid cells are identical with the nongranular leukocytes of the blood, many of them originated in the embryonic mesenchyme and stayed there. These cells can always enter the circulation. There is no reason for distinguishing hematogenous and histogenous cells among them; they all have the same potencies.

Mast Cells. Mast cells have been found, often in groups about the blood vessels, in the connective tissue of most vertebrates. Their cytoplasm is filled with granules which stain metachromatically with basic aniline dyes; with methylene blue or thionine the granules have a purple color. Neutral red stains them supravitally a dark, brick red (Fig. 4–8). The granules in most species are soluble in aqueous fixatives.

In the rat and mouse the mast cells are large and polyhedral; in other mammals, including man, they are smaller, irregularly oval or flattened cells. Slow amebism can be observed occasionally. The relatively small nucleus is inconspicuous. In the neighborhood of the nucleus is a diplosome.

In mammals the mast cells of the connective tissue and the basophile leukocytes of the blood are independent cell types, despite similar staining properties of their granules. There is an accumulating mass of evidence that the mast cells elaborate an *anticoagulant,* much like *heparin.*

Eosinophile Cells. In man these cells are occasionally found in the interstitial connective tissue of some glands, particularly the mammary gland, and of the lung, and in the omentum. Under certain pathological conditions they may accumulate in the connective tissue in large numbers. They are numerous in the loose connective tissue of the rat, mouse and guinea pig (Fig. 4–8).

Excluding the connective tissue of the intestinal mucosa, where special conditions prevail, the eosinophile cells of the connective tissue are eosinophile leukocytes which have migrated from the blood vessels and have settled in the tissue.

The nucleus in these cells always has the typical, polymorphous character of the mature eosinophile leukocyte of the respective species. Thus, in the rat or mouse it is a thick ring. Round, compact nuclei, as well as mitoses, which are typical for the young forms of the eosinophile leukocytes, do not occur in the connective tissue.

Plasma Cells. In the common connective tissues, plasma cells are extremely rare, although they occur frequently in the serous membranes and in the lymphatic tissue. They may be only as large as a small lymphocyte, or may be two or three times that size (Fig. 4–11). Their form is spherical or often flattened. In the living cell the spherical or polygonal body has a glassy, homogeneous appearance. Slow movements can sometimes be observed.

The nucleus is small, round or slightly oval, and has an eccentric position. In its interior and at the membrane, coarse, darkly staining, regularly distributed chromatin particles are seen. Binucleate cells occur, but mitoses are exceedingly rare.

The homogeneous cytoplasm is strongly basophile and forms a broad layer in the cell body. The middle of the cell is occupied by a round, pale area adjacent to the nucleus; this area is the cytocentrum with its diplosome. Scattered around the cytocentrum are mitochondria and a varying number of vacuoles, which stain supravitally with neutral red. These occupy the site of the Golgi net in fixed preparations.

In most of the foci of plasma cells, all transitions from small lymphocytes to fully developed plasma cells can be found, and the process of change has been followed in tissue cultures. The transformation of reticular cells and of large lymphocytes (hemocytoblasts) into plasma cells has also been observed. The possible role of plasma cells in

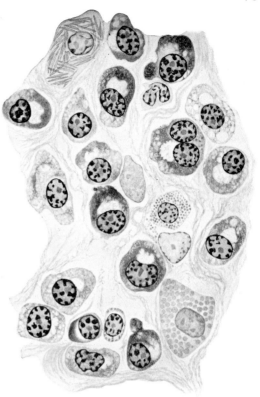

Fig. 4–11. Plasma cells from connective tissue near human tonsil. There are transitions from small lymphocytes to plasma cells. Several of the latter contain globular or crystalloid inclusions. Hematoxylin-eosin-azure. (A.A.M.)

antibody production, or storage, is discussed on page 79.

The plasma cells seem unable to change into any other cell type (except possibly into inflammatory macrophages); they are specifically differentiated elements which finally degenerate. During degeneration, large spherical drops or crystals of a peculiar, acidophile substance frequently accumulate in the cell body. When the cytoplasm disintegrates, these inclusions are set free and remain between the other elements of the tissue as *Russell's bodies.*

Pigment Cells. In the loose connective tissue of the mammals, pigment cells are rare; they occur more frequently in the dense connective tissue of the skin. They are elongated cells with short, irregular outgrowths; the cytoplasm contains small granules of *melanin.* The pigmented cells in the superficial layers of the derma are believed by many to be

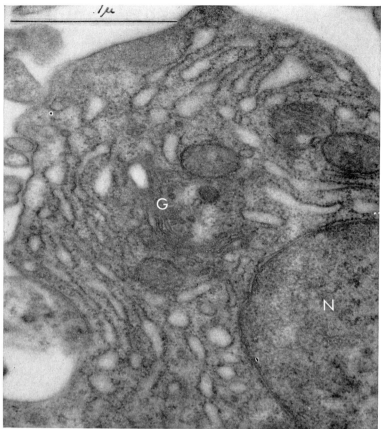

Fig. 4–12.   Electron micrograph of portion of a plasma cell from the nasal mucosa of a cat. G is part of the Golgi apparatus in which the pairs of delicate membranes are distinct. There are four mitochondria and the rest of the cytoplasm is largely filled with vesicles and membranes and the dense granules forming the so-called endoplasmic reticulum. These are the structures responsible for the intense basophilia of the plasma cell. N, nucleus. Buffered osmic acid fixation. (Courtesy of G. Palade.)

merely connective tissue phagocytes which receive their pigment from the epithelium; they may be called *dermal chromatophores.* Pigment cells containing melanin which they themselves have elaborated occur in the derma in the sacral region of the newborn of the Mongolian race. These cells had best be called *dermal melanocytes,* to distinguish them from the *epidermal melanocytes* (see Chap. 20). Melanocytes are found in most mammals in the pia mater of the ventral surface of the medulla oblongata. A large number of them are assembled in the pigment tissue of the choroid of the eye, where they are flattened and have broad, lobated processes.

The pigment granules in the melanocytes in hypophysectomized frogs retract about the nucleus. After the injection of extracts of the pars intermedia of the hypophysis and exposure of the frogs to sunlight, the pigment granules extend rapidly throughout the processes of these cells.

The pigment cells arise early in development from neural crest cells.

Fat Cells. Small droplets of neutral fat may occur in any cell of the connective tissue. There are, however, cells with a special fat-storing function; only these should be termed "fat cells." They are found scattered singly or in groups in the loose connective tissue, especially along the blood vessels. When they accumulate in large numbers and crowd out the other cells, the tissue is transformed into *adipose tissue.*

A living fat cell is a large, brilliant, spherical body. Every mature fat cell contains only one large drop of neutral fat, which can be

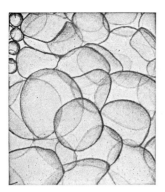

- *Fig. 4–13.* Fresh preparation of a human fat lobule, showing fat cells and smaller, extracellular fat drops (more highly refractile). 160 ×. (After Schaffer.)

chromatin. The individual fat cells are surrounded by a network of argyrophile fibers. In the brown fat tissue (interscapular gland) the cells, as a rule, contain not one large, but several small fat droplets.

New fat cells may develop at any time in the connective tissue of the adult organism, and fully developed fat cells may lose their fat when the organism does not receive sufficient nutritive material. In tissue cultures of adult loose connective tissue and in ear chambers in living rabbits, the development of fat cells from fibroblast-like cells has been observed. It is possible that, when new fat cells develop in the adult, they arise from the undifferentiated mesenchymal cells. This would

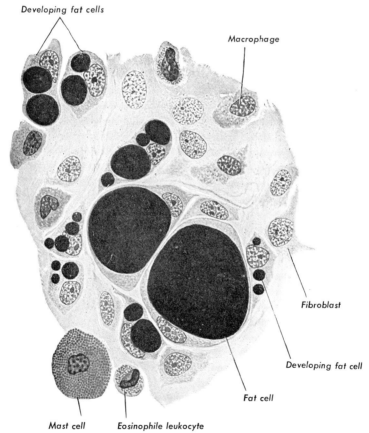

Fig. 4–14. Several fat cells from the subcutaneous, loose connective tissue of a rat. The fat has been stained black by the osmic acid of the fixation fluid. About 1000 ×. (A.A.M.)

stained black with osmic acid or orange with Sudan III. The cytoplasm is reduced to a thin membrane which surrounds the drop; it is thickened in that part which contains the flattened nucleus with its central mass of

agree with the fact that new fat cells—as in the embryo—always appear along the small blood vessels, which are accompanied by cells of undifferentiated mesenchymal nature.

The first step in the formation of a fat cell

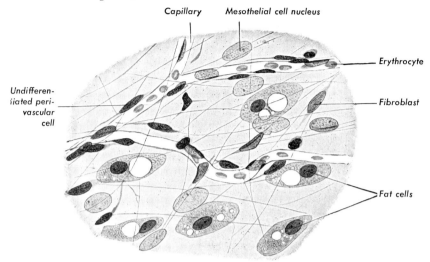

Fig. 4–15.   Portion of omentum of a starving rabbit. The fat cells have lost most of their fat and appear with much cytoplasm. 375 ×. (A.A.M.)

is the appearance of a few small droplets of fat in the cytoplasm. These increase in size and gradually fuse. Simultaneously, the cell body swells, the processes are withdrawn, and the cell becomes spherical. As the fat drop increases in size, the cytoplasm is reduced to a thin membrane, while the nucleus is compressed and flattened. Mitoses are not found in fat cells. When the fat cell loses its fat, the same series of transitional forms can be observed in the reverse sequence. The question of the exact nature of the cells into which the fat cells are transformed when they lose their fat is unsettled. They do not always resemble fibroblasts, but may remain, as in serous atrophy, as sharply outlined, spherical or oval elements. This has been confirmed by studies on living cells in chambers in the rabbit's ear (Clark and Clark).

The fat enters and leaves the cell in the invisible form of its soluble components. The idea that small droplets of fat (hemoconia) may penetrate the membrane and fuse with the large fat drop has not been confirmed.

Functions of the Loose Connective Tissue. The loose connective tissue is the medium supporting and surrounding the elements of the other tissues. It serves as packing material and fills out the spaces between the organs, and its flexible collagenous fibers allow a more or less distinct movement of the connected parts in relation to one another. This is its mechanical function.

In addition, this tissue plays an important role in the nutrition of the elements of other tissues which are embedded in it. The part each cell type takes in this function is unknown. But it is clear that all substances which the cells of the other tissues receive from the blood, and all the products of metabolism and water which they turn over to the blood and lymph, must pass through a layer of connective tissue. It has been claimed that some of the cells of this tissue have an endocrine function, but the evidence supporting this view is not convincing.

Inflammation. Of great importance is the role the loose (and dense) connective tissue plays as the arena of the local reactive process called inflammation. Even under physiological condition, endogenous noxious substances may appear in various places in the body. Some of them have to be neutralized or destroyed by the elements of the connective tissue; this process has been termed "physiological inflammation." Exogenous stimuli which cause a pathological inflammation call forth a much more intense local reaction which manifests itself in a series of complicated phenomena in which local elements of the connective tissue as well as cells and liquid from the blood participate. The results of this local reaction are the destruction, digestion and absorption of the foreign noxious substances and the reparation of the damage caused by them.

In inflamed connective tissue, leukocytes migrate from the vessels into the tissue at the

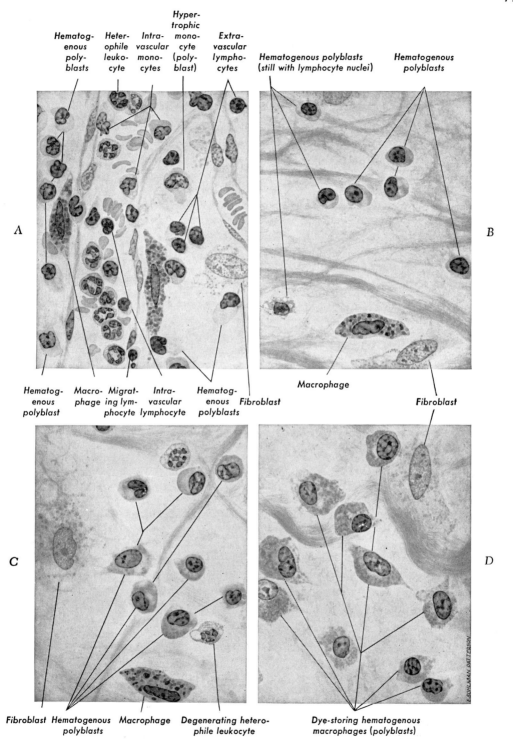

Hematogenous polyblasts | Heterophile leukocyte | Intravascular monocytes | Hypertrophic monocyte (polyblast) | Extravascular lymphocytes | Hematogenous polyblasts (still with lymphocyte nuclei) | Hematogenous polyblasts

A

B

Hematogenous polyblast | Macrophage | Migrating lymphocyte | Intravascular lymphocyte | Hematogenous polyblasts | Fibroblast | Macrophage | Fibroblast

C

D

Fibroblast | Hematogenous polyblasts | Macrophage | Degenerating heterophile leukocyte | Dye-storing hematogenous macrophages (polyblasts)

Fig. 4–16. Four stages in the early inflammatory reaction caused in the connective tissue of a rat by the local injection of trypan blue. *A,* at six hours, *B,* at eight hours, *C,* at twenty-four hours, *D,* at thirty-two hours after injection. These figures show the migration of lymphocytes and monocytes into the connective tissue and their rapid transformation into large, dye-storing macrophages by thirty-two hours. See text (p. 78). Hematoxylin-eosin-azure II. 700 ✕.

very beginning of the process. The heterophile leukocytes soon degenerate. The mononuclear blood cells (lymphocytes and monocytes) hypertrophy in a couple of days after the onset of inflammation and transform into large phagocytic elements, the hematogenous macrophages. In these early stages of inflammation, all transition forms from lymphocytes and monocytes to hematogenous macrophages can be seen. Another source of phagocytic elements is the macrophages already present in the connective tissue. A number of them turn into free macrophages (histogenous macrophages). There are thus in the field of inflammation a variety of mononuclear cells of different origin, called *inflammatory mononuclear cells* or *polyblasts*. There is some evidence that the fibroblasts can also turn into macrophages, but this transformation is denied by most investigators. In inflammation the endothelial cells of blood vessels swell and may divide mitotically, but they do not turn into leukocytes or macrophages. During the first two days of inflammation, the polyblasts of hematogenous origin can still be distinguished from those of local origin because of their smaller size. But they continue to grow, so that after this time the polyblasts of local and of hematogenous origin can no longer be distinguished.

In tuberculous lesions some polyblasts become changed into the epithelioid cells of the tubercle. The polyblasts may form, through fusion, giant cells of the foreign body or the tuberculous type. In the later course of the inflammatory process the fibroblasts proliferate. The polyblasts scattered among the fibroblasts settle down as resting macrophages; in still later stages, some become fibroblasts. The fibroblasts form collagen in the process of scar formation.

Tissue Cultures. Essentially the same cellular transformations occur in tissue cultures. The lymphocytes and monocytes of the circulating blood (Fig. 4–17) and the lymphocytes of the lymph and lymphatic tissue develop rapidly into macrophages. If the nutritive medium contains a vital dye, the hypertrophied lymphocytes and monocytes store it in granular form. In older cultures the transformation proceeds further; the cells proliferate mitotically and turn into fibroblasts which form large sheets of connective

tissue in which the development of argyrophile and collagenous fibers has been observed. In tissue cultures, as in inflammation, the fibroblasts proliferate, but fail to change into other cell types.

THE SYSTEM OF MACROPHAGES
(Reticulo-Endothelium)

In discussing inflammation it was pointed out that the macrophages of the tissue and those which developed from blood cells play the main role in disposing of local noxious agents. Generalized noxious stimuli are taken care of by similar cells scattered in the various connective tissues all over the body. Like the macrophages of the loose connective tissue, they have the ability to take up particulate matter, including bacteria, and to store foreign substances brought to them in colloidal solution. These cells form the *system of macrophages,* consisting largely of the macrophages of the loose connective tissue (already discussed), the phagocytic reticular cells of the lymphatic tissue, myeloid tissue and spleen, the Kupffer cells in the sinusoids of the liver, lining cells of the sinusoids in the adrenal gland and hypophysis, certain perivascular cells and the "dust" cells of the lung.

All these phagocytes, although dissimilar under physiological conditions, react similarly in response to the same noxious stimuli. This observation led to the idea that they constitute a single class of cells, to which a variety of names has been applied. Because Metchnikoff, who called them *macrophages,* was the first to recognize that they belong to a single physiological system and to see clearly their defensive function in inflammation and in immunity, the term *macrophage system* is probably the most appropriate for this collection of cells. So defined, the macrophage system is essentially the same as the "reticulo-endothelial system" of Aschoff.

As mentioned earlier, the most easily controlled criterion for deciding whether a cell of the connective tissue or blood is a macrophage is whether the cell will accumulate a colloidal dye from solutions so weak that the other elements of the connective tissue do not take up appreciable amounts of it. In animals which have had repeated injections of adequate doses of a vital dye, and in general infections, large numbers of free macro-

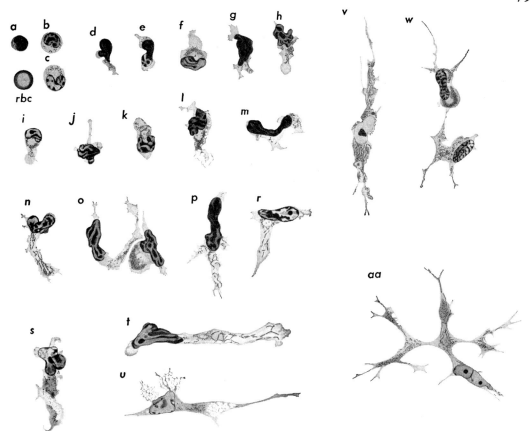

Fig. 4–17. Cells from sections of cultures of the leukocytes of the blood of guinea pig, showing the development of lymphocytes and monocytes into macrophages (polyblasts). *a* and *b,* lymphocytes and, *c,* monocyte from centrifuged blood; *d* and *e,* ameboid lymphocytes and *f,* ameboid monocyte, from a three-hour culture; *g* to *k,* from a ten-hour culture; *l* to *r,* from a twenty-five-hour culture; *s* to *u,* from a two-day culture; *v, w,* from a five-day culture; *w* is in mitosis; *aa,* macrophage from twelve-day culture. Note mitochondria in all cells; iron-hematoxylin stain. 750 ×. (A.A.M.)

phages are mobilized in the spleen, liver and bone marrow.

In tissue cultures, macrophages take up water by *pinocytosis* (W. Lewis). In the spleen and liver they phagocytose worn-out or damaged erythrocytes, with the result that iron-containing pigment may accumulate in their cytoplasm. Fat and lipoid inclusions are common. Dust and other materials entering the lungs are removed by the "dust cells." Foreign particulate material in the blood stream is removed by the macrophages in the liver, spleen and bone marrow, where they come in contact with the blood. Similarly, foreign particulate material in the lymph stream is removed by the macrophages of the lymph nodes. Foreign materials are gradually destroyed, at least in part, through intracellular digestion; in this way the organism gets

rid of some of the foreign substance. Macrophages while filled with a foreign substance are less capable of performing other functions.

Although it is widely believed that macrophages produce *antibodies,* there is considerable evidence that both macrophages and lymphoid cells are involved. In the so-called plasma cell theories, antibodies are supposed to be formed chiefly by lymphoid cells transitional between the fixed reticular cells and the mature plasma cells. These transitional cells have been variously termed: large lymphocytes, acute splenic tumor cells, myeloblasts, lymphoblastic plasma cells, developing immature plasma cells, macrohistiocytes and basophile macrophages (see p. 273 and review by Taliaferro, 1949).

In considering the source and behavior of

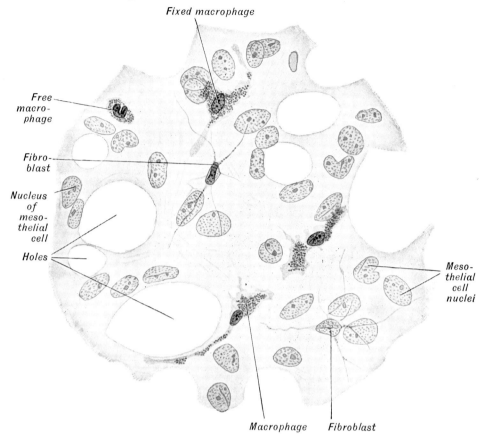

Fixed macrophage

Free macrophage

Fibroblast

Nucleus of mesothelial cell

Holes

Mesothelial cell nuclei

Macrophage   *Fibroblast*

Fig. 4–18.   Stretch preparation of a thin part of the omentum of a rabbit injected with lithium carmine. 375 ×. (A.A.M.)

macrophages in defense, it must be pointed out that they cannot be sharply separated from the lymphoid cells. It seems that in all defense reactions some new macrophages arise locally from the division of preexisting macrophages or by the assumption of phagocytic activity by cells having mesenchymal potencies. In the loose connective tissue the latter are the outstretched, undifferentiated perivascular mesenchymal cells; in the hematopoietic tissues they are the primitive reticular cells. In addition, many new macrophages arise from the hypertrophy and development of lymphocytes and monocytes. In the loose connective tissue these are hematogenous; in the spleen and other reticular tissue they represent lymphocytes which proliferate under the stimulus of the noxious agent. To signalize the fact that macrophages may develop homoplastically from macrophages and het-

eroplastically from lymphoid cells (and primitive reticular cells), Taliaferro and Mulligan proposed the term "lymphoid-macrophage system" to include both macrophages and all macrophage precursors.

Some believe that macrophages do not constitute a specific cell lineage, but represent a functional transformation of many different types of cells. The question whether the macrophages have hemopoietic potencies is discussed on page 114.

Tissue of the Serous Membranes. The serous membranes (the *peritoneum,* the *pleura* and the *pericardium*) are thin layers of loose connective tissue covered by a layer of mesothelium. When the membranes are folded, as the omentum or the mesentery, both free surfaces are covered with mesothelium. The serous cavities always contain a small amount of serous liquid, the *serous exu-*

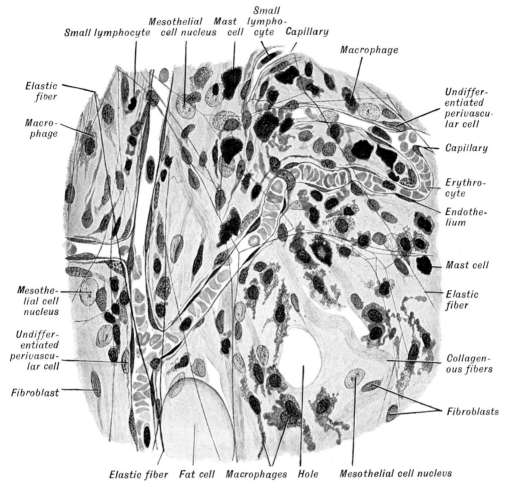

Fig. 4–19. Stretch preparation of human omentum. Hematoxylin-eosin-azure stain. 450 ×. (A.A.M.)

date. The cells floating in it originate from the serous membrane.

All the elements of the loose connective tissue are found in the serous membranes, where they are arranged in a thin layer. The mesentery contains a loose network of collagenous and elastic fibers, scattered fibroblasts, macrophages, mast cells and a varying number of fat cells along the blood vessels.

Physiologically, the most important and, histologically, the most interesting part of the serous membranes in mammals is the omentum. In places the membrane is pierced by innumerable holes and is thus reduced to a fine lacelike net formed by collagenous bundles covered by mesothelial cells. Such areas have few or no vessels.

In those areas of the omentum which are not provided with holes, undifferentiated cells occur along the vessels, and macro-

phages are numerous. There are also many small lymphocytes and plasma cells and, occasionally, eosinophile leukocytes and mast cells. The number of lymphocytes and plasma cells varies considerably in different animals.

In certain areas the macrophages are accumulated in especially dense masses. Such macroscopically visible areas are often arranged along the blood vessels as small or large, round or oval patches, called *milky spots*. These may or may not contain blood vessels, and are sometimes also found in the netlike part of the omentum. They are characteristic in the omentum of the rabbit. In the serous membrane which lines the pleural cavities there are cellular areas much like the milky spots of the omentum.

Free Cells of the Serous Exudate. Normally, the amount of serous exudate is small, but in pathological conditions it may in-

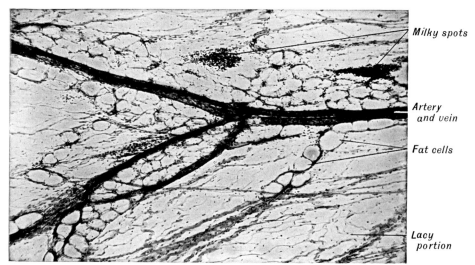

Milky spots

Artery
and vein

Fat cells

Lacy
portion

Fig. 4–20. Photomicrograph of stretch preparation of omentum of *Macacus rhesus.* Hematoxylin-eosin-azure II. 55 ×.

crease enormously. The exudate contains a number of freely floating cells. Among them the following can be distinguished:

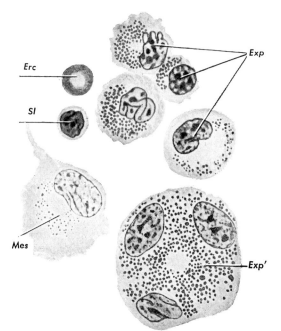

Erc

Sl

Mes

Exp

Exp'

Fig. 4–21. Cells from the peritoneal exudate of a rabbit which had several intravenous injections of lithium carmine. *Mes,* desquamated mesothelial cell; *Sl,* small lymphocyte; *Exp,* carmine-storing exudate polyblasts; *Exp',* exudate polyblast with three nuclei; *Erc,* erythrocyte. Moist fixed smear. Note carmine granules (dark gray). Hematoxylin stain. 1000 ×. (A.A.M.)

1. Free macrophages which originate in the milky spots of the omentum and migrate into the cavity. They correspond with those polyblasts of the inflammatory exudate which originate from the local macrophages.

2. Desquamated mesothelial cells which keep their squamous form or become spherical with small, budlike protuberances. The nucleus usually contains a heavily staining nucleolus. In inflammation and tissue culture they develop into fibroblasts.

3. Small lymphocytes, the vast majority of which have migrated from the blood vessels of the omentum. A few may have developed through proliferation of the undifferentiated mesenchymal cells of the omentum. In inflammatory exudates, transitions from lymphocytes to large macrophages can be found in great numbers.

4. Eosinophile leukocytes of hematogenous origin occur in some animals (guinea pig).

5. Free connective tissue mast cells occur in the rat and mouse.

6. In pathological inflammatory exudates there are great numbers of heterophile leukocytes from the blood.

THE DENSE CONNECTIVE TISSUE

This tissue is found mainly in the derma of the skin and the submucous layer of the intestinal and parts of the urinary tracts. Its constitution in the derma is typical. The elements are the same as in the loose variety,

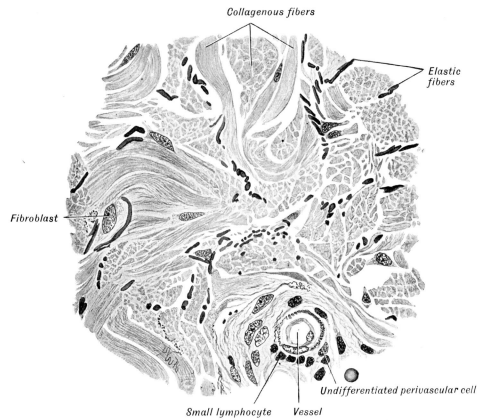

Fig. 4–22. Section of derma of man: dense, irregularly arranged connective tissue. Orcein and hematoxylin stains. 500 ×. (A.A.M.)

but the collagenous bundles are thicker and are woven into a compact feltwork. They are accompanied by many elastic networks. All the fibers from the derma continue directly into those of the loose, subcutaneous tissue, where their arrangement is correspondingly looser. There is less amorphous ground substance in the dense connective tissue. Between the two kinds of fibers and the amorphous cement substance are the cells; these are much more difficult to identify than in the loose tissue. The macrophages are easily recognized in vitally stained animals. Along the small vessels there are always many inconspicuous nuclei which probably belong to undifferentiated mesenchymal cells.

THE REGULAR CONNECTIVE TISSUE

The constituents of the regular connective tissue, especially the collagenous bundles, are arranged according to a definite plan. The particular arrangement reflects the mechanical requirements of the particular tissue, whether a tendon, a fibrillated membrane or lamellated connective tissue.

Tendons. Here the fibers form a flexible tissue which offers great resistance to a pulling force. Macroscopically, the tissue has a distinct fibrous structure and a characteristic, shining, white appearance.

The chief constituents of the tendon are thick, closely packed, parallel, collagenous bundles, in structure the same as those in the loose connective tissue. They show a distinct longitudinal striation and in many places fuse with one another at acute angles. In cross section they appear as finely dotted areas, usually separated from one another by broken, angular lines, although often continuing into one another. Fine elastic networks have been described between the collagenous bundles.

The fibroblasts are the only cells present;

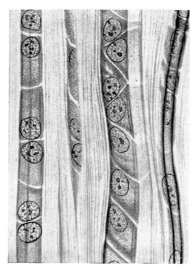

Fig. 4–23.　Freshly teased tendon of the tail of a rat, stained with methylene blue. The rows of tendon cells run between the collagenous bundles. 380 ×. (A.A.M.)

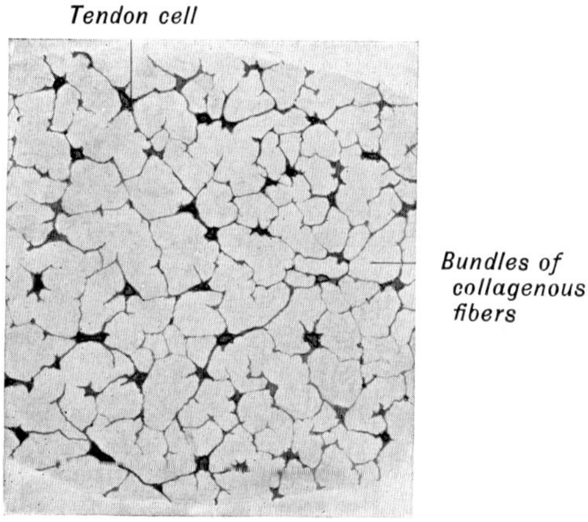

Tendon cell

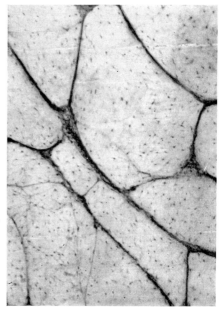

Bundles of collagenous fibers

Fig. 4–24.　Cross section of a tendon from tail of a rat. Hematoxylin-eosin-azure II stain. About 350 ×. (A.A.M.)

they are arranged in long, parallel rows in the spaces between the parallel collagenous bundles. The cell bodies are rectangular, triangular or trapezoid when seen from their surface, and rod-shaped when seen in profile. Their cytoplasm stains darkly with basic dyes and contains a clear attraction sphere adjacent to the single, round nucleus. Although the limits between the successive cells in a row are distinct, the lateral limits of the cells are indistinct, because here the cytoplasm continues into a thin membrane. Sometimes it can be followed in the transverse direction to another cell row. In a stained cross section

of a tendon the cells appear as dark, star-shaped figures between the collagenous bundles. A tendon consists of a varying number of small tendon bundles bound by loose connective tissue into larger bundles.

The *ligaments* are similar to the tendons, except that the elements are less regularly arranged.

Fibrous Membranes. The tissues of this group form membranes which surround various organs. On examination with the naked eye they show, in the fasciae, aponeuroses and tendinous center of the diaphragm, a parallel fibrillation, and are white and shiny like the tendons. In other situations the fibrillation is less regular, and the tissue is opaque and white—perichondrium, periosteum, dura mater, sclera, capsules of some organs and the tunica albuginea of the testis. In the cornea of the eye the tissue is transparent.

In the fasciae and aponeuroses the collagenous bundles and fibroblasts are arranged regularly in sheets. In each sheet the fibers follow a parallel and often slightly wavy course. In the different sheets the direction may be the same or it may vary. The fibers often pass from one sheet into another;

Fig. 4–25.　Cross section of a human tendon, showing the separation of the tendon bundles by loose connective tissue, which stains dark. Hematoxylin-eosin-azure II stain. Photomicrograph. About 120 ×.

therefore a clear isolation of the sheets is seldom possible. Between the collagenous bundles, fine networks of elastic fibers are usual. The cells correspond to the tendon cells and adapt themselves to the spaces between the collagenous bundles.

In the fibrous membranes with somewhat less regularly arranged elements (periosteum, sclera, and the like), a section perpendicular to the surface shows layers of collagenous bundles cut in the longitudinal, oblique or transverse directions, and cells which are irregular, flat or fusiform. In these tissues there are always gradual transitions to places where the elements have a quite irregular, dense arrangement. There is also no sharp distinction between them and the surrounding loose connective tissue.

Lamellated Connective Tissue. The lamellated connective tissue is found where small organs or parts of organs, usually of cylindrical shape, need thin and soft, but resistant, protective sheaths. It may be looked upon as a condensation of the loose connective tissue on the surface of these cylindrical structures. The elements cannot be sharply separated from those of the loose connective tissue.

Lamellated connective tissue is found outside the basement membrane in the wall of the seminiferous tubules in the testis; in the perineurium, which ensheathes the bundles of nerve fibers in a nerve trunk; and in the outer capsule of some sensory nerve endings, especially the corpuscles of Pacini. In a cross section through any of these structures, the periphery is found to be surrounded by a number of concentric, sometimes dotted lines between which are thin, rod-shaped nuclei. The lines are cross sections of thin lamellae, parallel or irregularly arranged collagenous fibers in an amorphous cement substance. These lamellae also contain elastic networks and reticular fibers. The surface of the lamellae is covered with a layer of flattened, endothelium-like fibroblasts, whose outlines can be made distinct by the use of silver nitrate. Macrophages are also present.

CONNECTIVE TISSUE WITH SPECIAL PROPERTIES

Mucous Connective Tissue. This tissue is found in many parts of the embryo, as under the skin, and is a form of the loose connective tissue. The classical object for its study is *Wharton's jelly* of the *umbilical cord* of the human fetus. The cells are large, stellate fibroblasts whose processes often are in contact with those of neighboring cells. A few macrophages and lymphoid wandering cells are also present. The intercellular substance is soft, jellylike and homogeneous in fresh condition; when fixed, it contains granules and fibrillar precipitates. It gives the reaction for mucin and contains thin, collagenous fibers which increase in number with the age of the fetus.

In the walls of large arteries (p. 237) the spaces between the elastic membranes and the cells are filled with a mucoid intercellular substance, which stains metachromatically because of the presence of chondroitin sulfuric acid.

Elastic Tissue. Some parts of the body have an elastic tissue which yields easily to a pulling force, but regains its original length as soon as the tension is released. Here the elastic fibers predominate, and the tissue has a yellow color macroscopically. It may appear in the form of strands of parallel fibers, as in the ligamenta flava of the vertebrae, in the true vocal cords, in the ligamentum stylohyoideum, the ligamentum suspensorium penis, and in the tendons of the smooth muscle of the trachea. In these situations the elastic fibers are thick, refringent, and round or flattened; they branch frequently and fuse with one another at acute angles, as in a stretched fishing net. In cross sections the angular or round areas representing the fibers form small groups; the spaces between the elastic fibers are filled with a delicate feltwork of collagenous fibers and a few fibroblasts.

The elastic tissue forms membranes in the walls of hollow organs upon which a changing pressure acts from within, as in the largest arteries, in some parts of the heart, in the trachea and bronchi.

In the large arteries the structural unit of the elastic tissue is a *fenestrated membrane,* a lamella of *elastin* of variable thickness provided with many irregular openings (Fig. 10–14). The fenestrated membranes are arranged in many layers around the cavity of the organ and are connected with one another by oblique, ribbon-like branches. The spaces between the lamellae contain a mu-

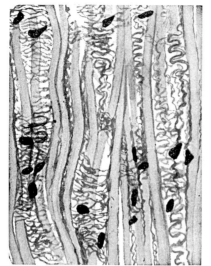

Fig. 4–26. Longitudinal section from ligamentum nuchae of an ox. The thick, elastic fibers form most of the tissue. Between them are dark fibroblast nuclei and wavy collagenous fibers. Eosin-azure stain. 300 ×. (A.A.M.)

fibers. These occur in the lymphatic tissue, myeloid tissue, spleen, and in the wall of the sinusoids of the liver. The cell types which are usually associated with the fibers of this reticulum are the primitive reticular cells and phagocytic reticular cells or macrophages. There are many transitions from the first cell type into the latter. In the meshes of this fibrous and cellular reticulum are free cells, varying in type and number, depending on the type and functional state of the tissue. This tissue is discussed at length in Chapter 5.

Adipose Tissue. The fat cells are closely packed and form the bulk of this tissue. In the narrow spaces between them, compressed fibroblasts, numerous lymphoid cells and mast cells are scattered. Collagenous fibers and elastic networks run in all directions between the fat cells. The argyrophile fibers are well developed, especially along the blood vessels, and form a netlike basket around

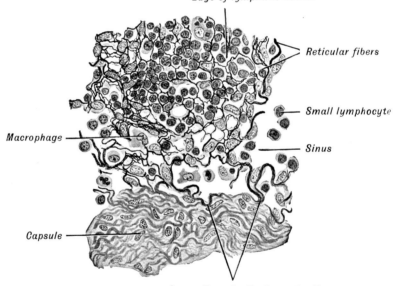

Fig. 4–27. Portion of cortex and capsule of human mesenteric lymph node. Bielschowsky stain. 500 ×. (A.A.M.)

coid amorphous mass and smooth muscular cells with irregular outlines. It is impossible to distinguish sharply between the fibrous elastic networks and the fenestrated elastic membranes.

Reticular Tissue. The fibrous elements of some types of connective tissues are *reticular*

each fat cell. The fat tissue always contains a rich network of blood capillaries. The fully developed fat tissue usually is more or less distinctly divided into lobules of varying size and shape, separated by partitions of fibrous connective tissue.

The most important function of the fat

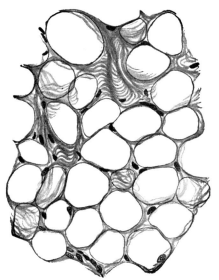

Fig. 4–28. Portion of a lobule of fat tissue from the subcutaneous tissue of man. The fat has been dissolved in preparing the section. About 200 ×. (A.A.M.)

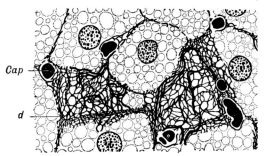

Fig. 4–29. Brown fat tissue from "hibernating gland" of white rat. *Cap*, capillary; *d*, intercellular fibrous network. Impregnation method of Hortega. 900 ×. (After Nageotte and Guyon.)

tissue is the storing of neutral fat. Since it consists of a multitude of closely packed liquid fat drops, the fat tissue forms soft and elastic pads between the various organs of the body.

The *brown fat tissue* must be distinguished from the common or white fat tissue. In rats and other rodents it is highly developed and forms yellowish, lobated masses in certain parts of the body—between the scapulae, on the neck, in the mediastinum, in the inguinal region, and elsewhere. Macroscopically, it suggests a gland, and so was called *interscapular* or *hibernating gland*. The latter name was given because this tissue was believed to play a peculiar role during hibernation. The brown fat contains a pigment which gives the tissue its color. The fat cells are assembled in groups separated by thin networks of collagenous or reticular fibers and numerous capillaries. The microscopic structure suggests an endocrine gland. While the common fat tissue loses or accumulates neutral fat with changes in the nutritional condition of the animal, these factors do not seem to affect the brown fat tissue. It has been claimed that the brown fat loses its lipids after hypophysectomy and that these changes can be prevented by injection of adrenocorticotropic hormone.

In adult man and other mammals the two kinds of fat tissue cannot be distinguished clearly. The morphological interrelationships between the two and the function of the brown fat tissue require further study.

Pigment Tissue. In the tunica suprachoroidea and in the lamina fusca of the sclerae of the eye, the majority of the cells in the loose connective tissue are melanocytes. Such a tissue can be termed "pigment tissue." It is described in the chapter on the Eye.

Connective Tissue (Lamina Propria) of the Intestinal and Uterine Mucous Membranes, the Interstitial Connective Tissue of the Lung, Testis, Ovary. The connective tissue which surrounds and supports the epithelial elements in these organs acquires a specifically differentiated structure. It is described in the chapters which deal with these organs.

REFERENCES

Allgöwer, M.: The Cellular Basis of Wound Repair. Springfield, Illinois, Charles C Thomas, 1956.

Allison, F., Jr., Smith, M. R., and Wood, W. B., Jr.: Studies on the pathogenesis of acute inflammation. II. The action of cortisone on the inflammatory response to thermal injury. J. Exp. Med., *102*:669, 1955.

Asboe-Hansen, G. (editor): Connective Tissue in Health and Disease. Copenhagen, E. Munksgaard, 1954.

Astbury, W. T., and Bell, F. O.: Molecular structure of the collagen fibres. Nature, *145*:421, 1940.

Bloom, G., Friberg, U., and Larsson, B.: Some observations on the fine structure of mast cell tumours (mastocytoma). Nordisk Veterinaermedicin, *8*:43, 1956.

Boedtker, H., and Doty, P.: On the nature of the structural element of collagen. J. Am. Chem. Soc., *77*:248, 1955.

Cappell, D. F.: Intravitam and supravital staining. J. Path. Bacteriol., *32*:595, 1929.

Clark, E. R., and Clark, E. L.: Microscopic studies of the new formation of fat in living adult rabbits. Am. J. Anat., *67*:255, 1940.

Creditor, M. C., Bevans, M., Mundy, W. L., and Ragan, C.: Effect of ACTH on wound healing in humans. Proc. Soc. Exper. Biol. & Med., *73*:245, 1950.

Cunningham, R.: The changes in the omentum of the rabbit during mild irritations, with especial reference to the specificity of the mesothelium. Bull. Johns Hopkins Hosp., *33:*257, 1922.

Downey, H.: The development of histiocytes and macrophages from lymphocytes. J. Lab. & Clin. Med., *45:* 499, 1955.

DuShane, G. P.: The development of pigment cells in vertebrates. Special Publ. New York Acad. Sci., *4:*1, 1948.

Ehrich, W. E., Harris, T. N., and Mertens, E.: The absence of antibody in the macrophages during maximum antibody formation. J. Exp. Med., *83:*373, 1946.

Evans, H. M., and Scott, K. J.: On the Differential Reaction to vital dyes exhibited by the two great groups of connective tissue cells. Carnegie Contrib. Embryol. No. 47, 1, 1921.

Fawcett, D. W., and Jones, I. C.: The effects of hypophysectomy, adrenalectomy and of thiouracil feeding on the cytology of brown adipose tissue. Endocrinology, *45:*609, 1949.

Felix, M. D., and Dalton, A. J.: A phase-contrast microscope study of free cells native to the peritoneal fluid of DBA/2 mice. J. Natl. Cancer Inst., *16:*415, 1955.

Foot, N. C.: Studies on endothelial reactions. X. On the origin of the pulmonary "dust cell." Am. J. Path., *3:* 413, 1927.

Cersh, I., and Catchpole, H. R.: The organization of ground substance and basement membrane and its significance in tissue injury, disease and growth. Am. J. Anat., *85:*457, 1949.

Gross, J. Highberger, J. H., and Schmitt, F. O.: Extraction of collagen from connective tissue by neutral salt solutions. Proc. Nat. Acad. Sci., *41:*1–7, 1955.

Kolouch, F., Jr.: The lymphocyte in acute inflammation. Am. J. Path., *15:*413, 1939.

Marchand, F.: Der Prozess der Wundheilung. Deutsche Chirurgie (v. Bermann u. v. Bruns) Lief, 16, Stuttgart, 1901. Die örtlichen reaktiven Vorgänge (Lehre von der Entzündung). Handb. d. allg. Pathol. (Krehl u. Marchand), Leipzig, (4), Pt. 1, 78, 1924.

Maximow, A.: Ueber die Zellformen des lockeren Bindegewebes. Arch. f. mikrosk.-Anat., *67:*680, 1906. The morphology of the mesenchymal reactions. Arch. Path., *4:*557, 1927. Bindegewebe und blutbildende Gewebe. Handb. d. mikrosk.-Anat. d. Menschen (v.

Möllendorff), (2), 232, Berlin, Pt. I, 1927. The Macrophages or Histiocytes, in Cowdry's Special Cytology. 2d ed. New York, (2), 709, 1932.

Menkin, V.: Dynamics of Inflammation. New York. Exper. Biol. Monographs, 1940.

Nature and Structure of Collagen. J. T. Randall and S. F. Jackson, editors. New York, Academic Press, Inc., 1953.

Odor, D. Louise: Observations of the rat mesothelium with the electron and phase microscopes. Am. J. Anat., *95:*433, 1954.

Paff, G. H., and Mergenthaler, D. D.: Vacuolation in normal mast cells and in mast cells treated with protamine sulfate. Anat. Rec., *121:*579, 1955.

Plenk, H.: Ueber argyrophile Fasern (Gitterfasern) und ihre Bildungszellen. Ergebn. d. Anat. u. Entwick., *27:* 302, 1927.

Porter, K., and Vanamee, P.: Observations on the formation of connective tissue fibers. Proc. Soc. Exper. Biol. & Med., *71:*513, 1949.

Ranvier, L.: Traité technique d'histologie. Paris 1875. Des clasmatocytes. Arch. d'Anat. micro., *3:*123, 1900.

Rebuck, J. W., and Crowley, J. H.: A method of studying leukocytic functions in vivo. Ann. New York Acad. Sci., *59:*757, 1955.

Schmitt, F. O., Gross, J., and Highberger, J. H.: States of Aggregation of Collagen. Symposia of the Society for Experimental Biology, No. IX; 148, 1955.

Schmitt, F. O., Gross, J., and Highberger, J. H.: Tropocollagen and the properties of fibrous collagen. Exp. Cell Research, Suppl., *3:*326, 1955.

Smith, D. N., and Lewis, Y. S.: Electron microscopy of mast cells after x-irradiation. Am. J. Physiol., *183:* 662, 1955.

Taliaferro, W. H.: The cellular basis of immunity. Ann. Rev. Microbiology, *3:*159, 1949.

Webb, R. L., and Simer, P. H.: The relation of lymph vessels to omental milk spots. Anat. Rec., *83:*437, 1942.

Wells, H. G.: Adipose tissue, a neglected subject. J.A.M.A., *114:*2177, 1940.

Wolbach, S. B.: Controlled formation of collagen and reticulum. A study of the source of intercellular substance in recovery from experimental scorbutus. Am. J. Path., *9:* Suppl., 689, 1933.

CHAPTER 5

Blood Cell
Formation and Destruction

THE SHORT-LIVED blood corpuscles are kept at a constant number in the blood by the continuous formation of new cells. Under normal conditions, blood cells are regenerated only within the lymphatic and the myeloid tissues and organs (*hemopoietic* organs and tissues). The process of their formation is called *hemopoiesis*.

The cells of the circulating blood may be divided into two groups, according to their origin. To the first group belong the lymphocytes (and probably the monocytes), which originate in the lymphatic tissue and are called *lymphoid elements*. The second group consists of the erythrocytes and the granular leukocytes; these originate in the myeloid tissue and are the *myeloid elements*. But this separation of myeloid and lymphatic tissue is not absolute; for it is effaced in certain abnormal conditions in postnatal mammals, and, in the early embryonic stages of the mammals as well as through life in most of the lower vertebrates, there is no such separation.

All the blood cell-forming tissues of adult mammals have the same fundamental structure—a fibrous and cellular stroma in the meshes of which hemopoiesis takes place. This framework is composed of reticular fibers and cells.

The reticular fibers are accompanied or sheathed by a thin layer of protoplasm in which are scattered pale oval nuclei. These *primitive reticular cells* often show no cell limits. They are not active phagocytes and only rarely contain a few granules of waste pigment; they do not store appreciable amounts of vital dyes (Fig. 5–2). Like the mesenchymal cells of the embryo, they are endowed with the ability to turn into all types of blood and connective tissue cells.

From these *primitive reticular cells* there are many transitions to larger cells which are active phagocytes, called *phagocytic reticular cells* or *fixed macrophages*. These have an abundant cytoplasm and a large pale nucleus. Most of them are stellate or spindle-shaped and adhere to the reticular fibers. They may contain debris of dead cells, foreign materials, engulfed erythrocytes in various stages of disintegration and, in vitally stained animals, numerous large dye granules. In fresh preparations stained supravitally with neutral red, the inclusions and vacuoles of the macrophages stain deeply. The fixed macrophages may become *free macrophages*.

LYMPHATIC TISSUE

In mammals the lymphatic tissue forms distinctly outlined organs, the *lymph nodes,* which are arranged along the course of the lymph vessels. It is present in small amounts in the bone marrow and in large amounts in the *spleen,* where it may undergo specific modifications depending on the peculiar type of blood circulation in this organ (see Chapter 12). In addition, lymphatic tissue is scattered in the mucous membranes of the alimentary canal and of the respiratory passages, in the conjunctiva and elsewhere. The *hemal nodes* are described on page 259. The *thymus,* which has a number of features in common with lymphatic tissue, is described in Chapter 13.

Two microscopic constituents can be distinguished in the lymphatic tissue: (1) a spongelike framework or stroma and (2) free cells in the meshes of the stroma. These constituents are present in different proportions in various parts of the lymphatic tissue, so that we may distinguish (*a*) *loose lymphatic tissue,* consisting predominantly of stroma; (*b*) *dense lymphatic tissue,* in which the free cells predominate; and (*c*) *nodular lymphatic tissue,* especially dense accumulations of free cells within the loose or dense lymphatic tissue. Under various physiological and pathological conditions, each of these types of tissue may turn into either of the others (p. 112).

The loose lymphatic tissue, as found in the lymph nodes, forms sinuses or pathways for the lymph which flows through the organ. Unlike the lymph vessels, which have a free lumen and a wall of their own, the sinuses are merely portions of the lymphatic tissue

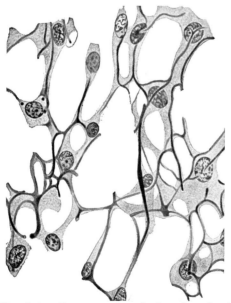

Fig. 5–1. From a section of a lymph node after the lymphocytes have been removed, showing the network of reticular cells and their intimate relations with the reticular fibers. Mallory-azan stain. (Redrawn after Heidenhain.)

which are especially loose in structure (see Chapter 11).

Stroma. The framework of lymphatic tissue is made up of (1) reticular fibers and (2) reticular cells (Fig. 5–1).

Fibers. The fibers are of the reticular type and are best shown by the silver impregnation method. At the periphery of the nodules the framework is dense and the meshes small, while the stroma within the nodules is loose, with thin fibers; in the loose tissue of the sinuses the large meshes are composed of coarse fibers (Fig. 5–6). Along the walls of all the blood vessels the reticulum is condensed.

Cells. The cells of the stroma are the primitive reticular cells and the phagocytic reticular cells or fixed macrophages. The primitive reticular cells of the lymphatic tissue have the ability to develop into phagocytes and lymphocytes, as well as into myelocytes in ectopic myelopoiesis (p. 114). Under certain conditions the fixed macrophages may become free macrophages anywhere in the lymphatic tissue; they are especially numerous in the sinuses. When the lymph contains foreign substances, such as lithium carmine or bacteria, the number of free macrophages greatly increases.

The fixed and free macrophages of the lymphatic tissue correspond closely with those of the loose connective tissue (p. 70). In the lymphatic tissue they increase by division and by development from primitive reticular cells.

The macrophages which help form the walls of the sinuses, and which are attached to the fibers passing through the cavity of these spaces, are often flattened and resemble endothelial cells (Fig. 5–2). For this reason they have been called endothelium, but, as the ability to store vital dyes and to transform into free macrophages has not been proved to be present in the endothelium of the common blood or lymph vessels, the term is not justified. The flattened form of these macrophages is an adaptation to their position on the wall of the channels through which the lymph flows. The term *littoral* or *lining cells* of the system of macrophages is perhaps the best to use.

The lymphatic tissue does not contain fibroblasts (except along the arteries and veins and in the trabeculae of the lymphatic organs), although, in inflammation and in

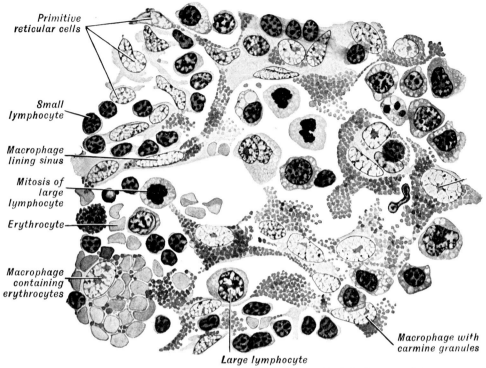

Fig. 5–2.   Medullary sinus of mesenteric lymph node of a rabbit which had repeated intravenous injections of lithium carmine. Hematoxylin-eosin-azure stain. 950 ×. (A.A.M.)

cultures of this tissue, fibroblasts develop from the primitive reticular cells and from the macrophages.

Free Cells. The meshes of the fibrous and cellular reticulum contain free cells. In dense lymphatic tissue and in the nodules the free cells are so densely crowded that the nuclei of the primitive reticular cells can be seen among them only in thin sections. The free cells are much less numerous in the meshes of the sinuses; here they float in the lymph which passes slowly through the channels. Except for the free macrophages described earlier, the free cells are all *lymphocytes.*

In the lymphatic tissue can be distinguished several types of lymphocytes: (1) The *small lymphocytes* form the vast majority (Fig. 5–3) (see Chapter 3). (2) The *medium-sized lymphocytes* are scattered everywhere among the small lymphocytes, but in a much smaller number. They are slightly larger than the small variety, and the nucleus is clearer and contains less chromatin; one or two nucleoli are prominent, and there is more cytoplasm. These cells divide mitotically. (3) *Large lymphocytes, macrolymphocytes,* are

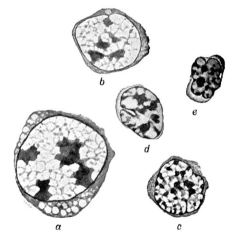

Fig. 5–3.   Lymphocytes from a human lymph node. *a,* large, *b, c,* medium-sized, and *d, e,* small lymphocytes. Hematoxylin-eosin-azure stain. 1500 ×. (A.A.M.)

scattered singly among the other lymphocytes and measure up to 15 microns in diameter, although occasional ones may measure 20 microns or more when rounded. They occur everywhere, even in the sinuses, but are more numerous in the lymphatic nodules, their number varying with the functional condition of the lymphatic tissue. Often, especially in human lymph nodes, they may be absent. Their cytoplasm forms a broad layer around the nucleus and is strongly basophile, presumably due to ribosenucleic acid. It may contain a few vacuoles at the indentation of the nucleus; the hemispherical cytocentrum with a diplosome is surrounded by a Golgi net. There are more rod-shaped mitochondria than in the smaller forms, and they are arranged around the cytocentrum. The large, usually kidney-shaped nucleus occupies a slightly eccentric position, with the excavation directed toward the large accumulation of cytoplasm. The nuclear membrane is coarsely outlined; the chromatin particles are widely scattered in a large quantity of clear nuclear sap. Always there are one or more large irregularly shaped nucleoli. The large lymphocytes divide by mitosis.

These three types of lymphocytes are connected with one another by an uninterrupted series of transitional forms. In the small lymphocytes mitoses are extremely rare under normal conditions, the main source of the lymphocytes of the blood being the medium-sized lymphocyte.

Under suitable conditions the small lymphocyte may hypertrophy into a larger one and regain the ability to divide. This transformation probably occurs but rarely in the lymphatic tissue. The small lymphocytes of the blood can hypertrophy in tissue culture within a day into typical large lymphocytes.

Plasma cells are of common occurrence in the lymphatic tissue, especially in the medullary cords of the lymph nodes; their number is subject to marked variation, particularly under pathological conditions. In some animals (rat, mouse) plasma cells are especially numerous. Sometimes, eosinophile leukocytes are found in the lymphatic tissue. Heterophile granulocytes are a sign of an inflammatory lesion. Young forms of granulocytes (myelocytes) are found only in *extramedullary myelopoiesis* (p. 112). Mast cells are often found scattered along the fibers of the reticulum; monocytes usually do not occur.

Development of Lymphocytes. In the postnatal mammals most lymphocytes arise by mitosis of preexisting lymphocytes within the lymphatic tissue. This occurs mainly in the nodular, but also to some extent in the diffuse and loose lymphatic tissue. The mother cell is usually a medium-sized lymphocyte, although dividing large lymphocytes are not uncommon. In some instances it has been possible to trace lymphocytes to their origin in primitive reticular cells—a source probably active only when the preexisting lymphocytes are unable, by their mitoses, to fill the demand for lymphocytes.

Lymphatic Nodules. The lymphatic nodules are especially dense accumulations of lymphocytes embedded in a relatively scanty cellular and fibrous reticulum, and are usually the expression of some stage of lymphocytopoietic activity focused at a small area in the lymphatic tissue. The nodules appear and disappear, or pass through a series of cyclic changes during which an intense new formation of lymphocytes proceeds through proliferation of preexisting lymphocytes and to a lesser extent through transformation of the primitive reticular cells.

In its fully developed form, a nodule consists of a central portion and a peripheral zone, sometimes called *corona*. The central portion of a nodule which is actively producing lymphocytes is called the *germinal center* (Figs. 5–4 and 5–5). This germinal center may attain a diameter of 1 mm. It often has a small artery supplying it with blood. This central area in such a nodule appears paler than the surrounding mass of small lymphocytes with their dark nuclei, for the majority of its cells are medium-sized lymphocytes. They contain more mitotic figures than do the medium-sized lymphocytes in loose and dense lymphatic tissue. Scattered among them are a few large lymphocytes and all transitions between them. A few small lymphocytes also are found. Among the lymphocytes of an actively lymphocytopoietic nodule are scattered primitive reticular cells with indistinct cytoplasm (Fig. 5–5). These also show occasional mitoses. Macrophages with phagocytosed inclusions are distributed along the capillaries in the nodule.

At the end of a proliferative phase, mitosis ceases in the germinal center, which gradually becomes depleted of lymphocytes. Such an *inactive center* contains reticular cells, macrophages and a few lymphocytes. In certain pathological conditions, such as diphtheria, burns and severe bacterial and plasmodial infections, the central portion may have a simi-

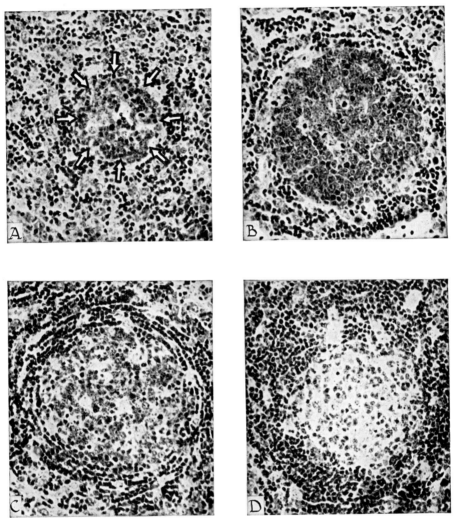

Fig. 5–4. Photomicrographs showing four nodules at different stages of development in mesenteric lymph node of guinea pigs, five days after injection of *B. monocytogenes*. *A,* small new "bare" germinal center consisting of dividing medium-sized lymphocytes. Its margins are indicated by the arrowheads. *B,* later stage in the development of a nodule. This "bare" germinal center contains twenty-seven mitoses in medium-sized lymphocytes. *C,* corona of densely packed small lymphocytes has been formed around the germinal center, which is actively lymphopoietic and contains fifteen mitoses in medium-sized lymphocytes. This is the type of nodule which is often regarded as typical, consisting of an outer dark-staining zone and a lighter central area. *D,* nodule with inactive center. It has a pale-staining central portion consisting mainly of reticular cells, free macrophages and a few scattered lymphocytes. This nodule with its center depleted of lymphocytes resembles the "reaction center" type. Hematoxylin-eosin-azure II. 300 ×. (After Conway.)

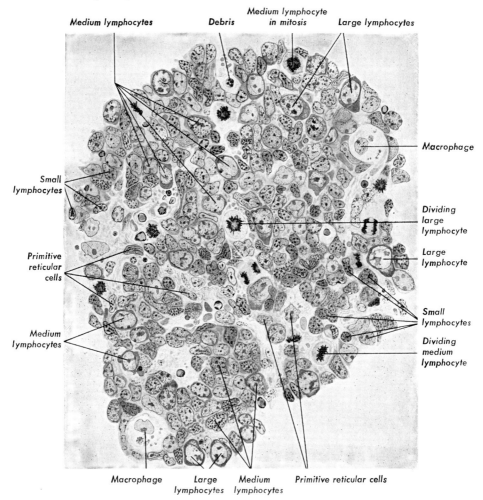

Medium lymphocytes   Debris   Medium lymphocyte   Large lymphocytes
                                     in mitosis

Macrophage

Small
lymphocytes

Dividing
large
lymphocyte

Large
lymphocyte

Primitive
reticular
cells

Small
lymphocytes

Medium
lymphocytes

Dividing
medium
lymphocyte

Macrophage   Large   Medium   Primitive reticular cells
              lymphocytes lymphocytes

Fig. 5–5.   Portion of actively lymphocytopoietic nodule of human lymph node. Hematoxylin-eosin-azure II. (A.A.M.)

lar appearance, although there are usually more active macrophages in these conditions. Such central areas have been described as *"reaction centers."* Some of the stages of their development are much like the "inactive centers."

The *peripheral zone* or *corona* appears in sections darker than the central portion of the nodule, for the majority of its cells are densely crowded small lymphocytes with their dark nuclei. These small lymphocytes are frequently seen arranged in concentric layers.

In a stage of complete rest the lymphatic nodule consists mainly of small lymphocytes, so compactly arranged that the nodule stands out as a dense, darkly-stained area in the diffuse lymphatic tissue. New nodules may de-

velop anywhere in the loose or dense lymphatic tissue. Indeed, they may even develop in a preexisting nodule. These new areas of lymphocytopoiesis start with the appearance of many, rapidly repeated mitoses in medium-sized lymphocytes. In some instances these have been shown to arise as free cells, with a narrow rim of cytoplasm by individual transformation or through mitoses of the primitive reticular cells (Figs. 5–4, 5–13). Such a small isolated mass of densely packed medium-sized lymphocytes is in every respect similar to a germinal center. Because of the absence of a corona of small lymphocytes, it may be described as a *"bare" germinal center.* Many of the medium-sized lymphocytes become large lymphocytes, and some of the primitive reticular cells become macrophages. The bare germinal center increases in size because of the continued mitoses of the medium-sized lymphocytes. The growth pressure may cause development of a corona of densely packed small lymphocytes, depending on the density of the surrounding lymphatic tissue.

As a lymphocyte-forming nodule becomes inactive, mitoses become less numerous, and the last divisions of the medium-sized cells give rise to small lymphocytes; some of the latter may originate from shrinkage of the larger cells. Plasma cells also appear. The decrease of the growth pressure effaces the sharp boundary line between the center and the periphery of the nodule, which then becomes uniform in appearance and composition.

New Formation of Lymphatic Tissue. New foci of lymphatic tissue and even lymph nodes can develop in any part of the loose connective tissue in the adult organism. When this happens, the lymphocytes and the elements of the stroma develop from the ubiquitous undifferentiated elements of the adult connective tissue (p. 68). When the lymphatic tissue involutes and disappears, the lymphocytes degenerate or wander away, while the reticular cells seem to be transformed into fat cells.

Function of the Lymphatic Tissue. The most conspicuous function of the lymphatic tissue is the production of lymphocytes. The lymphocytes which are newly formed in the lymph nodes—the vast majority of them are the small variety—migrate into the sinuses and are carried away by the lymph stream into the lymphatics and the thoracic duct, and hence into the blood. In addition, numbers of small lymphocytes migrate directly from the lymphatic tissue into the blood through the endothelium of the venous capillaries. In extramedullary myelopoiesis the lymphatic tissue can also become the source of granulocytes (see p. 112).

In the early stages of infection of rabbits and guinea pigs with *B. monocytogenes* the lymphocytes of the lymph nodes, and occasionally even of the nodules, turn into monocytes. Lymphoid hyperplasia in malaria builds up a reserve from which new macrophages are formed (p. 80). The other functions of the lymphatic tissue are concerned mainly with its macrophages and will be discussed with the structure of the lymph nodes and spleen. Evidence is accumulating that lymphocytes are rich in specific immune bodies and that the delivery of lymphocytes to the circulation is, in part, under control of the adrenal cortex and of the pars distalis of the hypophysis. The source of antibodies has not been determined, and the significance of the antibody content of lymphocytes awaits clarification.

The marked atrophy of lymphoid tissues which results from the action of a variety of noxious agents (part of the "alarm reaction" of Selye) is believed to result from the liberation of adrenal cortical hormones; it does not occur if the adrenal cortex is removed.

Some authors deny the importance of the nodules for the regeneration of the lymphocytes, believing them to be only centers of reaction of the lymphatic tissue to various toxic agents. As proof, they point to the degeneration of lymphocytes and reticular cells as evidenced by the nuclear debris in the macrophages of the centers, in intoxications, burns, inflammatory lesions and in certain infectious diseases. It is true that cellular debris occurs in the center of the nodule (Fig. 5–5). This is, however, not evidence that the center of the nodule is exclusively a site of cell destruction, since lymphocytes continue to proliferate (see mitoses in lymphocytes in Figure 5–5) and the germinal center can increase in size, while debris is present. Just as in all areas of rapid new formation of cells, some of the newly formed cells degenerate (see nervous system, Fig. 9–52), so do a number of the newly formed lymphocytes degenerate in the germinal center.

The lymphocytes are among the most sensitive cells in the body to ionizing radiations and certain toxins (mustard gas); the reticular cells are among the most resistant.

Embryonic lymphatic tissue has nodules which are dense masses of small lymphocytes, lacking pale-staining central areas. It is claimed that guinea pigs which have been reared for sixty days on sterile media do not show centers in the nodules.

Lymphatic Tissue in the Lower Vertebrates. In the lower vertebrates, although lymphocytes are plentiful, their regeneration is not localized in special lymphatic organs, but occurs in many places in the connective tissue; in fact, lymph nodes are usually ab-

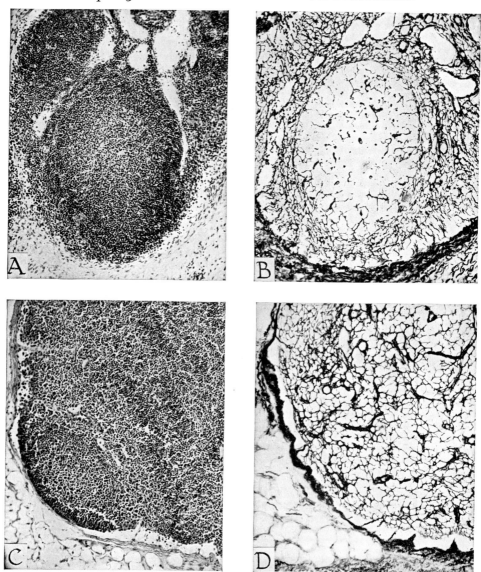

Fig. 5–6.   *A* and *B*, photomicrographs from sections of the same block of mesenteric lymph node of rabbit, thirty-six hours after injection of *B. monocytogenes;* *C* and *D*, from a block of mesenteric lymph node of rabbit, forty-eight hours after injection of the same bacterium. When nodular lymphatic tissue (*A*) becomes diffuse lymphatic tissue (*C*), the reticular-fiber framework, characteristic of the nodules (*B*), is lost (*D*). In all sections the subcapsular sinus is prominent. *A* and *C* stained with hematoxylin; *B* and *D* impregnated for reticular fibers by the Foot method. 107 ×. (After Conway.)

sent. The most important difference in comparison with the mammals is that the lymphatic tissue is not sharply separated from the myeloid tissue.

MYELOID TISSUE. THE BONE MARROW

Of the several kinds of bone marrow which differ macroscopically, the two most important varieties are the *red* and the *yellow,* or *fatty,* bone marrow. Only the red marrow, which consists of myeloid tissue, plays a role in hemopoiesis, producing the red blood cells and the granulocytes. In the embryo and the newborn, red marrow only is found in the bone cavities. With progressing age the red marrow is gradually replaced by the yellow marrow with its fat cells. In the normal adult, red marrow is found in the vertebrae, the ribs, the sternum, the *diploë* of the bones

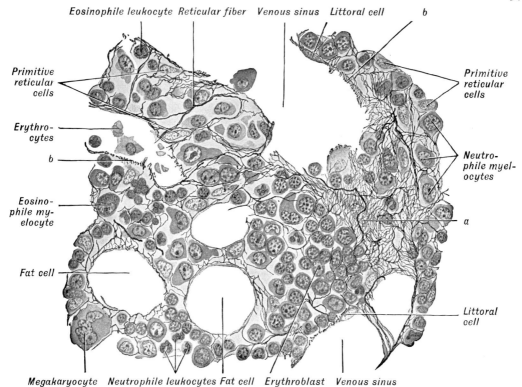

Eosinophile leukocyte Reticular fiber Venous sinus Littoral cell   b

Primitive
reticular
cells

Erythro-
cytes

b

Eosino-
phile my-
elocyte

Fat cell

Primitive
reticular
cells

Neutro-
phile myel-
ocytes

a

Littoral
cell

Megakaryocyte Neutrophile leukocytes Fat cell Erythroblast Venous sinus

Fig. 5–7. Bone marrow from upper epiphysis of a femur of a child of six years. The fibrous network of the wall of a vessel is seen from the surface at *a* and in cross section at *b*. Bielschowsky stain. 500 ×. (A.A.M.)

of the skull, and in the proximal epiphyses of the femur and humerus. Bone marrow forms 2 to 3 per cent of the body weight.

No sharp limit can be drawn between the two kinds of bone marrow. After considerable losses of blood or in the anemias, the fatty bone marrow is replaced to a greater or less extent by red marrow. After prolonged starvation or in some wasting diseases the bone marrow loses its blood cells, and the fat acquires a peculiar gelatinous appearance; it is then called gelatinous or "mucous" bone marrow. In myeloid leukemia the red bone marrow becomes rich in granulocytes and acquires a gray "pyoid" character. Figure 5–14 shows the effect of raising the temperature of fatty marrow.

The myeloid tissue, like the lymphatic, consists of (1) the spongelike framework or stroma which is intimately connected with the blood vessels and (2) the free cells in the meshes of the stroma.

Stroma. As in the lymphatic tissue, the stroma consists of primitive and phagocytic

reticular cells attached to the argyrophile fibers (Figs. 5–1, 5–7). The network of cells and fibers is looser and its meshes are larger than in the lymphatic tissue. Particulate matter and vital dyes injected into the blood are taken up rapidly by the fixed macrophages of the bone marrow.

Circulation in the bone marrow is characterized by the presence of many large vessels, called *sinusoids,* through the walls of which innumerable cells pass into the blood stream. The sinusoids are lined by flattened, fixed macrophages (littoral cells), like those forming the walls of the lymph node sinuses. These dye-storing and phagocytosing cells have indistinct limits and are in direct connection with similar cells of the stroma. They can round off and appear as free macrophages in the blood of the sinusoids. The manner in which the arteries connect with the sinusoids needs further study.

The stroma of the myeloid tissue is distinguished by the constant presence of fat cells. These are scattered singly in the red marrow (Fig. 5–7), but in the yellow bone marrow they crowd out practically all the other cells; between them remain (besides the blood vessels and reticular fibers) only scattered fixed macrophages and primitive reticular cells. The latter are probably the main source of the new blood cells when the yellow bone marrow is transformed into red marrow. Small accumulations of lymphatic tissue with nodules occur regularly in the bone marrow, but lymph vessels have not been found.

Free Cells. In contrast to the free cells of the lymphatic tissue, those of the myeloid tissue are extremely varied in form and are scattered irregularly throughout the tissue. The vast majority of them are immature myeloid elements.

MATURE MYELOID ELEMENTS

Mature, non-nucleated erythrocytes, and the three types of granular leukocytes as they occur in the circulating blood, are found everywhere between the other cells. Thus the tissue which produces these elements always contains a ready supply of them and in case of need can forward large quantities at once into the blood (Fig. 5–8).

IMMATURE MYELOID ELEMENTS

The other free cells in the bone marrow are *hemocytoblasts (free stem cells); erythroblasts*—the precursors of the red blood corpuscles; *myelocytes*—the precursors of the three principal types of granular leukocytes; and *megakaryocytes.*

Hemocytoblasts. The myeloid tissue of all adult mammals contains ameboid, nongranular, basophile cells of lymphoid nature. They vary in size, the largest measuring 15 microns, and are scattered singly or in groups of two or four. Their structure corresponds exactly to that of the lymphocytes. They are the free stem cells of all other myeloid elements. A suitable name for them is *hemocytoblast.* The small cells of this type are connected with the larger ones by a complete series of transitional forms. According to the unitarian theory of hemopoiesis, both lymphocytes and hemocytoblasts have identical developmental potencies (page 111).

Erythroblasts. The young forms of the red blood corpuscles are spherical cells with spherical nuclei and are called erythroblasts.

In living cells their cytoplasm is homogeneous, and of a yellow color which intensifies as the cells develop into erythrocytes. Supravital staining with neutral red produces red precipitates in their cytoplasm. Erythroblasts never show ameboid motion. In fixed and stained sections they show mitochondria, a Golgi net and a cytocentrum. The round nucleus of the erythroblasts always presents a checker-board distribution of angular particles of chromatin. The nucleoli gradually involute. The number of mitotic divisions in the cell lineage is not known. The changes in the erythroblasts as they develop into erythrocytes are clearly shown in Figures 5–9, 5–10.

The erythroblasts closest to the stem cell are called *basophile erythroblasts,* because of the intense basophilia of their protoplasm; it is deeper than that of the hemocytoblasts. An intermediate cell (*proerythroblast*) has been described.

The erythroblasts of the next youngest generation have a small amount of hemoglobin. After staining with the Romanowsky mixture (eosin-methylene-azure) the cytoplasm varies from a purplish-blue to lilac or gray. These erythroblasts are, therefore, called *polychromatophile.* This staining reaction is due to the appearance of pink-staining hemoglobin in the basophile cytoplasm of the erythroblast, which stains blue.

The polychromatophile erythroblasts divide mitotically. Some of them remain in the tissue in a resting condition for future use. In the others the amount of hemoglobin increases while the basophilia of the cytoplasm diminishes; in this way *normoblasts* arise in which the cytoplasm stains a bright pink with the Romanowsky mixture. Normoblasts are smaller than polychromatophile erythroblasts and only slightly larger than mature erythrocytes. The small round nucleus contains a dense accumulation of angular chromatin particles and stains very dark. After an unknown number of mitotic divisions, the nucleus is condensed to a darkly staining body. Each mature normoblast loses its pyknotic nucleus and is transformed into a red blood corpuscle. Some investigators hold that the nucleus is lost by *karyolysis,* but most believe this occurs by *extrusion.*

Myelocytes. Besides the erythroblasts, the young forms of the three types of leukocytes

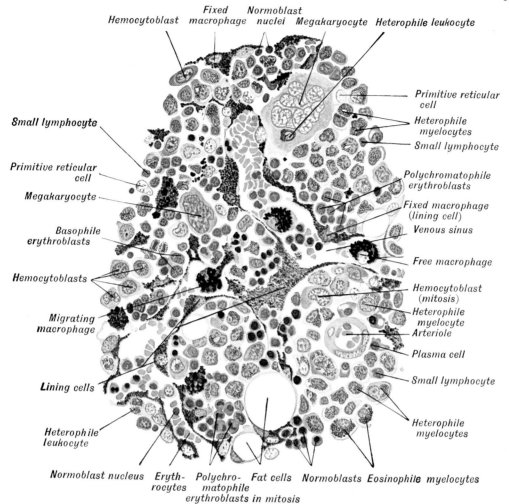

Fixed   Normoblast
Hemocytoblast macrophage nuclei   Megakaryocyte   Heterophile leukocyte

Primitive reticular
cell

Heterophile
myelocytes

Small lymphocyte

Small lymphocyte

Primitive reticular
cell

Megakaryocyte

Basophile
erythroblasts

Polychromatophile
erythroblasts

Fixed macrophage
(lining cell)

Venous sinus

Free macrophage

Hemocytoblasts

Migrating
macrophage

Hemocytoblast
(mitosis)

Heterophile
myelocyte

Arteriole

Plasma cell

Small lymphocyte

Lining cells

Heterophile
leukocyte

Heterophile
myelocytes

Normoblast nucleus   Eryth-   Polychro-   Fat cells   Normoblasts   Eosinophile myelocytes
rocytes   matophile
erythroblasts in mitosis

Fig. 5–8. Section of bone marrow of rabbit which had injections of lithium carmine and India ink. Hematoxylin-eosin-azure II. 460 ×. (A.A.M.)

(heterophile, eosinophile and basophile) are common cell types of the myeloid tissue. The myelocytes of each of the three types are provided with their characteristic granulation and cannot be transformed into myelocytes of another type or into elements of another kind. They have a compact, round or kidney-shaped nucleus, and proliferate intensely by mitotic division. Some of their progeny remain unchanged, while others undergo progressive maturation. Finally, each cell is transformed individually into a mature polymorphonuclear granular leukocyte. These details are clearly shown in Figures 5–9 and 5–10, which also illustrate the differences resulting from the use of the two technics.

MYELOCYTES WITH HETEROPHILE GRANULES

(NEUTROPHILE MYELOCYTES OF MAN). The heterophile myelocytes are larger than the mature heterophile leukocytes. In the youngest generation, sometimes called *promyelocyte,* the oval or kidney-shaped nucleus contains a loose chromatin network and several nucleoli. At the indentation of the nucleus there is a distinct cytocentrum. The ameboid cytoplasm is slightly basophile, although it often shows acidophile areas. The specific granules are scarce and usually are confined to the periphery of the cytocentrum and to the acidophile areas in the cell body. In dry smears the promyelocytes contain, in addition to the heterophile granules, azurophile granules which later disappear.

The promyelocytes often show mitosis. In

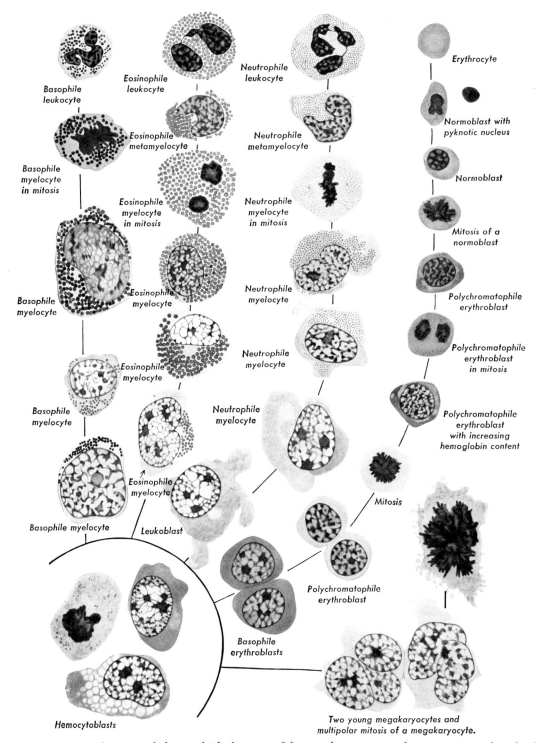

Basophile
leukocyte

Eosinophile
leukocyte

Neutrophile
leukocyte

Erythrocyte

Basophile
myelocyte
in mitosis

Eosinophile
metamyelocyte

Neutrophile
metamyelocyte

Normoblast with
pyknotic nucleus

Eosinophile
myelocyte
in mitosis

Neutrophile
myelocyte
in mitosis

Normoblast

Mitosis of a
normoblast

Basophile
myelocyte

Eosinophile
myelocyte

Neutrophile
myelocyte

Polychromatophile
erythroblast

Basophile
myelocyte

Eosinophile
myelocyte

Neutrophile
myelocyte

Polychromatophile
erythroblast
in mitosis

Basophile
myelocyte

Eosinophile
myelocyte

Neutrophile
myelocyte

Polychromatophile
erythroblast
with increasing
hemoglobin content

Basophile myelocyte

Eosinophile
myelocyte

Leukoblast

Mitosis

Polychromatophile
erythroblast

Hemocytoblasts

Basophile
erythroblasts

Two young megakaryocytes and
multipolar mitosis of a megakaryocyte.

Fig. 5–9. Development of the myeloid elements of human bone marrow from a common lymphoid stem cell as seen in sections stained with hematoxylin-eosin-azure II. The basophile myelocytes were fixed in absolute alcohol and stained with alcoholic thionine. The mature cells are from dry smears of human blood stained with May-Grünwald-Giemsa, except the basophile leukocyte, which is stained with alcoholic thionine. 1500 ×. (A.A.M.)

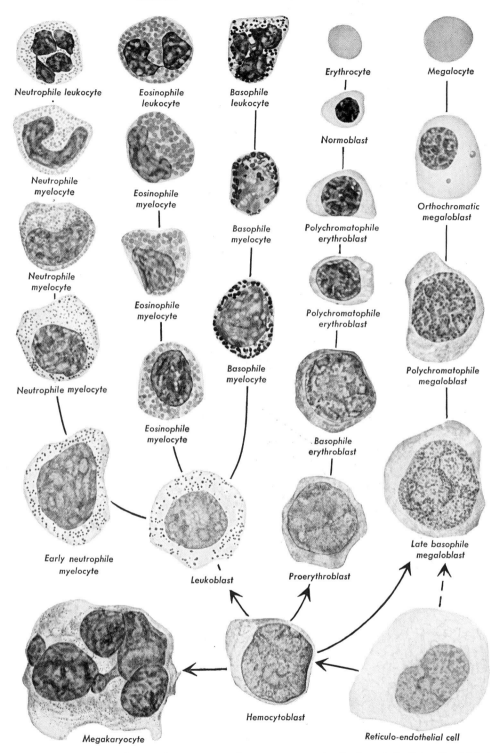

Fig. 5–10. Cells from human bone marrow dry smears, except reticulo-endothelial cell, which is from a smear of human embryonic liver. Note differences in size of cells and in nuclear structure of the erythroblast and megaloblast series (of pernicious anemia). Slides of O. P. Jones. May-Grünwald-Giemsa stain. 1350 ×. (Drawn by Miss Esther Bohlman.)

the following generation, the cytoplasm of the heterophile myelocytes becomes diffusely acidophile, while the specific granules increase in number and fill the whole cell body, except for the cytocentrum. The chromatin network of the nucleus becomes coarser and stains darker, and the nucleoli become indistinct. Mitoses are common; during division the granules are evenly distributed among the daughter cells and continue to increase in numbers as the latter grow. Some of the heterophile myelocytes are small and have a dark nucleus; these are called *micromyelocytes.*

After an unknown number of mitoses, a generation of heterophile myelocytes appears which does not divide. The nucleus in these cells shows a beginning polymorphism and has the shape of a horseshoe. Such cells are called *metamyelocytes;* each of them maturates by progressive constriction of the horseshoe-shaped nucleus into a mature heterophile leukocyte.

MYELOCYTES WITH EOSINOPHILE GRANULES. Less numerous than the heterophile myelocytes are the myelocytes with eosinophile granules, which undergo in general the same changes. Among them also different generations can be distinguished. They all have a slightly basophile protoplasm. The eosinophile promyelocytes contain a small number of specific granules which do not stain alike. The youngest among them show a distinct basophilia and stain bluish with eosin-azure; from these there are all transitions to mature, purely eosinophile granules. Mitoses are common in the eosinophile myelocytes, especially in the large ones. The horseshoe-shaped nucleus of the metamyelocytes becomes constricted, often into two lobes in the mature leukocytes.

MYELOCYTES WITH BASOPHILE GRANULES. These are much scarcer than the heterophile myelocytes and are difficult to study because their granules, in man, are easily soluble in water.

For the most part the basophile myelocytes are small cells with a paler nucleus than the other myelocytes. The protoplasm contains a widely varying number of specific, basophile, metachromatic granules of unequal size.

Megakaryocytes. These giant cells with a polymorphous nucleus are characteristic of the mammalian bone marrow, where they are scattered evenly among the other elements.

Some of them have a diameter as large as 40 microns. The form of the cell body is spherical, but its surface is often provided with irregularly shaped processes.

The nucleus is deeply constricted in many places; the lobes bulge at the periphery, while their central parts are interconnected by short, branched stalks. The interior of the nucleus shows a chromatin network and indistinct nucleoli. In the living cell the abundant cytoplasm is homogeneous and contains many groups of centrioles scattered in the furrows of the nuclear surface. Mitochondria and a Golgi net have also been described. With special fixation and staining, fine, azurophile granules are seen distributed in the cell body in large quantities, sometimes in small dense groups. The presumed role of the megakaryocytes in the production of platelets was mentioned on page 59.

In every normal bone marrow many megakaryocytes are found degenerating (Fig. 5–11), while there are frequent signs of their new formation from hemocytoblasts. The

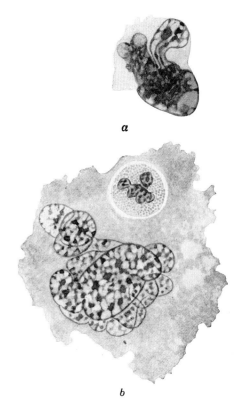

a

b

Fig. 5–11.   *a*, degenerating megakaryocyte; *b*, megakaryocyte containing a neutrophile leukocyte; both from human bone marrow. 1500 ×. (A.A.M.)

first stage is hypertrophy of the nucleus, which then becomes constricted in several places. Then follows a series of peculiar mitotic divisions which concern only the nucleus. The centrioles divide into several groups, and a complex spindle with several poles arises. The chromosomes are arranged in several equatorial planes and give rise to several daughter nuclei. There is no constriction of the cytoplasm, and the daughter nuclei at once fuse into a new, larger nucleus. After an interval a new mitosis with still more centers occurs, the daughter nuclei again fuse in the telophase, and the quantity of chromatin and the number of the centrioles again increase. The number of mitoses is not known. Sooner or later the cell degenerates; the giant nucleus shrinks, the cytoplasm disintegrates, and the final result is a naked, shrunken, nuclear remnant. Such degenerated nuclei often find their way into the sinusoids of the marrow and are carried with the blood into the right heart and thence into the capillaries of the lungs, where they remain and probably undergo autolysis. Under pathological conditions this embolism of the lung vessels by megakaryocytes may occur on a large scale; in fact, not only degenerating nuclei, but even whole cells with unchanged protoplasm may be found obstructing the pulmonary capillaries.

Plasma Cells. Plasma cells constitute 1 to 3 per cent of the hematopoietic cells of normal human marrow. They are found primarily within the reticular fiber sheath of the terminal portions of the arterial capillaries, but also occur as isolated cells or in small foci throughout the marrow. In certain diseases the level of globulins in the plasma seems to vary with the number of plasma cells in the marrow.

Monocytes. Many hematologists believe that monocytes are formed in the myeloid tissue. Under normal conditions they are found only in the lumen of the venous sinusoids. The origin of these cells is discussed on page 113.

Homoplastic and Heteroplastic Hemopoiesis. Under physiological conditions the needs of the adult organism for myeloid blood elements are usually supplied by *homoplastic hemopoiesis*—the production of mature cells by young elements of the same type. But not all the young forms reach maturity; some of them remain unused in the tissue. Whenever the requirements of the body for erythrocytes or leukocytes are greatly increased, homoplastic hemopoiesis does not suffice, and new *erythroblasts* and *myelocytes develop from stem cells.* This is called *heteroplastic hemopoiesis,* which also applies to the development of free stem cells from fixed ones.

In this process, when a hemocytoblast divides, either its daughter cells remain in the tissue as hemocytoblasts or one of its latent potencies develops and both daughter cells become erythroblasts or myelocytes. Transitional cells between the hemocytoblasts and early myelocytes have been described under the name of *leukoblasts* (Figs. 5–9, 5–10). Their structural differences are so insignificant that to recognize these elements as a separate cell type seems unwarranted.

In the embryo the hemocytoblasts of the bone marrow which produce the myeloid forms originate from outstretched mesenchymal cells. In the adult the same process may occur. It has been explained that some of the cellular elements of the reticulum always remain undifferentiated. But under physiological conditions it is rare for primitive reticular cells to become hemocytoblasts in the bone marrow. The mitoses of the myelocytes and erythroblasts—and occasionally of hemocytoblasts—usually are sufficient. Pathological stimuli sometimes facilitate the new formation of hemocytoblasts from the primitive reticular cells (Fig. 5–13). As described on page 92, heteroplastic development of lymphocytes may also occur (Fig. 5–12).

Entry of Myeloid Elements into the Blood. Because the myeloid elements arise outside the blood stream, it is obvious that the newly formed mature myeloid cells must pass through the walls of the blood vessels to enter the circulation. The thin-walled venous sinusoids make this possible. Through them easily pass, not only the ameboid mature granular leukocytes, but also the nonmotile erythrocytes. When these are ready for circulation, they slip through the membrane into the blood stream in the lumen of the sinusoid. The mechanism of this phenomenon is probably regulated by changes in the permeability of the vessel walls and in the surface energy.

The claim that red blood corpuscles in the

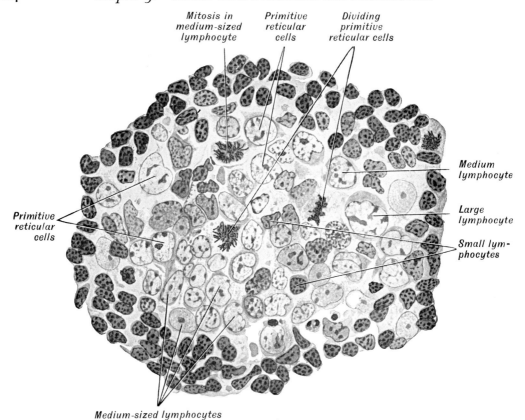

Fig. 5–12.   Heteroplastic development of lymphocytes from primitive reticular cells in a human lymph node. Hematoxylin-eosin-azure II. 750 ×. (A.A.M.)

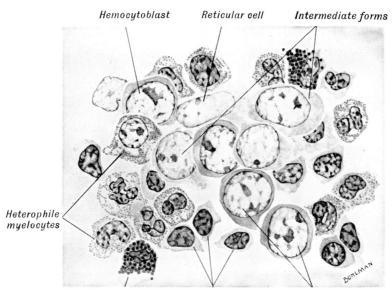

Fig. 5–13.   Section of human bone marrow from a case of polycythemia vera, showing stages in development of primitive reticular cells into hemocytoblasts and basophile erythroblasts. Zenker-formol and hematoxylin-eosin-azure II. From a preparation of C. Huggins. 1380 ×.

adult, normal man are formed intravascularly is based on unconvincing evidence. In the embryonic mammalian liver and bone marrow the red blood cells develop extravascularly, while in the yolk sac they are preponderantly of intravascular origin.

Functions of the Myeloid Tissue. The main function of the bone marrow seems to be the production of myeloid elements for the blood. The macrophages of the bone marrow also function like the macrophages in other tissues.

The cellular composition of the blood is intimately connected with the condition of the bone marrow. Under physiological conditions the relative numbers of the different cells in the bone marrow, as in the blood, vary only a little. But all general pathological processes immediately affect the composition of the bone marrow. In most general or severe local infections the heterophile granulocytopoietic apparatus is stimulated, and the percentage of myelocytes of this type increases greatly. In typhoid fever or in agranulocytic angina the heterophile myelocytes decrease in number. Whenever there is an increased need of erythrocytes or when the erythrocytes are destroyed in large quantities, they and their precursors predominate in the myeloid tissue. That temperature plays some role in the control of hemopoiesis in the marrow is shown by the fact that the fatty marrow of the tail bones of a rat becomes hematopoietic when the temperature of the bone is raised to that of the body, as by placing it in the body (Fig. 5–14).

The production of erythrocytes depends in part on an *anti-anemic factor* which is stored in the liver. This factor probably is the result of the interaction of a substance in the gastric juice (*intrinsic factor* of Castle) with some substance in the diet (*extrinsic factor*). The absence of the anti-anemic factor results in pernicious anemia, which can be treated successfully by the administration of liver or gastric extract or vitamin B_{12}.

The erythroblasts are about as sensitive to ionizing radiations as the hemocytoblasts (lymphocytes). The myelocytes are more resistant and the megakaryocytes much more so, while the reticular cells are extremely resistant.

Destruction of Blood Corpuscles. Both the red and the white corpuscles constantly

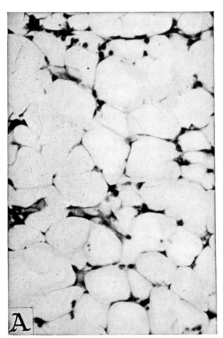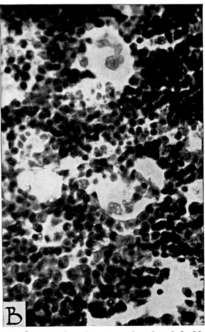

Fig. 5–14. A tail loop was constructed in a twenty-three-day rat by skinning the distal half of the tail and inserting it surgically in the peritoneal cavity, where it was kept for 125 days. The section on the left (A) is from the cool outside loop and shows fatty bone marrow; that on the right (B) shows hemopoietic marrow from the warm region of the tail in the abdominal cavity. 500 ×. (Courtesy of C. Huggins.)

perish in large numbers, even under normal conditions. With the aid of isotopes it has been shown that the life span of a human erythrocyte is about 120 days. The manner and site of the physiological destruction and final disposal of the erythrocytes have not been completely elucidated. It has long been known that there is destruction of red blood cells by the phagocytes of the spleen, liver and bone marrow. The hemoglobin of the ingested erythrocytes is broken into hematin and globin. The first is further split into bilirubin, which is excreted with the bile, and into iron, which is retained, especially by the spleen, and utilized for the formation of new erythrocytes. How this iron is transferred from the spleen to the bone marrow has not been described.

In addition, a constant disintegration of erythrocytes into hemoglobin-stained fragments in the circulation itself is thought to be an important factor, the fragments being taken up by the macrophages in various regions of the body. In certain pathological conditions when the erythrocytes degenerate in large quantities, erythrophagocytosis in the spleen is greatly increased, and the macrophages contain large amounts of hemosiderin and waste pigment. In these disturbances, other organs, especially the liver with its Kupffer cells, may also take part in the destruction of the erythrocytes.

The presence of degenerating leukocytes in the circulating blood, although often described, has never been confirmed conclusively. Destruction of granular leukocytes through phagocytosis by the Kupffer cells in the liver has been observed. Large numbers of lymphocytes may degenerate in the very place where they are formed in the lymphatic tissue. In addition, the organism always loses lymphocytes through migration into the cavity of the intestine.

EMBRYONIC DEVELOPMENT OF BLOOD AND CONNECTIVE TISSUE

The manner in which blood cells develop in embryonic and postnatal animals is one of the most controversial subjects in histology. In our opinion, the following presentation is the most accurate, although some hematologists do not agree. Downey's *Handbook of*

Hematology contains extended discussions of the subject.

Blood is formed in practically the same manner in all embryonic mammals. Beginning hemopoiesis is the same in almost all situations, and consists in the rounding up of outstretched mesenchymal cells into free basophile cells, which in turn give rise to all types of blood cells. The first site of this process is the walls of the yolk sac, succeeded by the body mesenchyme, liver, bone marrow, spleen, and lymph nodes. In the yolk sac most of the *primitive stem cells* become *primitive red blood corpuscles,* which serve as oxygen carriers until they are replaced by the permanent erythrocytes. The remaining stem cells give rise to the *definitive* or *permanent red blood cells, granulocytes* and *megakaryocytes.* In all other situations in which blood formation occurs, the process is the same except that primitive erythroblasts are not formed.

In all areas of embryonic blood formation the free stem cells are morphologically the

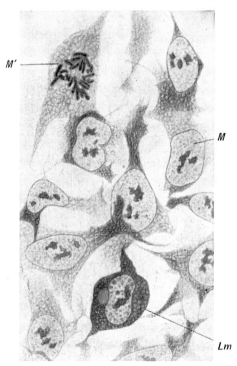

Fig. 5–15. Mesenchyme from head of a rabbit embryo of nine and three-quarter days. Development of large lymphoid wandering cell (*Lm*) from mesenchymal cells (*M* and *M'*). Eosin-azure stain. 1025 ×. (A.A.M.)

same as the various-sized lymphocytes (or hemocytoblasts) of the adult. Even in the primordia of the lymphatic tissue large numbers of erythrocytes, myelocytes and megakaryocytes are formed. It is only in the late embryonic stages that an apparent division of blood-forming tissues into myeloid and lymphatic takes place, and this division seems to hold for most of the normal adult life. Under abnormal conditions, however, the myeloid potencies of the cells of the lymphatic and loose connective tissues may become apparent even in the adult mammalian organism. *Blood formation in the embryo thus takes place through the development of a hemopoietic tissue whose constituent cells are qualitatively the same, but which vary quantitatively in the successive locations in which this process takes place.*

Origin of Mesenchyme. The mesenchyme arises from the mesoderm through the isolation from this layer of cells, which become distributed singly and in groups in the spaces between the three germinal layers. The sclerotomes are an especially abundant source of the mesenchyme. Some mesenchymal cells also arise from the surface of the parietal mesoderm facing the ectoderm, from the surface of the visceral mesoderm facing the entoderm, and from the lateral layer of the somites, the skin plate.

Yolk Sac. In early human ova irregular strands of primitive mesodermal cells traverse the small chorionic "cavity." As fluid accumulates in the blastocyst, these strands cover the surfaces of the chorionic, amniotic and yolk sac vesicles. As the embryo develops, the yolk sac becomes larger and its mesoderm assumes a more typical epithelium-like arrangement. This yolk sac mesoderm is apparently the source of the yolk sac mesenchyme, which then develops hematopoietically as in other mammals. The mesenchyme between the splanchnopleure and the entoderm gives rise to groups of spherical basophile cells the (*blood islands*) connected with one another by strands of elongated cells (Fig. 5–16). The peripheral cells of the islands and those of the strands become transformed into endothelial tubes. The endothelium secretes the blood plasma, which fills the tubes. In this way the first blood vessels, the yolk sac vessels, arise. The round cells of the islands are the first blood cells. In the first stages of development, the endothelial cells of the blood vessels in the area vasculosa are often seen to swell, and become free in the lumen as additional primitive blood cells (Fig. 5–17).

The first blood elements are hemocytoblasts. They are free mesenchymal cells and are usually called *primitive blood cells* (Fig. 5–17). Almost immediately after their formation most of them elaborate hemoglobin and become *primitive erythroblasts* (Fig. 5–18). They accumulate large quantities of hemoglobin and finally cease dividing, although the nucleus remains in the cell. Such older forms are called *primitive erythrocytes;* they serve the growing embryo as oxygen carriers, but finally die out. They do not form definitive erythrocytes. A few of the primitive blood cells remain unchanged as ameboid basophile hemocytoblasts. The intravascular hemocytoblasts at these early stages sometimes form atypical megakaryocytes. Free phagocytes arise from the primitive endothelial cells and are shed into the lumen. These are the first macrophages of the embryo; they engulf degenerating blood cells. In the human yolk sac vessels, the hemocytoblasts later produce a few secondary erythroblasts (Fig. 5–19) identical with those in adult bone marrow.

The primitive wandering cells (hemocytoblasts) in the mesenchyme outside the yolk sac vessels produce a few heterophile and eosinophile granulocytes. The hemopoietic activity of the yolk sac in man

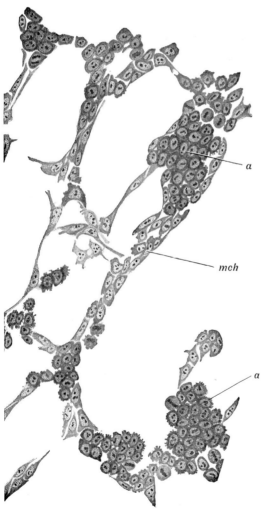

Fig. 5–16. Stretch preparation of the wall of the yolk sac of a guinea-pig embryo of thirteen days. Development of blood islands, (*a*) from the cells of the peripheral, mesenchymal mesoblasts (*mch*). Eosin-azure stain. 220 ×. (A.A.M.)

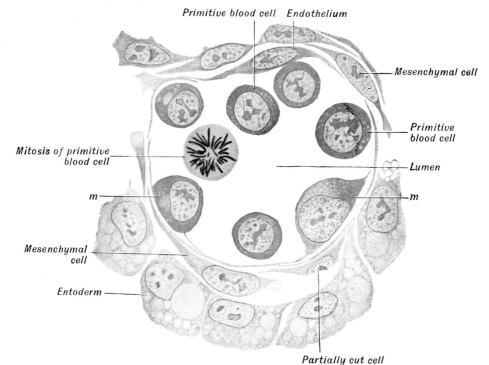

Fig. 5–17.   Cross section of a vessel of the area vasculosa of a rabbit embryo of eight and one-half days (five somites). *m,* rounding off of endothelial cells and their transformation into primitive blood cells. Eosin-azure stain. 1000 ×. (A.A.M.)

continues but a short time, and the organ soon atrophies. When the yolk sac of the rat is transplanted to the anterior chamber of the eye, the hemocytoblasts produce great numbers of myelocytes instead of primitive erythroblasts.

Body Mesenchyme. In the diffuse mesenchyme of the body, wandering cells of hemocytoblastic and macrophage appearance occasionally give rise to small extravascular groups of myelocytes and erythrocytes; most of these degenerate. The hemopoietic activity of the wandering cells in the diffuse mesenchyme soon subsides, but these same elements in the specialized blood-forming areas of the mesenchyme are the source of a most intense hemopoiesis.

Vascular Endothelium. In early embryonic stages the endothelium of the blood vessels is identical in its potencies with the common mesenchymal cells. Thus, in the yolk sac vessels and in the caudal portion of the aorta, the endothelial cells form clusters of hemocytoblasts. The endothelium of the vessels of the embryonic liver, bone marrow and spleen may take part for a short time in the production of hemocytoblasts. Later, this endothelium becomes the littoral cells of the macrophage system which either have lost or do not use their hemopoietic powers in the adult organism. In all the other vessels the endothelium loses its hemopoietic potency early (Chap. 10).

Liver. The liver, the second blood-forming organ of the embryo, develops as a network of branching epithelial strands from the epithelium of the intestine. Large, thin-walled blood vessels are located in

the meshes of this network from the very beginning. Between this endothelium and the epithelium are thin layers of mesenchyme which give rise to hemocytoblasts. They proliferate hemopoietically. The liver cells are soon outnumbered by the dense masses of extravascular definitive erythroblasts; a few megakaryocytes and myelocytes are also present.

The erythroblasts produce mature erythrocytes which slip through the walls of the sinusoids and enter the general circulation. The endothelium of these vessels is transformed into a layer of macrophages which become the Kupffer cells of the adult. Toward the end of gestation the hemopoietic activity of the liver gradually subsides, so that only small foci of erythroblasts can be found in the liver of the newborn. These, too, soon disappear.

Bone Marrow. The third hemopoietic organ of the mammalian embryo is the bone marrow. The myeloid tissue develops from the primitive bone marrow, the mesenchyme which resorbs the cartilage in the bones of endochondral origin and fills the spaces between the bone trabeculae of the endochondral or periosteal bone. Here again, the process is the same in principle as in the diffuse mesenchyme of the body and in the liver. Some of the fixed mesenchymal cells become wandering cells of hemocytoblastic or macrophage type. These proliferate and form dense, extravascular clusters of erythroblasts, groups of myelocytes of the three different types, and megakaryocytes. Soon, especially in the older regions, as in the diaphyses of the long bones, a solid mass of myeloid tissue develops. Of the original fixed mesenchymal

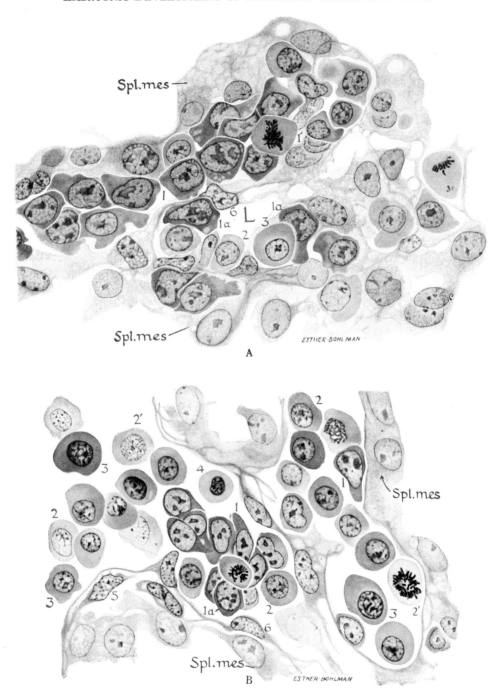

Fig. 5–18. Two sections through folds of the wall of the yolk sac of twenty-four-day human embryo (H1516 Univ. Chicago Emb. Coll.). A, early stage of hematopoiesis, consisting of proliferating extravascular hemocytoblasts (1, 1'); L, lumen of a small vessel containing a few primitive polychromatophile erythroblasts. B, later stage of hematopoiesis showing transformation of hemocytoblasts (1) into primitive basophile erythroblasts (1a), primitive polychromatophile erythroblasts (2, 3) and primitive erythrocytes (4); 5, mesenchymal cells; 6, endothelium; Spl. mes, splanchnic mesothelium. Hematoxylin-eosin-azure II. 1100 ×. (From Bloom and Bartelmez: Am. J. Anat., 67: No. 1, July, 1940.)

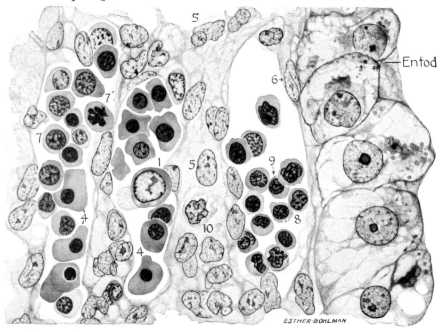

Fig. 5–19.   Section through yolk sac of a 20-mm. human embryo. In addition to circulating primitive erythrocytes, there are two foci of developing polychromatophile definitive erythroblasts. *1*, hemocytoblast; *4*, primitive erythrocytes; *5*, mesenchymal cells; *7* and *8*, early and late definitive polychromatophile erythroblasts with one in mitosis at *7'*; *9*, normoblast; *10*, lymphoid wandering cell. Hematoxylin-eosin-azure II. 1100 ×. (From Bloom and Bartelmez: Am. J. Anat., 67: No. 1, July, 1940.)

elements, only a few stellate cells remain between the meshes of the young blood cells; some of them remain as the primitive reticular cells of the stroma of the bone marrow, while the others develop into macrophages and fat cells. Argyrophile fibrils develop about them. The primitive endothelium of the vessels becomes the littoral macrophages in later stages.

Lymphatic Organs. The lymph nodes arise along the course of the lymphatics or in the walls of the primitive lymph sacs in relatively late stages of embryonic development. Here again, in circumscribed areas of the diffuse mesenchyme, many fixed mesenchymal cells are transformed into wandering cells. As in the other blood-forming organs, cells of hemocytoblastic and free macrophage types can be distinguished (Fig. 11–10). Wandering cells of the small lymphocyte type, rarely found in the bone marrow, now appear in large numbers. The number of large and small lymphocytes increases, in part, through continued mobilization of new, fixed mesenchymal cells, but mainly through intense mitotic proliferation of the free lymphocytes. The fixed mesenchymal cells which remain between the free cells become the cellular components of the reticular stroma, and in later stages elaborate argyrophile fibrils.

The lymphatic tissue in the embryo always contains many heterophile and eosinophile myelocytes and a few megakaryocytes and erythroblasts; these develop from the same wandering cells from which the small lymphocytes arise. Thus in the embryo

of the mammals the myeloid and the lymphoid elements are not sharply separated from each other.

In the *spleen* the lymphocytes develop in much the same way as in the lymph nodes, although more erythrocytes and other myeloid cells are formed. Some myelocytes also develop from the lymphoid wandering cells in the embryonic thymus.

Loose Connective Tissue. When connective tissue fibers appear in the mesenchyme, this tissue becomes the connective tissue. The exact moment when a mesenchymal cell changes into a fibroblast has not been determined, because there is no appreciable change in structure. In fact, in all regions of the body some fixed mesenchymal cells remain undifferentiated, mainly along the capillaries.

At the later embryonic stages the vast majority of the wandering cells in the connective tissue are macrophages; hemocytoblasts are rare except in the primordia of the lymphatic organs and the bone marrow.

Many of the wandering cells persist as such in the adult connective tissue. Most of them, however, become fixed macrophages. The primitive wandering cells also give rise to mast cells, which then proliferate mitotically.

The appearance of the primordia of the white and of the brown fat tissue is closely connected with the development of networks of blood vessels. The fibrillar intercellular substance of the connective tissue around the growing capillaries undergoes a peculiar dissolution, and the mesenchymal cells in these areas proliferate and form loose, cellular networks. Although some consider such accumulations

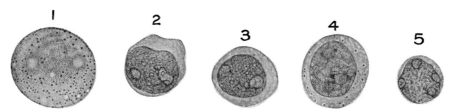

Fig. 5–20. *1*, myeloblast with azure granules from normal human bone marrow; *2*, myeloblast from the blood in chronic myeloid leukemia; *3* and *4*, lymphoblasts from the blood in chronic lymphatic leukemia; *5*, lymphoblast from the blood in subacute lymphatic leukemia. (Cells 2 to 5 are from pathological human blood.) May-Grünwald-Giemsa-stained dry smears. (After Downey.)

of cells as specific, primitive fat organs, it is more probable that these elements are common mesenchymal cells, which accumulate fat droplets and become fat cells. In the primordia of the brown fat tissue, stellate cells assume a polyhedral form, and the accumulated fat droplets fail to fuse.

POTENCIES OF DEVELOPMENT OF THE LYMPHOID STEM CELLS OF THE LYMPHATIC AND MYELOID TISSUES

Nearly all hematologists agree that the various myeloid elements of the bone marrow develop through proliferation and differentiation from a basophile free stem cell—designated here as the hemocytoblast. In the lymphatic tissue the small lymphocytes develop from young forms of larger size which have exactly the same structure as the hemocytoblasts in the bone marrow. *The question arises whether the lymphoid cells in both tissues have identical or different developmental potencies.* If they are identical, then all blood elements of the adult originate from one common stem cell which may appropriately be called the hemocytoblast (the "unitarian" theory of hemopoiesis). If, on the contrary, the large lymphoid cells of the lymphatic and of the myeloid tissues differ in their potencies, then each of these two tissues has a specific stem cell, and one of these could be called the *lymphoblast,* the other the *myeloblast* ("dualistic" theory of hemopoiesis). The "trialistic" theory holds that the monocytes, too, have a distinct stem cell. There are many variations of each of these theories.

The sum of all the facts speaks more in favor of the unitarian than of either of the pluralistic theories. Structural differences between the lymphoblasts and myeloblasts are not constantly present, and all the various morphological criteria for separating them which have been proposed, such as detailed structure of the nucleus, number of nucleoli (Fig. 5–20), mitochondria, supravital staining, oxidase and peroxidase reaction, are unreliable. Lymphocytes and myeloblasts have the same type of movement in tissue culture (De Bruyn). In fact, the stem cells which appear in the blood in leukemia are now frequently called "blasts" by most clinical hematologists until changes in the blood picture or in the clinical course of the disease permit the classification into myeloid or lymphatic type.

Much confusion is due to the fact that many hematological theories rest almost exclusively on studies of the peripheral blood of man in health and disease. The unitarian theory, however, is based on comparative and experimental histogenetic studies of blood and connective tissues in both embryonic and adult animals and is in agreement with results obtained from studies on *inflammation, extramedullary hematopoiesis* and *tissue cultures.*

In Lower Vertebrates. The boundary between myeloid and lymphoid tissue is completely effaced in the lower vertebrates. The developing lymphoid and myeloid elements are everywhere mixed with each other.

In Embryonic Development. In all hematopoietic foci in the mammalian embryo both lymphoid and myeloid elements arise from the same lymphoid wandering cell (see p. 106).

In Tissue Cultures. If a fragment of a lymph node of an adult rabbit is cultivated in a medium containing bone marrow extract, the large lymphocytes (lymphoblasts or hemocytoblasts) may differentiate into myelocytes and megakaryocytes. Lymphocytes of the thoracic duct of ascaris-immunized rabbits have also been observed to develop into heterophile leukocytes in cultures con-

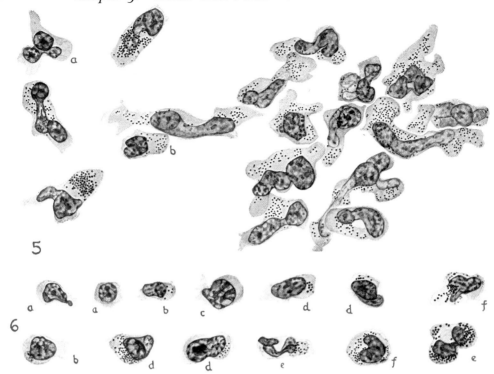

Fig. 5–21. Heterophile myelocytes and leukocytes which have developed from lymphocytes in tissue culture. The thoracic duct lymph of a rabbit immunized to ascaris extract was cultured with connective tissue in plasma and bone marrow and ascaris extracts. Cell 5*a* is an unchanged lymphocyte; 5*b* is an early myelocyte with a lymphocytic nucleus. The cells of 6 show stages in the development of lymphocytes *a, c* into myelocytes, *b, d, e, f*. Hematoxylin-eosin-azure II. 1490 ✕. (Drawn by Miss E. Bohlman, after Bloom, 1937. Courtesy of Wistar Press.)

taining bone marrow extract and ascaris extract (Fig. 5–21). The myeloblasts of the blood in myeloblastic leukemia develop into macrophages and fibroblasts in tissue culture, just as do the lymphocytes of lymphatic leukemia under the same conditions. The claim that myeloblasts can produce only myelocytes and erythroblasts is thus refuted. These experiments also refute the so-called "trialistic theories" of blood formation, for, in these cultures, both myeloblasts and lymphocytes often pass through a monocyte stage before becoming macrophages.

Extramedullary Myelopoiesis. Under physiological conditions in adult mammals, and especially in man, the formation of the myeloid elements is confined to the bone marrow. In various abnormal conditions *extramedullary* or *ectopic myelopoiesis* or *myeloid metaplasia* is of common occurrence.

Local myelopoiesis has been observed in the sclerotic aortic wall, in the adrenal and in other places; it develops after ligation of the renal artery and vein of the adult rabbit. More generalized extramedullary myelopoiesis occurs in various parts of the body in leukemia and certain intoxications and infections. It can be produced through repeated bleeding or chronic poisoning with blood-destroying substances. As a rule, the spleen is the first organ affected. Later the liver, the lymph nodes, the adrenal and other organs become involved. Nearly always, it is the heterophile and eosinophile myelocytes which first appear in the new place; megakaryocytes come later, and finally erythroblasts develop.

Experimental investigations have shown that the myelocytes and erythroblasts in extramedullary myelopoiesis originate in several different ways: (1) Sometimes the first myeloid elements appear in the lumen of the venous capillaries, where they originate from lymphoid cells which circulate in the blood.

From the viewpoint of the unitarian theory the latter are identical with lymphocytes. The newly formed myeloid elements may pass through the wall of the vessels into the tissue, where they continue to proliferate. (2) In the lymphoid organs, including the spleen, the free basophile cells of the tissue, the lymphocytes, are often the source of the myeloid elements; this process even occurs in the germinal centers where medium-sized and small lymphocytes transform directly into myelocytes. (3) In still other cases the first myelocytes may develop directly from undifferentiated perivascular cells or primitive reticular cells with or without passing through a hemocytoblast stage (p. 103).

Origin of the Monocyte. The questions of the origin and nature of the monocyte are among the most debated problems in morphological hematology. Some believe the monocyte to develop from specific monoblasts in the bone marrow, but the morphological specificity of the precursors has not been proved. Myeloblasts from the blood in myeloblastic leukemia pass through monocyte-like stages as they develop into macrophages in tissue culture. Most of the recent investigations indicate that endothelium does not furnish ameboid cells in the adult mammal.

The monocytes of the blood do not store vital dyes, as do the macrophages, both large and small. It is clear, however, that the monocytes, as they develop into macrophages, soon take on the ability to store vital dyes. While it is possible that monocytes may develop directly from the reticular cells of the blood-forming organs, such a process has never been demonstrated.

The unitarian hematologists consider the lymphocytes to be the source of monocytes. They point out that in blood smears of most animals it is impossible to separate all the monocytes as a cell type distinct from lymphocytes. In the rat and, to some extent, the monkey, supravital staining with neutral red and Janus green shows the monocytes to be connected with the common small lymphocytes by a complete series of transitional forms. Similar transition forms between lymphocytoid and monocytoid wandering cells are to be found in the loose connective tissue. In inflammation the hematogenous lymphocytes and monocytes rapidly become ameboid phagocytic elements (polyblasts). In this progressive development the lymphocytes often pass through a transitory state in which they cannot be distinguished from monocytes and, among other characteristics, have a typical neutral red rosette. In cultures of normal and leukemic blood leukocytes, as well as of lymphocytes of rabbit lymph, the small lymphocytes change into monocytoid cells and then into large macrophages and finally into fibroblasts. In rabbits in which an extensive monocytosis has been produced, as by B. monocytogenes, the monocytes develop by individual hypertrophy from the common smaller lymphocytes. In none of this experimental material is there any evidence for the existence of a specific monoblast different from a lymphocyte (hemocytoblast).

The majority of the facts support the idea that monocytes are lymphocytes, that is, hemocytoblasts, which have developed somewhat in the phagocytic direction. The main site of this transformation is the blood in the venous sinusoids of the spleen, liver and bone marrow, where transitional forms between lymphocytes and monocytes are common, especially in experimentally produced monocytoses (Fig. 5–22).

GENETIC INTERRELATIONSHIP AND POTENCIES OF THE CELLS OF THE BLOOD AND LYMPH, THE CONNECTIVE TISSUE AND ENDOTHELIUM

From a general histological point of view, three large groups of cells can be distinguished in the connective tissue and the blood: (1) fixed, highly specialized elements. As fibroblasts they produce collagen; as endothelium, they line blood channels; and as chondrocytes and osteocytes, they form the cells of cartilage and bone. (2) Fixed or free cells which phagocytose, store vital dyes and other colloidal substances, and play important roles in the general metabolism and especially in the "defense" reactions. These are the *macrophages.* (3) Free cells which circulate in the blood or are scattered throughout the connective tissue. These are the *hemocytes;* among them are to be distinguished: (*a*) the hemocytoblasts (lymphocytes) which serve as stem cells for (*b*)

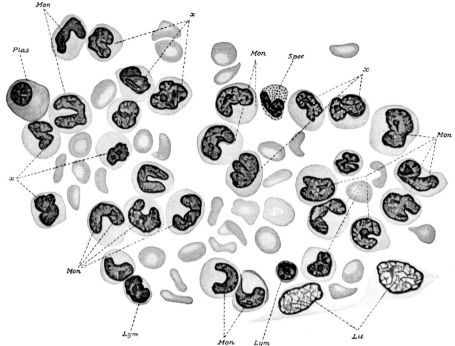

Fig. 5–22.   Section through a splenic sinus of a rabbit infected with *L. monocytogenes: Mon,* monocytes; *Lym,* lymphocytes; *x,* transitions from lymphocytes to monocytes; *Plas,* plasma cell; *Lit,* lining (littoral) cells; *Spec,* heterophile leukocyte. Hematoxylin-eosin-azure stain. 1200 ×. (After Bloom.)

granulocytes, monocytes, erythrocytes and megakaryocytes.

The relations between all these cells are not clearly observable under physiological conditions. Under pathological or experimental conditions, when there is an increased destruction of cells and a corresponding intense new formation, the genetic relationships may be analyzed more easily. Three processes especially favor such analysis: (1) the changes in the tissue in the local "defense" reaction, that is, in inflammation; (2) the reactions of tissue in culture; and (3) extramedullary myelopoiesis.

It is clear from such studies that the various-sized lymphocytes (hemocytoblasts) are all endowed with hemopoietic, phagocytic and fibrocytic potencies. The lymphocytes are free, mesenchymal cells which are scattered everywhere in the tissues of the adult body and circulate in the blood and lymph. Under normal conditions they keep the appearance of lymphocytes, but, in response to certain pathological stimuli, they may become granulocytes, erythroblasts, macrophages, and so on. They may be looked upon as an easily movable mesenchymal reserve.

It has been shown that fixed cells with unrestricted mesenchymal potencies are present in the connective tissues of the adult mammals. According to various investigators, these are fibroblasts or endothelial cells or fixed macrophages. But the most convincing evidence indicates that the original mesenchymal potencies are retained by cells scattered in the loose connective tissue along the blood vessels, by the primitive reticular cells of the hemopoietic tissues, and by some cells lining the venous sinuses of the liver.

Undifferentiated Fixed Cells; Primitive Reticular Cells. In the lymphatic and myeloid tissue the development of fixed and free macrophages from the primitive reticular cells can be observed in the body and in cultures of these tissues. Lymphoid cells, hemocytoblasts, also originate from the same source, particularly in the germinal centers. In the omentum the new formation of fixed macrophages from perivascular, undifferentiated cells has been described. In extramedullary myelopoiesis the myelocytes can often be traced directly to perivascular, fixed cells. If foreign substances, especially foreign proteins, are introduced into the organism, the

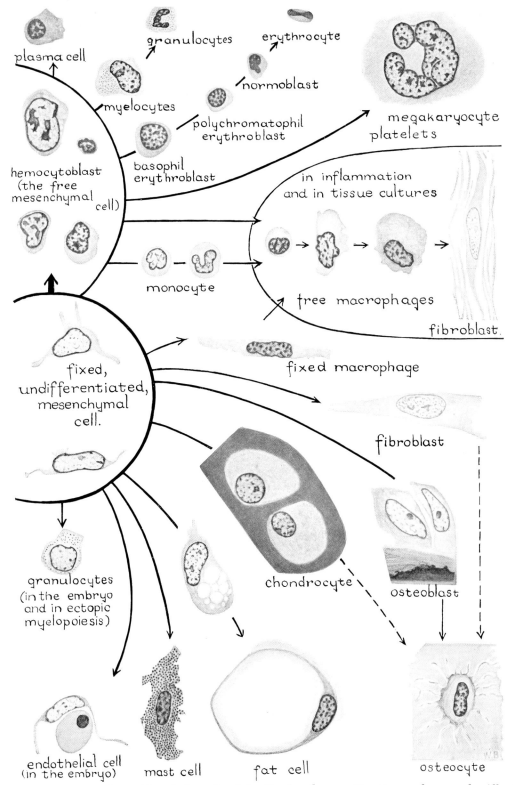

granulocytes

erythrocyte

plasma cell

myelocytes

normoblast

polychromatophil
erythroblast

megakaryocyte
platelets

hemocytoblast
(the free
mesenchymal cell)

basophil
erythroblast

in inflammation
and in tissue cultures

monocyte

free macrophages

fibroblast.

fixed,
undifferentiated,
mesenchymal
cell.

fixed macrophage

fibroblast

granulocytes
(in the embryo
and in ectopic
myelopoiesis)

chondrocyte

osteoblast

endothelial cell
(in the embryo)

mast cell

fat cell

osteocyte

Fig. 5–23.   Interrelationships of the cells of the blood and connective tissues of mammals. All cells
are from human tissues. The dotted lines indicate unusual transformations. The lymphocytes are included
with the hemocytoblasts. Hematoxylin-eosin-azure II. 720 ×. (W. B.)

macrophage system which has to dispose of them shows an increase in the size and number of its cells all over the body.

The question, which cells of the connective tissue represent undifferentiated elements, is answered in different ways by various authors. A few investigators believe that, under the influence of external stimuli, all fibroblasts can produce any other cell type of the blood and connective tissue. This has not been confirmed. According to another opinion, macrophages of every kind are endowed with full mesenchymal potencies.

But the histogenesis of the lymphocytes of the lymphatic tissue shows that the lymphocytes arise, not from the fixed macrophages, but from the primitive reticular cells, which are also the source of the fixed macrophages. The same is true for the development of myelocytes in extramedullary myelopoiesis in the lymph nodes. The question is undecided whether a fixed macrophage (phagocytic reticular cell) can cease its phagocytic activity and become a primitive reticular cell again, with all the potentialities of this cell type.

REFERENCES

The most important source book in English is Downey's Handbook of Hematology, New York, 1938.

Awrorow, P. P., and Timofejewsky, A. D.: Kultivierungsversuche von leukämischen Blute. Virchows Arch., *184:*216, 1914.

Bjørneboe, M., Gormsen, H., and Lundquist, F.: Further experimental studies on the rôle of the plasma cells as antibody producers. J. Immunol., *55:*121, 1947.

Block, M.: An experimental analysis of hematopoiesis in the rat yolk sac. Anat. Rec., *96:*289, 1946.

Bloom, M. A., and Bloom, W.: The radiosensitivity of erythroblasts. J. Lab. & Clin. Med., *32:*654, 1947.

Bloom, M. L., and Wislocki, G. B.: The localization of lipids in human blood and bone marrow cells. Blood, J. Hematology, *5:*79, 1950.

Bloom, W.: The origin and nature of the monocyte. Folia Haematol., *37:*1, 1928. Mammalian lymph in tissue culture. From lymphocyte to fibroblast. Arch. f. exp. Zellforsch., *5:*269, 1928.

Brown, J. W.: A quantitative study of cellular changes occurring in bone marrow following protein deficiency in the rat. Anat. Rec., *120:*515, 1954.

Conway, E. A.: Cyclic changes in lymphatic nodules. Anat. Rec., *67:*487, 1937. Reaction of lymphatic tissue in early stages of *Bacterium monocytogenes* infection. Arch. Path., *25:*200, 1938.

Custer, R. P.: Atlas of the Blood and Bone Marrow. Philadelphia, W. B. Saunders Company, 1949.

Danchakoff, V.: Origin of the blood cells. Development of the hematopoietic organs and regeneration of the blood cells from the standpoint of the monophyletic school. Anat. Rec., *10:*397, 1916.

Doan, C. A.: Current views on the origin and maturation of the cells of the blood. J. Lab. & Clin. Med., *17:*887, 1932.

Dougherty, T. F.: Effect of hormones on lymphatic tissue. Physiol. Rev., *32:*379, 1952.

Dougherty, T. F., and White, A.: An evaluation of alterations produced in lymphoid tissue by pituitary-adrenal cortical secretion. J. Lab. & Clin. Med., *32:*584, 1947.

Downey, H.: The myeloblast—Its occurrence under normal and pathologic conditions, and its relations to lymphocytes and other blood cells. Folia Haematol., Archiv., *34:*65, 145, 1927. The megaloblast-normoblast problem: A cytological study. J. Lab. & Clin. Med., *39:*837, 1952.

Drinker, C. K., Drinker, K. R., and Lund, C. C.: The circulation in the mammalian bone marrow. Am. J. Physiol., *62:*1, 1922.

Hall, B. E., and Watkins, C. H.: Experience with pteroylglutamic (synthetic folic) acid in the treatment of pernicious anemia. J. Lab. & Clin. Med., *32:*622, 1947.

Hamre, C. J.: Hematopoiesis in the bone marrow of rats recovering from nutritional anemia. J. Lab. & Clin. Med., *32:*756, 1947.

Jolly, J.: Traité technique d'hématologie. Paris, 1923.

Jones, O. P.: Morphologic, physiologic, chemical and biologic distinction of megaloblasts. Arch. Path., *35:*752, 1943.

Jordan, H. E.: The relation of lymphoid tissue to the process of blood production in avian bone marrow. Am. J. Anat., *59:*249, 1936.

Kindred, J. E.: A quantitative study of the hemopoietic organs of young adult albino rats. Am. J. Anat., *71:*207, 1942.

Lajtha, L. G., Oliver, R., and Ellis, F.: Incorporation of P^{32} and Adenine C^{14} into DNA by human bone marrow cells in vitro. Brit. J. Cancer, *8:*367, 1954.

Latta, J., and Henderson, J. W.: The hemopoietic disturbances induced in the albino rat by insulin administration. Folia Haematol., *57:*206, 1937.

Leduc, E. H., Coons, A. H., and Connolly, J. M.: Studies on antibody production. II. The primary and secondary responses in the popliteal lymph node of the rabbit. J. Exp. Med., *102:*61, 1955.

Maximow, A.: Bindegewebe und blutbildende Gewebe. Handb. d. mikr. Anat. (v. Möllendorff), (2), Pt. 1, Berlin, 1927.

Osgood, E. E., and Seaman, A. J.: The cellular composition of normal bone marrow as obtained by sternal puncture. Physiol. Rev., *24:*46, 1944.

Reinhardt, W. O.: Growth of lymph nodes, thymus and spleen, and output of thoracic duct lymphocytes in the normal rat. Anat. Rec., *94:*197, 1946.

Roberts, J. C., and Dixon, F. J.: The transfer of lymph node cells in the study of the immune response to foreign proteins. J. Exp. Med., *102:*379, 1955.

Sabin, F. R.: Bone Marrow, in Cowdry's Special Cytology. 2d ed. New York, (1), 505, 1932.

Schwind, J. L.: The supravital method in the study of the cytology of blood and marrow cells. Blood, *5:*597, 1950.

Taliaferro, W. H., and Mulligan, H. W.: The Histopathology of Malaria, with Special Reference to the Function and Origin of the Macrophages in Defence. Indian Med. Res. Memoirs, No. 29, 1, 1937.

Van Dyke, D. C., Contopoulos, A. N., Williams, B. S., Simpson, M. E., Lawrence, J. H., and Evans, H. M.: Hormonal factors influencing erythropoiesis. Acta Haematologica, *11:*203, 1954.

Weidenreich, F.: Die Leucocyten und verwandte Zellformen. Wiesbaden, 1911.

Wislocki, G. B., and Dempsey, E. W.: Observations on the chemical cytology of normal blood and hemopoietic tissues. Anat. Rec., *96:*249, 1946.

Yoffey, J. M.: The mammalian lymphocyte. Biol. Rev., *25:*314, 1950.

CHAPTER 6

Cartilage

CARTILAGE, a specialized, fibrous connective tissue, forms most of the temporary skeleton of the embryo, provides a model in which most bones develop, and is an important part of their growth mechanism. It persists in adult mammals as parts of joints, and in the respiratory passages and the ears. The intercellular component of cartilage predominates over the cells, which occupy special cavities within it. Because of differences in their intercellular substance, several types of cartilage may be distinguished; of these, the important are the hyaline, elastic and fibrous varieties. Hyaline cartilage is the most widespread and the most characteristic, the others being modifications of it. Blood vessels supplying other tissues occasionally pass through cartilage, but it has none of its own. With the exception of its naked surfaces in joint cavities, cartilage is always covered externally by a firmly attached layer of dense connective tissue—the *perichondrium.*

Hyaline or Glasslike Cartilage. In adult mammals hyaline cartilage is found on the ventral ends of the ribs, on the surfaces of bones within joints, and in the respiratory passages. It is much more widespread in the embryo. It is a flexible and somewhat elastic, semitransparent mass with an opalescent bluish tint, similar to that of frosted glass.

Cells of Cartilage (**Chondrocytes**). The cells of hyaline cartilage are usually spherical, although there are many exceptions. Thus, in the layers of the cartilage under the perichondrium or under the free joint surface, the cells are flattened in a plane parallel with the surface and, in the lower layers, are hemispherical or angular because of mutual

pressure. On the border between cartilage and perichondrium there are intermediate forms between cartilage cells and ordinary fibroblasts.

The body of the cartilage cell fills the

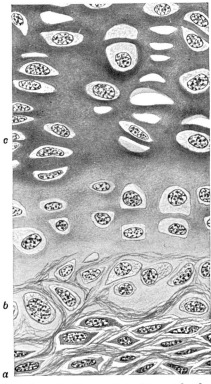

Fig. 6–1. Hyaline cartilage from xiphoid process of rat. *a,* transition layer adjacent to perichondrium; *b,* continuation of collagenous fibers from perichondrium into interstitial substance of cartilage; *c,* columns of isogenous groups of cartilage cells, some of which have fallen out of the cavities. Eosin-azure stain. 750 ×. (A.A.M.)

Page 117

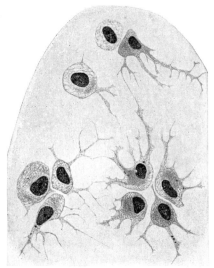

Fig. 6–2. Groups of cells with long, branching, anastomosing processes in the homogeneous interstitial substance of a cartilage of *Sepia officinalis.* 330 ×. (A.A.M.)

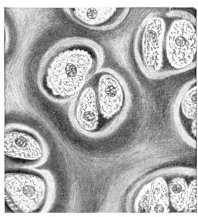

Fig. 6–3. Hyaline cartilage of a calf. 400 ×. (Redrawn and modified after R. Krause.)

cavity which it occupies in the interstitial substance. In adult higher vertebrates, the cartilage cells rarely have processes, and, since they are not connected with the wall of the cavity, they may drop out if the cavity is opened. Occasionally in the cartilage of the joints of higher vertebrates, and frequently in lower vertebrates and in early embryonic stages, the cytoplasm may extend into processes which enter the interstitial tissue (Fig. 6–2); the cells correspond in this respect with those of ordinary connective tissue.

The cytoplasm of the cartilage cells contains long mitochondria, vacuoles, fat drop-

lets and variable amounts of glycogen. The vacuoles in the peripheral portion of the cell body frequently are so large as to distend the cell like a bubble. Around the nucleus a cytocentrum with centrioles and a Golgi net can be distinguished. The nucleus contains one or several spherical nucleoli. Mitotic figures are practically never found in cartilage cells after growth has ceased. In the cartilage of the adult the cells are usually gathered into compact groups. These may be irregularly placed, rounded, or stretched into small columns of flattened cells. In growing bones the cartilage cells form characteristic columns before they are invaded by advancing bone (Fig. 7–20). Within the groups the interstitial substance is reduced to thin bands between the separate cells or may even be absent. This distribution of the cartilage cells is the result of their multiplication during the last stages of development. After they are surrounded by a dense interstitial substance, they divide several times in rapid succession. In this way individual cells give rise to closely adherent groups, imprisoned in the intercellular matrix. As these groups arise by division of one cell, they are called *isogenous.*

Interstitial Substance. When the cells are closely packed, the interstitial substance appears, in section, as a framework of thin cross beams surrounding the cartilage cavities. But more often it appears as a solid mass in which separate cells and groups of cells are dispersed at some distance from one another. In fresh condition and after ordinary fixation, the substance seems to be homogeneous, because the index of refraction of its collagenous fibers and the binding material which covers them is the same. However, the layers adjacent to the cell cavities and forming their walls are always distinguishable by their greater refractility, by their somewhat different staining reactions and, sometimes, by their concentric striation. They enclose the cartilage cells and are called *cartilage capsules.* The capsules belong to the intercellular substance, being its youngest layers and those nearest to the cells.

Despite its amorphous appearance with the light microscope, the interstitial substance is thoroughly permeated by thin fibrils which either form a dense feltwork running in all directions, or gather into definitely oriented bundles. The collagenous fibers can be demonstrated with the silver impregnation meth-

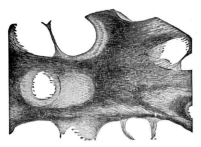

Fig. 6–4. Portion of tracheal cartilage of guinea pig from which all constituents except the collagenous fibers have been removed by digestion with trypsin. (Redrawn after Ruppricht.)

ods or by digesting the tissue with trypsin, which does not affect the fibers. The collagen from cartilage seems to be much the same chemically as that from the loose connective tissue.

The interstitial substance of hyaline cartilage is markedly basophile, owing to its content of *chondromucoid,* a glycoprotein which, on hydrolysis, yields the sulfonated polysaccharide, *chondroitin sulfate.*

The intercellular substance immediately surrounding the capsules is often especially basophile, presumably owing to a concentration of chondromucoid in these areas or to a change in its condition.

About one third of hyaline cartilage is in the intracellular phase, which in turn is one third protoplasmic solids and the rest water. Of the solids in the extracellular phase, one third is chondroitin sulfate and the rest mainly connective tissue components. S^{35}, injected as sodium sulfate, was shown by Dziewiatkowski to be incorporated into the chondroitin sulfate of growing cartilage. The role of the cartilage cells in the production of the chondromucoid is suggested by the experiments of Bélanger, in which injected S^{35} is detected first in the chondrocytes and later in the interstitial substance. Pelc and Glücksmann found this same sequence of uptake of S^{35} first by the cartilage cells and later by the matrix. Moreover, they showed that this happens in mature, "static" cartilage, as the pinna, trachea and xiphoid.

Because cartilage is devoid of blood vessels and forms large, compact masses, the nutritive fluid from the blood vessels in the perichondrium must pass through the interstitial substance, often for considerable distances, to reach the cells. A system of liquid-conduct-

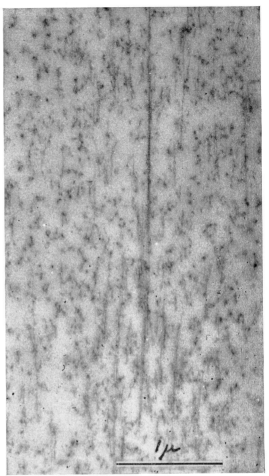

Fig. 6–5. Electron micrograph of section through epiphyseal cartilage, prior to calcification, of a young child. The fine fibrils are collagenous. Buffered osmic acid fixation. (Courtesy of R. Robinson and D. Cameron.)

ing canalicules, described as passing from one cell capsule to another, was considered a possible means for transferring substances through cartilage. It is now believed that these canalicules are artefacts. Direct observation of the action of a nontoxic stain upon living cartilage shows that the dye is quickly and evenly absorbed by the interstitial substance. In probably the same manner, the interstitial substance is permeated in the living condition by the tissue fluids from the perichondrium.

Elastic Cartilage. In mammals this variety of cartilage is found in the external ear, the walls of the external auditory and eustachian tubes, the epiglottis, and in parts of the corniculate and cuneiform cartilages. It differs

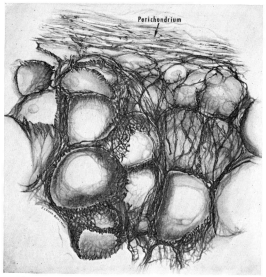

Perichondrium

Fig. 6–6. Section through elastic cartilage of the ear of a rabbit stained with orcein to show elastic fibers which form networks around the cartilage cells. 385 ✕.

from hyaline cartilage macroscopically by its yellowish color and by its greater opacity, flexibility and elasticity.

Its cells are similar to those of hyaline cartilage; they are of the same rounded shape, are also surrounded by capsules, and are scattered singly or in isogenous groups of two or three cells. The interstitial substance differs from that of hyaline cartilage by being penetrated in all directions by frequently branching fibers, which give all the tests for elastin. They form a network which is often so dense that the ground substance filling its loops is obscured; sometimes the network is especially dense at the periphery of the cells. In the layers beneath the perichondrium, the feltwork of the elastic fibers is looser. The elastic fibers of the cartilage continue into those of the perichondrium.

Fibrocartilage. Fibrocartilage occurs as indistinctly outlined, small accumulations in a few places in the bodies of mammals. It is found in the intervertebral disks, certain articular cartilages, in the symphysis pubis, in the ligamentum teres femoris, in the places of attachment of certain tendons to bones. Here, again, the tissue contains typical cartilage cells with homogeneous capsules which lie either singly or in pairs, and sometimes in larger groups extended lengthwise. The interstitial substance contains thick, compact, collagenous bundles, parallel with one another

and separated only by narrow clefts into which are squeezed the encapsulated cells. Usually little is seen of the ground substance.

Fibrocartilage is closely associated with the dense connective tissue of the capsules and ligaments of joints. It is a transitional form between cartilage and connective tissue, and this gradual transformation can be observed, in the embryonic histogenesis as well as in the adult organism, wherever there is fibrocartilage. Thus, in the intervertebral disks, the hyaline cartilage connected with the vertebrae shows distinct collagenous fibers in the apparently homogeneous interstitial substance. Then these fibers collect into thick bundles which almost entirely displace the homogeneous substance, while the cartilage cells retain their spherical form and their capsules. Finally, this typical fibrocartilage merges into connective tissue, the cells of which are provided with processes and are devoid of capsules.

Other Varieties of Cartilage and Chondroid Tissue. There is a transitory phase in the embryonic development of hyaline cartilage when it is composed of closely adjacent vesicular cells, provided with thin capsules, and with collagenous fibers in its interstitial substance. In this undeveloped condition the cartilage may remain throughout life in certain parts of the body of higher organisms. It occurs often in lower vertebrates (fishes, amphibians; as in the sesamoid cartilage of the tendon of Achilles in frogs) and is still more common in invertebrates. Such tissue has been called *pseudocartilage, fibrohyaline tissue, vesicular supporting tissue* or *chondroid tissue.* This tissue serves as a mechanical support for other parts of the body.

The tissue composing the *notochord* of vertebrates has a similar structure. Here, there is a shaft of variable thickness which consists of large, closely packed vesicular cells distended with fluid and with an elastic membrane. The notochordal tissue has a different embryological origin from that of the cartilage and of the other connective tissues.

Histogenesis of Cartilage. In those parts of the embryo where cartilage will develop, the mesenchyme cells round up and the spaces between them become smaller. In most cases, at early stages in the formation of cartilage, collagenous fibrils are present in the intercellular substance. This acidophilic material becomes enclosed by the basophile intercellular substance characteristic of cartilage, which stains metachromatically (purple) with methylene azure. It is probably a secretion of the cells and masks the collagenous fibrils embedded in it.

The cells enclosed by the interstitial substance soon acquire the distinctiveness of cartilage cells. They accumulate large amounts of fluid in vacuoles in their cytoplasm and become spherical or, through mutual compression, polyhedral. Mitoses may be observed among them for a long period; during the

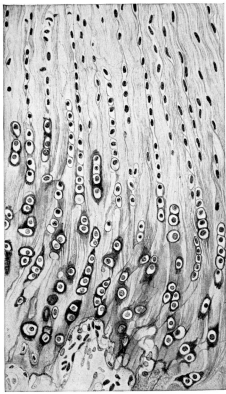

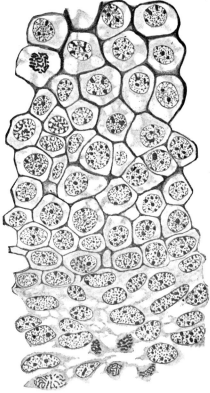

Fig. 6–7. Low-power drawing of insertion of tendon into the tibia of a rat. Note the direct transformation of rows of tendon cells (top) into cartilage cells surrounded by deeply staining cartilaginous matrix. Hematoxylin-eosin-azure II. From a preparation of F. C. McLean. (Drawn by Miss A. Nixon.)

Fig. 6–8. Development of cartilage from mesenchyme in a 15-mm. guinea pig embryo. The mesenchyme (below) gradually merges into the protochondral tissue with interstitial substance (above). Note mitoses. 750 ×. (A.A.M.)

constriction of the cytoplasm in such a division, a new partition of interstitial substance quickly develops and separates the two daughter cells. Some cells atrophy, become compressed between neighboring cells, and eventually disappear.

With the gradual increase of the interstitial substance, there appears a thin, shining layer—the capsule—along the line of its contact with the cytoplasm of the cartilage cells. This structure becomes progressively thicker, developing in the same manner as the rest of the interstitial substance, of which it represents the youngest layers. The multiplication of the cells by mitosis and the increase in mass of the intercellular substance are called *interstitial growth.*

The mesenchyme surrounding the cartilage primordium forms a special layer, the *perichondrium,* which merges gradually with the cartilage on one side and the adjacent connective tissue on the other. Throughout embryonic life there is a constant transformation of layers of this connective tissue into cartilage. Here the acidophile collagenous fibers of the dense connective tissue of the perichondrium are arranged in flat bundles; these are gradually covered with the basophile, cartilaginous ground substance. At the same time the fibroblasts of the connective tissue lose their spindle shape, change into spherical

cells, and thus are transformed directly into cartilage cells surrounded by capsules. This process is called *appositional* growth; it probably contributes more to the mass of the cartilage than does the interstitial growth. The ability of the perichondrium to form cartilage persists, although latent, in the adult organism.

Most of the hyaline cartilage of the embryonic skeleton is later replaced by bone (Chap. 7). Some cartilages are completely absorbed, as is the case with Meckel's cartilage.

At the site of the future elastic cartilage in the embryo, there is at first connective tissue containing fibroblasts and wavy fibrillar bundles which do not give characteristic reactions for either collagen or elastin. These indifferent fibers apparently are partly transformed into elastic fibers. The cells acquire capsules and become cartilage elements. On the surface of the elastic cartilage there is also a perichondrium which also initiates appositional growth of the cartilage during embryonic life.

Fibrocartilage develops in much the same way as ordinary connective tissue. In the beginning there are typical fibroblasts separated by a large amount of fibrillar substance. Then these cells become round, are surrounded by capsules, and are directly transformed into cartilage cells. The interstitial substance

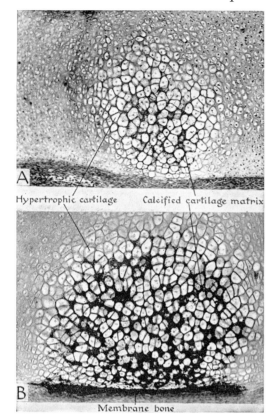

Hypertrophic cartilage   Calcified cartilage matrix

Membrane bone

Fig. 6–9. Two stages in the calcification of the cartilage model of the calcaneus in rats; *A,* two days and, *B,* four days after birth. The calcium salts appear black because of the silver nitrate stain. Undecalcified preparations stained with von Kossa's method and H+E. 75 ×. (After Bloom and Bloom.)

becomes infiltrated only slightly, if at all, with the basophile, amorphous, binding mass.

Regeneration of Cartilage. After a wound or excision of a portion of living hyaline cartilage in adult mammals, an independent regeneration of the cartilage does not take place, according to most observers. In the injured area only necrotic and atrophic changes can be seen in the cells. The defect is soon filled by newly formed connective tissue, which grows in from the perichondrium or nearest fascia. Then the fibroblasts of this granulation tissue become round, produce capsules around themselves, and may become transformed into new cartilage cells. Meanwhile, the fibrillar, interstitial substance of the scar tissue becomes homogeneous and gives rise to new interstitial substance in the same manner as in the embryonic development of cartilage. Accordingly, in adult organisms, new cartilage tissue is formed by metaplasia of the loose connective tissue.

Such a metaplasia sometimes takes place in connective tissue under the influence of simple mechanical forces acting from the outside, such as pressure, particularly when combined with friction. It is claimed that the presence of cartilage on the joint surfaces of bones is related to the constant mechanical influences to which a normal joint is subjected during its function. When these mechanical conditions disappear, as happens in dislocation of bones, the cartilage often undergoes dedifferentiation. On the other hand, cartilage is laid down in the primordia of the joint surfaces in the embryo at a time when there are probably no mechanical forces acting on the joint.

Regressive Changes in Cartilage. *Calcification,* the most important regressive change in cartilage, precedes and is closely related to one type of bone development (intracartilaginous ossification). The cartilage cells become arranged in groups as in a vertebra, or in more or less irregular columns separated by wide, parallel bands of interstitial tissue, as in the epiphysis of a long bone. In proceeding from the zone where cartilage cells are multiplying toward the area where bone formation will occur, one finds the cartilage cells becoming larger and their glycogen content rising greatly (zone of hypertrophic cartilage cells). This zone also contains much alkaline phosphatase, whose function here is not clear. Still closer to the zone of ossification, the matrix becomes calcified and the cartilage cells lose their glycogen. Minute granules of calcium phosphate and carbonate are deposited in the interstitial substance, primarily in the vicinity of the cells. As these enlarge and merge, the cartilage becomes opaque, hard and brittle. The great majority of the cells degenerate as vascular connective tissue invades the calcified cartilage preceding the formation of bone. Those few cartilage cells which do not perish probably turn into cells of bone. The process of ossification is described in Chapter 7. In man, ossification may take place in certain cartilages of the larynx as early as twenty years of age.

Hyaline cartilage may undergo the so-called *asbestos transformation.* Within the homogeneous intercellular substance, parallel fibers are deposited which have nothing in common with collagenous fibers. They do not swell in acetic acid, but dissolve in boiling water and in low concentrations of alkalies. They give the tissue a silky, glossy appearance similar to that of asbestos; they spread over wide areas and may lead to a softening of the tissue and even to the formation of spaces in it. It has been reported that new cartilage may develop in these spaces. In elastic as well as in hyaline cartilage, calcification and asbestos transformation may take place with advancing age.

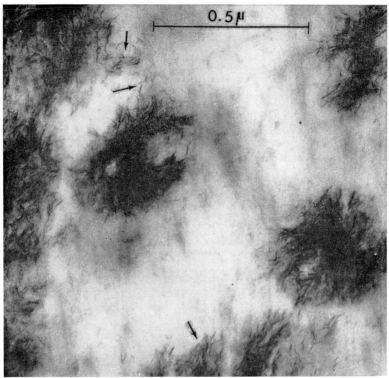

Fig. 6–10. Electron micrograph of section of cartilage in epiphyseal plate from kitten humerus. Calcification has started in foci; the arrows point to the small crystals which aggregate into dense masses. Buffered osmic acid fixation. (Courtesy of B. Scott and D. C. Pease.)

Histophysiological Remarks. Cartilage in joints has the remarkable property of sustaining great weight and at the same time allowing the bones which carry this weight to move easily and smoothly against one another. In other places, such as the ear and the respiratory passages, cartilage serves as a pliable yet resistant framework which prevents the collapse of the passages. Finally, cartilage in many bones makes possible their growth in length, and is important in determining their size and shape.

Far from being an inert tissue, cartilage, through its participation in the growth of bones, is a fairly delicate indicator of certain metabolic disturbances. It reflects *nutritional deficiencies,* especially in protein, minerals or vitamins. For example, the thickness of the epiphyseal cartilage plate diminishes rapidly when a young rat is placed on a protein-deficient diet or on one lacking in vitamin A. When vitamin C is withheld from guinea pigs, cessation of matrix formation may be accompanied by changes in the cells and by distortion of their columnar arrangement. In the absence of vitamin D or in a deficiency in calcium and phosphorus from an otherwise adequate diet, the cartilage continues to proliferate for some time, unchecked by calcification or by erosion by the vascular connective tissue.

The participation of cartilage in the growth in length of bones is in part under control of several hormones, the most important being the *growth hormone.* Hypophysectomy in young rats leads to a thinning of the cartilage plate, with cessation of mitosis and a decrease in number and especially in size of its cells. After a short time the cartilage fails to be eroded, with consequent cessation of growth of the bone. When growth hormone is injected into such animals, the cartilage undergoes a striking metamorphosis, and within a few days resembles that of a normal, young, growing animal, and the bone again resumes its growth. The response of the cartilage varies with the dose level and has been used to assay extracts containing the hormone. Long-continued administration of the hormone produces giant rats, this being made

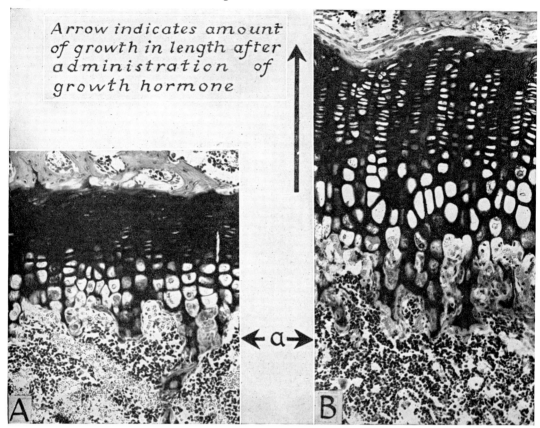

Fig. 6–11.   Photomicrographs of proximal metaphysis of tibias of young rats to show effects of growth hormone. *A,* atrophic cartilage of hypophysectomized rat; *B,* hypertrophy and growth of cartilage with new bone formation in hypophysectomized rat after injection for four days with purified growth hormone. *a,* tip of spongiosa. Zenker-formol, H+E. 165 ×.

possible in part by growth of cartilage after it would normally have ceased growing. Further, the injection of the hormone into old rats in which cartilage proliferation has stopped can to some extent reactivate its growth, with subsequent increase in size of bones.

When growth of cartilage has been retarded by removal of the thyroid from rats shortly after birth, it can be stimulated to renewed activity by administering *thyroxin.*

An excess of vitamin A accelerates the normal growth sequences of epiphyseal cartilage cells. It has been shown that these responses are not mediated through the pituitary. Mechanical injury to the cartilage may result in localized disturbance of growth. Lesions produced in the cartilage by x-rays or other high energy radiations frequently result in a marked stunting of growth.

Although much has been learned of the relation of the cells of cartilage to other mesenchymal cells, the interstitial substance is less well understood. Its mode of formation and growth, even its physical state, the organization of its polysaccharides, and the mechanism of calcification are all fundamental problems which need further study. Perhaps the most difficult problem is the mechanism of *interstitial growth* in the center of this supporting tissue with its dense, unyielding intercellular substance.

REFERENCES

Amprino, R.: On the incorporation of radiosulfate in the cartilage. Experientia, *11*:65, 1955.

Becks, H., Asling, C. W., Simpson, M. E., Li, Choh Hao, and Evans, H. M.: The growth of hypophysectomized female rats following chronic treatment with pure pituitary growth hormone. III. Skeletal changes: Tibia, metacarpal, costochondral junction and caudal vertebrae. Growth, *13*:175, 1949.

Bélangr, L. F.: Autoradiographic visualization of the entry and transit of S[35] in cartilage, bone, and dentine of young rats and the effect of hyaluronidase in vitro. Canadian J. Biochem. Physiol., *32:*161, 1954.

Clark, E. R., and Clark, E. L.: Microscopic observations on new formation of cartilage and bone in the living mammal. Am. J. Anat., *70:*167, 1942.

Dziewiatkowski, D. D.: Radioautographic visualization of sulfur-35 disposition in the articular cartilage and bone of suckling rats following injection of labelled sodium sulfate. J. Exp. Med., *93:*451, 1951.

Eichelberger, L., Brower, T. D., and Rosa, M.: The distribution of water, electrolytes, nitrogen and chondroitin sulphate in hyaline cartilages. Am. J. Physiol., *166:*328, 1951.

Fell, H. B., and Mellanby, E.: The biological action of thyroxine on embryonic bones grown in tissue culture. J. Physiol., *127:*427, 1955.

Follis, R. H., and Berthrong, M.: Histochemical studies on cartilage and bone. I. The normal pattern. Bull. Johns Hopkins Hosp., *85:*281, 1949.

Glücksmann, A.: Studies on bone mechanics in vitro. II. The role of tension and pressure in chondrogenesis. Anat. Rec., *73:*39, 1939.

Leblond, C. P., Bélanger, L. F., and Greulich, R. C.: Formation of bones and teeth as visualized by radioautography. Ann. New York Acad. Sci., *60:*629, 1955.

Montagna, W.: Glycogen and lipids in human cartilage, with some cytochemical observations on the cartilage of the dog, cat, and rabbit. Anat. Rec., *103:*77, 1949.

Pelc, S. R., and Glücksmann, A.: Sulphate metabolism in the cartilage of the trachea, pinna and xiphoid process of the adult mouse as indicated by autoradiographs. Exp. Cell Research, *8:*336, 1955.

Rouiller, C., Huber, L., and Rutishauser, E.: Les fibrilles de la substance fondamentale du cartilage hyalin. Etude au microscope électronique. Arch. Sciences, *5:* 215, 1952.

Schaffer, J.: Die Stützgewebe. Handb. d. mikr. Anat. d. Menschen (v. Möllendorff), (2), Part 2: 1, 1930.

Sheehan, J. F.: A cytological study of the cartilage cells of developing long-bones of the rat, with special reference to the Golgi apparatus, mitochondria, neutral-red bodies and lipid inclusions. J. Morphol., *82:*151, 1948.

Streeter, G. L.: Developmental Horizons in Human Embryos (Fourth Issue). A Review of the Histogenesis of Cartilage and Bone. Carnegie Institution of Washington, Publ. 583, Contributions to Embry., *33:*149, 1949.

Sylvén, B.: The Ground Substance of Connective Tissue and Cartilage. In "The Biochemistry and Physiology of Bone." (G. H. Bourne, Editor), Acad. Press Inc., New York, 1956.

Wolbach, S. B., and Maddock, C. L.: Vitamin-A acceleration of bone growth sequences in hypophysectomized rats. Arch. Path., *53:*273, 1952.

CHAPTER 7

Bone

BONE IS A HARD, specialized connective tissue, with a calcified collagenous intercellular substance. It performs a mechanical function in forming the *skeletal support of the body;* it protects the vital organs of the cranial and thoracic cavities and lodges the bone marrow. Its structure, even to minute details, is beautifully adapted to the performance of its supporting function with the least expenditure of material and with the least weight. As a second important function, related to its impregnation with minerals, bone serves as a store of calcium, and thus plays a part in meeting the immediate needs of the organism for this element.

Bone is a plastic tissue and is highly sensitive to alterations of its normal mechanical function. Thus disuse is followed by *atrophy,* in this case associated with a loss of substance; while increased use is accompanied by *hypertrophy,* with an increase in the mass of the bone. Owing to the ability of the bone to undergo internal reconstruction in response to external stimuli, it may to some extent be modified at will by surgical and experimental procedures.

Macroscopically, mammalian bone is either *spongy* (*cancellous*) or *compact* in structure. Spongy bone consists of intercrossing and connecting osseous bars of varying thickness and shapes. These branch, unite with one another, and partially surround intercommunicating spaces filled with bone marrow, by their arrangement giving the skeleton a maximum rigidity and resistance to changes in shape. Compact bone appears as a continuous hard mass in which spaces can be distinguished only with the aid of the microscope. No sharp boundary can be drawn between the two types of bone tissue; they are merely different arrangements of the same histological elements. Moreover, practically every bone contains both types of osseous tissue.

In typical long bones (femur and humerus) the *diaphysis* (shaft) consists of compact bone and contains in its center a voluminous, cylindrical, bone marrow cavity, the *medulla.* The *epiphysis* (at the end of the shaft) consists of spongy bone with a thin, peripheral cortex of compact bone. The cavities of this spongy bone are, in the adult animal, direct continuations of the bone marrow cavity of the diaphysis. In the growing animal the epiphysis and diaphysis are separated by the *epiphyseal cartilage* plate, which is united with the diaphysis by columns of spongy bone, often called the *metaphysis.* The epiphyseal cartilage, together with the spongy bone of the metaphysis, forms a *growth apparatus,* within which growth in length of the long bones occurs.

In the flat bones of the skull, the compact substance forms a relatively thick layer on both surfaces, between which there is a layer of spongy bone of varying thickness (*diploë*). The short and irregular bones usually are of spongy substance covered with a layer of compact bone.

All bones are covered with a specialized connective tissue called *periosteum;* a somewhat similar tissue, the *endosteum,* lines the marrow spaces, including those in spongy bone.

Bone develops through a transformation of connective tissue (*intramembranous ossification*) or by a replacement of cartilage (*intracartilaginous* or *endochondral ossification*) or through a combination of these processes. The formation of bone tissue takes place by apposition, new bone being laid down upon connective tissue, upon cartilage matrix, or upon bone itself. As a bone grows in size it undergoes *internal reconstruction,* which continues throughout the life of the animal, although at a greatly reduced rate in adults. As a result of the reconstruction during growth, bone acquires its definitive structure.

Microscopically, by far the greater part of the mass of bone is made up of layers (*lamellae*) of calcified *interstitial substance* or *bone matrix;* the arrangement of the lamellae differs in spongy and in compact bone. By appropriate methods the lamellae are found to be fibrillar in structure. Embedded within the interstitial substance are *lacunae* (cavities), completely filled with bone cells (*osteocytes*). In the walls of the lacunae are fine apertures, from which arise numerous thin canals, the *bone canalicules,* which penetrate the hard interstitial substance in all directions. They branch abundantly and anastomose with one another in a network, connecting all the lacunae into a system of cavities. On the surfaces of bone, and much more numerous during the active development and growth of the skeleton, are *osteoblasts* and *osteoclasts,* associated respectively with the apposition and the resorption of bone. The contribution of the cellular elements of bone to its total mass is small.

Cells of Bone. Osteoblasts, osteocytes and osteoclasts, peculiar to bone, are closely interrelated, in that transformations from one to another of the three cells are frequently observed.

The *osteoblast,* associated with the formation of osseous tissue, appears on the surface of bone which is undergoing growth and development. These cells are frequently present in a continuous layer, suggesting a cuboidal epithelium (Fig. 7–2) and are found in this location as long as active growth occurs. The body of the osteoblast has a diameter of 15 to 20 microns. The nucleus is large, and there is usually one fairly large nucleolus.

The cytoplasm of the osteoblast stains intensely with basic aniline dyes, suggesting the presence of ribose nucleic acids. This, together with the presence of *phosphatase* in these cells, suggests that the cells may be concerned with the synthesis of the proteins of the bone matrix. The cytoplasm also contains numerous threadlike mitochondria; near the nucleus is a pale-staining attraction sphere with a diplosome and a Golgi net. Spherical, cytoplasmic granules 0.3 to 0.6 micron in diameter have been demonstrated in many osteoblasts in sections of frozen-dried bones stained with the periodate-leuco-fuchsin method. There is evidence that the number of cells containing these granules as well as their number in each cell is greater when new bone is being formed.

The *osteocyte* is an osteoblast which has become embedded within the bone matrix (Fig. 7–1). It has a faintly basophile cytoplasm, containing a few mitochondria and a

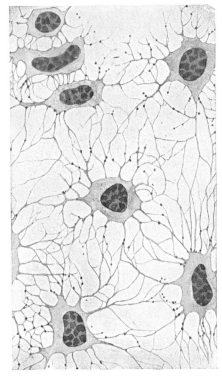

Fig. 7–1.   Thin, transparent membrane bone of a white mouse, stained supravitally with methylene blue, in glycerin. The interstitial substance appears homogeneous; the angular osteocytes with their nuclei fill the cavities. From the cells arise anastomosing processes which lie in the canalicules and in cross section appear as dots. 1040 ✕. (A.A.M.)

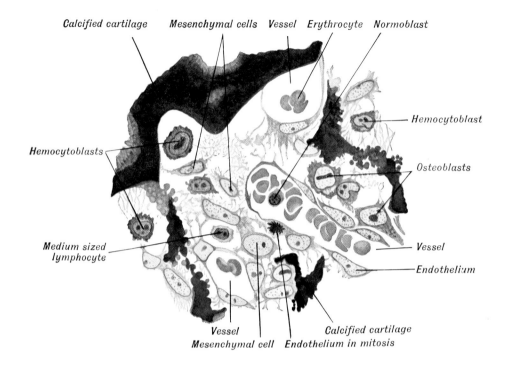

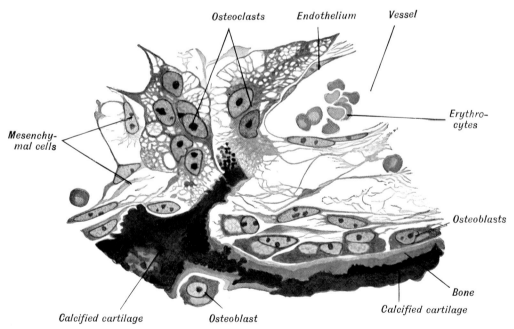

Fig. 7–2.   Two areas from sections of bone marrow cavity near the zone of endochondral ossification of the humerus of a human embryo of 70 mm. Hematoxylin-eosin-azure stain. About 700 ×. (A.A.M.)

small Golgi net. It is uncertain whether it contains a cytocentrum and centrioles. When stained supravitally with neutral red, it contains neutral red vacuoles, especially in young bone. Fat droplets and glycogen have been demonstrated in the cytoplasm, which also contains periodate-leucofuchsin-stainable granules indistinguishable from those in osteoblasts. The oval nucleus is large and filled with large chromatin particles and one or more nucleoli. In general, the appearance of the osteocyte suggests that of a somewhat shrunken fibroblast with a darker nucleus. Cells with two nuclei occur; mitoses have not been described in osteocytes.

The shape of the lacunae in which the osteocytes lie is usually flat and oval, resembling that of a melon seed. They range in size from 22 to 52 microns in length, 6 to 14 microns in width, and 4 to 9 microns in thickness. On the surfaces of the cells are many fine projections which enter the corresponding apertures in the walls of the lacunae. In the early stages of development of bone in mammals, thin cytoplasmic processes penetrate the bone canalicules so that the bone cells are directly connected. How far these cytoplasmic processes extend into the bone canalicules in adult mammals has not been determined.

The *osteoclast* is a multinucleated giant cell, varying greatly in size and in the number of nuclei. These cells are derived from the stromal cells of the marrow; at times they arise by the fusion of a number of osteoblasts, and they may also include osteocytes liberated from bone by resorption. Their pale-staining cytoplasm is often foamy; they frequently have branching processes with serrated edges (Fig. 7–2). The numerous nuclei are poor in chromatin, and each has a prominent, although small, nucleolus.

Interstitial Substance. The apparently homogeneous interstitial substance of fresh bone contains masked *osteocollagenous fibers* similar to the collagenous fibers of loose connective tissue. By silver impregnation and other methods it can be shown that the fibrils are often connected into small bundles 3 to 5 microns thick. They are united by a binding ground substance in which the mineral constituents of bone are laid down. The ground substance in fully formed bone is barely stainable with the periodate-leucofuchsin procedure. It becomes more vividly stained when bone is being deposited or resorbed rapidly. During bone formation and destruction, it is significant that a method which does not demonstrate phosphate in apatite crystals, or carbonate on their surfaces (see next section), will show much reactive phosphate and carbonate in just those areas of bone matrix which stain vividly with periodate-leucofuchsin.

A specialized, thin layer of the interstitial substance directly adjoins the lacunae and the canalicules and forms a sort of capsule for them. It differs from the rest of the interstitial mass in that it lacks fibrils, and does not dissolve when heated in a solution of strong alkali.

Chemical Composition of the Interstitial Substance. The hard interstitial substance is

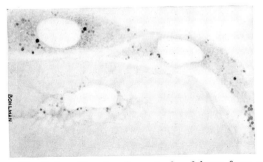

Fig. 7–3. Margin of a spicule of bone from a young rat; frozen-dried, undecalcified and stained with periodic acid-leucofuchsin. The cytoplasm of the osteocyte and two osteoblasts contains granules; the nuclei do not stain, and the matrix stains feebly. 3000 ×. (After Heller.)

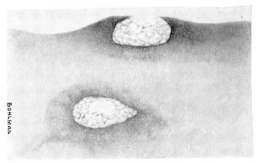

Fig. 7–4. Edge of a spicule of bone from a rat, six hours after injection of 1000 units of parathyroid extract. The dark-staining matrix around the osteocyte in the center and at the margin of the spicule indicates bone resorption. The upper osteocyte is partially liberated from the matrix. Cytoplasmic granules are absent. Frozen-dried, undecalcified, periodic acid-leucofuchsin stain. 3000 ×. (After Heller.)

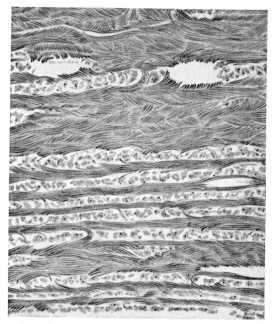

Fig. 7–5. Section of dense cortical bone of human femur stained to show variability of direction of the fibrils in successive lamellae. In places the fibrils of one lamella change direction and continue into another lamella. The oval openings are lacunae. Bielschowsky impregnation. 1225 ×.

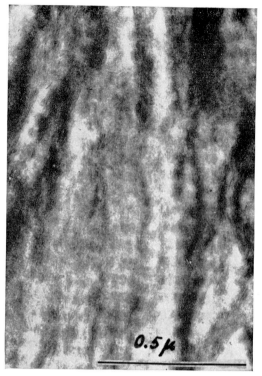

Fig. 7–7. Electron micrograph of section of undecalcified bone preparation of human metaphysis. The cross striation is due to the tiny crystals of bone salt being arranged in rows corresponding with the periodic banding of the collagenous fibers. (Courtesy of R. Robinson and M. Watson.)

chemically similar in different species of animals. Besides water, the amount of which varies greatly and which is abundant in young bones, the interstitial substance consists of two main components: the organic framework, and inorganic salts. Of compact bone, the inorganic part, or *bone salt* (*bone ash*) attains a maximum of approximately 65 per cent of the dry, fat-free weight in adult life. In developing bone, especially in the embryo, this proportion is lower, and may be as low as 35 per cent in the poorly calcified bone of *rickets* and *osteomalacia*. Bone salt consists essentially of submicroscopic crystals of *hydroxyapatite* $[Ca_3(PO_4)_2]_3 \cdot Ca(OH)_2$. From x-ray spectrograms the *apatite* lattice has been demonstrated. Certain ions such as

Fig. 7–6. Electron micrograph of section through decalcified, dense bone of human rib. The fibrils show the characteristic periodic banding of collagen. (Shadowed with uranium.) (Courtesy of M. Watson and R. Robinson.)

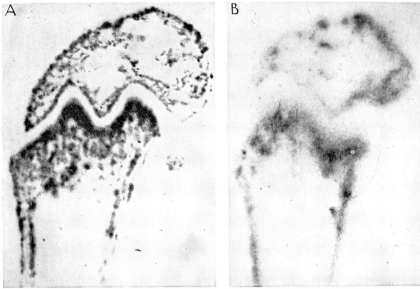

Fig. 7–8. Autoradiographs of distal ends of femur of rats to show deposition of bone-seeking, radioactive isotopes. Note the sharp localization of an α-emitting element (plutonium) in A, and the more indefinite localization of a long range β emitter (P^{32}) in B. Both sections of undecalcified bones after fixation in alcohol. About 10 $\times$.

radium or fluoride are sometimes found substituted in the lattice. The mineral of bone, however, includes other cations, notably magnesium and sodium, and considerable amounts of carbonate and citrate anions. These substances are at present believed to be on the surfaces of the crystals rather than within the crystal lattice. Owing to the small size of the crystals, the surfaces are large per unit of mass. Study of the turnover of the inorganic substances in bone is greatly aided by the use of radioactive isotopes (Fig. 7–8). Certain radioactive substances accumulate in bone and may cause severe damage to the bone tissue.

The organic portion of compact bone, amounting to 35 per cent or more, is made up chiefly of *bone collagen;* only a small fraction of the dry weight is contributed by the bone cells. The collagen yields gelatin when boiled.

A weak acid or a chelating agent (as EDTA) removes the inorganic salts, leaving the original appearance and microscopic structure. If a bone be ignited, only the inorganic constituents remain; a bone so treated becomes brittle, although it retains its external form and, to a certain degree, its microscopic structure.

Architecture of Bone. The cortex of a bone is commonly compact osseous tissue, while cancellous, or spongy, bone is found in the medulla. Spongy bone is simple in structure, but varied in form. It consists of plates and bars forming a network especially fitted for definite mechanical functions in individual bones; the parts are usually arranged in those directions which correspond with the lines of maximum pressure or tension. The trabeculae of the spongy substance are made up of a varying number of contiguous thin layers (*lamellae*). Embedded in the interstitial substance are the lacunae, containing osteocytes and intercommunicating with each other through a network of canalicules.

Except in the irregular, coarsely fibrillar compact substance, the lamellae are regularly arranged, in a manner closely connected with the distribution of the blood vessels which nourish the bone. The compact substance of the diaphysis of any long bone is penetrated by numerous cylindrical, branching and anastomosing canals. These are the *haversian canals;* they contain blood vessels with a small amount of connective tissue. They communicate by the *canals of Volkmann* with the external surface of the bone and with the bone-marrow cavity. It is by the haversian

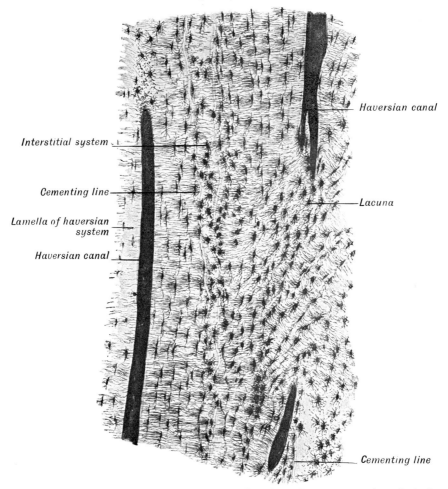

Fig. 7–9.   From a longitudinal, ground section of the ulna of man; stained with fuchsin. 160 ×.
(After Schaffer.)

canals and their related structures that the
internal structure of compact bone differs
from that of spongy bone.

Haversian Systems. The haversian system,
or *osteon,* is the unit of structure of compact
bone. It is an irregularly cylindrical, branching and anastomosing structure, with thick
walls and a narrow lumen, the haversian
canal. The canals are generally from 22 to
110 microns in diameter; they are surrounded
by concentrically arranged lamellae of bone,
of which there may be from four to twenty
in a single system, each from 3 to 7 microns
in thickness. The haversian systems are directed mainly in the long axis of the bone,
so that in cross section the canals appear as
round openings and the lamellae are ring-
shaped, while in longitudinal sections the

canals appear as long slits (Fig. 7–9). In
addition to the canals and lamellae, the haversian systems include large numbers of
lacunae, each containing an osteocyte, and
of canalicules, forming a network branching
out from the canals and intercommunicating
with each other and with the lacunae. The
broad surfaces of the lacunae are circum-
ferentially placed in the lamellae.

A haversian canal carries one or more,
usually two, blood vessels. These are for the
most part capillaries and postcapillary venules, lying in close association with the loose
connective tissue which fills the remainder of
the canal; occasionally an arteriole is found
in a canal. The canalicules of the haversian
system are extravascular, their function presumably being to promote diffusion of tissue

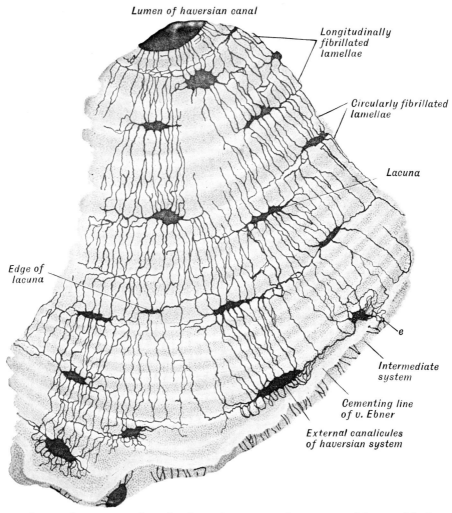

Lumen of haversian canal

Longitudinally fibrillated lamellae

Circularly fibrillated lamellae

Lacuna

Edge of lacuna

e

Intermediate system

Cementing line of v. Ebner

External canalicules of haversian system

Fig. 7–10. Sector of a cross section of a haversian system of a macerated human hip bone. The cavities and canalicules are filled with a dye: *e*, connection of canalicules of the haversian system with those of an intermediate system. 520 ×. (A.A.M.)

fluids required for maintenance of the osteocytes and interstitial substance. In a typical haversian system (Fig. 7–10) canalicules branch out from the canal and form a network which includes the lacunae. The canalicules for the most part are directed radially, forming the channels of communication between the canal and the successive lamellae of the haversian system and their lacunae. In the outermost lamella of a haversian system the external canalicules loop back into the system; intercommunication between the canalicules of adjacent systems is the exception rather than the rule.

In cross sections of a haversian system, stained for connective tissue fibers, longitudinally fibrillated lamellae alternate with circularly fibrillated ones. The alternation of perfectly longitudinal and circular lamellae, however, occurs rarely. More frequently this arrangement is only approximated, and the fibrils in all the lamellae run spirally to the axis of the canal. These spirals in adjacent lamellae cross at various angles and are sometimes perpendicular to one another. The direction of the fibrils within the lamellae of a haversian system is shown diagrammatically in Figure 7–12. The alternation in the direction of fibrillation in the lamellae causes the optic phenomena seen in cross sections of the systems in polarized light (Fig. 7–11).

Structure of Compact Bone. Compact

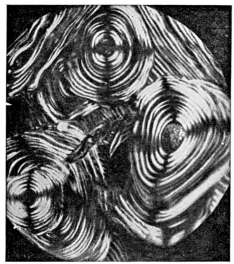

Fig. 7–11. Cross section of human hip bone in polarized light. The cross sections of three haversian systems are seen as bright Maltese crosses. Note the alternation of bright and dark lamellae. 130 ✕. (Redrawn after Gebhardt.)

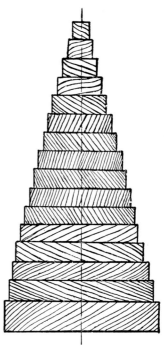

Fig 7–12. Diagram of the direction of the fibrils in successive lamellae of a haversian system. (Redrawn and slightly modified from Gebhardt.)

bone, e.g., the shaft of a long bone, is made up chiefly of large numbers of haversian systems. The irregular angular spaces between these systems are filled with the *interstitial* or *ground lamellae* (Fig. 7–13). Most of these are the remains of haversian systems which were only partly destroyed during the internal reconstruction of the bone (p. 141). On the external surface of the compact substance, and on the internal surface which forms the wall of the marrow cavity (Fig. 7–13) are the *basic* or *circumferential lamellae:* these vary in number and are arranged, as the name implies, in the circumference of the bone. Penetrating these lamellae, and opening on the free surface of the bone or in the marrow cavity, are the *canals of Volkmann,* within which are the blood vessels communicating with those of the haversian canals. They differ in appearance from the haversian canals in that they are not surrounded by concentrically arranged lamellae and usually contain larger blood vessels. Haversian canals frequently communicate with the marrow; such intercommunication is also carried out through the canals of Volkmann: in the periosteum, blood vessels communicating with haversian canals are carried solely by the canals of Volkmann.

Sharpey's Fibers. Compact bone also contains *Sharpey's* or *perforating fibers;* these are collagenous bundles of varying thickness passing from the periosteum through the systems of lamellae in different directions, independently of the collagen fibrils, lacunae and canalicules (Fig. 7–14, *SF*). They are found in those places where, during the formation of a new bone lamella, thick collagenous bundles of the surrounding connective tissue become surrounded by bone. When uncalcified, they occupy irregular, fairly wide canals in the compact bone substance. When calcified, they appear in sections as prominent, irregular stripes or spots against the background of interstitial substance.

Sharpey's fibers are encountered in the external basic and in the interstitial layers which develop by periosteal ossification. They are not found in the haversian and internal basic systems. Their number depends on the type of bone and varies greatly; they may appear singly or, as in some of the bones of the skull, in large numbers. They may be so numerous as to displace much of the interstitial substance and to compress and deform the lacunae.

In addition to Sharpey's fibers, it is said that *elastic fibers* also penetrate the bone

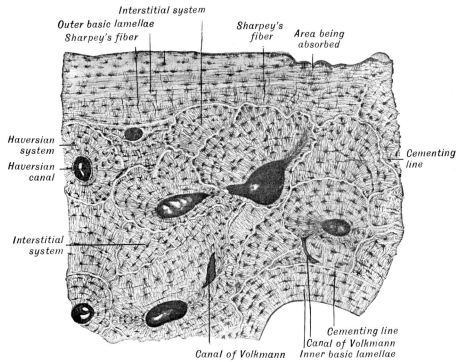

Interstitial system

Outer basic lamellae
Sharpey's fiber

Sharpey's fiber

Area being absorbed

Haversian system

Haversian canal

Cementing line

Interstitial system

Cementing line
Canal of Volkmann
Inner basic lamellae

Canal of Volkmann

Fig. 7–13.   Ground portion of a human metacarpal bone. Stained with fuchsin, mounted in Canada balsam. 160 ×. (After Schaffer.)

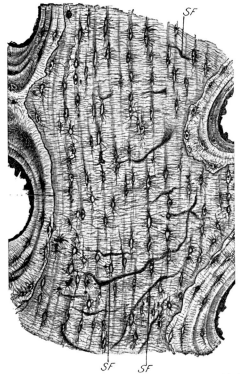

SF

SF   SF

Fig. 7–14.   From a cross section of a human fibula. SF, Sharpey's fibers. 160 ×. (After Schaffer.)

from the periosteum, and are to be found together with or independently of the collagenous bundles; their occurrence in bone is denied by some investigators.

Periosteum, Bone Marrow, and Endosteum. Except where it is joined to articular cartilage, bone is covered by the *periosteum,* a special, dense connective tissue layer. The attachment is tight on most of the surface of short bones, at the epiphyses of long bones, and where tendons and muscles are attached. This close connection depends mainly on the continuation of dense collagenous bundles from the periosteum into the bone as Sharpey's fibers. At such places, too, large blood vessels and nerves enter the bone. Where the periosteum is loosely connected, there are only a few, thin, collagenous bundles, and attachment to the bone is largely maintained by small blood vessels.

The periosteum in adults consists of two layers, not sharply defined. The external layer is a network of dense connective tissue containing blood vessels. The deep layer, adjacent to the bone, sometimes called the *cambium layer,* by a fancied analogy with the wood-forming zone of trees, is composed of more loosely arranged collagenous bundles; some of these change direction and enter the bone as Sharpey's fibers. The deep layer also contains spindle-shaped connective tissue cells and a network of thin elastic fibers. Blood vessels from the external layer enter the deep layer and pass through the canals of Volkmann to the haversian canals.

In the adult organism the periosteum has no osteogenic function under normal conditions and osteoblasts are not ordinarily recognizable among the spindle-shaped cells. If the bone is fractured, however, the bone-forming potentialities are activated and osteoblasts reappear in the deepest layer of the periosteum (p. 148).

The *endosteum* is a thin connective tissue layer lining the walls of the bone cavities, which are usually filled with bone marrow. It resembles the periosteum in some respects, and is the condensed peripheral layer of the stroma of the bone marrow where it is in contact with bone. All the cavities of bone, including the marrow spaces within spongy bone, are lined with endosteum after osteoblasts are no longer recognizable; that lining the compact bone of the shaft, however, is more prominent. The endosteum has both osteogenic and hematopoietic potencies.

HISTOGENESIS OF BONE

Bone always develops by a transformation of embryonic or adult connective tissue into a calcified connective tissue. When this occurs in cartilage it is called *intracartilaginous* or *endochondral ossification* in contrast with simple *intramembranous bone formation*. The only difference between them is that one occurs within cartilage, which must be removed before ossification can take place, although some of the cartilage matrix may remain as a framework upon which bone is laid down. In both cases the actual process of bone tissue formation is identical. The first bone formed is always spongy; some of it later becomes compact through internal reconstruction.

Occasionally, bone may arise in tissues not connected with the osseous system, and from connective tissue not ordinarily manifesting osteogenic potencies, in which case the process is called *ectopic ossification*.

Intramembranous Ossification. This process can be studied favorably in the developing bones of the calvarium. The place of origin of the first bone within the embryonic connective tissue is determined, to a large extent, by the course of the blood vessels. Bone first appears between and at equal distance from two neighboring blood vessels, and only later spreads toward the vessels. In an area where bone will develop, the connective tissue cells are connected with one another by their processes, and delicate bundles of collagenous fibrils run in all directions between them. The tissue is rather loose, and between its cells and fibrils is a semifluid, ground substance.

The first signs of bone development in such places are thin bars of dense intercellular substance between the cells; they soon become wider and thicker, and often unite to form a network in whose meshes the cells remain. Simultaneously, the cells increase in size and assume a polyhedral form while retaining their numerous processes connected with those of the adjacent elements and are now recognizable as osteoblasts (and later as osteocytes). Singly or in groups, the cells become surrounded by the dense interstitial substance, which gradually crowds out the intercellular material. Fibrils passing out of the newly formed bone substance continue into those of the surrounding tissue (Fig. 7–15).

When a certain stage in the transformation of the interstitial substance is reached, the tissue becomes calcifiable, bone salt is deposited in it, and it is now known as bone. The property of calcifiability is presumably conferred upon the transformed connective tissue by the osteoblasts. Osteoblasts arise in the early embryo by direct transformation from mesenchymal cells; similarly, they may arise in the adult from fibroblasts and reticular cells.

Soon after the initial stages of formation of bone from connective tissue, there are signs of further organization; osteoblasts appear on the surface of developing bone in a continuous layer (Fig. 7–16). Between their lateral surfaces remain spaces through which fibrils pass into the bone from the surrounding connective tissue. To these are added new fibrils which are presumably formed by the osteoblasts, and which make up the bulk of the fibrillar structure of the new bone.

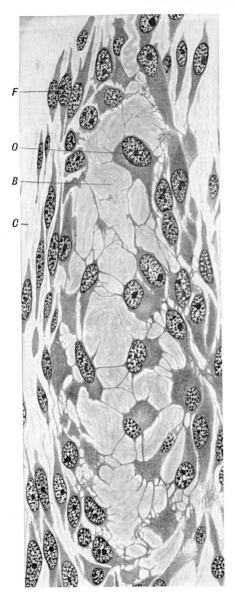

Fig. 7–15. Beginning intramembranous bone formation in the skull of an embryo cat of 5.5 cm. *F,* connective tissue cells; *C,* collagenous interstitial substance; *B,* homogeneous, thickened collagenous fibers which become the interstitial bone substance; *O,* connective tissue cells, with processes, which become osteoblasts and later bone cells. Eosin-azure stain. 520 ×. (A.A.M.)

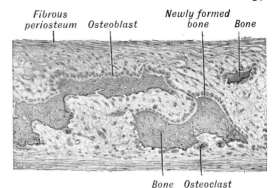

Fig. 7–16. Cross section through primordium of the parietal bone of a four-months' embryo. 100 ×. (After Schaffer.)

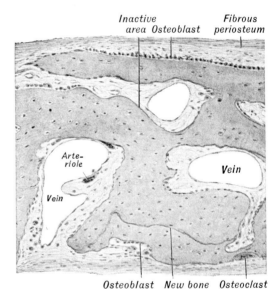

Fig. 7–17. Analogous section of a six-months' embryo. 100 ×. (After Schaffer.)

Through the activity of the osteoblasts the bone increases in thickness. Successive layers are added, by apposition, to the fibrillar mass which is being calcified while the osteoblasts remain on the exterior surface (Fig. 7–17). As the bone becomes thicker, some of the osteoblasts which lie on the surface are in-cluded, one by one, within its substance; these are the first bone cells or *osteocytes,* and they lie in the lacunae. They are formed directly from those osteoblasts which have become surrounded by the calcified interstitial substance they have produced. Most of the osteoblasts continue at the periphery and, with the gradual thickening of the interstitial substance, move away from those cells which remain in the lacunae. The osteoblasts maintain a continuous layer on the surface. As some of them become included in the bone as osteocytes, or as more are required for the formation of bone, new osteoblasts are formed by the transformation of cells

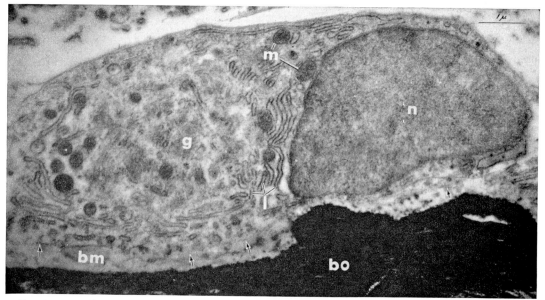

Fig. 7–18. Electron micrograph of section of undecalcified preparation of kitten humerus, showing contact of an osteoblast with the surface of bone matrix (arrows). *bo,* Calcified bone; *bm,* uncalcified, collagenous bone matrix; *g,* Golgi apparatus; *l,* lamellae of endoplasmic reticulum; *m,* mitochondria; *n,* nucleus of osteoblast. Buffered osmic acid fixation. (Courtesy B. Scott and D. Pease.)

from the surrounding connective tissue. Mitotic division seldom occurs among osteoblasts.

As osteoblasts are connected with one another by processes and as osteocytes are osteoblasts included within the ossifying substance, it is apparent how the processes of osteocytes penetrate the interstitial bone substance and connect the neighboring cells (compare Figs. 7–1 and 7–15). During the transformation of osteoblasts into osteocytes the latter even form a number of new processes. In a mature osteocyte only a few mitochondria remain; these are near the nucleus.

Bone which develops within the connective tissue has a spongy character for a long period. It consists of irregular plates and bars which branch and unite with one another, their fibrils becoming more regularly arranged as the plates thicken. The spaces between the plates are filled with connective tissue rich in blood vessels and dividing cells; this tissue is gradually transformed into myeloid tissue. The connective tissue surrounding a growing mass of spongy bone remains on its surface and gives rise to the periosteum. The osteoblasts which have remained on the surfaces of the bone during its active development assume a fibroblast-like appearance, and re-

main as the deepest layers of the periosteum and endosteum; their osteogenic potencies are recognizable only if they are again called upon to form bone, when they again assume the morphological characteristics of osteoblasts.

Intracartilaginous Ossification. In the process of intracartilaginous bone formation, the hyaline cartilage undergoes degenerative changes, is eroded by capillaries accompanied by osteogenic cells, and is replaced by bone which develops in the same manner as in intramembranous ossification. This process is most favorably studied in the zone of endochondral ossification, which is continuous with the epiphyseal cartilage plates of the long bones (7–20), and in which endochondral ossification continues until growth in length of the long bones is complete. In this zone cartilage cells multiply and form columns of flattened cells, instead of the irregular isogenous groups found in masses of hyaline cartilage. The cells in a column are separated by thin capsules; adjacent columns are separated by wide, parallel bands of interstitial substance.

Nearer the zone of ossification, the flat cells in the columns develop small, and then larger, vacuoles in their peripheral cytoplasm,

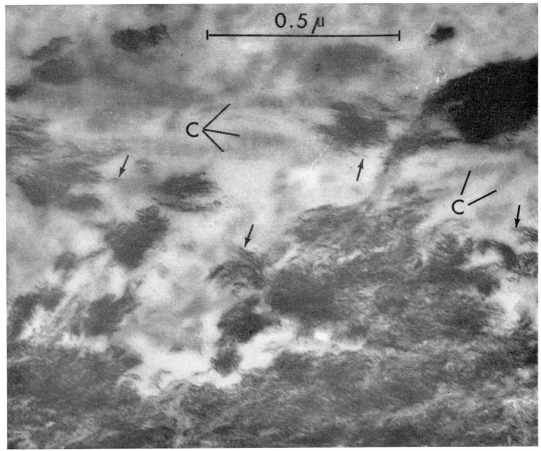

Fig. 7–19. Electron micrograph through epiphyseal plate of undecalcified kitten humerus. Area shows a site of active calcification. The cross striations are just visible in the collagenous fibers (C) and the tiny crystals of hydroxyapatite are indicated by arrows. Buffered osmic acid fixation. (Courtesy of B. Scott and D. Pease.)

causing the cells to swell. The nuclei also swell and lose most of their chromatin, and the cells degenerate. The matrix adjacent to these *vesicular* or *hypertrophic* cartilage cells becomes calcifiable, presumably under the influence of the cells. If there are adequate concentrations of calcium and phosphate in the blood plasma, the matrix then calcifies, especially the broad bands separating adjacent columns of cartilage cells; this forms the zone of *provisional* or *preliminary calcification,* which bridges and gives rigidity to the junction between hyaline cartilage and spongy bone.

The next stage in intracartilaginous ossification is due to the activity of the connective tissue and blood vessels of the bone marrow. Loops of blood vessels with accompanying connective tissue penetrate the cartilage. The interstitial substance separating the cartilage cells in the columns is dissolved in unknown fashion, and the distended cartilage cells are opened up, so that they are penetrated by the vascular connective tissue. In this way communicating canals arise, whose irregular walls are formed by the calcified cartilage matrix. The canals are filled with blood vessels and loose connective tissue; they lengthen as new capsules are opened up. Most of the vesicular cartilage cells perish during penetration of their capsules by the capillaries; a few of them may survive and become osteoblasts.

The process just described is dependent, for its orderly progress, upon the formation of the zone of provisional calcification, which advances just ahead of the penetration of the cartilage by capillaries and removal of the

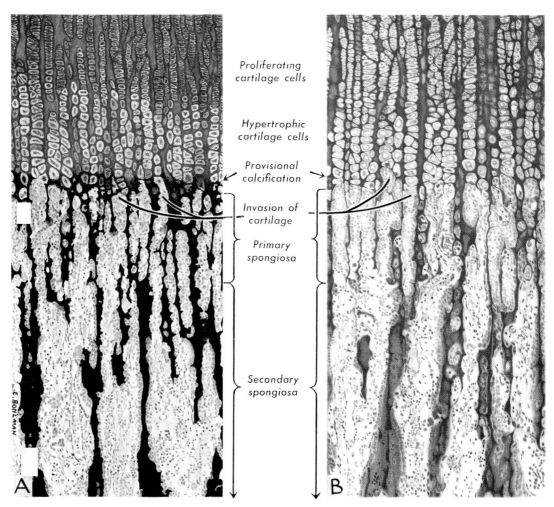

Proliferating
cartilage cells

Hypertrophic
cartilage cells

Provisional
calcification

Invasion of
cartilage

Primary
spongiosa

Secondary
spongiosa

Fig. 7–20. Endochondral ossification in longitudinal sections through the zone of epiphyseal growth of the distal end of the radius of a puppy. *A,* neutral formalin fixation; no decalcification. Von Kóssa and H–E stain. All deposits of bone salt are stained black; thus bone and calcified cartilage matrix stain alike. *B,* Zenker-formol fixation. Decalcified. Hematoxylin-eosin-azure II stain. Persisting cores of cartilage matrix in trabeculae of bone take a deep blue or purple stain, while bone stains red. It is impossible to tell where calcium deposits had been. 95 ×.

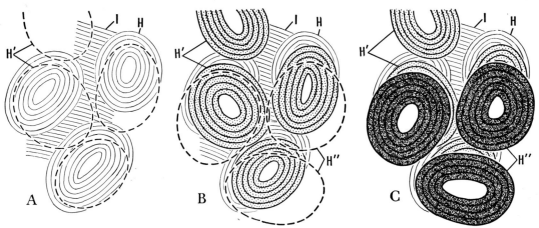

Fig. 7–21. Diagram of stages in formation of three generations of haversian systems, *H, H', H"; I,* interstitial lamellae. Modified after Prenant.

cartilage cells. If calcification in the cartilage matrix fails, owing to a deficiency of bone minerals, cartilage removal ceases; if multiplication of cartilage cells in columns continues, as is usually the case, the epiphyseal cartilage plate increases greatly in thickness. This, together with the appearance of uncalcified osteoid tissue in excessive amounts, constitutes the histological picture characteristic of *rickets* (Fig. 7–29).

When the vascular connective tissue penetrates the capsules, those connective tissue cells touching the cartilage matrix turn into a layer of osteoblasts. Then, between the osteoblasts and the cartilage matrix, which remains as a scaffolding, a thin, new layer of tissue appears, gradually thickens, and surrounds the cartilage bars (Fig. 7–2). This tissue, calcifiable when it is laid down, under favorable conditions begins to calcify as it is deposited and thus becomes bone. An intermediate stage of uncalcified osseous tissue, or *osteoid,* is not a necessary step in the formation of bone, but there may be a lag in calcification, even under physiological conditions, owing to a local failure in the supply or transport of bone mineral. When this failure becomes general, and osteoid tissue appears in excess, the condition is known as *rickets* or *osteomalacia* (p. 151). The calcification of new bone is best demonstrated in undecalcified sections, in which the bone salt is positively stained.

From this point, bone is formed by the osteoblasts just as in intramembranous bone formation. In quite the same fashion, the layers of the interstitial substance become thicker and surround isolated osteoblasts, transforming them into osteocytes. The spongy endochondral bone at this time consists of various-sized trabeculae, covered by osteoblasts, with a few osteoclasts, and containing the remains of cartilage matrix in their interior. The latter serve to differentiate bone formed by endochondral ossification from that arising by the intramembranous process alone. The wide spaces between the plates are filled with hematopoietic bone marrow.

Internal Reconstruction of Bone. Purely "membrane" bones enlarge by the deposition of new bone on one or more surfaces while bones developing in cartilage models increase in length by endochondral ossification and radially by the deposition of new periosteal (i.e., membranous) bone. As a bone increases in size, its structure is complicated by an internal reconstruction which serves to increase its strength and to provide a large cavity within it to lodge the bone marrow. These changes in a bone take place throughout its development and consist in the formation of new bone and a continued destruction and removal of areas of bone with subsequent formation of new layers of bone arranged differently from those which they have replaced (Fig. 7–21).

Even with the first appearance of bone, wherever formed, the destructive process also appears and is generally associated with the presence of osteoclasts. It is commonly believed that they produce a substance which dissolves the bone, but there is no direct evidence to support this belief. Osteoclasts are usually, but not always, seen where bone is dissolving, and are frequently found in deep grooves, *Howship's lacunae,* which have the appearance of having been eroded in the bone. Or an osteoclast may surround the free edge of the end of a trabecula of bone undergoing dissolution. The possibility that the osteoclast has a phagocytic function seems slight. Both organic matrix and inorganic bone salt are resorbed simultaneously, but neither cellular debris nor bone salt has been demonstrated in the osteoclasts, although, in certain circumstances, both appear in the macrophages of the bone marrow. However, plutonium, which deposits in bone, has been found in osteoclasts by autoradiography (Arnold and Jee).

When resorption of bone ceases in a particular location, the osteoclasts disappear, most of them becoming either osteoblasts or reticular cells, depending upon whether new formation of bone is to follow. Osteoclasts are rarely seen to degenerate.

The space resulting from the removal of bone is then filled with marrow or new bone. The sequence of bone formation, bone destruction, and formation of new bone oriented in different directions and of different degrees of compactness is repeated many times in the history of a bone. It must be emphasized that the reconstruction of bone must at all times be coordinated with the local mechanical stresses to which the bone is subjected and must also permit growth along those directions which will anticipate future weight bearing and other mechanical functions. For, in developing bone, as in practically all normal development, structure grows in such a fashion as to anticipate the functions it will mediate. The direct causes determining whether adjacent cells in a growing bone become either osteoblasts or osteoclasts are unknown.

A greatly diminished rate of reconstruction of bone, the "physiological turnover," continues throughout adult life. By releasing calcium it helps to maintain the level of calcium in the plasma. If, in adult life there is not sufficient calcium in the diet and the skeleton is called upon to furnish large amounts of calcium, as in pregnancy, the turnover of bone may be greatly accelerated. The condition known as *osteomalacia (adult rickets)* follows.

Formation of Haversian Systems. In parts of the skeleton spongy bone becomes transformed into compact bone. In the irregular, communicating cavities of the spongy bone, filled with bone marrow, the amount of marrow between the spicules of bone decreases as the osteoblasts covering the bone produce layer after layer of concentric bone lamellae. This process continues until all that remains of the former marrow cavity is a comparatively narrow canal containing the blood vessels surrounded by little of the bone marrow. In this manner, systems of concentric bone lamellae, called *primitive haversian systems,* are formed.

Then, at some places, the bone substance begins to dissolve, a process which may include parts or all of the newly formed primitive haversian systems as well as the periosteal bone, and which is associated with the presence of osteoclasts. Wide cylindrical cavities filled with blood vessels and with embryonic bone marrow are formed anew. Then the destruction of bone ceases, the activity of the osteoblasts begins, and concentric systems are once more laid down on the walls of the cavities. These are the haversian systems of the second generation. The dissolution may be renewed in adjacent areas of the bone, to be followed by the formation of haversian systems of the third generation (Figs. 7–21 and 7–22). Haversian systems are always formed by apposition of bone on the inner surfaces of lamellae of bone surrounding blood vessels; this results in a progressive decrease in the size of the haversian canals, and in an increase in the compactness of the bone.

This process of destruction and construction continues actively until the bones approach adult size, after which reconstruction continues throughout life at a sharply reduced intensity. It is upon this progressive reconstruction of bone that the complicated structure of the mature compact substance with its haversian and intermediate systems depends. As a bone increases in thickness, the periosteum and the endosteum lay down successive layers of *basic* or *circumferential lamellae* on its surfaces. During reconstruction of the bone these lamellae also undergo destruction and replacement by haversian systems. The intermediate systems, then, include

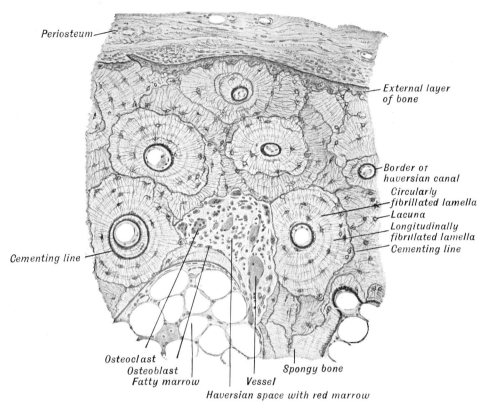

Fig. 7–22. Cross section of second phalanx of a human middle finger, showing replacement of spongy bone by compact bone. 110 ×. (After Schaffer.)

the remains of these lamellae, of which those of periosteal origin contain Sharpey's fibers and portions of former, partially destroyed haversian systems of various generations.

Development of Bones as a Whole. Most of the bones of the skeleton are first laid down in the embryo in hyaline cartilage; this group includes all the bones of the thorax, the limbs, the greater part of the bones of the skull, and the hyoid bone. The ossification of these cartilage models proceeds typically in the long bones of the limbs.

The external shape of the cartilage model suggests in general the future bone; in it a diaphysis, with an epiphysis at each end, may be distinguished early. Externally, the cartilage model is covered by a perichondrium of closely packed, embryonic connective tissue cells. Bone formation begins within a ring-shaped area surrounding the center of the diaphysis. The perichondrium is called the periosteum as soon as it begins to form bone, and the process is accordingly called "periosteal ossification," and is of the intra-

membranous type. The cells of the perichondrium adjoining the cartilage increase in size and become osteoblasts. Between them appear thin and later thicker bone lamellae with bone cells. These lamellae form a bone ring, the *periosteal bone band* or *collar,* which surrounds the middle of the diaphysis of the cartilage (Fig. 7–23). This band is a spongy bone network, through whose meshes the connective tissue of the periosteum continues in direct contact with the cartilage.

Before or shortly after the bone collar appears, the cartilage tissue inside the diaphysis changes markedly; the cells swell into vesicles, and the interstitial substance between them becomes thinner and calcified. Through the spaces in the periosteal band the connective tissue of the periosteum, together with the blood vessels, penetrates the transformed cartilage at one or several places (Figs. 7–24, 7–25). The capsules of the vesicular cartilage cells are quickly opened for a long distance, and become filled with embryonic bone marrow with its thin-walled blood vessels. In

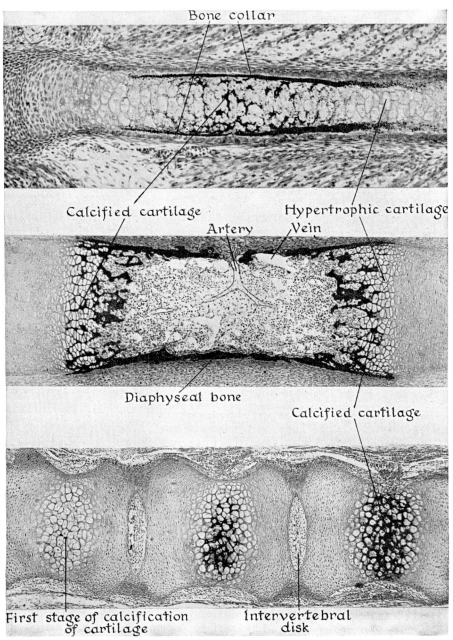

Fig. 7–23. Photomicrographs showing several stages of bone formation in developing rats. From formalin fixed, undecalcified sections stained with silver nitrate to show bone salt (black). Upper figure is a longitudinal section through second rib of eighteen-day rat embryo; calcification of the periosteal bone collar is further advanced than that of the cartilage. Middle figure is a section of metatarsal of four-day rat, in which ossification is proceeding toward the epiphyses; the hypertrophic cartilage is not completely calcified. Lower figure shows three stages in calcification of vertebrae in twenty-day rat embryo. 117 ×, 63 ×, and 57 × respectively. (Bloom and Bloom.)

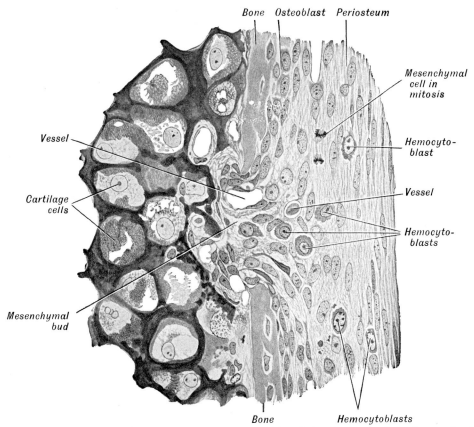

Bone Osteoblast Periosteum

Mesenchymal cell in mitosis

Vessel

Hemocyto-blast

Cartilage cells

Vessel

Hemocyto-blasts

Mesenchymal bud

Bone Hemocytoblasts

Fig. 7–24. Part of longitudinal section through the middle of the diaphysis of the femur of a 25-mm. human embryo. Mesenchyme with vessels entering calcified cartilage through an opening in the periosteal bone collar. Eosin-azure stain. 560 ×. (A.A.M.)

this manner a cavity with irregular walls is formed in the cartilage in the area surrounded by the periosteal band (Figs. 7–23, 7–26). This constitutes the *primary bone marrow cavity,* filled with embryonic bone marrow. The periosteal collar performs an important function by bridging the gap which would otherwise result from the formation of this cavity; it is the primitive shaft of the bone. Scattered between the elements of the marrow are angular remains of calcified cartilage. Some of the cells of the embryonic marrow become osteoblasts, which come in contact with these cartilaginous remains and surround them with layers of bone. Some of the cartilage cells also become osteoblasts. In other places osteoclasts are formed where the newly formed bone is being resorbed (Fig. 7–25).

With the continued growth of cartilage in the epiphyses, the entire cartilage model increases in size. The mass of the periosteal as well as of the endochondral bone in the diaphysis also grows progressively. The periosteal bone band widens toward the epiphyses. The endochondral bone may be distinguished by the remains of deeply staining cartilage matrix within its trabeculae. At a much later period, in man usually during the first few years of postnatal life, *ossification centers* appear in the epiphyses, until then formed of hyaline cartilage, and the process of endochondral ossification is repeated in these areas.

The epiphyseal cartilage plates (Fig. 7–20) between the epiphyses and the diaphysis are temporary formations which serve for the growth in length of the bone. Multiplication of cartilage cells, arranged in columns, occurs within the plate and movement is towards its epiphysis while removal of the degenerating cells is from the diaphyseal aspect. Under normal conditions of growth these two processes balance one another, and the disk remains at approximately constant thick-

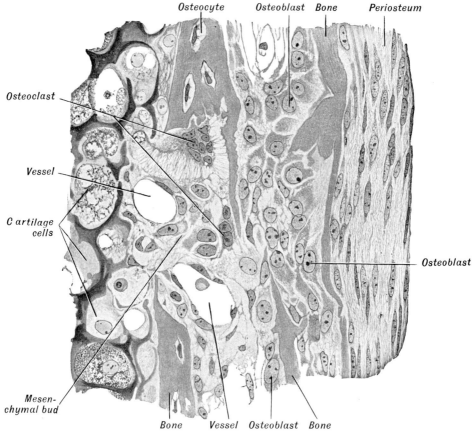

Fig. 7–25.   Similar place as in Figure 7–24 from the humerus of a human embryo of eight weeks. The process of ossification has advanced slightly farther than in that figure. Eosin-azure stain. 560 ×. (A.A.M.)

ness. Growth in length results from the fact that the cartilage cells continually grow away from the shaft, being replaced by bone as they recede; the net effect is an increase in length of the shaft. When proliferation of the cartilage ceases, at the end of the period of growth, the cartilage plates are entirely replaced by bone (*closure of epiphyses*), the epiphyses unite with the diaphysis, and longitudinal growth of the bone is no longer possible (Fig. 7–26). As mentioned in the chapter on cartilage, no satisfactory explanation has been proposed of the mechanics of interstitial growth in this tissue.

The contribution of each of the two epiphyses of a long bone to its growth may differ markedly; growth in length of the femur takes place mainly at the distal epiphysis, and of the tibia at the proximal one.

As the growing bone advances into the cartilage and replaces it, the cartilage matrix separating the columns of cartilage cells becomes covered with osseous tissue, forming the mass of spongy bone called the *metaphysis*. This bone normally undergoes extensive reorganization and thinning out as the growth process passes it by. Two parts of it become recognizable, the *primary* and *secondary spongiosa,* being differentiated by the fact that the latter has undergone reconstruction. As a part of this reconstruction, the tips of trabeculae of the spongiosa are continually being resorbed, with the result that the spongiosa as a whole tends to remain constant in length. The total picture in the growth zone, then, is that of an epiphyseal cartilage disk, a zone of provisional calcification, within which cartilage cells are being opened and destroyed, and a zone of spongy bone. All these zones remain at approximately constant dimensions, while the shaft of the bone increases in length, owing to the

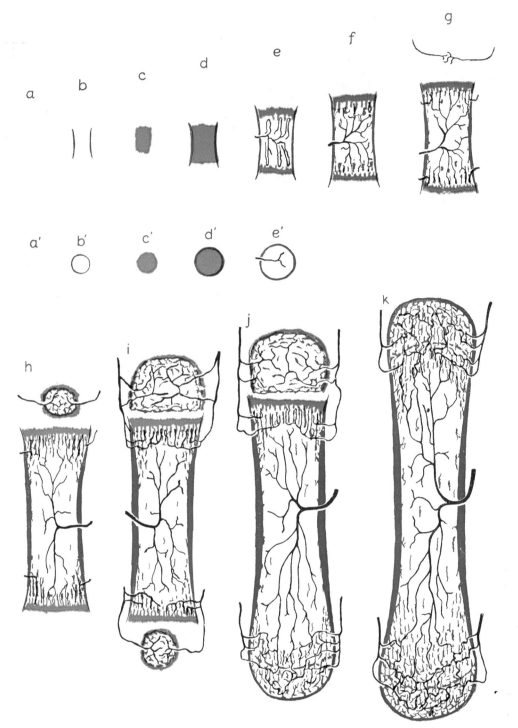

Fig. 7–26. Diagram of the development of a typical long bone as shown in longitudinal sections. *Pale green,* cartilage; *purple,* calcified cartilage; *blue,* bone; *red,* arteries. *a', b', c', d', e',* cross sections through the centers of *a, b, c, d, e* respectively. *a,* cartilage model; *b,* appearance of the periosteal bone collar before the development of calcified cartilage, *c,* or after it, *d; e,* vascular mesenchyme has entered the calcified cartilage matrix and divided it into two zones of ossification, *f; g,* blood vessels and mesenchyme enter upper epiphyseal cartilage; *h,* epiphyseal ossification center develops and grows larger; *i,* ossification center develops in lower epiphyseal cartilage; *j,* the lower and *k,* the upper epiphyseal cartilages disappear as the bone ceases to grow in length, and the bone marrow cavity is continuous throughout the length of the bone. After the disappearance of the cartilage plates at the zones of ossification, the blood vessels of the diaphysis, metaphysis and epiphysis intercommunicate.

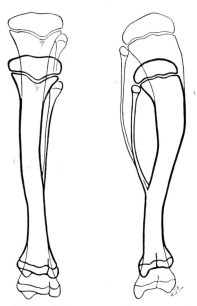

Fig. 7–27. Diagram to illustrate remodelling during growth of tibia and fibula of rat, viewed from anterior aspect and in profile. (After Wolbach.)

madder which deposits in newly formed bone. These findings have been verified and extended with the newer techniques using bone-seeking, radioactive isotopes.

In short bones developing in cartilage, a central point of endochondral ossification appears and progresses from the center to the periphery. This continues until only a thin cartilage layer remains. When the cartilage no longer regenerates and is completely used up, the surrounding layer of connective tissue becomes the periosteum, and begins to deposit upon the exterior of the endochondral spongy bone a layer of periosteal bone of varying thickness. This later becomes compact bone.

In flat bones which develop in cartilage (scapula), periosteal ossification is followed by endochondral bone formation, just as in the long bones. The bones of the calvaria, the sides of the skull and almost all the facial bones develop directly from connective tissue. In a limited region of this tissue a small center of spongy bone is formed. Its lamellae develop radially from this point of ossification. Such a growing bone consists of a solid mass in its interior and thin, bony rays at its periphery. The layers of connective tissue which cover the surfaces differentiate into periosteum and increase the thickness of the bone by apposition. The peripheral layers of the bone become compact substance through internal reconstruction. In the central layers, dissolution outstrips the formation of new bone, so that in the course of time there is formed a spongy substance with wide bone marrow spaces—diploë.

The lower jaw is an example of a special mode of ossification, for its model, although formed in the embryo of cartilage (*Meckel's cartilage*), does not undergo ossification, but simply serves as a surface for the deposition of bone by connective tissue. The cartilage is later resorbed.

Repair of Bone. After a fracture there are first the usual reactions of any tissue to severe injury, including hemorrhage and organization of the clot by ordinary granulation tissue, the *procallus.* The granulation tissue becomes dense connective tissue, and cartilage and fibrocartilage develop within it, forming the *fibrocartilaginous callus,* which fills the gap between the ends of the fragments. The new bone, which will ultimately

fact that the proliferating structures, the growth apparatus, constantly grow away from the diaphysis.

At first the only bone formed is of the spongy type, of periosteal and endochondral origin. Then the internal reconstruction begins in the periosteal bone and leads to the development of compact bone. In the diaphysis it finally forms a thick layer, which tapers gradually toward the epiphyses. Inside the central portion of the diaphysis, and extending toward the epiphyses, an extensive dissolution of bone begins, which is not compensated by a corresponding formation of new bone. In this manner the *definitive bone marrow cavity* arises. In a completed bone it occupies the entire diaphysis and continues into the spaces of the spongy substance toward the epiphyses.

As the bone has to support the larger articular cartilage, the epiphysis is broader than the shaft of the bone. With increase in length of the bone, the epiphyseal plate moves away from a fixed point on the shaft and the reconstruction of the old metaphysis occurs by resorption from the periosteal surface and new formation of endosteal bone (Fig. 7–27). Most of these phenomena in the reconstruction of the ends of growing bones have long been known as a result of studies with unite the fragments, begins to form at some distance from the fracture line, originating from the deeper layers of the periosteum and endosteum, and invading the fibrocartilaginous callus. It extends centripetally, replacing the tissues of the callus with new bone, the *bony callus,* which is calcifiable as it is laid down and, under favorable conditions, calcifies as it is formed. Ossification of the callus, then, like intracartilaginous bone formation, is essentially a process of replacement of the earlier tissue by bone, only enough of the first tissue remaining to furnish a framework for the deposition of the new bone. *Bony union* of the fracture is accomplished when the new spongy bone, invading the callus from the periosteum of the two fragments of bone, makes contact and unites. After this there is reorganization, with resorption of excess bone, and internal reconstruction, resulting finally in bridging the gap with compact bone. The fate of the cells of the fibrocartilaginous callus needs further study.

Ectopic Ossification. In the processes already described bone has been formed from connective tissue, with the transformation of mesenchymal cells, fibroblasts and reticular cells into osteoblasts, osteocytes and osteoclasts; the return of these cells to fibroblasts and reticular cells has also been described. All the processes described have in common the fact that bone has developed only in connection with the osseous system—the skeleton. The influences under which ordinary connective tissue gives rise to bone in the embryo are but little understood, but it is clear that previously undifferentiated connective tissue cells are capable of transformation to the cells characteristic of bone.

It would also appear that, once cells have exhibited osteogenic potencies, these potencies are readily evoked for an indeterminate period after the cells have returned to an indifferent morphological state. Thus, in the healing of fractures, cells in the deepest layers of the periosteum and endosteum, under the stimulus of trauma, reassume the form of osteoblasts and once again are actively engaged in osteogenesis. Moreover, cells grown from bone in tissue culture, and having lost the morphological characteristics of osteoblasts, once again form bone when implanted into the anterior chamber of the eye (Fig. 7–28).

Furthermore, under certain conditions bone may be formed spontaneously from connective tissue not in association with the skeleton. This ectopic ossification has been described in such diverse locations as the pelvis of the kidney, in the walls of arteries, in the eyes, in muscles and in tendons. From this it may be inferred that many types of connective tissue have latent osteogenic potencies, which are exhibited only rarely away from the skeletal system. This conclusion is supported by experimental production of bone in connective tissue after ligation of the renal artery and vein, after transplantation of bladder epithelium, and after the injection of alcoholic extracts of bone into muscle. In the latter case there is evidence that alcohol alone frequently induces osteogenesis in muscle, and that it shares this ability with other irritating substances.

Many attempts have been made to utilize the osteogenic potencies of periosteum and bone by transplanting these tissues to areas in which it is desired that new bone be formed; the modern "bone-bank," which supplies fragments of bone preserved by freezing or by other means, is the fruit of these efforts. When transplanted to a favorable environment cells with osteogenic potencies may form bone, as do autogenous grafts of fresh bone or periosteum in laboratory mammals, but homogenous grafts of preserved bone do not give rise to new bone. Such grafts do, however, favor the induction of new bone formation by the cells of the host.

Reticular cells within the orbit of advancing bone, e.g., in the formation of medullary bone in birds, assume the form of osteoblasts before they actually join in the process of osteogenesis. This observation, together with those upon the behavior of bone grafts just cited, suggests that the presence of bone itself may be an important aid in activating osteogenic potencies. There is thus histological evidence in favor of *induction* of formation of bone, although attempts to isolate a specific *inductor* substance have so far given equivocal results.

Histophysiological Remarks. The mechanism of the deposition of calcium in bone is still incompletely understood. At least two factors, local and humoral, are involved. The humoral factor is related to the supply of minerals in the fluids of the body, and to the

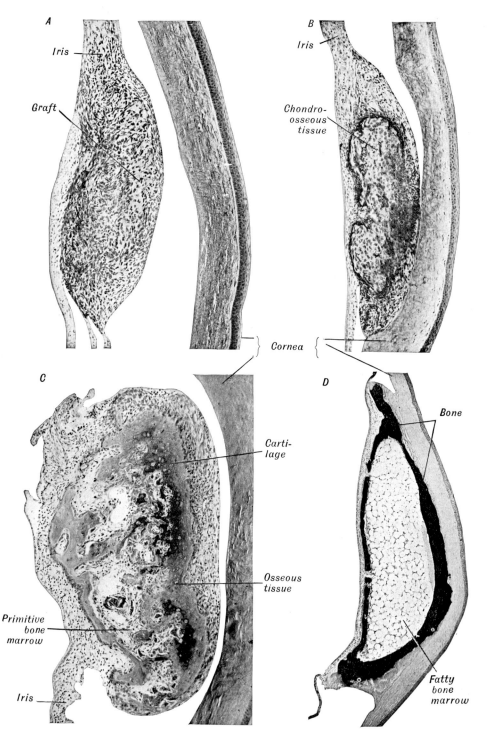

Fig. 7–28. Development of tissue cultures of bone grafted into the anterior chamber of the eye. Fragments of tibiae of twelve-day rats were cultured in rat plasma and embryo extract. The outgrowths were removed after four days *in vitro* and transplanted to the iris of normal rats. These outgrowths contained no bone or cartilage. *A,* after one and one-half days in the eye there was no cartilage or bone. *B,* after two and one-half days in the eye, chondro-osseous tissue developed from the culture. *C,* after six days in the eye, much bone and cartilage and some marrow appeared. *D,* after four months, a "bone" with central fatty marrow developed. *A, B, C,* Zenker-formol, hematoxylin-eosin-azure II. Photomicrographs, 80 ×. *D,* formalin fixation, silver nitrate-hematoxylin-eosin. Photomicrograph, 32 ×. (Courtesy of J. H. Heinen.)

solubilities of the difficultly soluble salts of calcium and phosphate; it may be defined in terms of the concentrations of these substances in the blood. But the local factor, which determines the occurrence and specific localization of the deposition of bone salt, when adequate concentrations of calcium and of phosphate are present in the blood, is not understood.

When calcification fails in growing animals or young children, the osseous tissue continues to grow, but the new uncalcified tissue is known as *osteoid*. This failure of calcification to keep pace with growth is known as rickets, and is usually associated with a diminished concentration of phosphate in the blood plasma. The preventive and curative action of *sunlight* and of *vitamin D* in rickets is generally attributed to increased absorption of calcium and phosphate from the gastrointestinal tract. That rickets is not due to failure in the local mechanism is shown by the fact that the cartilage matrix of rachitic bone calcifies readily, either *in vivo* or *in vitro*, when the surrounding medium is supplied with the necessary minerals in adequate concentrations (Fig. 7–29). *Phosphatase* is present in osteoblasts, but not in osteoid tissue; the staining reactions of these cells also indicate that they are rich in ribose-nucleic acids. It is suggested that these substances are associated with the formation of the bone matrix by osteoblasts, rather than with calcification.

The interstitial substance of bone acts as a store of calcium, there being a constant interchange of this substance between the blood and the bones, with the result that the calcium ion concentration in the plasma remains approximately constant. A dual mechanism for homeostatic control of the level of calcium in the plasma has been postulated. One part acts by simple chemical equilibrium with the labile fraction of the bone mineral, and is adequate to maintain a constant but low plasma calcium level of approximately 7 mg. per cent. The second part of the dual mechanism is required to raise the plasma calcium to the normal level of 10 mg. per cent, and to maintain it at this level. This action is mediated by the *parathyroid hormone* (Chapter 17) and depends upon a "feedback" mechanism, in which the calcium ion level itself exerts a direct influence upon parathyroid activity.

Since resorption of bone, as controlled by the parathyroid glands, results in destruction of the stable crystals of hydroxyapatite, as well as of the labile fraction of the mineral, this mechanism makes an otherwise inaccessible source of calcium available for homeostatic regulation.

In birds, an entire new system of *medullary bone*, produced chiefly by an outgrowth from the endosteal lining of the shafts of the long bones, is formed during the egg-laying cycle (or may be induced by the administration of *estrogens*) and serves to accumulate calcium to be used in the formation of the egg shell. When the egg shell is being calcified, calcium is made available by destruction of the medullary bone, including its organic matrix; osteoclasts are prominent during this resorptive stage. Mice react to the administration of estrogens in much the same way as do birds. Endosteal bone formation has not been reported in rats, in which estrogens inhibit the normal resorption of the spongiosa during growth by endochondral ossification. This results in a greatly elongated and dense spongiosa, containing cores of deeply stained cartilage matrix.

The growth of bone is markedly influenced by the *growth hormone* of the anterior pituitary. Hypophysectomy results in cessation of endochondral ossification; administration of growth hormone reinitiates growth, and, if continued for a sufficiently long time, may result in *gigantism*. Growth hormone, injected into rats which have been both thyroidectomized and hypophysectomized, produces skeletal growth, whereas thyroxine produces marked maturation and only moderate growth. Coordination between growth and maturation may be restored by the administration of both hormones.

Experiments with grafts of parathyroid gland to bone show that this organ causes a resorption of bone by direct action on this tissue (Fig. 17–3).

In *hyperparathyroidism*, bone is extensively resorbed, and is replaced by fibrous tissue containing large numbers of osteoclasts; this resembles the pathological picture of *osteitis fibrosa* (*von Recklinghausen*). When large doses of parathyroid hormone are given to animals, changes in the bones are profound. Within a few hours many osteoblasts die, although the majority change into fibro-

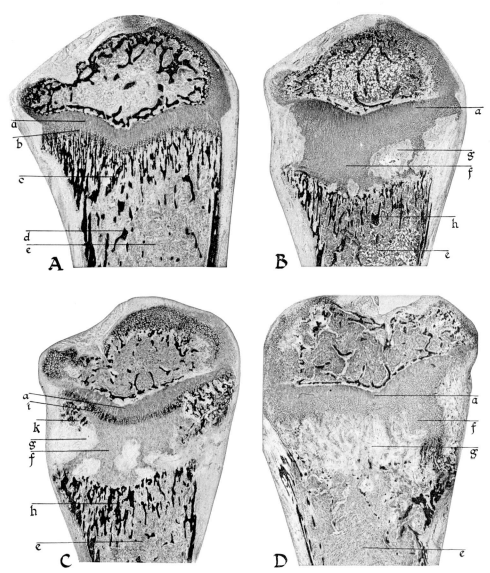

Fig. 7–29. Head of tibia in experimental rickets in rats. All sections from undecalcified bones stained with silver nitrate to show calcification, and counterstained with H and E. All rats weaned to experimental diet at twenty-one days. A, normal control, aged thirty-one days, Bills' stock diet. B, litter-mate of A, aged thirty-one days, same diet plus 2 per cent $BeCO_3$. C, age fifty-seven days, stock diet plus 1 percent $BeCO_3$, given daily intraperitoneal injections of sodium phosphates for last seven days. Note calcified cartilage matrix and beginning healing. D, age sixty-two days, rickets due to high calcium, low phosphate diet (Steenbock-Black). a, proliferating cartilage; b, zone of provisional calcification; c, tra-beculae of primary spongiosa; d, secondary spongiosa; e, bone marrow; f, hypertrophic cartilage; g, osteoid tissue; h, trabeculae calcified before onset of rickets; i, calcification preparatory to healing; k, healing with calcification of new bone. Photomicrographs, 15 ×. (Courtesy of F. C. McLean.)

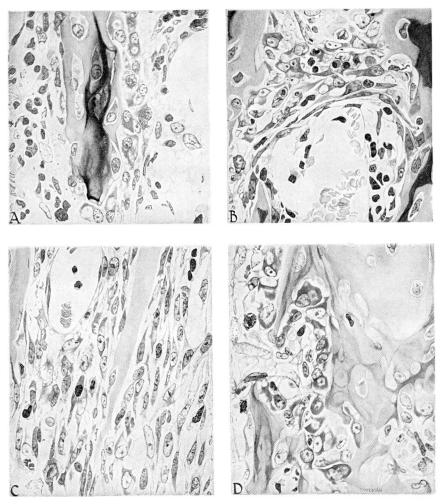

Fig. 7–30. Effect of large doses of parathyroid extract on proximal epiphysis of rat tibiae. The sections are from four members of a seven-weeks' litter. A, normal control, with prominent osteoblasts; B, nine hours; C, 24 hours; D, 96 hours after injection of 1000 units of parathyroid extract. B, extensive development of osteoblasts into fibroblast-like cells. C, bone marrow and osteoblasts have been replaced by densely packed fibroblast-like cells. D, the fibrous tissue has been replaced by newly formed bone, many of its cells having changed into osteoblasts. 505 ×. Hematoxylin-eosin-azure II. (After Heller, McLean and Bloom.)

blasts or osteoclasts or become phagocytic. There is widespread necrosis of the elements of the bone marrow and, in certain species, of the osteocytes. The calcium-containing trabeculae are rapidly resorbed and replaced by fibrous tissue. Salts of calcium have not been demonstrated within the osteoclasts, but have been found extracellularly as well as in the macrophages of the marrow. Recovery occurs when large numbers of osteoblasts develop from fibroblasts, and new bone, formed intramembranously, replaces the fibrous tissue (Fig. 7–30).

In long-standing deficiency of calcium and of vitamin D, especially when aggravated by pregnancy, the bones of adults contain much uncalcified osteoid tissue, and their mineral content is greatly diminished—a condition known as *osteomalacia (adult rickets)*. The diminution in calcium content is due to failure of calcification of new bone formed in the turnover of this tissue, rather than to simple decalcification of previously calcified bone. In osteomalacia, and in the form of rickets induced experimentally by deprivation of calcium, the parathyroid glands are en-

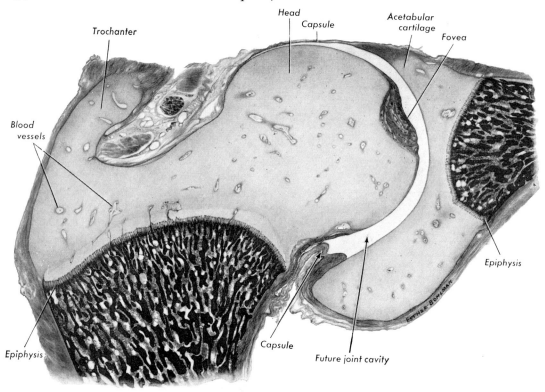

Fig. 7–31. Section through head of the femur of a human fetus of 26 cm. 6 ×. (From a preparation of H. Hatcher.)

larged; they are much less affected in the rickets associated with deficiency of phosphate.

The terms *atrophy, osteoporosis,* and *rarefaction* have been used loosely and interchangeably with reference to conditions in which there is a decrease in the hard portions of bone in favor of a relative increase in the soft portions. Such a condition is seen in elderly people, and especially in women after the menopause. It has not been shown that the mineral content per unit volume of the calcified bone substance is lessened in this condition. In *Paget's disease,* little understood, the bones are both thickened and softened, resorption and apposition of bone occurring simultaneously. In this condition the blood calcium and the parathyroid glands are normal.

Deficiency of *vitamin C* leads to profound changes in tissues of mesenchymal origin, producing the condition known as *scurvy,* which has been characterized as an inability of the supporting tissue to produce and maintain intercellular substance. In bone this re-

sults in destruction of the collagen of the matrix, with extensive reparative proliferation of fibroblasts. Deficiency of *vitamin A* results in a diminution in the rate of growth of the skeleton, without a corresponding retardation of growth of the central nervous system. The resulting damage to the central nervous system is regarded as mechanical, owing chiefly to the discrepancy in the relative sizes of the spinal cord and the vertebrae. Excessive administration of vitamin A accelerates remodelling of bone.

JOINTS AND SYNOVIAL MEMBRANES

Bones are joined to one another by connective tissue structures which permit varying degrees of movement between the adjoining bones. Such structures are called joints or articulations. These present extreme variations in character which depend primarily upon the type of bones which are joined and the varying degrees of motion permitted by the articulation. Thus, in some cases, as in the skull, the joints are immovable, and the

Articular surface

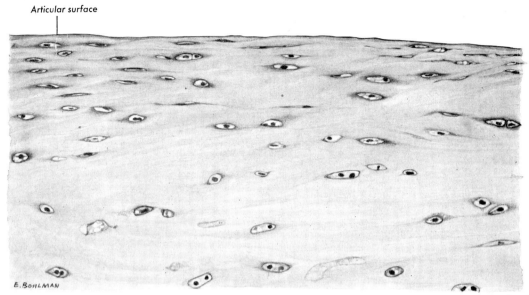

E. BOHLMAN

Fig. 7–32. Articular surface of head of the femur of a man. 300 ×. (From a preparation of H. Hatcher.)

connected bones are separated only by a thin connective tissue layer, the sutural ligament. Other joints are slightly movable, such as the intervertebral articulations. Here the succeeding vertebrae are joined to one another by dense fibrous tissue and cartilage. Still other bones are freely movable upon one another, and here the bones are completely separated by cartilage and fibrous capsules.

Joints in which there is little or no movement are called *synarthroses*. There are three types of these: If the connection between the bones is of bone, it is a *synostosis;* if of cartilage, a *synchondrosis;* and if of connective tissue, a *syndesmosis.* Joints which permit free movement of the bones are called *diarthroses.*

In the diarthrodial joints there is a cavity. Because this was thought by some to have a continuous lining of flattened, epithelium-like cells, the tissue was called "mesenchymal epithelium." However, the walls of the joint

Villi

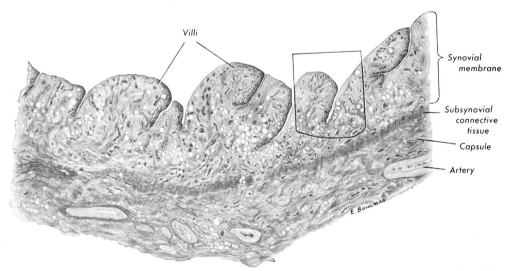

Synovial
membrane

Subsynovial
connective
tissue

Capsule

Artery

E. BOHLMAN

Fig. 7–33. Section through capsule of the knee joint of a young man showing the villi and connective tissue components. The area outlined is shown at higher magnification in Figure 7–34. 15 ×. (From a preparation of H. Hatcher.)

cavities are composed of a dense connective tissue whose cells are irregularly distributed and seldom suggest epithelium in arrangement. Occasionally, small amounts of cartilage and all transitions between the cartilage cells and the joint or synovial cells can be found.

The articular surface of the bones is covered with hyaline cartilage. Where the opposing cartilages touch, they are not covered with dense connective tissue, but at their bases a small area of perichondrium is reflected backward into the membrane of the joint capsule. At this point there are many cartilage cells extending into the synovial membrane. As is true of most of the cartilage of the body, the articular cartilages contain no blood vessels; it is generally believed that they are nourished by osmosis from the surrounding tissues. The articular cartilages are intimately adherent to a layer of compact bone which lacks haversian systems and has large lacunae, said to be free of canalicules.

Most of the joint capsules are composed of two fairly distinct layers. The external consists of dense fibrous tissue and is called the *fibrous layer.* The inner is the *synovial layer,* which is more cellular and is thought to secrete the viscid, colorless liquid of the joint cavity. However, the joint membrane exhibits many variations in structure. The synovial layer is sometimes thrown into marked folds which may project for surprising distances into the cavity. The larger of these folds frequently contain vessels. In other cases the two layers appear fused, or the synovial layer may rest directly on muscle or fatty tissue or periosteum. It has been suggested that the synovia be classified according to the tissues on which they lie: that is, loose connective, dense fibrous, or adipose tissue.

Synovial membranes which rest on loose

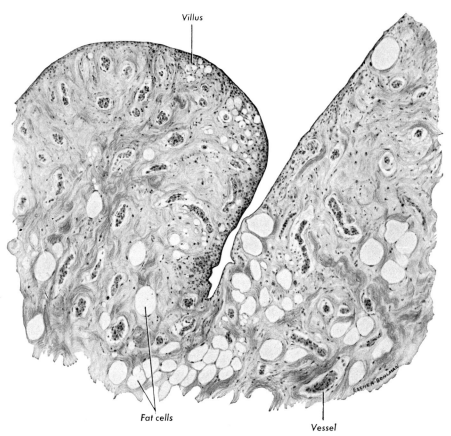

Villus

Fat cells

Vessel

Fig. 7–34.   Synovial membrane of young adult. (Higher magnification of the area outlined in Figure 7–33.) Note the irregularity in the concentration of cells toward the free surface of the villus and the irregular distribution of fat cells. 85 ×. (From a preparation of H. Hatcher.)

connective tissue usually cover those parts of the joints which are not subjected to strain or pressure. As a rule they have a definite surface layer, separated from the underlying tissue of the joint by loose connective tissue. The surface layer consists of collagenous fibers interspersed with fibroblasts whose processes may extend for long distances, although sometimes the cells are rounded. The collagenous fibers are either irregularly arranged or may be oriented along the main lines of stress. In addition to the fibroblasts, there are a few macrophages, leukocytes and lymphoid wandering cells. In addition to blood vessels, the loose connective tissue contains many lymphatics.

The fibrous synovial membrane covers the interarticular ligaments and tendons and lines those parts of the joints which are subject to strain. It consists of dense connective tissue; the surface zone is slightly more cellular than the rest. Some of the fibroblasts have capsules. When unusual pressure is applied to the synovial membrane, fibrocartilage develops.

The adipose type of synovial membrane covers the fat pads which project into the joint cavities. The synovial membrane in this case usually consists of a single layer of cells resting on a thin layer of connective tissue.

The fibroblasts of the synovial membrane rarely show mitoses. They may occasionally contain one or two vacuoles. There are no vacuoles within them which stain with neutral red. Mitochondria and a Golgi net have been demonstrated in them.

Folds of the synovial membrane may be either temporary formations which depend on the position of the joint, or they may form permanent *villi* which project into the joint cavity. Some of these villi have a broad base and a rather short stalk, while others may be thin and long. The larger folds contain blood vessels, lymphatics and occasionally lobules of adipose tissue. There is an increase in the size and number of the villi with age. New islets of cartilage are formed in them, mainly by metaplasia of the synovial fibroblasts.

Blood vessels probably do not lie free on the surface of the synovial membrane. There are two plexuses of lymphatics, as a rule, within the synovial membranes, a superficial and a deep plexus. The nerves which accompany the blood vessels end in the layer beneath the surface in terminal arborizations or end-bulbs or plates. Pacinian corpuscles are always present.

When injured, the synovial membrane reacts like any other connective tissue by the formation of granulation tissue, and after some weeks may be completely regenerated. The synovial fluid is normally small in amount and seems to be a dialysate of blood to which have been added small amounts of mucin and a very few cells, chiefly lymphocytes, monocytes and macrophages.

REFERENCES

Current surveys of bone from different points of view range from the relatively brief *Bone. An Introduction to the Physiology of Skeletal Tissue* by F. C. McLean and M. R. Urist (University of Chicago Press, Chicago, 1955) to the larger and more specialized *Bone and Bones. Fundamentals of Bone Biology* by J. P. Weinmann and H. Sicher (C. V. Mosby Co., St. Louis, 1947) and to the presentation by many authors in *The Biochemistry and Physiology of Bone* edited by G. H. Bourne (Academic Press, New York, 1956), and in the symposium on *Recent Advances in the Study of the Structure, Composition, and Growth of Mineralized Tissues* edited by R. O. Greep (Annals New York Acad. Sciences, *60:*541, 1955).

Amprino, R., and Engström, A.: Studies on x-ray absorption and diffraction of bone tissue. Acta Anat., *15:*1, 1952.
Asling, C. W., Nelson, M. M., Wright, H. V., and Evans, H. M.: Congenital skeletal abnormalities in fetal rats resulting from maternal pteroylglutamic acid deficiency during gestation. Anat. Rec., *121:*775, 1955.
Barnicot, N. A.: The local action of the parathyroid and other tissues on bone in intracerebral grafts. J. Anat., *82:*233, 1948.
Bast, T. H., Sullivan, W. E., and Geist, F. D.: The repair of bone. Am. J. Anat., *31:*255, 1925.
Bloom, W., Bloom, M. A., and McLean, F. C.: Calcification and ossification. Medullary bone changes in the reproductive cycle of female pigeons. Anat. Rec., *81:*443, 1941.
Duckworth, J., and Hill, R.: The storage of elements in the skeleton. Nutrition Abstr. and Rev., *23:*1, 1953.
Gebhardt, F.: Ueber funktionell wichtigen Anordnungsweise der gröberen und feineren Bauelemente des Wirbeltierknochens. Arch. f. Entwick., *11, 12, 20:* 1901, 1906.
Ham, A. W.: Cartilage and Bone. Special Cytology (Cowdry) 2d ed., New York, 1932, p. 981.
Heinen, J. H., Dabbs, G. H., and Mason, H. A.: The experimental production of ectopic cartilage and bone in the muscles of rabbits. J. Bone and Joint Surg., *31:* 765, 1949.
Heller, M.: Bone. Chapter 5 in Histopathology of Irradiation from External and Internal Sources. W. Bloom, editor. National Nuclear Energy Series. Vol. 21 I. McGraw-Hill Book Co., New York, 1948.
Heller, M., McLean, F. C., and Bloom, W.: Cellular transformations in mammalian bones induced by parathyroid extract. Am. J. Anat., *87:*315, 1950.
Heller-Steinberg, M.: Ground substance, bone salts, and cellular activity in bone formation and destruction. Am. J. Anat., *89:*347, 1951.
Hendricks, S. B., and Hill, W. L.: The nature of bone and phosphate rock. Proc. Nat. Acad. Sci., Geophysics, *36:*731, 1950.
Kirby Smith, H. T.: Bone growth studies. A miniature bone fracture observed microscopically in a trans-

parent chamber introduced in the rabbit's ear. Am. J. Anat., *53:*337, 1933.

Lacroix, P.: The Organization of Bones. J. and A. Churchill Ltd., London, and The Blakiston Division of McGraw-Hill, New York, 1951.

Levander, G., and Willstaedt, H.: Alcohol-soluble osteogenic substance from bone marrow. Nature, *157:*587, 1946.

Maximow, A.: Untersuchungen über Blut und Bindegewebe. III. Die embryonale Histogenese des Knochenmarks der Säugetiere. Arch. f. mikr.-Anat., *76:*1, 1910.

McLean, F. C., and Bloom, W.: Calcification and ossification. Calcification in normal growing bone. Anat. Rec., *78:*333, 1940.

Newman, W. F., and Newman, M. W.: The nature of the mineral phase of bone. Chem. Revs., *53:*1–45, 1953.

Owen, M., Jowsey, J., and Vaughan, J.: Investigation of the growth and structure of the tibia of the rabbit by microradiographic and autoradiographic techniques. J. Bone & Joint Surg. (Brit. No.), *37B:*324, 1955.

Petersen, H.: Die Organe des Skeletsystems, in v. Möllendorff's Handbuch der mikroskopischen Anatomie des Menschen. Berlin, 1930, Vol. 2, Pt. 2, p. 521.

Ray, R. D., Thomson, D. M., Wolff, N. K., and La Violette, D.: Bone metabolism, II. Toxicity and metabolism of radioactive strontium (Sr^{90}) in rats. J. Bone and Joint Surg., *38:*160, 1956.

Robinson, R. A.: An electron-microscopic study of the crystalline inorganic component of bone and its relationship to the organic matrix. J. Bone and Joint Surg., *34A:*389, 1952.

Ruth, E. B.: Bone studies. II. An experimental study of the haversian-type vascular channels. Am. J. Anat., *93:*429, 1953.

Scott, B. L.: Electron microscopy of the epiphyseal apparatus. Anat. Rec., *124:*470, 1956.

Silberberg, R., and Silberberg, M.: Skeletal effects of radio-iodine induced thyroid deficiency in mice as influenced by sex, age and strain. Am. J. Anat., *95:*263, 1954.

Vincent, J.: Recherches sur la constitution de l'os adulte. (Dissertation). Éditions Arscia, Brussels, 1955.

Watson, M. L., and Robinson, R. A.: Collagen-crystal relationships in bone. II. Electron microscope study of basic calcium phosphate crystals. Amer. J. Anat., *93:*25, 1953.

Weidenreich, F.: Das Knochengewebe, in Möllendorff's Handbuch der mikroskopischen Anatomie des Menschen. Berlin, 1930, Vol. 2, Pt. 2, p. 391.

Wolbach, S. B.: Vitamin A deficiency and excess in relation to skeletal growth. Proc. Inst. Med. Chicago, *16:*118, 1946.

CHAPTER 8

Muscular Tissue

THE MUSCULAR tissue performs mechanical work by contracting, that is, by a shortening and thickening of its constituents. The contracting muscle cells regulate the position and movements of the various parts of the body with respect to one another. In the hollow viscera, ducts and blood vascular system the muscles propel the body liquids and excretions from place to place. Muscle cells are always elongated in the direction of the contraction, and are usually grouped into bundles which sometimes reach a considerable length.

The vertebrates have two distinct types of muscle: *smooth muscle* and *striated muscle,* connected by many intermediate forms. As a rule, smooth muscles contract independently of voluntary control, while the striated muscles are subject to voluntary control. *Cardiac muscle,* although striated, is involuntary and contracts automatically and rhythmically.

SMOOTH MUSCULAR TISSUE

Smooth muscle shows a close relationship to the ordinary connective tissue and is found primarily in the internal organs. In man it forms the contractile portions of the wall of the digestive tract from the middle of the esophagus to the internal sphincter of the anus, of the ducts of the glands connected with the intestine, of the respiratory passages from the trachea to the alveolar ducts, and of the urinary and genital ducts. The walls of the arteries and veins and some of the larger lymphatics also consist to a consider-

able extent of smooth muscle. It is scattered in varying amounts in the connective tissue of the skin, in the capsule and trabeculae of the spleen, and in the connective tissue of

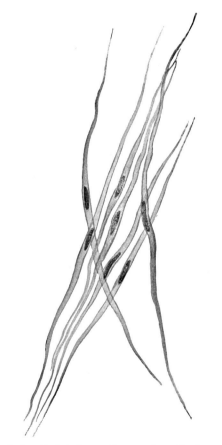

Fig. 8–1. Isolated smooth muscle cells from the wall of the stomach of a cat. 220 ×. (A.A.M.)

certain sensory organs, such as the eye. Peculiar smooth muscle cells are often closely connected with the epithelial tissue of the dermal and salivary glands.

Smooth Muscle Cells or Fibers. When a bit of fresh smooth muscle is examined under the microscope, the muscle cells (i.e., fibers) appear as long, spindle-shaped bodies which are thickened in the middle and become narrow toward their pointed ends. Occasionally, the cells are branched or star-shaped.

The smooth muscle cells may reach a length of 0.5 mm. in the pregnant human uterus, while their average length in the intestine of man is 0.2 mm., with a thickness of 6 microns. The smallest smooth muscle cells occur in the small blood vessels, where they are 15 to 20 microns in length.

The nucleus, as seen in cross sections, is slightly eccentric and occupies the middle, widest portion of the cell body. It is elongated in the long axis of the cell, and has an oval or cylindrical form with pointed or rounded ends. It contains several nucleoli and a pale chromatin net which lies along the internal surface of the nuclear membrane. During the contraction of the cell the nucleus becomes folded on its lateral surface or markedly twisted. In general, the size of

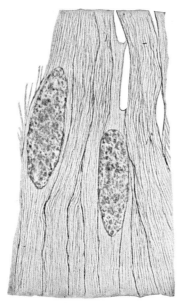

Fig. 8–2. Smooth muscle cells of the intestine of *Triton vulgaris;* the myofibrils are distinct. Biondi stain. 1430 ×. (After Levi.)

the nucleus increases with the size of the cell. Close to the nucleus, in a small indentation of its membrane, is a diplosome without an attraction sphere.

Smooth muscle cells do not have a distinct membrane which corresponds to the sarcolemma of the striated muscles (p. 163). The cytoplasm of smooth muscle cells in the living condition and sometimes after fixation and staining appears homogeneous. But some threads, the *myofibrils,* can always be made visible by maceration in nitric or trichloracetic acid. After this treatment the individual fibrils become visible as parallel threads running the length of the cell. The myofibrils, or better, *myofilaments,* are exceedingly fine in electron micrographs (Fig. 8–3).

The fibrils are homogeneous and lack the alternating sections characteristic of striated muscles. The fibrils are doubly refractile. The *border* or *external fibrils* are coarse and thick and stain deeply. In a cross section through a smooth muscle cell, they appear as sharply stained dots near the edge of the cytoplasm. The internal fibrils are thinner, measuring 0.3 micron. The number of fibrils in the smooth muscle cell varies, and in some cases the border fibrils may be few or absent.

It is generally believed that the fibrils represent the contractile elements of the smooth muscle cell. The actomyosin of smooth muscle is similar to that of striated muscle. The substance between the fibrils is called *sarcoplasm;* it usually accumulates in small amounts at both ends of the nucleus. Most of the cell body is occupied by fibrils so closely associated that sarcoplasm cannot be noticed between them. Mitochondria, a Golgi net and sometimes glycogen granules have been described in the sarcoplasm.

Contact of Smooth Muscle Cells with One Another. In many places in the body, but particularly in the skin, smooth muscle fibers are scattered singly or in small groups in the ordinary connective tissue. Here they are closely welded to the collagenous bundles and are often surrounded by thin elastic fibers. During contraction they throw the tissue into fine folds and wrinkles; this can be well seen in the skin of the mammary papillae or the scrotum. Sometimes several parallel fibers unite to form a small cylindrical bundle

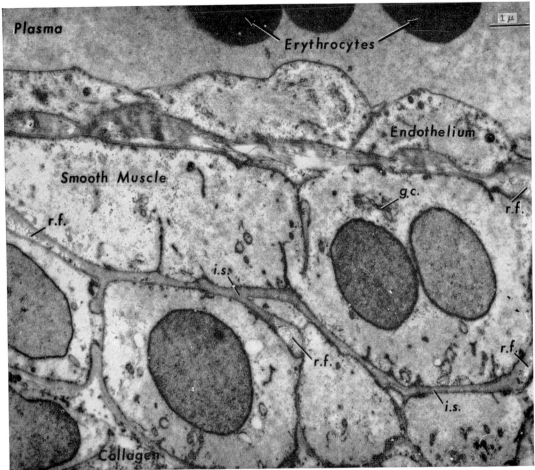

Fig. 8–3. Electron micrograph of cross section of smooth muscle cells in the wall of human arteriole. The myofilaments of smooth muscle cells are exceedingly fine and are barely perceptible here. *g.c.*, Golgi complex; *i.s.*, interstitial substance; the reticular fibrils, *r.f.*, are half the diameter of the fibrils in the collagenous bundle. Buffered osmic acid fixation. (Courtesy of D. Fawcett.)

whose ends are covered by elastic fibers. An example is the smooth muscles connected with the hairs.

In other cases the smooth muscle fibers are arranged parallel to one another in one plane where they form a layer of varying thickness, as in small arteries. Here, because of the small lumen, each fiber bends sharply to surround the vessel. In the walls of certain large hollow organs, such as the intestine, bladder and uterus, the smooth muscle cells are arranged in layers or bundles. The direction of the fibers is the same in each layer, while it varies in different layers or bundles. Thus, in the intestine the internal layer of the muscularis externa consists of circularly arranged fibers forming a close spiral, while the external layer

is composed of longitudinally arranged fibers forming a long spiral (Chapter 24).

The cells are so arranged that the thick middle portion of one cell is opposite the thin ends of adjacent cells. Consequently, in cross sections through a smooth muscle bundle, some of the cells have nuclei in the plane of the section, and some do not.

The connective tissue fibers outside the muscle cells continue into the spaces between them and bind them into the bundles. Between the thicker bundles and layers of smooth muscles, loose connective tissue is present in small amounts. It contains fibroblasts and wandering cells, collagenous and elastic fibers, and a thick network of blood vessels and nerves. But connective tissue cells

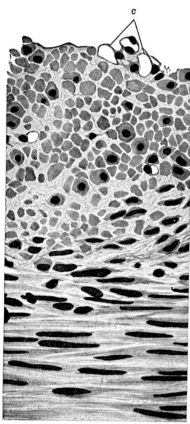

Fig. 8–4. Longitudinal section of part of the muscularis externa of intestine of a dog; external longitudinal layer (below), cross section of internal layer (above); *c*, blood capillaries. 530 ×. (A.A.M.)

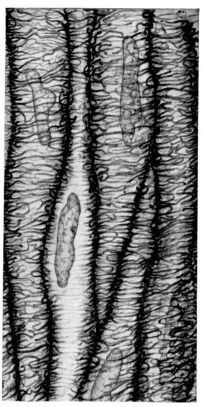

Fig. 8–6. Longitudinal section through smooth muscle of human intestine, stained with Bielschowsky silver method for reticular fibers and hematoxylin. 1875 ×. (Drawn by Miss E. Bohlman.)

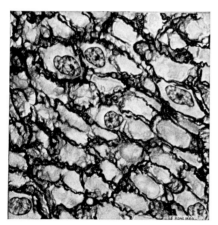

Fig. 8–5. Cross section through smooth muscle from human intestine, stained with the Bielschowsky silver method for reticular fibers and hematoxylin. The fibers form continuous networks about each of the muscle cells. Few of the cells have their nuclei in the plane of the section. 1875 ×. (Drawn by Miss E. Bohlman.)

do not occur in the narrow slitlike spaces between the individual smooth muscle cells; here there are only a few thin, collagenous bundles and dense networks of reticular and elastic fibers.

The reticular fibers branch irregularly and pass longitudinally and transversely between the bodies of the smooth muscle cells. They can be stained with Mallory's aniline blue method and still more sharply with the silver impregnation methods. They form a regular system of supporting and binding material which forms a *sheath* about each muscle cell (Fig. 8–5). A characteristic of smooth muscle all over the body is the intimate association it bears with elastic fibers. This is so extensive that some authors consider them as forming a "myo-elastic" tissue. These elastic fibers are continuous with those of the surrounding loose connective tissue.

In smooth muscles, the pull of each contracting cell is first transmitted to the sur-

Fig. 8–7. Smooth muscle cell from the stomach of a sparrow, showing six short contraction bands. (Redrawn after Soli, from Maximow.)

rounding sheath of reticular fibers which continue directly into those of the surrounding connective tissue. This arrangement permits the force of the contraction of the entire layer of the smooth muscle to be uniformly transmitted to the surrounding parts, as in the narrowing of the lumen of blood vessels or in peristalsis of the intestine.

If a bit of fresh smooth muscle is stimulated by an electric current, each spindle-shaped cell shortens and becomes thicker. In the spontaneous contraction of smooth muscle, sarcoplasm flows to a central point which thickens while the nucleus and the mitochondria move passively. No fibrils can be seen in such living cells. When living smooth muscle is fixed, some cells are often fixed in contraction, while adjacent cells are in relaxation. In such preparations, nodes of contraction may be seen over a small portion of the cell, and sometimes involve only a few fibrils (Fig. 8–7). Double refraction of the fibrils appears only in those contracted places, while the internodal portions are isotropic.

STRIATED MUSCULAR TISSUE

Muscle Fibers. The muscles attached to the skeleton of mammals consist of striated muscular tissue. In a teased preparation of fresh striated muscle, the tissue appears to consist of long cylindrical *muscle fibers.* These are large, multinucleated cells. As a result of teasing, only torn and broken sections of the fibers are seen, and the normal ends of the fibers are seldom found. When their undamaged ends are seen, however, the gradual tapering of the fibers toward a point is clearly visible. In other cases the end of the fiber appears rounded or notched; such an appearance is particularly frequent at the union of the muscle with a tendon.

Although the fibers are usually close to one another, they are entirely independent. Occasional anastomoses have been described between them. In nontapering muscles, such as the sartorius, the fibers apparently continue without interruption through the entire mus-

cle, so that their length is equal to that of the muscle. It is generally believed that in most muscles the fibers are usually shorter than the muscle; in this case, one end may be connected with a tendon, while the other end terminates among other fibers, or both ends may be free in the muscle. The thickness of the fibers fluctuates from 10 to 100 microns or more; apparently it depends, not on the length of the fiber, but on the type of animal and the particular muscle. In a given animal the more primitive muscles, such as those of the eye, are thinner. Fibers of varying caliber may be found in the same muscle. The thickness of the fibers increases with the age of the organism as well as under the influence of strenuous muscular activity.

Even in teased preparations of fresh muscle, the complex structure of the striated fibers is seen readily. The freshly teased fiber is usually slightly yellow and striated in both the longitudinal and transverse directions. These striations depend on the fact that the fibers consist of two parts: (1) a protoplasmic mass, the *sarcoplasm,* and (2) thin cross-striated fibrils, *myofibrils,* which are present in large numbers parallel to one another in the sarcoplasm. They give the fiber its unique appearance which is due to the fact that each myofibril consists of *disks* or sections which alternate regularly along its length. The corresponding disks of adjacent fibrils are usually arranged at the same level in the fiber (Fig. *1–2*).

The chief solid mass of the muscle fibers consists of several proteins, of which the most important are *myogen* and *myosin* combined with *actin.* Striated muscle contains more myogen and less myosin and one tenth as much nucleoprotein as smooth muscle. The fibers also contain carbohydrates, fats, lipids, and a pigment *myoglobin,* which is closely related to hemoglobin, and various metabolic intermediaries such as lactic acid, creatin-phosphate, and hexosephosphate.

Sarcolemma. The striated fibers are covered with the *sarcolemma,* a thin (perhaps

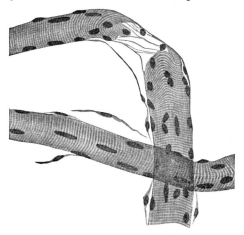

Fig. 8–8.　Two striated muscle fibers of man, in a teased preparation, with stained nuclei. The upper fiber is crushed in its middle, and here the sarcolemma is seen. Between the fibers are several spindle-shaped connective tissue cells. 250 ×. (A.A.M.)

0.1 μ) membrane which completely invests the fiber and follows its changes in form during contraction. In teased fresh preparations it can be seen as a transparent film where the fiber has been torn or crushed. It is probably a product of the cytoplasm of the muscle cell and is closely connected with the surrounding reticular fibers; its chemical reactions differ from those of collagen and elastin.

Nucleus. The nuclei of striated muscle fibers are rounded, oval, or elongated in the direction of the long axis of the fiber. Their size varies considerably. Their number fluctuates within wide limits, since it depends on the length of the fiber. The nuclei are always numerous, and in fibers several centimeters long they number several hundred.

The position of the nucleus varies according to the species of animal and the type of muscle. In the muscles of the lower vertebrates, and in many of the red muscles of mammals, the nuclei are scattered through the entire fiber. In the great majority of striated muscles of mammals, the nuclei are in the layer of sarcoplasm immediately beneath the sarcolemma.

Sarcoplasm. The cytoplasm of the muscle fiber which fills the spaces between the myofibrils is called sarcoplasm. It accumulates around the nuclei, especially at their ends, and is also present beneath the sarcolemma and in small islands about the endings of the motor nerves. The sarcoplasm must take part in the nutrition of myofibrils, since it completely surrounds them. It probably plays an important role in conducting excitation through the muscle fiber.

Variations in the Amount of Sarcoplasm. It is customary to distinguish striated muscle fibers rich in sarcoplasm from those poor in sarcoplasm. In certain vertebrates, as the rabbit, one can recognize two types of muscles with the naked eye; one appears red and the other white. Under the microscope the fibers of the first type are seen to be rich, and those of the second type poor, in sarcoplasm. In the pale fibers the fibrils are small and regularly arranged. In the fibers of red muscles the longitudinal striation is more prominent and the transverse striation is somewhat irregular. The red fibers contain many fat granules and have a "muddy" appearance. The nuclei of the red fibers occupy a more central position in the fiber and are rarely found at the periphery. As a rule, the red granular fibers in the lower vertebrates are confined to the most important muscles, while in the higher animals only the least active muscles are white. The red pigment is usually found in those muscles which contract repeatedly and over long periods of time. The "twitch" is longer in red muscles, which are more easily "tetanized." Those mus-

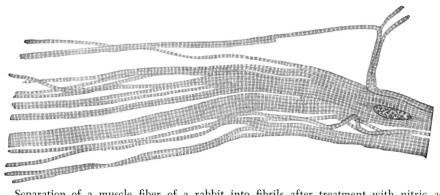

Fig. 8–9.　Separation of a muscle fiber of a rabbit into fibrils after treatment with nitric acid. One nucleus is seen within a spindle-shaped accumulation of sarcoplasm. 530 ×. (A.A.M.)

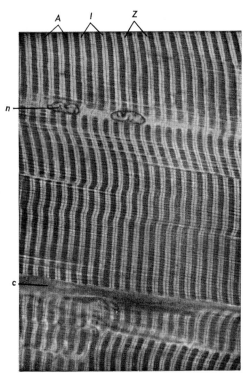

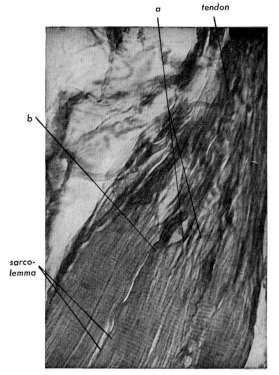

Fig. 8–10. Section of an infrahyoid muscle of man, showing characteristic cross striations with A, I and Z disks. *n*, nucleus; *c*, endomysium. Photomicrograph. Mallory-azan stain. 1125 ×. (After von Herrath and Abramow.)

Fig. 8–11. Section from human tongue, showing connection of striated muscle and its tendon. The fibrils of the tendon apparently are connected with myofibrils at (*a*) and with sarcolemma at (*b*) (but see text, p. 170). Photomicrograph. Mallory-azan stain. 500 ×. (After von Herrath and Abramow.)

cles which contract slowly are red, but not all red muscles contract slowly. The pigments which give these fibers their red color are probably muscle hemoglobin and cytochrome.

In the rabbit each type of fiber is generally gathered into separate muscles which show certain physiological differences. In the majority of animals, including man, both types of fibers enter into the composition of all the muscles; according to the type of muscle, one or the other type of fibers predominates. Sarcoplasm is very prominent in some species, as the frog.

Organelles and Inclusions. The sarcoplasm of striated muscle fibers contains numerous mitochondria (also called sarcosomes) in both I and A disks. (See next section on *myofibrils.*) There is a small Golgi net, frequently at each pole of the nucleus. With the light microscope a vague network had been described in the I disks close to the Z disks and sometimes extending into the A disks. With the electron microscope it has been found that this network is composed of a system of cytoplasmic membranes (endo-

plasmic reticulum) such as are found in various forms in practically all cell types. A better term in the case of muscle is *sarcoplasmic reticulum.* There are fat inclusions which diminish or disappear in starvation. In fixed preparations, glycogen appears as granules of irregular shape and size between the myofibrils.

Myofibrils. In longitudinal sections through muscle fibers or in preparations where they have separated into individual fibrils, the latter appear as long, parallel threads (Fig. 8–9), which do not branch. Their thickness fluctuates, but they are not larger than 2 to 3 microns in ordinary preparations. They extend in relatively parallel straight lines for indefinite lengths in the fibers. With the electron microscope the *myofibrils* are found to be composed of bundles of *myofilaments,* ranging from 100 to 120 A in diameter and 300 to 400 A apart.

Myofibrils are distributed evenly or in

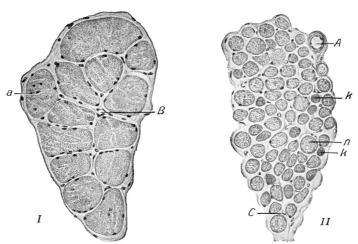

Fig. 8–12.   Cross section of muscle bundles from two muscles of the same man. *I*, Gastrocnemius muscle; *a*, fiber with central nuclei; *B*, blood vessel. *II*, ocular muscle; *n*, normal fiber with Cohnheim's fields; *k*, dense portion of fiber; *A*, artery; *C*, capillary. Both figures 110 ×. (After Schaffer.)

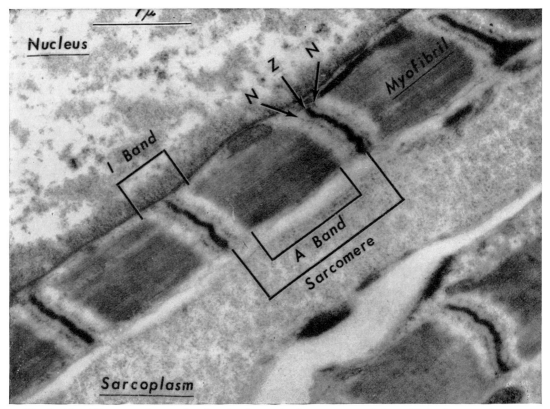

Fig. 8–13.   Electron micrograph of striated muscle from tongue of frog. Note the granular nature of the sarcoplasm. The *A*, *I*, *N* and *Z* disks are especially clear in the myofibril. Buffered osmic acid fixation. (Courtesy of D. Fawcett.)

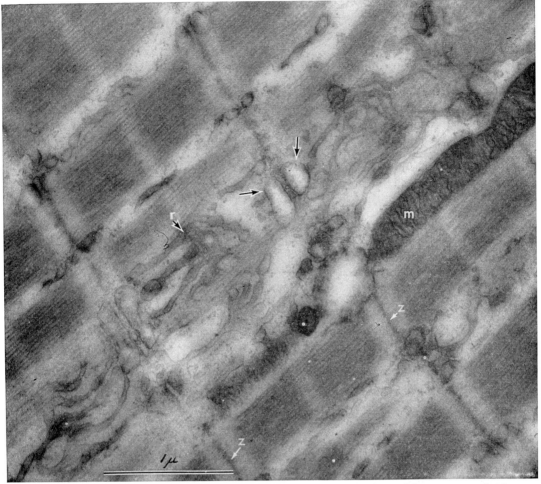

Fig. 8–14. Electron micrograph of section of striated muscle of caudal myotome of 12 mm. Amblystoma larva, showing the complicated sarcoplasmic reticulum, *r*, running predominantly in the long axis of the muscle fiber. Note the dilatations (arrows) on each side of the Z disks. *m*, mitochondrium. Buffered osmic acid fixation. (Courtesy of K. Porter.)

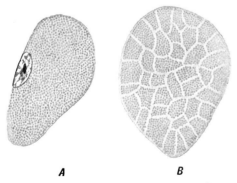

Fig. 8–15. Cross section of two striated muscle fibers of a rabbit. A, uniform distribution of fibrils; B, Cohnheim's fields. 1000 ×. (Redrawn after Szymonowicz.)

compact bundles in the cytoplasm, the spaces between the fibrils being occupied by sarcoplasm. In cross section the separate fibrils appear as fine dots; when packed in bundles, they are separated by sarcoplasm, forming fields of Cohnheim (Fig. 8–15).

The appearance of the striated muscle fiber depends on whether it is at rest, contracted, or passively stretched. The myofibril is composed of two main (and several subordinate) structures which alternate regularly along its length as short cylinders and are called disks. One type is markedly refractile and appears dark and shining; it stains intensely with iron hematoxylin and, since it is doubly refractile, or *anisotropic*, in living cells and after fixation, it is called A *disk.*

Alternating with the A disks are *isotropic* (singly refractile) or I disks. With the usual stains the I disks remain colorless. In resting fibrils the A and I disks are approximately the same height. When the fibers are passively stretched, the I disk appears taller than the A disk; when the fiber contracts, the I disk shortens more than the A disk.

There are other disks in the myofibril. The most obvious of these is the Z *disk* which occupies the middle of the I disk and is doubly refractile. It seems to be attached, perhaps loosely, to the sarcolemma. During contraction the center of the A disk appears paler than the rest and is called Hensen's disk (H) within which is a thin middle stripe indicated by the letter M. The N disk may be seen at times within the I disk between the Z and A disks. The amount of substance included between two Z disks is called a *sarcomere,* the structural and functional muscular unit. All of these disks are visible in electron micrographs which also show that the Z disks are not collagenous (as some had believed) and that the myofilaments extend for great distances in the fibers. They apparently pass through the Z bands as they go through successive sarcomeres.

The ability of striated muscle fibers to contract and relax rapidly may not depend on the transverse striation of the fibrils, since cardiac muscle cells in culture which had lost their cross striations were seen to continue to contract rapidly. But these observations were made with the optical microscope and it is possible that the cells still contained submicroscopic aggregates of cross striated myofilaments.

In contracting, the striated muscle fiber, as well as the entire muscle, may shorten to as little as one tenth of its original length. Its thickness increases greatly, and its volume decreases only by 0.05 per cent. In warm-blooded animals the contraction wave is so long and rapid that the entire striated muscle shortens at once. Numerous nerve endings scattered along their length permit all the fibers of a muscle to contract simultaneously.

When a living muscle is teased under the microscope, its fibers are seen to contract for a long time. On fixation, the entire fiber may contract, or agonal, local contraction waves

may become fixed. One can thus follow all the steps in the change from resting, thin, cylindrical fibers into the condition of maximal contraction when they are thick and spheroidal. In such fixed preparations the fibrils thicken and the disks become wider and thinner; indeed, the I disk may become so thin that it disappears completely. When the shortening of the fibrils of the fiber reaches 50 per cent or more, a *reversal of striation* takes place. This is the appearance of thick, dark, transverse stripes in place of the Z disk. This is because the darkly stainable substance of the A disk spreads in both directions from the middle disk M, penetrates the I disk, and closely approaches the Z disk. However, during this change the double refraction of the A disk retains its location, although the disk itself no longer stains darkly. In the return to the resting stage, these changes are repeated in the reverse order. The M and especially the Z disks apparently do not change in contraction of the myofibril. It has been suggested that they help support the fiber by interfering with the shifting of fibrils in relation to one another.

The fine structure of striated muscle and its changes during contraction are being actively investigated by x-ray diffraction and by phase contrast, polarization and electron microscopy. Coupled with the rapid advances which are being made with these methods come equally rapid changes in interpretation of the findings and their correlation with the results of biochemical study of resting and contracting muscle. Indeed, the morphological and biochemical approaches to some facets of the problem have become mutually indispensable and often inseparable. On the basis of recent experience it can be predicted with confidence that the present theories will soon be modified or even discarded in the light of new experiments and consequent new interpretations. Nevertheless it seems desirable to summarize a few of the important points of view to give a glimpse of some of the trends in this field.

Huxley and Hanson have proposed a model of the structure of striated muscle (Fig. 8–16) which rests on their belief that there are two types of longitudinal filaments in the sarcomere: (1) Thin actin filaments, about 40 A in diameter, which extend from the Z membranes through the I bands into the A bands and terminate at the A band-H disk junction, where they are connected by a hypothetical material, S. (2) Thick myosin filaments (about 110 A in diameter) which are hexagonally arranged and are confined to the A band, including its H disk. Thus the two sets of filaments interdigitate in the A band proper—there being only a thin set in the I band. They postulate that shortening and stretch involve a slippage of the thin actin filaments relative to the thick myosin filaments, with consequent decrease or increase respectively in the length of the I band as the thin filaments are either drawn into or pulled out of the A band.

According to Hodge (Fig. 8–17) there is only a single set of myofilaments in insect muscle (and presumably also of vertebrate muscle). They have a lightly staining core which runs continuously through all bands along successive sarcomeres. In the A bands, the cores of the myofilaments are covered by a densely staining cortex which is absent or much thinner in the I band. Except in the H (and M) bands, the myofilaments are joined laterally at regular intervals by thin filamentous bridges. Interstitial material appears to be present to some extent in all bands. The Z disks consist of extremely dense interstitial material and there is definite continuity of myofilamentous material through them. Hodge believes it is premature to attempt a description of the flight muscle of insects in terms of actin and myosin, but "The results are certainly consistent with a model in which F actin filaments form the core of the continuous myofilaments and are joined laterally by regularly spaced filamentous bridges. . . . . . These may represent the tropomyosin of the myofibril . . . (The micrographs) appear to be compatible with either a localization of myosin in the A band or a uniform distribution of it throughout the sarcomere. In the latter case, the increased thickness of the myofilament in the A band could be ascribed to the presence of the unknown protein of Szent-Györgyi et al."

Another view is presented by Spiro (Fig. 8–18) who studied chick and rabbit muscle at varying amounts of shortening. At rest length the sarcomere is characterized by thick filaments (about 140 A) in the H disc; the A band proper and the I bands contain

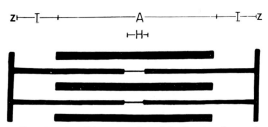

Fig. 8–16. Diagram of model of striated muscle after Hanson and Huxley (1955). The filaments running from Z to Z are thought to be actin, joined at the region of the H band by an elastic segment. The thicker bands confined to the A disk are supposedly myosin. See text.

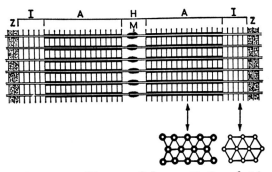

Fig. 8–17. Diagram of the constitution of striated flight muscle of an insect in longitudinal section, as conceived by Hodge (1955). F-actin filaments run through the sarcomeres and are covered with a thin coating in I and a much thicker one in the A band proper. Cross sections of A and I are indicated by arrows. See text.

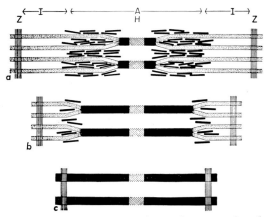

Fig. 8–18. Diagram of muscle at rest length (a), 65% of rest length (b) and 60% of rest length (c), according to Spiro (1956). The molecules of myosin are indicated as rodlets. The cross hatched area H is presumably of different composition from the rest of the A band. Note the disappearance of I at 60% contraction. See text.

Fig. 8–19.   Electron micrograph of section through rabbit psoas muscle fixed at rest length. Myofilaments at *H* are decidedly thicker than in the rest of the *A* and in the *I* bands, as indicated by the arrowheads. Buffered osmic acid fixation. (Courtesy of D. Spiro.)

thinner filaments (60–70 A), possibly composed of actin, which are three times as numerous as the thick H disk filaments. Several thin filaments associate at the A-H junction to form the individual, thick H filaments. Myosin may be present as macromolecules between the thin filaments in the A band, and thus account for the interfilamentous density of this region. On shortening there is a progressive transformation of numbers of thin filaments into single thick ones. To explain this, he suggests that shortening involves the association of several thin (actin?) filaments with myosin macromolecules by a supercoiling mechanism to form individual thick filaments. This results in the pulling in of the I band, with consequent decrease in the length of the sarcomere.

The student interested in these questions might consult the book by Albert Szent-Györgyi and the older review by Barer and find references to pertinent current work in the annual review journals and books on biochemistry, physiology and biophysics.

Union of Striated Muscle Fibers with One Another to Form Muscles. Muscles are formed of parallel muscle fibers held together by connective tissue. The arrangement of muscle fibers within the muscle is clearly seen in cross sections and is similar to the structure of tendons. Like the collagenous bundles in

tendons, so the muscle fibers here combine to form the *primary bundles;* several primary bundles combine to form *secondary bundles; tertiary bundles* are formed by the secondary ones, and so on. Large bundles and layers of interstitial connective tissue at the periphery of the muscles, the *epimysium,* project into the spaces between the bundles of muscular fibers as the *perimysium.* They consist of irregularly arranged collagenous, reticular and elastic fibers, and many varieties of connective tissue cells, including fat cells. These thick layers branch and send thin layers between the smaller bundles (Fig. 8–20).

Between the separate muscle fibers inside the primary muscle bundles, the *endomysium* consists, as in smooth muscles, of thin fibrous networks which form capsules for the fibers. The endomysium also contains fibroblasts and fixed macrophages. The latter play an important role as phagocytes in inflammation of the muscle.

The number of elastic fibers in the interstitial connective tissue varies with the type of muscle and is probably closely connected with its functional peculiarities. They are extremely abundant in the eye muscles and in muscles which attach to soft parts (muscles of the tongue and face).

Where a muscle is attached to a tendon there is a close union of the muscle fibers

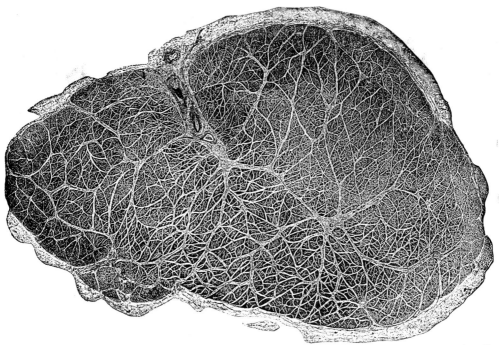

Fig. 8–20. Cross section through the sartorius muscle of man, showing the subdivision into bundles of various sizes by connective tissue. 4 ×. (Photograph by Müller, from Heidenhain.)

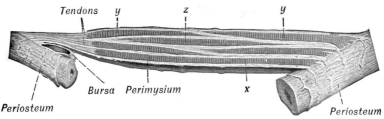

Fig. 8–21. Diagram showing connections between a muscle and the bones to which it is attached. Muscle fiber, *x*, begins and ends in tendons attached to the bones; *y*, terminates at one end in the muscle; *z*, terminates at both ends in the muscle. (After Braus.)

with the collagenous bundles of the tendon. The collagenous bundles of the perimysium pass directly over into those of the tendon; the sarcolemma covering the rounded, cone-shaped ends of the muscle fiber is fused with the ends of the collagenous bundles. The cone-shaped ends of the muscle fiber fit into grooves in the tendon. The connection of the sarcolemma with the collagenous bundles is much more rigid than with the substance of the muscle fiber itself; for, if a fresh muscle is put into hot water, the contents of the muscle fiber at the ends separate from the sarcolemma.

Electron micrographs show that the end of the myofibril is connected with the sar-

colemma by a very short nonstriated fibril. The myofibrils thus do not continue directly into the collagenous fibrils of the tendon as some had claimed on the basis of light microscope studies (Fig. 8–22).

Blood Vessels and Nerves. The blood vessels of skeletal muscle tissue (particularly red muscles) are abundant; capillaries which directly enlace separate fibers form a dense network with meshes stretched along the length of the fiber (Fig. 8–23). The short sides of these meshes sometimes appear as swollen spindles.

Lymphatics have been found in certain muscles within the layers of the perimysium and around the blood vessels.

The main nerve supply of the skeletal muscles is from the myelinated cerebrospinal afferent and efferent nerves.

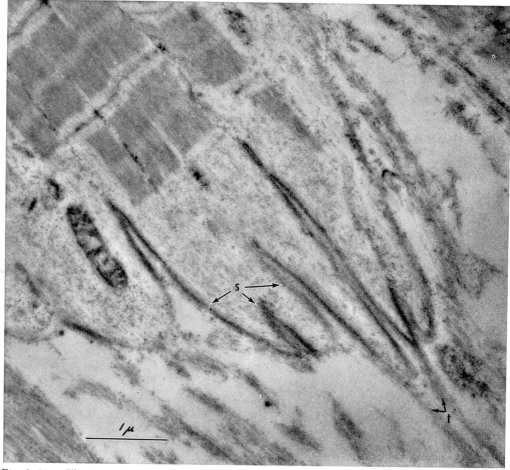

Fig. 8–22. Electron micrograph of the terminal of a myoblast of Amblystoma showing ending of the cross-striated fibrils some distance from the sarcolemma (*s*) and the connection of the latter with the fibrils of the tendon (*t*). Fixation in buffered osmic acid. (Courtesy K. Porter.)

CARDIAC MUSCULAR TISSUE

The heart of all vertebrates is composed of a network of peculiar striated muscle fibers. It contracts rhythmically and automatically. Its structure differs in several respects from that of skeletal striated muscles.

In a section of mammalian cardiac muscle, parallel to the surface of the heart, one can see that the fibers form networks with narrow meshes stretched in one main direction. In cross section the fibers appear as rounded or irregular areas of various sizes. Free endings can be found in cardiac muscle fibers only in teased, macerated preparations taken from the region of the atrioventricular openings and from the papillary muscles.

The cardiac muscle fibers consist of (1) nuclei, (2) myofibrils, (3) sarcoplasm, (4) a sarcolemma, according to some authors, and (5) intercalated disks.

Nuclei. The nuclei in cardiac muscle fibers, in contrast to those of striated muscle, are always arranged in the interior, usually in the axial part, of the fiber. They are scattered in the network of the fibers at various distances from one another. Their shape is oval, and their internal structure shows nothing peculiarly different from that of the nuclei of skeletal muscle fibers.

Myofibrils. The myofibrils are similar to those of ordinary striated fibers, and are composed of the same types of disks, A, I, Z, and the like.

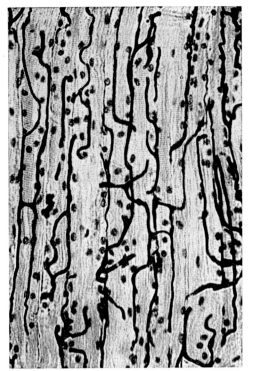

Fig. 8–23. Photomicrograph of striated muscle of monkey injected with India ink to show pattern of small blood vessels. Note arrangement of capillaries parallel to muscle fibers and transverse branches. 250 ×.

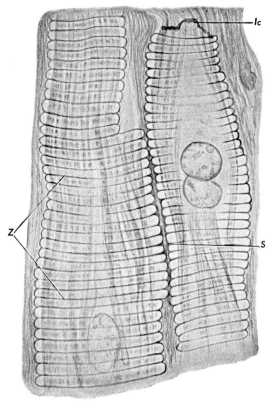

Fig. 8–24. Section of human cardiac muscle fibers, showing connection between the Z disks (Z) and the sarcolemma (S); Ic, intercalated disk. Mallory-azan stain. 1400 ×. (Drawn by Miss Agnes Nixon.)

The fibrils in cardiac muscle pass uninterruptedly along the length of the fiber, so that their free ends are not seen. The cross-striated fibers here, too, are gathered into bundles or columns. The individual fibrils have been seen in living tissue cultures.

Sarcoplasm. As sarcoplasm in the cardiac muscle fibers is usually rather abundant, the longitudinal striation is well pronounced. In the nuclear areas it forms elongated accumulations devoid of fibrils; the swollen middle portion of these accumulations contains the nucleus and tapers gradually to the ends. Mitochondria are much more numerous than in striated muscle and are frequently arranged in columns between the fibrils. In the spindle-shaped accumulations which surround the nuclei there are also fat droplets, a poorly developed Golgi net and pigment granules which increase with age.

Sarcolemma. The free surface of the cardiac muscle fibers is provided with a thin sheath which is well seen in sections as a sharp line. It is not so easily isolated as that of striated skeletal muscle. It may be selectively stained with certain dyes, and the Z disks seem attached to it. Well-pronounced, interstitial connective tissue areas are found only in the cardiac muscle of adult mammals.

Intercalated Disks. For a long time the attention of investigators has been attracted by short lines called *intercalated disks*, oriented transversely to the long axis of the fibers. The height of the stripes is somewhat less than that of a sarcomere; but, like a sarcomere, the intercalated disks are practically always bounded on both sides by Z disks. Where the fibers branch, intercalated disks are sometimes found which are cone-shaped in sections.

The substance of the intercalated disks stains sharply with various dyes. It appears to consist of vertical rods whose ends are directly fused with the myofibrils approaching the disks from both sides. The myofibrils are

Fig. 8–25. Section of human cardiac muscle, showing intercalated disks. Sublimate fixation; stained in thiazin red and toluidin blue. About 450 ×. (Slightly modified after M. Heidenhain.)

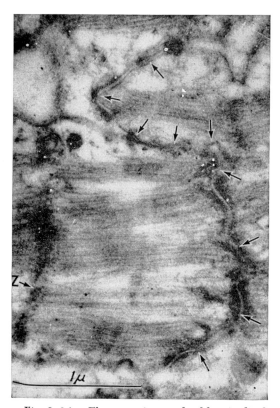

Fig. 8–26. Electron micrograph of longitudinal section through myofibril of guinea pig cardiac muscle. The arrows point to an intercalated disk, with a pale center, extending across the myofibril. Buffered osmic acid fixation. (Courtesy of F. Sjöstrand.)

believed to pass uninterruptedly through the intercalated disks.

The significance of the intercalated disks is unknown. According to one opinion, these areas act as fine, elastic interstitial tendons. They have also been considered to be thickenings which divide the network of cardiac muscle fibers into cell territories. This view is supported by the electron-microscopic studies of Sjöstrand (Fig. 8–26).

The intercalated disks appear comparatively late in the development of the cardiac muscle, and their number gradually increases with age, independently of cell multiplication.

It has been shown in tissue culture that two heart muscle cells, which are not completely separated by a cell membrane and which seem to have a partially continuous cytoplasm and common fibrils, may beat with independent rhythms (Fig. 8–27). Although these cells may have had a certain degree of morphological continuity, they were obviously discontinuous functionally—otherwise it is difficult to see how they could beat with different rhythms. It would be interesting to study such cells with an electron microscope.

Purkinje Fibers. Fibers of the Impulse-Conducting System. Under the endocardium which lines the internal surface of the heart, particularly of the interventricular septum, there is a net of atypical muscle fibers, called "Purkinje fibers" after the man who discovered them.

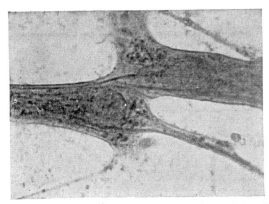

Fig. 8–27. Two cells from a seven-day culture of the heart of a four-day chick embryo. The two cells were beating with different rhythms. Two smooth fibrils continue from one cell into the other. There is no distinct cell membrane separating the two cells. The dark granules are mitochondria. Stained with Janus green and fixed with iodine. 1450 ×. (Courtesy of W. H. Lewis.)

Fig. 8–28. Cells of Purkinje in a papillary muscle of a sheep; concentric arrangement of the myofibrils in the peripheral part of the cells. 475 ×. (After Levi.)

It is now established that, just as in the ordinary cardiac muscle, the Purkinje fibers form a continuous, sarcoplasmic network. It appears to be divided into separate sections because of the extremely irregular arrangement of the continuous bundles of striated fibrils; these pass mainly in the peripheral portions of the fibers. These are also provided with intercalated disks. Large amounts of sarcoplasm are accumulated about the nuclei. The sarcoplasm of the fibers of Purkinje often has a large amount of glycogen, particularly in children. In many places a gradual passage of these Purkinje fibers into ordinary cardiac fibers can be noticed.

The coordinated contractions of separate parts of the cardiac muscle depend on the presence of a mechanism for conducting the stimuli for contraction. The fibers of Purkinje form part of this mechanism. Nerves may also participate in the conduction of the contractile impulse (see p. 178).

The sino-atrial and atrio-ventricular nodes have the same structure as the Purkinje fibers.

Connective Tissue and Blood Vessels of Cardiac Muscle. Loose connective tissue is found in the slitlike spaces of the cardiac muscle. The muscle fibers are everywhere surrounded by dense, basket-like networks of blood capillaries. These arise from the coronary arteries and are collected in the cardiac veins.

Histogenesis of Smooth Muscle. Smooth muscle cells arise from the mesenchyme. In those places where a layer of smooth muscle will later develop, the mesenchymal cells begin to stretch out, the nuclei become elongated, and fibrils appear in the cytoplasm. They, at least in the beginning, apparently run continuously through a whole series of cells. In blood vessels, which at first consist only of endothelium, mesenchyme cells become arranged at regular intervals along the outside of the tube. They stretch out transversely, multiply by mitosis, and then produce myofibrils within their cytoplasm. Then the edges of these *myoblasts* come in contact with one another, and a continuous layer of smooth muscle is produced.

The reticular fibers between the muscle cells are probably produced by the same cells which become muscle fibers—the developing smooth muscle cells function as both myoblasts and fibroblasts.

It is claimed that some of the new smooth muscle cells which develop in the uterus during pregnancy arise from the undifferentiated connective tissue cells in this tissue, as well as from lymphocytes which wander into the myometrium. In a virgin rabbit, after injection of the female sex hormone, there is mitotic proliferation of the smooth muscle cells of the uterus. The smooth muscle elements (myoepithelial cells, p. 339) in certain glands arise from the epithelium from which the glandular elements arise.

Histogenesis of Striated Muscle Tissue. The striated muscular tissue arises in vertebrates from the mesoderm and in particular from its somites, except in the head, where it develops directly from mesenchyme. Those cells which give rise to the muscle tissue are called *myoblasts*. Within the myotome they are regular and cylindrical, but soon become spindle-shaped and arrange themselves into parallel bundles. At the same time they multiply rapidly by mitosis. Within the myoblasts, myofibrils appear and gradually develop the characteristic cross striations.

There are several explanations of how the large, multinucleated, skeletal muscle fibers arise from the myoblasts: (1) Each muscular fiber is a syncytium resulting from fusion of many separate cells. (2)

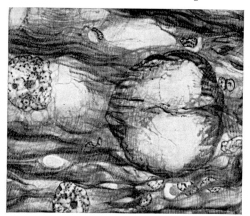

Fig. 8–29. Large, centrally vacuolated Purkinje cells of human heart. The myofibrils are concentrated at the periphery of the cells. 950 ×. (Drawn by Miss E. Bohlman.)

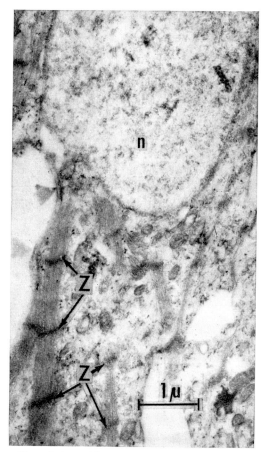

Fig. 8–30. Electron micrograph of section through heart muscle of 72 hour chick embryo. Myofilaments are forming in thin bundles and only the Z disk seems visible at this stage. *n,* nucleus. Buffered osmic acid fixation. (Courtesy of D. Spiro.)

Each myoblast grows markedly in length, and the rapid multiplication of the nuclei by mitosis is not accompanied by division of cytoplasm, so that a multinuclear cell is produced. (3) Both methods of development occur. A final decision of this question must be left to future investigations.

In the further development of the muscular tissue the separate fibers increase in thickness and length, and their number increases through transformation of new myoblasts. The increase in number of fibers in the sartorius muscle stops when the human embryo is 130 to 170 mm. long. The future growth of the muscle depends only on the continued increase in the size of the fibers already present.

The sarcolemma appears at the surface of the embryonic muscle fibers at comparatively late stages. The nuclei, during the gradual growth of the muscle fiber, increase in number by mitosis and, in later stages, perhaps by amitosis. In mammals the nuclei at first are in the center, and the fibrils occupy the periphery of the fiber. In later stages the nuclei move toward the periphery, so that the central parts become occupied by fibrillar columns.

Contractility begins in the embryonic muscular elements about the time or shortly before the first myofibrils arise in their protoplasm. This contractility, at first slight and slow, gradually increases with the increase in number of myofibrils and their arrangement in bundles. The appearance of voluntary movements is connected with the development of the nervous motor tracts which lead from the spinal cord to the myotomes.

During the embryonic histogenesis of the striated muscle tissue, degenerative processes accompany the phenomena of progressive character. These sometimes include a considerable portion of the muscle fibers and may lead to their complete destruction.

Histogenesis of Cardiac Muscular Tissue. Cardiac muscle in the embryo forms from the splanchnopleure adjoining the endothelium of the heart primordium. At first a layer of loosely connected cuboidal cells, this part of the splanchnopleure becomes stratified. Its star-shaped cells anastomose with one another by processes which gradually thicken, forming a syncytium of protoplasmic shafts. The nuclei, scattered in the syncytium, multiply energetically by mitosis. The cytoplasm contains many rod-shaped mitochondria, often in groups. Electron micrographic study of embryonic cardiac muscle shows fine bundles of myofilaments developing in the myoblasts; the first cross striations are Z disks (Fig. 8–30). The old idea of longitudinal splitting of myofibrils receives no confirmation from this study.

The *Purkinje fibers* develop from the same primary syncytium as the cardiac muscle fibers. They soon become distinguishable from the remaining myocardiac mass as thick protoplasmic shafts, swollen about the nuclei; they lie directly under the endocardium. A few myofibrils are irregularly distributed at their periphery.

Toward the end of the embryonic period, cardiac muscular tissue is well differentiated. But how it grows to form the mature organ is not yet clear. It is clear that the nuclei increase at first by mitosis and later perhaps by amitosis. The manner in which the fibers of the myocardium increase in number is un-

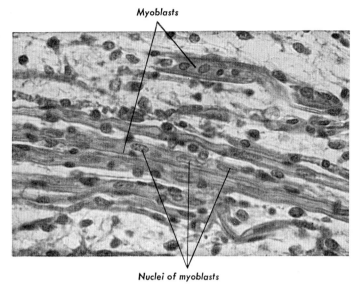

Myoblasts

Nuclei of myoblasts

Fig. 8–31. Myoblasts in a muscle of the lower jaw of an eleven-week embryo. The myoblasts contain rows of centrally placed nuclei and a longitudinal fibrillation, but lack cross striations. Photomicrograph. H + E. 500 ×. (After von Herrath and Abramow.)

known, although it has been supposed that this happens by longitudinal splitting of the existing fibers.

Regeneration of Smooth Muscle. In the vicinity of injured regions in the walls of the intestine or stomach, mitosis has been observed in the smooth muscle cells. But this capacity for regeneration is small, and great defects in smooth muscle heal by scar formation. Whether smooth muscle cells in the adult organism may be formed anew from fibroblasts has not been established; it is practically certain that they may develop from the perivascular mesenchymal cells of the adult (p. 70).

Regeneration of Striated Muscle. During intensive activity, the skeletal muscles increase in volume by enlargement of the existing fibers through an increase in the sarcoplasm and not of the fibrils.

The regenerative capacity of the striated muscular tissue of higher vertebrates does not always lead to the formation of functioning fibers. After destruction of muscle fibers, regeneration always starts from existing fibers. The most successful regeneration takes place when the nuclei with the surrounding sarcoplasm remain alive. These become separate cells called *sarcoblasts* or *myoblasts*. The ends of the fibers become thicker and grow out toward the place of injury as muscular buds. The sarcoblasts

hypertrophy, multiply, digest the degenerating fibers, and fuse in groups. Inside the old sarcolemma they form new fibers in which striated fibrils appear. In such a regenerative process, the sarcoblasts or myoblasts can be easily distinguished in vitally stained animals from the macrophages which have penetrated the fiber. It has been claimed that muscle cells turn into macrophages under the influence of choline in tissue cultures. A large defect in the muscular tissue is replaced by a connective tissue scar. Connection with motor nerve fibers is necessary for the existence of skeletal muscular tissue as well as for its successful regeneration.

Regenerative Capacity of Cardiac Muscle. In various pathological conditions in the adult organism, an increase in volume of the cardiac muscle may take place. This probably depends in part on the increase in thickness and length of the existing fibers and in part on continued splitting of the muscular network, as in its normal development.

The regenerative capacity of cardiac muscle tissue is insignificant and healing takes place by the formation of scar tissue. The large cells of the Aschoff nodules in the myocardium in rheumatic fever are no longer thought to arise from the muscle fibers. A yellowish pigment, possibly an abnormal metabolite, accumulates in smooth, cardiac and

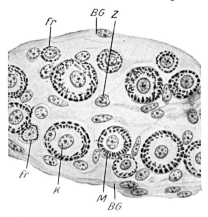

Fig. 8–32. Cross section through embryonic muscle bundle of a sheep. *BG,* cells of the primordium of the perimysium; *fr,* muscle fibers in cross section with a single layer of primitive fibrils; *K,* nucleus in the axial sarcoplasm; *M,* primitive muscle fibers; *Z,* connective tissue cell. 740 ×. (After Schaffer.)

skeletal muscle of rats on a diet deficient in vitamin E.

Participation of Nerves in Muscular Contraction. All muscles are under more or less continuous nervous stimulation whose nature varies with the type of muscle and its nervous connections. Smooth and cardiac muscle are under autonomic nervous control and contain autonomic nerve cells. The striated skeletal muscles receive their motor impulses from the central nervous system by way of craniospinal nerves. They probably do not receive additional innervation from the autonomic system.

When a skeletal muscle, preferably of a cold-blooded animal to avoid the effect of cooling, is removed from the body and its attached nerve is stimulated by a single electric shock, the muscle contracts quickly and relaxes almost immediately. This process is called a "twitch." When the nerve is stimulated by a rapid series of shocks, the muscle remains contracted, and the condition is called "tetanus." The muscles are in this condition when executing any voluntary movements. In the body, change in the position of any of its parts depends on a constant series of nervous impulses mediated by the myelinated efferent nerves. These cause a beautifully coordinated series of contractions and relaxations of the antagonistic muscles involved.

In addition to this neuromuscular mechanism which controls the movements of the limbs and other parts, and is based on typical reflex arcs (p. 210), there is another mechanism which controls the position of the limbs in space. This involves a series of unconscious, involuntary proprioceptive reflexes

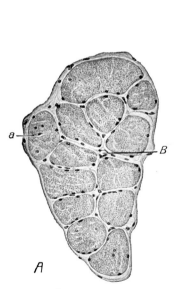
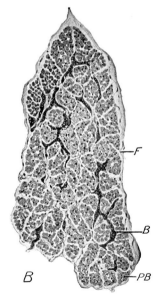

Fig. 8–33. Cross section through gastrocnemius muscle of an adult (*A*) and of a six-month fetus (*B*). Notice the difference in thickness of the fibers. *a,* fiber with central nuclei; *B,* blood vessel; *PB,* primary bundle, the number of whose fibers corresponds to those in Figure *A; F,* connective tissue. 110 ×. (After Schaffer.)

from the muscles themselves (see p. 198), from pressure organs, the labyrinths, eyes, and so forth. These are mediated through the central nervous system by myelinated nerve fibers and probably affect the same muscles as those involved in the voluntary movements. The impulses responsible for this "tone" are carried by the same nerves that carry the voluntary impulses. This is clearly shown when a nerve bundle was dissected until only one fiber was left undivided. When stimulated, this nerve fiber caused the muscle to contract; when not stimulated, it still carried sufficient impulses to maintain the tone of the muscle. Thus it appears highly probable that tone in skeletal muscle depends on the contraction of a few fibers. The normal stimulus for tone is probably in part the stretch put on the fibers as a result of the position the members of the body occupy after all movements. Those voluntary muscles which normally oppose the pull of gravity show tonus except during deep sleep and general anesthesia.

Between the extremes of skeletal and smooth muscle is the fairly quick contraction of cardiac muscle. In addition, it contracts rhythmically and does not develop fatigue—its rest periods are slightly longer than its periods of contraction. It is not under voluntary control. Its rhythmical activity is an intrinsic characteristic of the muscle, for in embryos the heart contracts for several days before any nerves have reached it. Moreover, in tissue cultures of embryonic heart muscle, individual muscle cells which have wandered into the plasma beat with characteristic rhythms. Indeed, two apparently connected cells may have individual rhythms.

REFERENCES

Adams, R. D., Denny-Brown, D., and Pearson, C. M.: Diseases of Muscle. A Study in Pathology. Paul B. Hoeber, Inc., New York (Med. Book Dept. of Harper & Bros.), 1953.

Barer, R.: The structure of the striated muscle fibre. Biol. Rev., 23:159, 1948.

Bennett, H. S.: Modern concepts of structure of striated muscle. Amer. J. Physical Med., 34:46, 1955.

Bennett, H. S., and Porter, K. R.: An electron microscope study of sectioned breast muscle of the domestic fowl. Am. J. Anat., 93:61, 1953.

Cohn, A. E.: Cardiac Muscle, in Cowdry's Special Cytology. 2d ed. New York, 1932, Vol. 2, p. 1127.

Fischer, E.: Vertebrate smooth muscle. Physiol. Rev., 24:467, 1944.

Goss, C. M.: First contractions of the heart without cytological differentiation. Anat. Rec., 76:19, 1940.

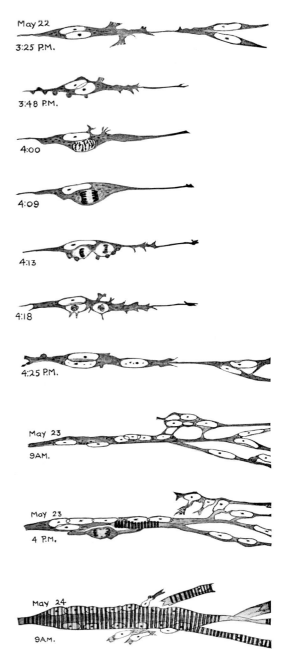

Fig. 8–34. Differentiation of myoblasts into cross-striated muscle fibers as seen in living regenerating zone, following removal of the tip of a tadpole's tail. One of a pair of closely associated myoblasts was watched throughout its nuclear division. The next day many nuclei were present. At 4 P.M. the first faint cross striations were visible. The following day many cross striations were in evidence in all fibers. (Redrawn after Speidel.)

Hall, C. E., Jakus, M. A., and Schmitt, F. O.: An investigation of cross striations and myosin filaments in muscle. Biol. Bull., *90:*32, 1946.

Hanson, J., and Huxley, H. E.: The structural basis of contraction in striated muscle. Symposia of the Society for Experimental Biology. Cambridge University Press, *9:*228, 1955.

Harman, John W.: Relation of mitochondria to enzymic processes in muscle. Amer. J. Physical Med., *34:*68, 1955.

Hartz, P. H.: Proliferation of muscle cells in the myometrium of the nonpregnant uterus. Arch. Path., *39:*323, 1945.

Heidenhain, M.: Plasma und Zelle. Jena, 1911.

Hodge, A. J., Huxley, H. E., and Spiro, D.: Electron microscope studies on ultrathin sections of muscle. J. Exper. Medicine, *99:*201, 1954.

Hogue, M. J.: Studies of heart muscle in tissue cultures. Anat. Rec., *67:*521, 1937.

Huxley, A. F., and Niedergerke R,.: Structural changes in muscle during contraction. Nature, *173:*971, 1954.

Huxley, H. E., and Hanson, J.: Changes in the cross-striations of muscle during contraction and stretch and their structural interpretation. Nature, *173:*973, 1954.

Jordan, H. E.: The structural changes in striped muscle during contraction. Physiol. Rev., *13:*301, 1933.

Lewis, W. H., and Lewis, M. R.: Cultivation of Embryonic Heart Muscle. Contrib. to Embryol., Carnegie Inst., 1926.

Lockhart, R. D., and Brandt, W.: Notes upon length of striated muscle fibre. J. Anat., *72:*470, 1938.

Mason, K. E., and Emmel, A. F.: Vitamin E and muscle pigment in the rat. Anat. Rec., *92:*33, 1945.

Meigs, E. B.: Striated and Smooth Muscle, in Cowdry's Special Cytology. 2d ed., New York, 1932, Vol. 2, p, 1087.

Nicholas, J. S.: Development of contractility. Proc. Am. Philosophical Soc., *94:*175, 1950.

Pease, D. C., and Baker, R. F.: The fine structure of mammalian skeletal muscle. Am. J. Anat., *84:*175, 1949.

Policard, A., and Baud, A.: Sur l'histologie inframicroscopique de la fibre musculaire striée. Bull. d'Histologie Appliquee, *27:*121, 1950.

Renaut, J., and Maillard, J.: Le myocarde. Rev. gén. d'histologie, 1905.

Schmitt, F. O.: Morphology in muscle and nerve physiology. Biochemica et Biophysica Acta, *4:*68, 1950.

Sjöstrand, F. S., and Anderson, E.: Electron microscopy of the intercalated discs of cardiac muscle tissue. Experientia, *10:*369, 1954.

Szent-Györgyi, A.: Chemical Physiology of Contraction in Body and Heart Muscle. Academic Press Inc., New York, 1953.

Truex, R. C., and Copenhaver, W. M.: Histology of the moderator band in man and other mammals, with special reference to the conduction system. Am. J. Anat., *80:*173, 1947.

CHAPTER 9

The Nervous Tissue

THE ENTIRE mass of nervous tissue in the body forms the nervous system. The essential function of this tissue is to receive stimuli from the environment, to transform them into nervous excitations and to transmit them to the nervous centers, where they are reorganized to call forth appropriate responses. By these means the individual adjusts to the events of the world in which it lives and so coordinates the functions of its organs that they maintain the integrity of the body. The nervous system also includes the specific apparatus of all conscious experience. It is the dominant mechanism for the regulation of behavior and the maintenance of unity of the personality.

In the brain and spinal cord, the *central nervous system,* nervous impulses from all parts of the body come together and are integrated with other nervous impulses resulting from stimuli coming from outside the body. The *peripheral nervous system* is made up of all nerve tissue outside the brain and spinal cord and serves to interconnect all other tissues with the central nervous system. In this way, all parts of the organism are integrated by a central clearing house which controls the activity of the organism as a biological entity.

The function of the nervous system is based on two fundamental properties of living substance. The first is the ability to react to various physical and chemical agents. The second is the ability to transmit the excitations thus elicited from one locality to another. The first property is called *irritability;* the second, *conductivity.*

The nervous system of the higher organisms evolved from these primitive properties of living substance in lowly forms. In the Metazoa certain cells developed the properties of irritability and conductivity to a high degree, forming a rudimentary nervous system. By further specialization some of the nerve cells evolved the capacity to react to special kinds of exogenous energy. These cells, with the corresponding accessory structures distributed throughout the body or near its surface, produced three sensory systems: the *exteroceptive system,* concerned with receiving impulses from the surface of the body; the *interoceptive system,* responsive to impulses from the internal organs; and the *proprioceptive,* receiving excitations from the muscles, tendons and joints. Other nerve cells became connected with the peripheral *effector organs,* as the muscles and glands, forming the *neuromotor* and *secretory systems.* Still other nerve cells, mostly collected in a large, central mass, assumed the role of *correlators* or *integrators.* These receive, select, combine, distribute, inhibit or otherwise modify the excitations arriving from the receptive surfaces or from the inner organs, and finally influence properly the peripheral effectors.

The cells within the nervous system which carry out its special functions are called nerve cells or *neurons.* Their numbers, although enormous, are exceeded by other cells which

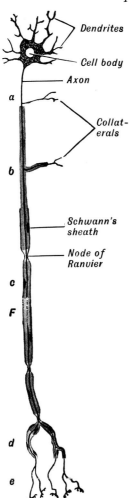

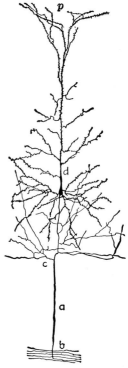

Fig. 9–2.   Pyramidal neuron (type I of Golgi) from cerebral cortex of rabbit. The axon gives off numerous collateral branches close to the cell body and then enters the white substance, within which it extends for a long distance. Only a small part of the axon is included in the drawing. *a,* axon; *b,* white substance; *c,* collateral branches of axon; *d,* ascending or apical dendrite; *p,* its terminal branches at the outer surface of brain. (After Ramón y Cajal.)

Fig. 9–1.   Diagram of a peripheral motor neuron. *a,* naked axon; *b,* axon invested only with myelin; *c,* axon covered with both myelin and Schwann's membrane; *F,* broken lines indicating great extent of the fiber; *d,* the axis cylinder, covered only with Schwann's sheath and its nuclei; *e,* the naked axis cylinder ending.

serve to maintain the physical integrity of the tissue, and also supply its nutritional and biochemical requirements. The cells not specifically concerned with conduction of nervous impulses are the *neuroglia cells* and the cells of the rich vascular plexus which pervades the central nervous system.

The neurons have a body made up of a nucleus and surrounding cytoplasm (*perikaryon*) which expands into a number of processes (Fig. 9–1). These usually comprise several short *dendrites* and only one *axis*

cylinder, or *axon,* which may have a great length (Fig. 9–2).

The size, shape and the other peculiarities of the body, and the number and mode of branching of the processes, vary, producing countless varieties of nerve cells. It has been assumed that with the morphological diversity there goes some sort of functional specialization. The neurons are related anatomically and functionally by their processes which are in contact with other nerve cells, or with epithelial, muscular or glandular cells. The point of contact of two nerve cells, called a *synapse,* transmits functional influence from one cell to another in one direction only (p. 207). Nearly every nerve cell has many synapses with other cells. The evidence —morphological, physiological and pathological—indicates that the nervous system is built of countless individual cells that are structurally and functionally independent to a greater or lesser degree.

MINUTE STRUCTURE OF THE NEURON

The nerve cell or neuron has a body containing a nucleus and threadlike processes or expansions. Often the mass of the cytoplasm in the processes is much greater than that in the cell body.

Nucleus. The relatively large nucleus has a thin nuclear membrane and in most cases a single large prominent nucleolus. The basichromatin is scanty so that the nuclei of nerve cells appear as pale vesicles when stained with basic dyes.

Nerve Cell Body or Perikaryon. The undifferentiated cytoplasm or matrix of the nerve cell body is called *neuroplasm*. In it are (1) neurofibrils, (2) chromophile substance or Nissl's bodies, (3) mitochondria, (4) Golgi apparatus, (5) various inclusions and (6) a centrosome in embryonic nerve cells. The neuroplasm extends into the cell processes and is called *axoplasm* in the axon. The nature of the neuroplasm, homogeneous in the fresh condition and showing some granules with dark-field illumination, requires further study with the electron microscope.

Neurofibrils. The *neurofibrils* are best developed in large neurons, but their presence has been demonstrated in almost every variety of nerve cell. When impregnated with silver methods they appear as homogeneous threads. They have been seen in living tissue cultures (Fig. 9–6) and can be stained vitally with methylene blue. Neurofibrils are distributed as a complicated network throughout the cell body, and spread into all the processes, where they can be followed into the finest terminal ramifications (Figs. 9–27, 9–29, 9–43). It is possible that the neurofibrils seen with the optical microscope are aggregates of minute filaments, 60 to 200 A thick, which have been found with the electron microscope.

The function of the neurofibrils is not clear. It now seems assured that they are confined to the territories of their respective neurons.

The Neuroplasm. The *neuroplasm* is the undifferentiated part of the cytoplasm of the nerve cells wherein the neurofibrils are embedded. Neuroplasm in the processes is called

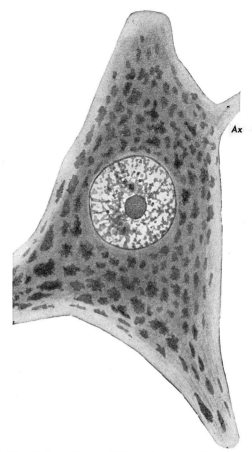

Fig. 9–3. Motor cell from the gray substance of the ventral horn of the spinal cord of a cat, showing granular chromophile substance. *Ax,* axon hillock. 670 ×. (A.A.M.)

interfibrillar substance; in the axis cylinder it is called axoplasm. In fresh condition the axoplasm appears homogeneous; in the dark field it contains scattered bright granules.

Chromophile Substance. The *chromophile substance,* or *Nissl's bodies* (Figs. 9–3, 9–7, 9–42, 9–9), are conspicuous structures of the nerve cells and show important changes in some pathological conditions. They are invisible in living or fresh material, and are best shown by staining with toluidin blue or thionine or other basic aniline dyes. Thus treated, the bodies appear intensively stained, much like the chromatin of the nucleus; neurofibrils pass between them (compare Figs. 9–3 and 9–5).

The physiological significance of the chromophile substance is undetermined. It is absent from certain neurons and from the

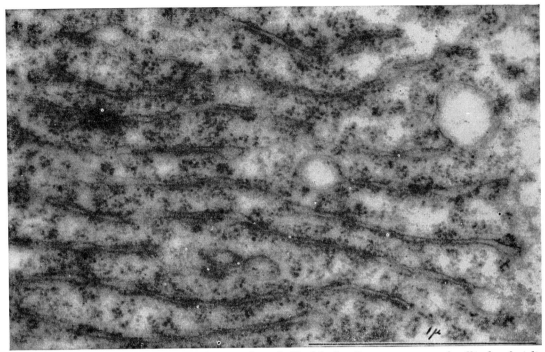

Fig. 9–4.   Electron micrograph of section through Nissl body of motor neuron of colliculus facialis of rat. Note the double membrane lamellae and the dense, RNA rich granules closely associated with and scattered between them. Buffered osmic acid fixation. (Courtesy of G. Palade.)

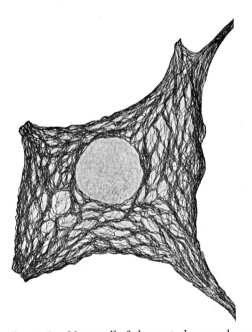

Fig. 9–5.   Motor cell of the ventral gray column of spinal cord of rabbit; the net of neurofibrils in the perikaryon continues into the processes; the nucleus appears as a pale disk. Bielschowsky method. 500 ×. (A.A.M.)

axis cylinders. Possibly it represents reserve material easily utilizable during the activity of the nerve cell—a view supported by the marked changes observed in the chromophile material under varying physiological and pathological conditions.

The chromophile bodies are distributed in the entire cell body except in its most peripheral layer and the zone immediately adjacent to the nucleus. They are also present in the dendrites, but absent from the axon and its origin from the cell body, the axon-hillock. The form, size and distribution of the chromophile bodies vary in the extreme, appearing in as many patterns as there are varieties of nerve cells. As a rule they are coarser and more abundant in large cells, especially motor ones, and scarce and fine in small cells. Under different conditions, such as rest and fatigue, the bodies change their aspect. In pathological processes they may disappear. Their disappearance may be the consequence either of direct injury to the cell body or to the axis cylinder anywhere along its course, and is called *chromatolysis* (Fig. 9–9); the process that brings it about, if caused by injury to the axon, is called Nissl's reaction or primary irritation of the nerve cell (p. 218).

The study of this substance with the freezing-drying method favors the view that it is not distributed homogeneously in the living cell (Fig. 9–7). With the aid of ultraviolet microscopy and the use of ribonuclease, it has been shown that ribose nucleo-protein is one of the main constituents of the Nissl

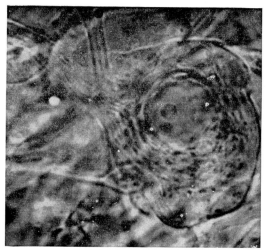

Fig. 9–6. Ganglion cell from an eight-day chick embryo cultivated *in vitro* for seven days. Unretouched photograph of the living cells showing neurofibrils. 1650 ×. (After Weiss and Wang, 1937; courtesy of The Wistar Press.)

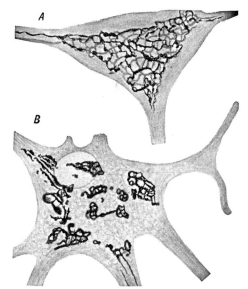

Fig. 9–8. *A,* normal cell of the nucleus of the sublingual nerve of rabbit, showing the intracellular reticular apparatus; *B,* similar cell four days after cutting the nerve. (Redrawn after Marcora.)

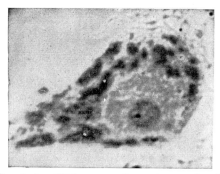

Fig. 9–7. High-power photomicrograph of anterior horn nerve cell of spinal cord of rabbit, fixed by the freezing-drying method, untreated, undenatured, and stained with toluidin blue. (After Bensley and Gersh.)

substance. Treatment of the sections with ribonuclease results in the loss of stainability with basic dyes, although the protein structure of the Nissl bodies is left intact.

Like the chromophile substance in other cell types (page 18) the Nissl bodies, as seen in electron micrographs, are composed of varying proportions of parallel cytoplasmic lamellae and of fine granules thought to contain ribose nucleic acid (Fig. 9–4).

Golgi Apparatus. The *intracellular reticular apparatus of Golgi* (Fig. 9-8) is present in all nerve cells and appears as a network of irregular, wavy threads and bands, coarser than the neurofibrillar network. The form varies considerably in different types of neurons.

Mitochondria. The rodlike or filamentous *mitochondria* are scattered everywhere between the Nissl's granules and neurofibrils (Fig. 9–10). They can be demonstrated in many fresh nerve cells by supravital

staining. Their number varies from a few to many. They are especially numerous in axon endings.

Centrosome. The *centrosome* is a spherical structure characteristic of the immature, multiplying nerve cells during the early stages of embryonic development. In adult neurons of vertebrates, a typical centrosome is rarely seen. Most of the structures so designated have another significance.

Inclusions. Besides the structures mentioned, there are inclusions in the nerve cells which are less widespread and less constant. Bright *vacuoles* have been described in the fresh nerve cells of lower animals. *Pigment granules* are frequently encountered. The coarse, dark-brown or almost black granules are undoubtedly melanin and are found in certain cells only, in the substantia nigra of the midbrain, in the locus caeruleus in the floor of the fourth ventricle, in the dorsal vagus nucleus, and in the spinal and sympathetic ganglia. Its physiological significance is unknown. More frequent, especially in man, are fine lipochrome granules of yellowish color. They are probably a product of normal activity which remains within the protoplasm in a useless although noninjurious capacity. In favor of this view is the gradual increase in the amount of the pigment with advancing age. *Fatty substances* are encountered in the form of inclusions in the protoplasm of the nerve cells, either as reserve material or as a product of normal or pathological metabolism. *Glycogen* is found in the ependyma, choroid plexus and nerve cells of the embryonic, but not in a demonstrable quantity in the adult, nervous tissue. *Iron-containing granules* are found in the nerve cells of the substantia nigra, the globus pallidus and elsewhere. Their number increases as the tissue grows older.

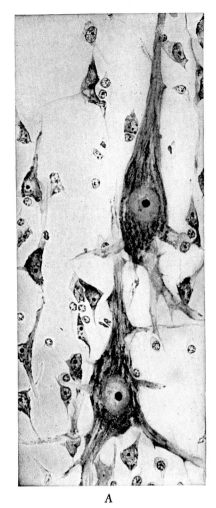

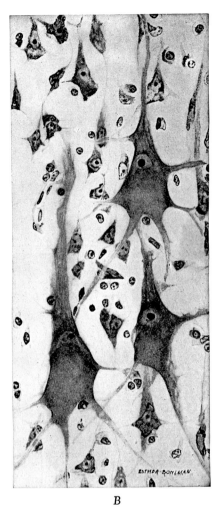

A   B

Fig. 9–9.   *A*, normal cells of motor cortex of macaque; *B*, chromatolysis in similar cells after hemisection
of the cervical spinal cord. Stained after Nissl-Lenhossék. (Courtesy of S. Polyak.)

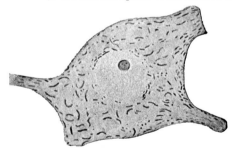

Fig. 9–10.   Nerve cell body of a rabbit, showing
mitochondria. (Redrawn after Schirokogorow.)

Processes or Expansions. The processes or
expansions of the nerve cells are their most
remarkable characteristics. In almost every
one of the many varieties of neurons there
are two kinds of processes: the dendrites, and
the axis cylinder.

The *dendrites* are direct expansions of the
body (Fig. 9–1). Nissl's chromophile bodies
and mitochondria are found in the thicker
portions of the dendrites (Figs. 9–3, 9–7,
9–10). A neuron usually has several main
dendrites; more rarely there is only one
(Fig. 32–23). At the point where the
dendrites emerge from the cell body they are
thick, rapidly becoming slender toward their
ends. Each dendrite usually divides into primary, secondary, tertiary and more branchlets. These are of the most varying shapes and
sizes, distributed in the most diverse ways,
but they are typical for each variety of neuron.
As seen in Golgi preparations, the surface of
many dendrites is covered with a great number of minute, thorny "spines," or "gem-

mules," giving the dendrites the appearance of a test-tube brush. These "spines" and other similar terminal twigs often serve as synaptic organs. In the majority of the neurons the dendrites are short and are confined to the immediate vicinity of the cell body. The number, length and arrangement of the terminal twigs of the dendrites vary in the extreme, and are not directly dependent upon the size of the perikaryon.

The dendrites, through their synapses with the axon endings of functionally related neurons, receive nervous impulses from other neurons.

The *axis cylinder* or *axon* differs considerably from the dendrites. While there are usually several dendrites, there is only one axis cylinder to each neuron (*a* in Fig. 9–1). This process often arises from a small conical elevation on the cell body, devoid of Nissl's substance, called axon-hillock (Fig. 9–3). The axon does not contain Nissl's bodies and usually is thinner and much longer than the dendrites of the same neuron.

Along its considerable course the axis cylinder may or may not emit collateral branchlets. The chief arborization, however, is at the end of the main branch and is called *axon ending* (also *telodendron*). It is composed of primary, secondary and other branches and buds varying greatly in number, shape and distribution. Often its branches are assembled into baskets that surround the body of the related neuron, or they twist around the dendrites of the latter. In simpler cases one or two twigs of an axon ending just touch the surface of a dendrite or the body of another related neuron (Fig. 9–46).

The axon normally receives nervous excitations from its own cell body, and thus indirectly from its dendrites. Occasionally, an axon may arise from a principal dendrite rather than from the cell body. In such instances there may be direct conduction from dendrite to axon of the same cell (as in the second S—ganglion cell from the left in Fig. 32–25). The axon transmits the excitation through its ending to other neurons or to effector cells, as muscle fibers or glandular cells. There are many modes or types of axon endings (Fig. 9–46) and indeed the same axis cylinder may terminate in several

different ways and be synaptically connected with several different neurons (Fig. 32–25).

Some exceptions to these features characterizing dendrites and axons are encountered, as in the peripheral sensory neurons of the spinal ganglia. In these the afferent fiber in the adult has the histological and conducting properties of an axon, although it normally conducts impulses toward its cell body in the same way as dendrites of other neurons.

A recent development in our knowledge of nerve cells is the concept that the nerve cell body is continuously forming new cytoplasm that flows continuously down the nerve cell processes, perhaps at about 1 mm. per day. According to Weiss and Hiscoe, "the perpetual growth of the neuron presumably serves to replace catabolized protoplasmic systems, especially proteins, which cannot be synthesized in the peripheral cytoplasm."

Forms and Varieties of Neurons. Depending on the number, length, thickness, and mode of branching of the processes, and also on the shape, size and position of the cell body, and on the synaptic relationships, an infinite number of types of neurons can be distinguished in the nervous system. In general, the neurons may have axis cylinders of considerable length that leave the place of their origin in the gray substance and traverse the so-called "white or fibrous mass," or become peripheral nerve fibers, and terminate at some distance in another locality. Such are termed *Golgi type I* neuron with the long axon (Fig. 9–2). To this type belong all the peripheral nerves and neurons whose axis cylinders form long fiber tracts of the brain and spinal cord. In other neurons the axis cylinder is relatively short and does not leave the confines of the gray substance where its body lies. These represent *Golgi type II* neuron with the short axon. Such neurons are especially numerous in the cerebral and cerebellar cortex and in the retina.

The shape of the cell bodies is variable; it may be spherical, oval, piriform, spindle-shaped or polyhedral. The absolute size of the neurons likewise varies between extreme limits, from midgets to those of giant size.

True *unipolar neurons* having a single process, the axon, are rare, except in early embryonic stage (Fig. 9–54). In the *bipolar*

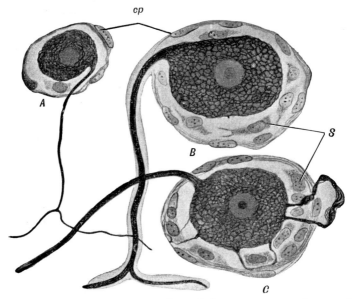

Fig. 9–11.   Three cells from the nodose ganglion of the vagus nerve of man, *A* and *B,* with two T-shaped dividing processes; *cp,* capsule; *S,* satellites; cell *C* has looped processes. (Redrawn after Ramón y Cajal.)

neurons each cell has one main dendrite and one axis cylinder projecting from opposite ends of the fusiform body. Typical bipolars are found in the retina (Figs. 32–23, 32–25), in the vestibular and cochlear ganglions, and in the olfactory nasal epithelium. In vertebrate embryos all neurons of the craniospinal ganglia are at first bipolar (Fig. 9–53); during further development they undergo changes resulting in the peculiar forms to be described. The single process shown by most of these cells does not represent a simple axon; because of this these elements may be called *pseudo-unipolar* (Fig. 9–11).

In the multipolar neurons, representing by far the great majority of neurons, the shape is determined by the number and arrangement of their dendrites (Fig. 9–1). The *star-shaped neurons* are the motor cells of the ventral gray columns or anterior horns of the spinal cord (Figs. 9–3, 9–8). The *pyramidal neurons* (Figs. 9–2, 9–42, 9–9) are one of the characteristic elements of the cerebral cortex.

Of remarkable shape are *Purkinje's cells* in the cerebellar cortex. In these, from the upper end of the body arise two thick, rapidly dividing dendrites covered with a multitude of tiny "spines." The large dendritic tree-top is confined to a narrow zone; it resembles a richly arborized fan oriented across the longitudinal axis of one of the cerebellar convolutions and vertical to its surface. The axis cylinder enters the white subcortical mass.

Many more varieties are found both in the cerebral and cerebellar cortex and elsewhere, among which are conspicuous diminutive *granule cells.* In these the few short dendrites radiate in all directions, while the axis cylinder and its branches are also confined to the immediate neighborhood of the cell.

Of special interest are the ganglion cells of the root ganglia of the cranial and spinal nerves (Fig. 9–11). These are mostly pseudo-unipolar. From the globular or pear-shaped body a single process arises which divides like the letter T into a peripheral or dendritic branch (structurally an axon) of a peripheral nerve, and into a central or axonic branch traveling in a sensory or posterior root to terminate in the central nervous system. Although unipolar, these neurons are physiologically bipolar. Except in the smallest cells the initial single expansion and both central and peripheral branches are myelinated. The body of each cell is enveloped by two cellular capsules. The inner is made up of small, flat, epithelium-like satellite cells continuous with similar cells enveloping the peripheral proc-

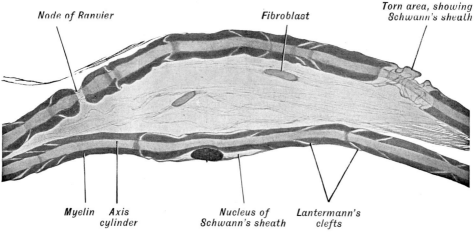

Node of Ranvier   *Fibroblast*   *Torn area, showing Schwann's sheath*

Myelin   *Axis cylinder*   *Nucleus of Schwann's sheath*   *Lantermann's clefts*

Fig. 9–12. Two myelinated fibers of the sciatic nerve of a frog; treated with osmic acid and picrocarmine and teased. 330 ×. (A.A.M.)

esses. The outer capsule of vascular connective tissue extends along the cellular process, becoming continuous with the endoneurium of the nerve fiber.

The few examples described give an incomplete picture of the wealth of the varieties of neurons. Many more have been discovered by numerous investigators, especially by Ramón y Cajal and his pupils, but probably many more remain unknown. It is apparent that each ganglion or cortical area is composed of a multitude of varieties of neurons differing from place to place, and occurring side by side.

THE NERVE FIBER

The nerve fiber is composed of an axon and such of its coverings as are of ectodermal origin. All axons in the peripheral nervous system are associated with a sheath composed of Schwann cells. These cells are absent from the central nervous system and possibly certain neuroglial cells distributed along fiber tracts are their central homologues.

As seen with the light microscope, all but the smallest axons are enveloped in a myelin sheath (see below) which, in the peripheral nervous system, is contained in cells of Schwann. It has accordingly been common practice to designate fibers as *myelinated* or *unmyelinated*. With the polarizing microscope, separation of fibers into myelinated and unmyelinated types becomes less clear, since even the smallest visible fibers contain birefringent material.

As discussed on page 193, the investigation of the myelin sheath by polarized light, x-ray diffraction and, more recently, electron microscopy shows it to be composed of many concentric layers (myelin lamellae) laid down by the Schwann cell. It may well be that in the future new terms will be introduced to distinguish between nerve fibers more or less devoid of lamellated coverings as in Figure 9–21, from those with multiple lamellae (Fig. 9–20). For the present we shall continue to use the terms of light microscopy.

Fresh myelinated fibers appear, with the light microscope, as homogeneous glistening tubes. It is this property of myelin that is responsible for the white color of fiber masses of the brain and spinal cord, and of numerous peripheral nerves. In stained preparations, the appearance of various constituents of the nerve fiber differs according to the technique applied. The vital methylene blue, and silver methods, stain the axis cylinder blue, brown or black, the myelin remaining unstained (Fig. 9–24). Unmyelinated fibers, often difficult to observe by routine histological methods, are well demonstrated by these special techniques. Weigert's method or osmic acid darkens the myelin, leaving the axon colorless or light gray. Myelin sheaths are stained blue-green by the Klüver-Barrera method (Fig. 9–13). Nuclei of Schwann cells

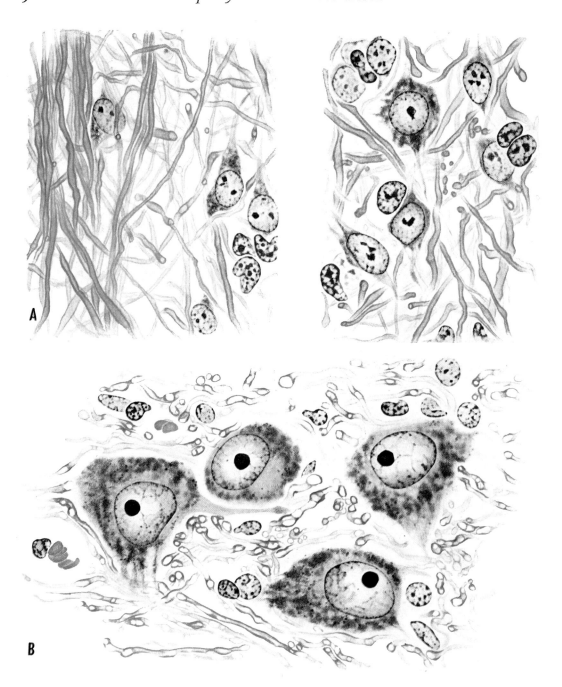

Fig. 9–13.   *A,* two areas of section through the optic tectum of a leopard frog showing blue stained myelin sheaths and the nerve cell bodies. The small dark nuclei are supporting cells. *B,* section from pons of man, showing myelin sheaths, nerve cell bodies and glia cells. *A,* is from a frozen section fixed in formalin, *B,* a paraffin section after post mortem formalin fixation. Klüver and Barrera staining method for cells and myelin sheaths. 1100 ×. (Drawn by Esther Bohlman.)

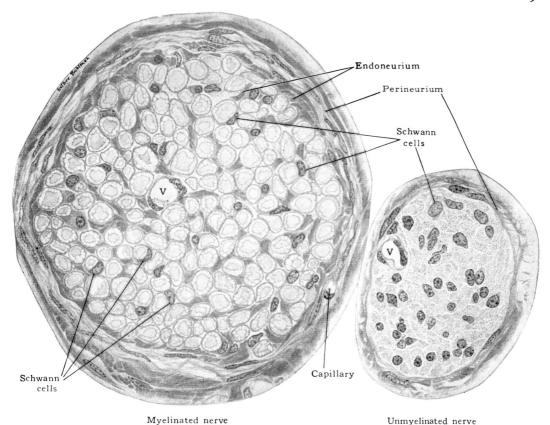

Myelinated nerve   Unmyelinated nerve

Fig. 9–14. Drawings of myelinated and unmyelinated nerves of *Macacus rhesus.* As a result of fixation by perfusion with Zenker-formol, the vessels (*V*) are empty. 700 ×.

are conspicuous in teased preparations of peripheral nerves (Fig. 9–12), but in sectioned material they may be difficult to distinguish from nuclei of surrounding connective tissue cells.

Axis Cylinder. The axis cylinder is a thin thread of fairly uniform thickness and smooth appearance. At the nodes of Ranvier (below) it is thinner than between them. It contains neurofibrils, neuroplasm and mitochondria but lacks Nissl granules.

Schwann's Sheath. Schwann's sheath, or *neurolemma,* envelops all axis cylinders of peripheral nerves. It is composed of *Schwann's cells,* that follow one another along the nerve fiber from its beginning, at the spinal root or in some ganglion, almost to its peripheral termination. Each Schwann cell has a flat and oval nucleus surrounded by cytoplasm containing a Golgi net and mitochondria.

Like the neurons, Schwann's cells are of ectodermal origin. They can be considered a peripheral neuroglia that has left the

central nervous system and has become adapted to the special conditions of the peripheral nervous system (Harrison). As the peripheral axons grow, embryonic cells of Schwann follow them, enveloping one segment after another, and freely migrate from branch to branch until they form complete neurolemmal sheaths.

In the adult unmyelinated fibers frequently form small groups, up to a dozen or more, the individual fibers of which occupy invaginations of the surface of a Schwann cell as shown in Figure 9–21.

The obviously myelinated nerve fibers have individual neurolemmal sheaths divided into segments by the *nodes of Ranvier.* In these fibers the myelin sheath is missing at the nodes and each segment is composed of a Schwann cell with its contained myelin. These are shorter in the terminal portion of the fiber. The length varies in different nerve fibers and in different animals from about 200 to over 1000 μ. The longer and/or

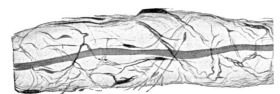

Fig. 9–15. Myelinated nerve fiber from ventral column of the white matter of the spinal cord of a cat; the axis cylinder is surrounded by a myelin sheath enveloped by neuroglia fibers. (Redrawn after Paladino.)

thicker the fibers, the longer the segments. If the peripheral nerve fiber gives off collateral branches, this takes place at a Ranvier node. (Fig. 9–1).

In fixed preparations of the peripheral nerves the myelin of each segment is interrupted by oblique partitions, the *incisions* or *clefts of Schmidt-Lantermann,* several to each Schwann's segment (Fig. 9–12). The clefts have been seen in teased fresh nerves of rats.

Many nerve fibers in the brain and spinal cord, especially those that form the white subcortical substance, have myelin sheaths but lack the neurolemma, for which is substituted neuroglia, particularly the oligodendroglia (Figs. 9–15, 9–39). Both Ranvier's nodes and Schmidt-Lantermann's clefts do occur in the central nervous system.

Schwann's cells are indispensable for the life and function of the axons of the peripheral nerve fibers. In regeneration the new axon always grows out of the central stump, which remains continuous with the cell body of the neuron, and spreads along the bridges formed by Schwann's cells (p. 219). In tissue cultures, Schwann's cells may transform into macrophages.

Myelin Sheath. According to conventional views based on light microscopy peripheral axons were thought to be encased in two sheaths, with the myelin sheath between the axon and the neurolemmal sheath. Ultramicroscopic methods indicate that the myelin

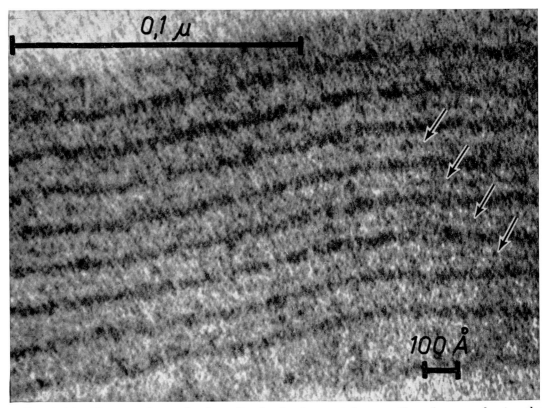

Fig. 9–16. Electron micrograph of myelin sheath of a central nerve fiber of mouse showing the lamellae about 130 A apart. A faint intermediate line is indicated by the arrows. Buffered osmic acid fixation. (Courtesy of H. Fernandez-Moran.)

lamellae are an integral part of the Schwann cell.

Schmitt, Bear and Palmer, on the basis of x-ray diffraction patterns, describe the myelin sheath as "being composed of concentrically wrapped layers of mixed lipides alternating with thin, possibly unimolecular, layers of neurokeratinogenic protein material. Within the layers the lipide molecules are oriented with paraffin chains extending radially and with polar groups in the aqueous interfaces, loosely bonded to those of the protein. . . . The specific structure of the sheath is relatively insensitive to the action of temperature, electrolytes, and detergents." This view of the structure of the myelin sheath is supported by studies with the electron microscope which show its lamellar structure (Fernandez-Moran and others).

Additional verification of this arrangement has been derived from electron microscope studies of developing myelin in fetal peripheral nerves by Geren, which show that the axon is first enveloped by the Schwann cell (Figs. 9–16 to 9–20). Then the Schwann cell progressively encircles the axon, and with further development, forms many turns about it. How this occurs is not clear, but the result is that the axon becomes surrounded by a many-layered myelin sheath. The measurements across lamellae indicate a thickness of about 130–180 A, depending on the species and the mode of study.

The development of myelin in fibers of cultured spinal ganglion cells in the absence of functional connections has been observed by Peterson and Murray. The myelin first becomes evident in discontinuous segments on the axon at the site of Schwann cells.

In ontogenesis myelin appears relatively late, and the process of myelinization ends only some time after birth. Different fiber systems or tracts of the brain and spinal cord become myelinated at different times.

The role of the myelin sheath and the other coverings of the nerve cell processes in facilitating nervous conduction is under investigation.

Physiological Properties of the Nerve Fiber. The nerve fiber is essentially a highly irritable conductor. Along it the dynamic nervous excitation propagates in waves, faster in large than in small axons. During the conduction of excitation the activity of one portion of the axon serves as a stimulus activating the next portion, and so on. As the nerve fiber becomes active, it changes its electric potential, the outside of each active portion becoming negative relative to resting portions. Action currents then flow between active and resting regions.

Studies on giant nerve fibers of squid demonstrate that changes in the permeability of the axon membrane, permitting sodium ions to enter the axon and potassium ions to migrate from it, are of great importance in conduction. When artificially stimulated, the nerve fiber increases its metabolism. The electrical changes in active nerves and the accompanying chemical reactions are discussed in detail in textbooks of physiology.

The following features are characteristics of the activity of the nerve fiber or axis cylinder: (1) Like all living substance, it has *irritability,* the ability to respond to various stimulating agents, and *conductivity,* the ability to transmit impulses from point to point. (2) To act as a transmitter, the nerve fiber must be anatomically continuous and physiologically in an appropriate condition. (3) After the passing of the impulse the fiber remains for a short time unexcitable ("refractory period"). (4) The axon can conduct an impulse with equal ease in the normal direction and in the opposite, *antidromic,* direction. (5) The impulse normally remains confined to the stimulated axon, spreading only along it and its branches to the synapses. (6) The impulse traveling along an axon can be weakened temporarily or blocked by the local action of heat, cold, pressure, electric current and by many drugs (anesthetics, narcotics). (7) Any stimulation intense enough to cause the axon to respond calls forth the maximum discharge of which the axon is capable ("all or nothing law").

The properties of simple nervous conductors, as listed, differ profoundly in several respects from those of the synaptic gray nervous substance of the brain, the spinal cord and the ganglia, as discussed on page 215.

Nerve Fibers as Constituents of Peripheral Nerves, Brain and Spinal Cord. In their peripheral course outside the central nervous system, both myelinated and unmyelinated nerve fibers are bound into bundles by connective tissue, forming peripheral *nerve*

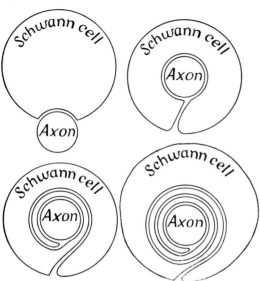

Fig. 9–17.   Diagram of development of myelin sheath in young mice showing the envelopment of the axon by the Schwann cell and the progressive spiral wrapping of the Schwann cell surface about the axon. (Courtesy of B. Geren-Uzman.)

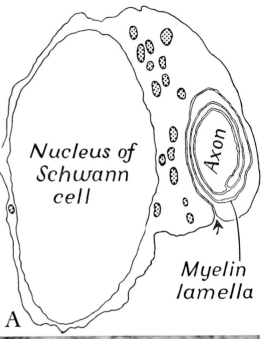

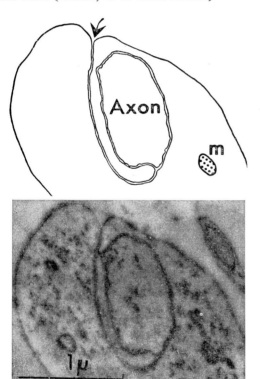

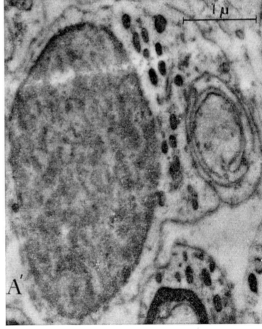

Fig. 9–18.   Electron micrograph and tracing of early stage in the wrapping of the Schwann cell surface about the axon of 7 day mouse. The arrow indicates the point of inclusion of the plasma membrane; *m,* mitochondrium. Fixation in buffered osmic acid. (Courtesy of B. Geren-Uzman.)

Fig. 9–19.   Electron micrograph and tracing of further stage of the spiral wrapping of the Schwann cell surface about the axon. The arrow indicates the inclusion of the plasma membrane; the mitochondria are stippled. 7 day mouse. Buffered osmic acid fixation. (Courtesy of B. Geren-Uzman.)

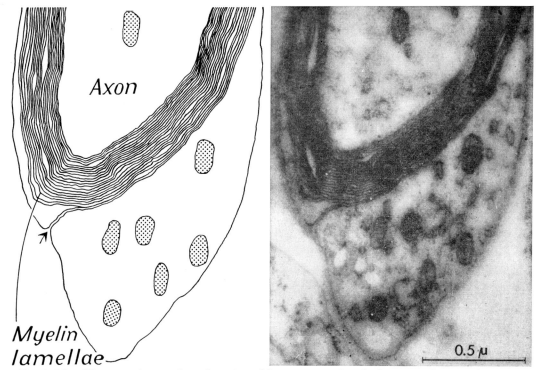

Fig. 9–20. Electron micrograph and tracing of later stage and at higher magnification of developing myelin sheath in 7 day mouse. The inclusion of the surface of the Schwann cell is indicated by the arrow. The layers of the myelin sheath are distinct. Mitochondria are stippled. Buffered osmic acid fixation. (Courtesy of B. Geren-Uzman.)

trunks and their branches (Figs. 9–14, 9–24). While most of the nerve fibers are myelinated, they are characteristically white and glistening in appearance. The *white matter* of the brain, the various bundles of the brain stem, the core of the cerebellum and the white columns of the spinal cord, consist mainly of nerve fibers; here there are few, if any, nerve cells. The *gray matter,* found in both the cerebral and cerebellar cortex, in the basal ganglia of the brain, in the numerous nuclei of the brain stem, in the gray columns of the spinal cord, in the peripheral ganglia and in the retina of the eyes, is chiefly composed of the bodies of numerous nerve cells, their dendrites, and the initial and terminal unmyelinated portions of axis cylinders. The nerve fibers of some sympathetic nerves are mostly unmyelinated gray fibers. Both white and gray matter contain neuroglia and blood vessels, although these elements are more abundant in the gray matter. In certain regions of the central nervous system the constituents of both white and gray substance are mixed in various degrees, as along the sides

of the thalamus, in the subthalamus and hypothalamus, in the tegmentum of the brain stem and at the junction of the anterior and posterior gray horns of the spinal cord. Such regions are called *reticular formations.*

The *peripheral nerves* are composed of fascicles of nerve fibers of varying thickness (1, 2 and up to 30 microns), held together by connective tissue. The outer layer of the latter, the *epineurium* (Fig. 9–23), is made up of connective tissue cells and of collagenous fibers, mainly arranged longitudinally. Fat cells may also be found here. Each of the smaller fascicles of a nerve is in turn enclosed in a membrane of dense, concentric layers of connective tissue called *perineurium.* From this, fine longitudinally arranged strands of collagenous fibers, fibroblasts and fixed macrophages pass into the spaces between the individual nerve fibers; this is the *endoneurium.* Where the nerve trunks divide into branches, the connective tissue sheaths become thinner. The smaller branches show no epineurium, and here the perineurium cannot be distinguished from

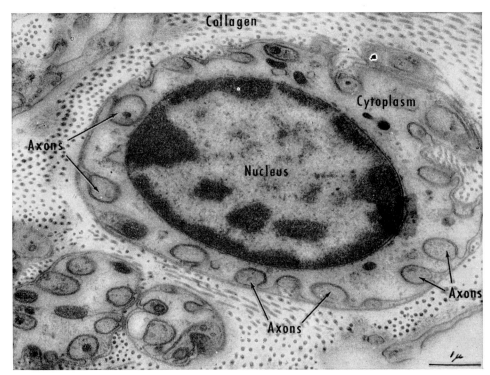

Fig. 9–21. Electron micrograph of section of Schwann cell and associated unmyelinated axons from a delicate nerve in interstitial tissue of cat testis. The inner of the two black lines at the edge of the sheath is the Schwann plasma membrane. It turns inward to surround the axons. Inside the loops a second line evinces the axon plasma membrane. Note that none of the axons is completely separated from the exterior by cytoplasm of the Schwann cell. Buffered osmic acid fixation. Electron micrograph by D. Fawcett. (Courtesy of H. S. Gasser.)

Fig. 9–22. Unmyelinated sympathetic nerve fibers of cat, teased and stained with hematin. (Redrawn after Ramón y Cajal.)

the endoneurium, being reduced to a thin, transparent, fibrillated membrane covered with flat connective tissue cells resembling endothelial cells whose outlines can be demonstrated with silver. From this membrane filaments extend to wrap around each nerve fiber, thus forming the delicate *endoneural* or *connective tissue sheath of Key and Retzius,* a network of elastic fibers attached to the neurolemmal sheath of Schwann. This sheath is also known as the sheath of Henle, although he called it neurilemma. Blood vessels are embedded in the epineurium and perineurium and in the thicker layers of endoneurium.

It has become customary to classify nerve fibers according to their diameter, since the speed of impulse transmission and size of the action potential vary with the square root of the diameter. Fiber diameters cover a wide and continuous range from large myelinated to small unmyelinated fibers. It is found in peripheral nerve that fibers are collected into three distinct diameter groups. The large fibers of group A, conducting at 15 to 100 meters per second, contain motor and some sensory fibers. The B group conducts at 3 to 14 meters per second and contains mainly visceral sensory fibers. The C group consists of unmyelinated fibers, conducting at 0.5 to 2 meters per second, and carries autonomic and some sensory impulses.

The following rule on the *functional characters of the nerve fibers* holds good: the

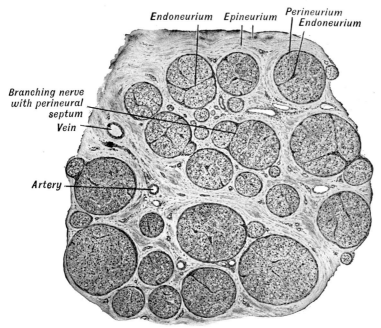

Endoneurium   Epineurium   Perineurium   Endoneurium

Branching nerve with perineural septum

Vein

Artery

Fig. 9–23. Portion of cross section through sciatic nerve of a newborn. 42 ×. (After Schaffer.)

motor nerve fibers of the skeletal muscles are thick and heavily myelinated; those of the smooth visceral muscles are thin and lightly myelinated or without myelin; those of tactile sensibility are of medium size and moderately myelinated; those of pain and taste are thinner, with less myelin or none at all; and those of the olfactory nerve are always unmyelinated. Such histologically defined fiber aggregates are therefore functional systems: tactile, gustatory, somatic motor, visceral motor, and so forth.

A particularly clear segregation of functionally different nerve fibers is found in the *spinal roots.* In general, each segmental spinal nerve contains in its ventral roots motor fibers of several types: (1) some coarse and heavily myelinated for ordinary skeletal muscle fibers, (2) others small and myelinated for intrafusal muscle fibers (see p. 200), and (3) visceral motor fibers, thinner and more lightly myelinated for the autonomic nervous system. Its dorsal roots contain cutaneous fibers of several types, as those of deep sensibility, proprioceptive fibers from muscles and tendons, and afferent fibers of visceral sensibility from the sympathetic system. More than half of the dorsal root fibers are very small axons, and most of these are distributed with the cutaneous rami. The

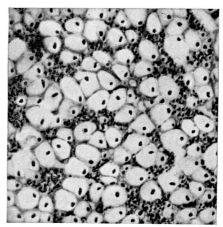

Fig. 9–24. Photomicrograph from a cross section of human medial cutaneous nerve, prepared by Davenport's reduced silver method and kindly furnished by S. W. Ranson. 450 ×.

relative number of myelinated and unmyelinated fibers varies widely in different spinal segments and in the same segment of different mammalian species. In the mixed trunks peripheral to the spinal ganglia, the fibers of the motor and sensory roots mingle, and to those are added sympathetic fibers from the communicant rami (Fig. 9–24). The myelinated fibers of various sizes are readily identified by the clear zones of unstained

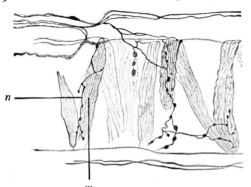

m

Fig. 9–25. Nerve endings (*n*) on the smooth muscle cells (*m*) of an artery from the vascular membrane of a rabbit's eye. (Redrawn after Retzius.)

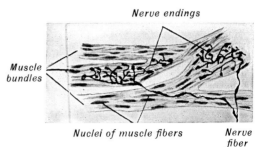

Nerve endings

Muscle bundles

Nuclei of muscle fibers   *Nerve fiber*

Fig. 9–26. Smooth muscle spindles in small bronchial muscle bands. Child eight months old. Intravitam methylene blue and borax carmine. Camera lucida. 356 ×. (Redrawn after Larsell and Dow.)

myelin surrounding the darkly stained axis cylinders. The unmyelinated fibers tend to assemble in small fascicles. Some of these are sensory fibers from the spinal ganglia; others are postganglionic sympathetic fibers.

In the *central nervous system,* in the brain and spinal cord, numerous nerve fibers are also segregated into functional systems. Such are especially the afferent and efferent pathways (cortico-spinal, cortico-nigral, spino-cerebellar, spino-thalamic and many other fiber tracts). Each of these has a special function, partly well known, partly still obscure.

Peripheral Nerve Endings. Each peripheral nerve fiber, be it sensory, motor or secretory, sooner or later terminates in some peripheral organ with one or several terminal arborizations. Some nerve fibers spread as free endings among the non-nervous tissue cells; others are attached to these by means of complicated structures. The nerve fibers ending as *receptors* are homologues of dendrites; those with *motor* or *secretory* endings are homologues of axis cylinders, and their terminations are equivalent to axon endings. In general, the structure of the nerve endings is adapted to increase the surface of contact between the neuron and its related non-nervous element. The chemical-physical changes which mediate the transfer of the various "sensory" stimuli from, or of the efferent impulses to, a peripheral non-nervous organ have been the subject of intense investigation (see p. 209). According to the tissue, three groups of nerve terminations can be distinguished: (1) endings in muscle, (2) endings in epithelium, and (3) endings in connective tissue.

Nerve Endings in Smooth and Cardiac Muscle. These belong to the unmyelinated type of fibers. From complicated plexuses, thin nerve fibers are given off that eventually come in contact with the surface of the muscle cells. Some of these, the *visceral motor endings* (Figs. 9–25, 9–26), terminate here by means of one, two or more terminal swellings. Possibly, some even penetrate the substance of the muscle fibers. The *visceral sensory fibers* spread in the connective tissue between the smooth muscle bundles, or are in contact with the muscle fibers themselves. In the cardiac muscle the tissue is permeated by a multitude of thin fibers passing between the muscle trabeculae, on whose surface they form varicosities.

Terminations of the Myelinated Somatic Motor Nerve Fibers on Striated Muscles (Motor Plates). These have a more complex structure (Figs. 9–27, 9 28). As the nerve fiber approaches the muscle fiber, it loses its myelin sheath. The connective tissue membrane of Key and Retzius with its nuclei extends over the surface of the sarcolemma and disappears. The neurolemma, according to some, also terminates abruptly in the sarcolemma, while, according to others, it may run for a short distance within the plate. At the junction of the nerve and muscle fibers the sarcoplasm forms a mass that varies in form and size beneath the sarcolemma. This is the *motor plate.* It receives the naked axis cylinder, which here breaks up into a number of terminal ramifications. The deep layer of the motor plate adjacent to the contractile substance is its *sole.* Here muscle nuclei may be found in large numbers. The ramifications of the axis cylinder are accompanied by small, dark nuclei interpreted as those of neurolemmal cells. The nature of the so-called "periterminal net" in the muscle plate (Fig. 9–27) is obscure. It is considered an artefact by some.

Sensory Nerve Endings in Striated Muscles. These are always present in considerable numbers. Some are located in the muscular tissue, others on tendons or at musculo-tendon junctions. Some terminations are simple, others complex. The interstitial terminations are distributed in the connective tissue; the epilemmal terminations are in close contact with the muscle fibers, but, in contrast with the motor plates, remain on the surface of the sarcolemma. The inter-

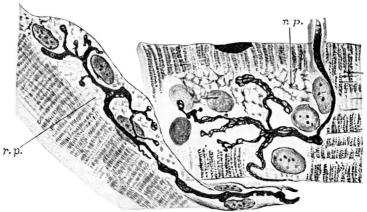

Fig. 9–27. Motor end plate from tongue of rabbit, showing the "periterminal net" (*r. p.*) of the end plate. (Redrawn after Ramón y Cajal.)

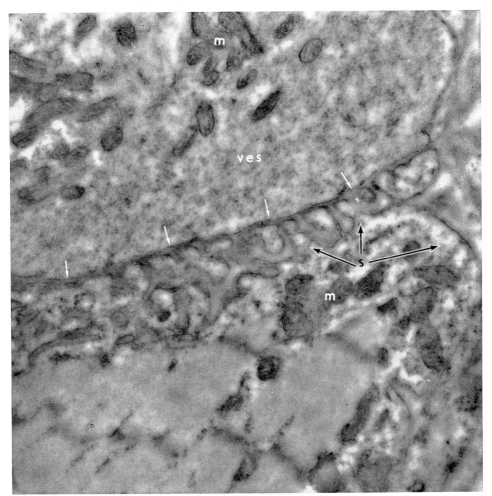

Fig. 9–28. Electron micrograph of neuromuscular synapse in rat diaphragm. The axon (above) ends abruptly (white arrows). The processes of the sarcoplasm (*s*) interdigitate with an irregular, homogeneous material in contact with the axon ending. *ves*, presynaptic vesicles in the axon; *m*, mitochondria. Compare with the synapses in Figures 9–44 and 9–45. Buffered osmic acid fixation. 25,000 ×. (Courtesy of G. Palade.)

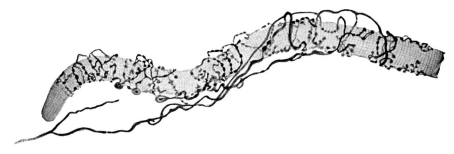

Fig. 9–29.   Sensory nerve ending enveloping a fiber of an ocular muscle. (Redrawn after Dogiel.)

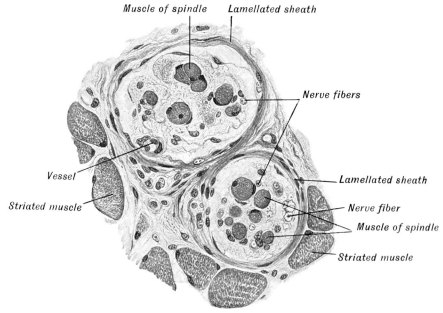

Fig. 9–30.   Cross section of a double muscle spindle from human tongue. 380 ×. (After Schaffer.)

stitial terminations may be simple naked branches of the axis cylinders or encapsulated structures. The epilemmal endings likewise may be simple: one or more tortuous axis cylinders, after shedding their myelin sheath at approximately the middle of a muscle fiber, envelop the sarcolemma by continuous circular and spiral twists. Their varicose twigs terminate with nodular swellings (Fig. 9–29). More complicated are the *neuromuscular spindles,* found in higher vertebrates only (Figs. 9–30, 9–31). They are narrow, long (0.75 to 7 mm. or more) structures slightly thickened in the middle, arranged lengthwise with the bundles of ordinary muscle fibers, and present mainly at the junction of muscles with tendons. Each spindle, enveloped by a connective tissue capsule, consists of one or several long striated muscle fibers, the intrafusal fibers. Near the middle of each fiber the striations are replaced by a collection of nuclei, the nuclear bag. Each spindle is supplied by thin motor nerves, *gamma fibers,* that terminate at the muscle fibers of the spindle with typical motor plates. These motor nerve fibers have been shown to affect the sensitivity of the sensory

endings on the muscle spindle. In addition, the spindle is approached by one or more thick sensory nerve fibers. Their axis cylinders, covered with a thin layer of Schwann's cytoplasm and nuclei, wind around the intracapsular portion of the axial muscle fibers and are in close contact with the sarcolemma, forming spirals. The muscle fibers of the spindles are distinguished by their thinness, abundant sarcoplasm and their peripheral nuclei; in this they resemble the so-called "red muscle fibers."

Sensory Nerve Endings in Tendons. These are of several kinds, and are also either simple or encapsulated. In simple forms the naked nerve fibers and their branches spread over the surface of the somewhat changed tendon fibers in small treelike figures of different forms (Fig. 9–32). The composite forms, such as the neurotendinal spindles, the organs of Golgi, resemble the neuromuscular spindles and are always found at the very border of the muscular tissue.

The physiological significance of the muscular and tendinous sensory apparatus probably is their responsiveness to various peripheral stimuli of gen-

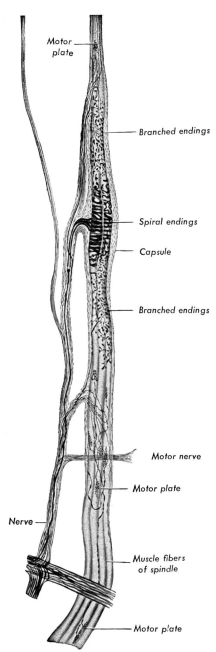

Motor plate

Branched endings

Spiral endings

Capsule

Branched endings

Motor nerve

Motor plate

Nerve

Muscle fibers of spindle

Motor plate

Fig. 9–31. Neuromuscular spindle of a cat, showing nerve endings. (Redrawn after Ruffini.)

eral character, giving sensations of pain, pressure, and particularly of muscle sense.

Nerve Endings in Epithelial Tissue. These are of both receptor and effector type. Histologically, they can be distinguished only in rare instances. The terminations in the epithelial layers of the skin and mucous membranes are regarded as sensory receptors, those in the epithelial glands partly as secretory, partly as sensory. The terminations of the cochlear and vestibular nerves are undoubtedly sensory in their function. The *nervous terminations in glands* (lacrimal, salivary, kidneys, and so on) are all unmyelinated sympathetic fibers forming dense nets on the outer surface of the basement membrane, with branches penetrating the latter and often forming a second network on its inner surface. They end between the glandular cells as thin varicose threads.

Free Sensory Epithelial Endings. These are found in the epithelium of the cornea (Fig. 9–33), epithelium of the mucous membrane of the respiratory passages, skin, and oral cavity, and are especially abundant in places which have a well-developed sensitiveness. In the epidermis these branches do not penetrate farther than the granular layer. Nerve endings in hair follicles are important tactile organs. There are two sets of free nerve endings: an outer one circularly arranged in the middle layer of the dermal sheath; the other consisting of fibers running parallel to the hair shaft and terminating in the outer root sheath.

Nerve Endings in Connective Tissue. These are numerous and of many forms, particularly in the derma, under the epithelium and mesothelium of the mucous and serous membranes, around the joints, in the endocardium and elsewhere. The terminations of the somatic cerebrospinal nerve fibers in the connective tissue are either free or encapsulated endings, or are connected with special tactile cells of epithelial origin. More complex endings are in the skin and hypodermis, in mucous and serous membranes, endocardium, cornea, sclera, periosteum and elsewhere. *Nonencapsulated nerve glomeruli* are frequent in the papillary layer of the skin, in the connective tissue of the mucous membranes as that of the urinary bladder, in the pericardium and endocardium, periosteum, and so forth. In these the terminal branches of the nerve fibers form spherical or elongated structures resembling glomeruli.

Encapsulated Terminal Sensory Apparatus. In these there is a special connective tissue capsule of varying thickness surrounding the actual nerve endings. The capsule attains its greatest thickness in the *corpuscles of Vater-Pacini* (Fig. 9–34). Terminations of this type are found in the deeper layers of

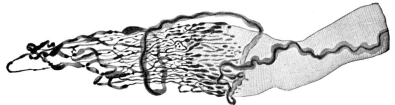

Fig. 9–32. Sensory nervous apparatus, consisting of palisade-like terminal branches, located at the junction of a muscle fiber with a tendon. (Redrawn after Dogiel.)

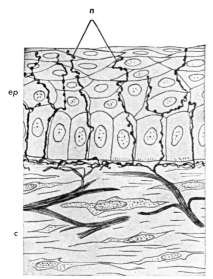

Fig. 9–33.   Free nerve endings (*n*) in the epithelium (*ep*) of rabbit cornea; *c,* connective tissue of the corneal substance proper. Impregnation with gold chloride. (Redrawn after Ramón y Cajal.)

the skin, under the mucous membranes, in the conjunctiva, cornea, heart, mesentery, pancreas, and in loose connective tissue in general. The size of these structures is considerable (1 to 4 by 2 mm.), and they are white. Each corpuscle is supplied with one or more thick myelinated fibers which lose their myelin. Their sheaths of Schwann and of Key-Retzius are continuous with the capsule. Of the same type are the so-called *genital corpuscles* found in the skin of the external genital organs and of the nipple. *Meissner's corpuscles* (Fig. 9–35) are found in the connective tissue of the skin of the palms, soles and tips of the fingers and toes. They are elongated, pear-shaped or elliptical formations with rounded ends, located in the cutaneous papillae, with the long axis vertical to the surface. Their size varies (40 to 100 by 30 to 60 microns). The *corpuscles of Golgi-Mazzoni* or *the terminal bulbs of Krause* are similar in structure to the corpuscles of Vater-Pacini, but are smaller in size and simpler in construction. (On terminations of the dendrites and axis cylinders in the brain and spinal cord, see p. 207.)

VISCERAL NERVOUS SYSTEM

All motor neurons of the central and peripheral nervous systems primarily concerned with the regulation of visceral activities form the *autonomic* portion of the *visceral*

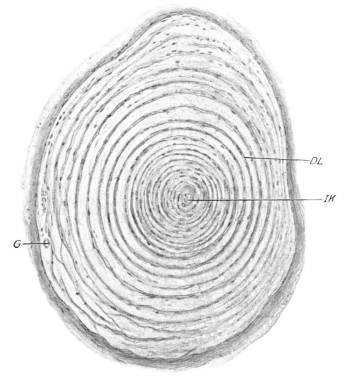

Fig. 9–34.   Cross section of corpuscle of Vater-Pacini, from derma of the sole of a human foot. *DL,* Lamellae; *G,* blood vessel between superficial lamellae; *IK,* inner bulb. 110 ×. (After Schaffer.)

nervous system. Not included under the term autonomic are the *visceral sensory neurons* which form the afferent side of visceral reflex arcs.

The autonomic system is composed of numerous small ganglia, some of which are arranged in two chains along the spinal column, and more of which are scattered among other tissues of the body. The autonomic system consists of the *sympathetic* (*thoracolumbar*) and *parasympathetic* (*craniosacral*) outflows.

The sympathetic trunks and their ganglia, the *vertebral ganglia,* as well as the more ventrally situated *prevertebral ganglia,* are the chief avenues of communication for the thoracolumbar outflow between the central nervous system and the viscera. Each sympathetic trunk contains ganglia at the level of exit of most of the spinal nerves. The *communicating branches* (rami communicantes) pass between the trunk and the spinal nerves.

The bodies of the sympathetic neurons are segregated in the intermedio-lateral gray column of the thoracic and upper lumbar spinal cord (Fig. 9–36, *int. lat.*). Their axons pass out of the cord into the ventral roots and through the white communicating branches, to end either in a vertebral ganglion of the sympathetic trunk or in a prevertebral ganglion. Most of these axons, the *preganglionic fibers,* with thin myelin sheaths, terminate in a sympathetic ganglion. Here they effect synaptic junction with secondary visceral motor neurons, whose axons—the mostly unmyelinated *postganglionic fibers*—transmit the impulse to visceral muscles or glands. Some postganglionic fibers travel to internal viscera over sympathetic nerves, like the cardiac or splanchnic nerves, others extend from vertebral ganglia through gray communicating branches and spinal nerves to visceral structures of the body wall and extremities. Among the latter are the *vasomotor* fibers going chiefly to arteriolar muscles, the *pilomotor* fibers to the small muscles of the hair follicles, and the sudomotor fibers to the sweat glands.

The craniosacral division of the autonomic system has preganglionic neurons situated in the brain and spinal cord. Axons of the cranial component emerge from the brain in the oculomotor, facial, glossopharyngeal and vagus nerves to synapse with terminal

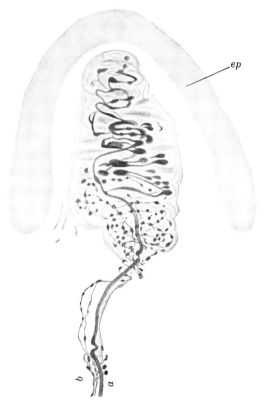

Fig. 9–35. Meissner's corpuscles of a dermal papilla of a human finger. *a,* thick and, *b,* thin myelinated fiber; *ep,* epithelium. Methylene blue. (Redrawn after Dogiel.)

ganglia innervating the head and trunk. From the second, third and fourth sacral segments of the spinal cord axons leave via ventral roots and sacral nerves to reach postganglionic neurons in terminal ganglia associated with pelvic viscera.

Postganglionic neurons which lie wholly within the peripheral autonomic system may exercise a local regulatory control over the viscera to which they are related. These local adjusters are under modification by the visceral centers of the central nervous system.

Distributed with both divisions of the autonomic nervous system, the peripheral processes of the visceral sensory neurons extend from the viscera through communicating branches, or through cranial or sacral nerves to sensory ganglia. Their cell bodies are morphologically indistinguishable from those of the somatic sensory neurons with which they are mingled in craniospinal ganglia.

Autonomic Nerve Cells. The cell bodies of the preganglionic visceral efferent neurons

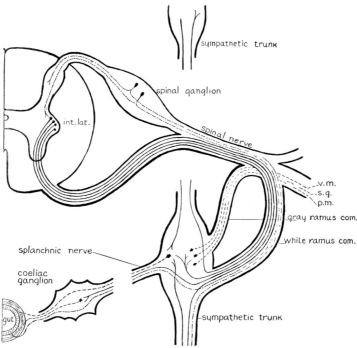

Fig. 9–36.   Diagram of relations of sympathetic trunk to spinal cord and spinal nerves. Visceral sensory fibers are drawn in dot-and-dash lines, preganglionic fibers in continuous lines, and postganglionic fibers in broken lines. For clearness the rami communicantes are drawn farther separated from the spinal ganglion than natural. *Int. lat.,* Intermediolateral gray column of the spinal cord, axons of whose cells form preganglionic fibers; *p.m.,* pilomotor postganglionic fiber; *s.g.,* postganglionic fiber for sweat glands; *v.m.,* vasomotor postganglionic fiber. (From Herrick's Introduction to Neurology.)

are small, spindle-shaped elements in the intermediolateral gray column.

The postganglionic neurons of the craniosacral visceral nervous system lie, as a rule, close to the viscera innervated. The preganglionic fibers, accordingly, are relatively long—as in the vagus nerve—and the postganglionic fibers are short. On the other hand, most of the synapses of the thoracolumbar system are in the ganglia of the sympathetic chains or trunks; therefore their postganglionic fibers are relatively longer.

The nervous elements of the sympathetic ganglia are generally small and have such diverse shapes and structure that some maintain that no morphological classification is practicable. The cells are generally multipolar, with the dendrites and axon sometimes being clearly distinguishable, in other cases showing no obvious difference. Preganglionic fibers often synapse with the dendrites of the ganglion cell in dense glomeruli. For a typical example see the description of the postganglionic neurons of the intestine.

The cell body may be surrounded by a capsule of satellite cells, which, like those of the craniospinal ganglia, are ectodermal elements related to the cells of Schwann in the nerve sheaths. In the outlying sympathetic ganglia these capsules may be absent, but the cells of Schwann accompany the peripheral sympathetic fibers everywhere.

NEUROGLIA

The term "neuroglia" is applied to the following interstitial tissues: the *ependyma* which lines the ventricles of the brain and spinal cord, *neuroglial cells* and their expansions or "fibers" which bind together the neurons in the central nervous system and in the retina, and the *satellite* or *capsular cells* of the peripheral ganglia. The *cells of Schwann* of the peripheral nerves may be considered equivalent to peripheral neuroglia.

Ependyma. In the early embryonic stages of the brain and spinal cord the wall of the neural tube is a simple epithelium (Fig. 9–

the wall enclosing the ventricular cavities always retains an epithelial character (Fig. 9–37, 9–60). This lining membrane, the adult ependyma, is composed of the inner ends of the persisting epithelial cells, with their nuclei and some of their cytoplasm, and such derivatives of the primitive embryonic epithelium as remain in connection with it.

The embryonic ependyma is ciliated, and in some parts of the ventricular lining the cilia may persist in adult life. In the mature brain, their broad bases taper to long, threadlike processes that may branch and that are lost among other elements of the brain (Fig. 9–37). In a few places, where the nervous wall is thin, as in the ventral fissure of the spinal cord, some ependymal cells span the entire distance between the ventricular and external surfaces. All of them do so in the early embryonic stages (Fig. 9–38). In these cases the ependymal cells form a dense *internal limiting membrane* at the ventricular end.

At the external surface under the *pia mater* the ependymal threads and bars expand into pedicles which fuse into a thin, smooth and dense membrane, the *external limiting membrane* of the central nervous system (Fig. 9–38). Similar membranes are formed around the blood vessels (Figs. 9–39, 9–40). In most parts of the adult human brain and spinal cord, with the increase in the thickness of the wall, the ependymal threads are stretched between the internal and external limiting membranes beyond the breaking point. Finally the ependymal threads lose contact with the opposite face of the wall, remaining connected with their own ependymal cells.

Neuroglia Proper or "Glia." In any section of the central nervous system prepared by ordinary histological methods, small nuclei are seen scattered among the nerve cells and their processes (Figs. 9–42, 9–9). The cytoplasm and long processes of these neuroglial elements are revealed by special histological technique.

Three types of neuroglia are distinguished: *astrocytes, oligodendrocytes,* and *microglia.* The first two, called *macroglia,* are undoubtedly of ectodermal origin, as are the nerve cells proper. The third, or microglia, originates from mesodermal cells of the pia mater which migrate into the central nervous system along the blood vessels.

The *astrocytes,* termed also "astroglia," "macroglia," or "spider cells," are of two varieties. The first is the *protoplasmic astrocyte* with nucleus larger than in oligodendrocytes and microglia, and with relatively abundant granular cytoplasm and numerous, rather thick plasmatic expansions (Fig. 9–39). Many of their processes are attached to the blood vessels and to the pia mater by means of expanded pedicles. In other cases, the body of the cell lies

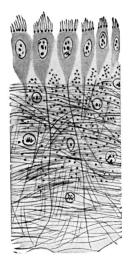

Fig. 9–37. Neuroglia from the ependymal layer of the fourth ventricle (tuberculum acusticum) of a cat, with ciliated ependymal cells. (After Rubaschkin.)

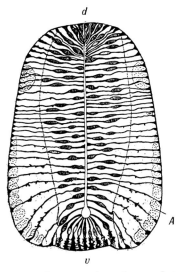

Fig. 9–38. Cross section of neural tube of a three-day chick embryo. Spongioblasts stain black; neuroblasts between them are unstained. *v,* ventral side; *d,* dorsal side; *A,* region of future anterior column of the white substance. Method of Golgi. (Redrawn after Ramón y Cajal.)

52). Certain thin, non-nervous parts of the brain retain this structure throughout adult life, as the epithelial layer of the choroid plexus (Fig. 9–58). In most other parts of the neural tube, the wall is greatly thickened by the differentiation and multiplication within it of neurons and neuroglial elements. The lining of the inner surface of

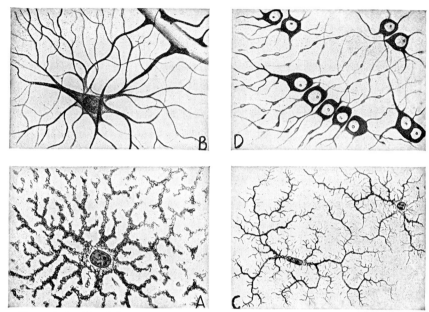

Fig. 9–39.   Neuroglial cells of the central nervous system. *A*, protoplasmic astrocyte; *B*, fibrous astrocyte; *C*, microglia; *D*, oligodendroglia. (After del Río-Hortega.)

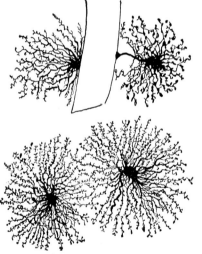

Fig. 9–40.   Short-rayed astrocytes from the gray matter of the brain of an adult man; the two upper ones are connected with the walls of a blood vessel by their processes. Golgi method. (After Ramón y Cajal.)

directly on the wall of the blood vessel or on the inner surface of the pia. Some of the smaller cells of this variety lie close to the bodies of the neurons and are called *satellite cells.* The other variety is the *fibrous astrocyte* (Fig. 9–39), distinguished from the first by long, relatively thin, smooth, and little branched expansions. Embedded within the cytoplasm of their bodies and expansions are fibrillar structures or *neuroglial fibers* (Fig. 9–41). These cells also are often attached to the blood vessels by

means of their processes. The protoplasmic astrocytes are found chiefly in the gray substance, the fibrous astrocytes in the white substance of the brain insinuated between the fascicles of nerve fibers. Mixed or *plasmato-fibrous astrocytes* are occasionally encountered at the boundary between the gray and white substance, those of their processes that spread into the gray substance have a protoplasmic character, while those that pass into the white substance are fibrous.

The *oligodendrocytes,* also called "oligodendroglia" and "oligoglia" (Fig. 9–39), are closely akin to the astrocytes, which they resemble in most respects. They are smaller and have smaller nuclei, although there are many transitional forms. The name is derived from the fact that their few and slender processes have few branches. No true neuroglial fibers are related to them. They seem to be in an especially intimate relationship with the nerve fibers along which they are frequently found in rows or columns. Because of this they are regarded as the central homologue of the neurolemmal cells of Schwann. In the gray substance those oligodendrocytes that adjoin the nerve cells proper are called "satellites" (Fig. 9–42, *A*). The criteria for identification of the several types of macroglia in electron micrographs have not been agreed upon.

In the *microglia* (Fig. 9–39, *C*), the nucleus is small but deeply stained and surrounded by scanty protoplasm. The few expansions are rather short and, unlike the more or less straight expansions of the astrocytes, are twisted in various ways. Also, the processes and the body do not appear smooth, but are covered with a considerable number of tiny pointed twigs or "spines." The microglial cells are scattered everywhere throughout the brain and spinal cord.

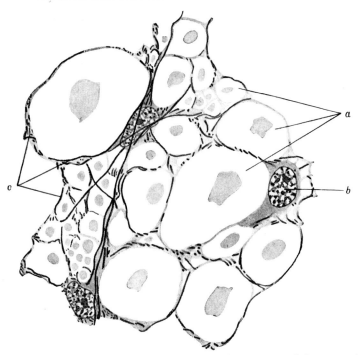

Fig. 9–41.   Cross section of white matter of spinal cord of a cat stained for neuroglia fibers. *a,* nerve fibers of different calibers, with a centrally located axis cylinder and with a wide, pale myelin sheath; *b,* neuroglia cell; *c,* neuroglia fibers. Weigert method. 1000 ×. (A.A.M.)

The neuroglia of the adult central nervous system develops from the primitive spongioblasts of the embryo (Fig. 9–51), and is of ectodermal origin. An exception is the microglia, which possibly is mesodermal. In the mature brain and spinal cord the neuroglial tissue as a whole forms an extremely complicated supporting framework of cells and their expansions, with a multitude of passages, in which the nerve cells proper or neurons and their processes are suspended. Like the nerve cells, the supporting neuroglial cells do not form an actual syncytium (as assumed by some), but they, too, retain a certain degree of individuality, although apparently less than do the neurons, since the adjoining neuroglial cells form virtually a sealed honeycomb. In the chambers of this honeycomb the nerve cells and their expansions are individually encapsulated and thus separated or insulated from one another (Fig. 9–41). Only at the points of the synapses are the neuroglial barriers broken, and only here is a direct contact between the neurons possible.

The neuroglia appears also to be an important mediator for the normal metabolism of the nervous elements proper, although little is known in this respect. More is known about the activity of the neuroglia in pathological processes. Whenever the neurons are affected by a local or distant pathological process, the surrounding neuroglial elements always react in some way. They are actively involved in the degeneration and regeneration of the nerve fibers, in vascular disorders, in various infectious processes, and are the chief source of tumors of the central nervous system. In particular, the microglial cells assume a great variety of forms, with active migration and phagocytosis. They probably play a role in the metabolism of the nerve cells, and phagocytose disintegrating nervous elements.

SYNAPSE AND THE INTERRELATIONSHIPS OF NEURONS

Essentially, the nervous system is composed of complex chains of neurons so arranged as to permit transmission of excitation from one neuron to another in one direction only. The site of transneuronal transmission is called a *synapse.* Physiologically, it is of the utmost importance, for functional polarization is established here, and not along the nerve fiber where conduction in either direction is possible. What the basis of irreciprocal conduction across the synapse may be is uncertain.

Anatomically the synapse has been traditionally described as a place of contact between two neurons and may be from axon to dendrite, from axon to perikaryon, more rarely from axon to axon.

The number of synapses on a neuron may vary from only a few to as many as 1800 on the body of a single motor neuron. The forms

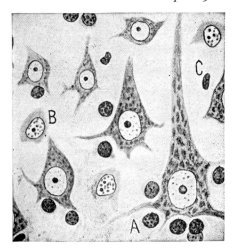

Fig. 9–42. Portion of human cerebral cortex stained by Nissl's method. *A,* naked nuclei of oligodendroglia cells; *B,* protoplasmic astrocyte; *C,* nucleus of microglia cell. In addition, large and small pyramidal neurons. (After del Río-Hortega.)

of the synapses vary in the extreme (Fig. 9–43). Usually they are tiny swellings at the ends of the axon endings. Or the twigs form bouquets or loose baskets, and the like, adhering to the body or dendrites of another nerve cell. Each variety of neuron is distinguished by its own form of synaptic terminations, some having endings of several kinds. Neurons that have no direct or even indirect synaptic relationship with one another are independent of one another.

In electron micrographs showing central nervous system synapses (Figs. 9–44 and 9–45), the membrane of the end feet of axons, called presynaptic membrane, is separated from the membrane of the dendrite or perikaryon (post-synaptic membrane) by a space of about 200 A, the constitution of which is unknown. The cytoplasm of the axon terminal is characterized by a collection of mitochondria and by numerous clusters of vesicles. In the cytoplasm immediately

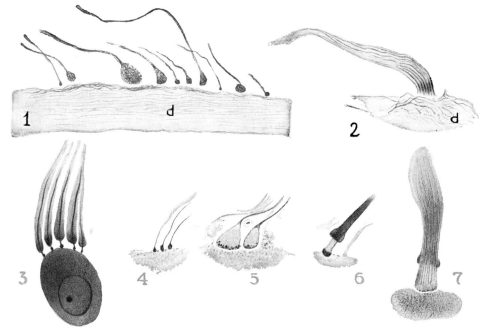

Fig. 9–43. Types of nerve fiber endings in the vertebrate central nervous system. *1,* end-feet of Held of unmyelinated nerve fibers ending on dendrite of another neuron (*d*). *2,* club ending of Bartelmez which ends abruptly on dendrite of another neuron (*d*). *3,* fine myelinated fibers ending on nerve cell by means of tiny "end-feet." *4,* similar endings of unmyelinated fibers on dendrite of another nerve cell. *5,* large "end-feet" on dendrite of another nerve cell. Note red-stained granular mitochondria at terminal surfaces of the "end-feet." *6, 7,* clublike endings of myelinated fibers ending on dendrites of other cells. Neurofibrils in dendrite of *7* are cut transversely and appear as fine dots. *1* and *2* stained for neurofibrils with reduced silver. 3 to 7 fixed by injecting Zenker-formol into blood vessels of living animal; silver followed by Mallory-azan stain. All from the brain of the goldfish. 1440 ×. (After Bodian, 1937; Courtesy of Wistar Press. Drawn by Miss Agnes Nixon.)

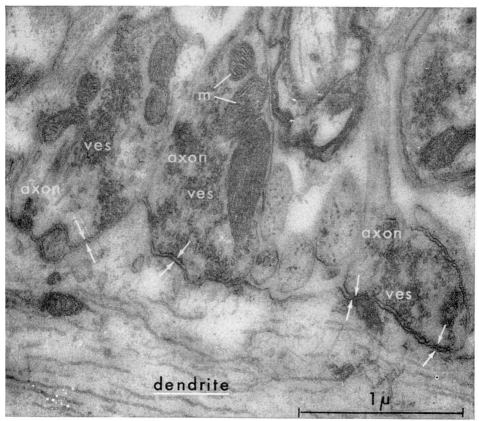

Fig. 9–44. Electron micrograph through synapses of three axon endings on a dendrite from the region of abducens nucleus of a rat. *m*, mitochondria; *ves*, the small vesicles characteristic of presynaptic endings. The apposing synaptic membranes, indicated by arrows, are separated by a space about 200 A in diameter. Buffered osmic acid fixation. (Courtesy of S. Palay.)

beneath the post-synaptic membrane, mitochondria and especially the vesicles are usually much fewer.

The absence of cytoplasmic continuity between neurons forms the basis for the almost universally held neuron doctrine which maintains that each mature nerve cell represents a cellular unit, anatomically separate from, and trophically independent of, other neurons. The claim of cytoplasmic continuity between neurons of the intestinal autonomic plexus should be tested with the electron microscope.

The processes of a nerve cell are dependent on the body with its nucleus; when cut off, they die, although peripheral processes may regenerate from the perikaryon (p. 219). The body and nucleus of the nerve cell are the trophic center of the whole neuron. If a nerve cell suffers irreparable injury, adjoining nerve cells are not necessarily affected.

Various theories based on chemical and electrical changes observed in nerves have been advanced to explain the transmission of the nervous impulse from one neuron to another or to another effector ending. Of particular interest is acetylcholine which is found in the central nervous system, as well as in peripheral autonomic ganglia and motor end plates. Its specific destructor, acetylcholinesterase, has been found in plexiform layers, rich in synapses, of the cerebral cortex; the full significance of these findings is not known. It is suspected that there are other, as yet unidentified, transmitter substances at central synapses.

Examples of Interrelationships of Neurons. Except in the primate retina, where one-to-one synapses are found (Fig. 9–46), practically all neurons are connected with several or many other neurons. With the aid of the Golgi impregnation and other meth-

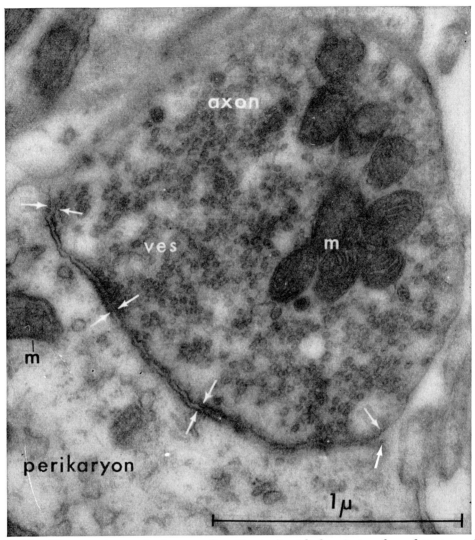

Fig. 9–45. Electron micrograph of axon ending (bouton) applied against surface of a neuron in the abducens nucleus of a rat. The presynaptic ending with its mitochondria (*m*) and the characteristic small vesicles (*ves*) are shown. The actual synapse is indicated by arrows. Buffered osmic acid fixation. (Courtesy of S. Palay.)

ods, several different types of relationships between neurons have been shown to be present. These vary from extremely complex relationships involving the processes of hundreds of cells to relatively simple configurations. It will suffice here to give examples of a few extreme categories. For instance, attached to the body and dendrites of many large motor cells of the anterior gray columns of the spinal cord are many hundreds of synaptic buttons of axon endings of neurons in the cerebral cortex, medullary nuclei and elsewhere in the spinal cord. The spinal motor cells serve, accordingly, as the *final common*

pathway where the nervous impulses from a variety of sources are transmitted to effector organs. A clear instance of this is found in the giant Mauthner's cells in the medulla oblongata of fishes (Fig. 9–43). In the retina, the *d*-bipolars serve as a common pathway for impulses from both rods and cones (Fig. 9–46, *A*). The reverse arrangement is shown in Figure 9–46, *C,* where one retinal cone is in contact with three neurons (*d, f, h*).

In the frequent arrangement in which a few neurons are related to a large group of neurons, the reaction is not commensurate with the initial stimulus, but is determined

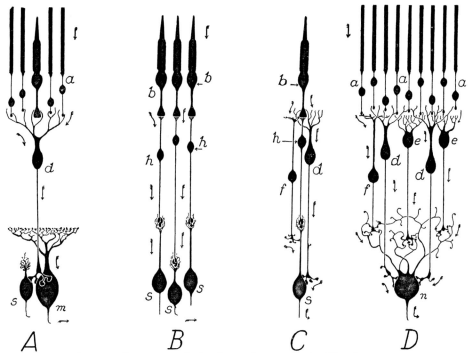

Fig. 9–46. Several types of synaptic relationships of neurons. *A*, *d*-Bipolar neuron serving as a common pathway for both rods and cones (*a*); *B*, isolated conduction or one-to-one relationship of neurons (*b-h-s*); *C*, a single excitation (in *b*) is transferred to each of the three related neuron varieties (*d, f, h*); *D*, excitations from a number of rods (*a*) pass through intermediary neurons (*d, e, f*) to a single large neuron (*n*). Examples from the primate retina (see Figure 32–25). (Courtesy of S. Polyak.)

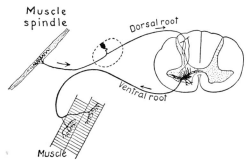

Fig. 9–47. Diagram illustrating simple spinal reflex arc consisting of a sensory neuron connected with a receptor ending and a motor neuron connected with a muscle. Physiological connection between the two neurons is effected within the spinal cord. (Modified from van Gehuchten.)

by the number and kinds of reacting neurons, often arranged in internuncial chains effecting inhibition or facilitation of the impulse. Thus, in a spinal reflex arc (Fig. 9–47) the excitation of a few peripheral sensory elements may activate a great number of motor neurons, and the total response or effect may exceed many times the energy that

initiated it. Another example is the excitation of a few photoreceptor cells of the retina and the subsequent turning of the eyes and head toward the source of the stimulus.

These glimpses of the exceedingly intricate interconnections between neurons, coupled with their enormous numbers (it is estimated that there are 9,200,000,000 neurons in the cerebral cortex alone), and their extreme variability in the various parts of the nervous system, indicate the extreme complexity of structure and function.

White Matter Conducts, Gray Matter Integrates Impulses. The details of the extremely complex organization of the central nervous system must be sought in manuals of neurology. But it may be helpful to include here a few photomicrographs of three different parts of the nervous system. Figure 9–48 of the spinal cord emphasizes the external position of the great masses of myelinated fibers with the relatively small amount of gray substance with nerve cell bodies. Figures 9–49 and 9–50 show the gray matter outside the white in cerebral cortex and cerebellum. The

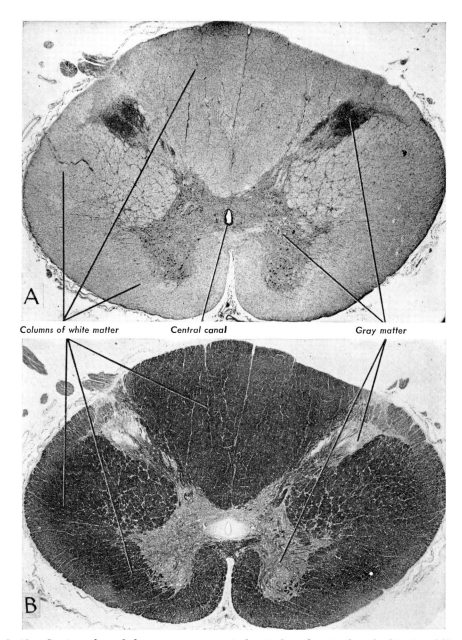

Columns of white matter   Central canal   Gray matter

Fig. 9–48. Sections through human, upper cervical spinal cord stained with thionine (*A*) to show cells, and with the Weigert-Weil method (*B*) to show myelinated fibers. Note the external arrangement of the fibers (white matter) and the central, cruciate area containing the cell bodies (gray matter). The ventral surface is below. A portion of the dorsal root is seen in the upper left. 12 ×. (Courtesy of P. Bailey.)

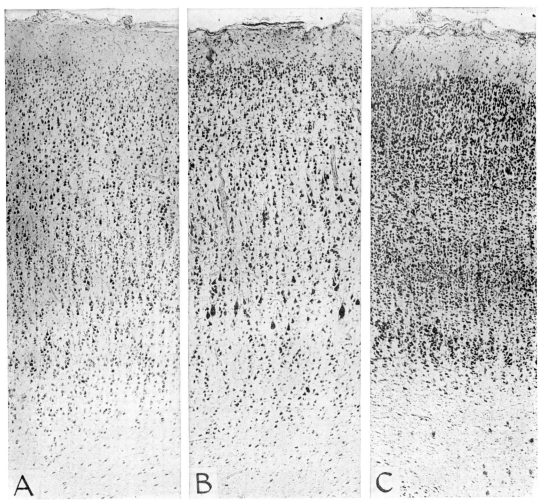

Fig. 9–49. Sections from three areas of human cerebral cortex, showing distribution of nerve cell bodies in the temporal eulaminate (associational) cortex (*A*), precentral agranular cortex (motor area) (*B*) and occipital koniocortex (striate visual cortex) (*C*). Much stress has been laid on minute differences in lamination of the nerve cells and fibers in these and other areas of the cortex, but there is now a tendency toward minimizing some of these differences. 53 ×. (Courtesy of P. Bailey.)

white matter of the brain, the numerous tracts of the brain stem and spinal cord, and practically all peripheral nerves, are chiefly or entirely made up of myelinated or unmyelinated axis cylinders. These parts serve, accordingly, to transmit nervous excitations from the viscera to the central nervous system, or vice versa, or from one part of the brain or cord to other parts. There is no evidence that any essential modification of the passing excitations occurs in the fibrous parts.

In the regions composed chiefly of nerve cells, unmyelinated and some myelinated nerve fibers, in the nerve centers which constitute the so-called "gray matter" (cerebral and cerebellar cortex, various subcortical nuclei, gray columns of the spinal cord, peripheral ganglia), the situation is reversed. Here innumerable reciprocal contacts between the various types of neurons make possible an endless variety of mutual influences. It is here that the centralizing, selecting, combining, dividing and intensifying of incoming impulses is performed and the resulting impulses sent back to the peripheral organs of execution. A preparation of such an area shows the bodies of the cells arranged in a certain order, usually in layers. The space between the cellular layers, and also between the individual cells, is filled with innumerable

Outer molecular layer

Granular layer

Purkinje cells

Molecular layer

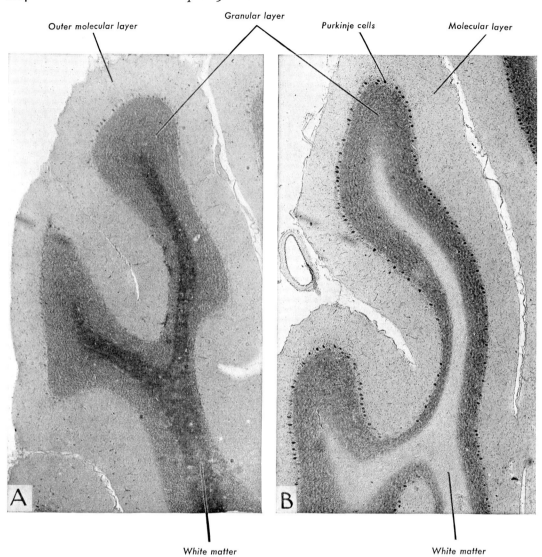

White matter

White matter

Fig. 9–50.   Sections of human cerebellar folia stained with Weigert-Weil (*A*) for myelinated fibers and with thionine for cells (*B*). Note the central disposition of the white matter with its myelinated fibers, which stain black with Weigert-Weil and pale with thionine, the outer molecular layer (pale gray) with scattered neurons and the large Purkinje cells, and the intermediate or granular layer composed of cells and fibers. 32 ×. (Courtesy of P. Bailey.)

axis cylinders and dendrites, and also with neuroglia and blood vessels. The nervous expansions usually are without myelin sheaths, which accounts for the gray appearance of these parts in fresh condition.

When stained with routine methods, the nervous plexiform substance between the cell bodies has a dotted aspect, and was often called *neuropil.* Where the separation of cellular elements from the plexiform substance is complete (as in the molecular layer of the cerebellar cortex, in the plexiform layer of

the cerebral cortex, and in the retina) certain layers are composed almost exclusively of the naked expansions of the neurons and of the neuroglia. Since, in these layers, huge numbers of synaptic contacts take place, they can be called *synaptic fields* (layers 5 and 7, Fig. 32–25).

The pattern of the cells and fibers (cytoarchitecture) in the gray substance varies much in detail from place to place. Every subcortical nucleus, peripheral ganglion, and locality of the cerebral cortex has architectural features of its own. Thus the cortex in the precentral convolution of the primate brain, which coincides with the so-called *motor area,* differs from that of the postcentral convolution, where the combined *somatosensory function* is represented, or from any other portion of the cerebral cortex. One of the most characteristic cortical areas is along the calcarine fissure of the occipital lobe which corresponds with the *visual center* (area striata). Another, in the Sylvian fossa, is the *auditory center.* Careful attempts to correlate cytoarchitectonic and functional findings have, however, failed up to the present time. Some functions of the central nervous apparatus are territorially well localized, whereas others are properties of large volumes of tissue.

The gray nervous substance differs profoundly from the simple nerve fibers or axons in several respects. Although most reflexes are transmitted over several intercalated neurons, a monosynaptic reflex arc may serve as an example. It can be conceived to be composed of a sensory (afferent) and a motor (efferent) neuron connected in the nervous center, together with the corresponding peripheral receptor and effector (Fig. 9–47). Such a mechanism is functionally characterized by the following: (1) It fatigues rapidly in contrast to the simple nerve fibers, which are exhausted slowly—or never as the myelinated fibers. (2) The reflex is blocked in the center by a fraction of the amount of a drug which suffices to block the peripheral nerve fiber. (3) The direction of the excitation is always from the sensory fiber to the motor or secretory fiber, indicating the functional polarity of the gray substance, termed irreversibility or irreciprocal conduction. (4) The response varies greatly with respect to the latent period and the intensity, depending on various conditions of the central nervous system itself; this is termed "variability." (5) The latent period is much longer than in the nerve fiber, and there may be an afterdischarge; that is, the response may continue for some time after the stimulus ceases. (6) Whereas one or a few stimuli may have no effect, an effect may result from numerous stimuli applied in sequence, which indicates summation. (7) Certain nerves are capable or decreasing or stopping the reflex response induced by the stimulation of other nerves,

an effect interpreted as inhibition. (8) The rhythm of the response in a reflex is usually slower than that of the applied stimulus (Sherrington).

Little is known of the mechanism underlying these phenomena. Some features may be due to difference in size, number of contacts and minute structure and organization of the various types of synaptic junctions and dendrite trees.

Electric Manifestations of the Brain. Considerable attention has been paid to two kinds of electric activity of the cortical gray substance. The spontaneous potentials manifest themselves by automatic rhythmic "beats" even in the absence of outside impulses; the other, the evoked potentials, often likewise rhythmic, arise only when a peripheral sensory organ is stimulated or a motor action initiated. These potential changes often have some characteristic local features limited to a particular architectural area. The subcortical pathways, various nuclei, the spinal cord and even the peripheral ganglia may show a like activity.

It would thus seem that the normal cerebral cortex is in a state of constant activity, irrespective of the stimuli from the peripheral sense organs. This is paralleled by its high metabolism, which, for oxygen, has been shown to be twenty-five times as great as in muscle or peripheral nerve. A great deal of automatic rhythmic activity seems to be inherent even in single neurons or agglomerations of these. The brain activity seems, therefore, to be the result of the interplay of the central autonomous forces and the excitations coming from the peripheral organs. When a particular peripheral sense organ (e.g., eye) is stimulated, the electrical reaction is primarily in the afferent pathway (optic nerve, tract, radiation in the case of the eye) and in the particular cortical field of projection (area striata).

DEVELOPMENT OF THE NEURONS AND OF THE NERVOUS TISSUE

The neurons of the nervous system develop from embryonic ectoderm; an exception is the peripheral olfactory neurons, which develop from the sensory epithelium of the nasal sacs. Likewise of ectodermal origin are the neuroglial cells (with the probable exception of microglia), the neurolemmal cells of the peripheral nerves and the satellite cells of the

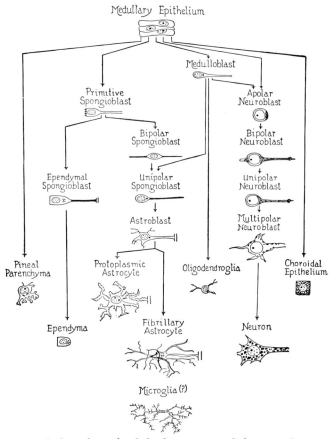

Fig. 9–51.   Diagram, partly hypothetical, of the histogenesis of the central nervous system. Especially hypothetical are the medulloblasts, yet their existence seems to be necessary to explain the histogenesis of the nervous system, its malformations, and its tumors. (After Bailey.)

peripheral ganglia—and apparently also certain elements of the meninges.

In early embryonic stages the future central nervous system separates by folding from the primitive ectoderm to form the *neural tube.* Next, other cells detach from the neural tube to form cellular bands between the neural tube and the ectoderm that later becomes epidermis. These bands, the *neural crests,* soon become segmented, the precursors of the cranial and spinal ganglia, and probably the autonomic ganglia. The epithelium that forms the neural tube is gradually differentiated into *spongioblasts,* which will become the ependyma and neuroglia, and *neuroblasts,* the future neurons. In a similar way some cells of the neural crests become peripheral neurons; others, satellite cells; still others, neurolemmal cells. These ectodermal tissues are at first sharply separated from the surrounding mesenchyme, from which the meninges and the connective tissue of the central nervous system and of the ganglia are derived. The intimate association of the nervous and the connective tissues found in the adult is achieved only gradually.

The sensory neurons of the craniospinal nerves arise from the cells which remain in the vicinity of the original neural crests where they form ganglia of

these nerves. The peripheral (dendritic) processes of these cells grow outward and become the axis cylinders of the sensory nerve fibers. Their central processes enter the central nervous system as dorsal roots. The cell bodies of the peripheral motor and visceral neurons remain within the brain or spinal cord, their axons form the motor roots of the peripheral nerves and terminate in the muscles or in the visceral ganglia. Some of the indifferent cells leave the central nervous system and migrate into various parts of the body, where they become sympathetic or visceral ganglia. The steps by which the various cells of the central nervous system are derived from the primitive epithelium of the neural tube are diagrammed in Figure 9–51.

As soon as the immature neurons of the neural tube and crest can be distinguished from other cells, they are called *neuroblasts* (Fig. 9–53). Those of the spinal ganglia (*o*) send their axons through the dorsal roots (*B*) into the spinal cord; those in the ventral part of the neural tube (*e*) send their axons through the ventral roots (*A*) outward toward the muscles and viscera; those in the dorsal part of the neural tube (*a*) become correlation neurons of the spinal cord. The protoplasm of the growing axons shows ameboid movements and insinuates itself between the other tissue elements by a positive out-growth. At its advancing tip there is a bulbous en-largement, called "growth cone" (Fig. 9–54), from which slender, spinelike projections are thrust be-tween obstructing cells and fibers.

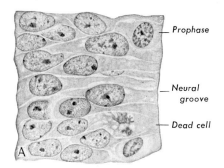

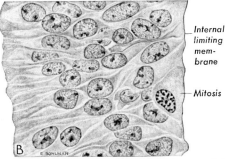

Fig. 9–52.   A, portion of neural fold just caudal to the posterior neuropore of an eighteen-somite hu-man embryo (about twenty-four days old). It is a pseudostratified epithelium with cell boundaries clearly defined. The internal limiting membrane is developing, but the external one has not appeared. As in most rapidly growing tissues, there is an occa-sional degenerating cell. 845 ×. B, part of lateral wall of neural tube in the region of the medulla oblongata from a twenty-six-somite human embryo (about four weeks old). The cells are much longer and more irregular than in A, but it is occasionally possible to follow one through the entire thickness of the wall. Cell boundaries indicate that the origi-nal epithelial condition persists. Both external and internal limiting membranes are present. 845 ×. (Courtesy of G. W. Bartelmez.)

The knowledge of the development of the neurons expounded above is based chiefly upon the study of the fixed and stained material, and was confirmed in all essential points by Harrison's observations on living nerves in tissue culture, a method which he devised for this purpose. This was amplified by Speidel's studies of the growing nerves in the trans-parent tail of the living frog tadpole. These observa-tions showed that the axons of the unipolar neuro-blasts grow into the intercellular spaces as slender, protoplasmic strands. It is clear that in the peripheral nerve fibers all newly formed nerve sprouts are at first devoid of neurolemmal and myelin sheaths. Next they are joined by Schwann's cells. The earliest myelin seen with the light microscope appears near the nucleus of the sheath cells, from which locality it spreads proximally and distally.

The forces that in the course of phylogeny and ontogeny have brought about the complex nervous

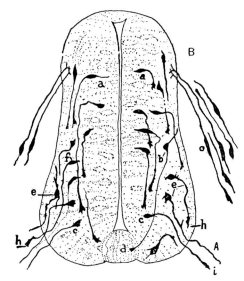

Fig. 9–53.   Section through spinal cord of a three-day chick. A, anterior and, B, posterior roots; a, b, c, etc., neuroblasts whose axons frequently end in swellings (d, h, i); o, spinal ganglion cells whose processes have penetrated the spinal cord. Golgi method. (Redrawn after Ramón y Cajal.)

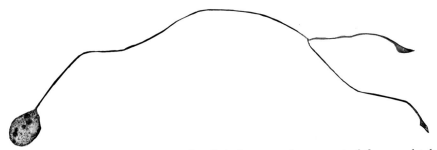

Fig. 9–54.   Isolated unipolar neuroblast with a forked process, from a part of the neural tube of Rana palustris explanted in a drop of lymph of Rana pipiens two days previously. 350 ×. (Redrawn after Harrison.)

tissue of vertebrates are unknown. Some saw in *mechanical factors* the chief cause directing the growth of the neuroblasts and their expansions. Others thought that in addition the various peripheral tissues secrete substances which exert *chemotactic influences* upon the sensitive growing buds of the axons, a process called *neurotropism*. In the central nervous system a similar force is believed to attract the dendrites and the bodies of the neurons toward the points whence this force emanates.

The concept of *neurobiotaxis* assumes the driving force to be a difference in electric potential between the dendrites and the axis cylinder. In this theory a neuron, or a group of them, is attracted by the axis cylinders and endings of other related neurons, this attraction being at first expressed by the shortening of the dendrites and later by the migration of the bodies in the direction of the source whence their stimuli come.

The role of *purely mechanical factors,* of the oriented ultrastructure (micellar orientation and aggregation), as the guide along whose channels the developing axis cylinders spread, has lately been experimentally tested, and the importance of the chemotactic, electrical and electromagnetic factors has been questioned. No effect of a galvanic or faradic current has been seen upon either the rate or the direction of the growth of nerves in the living vertebrate.

The ultimate causes are not known which determine the orientation of the ultramicroscopic micellar units in the media wherein the nervous processes expand, and induce the selecting of particular micellar pathways by particular axons. Although most attention has been directed to problems of outgrowing fibers, it now seems likely that the periphery can affect the central connections after contact has been established between outgrowing fibers and the periphery.

DEGENERATION AND REGENERATION OF THE NERVOUS TISSUE

The neuroglia of the adult central nervous system and the cells of Schwann and allied elements of the peripheral system are less specialized than the neurons. In certain circumstances they are capable of rapid proliferation. This occurs in certain tumors (gliomas), in scar tissue, in various other pathological conditions, and in a special form during the process of regeneration of peripheral nerve fibers.

Mammalian nerve cells, on the contrary, as soon as they reach that early stage of differentiation when they can be recognized as neuroblasts, appear to lose the power of multiplication. If any neurons are destroyed, they are not replaced.

Though mature neurons cannot proliferate, they show visible changes in the course of normal physiological activity and in various pathological conditions. The change in size and shape is particularly manifest in the following instances: (1) transplantation or explantation of nerve cells, (2) pathological or operative destruction of portions of the central nervous system, and (3) after injury to peripheral nerves.

The chromophile substance of Nissl is especially sensitive to both artificial stimulation and normal fatigue. In nervous elements which were highly active or were in some way impaired, the chromophile substance partly disintegrates into granules distributed throughout the cytoplasm and partly dissolves. This phenomenon is called *chromatolysis* or *tigrolysis* (Fig. 9–9). The Nissl substance may even disappear completely in consequence of extreme fatigue or exhaustion. After a period of rest this substance again accumulates and the cell assumes its original appearance. If too high a degree of fatigue is produced, complete degeneration and death of the neuron may result.

Accompanying chromatolysis may be an increase in the volume of the cell due to an increased water content of both nucleus and cytoplasm. With the advance of exhaustion of the cell, a decrease in its volume is evident; the cytoplasm becomes vacuolated, and finally the cell perishes. During intense activity the neurofibrils likewise increase in number and become thinner and paler staining. During hibernation they diminish in number, and become thicker and more deeply stained.

The changes in chromophile substance in fatigue and in various pathological conditions has been much studied. Most of these changes take the form of chromatolysis, with considerable variety in detail. The most complete observations concern the change in the cell body after its axon is severed. This is the so-called *primary reaction of Nissl,* the *axon reaction* or the *retrograde cell degeneration.* The cell body grows larger, chromatolysis is observed, the nucleus migrates to one side of the body, and the nuclear membrane shrivels. The reaction may be more or less severe, depending on the variety of the neuron, the nature of the injury, the distance from the cell body at which the axon was cut, and the degree of regeneration, if any, which follows the injury. When the axon is not destroyed completely, so that the remaining part may still perform some function, and when regeneration occurs, the injured neuron may make a complete recovery. In more severe injury the changes in the cell body are more rapid and continue until degeneration is complete and the cell dies. In the brain the neurons probably always degenerate and disappear completely whenever their axis cylinders are interrupted. The axis cylinder exhibits immediate changes in form and structure after subjection to drugs, heat, cold, starvation, and after mechanical injury.

It is difficult and frequently impossible in normal material to follow the axons of some particular group of nerve cells as they make their devious ways through the central or peripheral nervous system, mingled with other fibers. If some of these fibers are severed by accident or disease, or if they are cut in an experiment, the cell bodies from which the injured fibers arise will show chromatolysis. On the other hand, the myelinated fibers which have been separated from their cell bodies, or whose cells have been destroyed, degenerate. During the period of from one to twelve weeks or more after the injury, before the degenerating myelin is resorbed, it can be specifically stained by a *method devised by Marchi.* Since the altered myelin stains black in contrast to the unstained myelin of the uninjured fibers, the course of the injured fibers distal to the injury can be accurately followed. These two methods—Nissl's method of retrograde chromatolysis and the method of Marchi—are extensively used in the investigation of the fiber tracts of the brain and the spinal cord. Fine fibers can be studied during early stages of degeneration by following their structural changes in silver-stained preparations.

When a nerve trunk is severed, the peripheral or distal portion soon loses its glossy white aspect and becomes dull and gray. The central or proximal portion remaining continuous with the cell bodies apparently does not change much. Artificial stimulation of the peripheral portion three or four days after the operation fails to produce a contraction of the muscles which it supplies, if it contains motor fibers. However, stimulation of the central portion, if it be a sensory or mixed nerve, produces the usual pain sensations and more or less widespread motor reflexes. Microscopic examination shows that the immediate result of the operation is a primary degenerative change which involves the ends of both the central and peripheral portions for a short distance. This is *traumatic degeneration*. But the changes in the whole length of the peripheral portion depend upon a different process. This is called *secondary* or *wallerian degeneration* of the nerve fiber (Fig. 9–55). It affects the entire length of the peripheral portion of the nerve.

In wallerian degeneration those parts of the severed peripheral fiber which are organic parts of the neuron, and hence trophically dependent upon its cell body, undergo complete degeneration. However, if conditions are favorable for regeneration, they may be restored to perfect function. This applies to the axis cylinder, and to the myelin sheath if present. On the other hand, the sheath of Schwann, being trophically independent of the neuron, survives and is reorganized with the active proliferation of nuclei and the growth of cytoplasm. It assists in the regeneration of the axon.

The axis cylinder of the peripheral stump always perishes. But in many cases there is ultimately a complete *regeneration* of this degenerated portion of the nerve and its terminal apparatus (Fig. 9–56). This regenerative process always proceeds from the end of the central stump. It progresses much slower than the rapidly occurring wallerian degeneration. It is accomplished relatively easily and quickly when the two severed ends of the nerve are immediately brought into close contact with each other. If the ends have been widely separated, the regenerative process may require a long time or may never take place. It occurs much more rapidly and successfully in a young person than in an old one.

The nonmyelinated fibers also undergo a secondary degeneration peripheral to the injury. Here, too, the axis cylinder disintegrates, and its fragments are absorbed by the protoplasm of Schwann's sheath. This process differs from that in the myelinated fibers only by the absence of the myelin sheath.

The degenerative processes cannot be sharply separated from those of regeneration, for the entire response of the neuron to injury seems to be reparative from the start. It is now definitely established that

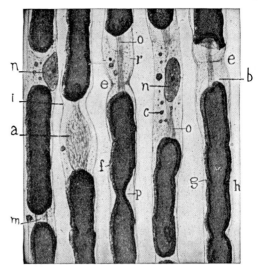

Fig. 9–55.   Fibers of the peripheral stump twenty-four hours after section of a nerve of a rabbit. *a,* widening of the axon next to a constriction (*i*); *B,* vacuole of the constriction; *c,* spherules of Erholz; *e,* cementing disk; *f,* incisure of Schmidt-Lantermann; *g,* infundibulum of incisure; *m,* protoplasmic bridges formed at the level of the incisures; *n,* nuclei; *o,* subsistent axon in the protoplasm of Schwann's cells; *r,* protoplasm accumulated next to the disks of Ranvier. (After Ramón y Cajal.)

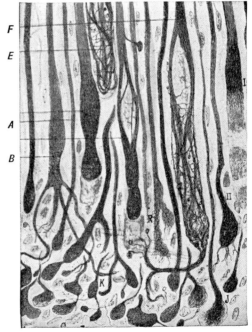

Fig. 9–56.   Central stump of sciatic nerve of adult cat, two days after the section. *A,* nonmedullated fiber; *B,* medullated axon ending in terminal branches; *E, F,* structures of Perroncito. (After Ramón y Cajal.)

the regeneration can be carried through to completion only by the outgrowth of nerve fibers from the uninjured axons of the central stump.

Although there is considerable variation in the extent and rate of regeneration, even among fibers of the same nerve, the time sequence of events is indicated very generally in the following description.

Very soon after section of a nerve the axons near the injury, and distal to it, swell. Within a few days they become fragmented. From the central ends of cut axons numerous new sprouts appear. Late in the first week the myelin segments become discontinuous, forming large irregular ovoids. Schwann cells proliferate, forming strands along the pathway of degenerating fibers. Connective tissue cells increase in number and may form scar tissue at the site of interruption of the nerve.

During the second week, and continuing for many weeks, the myelin ovoids break up into small globules which are gradually removed by macrophages. If the cell bodies in craniospinal ganglia or in motor nuclei of the central nervous system are examined late in the second week, maximal chromatolysis will usually be observed, although there is much variation depending on the type of injury and distance of cell bodies from the site of trauma. Unless conditions are unfavorable for regeneration, new axons may be found in the distal stump at this time. The rate of progress of the growing axons depends on several factors, but after crossing the injured area, they usually proceed at 1–2 mm. per day, establishing close association with the Schwann cells.

In the third week, careful scrutiny may reveal the first new myelin. During succeeding weeks, axons in the distal stump increase in length and diameter, and the new myelin sheaths become progressively thicker. If the growing axons reach and connect with appropriate end organs, function can be restored.

CONNECTIVE TISSUE, CHOROID PLEXUS, VENTRICLES, AND MENINGES OF THE CENTRAL NERVOUS SYSTEM

In addition to the neurons and the supporting neuroglia, both of ectodermal origin, the brain and the spinal cord everywhere contain blood vessels derived from mesenchyme. The membranes enveloping the brain and spinal cord are likewise composed chiefly of connective tissue. There are three such membranes. The outermost, the dura mater or pachymeninx, is dense and firm. Both the inner membranes, the innermost or the pia mater and the one next to it, the arachnoid membrane, are composed of much looser connective tissue and are called leptomeninges.

Dura Mater. The relation of the dura to the surrounding bones differs in the spinal cord and in the brain. In the vertebral canal the inner surface is lined by its own periosteum, and within this a separate cylindrical dural membrane loosely encloses the cord.

There is a rather wide epidural space between the periosteum and the dura which contains much loose connective and fatty tissue with many veins. The dura is firmly connected to the spinal cord on each side by a series of denticulate ligaments. The inner surface of the spinal dura is lined with squamous cells. Its collagenous bundles run for the most part longitudinally, and the elastic nets are less prominent than in the cerebral dura.

The dura mater of the brain at the beginning of its embryonic development also has two layers, but in the adult these are more or less closely joined. Both consist of loose connective tissue with elongated fibroblasts. The outer layer adheres to the skull rather loosely except at the sutures and the base of the skull. It serves as periosteum, is looser and richer in cells than the inner layer, and contains many blood vessels; its thick collagenous fibers are arranged in bundles. The inner layer is thinner, with finer fibers forming an almost continuous sheet. Its fibers run from in front and below backward and upward, thus with orientation opposite to those of the outer layer. These fibers are so arranged as to equalize tensions and pressures within the cranial cavity. The inner surface of the dura is smooth and covered with a layer of squamous mesothelial cells.

Arachnoid. In the brain and spinal cord the leptomeninges are similar in structure. The arachnoid is a thin, netlike membrane devoid of blood vessels, resembling the transparent parts of the omentum. Its outer surface is smooth, but from its inner surface run a multitude of thin, branching threads and ribbonlike strands, attached to the pia. The tissue on macroscopic examination has a cobweb-like appearance. The arachnoid membrane bridges over the sulci and the fissures on the surface of the brain and the spinal cord, forming subarachnoid spaces of various extent within these sulci.

Pia Mater. This inner membrane is a thin connective tissue net that closely adheres to the surface of the brain and the spinal cord. It contains a large number of blood vessels from which most of the blood of the underlying nervous tissue is derived. Attached to the pia are the inner fibrous strands of the arachnoid, and these two membranes are so intimately related that their histological structure can best be described together. In fact, these two membranes are often treated as one, the *pia-arachnoid*.

The main elements of both the arachnoid and the pia are interlacing collagenous bundles surrounded by fine elastic networks. In the spinal pia an outer longitudinal and an inner circular layer can be distinguished. Among the cells are fibroblasts and fixed macrophages; these are especially numerous in the pia along the blood vessels. They correspond in their general histological properties to the macrophages of the other parts of the body. They store vital dyes injected directly in the subarachnoid space. In inflammation, especially in tuberculous meningitis, they are transformed into large, free macrophages or epithelioid cells. In man they often contain, even under apparently physiological conditions, considerable amounts of a yellow pigment that sometimes reacts positively to tests for iron.

Along the blood vessels of the pia mater are scattered single mast cells and small groups of lymphocytes. In certain pathological conditions the latter increase enormously in number and may become transformed into plasma cells. The tissue of the leptomeninges, especially along the blood vessels of the pia, also contains many embryonic mesenchymal elements. In the pia mater, particularly on the ventral surface of the medulla oblongata, a varying number of melanoblasts can be found.

The outer and the inner surfaces of the arachnoid, the trabeculae, and the outer surface of the pia are lined with a layer of squamous mesenchymal epithelial cells. Whereas some investigators describe their rounding off, mobilization and transformation into free macrophages under the influence of inflammatory stimuli, others trace the origin of macrophages exclusively to fixed macrophages. This question requires further study.

During development of the meninges two zones may be distinguished: an outer zone of condensation of mesenchyme which gives rise to periosteum, dura, and membranous arachnoid; and an inner zone which becomes pia. Between these two zones the mesenchyme remains loose and later forms spongy tissue permeating the subarachnoid spaces.

In lower vertebrates the mesenchyme of the head is formed of cells derived in part from the entoderm (mesentoderm) and in part from the ectodermal neural crest (mesectoderm). Both types of mesenchyme have been shown to participate in the formation of the meninges. Working with amphibians and birds, Burr and others have transplanted portions of the early neural tube with and without the neural crest into foreign tissue. In subsequent development the transplants with the neural crest acquire typical pia mater containing cells of neural crest origin, while those lacking the neural crest show an atypical and defective pia.

If the mammalian pia mater likewise contains elements derived from both mesectoderm and mesentoderm, then it is uncertain whether the microglia, which is said to migrate into the brain from the pia mater, is ultimately of ectodermal or entodermal origin. It has been suggested, moreover, that this twofold origin of the elements of the leptomeninges explains some peculiarities of meningeal tumors.

Nerves of the Meninges. The dura and pia are richly supplied with nerves. All vessels of the pia and of the choroid plexus are surrounded by extensive nervous plexuses in the adventitia, from which fine fibrils penetrate the media. These nerves have their origin in the carotid and vertebral plexuses and in certain cranial nerves, and belong to the sympathetic system. Some fibers seem to emerge directly from various places of the brain. Sensory, non-encapsulated nerve terminations, and even single nerve cells, are also present on the adventitia of the blood vessels.

The cerebral dura contains, besides the nerves of the vessels, numerous sensory nerve endings in its connective tissue. The connective tissue of the cerebral pia contains extensive nervous plexuses. They are especially abundant in the tela choroidea of the third ventricle. The fibers end either in large, pear-shaped or bulbous swellings or in skeins and convolutions similar to those of the corpuscles of Meissner. In the spinal pia the vessels receive their nerves from the plexuses following the larger blood vessels to the cord. Afferent nerve endings are also present, but are very unevenly distributed.

Both myelinated and unmyelinated nerve fibers accompany the blood vessels into the substance of

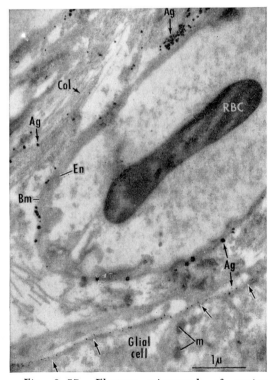

Fig. 9–57. Electron micrograph of section through the area postrema of rat vitally stained with silver (*Ag*) around the vessel and at the edge of the glial cell, indicating the hematoencephalic barrier. *BM*, basement membrane; *Col*, collagenous fibers; *En*, endothelium; *m*, mitochondria; *RBC*, red blood corpuscles. Buffered osmic acid fixation. (Courtesy of V. L. Van Breemen and C. D. Clemente.)

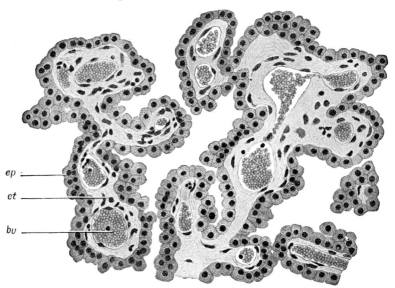

Fig. 9–58. Choroid plexus of the fourth ventricle from man. *ep,* Epithelium; *ct,* connective tissue; *bv,* blood vessels. 190 ×.

the spinal cord and the brain, ending on the muscle cells of the vessels. These come from similar nerves of the pial vessels, and the two nervous plexuses are continuous.

Meningeal Spaces. Between the dura mater and the arachnoid, the subdural space is comparable to a serous cavity. It contains a minimum of fluid and in reality is scarcely more than a potential space. Between the outer sheet of arachnoid and the pia, the subarachnoid space is traversed by cobwebby connective tissue trabeculae. It is independent of the subdural space and contains a large amount of fluid. At the summits of the convolutions it is narrow, but in the sulci it is wide and deep. The subarachnoid space is especially wide throughout the length of the spinal cord. In the brain it is greatly enlarged in a few places termed "cisterns," where the arachnoid is widely separated from the pia and the trabeculae are rare or absent. The most important of the cisterns lies above the medulla oblongata and below the posterior border of the cerebellum (cisterna cerebellomedullaris, or cisterna magna). The fourth ventricle communicates with this cistern through three openings in the tela choroidea: a medial foramen of Magendie—recently questioned by Meulen—and the two lateral foramina of Luschka.

Ventricles. The central nervous system begins its development as a neural tube with a wide cavity throughout its length, and it preserves its character as a hollow organ throughout life. The ventricle of the spinal cord, or central canal, in the adult is minute, or it may be obliterated. It does not seem to perform any important function. But in the normal adult the ventricular cavities of the brain always form a continuous channel for flow of cerebrospinal fluid throughout its length. If any part of this channel is occluded by disease so as to prevent free circulation of its fluids, an increased intracerebral pres-

sure develops, with resulting hydrocephalus or other serious pathological consequences.

The ventricular cavity is dilated in four regions: the two lateral ventricles in the cerebral hemispheres, the third ventricle in the thalamic region, and the fourth ventricle in the medulla oblongata and pons. Choroid plexuses develop in these four regions, and most of the ventricular fluid is derived from the blood vessels of these plexuses.

Choroid Plexus. There are four places where the wall of the brain retains its embryonic character as a thin, non-nervous epithelium. This part of the brain wall is the lamina epithelialis. The pia mater which covers it is extremely vascular and otherwise modified to form a choroid plexus. The lamina epithelialis is closely joined to the choroid plexus, and the whole is called tela choroidea or, less exactly, choroid plexus.

These choroid plexuses are found in the roof of the third and fourth ventricles, and in a part of the wall of the two lateral ventricles. In each case the tela choroidea is much folded and invaginated into the ventricle, so that the free surface exposed to the ventricular fluid is large, with branching tufts of tortuous vessels and a rich capillary net.

The epithelium early acquires a peculiar structure, different from that of the ependymal cells lining the ventricles. In embryonic stages it contains glycogen and carries cilia. In the adult its cells are cuboidal and are arranged in a single, regular layer. Each contains a large, round nucleus and a varying number of rod-shaped and granular mitochondria. Common inclusions are large, transparent vacuoles in the distal part of the cell, or large, usually single, fat droplets. On the free surface some have a brush-

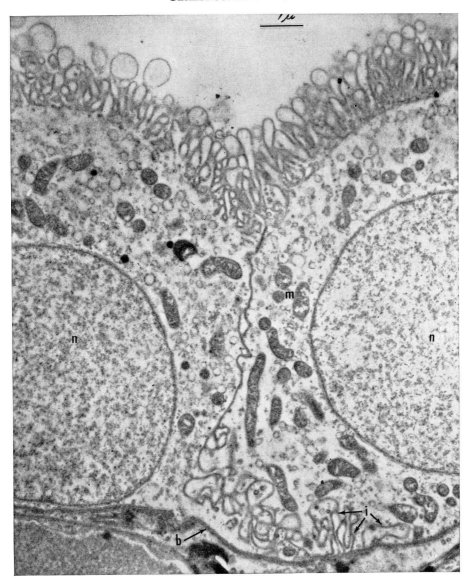

Fig. 9–59. Electron micrograph of choroid plexus of rat. The free surface of the cells has characteristic polypoid processes and the basal surface is provided with numerous, complicated basal infoldings, *i,* in the region between cells. *b,* basement membrane; *n,* nucleus; *m,* mitochondria. Buffered osmic acid fixation. (Courtesy of D. Maxwell and D. Pease.)

like border and, in the guinea pig, long, motile cilia. In animals repeatedly injected intravenously with vital dyes, such as trypan blue, the epithelium of the choroid plexus stores large amounts of the dye in granular form. In the perivascular connective tissue core of the plexus are many fixed macrophages which store large amounts of dye in contrast to those of the leptomeninges.

Cerebrospinal Fluid. The central nervous system is surrounded on all sides by cerebrospinal fluid; it is suspended in it as in a water bed. This fluid protects it from concussions and mechanical injuries and is of importance for its metabolism. The sub-

arachnoid spaces are in free communication, so that cerebrospinal fluid may pass through them from end to end of the central nervous system. The amount of the fluid is variable, estimated as 80 to 100 cc., or even as much as 150 cc. It is limpid and slightly viscous and has a low specific gravity (1.004 to 1.008). It contains traces of proteins, small quantities of inorganic salt and dextrose, and few lymphocytes (about two or three, and not more than ten in 1 cu. mm.). It resembles the aqueous humor of the eye more closely than any other liquid of the body.

The cerebrospinal fluid is constantly renewed. It

circulates slowly through the brain ventricles and through the meshes of the subarachnoid spaces. If these spaces are opened to the outside by injury (subarachnoid fistula), large amounts of fluid steadily drain off—200 cc. or more in a day. The sources of this fluid are primarily the blood vessels of the choroid plexus, the pia mater, and the brain substance. From the brain substance the flow is outward into the subarachnoid spaces; from the choroid plexus it is inward into the ventricles. Fluid may be added to the ventricles in a few other places, notably in the area postrema at the lower end of the fourth ventricle. The ependymal surfaces in general do not seem to discharge fluid into the ventricles. On the other hand, the absorption of fluid from the ventricles into neighboring veins takes place through the ventricular walls. The plexuses are wholly secretory, not resorptive, in function. They are the chief source of the cerebrospinal fluid. The chief channel of discharge of ventricular fluid outward into the subarachnoid spaces is through specially modified localities of the membranous roof of the fourth ventricle.

The flow of ventricular fluid normally passes from the lateral ventricles of the cerebral hemispheres, where it is derived chiefly from the lateral choroid plexuses, through the foramina of Monro into the third ventricle. Here fluid is added from the choroid plexus, and the augmented flow passes through the aqueduct of Sylvius into the fourth ventricle, where more fluid is added from the choroid plexus. From the fourth ventricle the fluid passes into the cerebellomedullary cistern, and from here it diffuses in all directions through the subarachnoid spaces. Some of it apparently gets into the extracranial lymphatics by way of the perineural spaces within the sheaths of the cranial nerve roots, part reaching the nasal cavity along the perineural sheaths of the olfactory nerve filaments. Around the spinal nerve roots there is an arrangement of the dural veins and sinuses adapted for the passage of cerebrospinal fluid directly into the venous blood, rather than into the lymphatic vessels. A small part of the cerebrospinal fluid enters the lymphatics or the veins by the routes just mentioned. Most of it passes directly into the big endocranial venous sinuses through the arachnoid villi.

Arachnoid Villi. The large endocranial venous sinuses are entirely enclosed by massive walls of dura mater except in definite places, chiefly in the sagittal sinus of the falx, where the dura is perforated by numerous protrusions of the arachnoid membrane, through each of which a finger-like evagination of the arachnoid mesothelium is thrust into the lumen of the sinus. This is the arachnoid villus. Its cavity, which contains a small amount of loose arachnoid tissue, is in free communication with the subarachnoid spaces, so that here the fluid of these spaces is separated from the blood of the sinus only by the thin mesothelial membrane.

These villi have been found in dogs, cats, monkeys, human infants, and adults. In man, with advancing age, they are enlarged and in this condition have long been known as Pacchionian corpuscles (granulations).

The arachnoid villi provide the main pathway for the outflow of cerebrospinal fluid directly into the venous circulation. This flow is rapid. Dyes and other chemicals injected into the subarachnoid spaces can be detected in the blood stream in ten to thirty seconds, and only after thirty minutes can they be found in the lymphatics.

Blood Vessels of the Central Nervous System. The arteries reach the spinal cord with the ventral and dorsal nerve roots (anterior and posterior radicular arteries) and form a dense arterial network in the spinal pia mater. Here several longitudinal arterial pathways can be distinguished (spinal arterial tracts). The most important among them is the anterior arterial tract; it gives off a multitude of small branches (central arteries) which enter the ventral medial fissure and penetrate to the right and left into the medial part of the anterior gray columns. They supply the major part of the gray substance with blood. Numerous smaller branches of the pial arterial net, the peripheral arteries, penetrate the white substance of the cord along its entire circumference. The capillary nets in the white substance are loose and have meshes which are drawn out longitudinal. The capillaries of the gray substance are much more numerous and dense. The course of the veins does not correspond with that of the arteries. Numerous venous branches emerge from the periphery of the cord and from the ventral median fissure and form a diffuse plexus in the pia; this is especially prominent on the dorsal surface of the cord. From this plexus the blood is led away by veins accompanying the ventral and dorsal roots.

The arterial supply of the brain is derived almost entirely from the carotids and the large arteries at its base, chiefly the basilar artery and the circle of Willis. Most of the arteries from these large vessels pass upward in the pia mater, from which smaller vessels dip into the brain substance. These vessels, after penetrating the brain, were commonly supposed to be end arteries, with no appreciable amount of anastomosis from one to another; this problem requires further study in mammals.

As in the spinal cord, the capillary net in the cerebral white matter is relatively meager, with elongated meshes; in the gray matter the net has a closer mesh. It is assumed that the density of capillaries is a crude indication of the rate of metabolism of the tissue supplied by it. On this assumption, it is clear that the metabolism of the gray substance is much more active than that of the white.

The linear extent of capillaries per unit volume of brain substance has been measured by Craigie in a number of representative parts of the central nervous substance in various animals. He finds, for instance, in the rat that parts of both white and gray matter differ in vascularity, all the gray being more vascular than the white. The motor nuclei are less vascular than the sensory nuclei and correlation centers. In the cerebral cortex the fourth layer of Brodmann is more vascular than the other layers, and the supragranular layers tend to be more vascular than the infragranular layers. The parietal area is more vascular than the others, and the vascularity of the cerebellar cortex is about the same as that of the cerebral cortex taken as a whole. In studying the postnatal development of this vascular

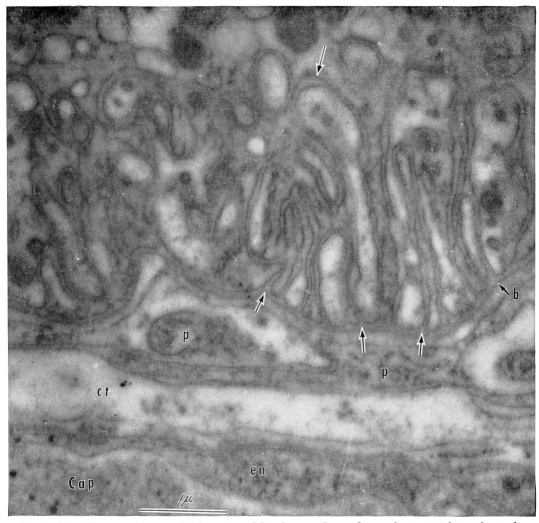

Fig. 9–60. Electron micrograph of section of basal part of ependyma of rat at right angles to basement membrane (*b*) showing the infolded basal membranes (arrows) in region between cells. *Cap,* capillary; *ct,* connective tissue space; *en,* endothelium; *p,* pia. Compare with similar basal infoldings in Figure 21–13 in the secretory duct of parotid gland and Figure 28–13 in distal convolution of kidney. Buffered osmic acid fixation. (Courtesy of D. Pease and D. Maxwell.)

pattern, it was concluded that the richness of the capillary supply is directly related to functional activity, and that the metabolism involved in the latter requires a greater blood supply than does the metabolism of growth.

There are no lymphatics in the central nervous system. Blood fluids which pass out from the capillaries seep through the tissue and are not collected in lymphatic vessels, as in most other parts of the body. The blood vessels that penetrate from the pia mater are surrounded by perivascular spaces which open freely at the brain surface into the subarachnoid spaces. Thus the cerebrospinal fluid, derived from the blood, is drained from the brain tissue outward toward the meninges without at any time being enclosed in definite lymphatic vessels.

When certain vital dyes, pigments or metals are present in circulating blood of adult animals, the tissues of the central nervous system remain colorless except the choroid plexus and certain subependymal areas. In these regions, most dyes and pigments are found within extravascular cells but silver particles remain on cell surfaces. From such experiments the concept of a barrier between the blood and the nervous tissue intervening between capillaries has been developed. There are several views as to the location of the *blood-brain* or *hematoencephalic barrier;* some maintain that the capillary endothelium is less permeable than in the rest of the body; others believe that the membrane formed by sucker feet of neuroglial cells on vessel walls excludes certain substances; still others designate the specialized subependymal areas as the barrier. Wislocki and Leduc suggest that the blood-brain barrier is composed of a succession of thresholds including the structures named above.

In young animals given intravenous dye injections, however, there can be found a distinct, although small, storage of the dye in the cells in different places of the brain stem, so that the apparent impermeability of the walls of the blood vessels develops gradually.

The choroid plexus is often considered separately as the blood-cerebrospinal fluid barrier.

REFERENCES

Adrian, E. D.: The Mechanism of Nervous Action. Philadelphia, University of Pennsylvania Press, 1933.

Ariëns Kappers, C. U., Huber, G. C., and Crosby, E. C.: The Comparative Anatomy of the Nervous System of Vertebrates, Including Man. 2 vols. New York, 1936.

Bailey, P., and Bonin, G. von.: The Isocortex of Man. Urbana, University of Illinois Press, 1951.

Bartelmez, G. W., and Hoerr, N. L.: The vestibular club endings in Ameiurus. Further evidence on the morphology of the synapse. J. Comp. Neur., *57:*401, 1933.

Bethe, A., Bergmann, G., Embden, G., and Ellinger, A.: Handbuch der Norm. u. Pathol. Physiologie. Berlin, 1927–31, vols. 1, 9, 10, 11, 12.

Bodian, D.: Cytological aspects of synaptic function. Physiol. Rev., *22:*146, 1942.

Cole, K. S.: Ions, Potentials and the Nerve Impulse. Lecture and Review Series, No. 53–7, p. 89 Naval Med. Research Inst. 1953.

Coombs, J. S., Eccles, J. C., and Fatt, P.: Several papers on electrical properties of neurons. J. Physiol., *130:*291–413, 1955.

Dempsey, E. W., and Wislocki, G. B.: An electronmicrograph study of the blood brain barrier in the rat, employing silver nitrate as a vital stain. J. Biophys. Biochem. Cytol., *1:*245, 1955.

De Robertis, E. D. P., and Bennett, H. S.: Some features of the submicroscopic morphology of synapses in frog and earthworm. J. Biophys. Biochem. Cytol., *1:*47, 1955.

Economo, C.: The Cytoarchitectonics of the Human Cerebral Cortex. Oxford, 1929.

Elliott, K. A. C., Page, I. H., and Quastel, J. H.: Neurochemistry. Charles C Thomas, Springfield, Ill., 1955.

Fernández-Morán, H.: The Submicroscopic Structure of Nerve Fibres. Progress in Biophysics, Vol. 4, 1954.

Flexner, L. B.: Events associated with the development of nerve and hepatic cells. Ann. New York Acad. Sci., *60:*986, 1955.

Gasser, H. S.: Properties of dorsal root unmedullated fibers on the two sides of the ganglion. J. Gen. Physiol., *38:*709, 1955.

Gerard, R. W.: Metabolism and Function in the Nervous System. Chap. XVII of Elliott, Page and Quastel, Editors: Neurochemistry. Charles C Thomas, Springfield, Ill., 1955.

Geren, B. B.: The formation from the Schwann cell surface of myelin in peripheral nerves of chick embryos. Exper. Cell Res., *7:*558, 1954.

Gersh, I., and Bodian, D.: Some chemical mechanisms in chromatolysis. J. Cell. Comp. Physiol., *21:*253, 1943.

Glees, P.: Neuroglia: Morphology and Function. Springfield, Charles C Thomas, 1955.

Granit, R.: Receptors and Sensory Perception. Yale University Press, 1955.

Harrison, R. G.: Observations of the living developing nerve fiber. Anat. Rec., *1:*116, 1908. The outgrowth of the nerve fiber as a mode of protoplasmic movement. J. Exper. Zool., *9:*787, 1910.

Hartmann, J. F.: An electron optical study of sections of central nervous system. J. Comp. Neur., *99:*201, 1953. Electron microscopy of motor nerve cells following section of axones. Anat. Rec., *118:*19, 1954.

Herrick, C. J.: An Introduction to Neurology. Philadelphia and London, 1931; The Brain of the Tiger Salamander. University of Chicago Press, 1948. The Evolution of Human Nature. Austin, Univ. of Texas Press, 1956.

Hines, M.: Studies in the innervation of skeletal muscle. J. Comp. Neur., *56:*105, 1932.

Hinsey, J.: The innervation of skeletal muscle. Physiol. Rev., *14:*514, 1934.

Hodgkin, A. L., and Katz, B.: The effect of sodium ions on the electrical activity of the giant axon of the squid. J. Physiol., *108:*37, 1949.

Hogue, M. J.: A study of adult human brain cells grown in tissue cultures. Am. J. Anat., *93:*397, 1953.

Huxley, A. F., and Stämpfli, R.: Effect of sodium and potassium on resting and action potentials of single myelinated nerve. J. Physiol., *112:*496, 1951.

Klüver, H., and Barrera, E.: A method for the combined staining of cells and fibers in the nervous system. J. Neuropath. and Exp. Neurol., *12:*400, 1953.

Kuntz, A.: The Autonomic Nervous System. Philadelphia, Lea and Febiger, 1953.

Lorente de Nó, R.: On the existence of a gradient of sensitivity to the lack of sodium in the spinal roots of the bullfrog. Studies of the Rockefeller Institute for Medical Research, *144:*253, 1952.

Maxfield, M.: Axoplasmic proteins of the squid giant nerve fiber with particular reference to the fibrous protein. J. Gen. Physiol., *37:*201, 1953.

Ortiz-Picón, J. M.: The neuroglia of the sensory ganglia. Anat. Rec., *121:*513, 1955.

Palay, S. L., and Palade, G. E.: The fine structure of neurons. J. Biophys. and Biochem. Cytol., *1:*69, 1955.

Penfield, W.: Cytology and Cellular Pathology of the Nervous System. New York, 2 vols.; Neuroglia, Ibid., *2:*423, 1932.

Peterson, E. R., and Murray, M. R.: Myelin sheath formation in cultures of avian spinal ganglia. Am. J. Anat., *96:*319, 1955.

Polyak, S.: The Main Afferent Fiber Systems. Berkeley, 1932. The Retina. Chicago, 1941. Vertebrate Visual System. Chicago, Univ. of Chicago Press. 1957.

Pomerat, C. M.: Dynamic neurogliology. Texas Reports on Biology and Medicine, *10:*885, 1952.

Pope, A.: Application of quantitative histochemical methods to the study of the nervous system. J. Neuropath. and Exper. Neurol., *14:*39, 1955.

Ramón y Cajal, S.: Histologie du système nerveux de l'homme et des vertébrés. Paris, 1909–11. Degeneration and Regeneration of the Nervous System. Oxford, 1928.

Ranson, S. W., and Clark, S. L.: The Anatomy of the Nervous System. 9th ed. Philadelphia, W. B. Saunders Company, 1953.

Rasmussen, A. T.: The Principal Nervous Pathways. New York, 1951.

Rodriguez, L. A.: Experiments on the histologic locus of the hemato-encephalic barrier. J. Comp. Neur., *102:*27, 1955.

Sauer, F. C.: Mitosis in the neural tube. J. Comp. Neur., *62:*377, 1935.

Scharrer, E., and Scharrer, B.: Neurosekretion. Handb. d. mikrosk. Anat. d. Menschen (v. Moellendorff-Bargmann). Berlin, Springer Verlag, *6:*pt. 5, 953, 1954.

Schmitt, F. O.: The structure of the axon filaments of the giant nerve fibers of Loligo and Myxicola. J. Exp. Zool., *113:*499, 1950.

Schmitt, F. O., Bear, R. S., and Palmer, K. J.: X-ray diffraction studies on the structure of the nerve myelin sheath. J. Cell. Comp. Physiol., *18:*31, 1941.

Sherrington, C. S.: The Integrative Action of the Nervous System. New York, 1906.

Speidel, C. C.: Studies of living nerves. VII. Growth adjustments of cutaneous terminal arborizations. J. Comp. Neur., 76:57, 1942.

Sperry, R. W.: Neuronal Specificity, Genetic Neurology (Weiss). The University of Chicago Press, 1950.

Tobias, J. M., and Bryant, S. H.: An isolated giant axon preparation from the lobster nerve cord. J. Cell. Comp. Physiol., 46:163, 1955.

Van Breemen, V. L., and Clemente, C. D.: Silver deposition in the central nervous system and the hematoencephalic barrier studied with the electron microscope. J. Biophys. Biochem. Cytol., 1:161, 1955.

Waelsch, Heinrich, ed.: Biochemistry of the Developing Nervous System. New York, 1955.

Weddell, G., Palmer, E., and Pallie, W.: Nerve endings in mammalian skin. Biol. Rev., 30:159, 1955

Weed, L. H.: Certain anatomical and physiological aspects of the meninges and cerebrospinal fluid. Brain, 58:383, 1935.

Weiss, P.: Genetic Neurology. Problems of the Development, Growth, and Regeneration of the Nervous System and Its Functions. University of Chicago Press, 1950.

Weiss, P., and Hiscoe, H. B.: Experiments on the mechanism of nerve growth. J. Exp. Zool., 107:315, 1948.

Wislocki, G. B. and Leduc, E. H.: Vital staining of the hematoencephalic barrier by silver nitrate and trypan blue, etc. J. Comp. Neur., 96:371, 1952.

Young, J. Z.: Functional repair of nervous tissue. Physiol. Rev., 22:318, 1942.

CHAPTER 10

The Blood Vascular System

Multicellular organisms require a mechanism to distribute nutritive materials, oxygen and hormones to the various parts of the body and to collect the products of metabolism from the whole body and transmit them to the excretory organs. In the vertebrates this function is carried out by the vascular system. It consists of tubelike vessels, the *arteries, capillaries* and *veins,* and the central motor apparatus, the *heart,* which maintains a constant circulation of the blood by its contractions. The arteries lead from the heart to the capillaries, the veins from the latter to the heart. Lymphatic vessels are described in Chapter 11.

The circulation of the blood in a living animal may be studied directly in a thin vascular membrane, such as the web of a frog's tongue, the wing of a bat or the special chambers inserted in the ear of a rabbit (Sandison). The vessels of thicker organs may be studied with the aid of illuminated glass or quartz rods (Knisely).

CAPILLARIES

The main component of the wall of a capillary is the endothelium; this is the characteristic structure in every vessel, including the heart. In the living animal it is usually possible to distinguish the endothelial nuclei scattered along the outlines of the capillaries. After fixation and staining, the wall of the capillaries stands out clearly as a thin, homogeneous membrane, within which the endothelial nuclei are located at various distances from one another.

The endothelial cells are structurally similar to fibroblasts. The elongated or oval nucleus is flattened, sometimes curved with the lumen of the vessel, and contains fine, dust-like chromatin particles similar to those in the nucleus of the fibroblast; it lacks, however, the large nucleoli. Its membrane often shows longitudinal folds. These slight differences are rapidly effaced when the endothelial cells turn into fibroblasts.

The flat endothelial cells are usually stretched along the axis of the capillary and have tapering ends. In the wider capillaries they are shorter and broader. In the lung their outlines are irregularly scalloped. In capillaries of medium width, only two curved cells surround the lumen. In wider capillaries the aperture may be surrounded by a greater number of cells, while in narrow ones a single endothelial cell may form the wall of the tube.

The caliber of the capillaries in various parts of the body of a given animal varies within narrow limits and is closely related to the size of the red blood corpuscles. In man it averages about 8 microns. Patent thin capillaries, through which only blood plasma circulates, probably are not present, although great numbers of the capillaries are collapsed when the organ or tissue is in a resting condition. When the organs begin to function actively, these collapsed capillaries open up, and blood circulates through them. In sections of tissues fixed in the usual manner, the capillaries appear narrower than in the living animal, while artificially injected capillaries are often distended beyond their normal limits.

In the majority of capillaries it is possible to show by the injection of silver nitrate that their walls consist of separate endothelial cells whose boundaries stand out as sharply stained black lines; each cell contains a single nucleus (Fig. 10–1). In such preparations the cell boundaries are frequently covered with angular, dark spots. They were originally thought to be openings in the walls of the capillaries between the endothelial cells, the so-called *stigmata* or *stomata;* they are now known to be artefacts. In the living frog intravascularly injected India ink particles were seen to accumulate first in the cementing lines.

The capillaries originate from the embryonic connective tissue. As they penetrate everywhere between the elements of various organs and tissues, they are accompanied along their entire course by connective tissue cells and layers of thin, collagenous or reticular fibers, which closely adjoin the endothelium in most places. The network of reticular fibers forms a thin membranous sheath around the capillaries and separates them from the elements of the other tissues.

The connective tissue which accompanies the capillaries is sometimes called *perithelium.* This is an indefinite term which includes several types of cells; because of its indefiniteness, it should be discarded. The usual capillaries are accompanied by fixed macrophages, cells of probably undifferentiated mesenchymal nature, and a few scattered nerve cells which can be identified only through the use of special histological methods. The pericapillary mesenchymal cells are beautifully demonstrable in the serous membranes (Fig. 4–10). In certain instances the pericapillary cells are of quite different nature. Thus, along the capillaries of the nictitating membrane of the frog's eye are peculiar cells with long, branching processes which surround the capillary wall (Rouget cells). These cells have been seen to contract under electric stimulation. Hence, in this membrane, these cells may be considered to be of the nature of smooth muscle cells. The Rouget cells round up, but do not contract

Fig. 10–1. Capillary from the mesentery of frog. Boundaries of the endothelial cells are stained black with silver nitrate. 350 ×. (Redrawn after Ranvier.)

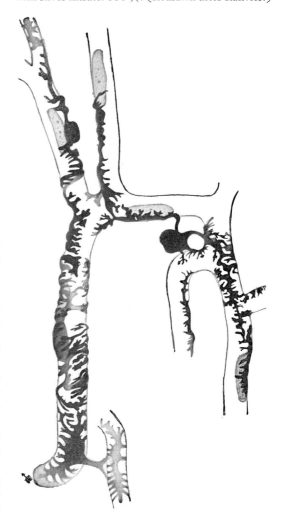

Fig. 10–2. Arterial capillaries from the heart of a forty-three-year old man. Four polymorphous perivascular cells continue into those of the capillaries. The arrow points toward the artery. Chrome-silver impregnation. 1000 ×. (Redrawn after Zimmermann.)

when prodded, and lack the birefringent myofibrils characteristic of smooth muscle. Studies made on living blood vessels in chambers inserted in the rabbit's ear indicate that capillary contractility in the mammals does

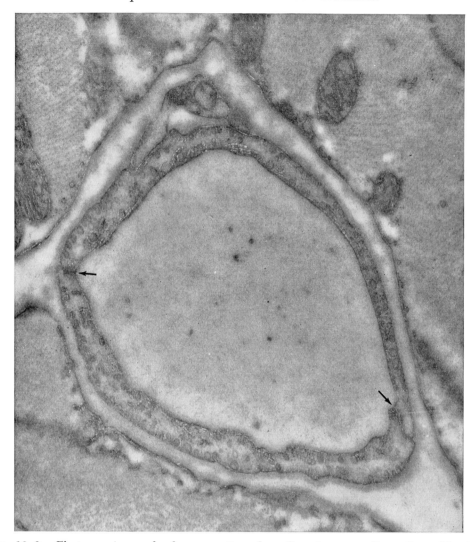

Fig. 10–3. Electron micrograph of cross section of capillary in myocardium of rat. The intimate connection between the cytoplasm of two endothelial cells is seen (arrows). Along the inner and outer surfaces of the endothelium, small vesicles, possibly of endoplasmic reticular nature, are concentrated. In contrast to the endothelium in Figures 10–4 and 10–5, the endothelium here does not show great variations in thickness. Buffered osmic acid fixation. 28,500 ×. (Courtesy of Palade.)

not depend on the Rouget cells (Clark). Microdissection studies have shown that the endothelial cells may contract after direct mechanical stimulation.

The fluid part of the blood reaches the elements of the tissues only by passing through the endothelial protoplasm of the capillaries. With a few important exceptions, in most of the organs so far examined with the electron microscope, the endothelium of the capillaries forms a regular cytoplasmic membrane encompassing the lumen and becoming much thicker near the nucleus. In such vessels the junction of adjacent endo-thelial cells is by close contact (Fig. 10–3). In the capillaries of the intestinal villi the endothelial thickness is variable and may become irregularly attenuated as shown in Figure 10–4. Even more striking are apparent discontinuities in the endothelium of the glomerular capillaries in which there seem to be irregularly spaced small openings in immediate contact with the basement membrane. If these openings exist in the living animal and are not technical artefacts, they must be of importance in the production of the glomerular filtrate (Figs. 10–5; 28–8, 28–9).

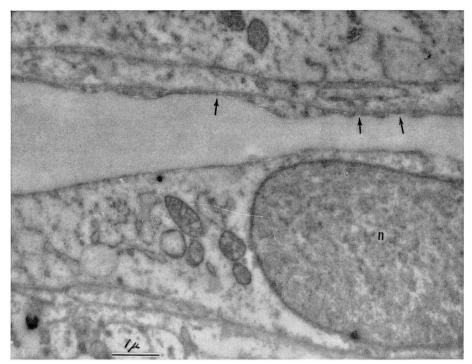

Fig. 10–4. Electron micrograph of section through capillary in an intestinal villus of rat. The endothelium, thick near the nucleus (*n*), becomes very tenuous on the opposite side of the lumen of the capillary as indicated by the arrows. Buffered osmic acid fixation. (Courtesy of G. Palade.)

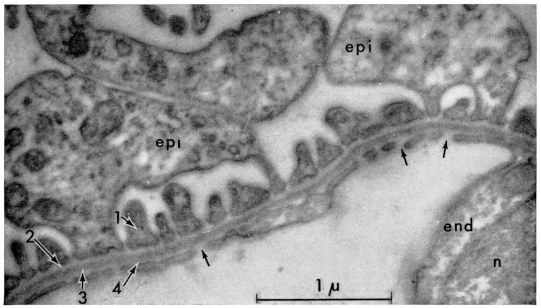

Fig. 10–5. Electron micrograph of section through glomerular capillary of rat showing major processes (*epi*) of the epithelial cells and the minor extensions of these processes, the pedicels (1). The pale layers of the basement membrane are shown at 2 and 4 and the darker central zone at 3. Endothelium (*end*) seems incomplete in places (arrows). *n,* Nucleus. Buffered osmic acid fixation. (Courtesy of D. Pease.)

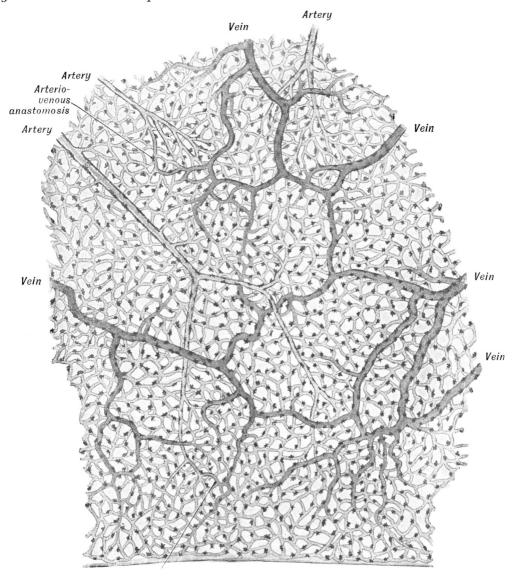

Arteriovenous anastomosis

Fig. 10–6.   Network of blood vessels in the web of a frog, showing the connection of arteries and veins with the capillary network and direct connections between arterioles and venules. Many chromatophores are scattered along the capillaries. Medium magnification. (A.A.M.)

Leukocytes pass through the wall by their ameboid movement, in which they push apart the processes of the endothelial cells, or pass through the protoplasm of these cells and form temporary openings which close immediately after their passage.

The capillaries connect the terminal branches of arteries and the beginnings of the veins. They always form extensive networks by their frequent branchings and anastomoses; these networks thoroughly penetrate the various tissues which they nourish. In most instances the meshes of the capillary network, adjusting themselves to the available free spaces between the elements of the tissues, have a polygonal shape and are of approximately equal size in all planes (Fig. 10–6).

It is obvious that, if the tissue consists of a thin membrane, its capillary network will be arranged in the same plane. If the tissue elements are all elongated and lie parallel to one another, as in nerves, tendons or muscles, the capillaries between them form a network with elongated meshes, often with right angular meshes in some of the muscles (Fig. 8–23).

The higher the metabolism of the organ, the denser is its network, and vice versa. In the pulmonary alveoli the meshes are somewhat less than the diameter of the capillary tubes themselves. The capillary networks are dense in various glands, in the mucous membrane of the intestinal tract, and elsewhere. In the gray matter of the central nervous system the vascular network is considerably denser than it is in the white matter, which consists only of nerve fibers. In tendons the capillaries are scarce, while in adipose tissue they are abundant.

The transitions between arteries and capillaries and between capillaries and veins are gradual. This applies to the structure of the wall as well as to the caliber of the vessel. However, capillaries are often found which project directly from small arteries before a complete ramification of the latter has taken place; similarly, accessory capillaries frequently enter directly into a well-developed small vein.

In following the ramifications of an artery in the direction of the flow of the blood, only that part of the wall of the vessel which has entirely lost its muscular elements and consists only of endothelium should be called a capillary (Fig. *10–7, x*). The first stretches of the capillary network are ordinarily called the *arterial capillaries;* they are usually a little wider than the main mass of the network. Where the veins are formed from the capillary network, the capillary tubes again become gradually wider and at the same time less numerous—these are the so-called *venous capillaries,* which not infrequently have a considerable diameter. The appearance of the first smooth muscle cells or of denser collagenous fibers in their walls indicates the beginning of a small vein. The concept of arterial and venous capillaries is rather indefinite, and it is often impossible to distinguish them by the width of their apertures from ordinary capillaries.

Sinusoids. In certain organs there is another type of connection between arteries and veins. These are called "sinusoids" and are structurally quite different from the capillaries. The capillaries have a constant bore and a complete endothelial lining in which the cell boundaries are clearly demonstrable in most cases by treatment with silver nitrate. The sinusoids, on the contrary, have irregular, tortuous walls which vary from 5 to 30 microns or more in diameter in fixed material. Their walls are not formed by a continuous layer of endothelial cells, as in the capillaries, but by irregularly scattered phagocytic and nonphagocytic cells. The ordinary capillary endothelial cells do not store vital dyes or phagocytose bacteria as do the phagocytes of the sinusoids. The outlines of the cell bodies in the sinusoids are not demonstrable in

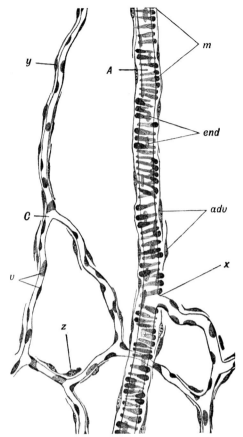

Fig. 10–7. Small artery, *A,* and capillaries, *C,* from mesentery of a rabbit; *m,* muscle cells in the media; *adv,* adventitia; *x,* origin of a capillary from the artery; *y,* pericyte; *z,* perivascular (adventitial) histiocyte; *end, v,* endothelial nuclei. 187 ×. (A.A.M.)

most instances by treatment with silver nitrate. The sinusoids are accompanied by a dense, membranous network of reticular fibrils. The sinusoids probably represent a primitive type of capillary. In the adult mammalian body, sinusoids occur in the blood-forming tissues, the liver and certain endocrine glands.

The concept that phagocytosis by cells lining vessels depends on a sluggish circulation should be dropped. Studies of the living circulation show that the rate of flow varies considerably in all capillaries (and sinuses) and that it often ceases for hours in many vessels which are not sinuses. But phagocytosis and dye storage by the common endothelial cells in these vessels, as in muscle and in the glomeruli, have not been reported.

ARTERIES

The blood is carried from the heart to the capillary networks of the tissues and organs of the body by arteries. These are tubes which begin with the aorta and pulmonary artery on the left and right sides of the heart, respectively, and then split into smaller branches. The caliber of the arteries gradually decreases as they recede from the heart, while the sum of the diameters of the lumens of all the branches of these arteries increases greatly the further they are from the heart. The lining of the walls of all the arteries consists of the same kind of endothelium as is found in the capillaries. But external to the endothelium in the arteries, other elements can be distinguished which cause the strength, rigidity and complexity of the arterial walls. All these qualities decrease progressively in passing from the larger arteries which originate in the heart to the capillaries. Besides the endothelium, the arteries are composed of: (1) fibroblasts and collagenous fibers, (2) bands and networks of elastic fibers, and (3) smooth muscle cells. The arterial walls are abundantly provided with nerves, and in the large arteries small blood and lymphatic vessels are present.

The wall of the largest arteries (such as the aorta) differs from the wall of arteries of medium caliber (such as the radial artery) by its absolute thickness and by its structure. In the aorta the middle layer of the vessel is distinctly yellow, because of the predominance of elastic elements; in the second instance it is red-gray because of smooth muscles. The arteries of *elastic type* are of large caliber and include the aorta, innominate, subclavian, the beginning of the common carotid, and the pulmonary arteries; these are also called the *conducting arteries.* The arteries of *muscular type* (the *distributing arteries*) include the majority of the arteries; they continue from the afore-mentioned large vessels close to the heart and extend to the unnamed arteries which are difficult to distinguish with the naked eye. The smallest arteries, 0.3 mm. in diameter or smaller, are usually grouped in a separate class and are called *arterioles.* In the transition between the arterioles and the capillaries some authors distinguish *precapillary arterioles*—an ill-defined concept. The peculiarities in the structure of the different types of arteries are reflected in their physiological significance.

In the walls of every artery, three layers can be distinguished: (1) the inner coat, *tunica intima* or *interna,* whose elements are oriented mainly longitudinally; (2) the intermediate coat, *tunica media,* most of the elements of which are directed circularly. This is the thickest layer of the wall, and its character determines the type of artery. (3) The external coat, *tunica adventitia* or *externa,* most of the elements of which run parallel to the long axis of the vessel. The elements of this tunic gradually merge with those of the surrounding loose connective tissue which accompanies every blood vessel. The boundary between the tunica intima and tunica media is formed by the *internal elastic membrane,* which is particularly noticeable in arteries of medium caliber. Between the tunica media and the tunica adventitia, an external elastic membrane can be distinguished in most cases.

Small Arteries—Arterioles. The *tunica intima* consists only of endothelium and the internal elastic membrane (Fig. 10–8). In cross section the elastica interna usually appears as a thin, bright line just beneath the endothelial nuclei. It is markedly scalloped in sections, because the agonal contraction of the muscle fibers throws it into longitudinal folds.

The *tunica media* of small arteries consists of smooth muscle cells, 15 to 20 microns in length. They are always oriented transversely to the length of the vessel, and are bent with the curvature of the arterial wall. The number of layers of muscle cells depends on the caliber of the artery.

The *tunica adventitia* approximately equals the tunica media in thickness; it is a layer of loose connective tissue with longitudinally oriented, collagenous and elastic fibers, and a few fibroblasts. It merges with the surrounding connective tissue. The small arteries lack a definite external elastic membrane.

When these small arteries merge into capillaries, the endothelium remains uninterrupted and unchanged, while the internal elastic membrane becomes progressively thinner and disappears when the vessel has a diameter of 62 microns. The spindle-shaped muscle cells disappear when the caliber of the blood vessel decreases to that of the capil-

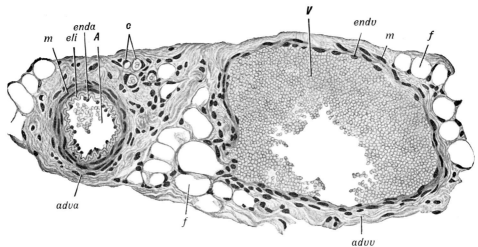

Fig. 10–8. Cross section through a small artery (A) and its accompanying vein (V) from the submucosa of a human intestine. *adva* and *advv*, adventitia of the artery and vein; *c*, cross sections of capillaries; *enda* and *endv*, endothelium of the artery and vein; *eli*, elastica interna; *m*, muscle cells of the media; *f*, fat cells in the loose connective tissue. 187 ×. (A.A.M.)

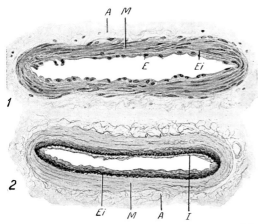

Fig. 10–9.   Cross section of central artery of human retina. *1*, stained with H + E, *2*, stained with orcein; *A*, adventitia; *E*, endothelium; *Ei*, internal elastic membrane; *I*, intima; *M*, muscular layer. 160 ×. (After Schaffer.)

lary. The tunica adventitia loses its elastic fibers, which are replaced by networks of reticular fibers and the perivascular cells of the capillaries.

Arteries of Medium Caliber or of Muscular Type. This group comprises most of the arteries. The *tunica intima* is lined by the endothelium, which is continuous with that of the arteries of small caliber. Beneath the endothelium in the smaller arteries of this group is the internal elastic membrane. In larger vessels, collagenous and elastic fibers

and a few fibroblasts lie beneath the endothelium.

The *internal elastic membrane* is well developed. In cross section it appears homogeneous and bright; because of agonal contraction of the tunica media it is typically scalloped (Fig. 10–10). In large blood vessels it is a thick, "fenestrated" elastic membrane provided with a number of irregular, rounded or oval openings (Fig. 10–14). In many arteries the elastica is split into two or more layers (Fig. 10–11).

The *tunica media* of arteries of muscular type consists almost exclusively of smooth muscle cells arranged in concentric layers. Thin reticular fiber membranes can be demonstrated to form sheaths for the individual muscle cells. Thin elastic fiber networks with wide meshes course circularly in the tunica media and continue into the external and internal elastic membranes (Fig. 10–11, G).

The *tunica adventitia* of arteries of the muscular type is sometimes thicker than the tunica media. It consists of loose connective tissue whose collagenous and elastic fibers pass predominantly in the longitudinal or tangential directions. The elastic layer immediately adjacent to the smooth muscles stands out as a well-defined, perforated membrane, the external elastic membrane. The tunica adventitia passes over into the surrounding connective tissue without sharp boundaries.

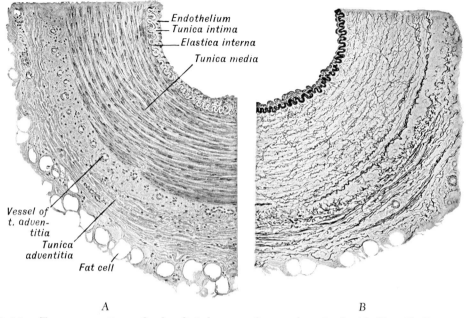

Fig. 10–10.   Two cross sections of volar digital artery of man; *A*, stained with H + E; *B*, stained with orcein to show elastic tissue. 80 ×. (Slightly modified after Schaffer.)

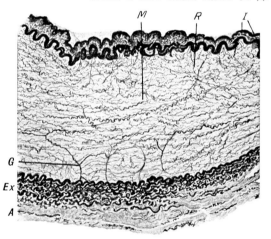

Fig. 10–11.   Portion of cross section of mesenteric artery of man. *A*, adventitia; *Ex*, external elastic layer; *G*, branching elastic fibers; *I*, elastica of the intima, which is here split into two layers; *M*, tunica media; *R*, radial elastic fibers. Orcein stain. 110 ×. (After Schaffer.)

Fig. 10–12.   Longitudinal section through posterior wall of human descending aorta. Elastic tissue is black—the other elements are not shown clearly. *I*, intima; *M*, media; *A*, adventitia; *a*, subendothelial layer; from *b* to *c*, the longitudinally striated layer, which becomes a fenestrated membrane at *c*; *d*, fenestrated elastic membrane; *e*, the last membrane, elastica externa, on the boundary between adventitia and media; *vv*, vasa vasorum. Elastic fiber stain. 85 ×. (After Kölliker-von Ebner.)

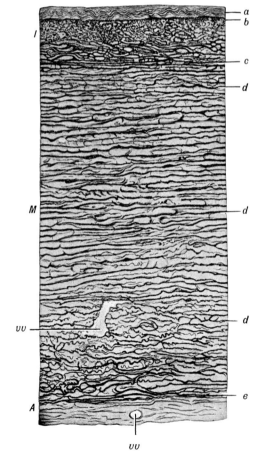

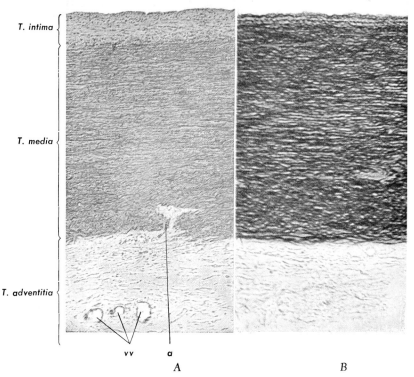

T. intima

T. media

T. adventitia

vv   a

A   B

Fig. 10–13.   Sections of human ascending aorta stained (A) with H + E and (B) with resorcin-fuchsin for elastic fibers. Vasa vasorum (vv) penetrate the tunica media at a. Photomicrographs. About 50 ×. (After von Herrath and Abramow.)

Owing to this loose consistency of its external layers, the tunica adventitia permits the arteries to move within certain limits and allows the constant changes in the size of the lumen; it also limits the amount of shortening of the arteries which takes place after they are cut.

Arteries of Large Caliber or of Elastic Type. The resistant, elastic wall of these blood vessels (such as the aorta) is much thinner, in comparison with the size of their lumen, than that of the vessels of the preceding group.

Tunica Intima. The tunica intima in an adult man is rather thick (127 microns) (Fig. 10–12, *I*). The endothelium differs from the endothelium in smaller arteries by the fact that the cells are not elongated, but have an oval or polygonal form. The layer directly beneath the endothelium is normally thin. It consists of a few thin interlacing fibers and fibroblasts. A few wandering cells may normally be present. The next layer consists of many branching elastic fibers which fuse in places into a more or less well-pronounced,

striated membrane. Between these fibers are a few collagenous fibers, fibroblasts and small bundles of smooth muscle cells. Externally, this layer of elastic fibers passes into a fenestrated elastic membrane, which by its location corresponds with the internal elastic membrane. But it does not differ from the many similar membranes which follow toward the exterior and form the tunica media of the aorta. Thus, the tunica intima in the largest blood vessels is but poorly delimited from the tunica media.

Tunica Media. The tunica media consists mainly of elastic tissue (Fig. *10–12, M*). In the human aorta it appears in the form of fifty to sixty-five concentric "fenestrated" elastic membranes, 2.5 microns thick, between which the interspaces measure 6 to 18 microns. The neighboring membranes are frequently connected with one another by elastic fibers or bands.

In the spaces between two adjacent elastic membranes are thin layers of connective tissue with thin collagenous and elastic fibers, fibroblasts and smooth muscle cells (Fig.

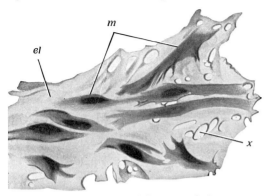

Fig. 10–14.   Portion of fenestrated elastic membrane from aorta of a calf; *el,* elastic substance; *x,* openings; *m,* smooth muscle cells adherent to the membrane. 250 ×. (Redrawn after Prenant.)

Tunica Adventitia. The tunica adventitia in arteries of large caliber is relatively thin. It cannot be sharply distinguished from the surrounding connective tissue. The most external of the fenestrated membranes of the tunica media serves as an external elastic membrane, from which numerous elastic fibers project. There is a gradual transition from the tunica adventitia into the surrounding loose connective tissue with its fat cells.

Connection between Arteries of Different Types. As one type of artery goes over into another without marked boundaries, it is sometimes difficult to classify an artery as of a given type. Some arteries of rather small caliber (popliteal, tibial) have walls which suggest large arteries, while some large arteries (external iliac) have walls like those of medium-sized arteries. The change of an artery of elastic type into an artery of muscular type usually takes place gradually, so that the intermediate regions are often designated *arteries of mixed type.* Such are the external carotid, axillary, and common iliac arteries. In their middle tunics are islands of smooth muscle fibers which interrupt the elastic membranes in many places.

10–15). The latter, particularly in the inner layers of the tunica media of the aorta, are flattened, branched elements with irregular outlines and serrated edges; they have characteristic, rodlike nuclei. Most of them are arranged circularly. These smooth muscle cells are closely surrounded by collagenous fibers which bind them to the elastic membranes. Between these various structures is an appreciable amount of basophile amorphous ground substance which stains like mucus with certain dyes. The basophilia of this ground substance is believed to be due to the presence of chondroitin sulfuric acid.

Where arteries of mixed or elastic type pass suddenly into arteries of the muscular type, short transition regions occur; these are called *arteries of hybrid type,* and are found

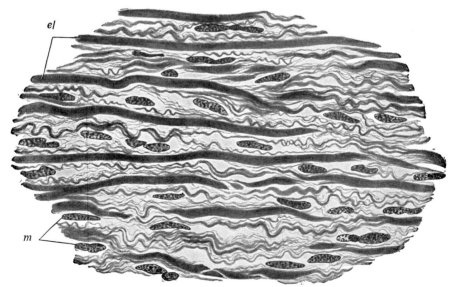

Fig. 10–15.   Cross section from media of aorta of a five-year-old boy. *el,* cross sections of fenestrated elastic membranes, between which are fine collagenous fibers; *m,* smooth muscle nuclei. Orcein and hematoxylin. 500 ×. (A.A.M.)

in the visceral arteries which arise from the abdominal aorta (Fig. *10–11*). In them, for a varying distance, the tunica media may consist of two different layers—the internal is muscular and the external is composed of typical elastic membranes.

Special Types of Arteries. In the tunica media of the arteries of the lower limbs, the muscular tissue is more highly developed than in the arteries of the upper limbs.

The *arteries of the skull,* which are protected from external pressure or tension, have a thin wall and a well-developed elastica interna. In the tunica media the elastic fibers are almost entirely absent.

The *umbilical artery* has an atypical, special structure. Its intima consists only of endothelium and lacks an internal elastic layer. The tunica media contains a small number of elastic fibers and two thick, muscular layers which are sharply separated from each other. The inner layer is composed of longitudinally directed fibers; in many places these form longitudinal protrusions into both the lumen and the outer circular muscular layer. The extra-abdominal portion of the umbilical artery is provided with numerous oval swellings; in these regions the wall becomes thin and consists almost exclusively of circularly arranged muscles.

The various organs show differences in their arteries. These are described in the following chapters.

Physiological Significance of the Structure of Arteries.

As the movement of the blood in the arteries is caused by the contractions of the heart, it is rhythmically interrupted. If the walls of the arteries were inflexible, the flow of blood in their terminal branches would also be irregular. But the walls of the largest vessels near the heart are composed of an elastic, easily expanding tissue, and only a part of the force of contraction (systole) immediately advances the blood. The remainder of the force of the contraction expands the large elastic arteries and is accumulated as potential energy in the increased elastic tension of the arterial wall. With the closure of the aortic and pulmonary valves, this tension becomes transformed into kinetic energy which moves the blood forward while the ventricles are at rest (diastole). At the beginning of the arterial system the flow of blood is irregular; it becomes more and more continuous in the direction of the terminal ramifications.

The arteries of elastic type can be regarded as regulating the general blood circulation, while the muscular arteries, by contracting or relaxing, decrease or increase the supply of arterial blood in any region of the body.

These contractions and dilatations of the muscular arteries are regulated by the *vasoconstrictor* and *vasodilator nerves* of the autonomic nervous system which terminate in the smooth muscles.

The muscular tissue of the arterial walls is normally somewhat contracted; this is the basis of the tone of the vessels. The degree of tone fluctuates continuously.

Changes in the Arteries with Age. The arterial blood vessels reach their mature form only in adult life. During the fourth month of embryonic life in man, the arteries acquire their three main layers. From this time the wall of the vessels changes gradually, so that the intima of the aorta, for example, becomes complete only at about thirty years of age. The arterial system, with the heart, is always active mechanically and seems to wear out more than any other system of organs. Indeed, the final differentiation of the structure of the wall frequently cannot be sharply separated from the regressive changes which develop gradually with age and lead to *arteriosclerosis.* Some authors view this process as a physiological, others as a pathological, progression. In general, arteriosclerosis is a pathological process when its intensity in a given vessel is beyond the norm for this vessel at a particular age. The arteries of elastic type, particularly the aorta, show much greater changes with age than do the arteries of muscular type. The small arteries hardly participate in this process under physiological conditions.

In the aorta of a four months' human embryo, the intima consists only of the endothelium and of one rather thick, elastic membrane—the elastica interna. The media consists of several layers of circular smooth muscles, between which are flat networks of elastic fibers. The adventitia is thicker than the media and consists of embryonic connective tissue.

At the end of embryonic life the internal elastic membrane becomes thicker, while the flat networks of elastic fibers in the media turn into thick elastic membranes. The muscular elements have increased slightly in number, but are still inconspicuous. The adventitia by this time has become smaller.

After birth the number and thickness of the elastic membranes in the media of the aorta gradually increase. They are much like the elastica interna now. Between the endothelium and the elastica interna in the intima, an elastic muscular layer appears. It arises in part by a splitting of the elastica interna and in part by the new formation of collagenous and elastic fibers, and gradually increases in thickness. At about the age of twenty-five, these layers are completely differentiated.

The medium-sized muscular arteries, such as the brachial, even in the middle of embryonic life, have an intima composed of an endothelium and an elastica interna, a media of circular smooth muscles, and an adventitia. The last has a pronounced elastica externa surrounded by a connective tissue layer rich in elastic fibers. Toward the end of the embryonic period the greatly thickened media consists only of circular muscles bounded by the external and internal elastic membranes. After birth, in the arteries of muscular type, in addition to the thickening of the wall as a whole, a connective tissue layer gradually develops between the endothelium, and the elastica interna.

The wearing out of a large vessel, such as the aorta, is shown mainly in an irregular thickening of the tunica intima. Later on, fat infiltrates the interstitial substance, and the degenerative processes begin. In the tunica media, the elastin of the fenestrated membrane may transform into the nonelastic *elacin*. In the medium-sized arteries of muscular type, the main change is a calcification within the tunica media, although the intima frequently thickens through a splitting of the elastica interna and the new formation of collagenous and elastic fibers.

VEINS

The blood is carried from the capillary networks toward the heart by the veins. In progressing toward the heart, the caliber of the veins gradually increases, while the wall becomes thicker. The veins usually accompany their corresponding arteries. As the caliber of an artery is always less than that of the corresponding vein or veins, the venous system has a much greater capacity than the arterial. The wall of the veins is always thinner, softer and less elastic than that of the arteries. Hence in sections the veins, if empty, are collapsed, and their lumen is irregular and slitlike.

One can frequently distinguish three types of veins: those of small, medium-sized, and large calibers. This subdivision is often unsatisfactory, for the caliber and structure of the wall cannot always be correlated. Individual veins show much greater variations than do the arteries, and the same vein may show great differences in different parts.

Most authors distinguish three layers in the walls of the veins: tunica intima, tunica media, and tunica adventitia. But their boundaries are frequently indistinct, and in certain veins these coats, particularly the tunica media, cannot be distinguished. The muscular and elastic tissue is much more poorly developed in the veins than in the arteries, while the connective tissue is much more prominent in the veins.

Veins of Small Caliber. When several capillaries unite, they first form a tube about 20 microns in diameter. This consists of a layer of endothelium surrounded by a thin layer of longitudinally directed collagenous fibers and fibroblasts (Fig. 10–16). When the caliber has increased to about 45 microns, partially differentiated, smooth muscle cells appear between the endothelium and the connective tissue. These cells are at first located at some distance from one another;

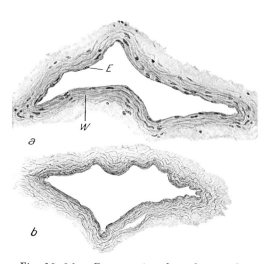

Fig. 10–16. Cross section through central vein of human retina. *a,* stained with H + E; *b,* with acid orcein. *E,* endothelium; *W,* connective tissue wall whose fine elastic fibers are visible in *b.* 160 ✕. (After Schaffer.)

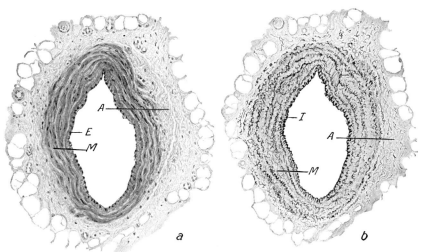

Fig. 10–17.   Cross section through common digital vein of a man. Stained with H + E (*a*) and with acid orcein (*b*); *A*, adventitia; *E*, endothelium; *I*, internal elastic membrane; *M*, muscular coat. 80 ×. (After Schaffer.)

they later become arranged closer and closer together. In veins with a diameter of 200 microns these elements form a continuous layer and have a typical, long, spindle shape. In still larger veins thin networks of elastic fibers appear. In them the tunica intima consists only of endothelium, while one or several layers of smooth muscle cells form the media. The tunica adventitia consists of scattered fibroblasts and thin elastic and collagenous fibers; most of them run longitudinally, and some enter the spaces between the muscle cells of the tunica media.

Veins of Medium Caliber. The veins of medium caliber (2 to 9 mm.) include the cutaneous and deeper veins of the extremities up to the brachial and the popliteal, and the veins of the viscera and head with the exception of the main trunks. In the *tunica intima* of these veins the endothelial cells are irregular polygons. Sometimes the tunica intima also contains an inconspicuous connective tissue layer with a few cells and thin elastic fibers. Externally, it is sometimes bounded by a network of elastic fibers. As it is frequently feebly developed, some authors consider the inner and middle coats as forming one layer.

The *tunica media* is much thinner than in the arteries, and consists mainly of circular smooth muscle fibers separated by many longitudinal collagenous fibers and a few fibroblasts (Fig. *10–17*).

The *tunica adventitia* is usually much thicker than the media and consists of loose connective tissue with thick, longitudinal, collagenous bundles, and elastic networks. It often contains in the layers adjacent to the media a number of longitudinal smooth muscle bundles.

Veins of Large Caliber. The *tunica intima* has the same structure as in the medium-sized veins. In some of the larger trunks its connective tissue layer is of considerable thickness (45 to 68 microns).

The *tunica media,* in general, is poorly developed and is sometimes absent. Its structure is the same as in the veins of medium caliber. The *tunica adventitia* composes the greater part of the venous wall and is usually several times as thick as the tunica media (Fig. *10–18*). It consists of loose connective tissue containing thick elastic fibers and mainly longitudinal collagenous fibers. In the layer adjacent to the tunica media or, if the latter is absent, to the tunica intima, the tunica adventitia contains prominent longitudinal layers of smooth muscles and elastic networks. This is the structure of the inferior vena cava and the portal, splenic, superior mesenteric, external iliac, renal and azygos veins.

Special Types of Veins. There are longitudinal or tangential smooth muscle fibers in the subendothelial connective tissue layer of the tunica intima of the iliac, femoral, popliteal, saphenous, cephalic, basilar, median, umbilical and other veins. In certain veins the longitudinal orientation is also noticed in the innermost muscular layers of the tunica media.

In a considerable portion of the inferior vena cava, the tunica media is absent and the well-developed longitudinal muscle bundles of the tunica adventitia are directly adjacent to the intima. In the pulmonary veins the media is well developed with circular muscles and is like an artery in this respect. Smooth muscles are particularly prominent in all the layers of walls of the veins in a pregnant uterus.

Certain veins are entirely devoid of smooth muscle tissue and consequently of a tunica media. In this group belong the veins of the maternal part of the placenta, of the spinal pia mater, of the retina, of bones, the sinuses of the dura mater, the majority of the cerebral veins, the veins of the nailbed and of the trabeculae of the spleen. The last two are simply channels lined by endothelium with a fibrous connective tissue covering.

The adventitia of the vena cava and particularly of the pulmonary vein is provided for a considerable distance with a layer of cardiac muscle fibers arranged in a ring with a few longitudinal fibers where these vessels enter the heart. In the rat, the pulmonary veins up to their radicles contain much cardiac muscle in the tunica media.

Valves of the Veins. Many veins of medium caliber, particularly those of the extremities, are provided with valves which prevent the blood from flowing away from the heart. These are semilunar pockets on the internal surface of the wall and are directed with their free edges in the direction of the blood flow. In man they are usually arranged in pairs, one opposite the other, distal to the branches entering the veins. Between the valves and the wall of the veins there is the so-called *sinus of the valve;* in this place the wall of the blood vessel is usually distended and thin.

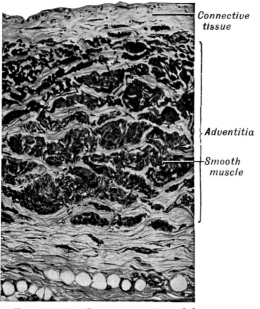

Fig. 10–18. Low-power view of human vena cava. Note the muscular adventitia. (Drawn by E. Bohlman.)

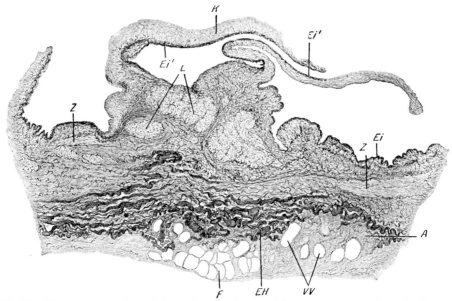

Fig. 10–19. From cross section of femoral vein of man. The section passes through the origin of a valve. *A,* adventitia with its elastic membrane, *EH; Ei,* elastic fiber network in the intima; *Ei',* the same on the inner surface of the valve leaflet; *F,* fat cells; *K,* leaflet of the valve; *L,* longitudinal muscles at the base of the valve; *VV,* vasa vasorum; *Z,* circular muscle bundles in the media. Acid orcein stain. 70 ×. (After Schaffer.)

The valve is a thin, connective tissue membrane; on the side toward the lumen of the vessel, it contains a thick network of elastic fibers continuous with those of the tunica intima of the vein. The wall of the vein is thinner in the region of the sinus; here its intimal and medial tunics contain only longitudinal smooth muscles; these do not enter into the substance of the valve in man.

Both surfaces of the valve are covered by endothelium which is reflected from the internal surface of the intima. The endothelial cells lining the surface toward the lumen of the vessel are elongated in the axis of the vessel; those which line the valves facing the sinus are elongated transversely.

Blood Vessels of Blood Vessels (Vasa Vasorum). The walls of all arteries and veins with a caliber greater than 1 mm. are provided with their own blood vessels, the vasa vasorum. These originate from the adjacent small arteries and from a dense capillary network in the adventitia. In even the larger arteries they do not penetrate further than the external layers of the media (Fig. 10–12, *vv*). In the veins, however, they are in general more abundant and may even penetrate up to the intima; the veins of these blood vessels often open into the lumen of the vessels which they drain. Networks of thin-walled, frequently wide lymphatics have been proved to be present in all the larger arteries and veins. They connect with the *perivascular lymphatics* and, according to some authors, may even be traced into the media. The blood vessels in the central nervous system are surrounded by perivascular lymphatic spaces bounded externally by a limiting membrane of neuroglia.

Nerves of Blood Vessels. All the blood vessels, particularly the arteries, are well supplied with nerves. These are of two types, vasomotor and receptor or sensory nerves (see p. 198).

Other Connections between Arteries and Veins.

As a general rule, a capillary network connects the terminal ramifications between the arteries and veins, and the transition occurs gradually. In many organs and tissues, however, modifications of this vascular plan are adapted to the peculiar functions of the particular tissues.

In certain cases an artery or vein may ramify into a number of capillaries, which are then collected into larger vessels of the original type, i.e., an artery or vein. An example of this is found in the arteries which form the glomeruli of the kidney; the afferent artery suddenly breaks up into a mass of twisting capillaries which coalesce to form the efferent artery. The portal vein of the mammalian liver arises from the capillary networks of the abdominal viscera, enters the liver, and separates into a network of sinusoids. They penetrate the organ and are then gathered into the hepatic vein. This is a "portal" system.

Arteriovenous Anastomoses. The terminal ramifications of arteries are connected with veins, not only by capillaries, but also by direct arteriovenous anastomoses in many parts of the body. As the lumen of these anastomoses changes within wide limits and is often closed, the anastomoses are probably a mechanism for the local regulation of blood circulation and pressure. In addition to these simple direct communications, Masson has described highly organized connections between arteries and veins which occur as part of a specific organ, the *glomus,* found in the nailbed, the pads of the fingers and toes, ears, hands and feet. The afferent arteriole enters the connective tissue capsule of the glomus, loses its internal elastic membrane, and develops a heavy epithelioid muscle coat and narrow lumen. This arteriovenous anastomosis of the glomus may be branched and convoluted, and is richly innervated by sympathetic and myelinated nerves. The anastomosis empties into a short, thin-walled vein with a wide lumen which drains into a periglomic vein and then into the ordinary veins of the skin.

In addition to helping regulate the flow of blood in the extremities, it is claimed that the glomus is concerned with temperature regulation and conservation of heat.

A special place in the blood vascular system is occupied by the cavernous tissue of erectile organs (see Chapter 29).

Coccygeal Body. This organ, erroneously included in the paraganglia, does not contain chromaffin cells. It is situated in front of the apex of the coccyx and measures 2.5 mm. in diameter. It consists of numerous arteriovenous anastomoses embedded in a dense fibrous matrix. The smooth muscle cells have undergone extensive "epithelioid" change. An internal secretion has not been demonstrated in this organ.

THE HEART

The heart, a thick, muscular, rhythmically contracting portion of the vascular system, is

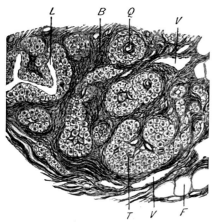

Fig. 10–20. Coccygeal body of man: portion of a cross section. *B,* connective tissue; *F,* fat cells; *L,* vessel in longitudinal, *Q,* in cross, and, *T,* in tangential sections; *V,* veins. Mallory's aniline blue stain. 110 ×. (After Schaffer.)

a roughly conical organ. It lies in the pericardial cavity within the mediastinum. It is about 12 cm. long, 9 cm. wide, and 6 cm. in its anteroposterior diameter. It consists of four main chambers: a right and left *atrium* and a right and left *ventricle.* The superior and inferior venae cavae bring the venous blood from the body to the right atrium, whence it passes to the right ventricle. From here the blood is forced through the lungs, where it is aerated and brought to the left atrium. It then passes to the left ventricle and is distributed throughout the body by the aorta and its branches. The atria are separated from the ventricles by the tricuspid and mitral valves on the right and left sides. The pulmonary artery and the aorta are separated from the right and left ventricles, respectively, by the semilunar valves.

The wall of the heart, in both the atria and the ventricles, consists of three main layers: (1) the internal, or *endocardium;* (2) the intermediate, or *myocardium;* (3) the external, or *epicardium.* The internal layer is in immediate contact with the blood; the myocardium is the contractile layer; and the epicardium is the visceral layer of the *pericardium,* a serous membrane which forms the pericardial sac in which the heart lies.

Most authors believe that the endocardium is homologous with the tunica intima of the blood vessels, the myocardium with the tunica media, and the epicardium with the tunica adventitia.

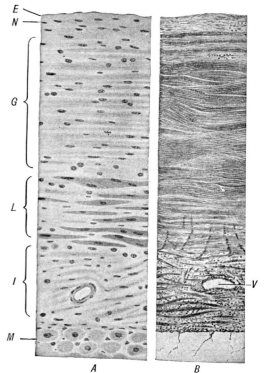

Fig. 10–21.   Cross section through left atrium of a man; *A,* stained with H + E; *B,* after orcein. *E,* endothelium; *N,* subendothelial layer; *G,* inner layer, and, *L,* outer layer with smooth muscle fibers of the endocardium; *I,* subendocardial layer; *M,* myocardium; *V,* blood vessel. 200 ×. (Redrawn after Favaro.)

Endocardium. The endocardium is lined with ordinary endothelium which is continuous with that of the blood vessels entering and leaving the heart. This endothelium consists of rounded or polygonal cells. In most places, directly under the endothelium, there is a thin *subendothelial layer;* it contains collagenous and a few elastic fibers and fibroblasts. External to this layer is a thick layer of connective tissue which composes the main mass of the endocardium and contains great numbers of elastic elements. In the left atrium these elastic fibers pass into a typical, fenestrated elastic membrane. Bundles of smooth muscle fibers are found in varying numbers in this layer, particularly on the interventricular septum.

A *subendocardial layer,* absent from the papillary muscles and the chordae tendineae, consists of loose connective tissue which binds the endocardium and the myocardium together and is directly continuous with the

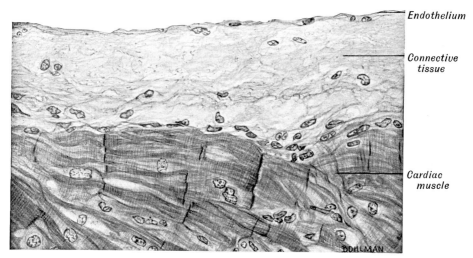

Endothelium

Connective
tissue

Cardiac
muscle

Fig. 10–22.   Section of the endocardium of the ventricle of man. 265 ×.

interstitial tissue of the latter. It contains blood vessels, nerves, and branches of the conduction system of the heart. In the spaces between the muscular bundles of the atria, the connective tissue of the endocardium continues into that of the epicardium, and the elastic networks of both layers intermingle.

Myocardium. The minute structure of the cardiac muscle has been described on page 172. In the embryos of the higher vertebrates the myocardial fibers form a spongy network. In the adult stage, however, they are bound by connective tissue into a compact mass. This condensation of the myocardium progresses from the epicardium toward the endocardium. Many embryonic muscular bars remain in a more or less isolated condition on the internal surface of the wall of the ventricular cavities. These bars are covered with endocardium and are called "trabeculae carneae."

Elastic elements are scarce in the myocardium of the ventricles of adult mammals, except in the tunica adventitia of the larger blood vessels of these chambers. In the myocardium of the atria, however, there are networks of elastic fibers which run everywhere between the muscle fibers and are directly connected with similar networks in the endocardium and epicardium. They are also continuous with the elastic networks in the walls of the large veins. A large part of the interstitial connective tissue of the cardiac muscle consists of extensive networks of reticular fibrils.

Epicardium. The epicardium is covered on its free surface by a single layer of mesothelial cells. Beneath the mesothelium is a thin layer of connective tissue with flat networks of elastic fibers, blood vessels and many nervous elements. About the adventitia of the coronary vessels there is a loose layer of considerable thickness which contains much adipose tissue.

The parietal layer of the pericardium is a serous membrane of the usual type—a flat layer of connective tissue which contains elastic networks, collagenous fibers, fibroblasts, fixed macrophages and a covering layer of mesothelial cells. Removal of the parietal pericardium in cats results in thickening of the epicardium and enlargement of the heart.

Cardiac Skeleton. The central supporting structure of the heart, to which most of the muscle fibers are attached and with which the valves are connected, is the cardiac skeleton (Poirier, Tandler). It has a complicated form and consists mainly of dense connective tissue; its main parts are the *septum membranaceum,* the *trigona fibrosa,* and the *annuli fibrosi* of the atrioventricular and the arterial foramina.

In man the fibrous rings consist mainly of dense connective tissue which contains some fat and thin elastic fibers. The structure of the septum membranaceum suggests that of an aponeurosis, with its more regular distribution of collagenous bundles in layers. The connective tissue of the trigona fibrosa contains islands of chondroid tissue. The cells of the latter are globular as in cartilage, although they lack true capsules. The interstitial substance stains deeply with basic aniline dyes and hematoxylin, and is pene-

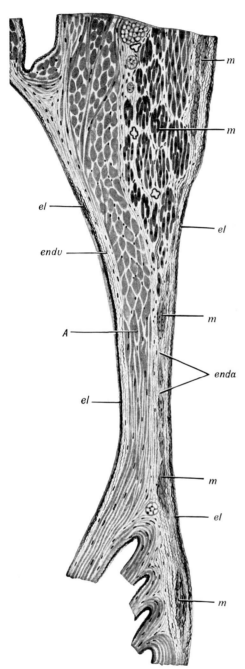

trated by collagenous fibers and practically no elastic fibers. In aged persons the tissue of the cardiac skeleton may in places become calcified and sometimes even ossified.

There are important differences in the histological structure of the cardiac skeleton among different animals, and even in persons of different ages. In some cases it is a simple, dense connective tissue with a few elastic fibers and is directly continuous with the interstitial tissue of the myocardium; in some cases it approaches cartilage in its structure (horse and pig); in the dog it forms true hyaline cartilage, and contains bone in the ox. These tissue types may be located in islands side by side; one type may merge into another.

Cardiac Valves. *Atrioventricular Valves.* These consist of a plate of connective tissue which begins at the annulus fibrosus and is reinforced by ligamentous threads. It is covered on the atrial and ventricular sides by a layer of endocardium. At the free edge of the valve these three layers blend.

The ground plate consists mainly of dense chondroid tissue with small spindle-shaped or rounded cells and a basophile, fibrillated, interstitial substance. The endocardial layer is thicker on the atrial side. Here the subendothelial layer has a small amount of chondroid tissue and rests upon a connective tissue layer which contains many elastic fiber networks and some smooth muscles. In the vicinity of the annulus fibrosus the subendocardial layer is quite loose, and the musculature of the atrium penetrates far into it. On the ventricular side the endocardial layer has a similar structure, but is much thinner. In many places the chordae tendineae enter it, and at the base of the valves are some muscle fibers from the ventricle.

Aortic and Pulmonic Valves. The aortic and pulmonic valves have the same general structure as the atrioventricular valves. In the middle of the valve are plates of chondroid tissue with collagenous and thin elastic fibers. At the root of the valve these all continue into the annulus fibrosus of the arterial foramen, and at the middle of the free edge they form the noduli Arantii.

On the arterial side this plate is covered with a thick, uneven endocardium consisting of (1) connective tissue with coarse, collagenous bundles (Fig. 10–24, *III a*) and a few elastic fibers; (2) a thin subendothelial layer with an elastic network and a peripheral endothelium (Fig. 10–24, *III b*). On the ventricular side the central plate (Fig. 10–24, *II*) is covered with a thick endocardium composed of (1) a connective tissue layer with longitudinal collagenous and elastic fibers (Fig. 10–24, *I c*) and (2) two connective tissue layers not sharply outlined from each other; one of these contains longitudinal (Fig. 10–24, *I a*) and the other transverse (Fig. 10–24,

Fig. 10–23. Cross section through mitral valve of man. Atrial surface on the right, ventricular on the left. In the upper left-hand corner is the attachment of the aortic valve; on the left, below, is the passage of chordae tendineae into the valve. *A,* dense tissue plate; *enda,* endocardium from the atrial, and, *endv,* from the ventricular side; *el,* elastic fibers; *m,* myocardium. Low magnification. (After Sato.)

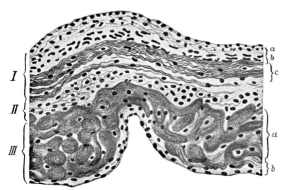

Fig. 10–24. Section through human aortic valve. Above is the ventricular surface; below is the lumen of the aorta. Elastic fibers unstained. See text (p. 246) for detailed explanation. (Redrawn from Mönckeberg.)

I b) elastic fibers; the covering is endothelium. There is here also a dense network of particularly thick elastic fibers which suggest the elastica interna of arteries.

Impulse-Conducting System. In the vertebrate embryo and in the adult lower vertebrates, the heart is a bent tube whose contractile walls are dilated and constricted in several places. The tube consists of four portions which lie behind one another in the caudocranial direction: (1) sinus venosus, (2) atrium, (3) ventricle, (4) conus arteriosus. Patten and Kramer studied living chick embryos and noted that the heart develops by "progressive fusion of paired primordia, ventricular end first, then atrium, and last of all sinus." As each part forms, it begins to beat and controls the rate of contraction of the parts previously laid down. Thus the regular activity of a primitive vertebrate heart is based on (1) the origin of the stimulus in a definite area of the organ, and (2) the transmission of this stimulus to the following portions.

In the adult mammalian heart, too, the motor impulse arises in that part of the heart which develops from the embryonic sinus venosus, that is, where the superior vena cava enters the right atrium. There is a specialized mechanism by which the contraction spreads to the atria and then to the ventricles.

Beginning with the sinus node and extending up to the papillary muscles and the other portions of the myocardium of the ventricles, there is a continuous tract of atypical muscles (the Purkinje fibers, p. 174), the *sinoventricular system.* This system serves for the origin and transmission of the contractile impulse. This conduction system is accompanied by many nerves which also play a part in carrying the contractile impulse. The usual descriptions picture the Purkinje fibers as arising at the sinus node, spreading over the atria, concentrating at the atrioventricular node, and passing by one main bundle (the atrioventricular bundle) to the ventricles, where they again branch out over the whole inner surface of these cavities. This description is but partially correct. The atypical fibers of the conduction system do appear in these positions; in addition, however, they pass from the atria to the ventricles by several other routes which have not been studied as thoroughly as the atrioventricular bundle.

This system of conduction fibers, even up to the terminal ramifications in the ventricles, is covered with a connective tissue membrane which separates it from the remaining muscular mass of the heart.

At the boundary between the right atrium and the superior vena cava, in the region of the sulcus terminalis, is the sino-atrial node, 1 cm. in length and 3 to 5 mm. in width. Although not sharply outlined, it can be seen with the naked eye. It consists of a dense network of twisted Purkinje fibers.

The atrioventricular node is a flat, white structure about 6 mm. long and 2 to 3 mm. wide; it is located in the posterior lower part of the interatrial septum under the posterior aortic valve. The node consists of Purkinje fibers, which form a tangled dense network whose meshes are filled with connective tissue. These fibers pass into (or between) the usual myocardial fibers, so that the boundary of the node is indistinct over much of its periphery. Toward the ventricles the substance of the node contracts abruptly into a shaft about 1 cm. long, the atrioventricular bundle. It is located in the dense connective tissue of the trigonum fibrosum dextrum and continues into the septum membranaceum, where it divides into two branches.

The first branch, a cylindrical bundle 1 to 2 mm. thick, runs downward along the posterior circumference of the membranous septum and is located in part directly under the endocardium of the right ventricle. It proceeds along the interventricular septum and splits into many branches which spread along the entire internal surface of the right ventricle and along the papillary muscles of the trabeculae carneae and disappear in the substance of the myocardium.

The left branch is a wide, flat band which comes forward under the endocardium of the left ventricle in the upper portion of the interventricular septum, under the anterior edge of the posterior cusps of the aortic valve. It divides into two main branches of the border between the upper and middle thirds of the septum; then it separates, as in the right ventricle,

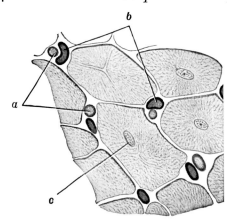

Fig. 10–25. Section of human myocardium, perpendicular to the muscle fibers, showing injected blood vascular capillaries, *a,* and lymphatic capillaries, *b; c,* nucleus of muscle fiber. High magnification. (Redrawn after Bock.)

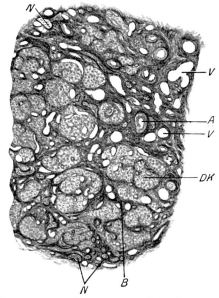

Fig. 10–26. Cross section through part of a carotid body of a man. *A,* artery; *B,* connective tissue; *DK,* cords of epithelioid cells; *N,* nerves; *V,* veins. Mallory's aniline blue stain. 42 ×. (After Schaffer.)

into numerous, anastomosing thin threads which are lost to view in the myocardium.

Blood Vessels of the Heart. The blood supply to the heart is carried by the coronary arteries, usually two in number, which arise in the aortic sinuses. They are distributed to the capillaries of the myocardium. The blood from the capillaries is collected by the cardiac veins, most of which empty by way of the coronary sinus into the right atrium. A few small cardiac veins empty directly into the right atrium.

In the coronary arteries of the human heart, the tunica media, which is limited on both sides by the usual internal and external elastic membranes, is divided by a thick fenestrated membrane into an inner and an external layer.

In ordinary preparations it is difficult to see blood vessels in the cardiac valves. Most authorities now believe that normal valves are practically devoid of vessels and that those which have been demonstrated are the result of chronic inflammatory processes (endocarditis).

There are a few vessels in the chordae tendineae; they run for the most part under the endothelium and arise from the vessels of the papillary muscles.

The sinoventricular system and, particularly, both its nodes are abundantly supplied with blood from special, rather constant branches of the coronary arteries.

Lymphatic Vessels of the Heart. Three groups of lymphatic vessels are described in the heart: (1) large lymphatic vessels which lie in the grooves of the heart together with the blood vessels; they are connected with the lymphatic nodes beneath the loop of the aorta and at the bifurcation of the trachea; (2) the lymphatic vessels of the epicardial connective tissue; and (3) lymphatic vessels of the myocardium and the endocardium.

In the subepicardial connective tissue ordinary flat networks of lymphatic capillaries may be demonstrated easily. These are connected with large efferent lymphatic capillaries and vessels.

Within the subendothelial connective tissue there

is an even larger network of typical lymphatic capillaries; the larger vessels have valves. Lymphatic capillaries have been described in the atrioventricular and semilunar valves.

This lymphatic network in the endocardium was formerly often confused with the netlike ramifications of the sinoventricular system, for both structures may be demonstrated by the same injection method. But the conducting system forms much wider meshes, and its cross bars are thicker and coarser.

The myocardium is penetrated by an abundant lymphatic network, which is everywhere connected with the subendocardial one and also continues into the pericardial network. Each muscular fiber is surrounded by several lymphatic capillaries longitudinally oriented along its surface. These are connected by means of cross and tangential anastomoses and closely adjoin the blood vessel capillaries, which follow approximately the same direction.

Nerves of the Heart. The numerous nerves of the heart belong in part to the vagus nerve and in part to the sympathetic nerves. For a detailed description, see Kuntz (1953).

Some nerve endings in the heart are apparently of effector type, while other endings are of receptor or sensory character. The nerve endings in the myocardium have been described (p. 198). Nonidez has given detailed descriptions of the nerve endings in the large arteries, near the heart, which are affected by changes in pressure in these vessels.

Carotid and Aortic Bodies. These structures have until recently been erroneously included with the paraganglia. They do not contain chromaffin cells and have not been shown to have an internal secretion. The carotid and aortic bodies are similar in structure and presumably in function.

The carotid bodies are flattened, inconspicuous structures at the bifurcation of each common carotid artery. They contain irregular masses of pale-staining epithelial-like cells with pale nuclei closely applied to the endothelium of sinuses. The epithelioid cells are richly supplied with nerve endings apparently specialized to receive chemical stimuli (hence the name *chemoceptors*) indicating a fall in pH, a rise in carbon dioxide and a decrease in oxygen of the circulating blood. Hollinshead found a degranulation of the epithelioid cells when the oxygen tension was reduced to lethal levels. He believes that the granules "are directly concerned with the initiation of chemoreceptor reflexes." The specific nerves from the carotid body reach the central nervous system by the sinus branch of the glossopharyngeal nerve.

The aortic body on the right side lies between the angle of the subclavian and the carotid, while on the left it is found above the aorta mesial to the origin of the subclavian, in each case occurring where the aortic nerve reaches the externa of the artery on which it ends (Nonidez). The structure of these bodies is identical with that of the carotid bodies.

The carotid body arises from the mesenchyme of the third branchial cleft artery and from the glossopharyngeal nerve. It is believed that the aortic bodies have a similar origin from the fourth branchial cleft artery and the vagus nerve.

The impulses from the aortic bodies are carried by the aortic nerve (depressor nerve of the vagus).

Chromaffin Cells. In the connective tissue between the aorta and pulmonary artery, approximately at the level of the semilunar valves, and also within the subepicardial connective tissue in the sulcus coronarius, mainly along the left coronary artery, small islands of chromaffin cells, similar to the elements of the medullary substance of the suprarenal glands, are scattered (p. 316). They are in close connection with nerve networks and ganglion cells. They are more highly developed in the newborn than in adults.

Histogenesis of the Blood Vessels and of the Heart. *Blood Vessels.* The blood vessels and the heart first appear as a layer of endothelial cells. In mammals the first vessels are laid down in the area vasculosa, where they develop from the mesenchymal cells (p. 107). In the organism proper the blood vessels and the heart appear later; at first they are devoid of blood cells and are empty.

In the spaces between the germ layers, groups of mesenchymal cells flatten around spaces filled with fluid which are thus surrounded by a thin endothelial wall. In this way, in given places in the body, the primordia of the heart and the main blood vessels, such as the aorta, cardinal and umbilical veins, and so forth, are laid down. Then, these at first independent primordia rapidly unite with one another and with the vessels of the area vasculosa, after which the blood circulation is established. The endothelial cells in these first stages are merely mesenchymal cells adjusted to the new and special function of bounding the blood vessel lumen. The idea that the vascular system in the embryo proper arises as an ingrowth of vessels from the area vasculosa has been rejected by most observers.

After the closed blood vascular system has developed and the circulation begun, new blood vessels always arise by "budding" from pre-existing blood vessels.

The new formation of blood vessels by budding may be studied in sections of young embryos or in the living condition in the margin of the tail in larval amphibians, the mesentery of newborn mammals, or the thin layer of inflamed tissue which grows in between two cover slips introduced under the skin of an animal (Fig. 10–27). A method has been devised for the continued observation of such chambers in the living rabbit for weeks and even months (Clark, Sandison).

In the process of budding, a protrusion appears on the wall of the capillary and is directed into the surrounding tissues. From the beginning it often appears to be a simple, hollow expansion of the endothelial wall; in other cases it is at first a solid accumulation of endothelial cytoplasm. This *vascular bud* or sprout enlarges, elongates, and assumes many shapes. Most frequently it appears as a pointed cylinder. It always becomes hollow and thus represents a local outpouching of the blood vessel into which blood cells penetrate.

An endothelial bud may encounter another bud and fuse with its end, or its lateral wall may come in contact with another bud or with another capillary. A lumen appears within the fused endothelial protoplasm and unites the two capillaries. In this way a new mesh is formed in the capillary network, and blood begins to circulate in it. Later, new buds may arise from the newly formed vessels.

The developing vascular buds are often accompanied by undifferentiated cells, phagocytes and fibroblasts, stretched parallel to the long axis of the buds; sometimes there are also wandering cells.

The most probable explanation for the cause of the capillary bud is that the increase of metabolism within the tissue causes an increase in circulation of substances through the endothelium and thereby induces the growth of the endothelium in the direction of this current.

Arteries and veins of all types are always laid down at first as ordinary capillaries. The primary endothelial tube expands and thickens as new elements, uniting with the outside of the wall, differentiate in several directions. These elements originate from the surrounding mesenchyme in the embryo, and form cells with mesenchymal potencies along the capillaries in the adult. They play an important part in the new formation of arteries and veins from capillaries, as well as in the formation of large vessels from smaller ones in the development of a "collateral circulation" of the blood. The mesenchymal cells outside the endothelium become young smooth muscle cells, and myofibrils differentiate in their cytoplasm. Soon more layers of smooth muscle fibers join in the first layer; these arise in part by multiplication of the smooth muscle cells and in part by the addition of new mesenchymal cells. In addition, networks of reticular fibers appear and form sheaths around the smooth muscle cells.

The factors which cause the larger arteries and veins to develop into more or less constant shapes in definite places and in definite directions are not

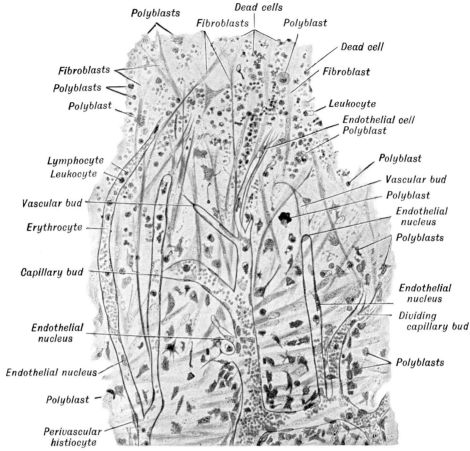

Polyblasts

Dead cells

Fibroblasts

Polyblast

Fibroblasts
Polyblasts
Polyblast

Lymphocyte
Leukocyte

Vascular bud

Erythrocyte

Capillary bud

Endothelial
nucleus

Endothelial nucleus

Polyblast

Perivascular
histiocyte

Dead cell

Fibroblast

Leukocyte

Endothelial cell
Polyblast

Polyblast

Vascular bud
Polyblast

Endothelial
nucleus
Polyblasts

Endothelial
nucleus

Dividing
capillary bud

Polyblasts

Fig. 10–27.   Young connective tissue with budding vessels growing into the space between two cover-slips inserted twenty days previously into the subcutaneous connective tissue of a rabbit. (A.A.M.)

completely solved. It is probable that in the earliest embryonic stages the formation of the vessels takes place through forces of heredity, while in the later stages the shape and growth of the blood vessels are determined by local mechanical and chemical stimuli.

The Heart. The heart at the beginning of the circulation is a tube with a double wall: the internal, endothelial layer from which the endocardium develops, and the external, myo-epicardial. The latter consists of several layers of cells with indistinctly outlined boundaries. In the beginning (human embryo of 3 mm. length) the distance between the two layers of the wall is rather great and is filled with a gelatinous, intercellular substance, which is penetrated by long, protoplasmic processes passing from the endothelium to the myo-epicardial layer.

In a human embryo 3.5 mm. in length, beginning with the sinus venosus and passing over to the atrium and the ventricle, this mucoid tissue disappears, and the endothelium closely adjoins the myocardial layer. But in the vicinity of the opening which connects the atrium with the ventricle and in the bulbus, this tissue remains. In this way, cushion-like thickenings of the endocardium are formed; they consist of a mu-

coid connective tissue. The myocardium differentiates at the same time into an external peripheral layer of flat cells, the primordium of the serous membrane of the epicardium, and into the internal, thicker layer of irregular cells united into a syncytium by intercellular bridges. The histological differentiation of the developing cardiac muscle from the syncytial layer located between the endocardium and epicardium has been described in the section on Cardiac Muscular Tissue.

The endocardial, cushion-like thickenings play an important role in the formation of partitions which separate the primary single cavity of the heart into compartments, and are particularly important in the formation of valves.

In the earlier stages of development the myocardium is continuous from the atria to the ventricles. But later, from the epicardium, along the course of the atrioventricular ridge, a transverse band of embryonic connective tissue develops which completely encircles the heart. It cuts into the myocardium from the exterior and separates entirely the muscle of the atria from that of the ventricles, save for the connection between them due to the atypical fibers of the conduction system.

REFERENCES

Aagard, O. C.: Les vaisseaux lymphatiques du cœur chez l'homme et chez quelques mammifères. Copenhagen and Paris, 1924.

Abell, R. G., and Page, I. H.: The reaction of peripheral blood vessels to angiotonin, renin, and other pressor agents. J. Exper. Med., 75:305, 1942.

Altschul, R.: Endothelium. The Macmillan Co., New York, 1954.

Benninghoff, A.: Blutgefässe und Herz. Handb. d. mikr. Anat. (v. Möllendorff), 1930, Vol. 6, pt. 1, p. 1.

Bloch, E. H.: Microscopic observations of the circulating blood in the bulbar conjunctiva in man in health and disease. Ergeb. Anat. Entwickl., 35: 1956.

Boyd, J. D.: The development of the human carotid body. Contrib. Embryol., Carnegie Inst. 152:3, 1937.

Chambers, R., and Zweifach, B. W.: Capillary endothelial cement in relation to permeability. J. Cell. & Comp. Physiol., 15:255, 1940.

Clark, E. R.: Growth and development of blood vessels and lymphatics. Ann. Int. Med., 9:1043, 1936; Arteriovenous anastomoses. Physiol. Rev., 18:229, 1938.

Clark, E. R., and Clark, E. L.: Microscopic observations on the extra-endothelial cells of living mammalian blood vessels. Am. J. Anat., 66:1, 1940.

Ebert, J. D., Tolman, R. A., Mun, A. M., and Albright, J. F.: Patterns of synthesis in differentiation. The molecular basis of the first heart beats. Ann. New York Acad. Sci., 60:968, 1955.

Gregg, D. E.: The coronary circulation. Physiol. Rev., 26:28, 1946.

Goss, C. M.: The physiology of the embryonic mammalian heart before circulation. Am. J. Physiol., 137: 146, 1942.

Harper, W. F.: The blood supply of human heart valves. Brit. M. J., 2:305, 1941.

Hollinshead, W. H.: Effects of anoxia upon carotid body morphology. Anat. Rec., 92:255, 1945.

Knisely, M. H., Bloch, E. H., and Warner, Louise: Selective phagocytosis. I. Microscopic observations concerning the regulation of the blood flow through the liver and other organs and the mechanism and rate of phagocytic removal of particles from the blood. Det. Kongelige Danske Videnskabernes Selskab, Biol. Skrifter, 4:2, 1948.

Kuntz, A.: The Autonomic Nervous System. Philadelphia. Lea and Febiger, 1953.

Lutz, B. R., Fulton, G. P., and Akers, R. P.: The neuromotor mechanism of the small blood vessels in membranes of the frog (Rana pipiens) and the hamster (Mesocricetus auratus) with reference to the normal and pathological conditions of blood flow. Exper. Med. & Surg., 8:258, 1950.

McClure, C.: The endothelial problem. Anat. Rec., 22: 219, 1921.

Nonidez, J. F.: Identification of the receptor areas in the venae cavae and pulmonary veins which initiate reflex cardiac acceleration (Bainbridge's reflex). Am. J. Anat., 61:203, 1937. The aortic (depressor) nerve and its associated epithelioid body, the glomus aorticum. Am. J. Anat., 57:259, 1935.

Patten, B. M., and Kramer, T. C.: The initiation of contraction in the embryonic chick heart. Am. J. Anat., 53:349, 1933.

Sabin, F. R.: Studies on the origin of blood vessels and of red blood corpuscles as seen in the living blastoderm of chicks during the second day of incubation. Contrib. Embryol. Carnegie Inst., 9:213, 1920.

Sandison, J. C.: Contraction of blood vessels and observations on the circulation in the transparent chamber in the rabbit's ear. Anat. Rec., 54:105, 1932.

Schmidt, C. F., and Comroe, J. H., Jr.: Functions of the carotid and aortic bodies. Physiol. Rev., 20:115, 1940.

Vimtrup, Bj.: Beiträge zur Anatomie der Capillaren. I. Ueber contractile Elemente in der Gefässwand der Blutcapillaren. Zeitschr. f. Anat. und Entwicklungs., 65:150, 1922.

Weidenreich, F.: Allgemeine Morphologie des Gefässsystems. Handb. d. vergleich. Anat., 6:375, 1933.

Zimmermann, K. W.: Der feinere Bau der Blutkapillaren. Zeit. f. Anat. u. Entwicklungs., 68:29, 1923.

Zweifach, B. W.: A micro-manipulative study of blood capillaries. Anat. Rec., 59:83, 1934.

CHAPTER 11

The Lymphatic System

AN EXCHANGE of nutritive materials and oxygen proceeds continuously between the blood within the capillaries and the tissue juice bathing the cells of the various tissues. Most of the waste products of metabolism are returned from the tissues to the capillaries and capillary veins. In the vertebrates the vessels of the closed lymphatic system return some of the tissue fluids to the general circulation by a roundabout route.

The lymphatic system is composed of *lymphatic vessels* and *organs*. The smallest vessels, the *lymphatic capillaries,* are thin-walled, blindly ending tubes which form a dense network in most of the tissues of the body. They collect tissue juice which is called lymph as soon as it enters these capillaries. The lymphatic capillaries unite to form larger vessels, the largest of which empty into veins. The lymphatic system thus differs from the blood vascular system in that it is not a closed vascular ring. The lymphatic organs are located along the course of the lymphatic vessels and contribute various-sized lymphocytes to the lymph passing through them. The lymph of the finest lymphatic radicles is almost devoid of cells.

Connected with the lymphatic system are the serous cavities, the spaces surrounding the meninges, the chambers of the eye, Tenon's cavity around the eyeball, the cavity of the internal ear, the ventricles of the brain, and the central canal of the spinal cord. The liquids in these cavities are different from the lymph and have a different physiological significance, although the liquid in the serous cavities is much like lymph. Nevertheless, injected colloidal solutions and particulate matter may penetrate from these cavities into the lymphatic vessels, and vice versa.

LYMPHATIC CAPILLARIES AND VESSELS

Lymphatic capillaries are thin-walled, tubular structures of slightly greater caliber than blood capillaries. Unlike the latter, which usually have a regular cylindrical form, they have irregular shapes and are constricted in some places and dilated in others. They branch abundantly and anastomose freely with one another. Dilatations occur frequently where several capillaries join. The lymphatic networks are often located beside networks of blood capillaries, but are always independent of them. As a general rule, the lymphatic networks are farther from the surface of the skin or mucous membranes than the blood capillary networks.

Further, the lymphatic networks are distinguished from the blood capillaries by ending blindly in rounded or swollen ends. This is best seen in the mucous membrane of the small intestine, where a network of lymphatic capillaries or a single, blindly ending vessel, the *central lacteal,* extends in the lamina propria up to the end of the villus (Fig. 11–1). The lymphatic capillaries form expanded networks of considerable size around the solitary and aggregated lymphatic nodules of the intestine, and in the thyroid and mammary glands.

The wall of the lymphatic capillaries is formed by a single layer of flat endothelial cells; these are slightly larger and thinner than those of the blood capillaries. Hence, in sections of collapsed lymphatic capillaries, only the endothelial nuclei can be seen, and these cannot be distinguished from the nuclei of the surrounding fibroblasts. The lymphatic capillaries abut directly against the surrounding tissues and are not provided with a layer of pericytes like the blood capillaries.

The lymph passes from these capillary networks into lymphatic vessels which have slightly thicker walls and valves. They are covered at first by thin, collagenous bundles, elastic fibers and a few smooth muscle cells, arranged tangentially or transversely to the vessel. Those lymphatic vessels with a diameter greater than 0.2 mm. have thicker walls in which three layers, corresponding to the inner, medial, and adventitial coats of arteries and veins, can be distinguished. The boundaries between these layers are often indistinct, so that the division is somewhat artificial. The tunica intima consists of endothelium and a thin layer of longitudinal, interlacing elastic fibers. The tunica media is composed of several layers of mainly circular and a few tangential smooth muscles, and several thin elastic fibers. The tunica adventitia is the thickest layer and consists of interlacing collagenous and elastic fibers, and smooth muscle bundles. The elastic fibers of the tunica adventitia continue into those of the surrounding connective tissue.

Valves. The valves of the lymphatic vessels always occur in pairs; they are placed on opposite sides of the vessel, and their free edges point in the direction of the lymph flow. The valves are often unable to withstand the pressure of a retrograde injection.

As in the veins, the valves of the lymphatic vessels are folds of the tunica intima. They have a thin connective tissue base and are covered on both sides by a layer of endothelium continuous with that of the rest of the vessel. Although valves are not present in all lymphatic vessels, when they occur, they are usually much closer together than those in the veins. Above each pair of valves, the lymphatic vessel is more or less distinctly expanded, and the wall in these places has several prominent layers of smooth muscles in its media. It is believed by some that the contractions of these muscles may help move the lymph along the vessel.

Large Lymphatic Vessels. Thoracic Duct. The lymphatic vessels unite with other simi-

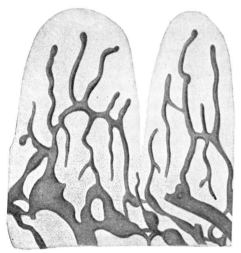

Fig. 11–1. Lymphatic capillaries (lacteals) filled with Berlin blue in the villi of the intestine of a rat. (Redrawn after Ranvier.)

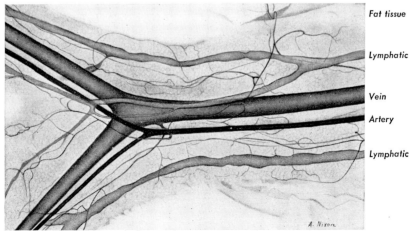

Fat tissue

Lymphatic

Vein

Artery

Lymphatic

A. Nixon

Fig. 11–2. Vital injection of lymphatic vessels with alpha-azurine F. G. and of the blood vessels with colloidal mercuric sulfide. Mesentery of rabbit. About 20 ×.

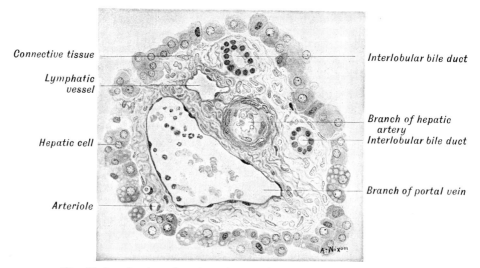

Fig. 11–3.   Section of periportal area of a human liver. 480 ×.

lar vessels and become larger and larger, while their walls become thicker. They form networks which often surround blood vessels. This is very marked about the mesenteric vessels of some mammals.

Finally, all the lymphatics come together and form two main trunks—the right lymphatic duct, and the thoracic duct. The former is the smaller; it carries the lymph from the upper right portion of the body and usually opens into the right innominate vein, where it arises from the right internal jugular and subclavian veins. The thoracic duct carries the lymph from all the remaining parts of the body (including the digestive system) and opens into the point of junction of the left internal jugular and subclavian veins. Both ducts are provided with valves where they enter the veins.

The wall of the thoracic duct differs from that of the great veins by the greater development of the muscles in the tunica media, by a less distinct division into three layers, and, particularly, by the great irregularity in the structure of adjacent portions.

The tunica intima consists of the endothelial lining and several thin layers of collagenous and elastic fibers; the latter condense into a layer similar to an internal elastic membrane near the junction with the tunica media. The transverse smooth muscle bundles in the tunica media are penetrated by elastic fibers coming from the elastica interna. The tunica adventitia is composed of longitudinal collagenous fibers, interlacing elastic fibers, and a few longitu-

dinal smooth muscle bundles. The tunica adventitia gradually merges into the surrounding loose connective tissue.

Blood Vessels of Lymphatics. The wall of the thoracic duct is provided with many blood vessels which extend into the outer layer of the middle tunic; these vessels are similar to the vasa vasorum of the larger blood vessels. The narrow, thin-walled lymphatic vessels are often accompanied by a small artery and a vein which run parallel to it. Capillaries arise from them and encircle the lymphatic vessel or form regular networks on its surface.

Nerves of Lymphatics. Both the large thoracic duct and the smaller lymphatic vessels are abundantly supplied with nerves. In both adventitial and medial coats some of the fibers terminate in sensory endings. The other fibers are motor nerves for the smooth muscles, as in the blood vessels.

Passage of Lymph from the Tissues into the Lymphatics. Investigation with the aid of injection methods has shown that the lumen of lymphatics does not communicate directly with the "tissue spaces." The so-called "stomata" seen in silver nitrate preparations are undoubtedly artefacts. As the lymphatics form a closed, endothelium-lined system of tubes, the tissue juice must pass through the endothelial cytoplasm to reach the lumen of the lymphatics. In inflammation the permeability of the local lymphatics to certain dyes is increased.

LYMPHATIC ORGANS

Closely connected with the lymphatic vessels are collections of *lymphatic tissue* aggregated into the *lymphatic organs*. The

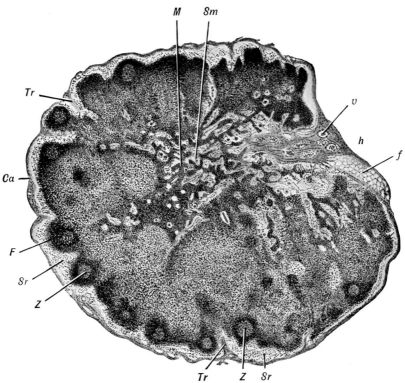

Fig. 11–4. Section through small jugular lymph node of man. *Ca,* capsule; *F,* nodules with their centers *Z; f,* fat tissue; *h,* hilus; *M,* medullary cord; *Sm,* medullary and, *Sr,* subcapsular sinus; *Tr,* trabeculae; *v,* blood vessel. 18 ×. (Redrawn and slightly modified from Sobotta.)

lymphatic tissue has been discussed in Chapter 5. The solitary and aggregated lymphatic nodules of the gastrointestinal, respiratory and genitourinary systems will be described with those organs. Here only the lymph nodes will be considered.

LYMPH NODES

The lymph nodes are large accumulations of lymphatic tissue organized as a definite lymphatic organ. They are always located along the course of lymphatic vessels, whose contents pass through the nodes on their way to the thoracic and the right lymphatic ducts. Lymph nodes are scattered in large numbers, usually in groups, throughout the prevertebral region, in the mesentery, and in the loose connective tissue of the inner surfaces of joints, such as the axilla, groin, and elsewhere. They are flat, well-defined bodies varying from 1 to 25 mm. in diameter. Their form is rounded or kidney-shaped, and their surface is somewhat rough. Usually there is a slight indentation, the *hilus,* on one side of

the node, where blood vessels enter and leave the organ. Lymphatic vessels enter the node at many places over its convex surface; they leave it only at the hilus.

Framework. The lymph node is covered by a *capsule* of dense collagenous fibers with a few fibroblasts and, particularly on its inner surface, networks of thin elastic fibers. A few smooth muscle cells are also found in the capsule about the points of entry and exit of the afferent and efferent lymph vessels. At the *hilus* the capsule is greatly thickened. *Trabeculae* of dense collagenous connective tissue arise from the capsule and penetrate the organ. Towards the hilus they become highly branched and finally fuse with the collagenous tissue of the hilus. Near the capsule, they divide the interior of the lymph node into roughly round areas, sometimes called ampullae or alveoli. As the trabeculae are frequently interrupted, adjacent ampullae connect with each other. The capsule, the hilus and the trabeculae constitute the collagenous framework of the lymph node. Suspended within this collagenous framework is

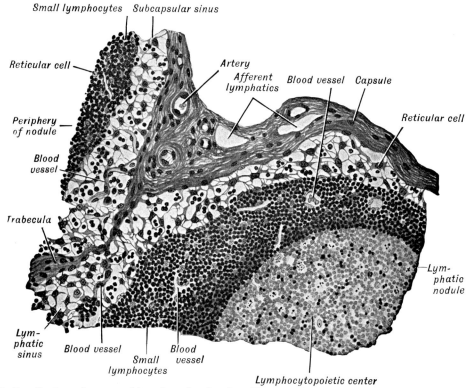

Small lymphocytes   Subcapsular sinus

Reticular cell

Artery
Afferent lymphatics   Blood vessel   Capsule

Reticular cell

Periphery of nodule

Blood vessel

Trabecula

Lym-phatic nodule

Lym-phatic sinus   Blood vessel   Blood vessel
Small lymphocytes

Lymphocytopoietic center

Fig. 11–5.   Portion of cortex of lymph node of a dog. Hematoxylin-eosin-azure stain. 187 ×. (A.A.M.)

the *reticular framework.* The reticular fibers are frequently continuous with fibers of the collagenous framework. The reticular fibers penetrate all parts of the node and form a network of varying density in different locations. The loosely meshed areas constitute the sinuses, through which the lymph percolates. Such loosely meshed areas occur under the capsule and along the trabeculae, where they are called subcapsular or trabecular sinuses respectively. The *cellular stroma* of the lymph node is made up of the primitive reticular cells and the dye-storing fixed macrophages. These are associated with the reticular fibers. It is generally believed that the primitive reticular cells or the fixed macrophages (or both) form the reticular fibers, since typical fibroblasts are found only in the collagenous framework. In the meshes of the stroma are the free cells, mostly lymphocytes of various sizes. Plasma cells often occur, especially in the rat. A few hematogenous eosinophile leukocytes can be found in most lymph nodes. The sinuses, particularly of the medulla, contain free macrophages, even under normal conditions. Usually there are

fewer free cells in the sinuses than in the tissue, since the cells are swept away by the flowing lymph.

Cortex and Medulla. The sectioned surface of a lymph node under low magnification shows the organ divided into an outer cortical and an inner medullary part. The difference in appearance between the cortex and medulla consists mainly in differences in arrangement of the lymphatic tissue in the two zones. The cortex occupies the surface of the organ, with the exception of the hilus, and consists primarily of dense lymphatic tissue which continues into the medulla as medullary cords. As mentioned before, a rim of loose lymphatic tissue is present under the capsule and bordering the trabeculae. The cortex contains lymphatic nodules about 1 mm. in diameter. The nodules are temporary structures (see p. 92), expressing the cytogenetic and defense functions of the lymphatic tissue, which depend on age, condition or nutrition of the organism, and the like. They may develop and disappear, to reappear again at the same or another place. The number and size of the nodules fluctuate remark-

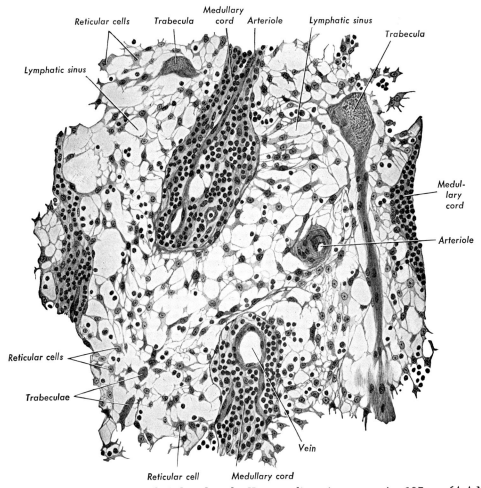

Fig. 11–6. Portion of medulla of a dog's lymph node. Hematoxylin-eosin-azure stain. 187 ×. (A.A.M.)

ably. In the embryo and in the first months after birth they lack the central "germinal" or "reactive" areas. With the growth and development of the organism these centers appear and then become more numerous and larger. With advancing age they become less conspicuous and smaller, and in old age and in various diseases may disappear. The medulla consists of the same cytological constituents as the cortex. It is not sharply separated from the cortex and usually occupies the inner portion of the node radiating from the hilus. The medullary cords are dense lymphatic tissue and rarely contain nodules. The cords branch and anastomose freely with one another. Near the hilus they terminate with free ends, or, more frequently, they form loops which continue into other cords. The cords are accompanied and surrounded by the medullary sinuses, which separate them from the trabeculae and are continuations and amplifications of the cortical sinuses. The substance of the sinuses is also composed of lymphatic tissue, but its meshes are so wide that they constitute relatively broad channels for the passage of lymph.

Lymphatic Vessels and Sinuses. The vessels which supply lymph to the node (vasa afferentia) are provided with valves which open toward the node (Fig. 11–7). These afferent vessels approach the convex surface of the node, pierce its capsule and open into the subcapsular sinus. From here the lymph passes through the looser parts of the lymphatic tissue, the sinuses, of both the cortex and medulla, and then into the efferent lymphatic vessels at the hilus.

Unlike the tubular, endothelium-lined

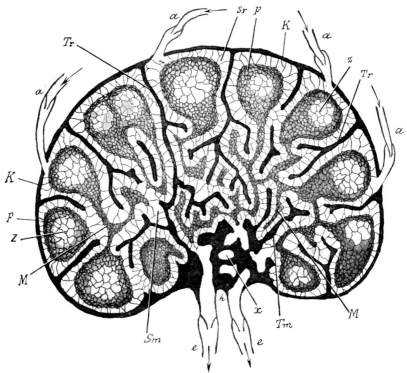

Fig. 11–7. Diagram of lymph node. *a,* afferent and, *e,* efferent lymphatic vessels with valves; the arrows indicate the direction of lymph flow; *F,* cortical tissue; *K,* capsule; *M,* medullary cords; *Sm,* medullary and, *Sr,* cortical sinuses; *Tm,* medullary trabeculae, continuous with those of the cortex; *Tr,* trabeculae originating in the capsule and dividing the cortex into ampullae; *x,* lymphatic vessels in the dense connective tissue of the hilum, *h; Z,* nodules.

blood vascular and lymphatic *vessels,* the lymphatic *sinuses* are irregular, tortuous spaces within the lymphatic tissue. Their walls are not continuous, and are formed of reticular cells and fixed macrophages supported by the reticular fibers. As a continuous stream of lymph flows through the sinuses, lymphocytes are swept into the efferent lymphatic vessels, and new lymphocytes enter the sinuses by their own ameboid movement.

The sinuses of the medullary substance at first pass over into a network of twisted tubes, which penetrate the thickened portion of the capsule at the hilus and then continue into the efferent vessels, which lead the lymph away. These are wider and less numerous than the afferent vessels; they are provided with valves which open away from the node. The arrangement of the valves in the afferent and efferent vessels thus permits a flow of lymph in only one direction through the node.

The margins of the endothelial cells in the

lymphatic vessels can be outlined by treatment with silver nitrate. The outlines of the reticular cells which form the walls of the lymphatic sinuses may sometimes be demonstrated by this means when they are so closely packed as to simulate endothelial cells. In all cases their reticular nature is easily recognizable.

Variations in Structure of Lymph Nodes. The described arrangement of the constituents of a typical lymphatic node is realized in but few instances, for the lymph nodes show great variations in structure, depending on the animal species as well as the location of the node. But none of these deviations affects the fundamental structure.

In large nodes the trabeculae are prominent; in small nodes they are thin and frequently interrupted, so that they may be absent for long stretches. The nodes deep in the body, as in the peritoneal cavity, are also distinguished by the poor development of their trabeculae as contrasted with the more peripheral nodes.

In some cases a hilus may be absent, while in others it may be so highly developed that its connective tissue may penetrate far into the node and divide it completely. In the ox the trabecular system is so well developed that the ampullae of the cortex are completely separated from one another. When the trabecular system is poorly developed, as in man, the nodules of the cortical substance and the sinuses may lose their sharp outlines and often fuse into a continuous, diffuse mass of lymphatic tissue, in which there are occasional looser strips or passages along which the lymph flows. Such areas, when filled with macrophages, have been called "interfollicular tissue." The term should be discarded, since the only tissue in the node is lymphatic tissue.

The relative amounts of cortical and medullary substance and their mutual arrangement fluctuate within wide limits. The nodes of the abdominal cavity are especially rich in medullary substance. In those cases in which the cortical substance predominates, the nodules may be arranged in several layers. Sometimes the cortical substance may surround the medulla completely, while in other cases the medullary substance may be adjacent to the capsule for long distances. In some cases the medulla and cortex may accumulate at opposite poles of the node, while in the pig the cortical substance with its nodules is collected in the central portion of the node, and the medullary cords with their wide sinuses may occupy only small portions of the periphery.

Blood Vessels. Almost all the blood vessels destined for the lymph node enter it through the hilus; only occasionally small ones enter through the capsule. The larger arterial and venous branches pass along the trabeculae, while the smaller ones pass along the axis of the medullary cords toward the cortex. The capillaries form particularly dense networks in the peripheral layers of the medullary cords and of the nodules. In the latter they form radially arranged meshes. In the cortex, they have a thickened endothelium, so that in cross section they often appear as though lined by cuboidal epithelium. Large numbers of small lymphocytes are present and pass through this endothelium into the blood.

Nerves. Nerves enter the hilus of the node with the blood vessels forming perivascular networks. In the trabeculae and in the medullary cords, independent nervous networks may be noticed. But in the nodules nerves are present only along the vessels and are probably of vasomotor type.

Hemal Nodes. Even in normal lymph nodes varying numbers of erythrocytes are found; these have either entered the lymph from the afferent vessels or have come from the blood vessels of the node. Some of them pass with lymph into the efferent vessels, but most of them are engulfed by the fixed macrophages. Some nodes, however, are characterized by their great content of erythrocytes; macroscopically, such organs are called *hemal nodes*. They are most numerous and well defined in the ruminants (sheep); they probably do not occur in man.

They vary from the size of a hardly noticeable granule to that of a pea or larger, and are scattered near large blood vessels in the retropleural and retroperitoneal tissues along the vertebral column from the neck to the pelvic inlet. They are also found near the kidneys and spleen, where they are believed by some to be accessory spleens.

Each node is covered by a dense capsule loosely connected with the surrounding tissue. At the hilus a small artery and a large vein enter and leave. The nodes are devoid of lymphatics.

The hemal node is a mass of lymphatic tissue, separated from the capsule by a sinus filled with blood. The lymphatic tissue is often penetrated by sinuses originating from the peripheral sinus and emptying into the "central" sinuses. All are filled with blood. A connection between the blood-containing sinuses and branches of arteries or veins has not been demonstrated.

The hemal nodes are "filters" of lymphatic tissue, situated in the course of blood vessels, and their structure is closer to that of the spleen than of lymph nodes. In the pig a special type of hemolymphatic node occupies a position halfway between the ordinary lymph node and the typical hemal node. It has blood as well as lymphatic vessels, and the contents of both types of vessels mix in the sinuses. It is possible that even in adult animals a simple lymph node may change into a hemal node, and vice versa. The functions of the hemal nodes are probably like those of the spleen.

Function of Lymphatic Nodes. Although they share this function with all the other accumulations of lymphatic tissue in the body, they are the most active structures for the formation of the lymphocytes. The stimuli for lymphocyte production are probably brought to the lymph nodes by both lymphatic and arterial vessels. Although great numbers of lymphocytes are produced in certain infections, the lymphatic leukemias and in some intoxications—such as diphtheria—the actual stimuli for lymphocytopoiesis in these conditions, as well as in physiological states, are unknown. As the lymph nodes are composed essentially of lymphocytes and phagocytes, it is obvious that their main functions depend on these cells. The functions of these cells are discussed in Chapters 4 and 5.

In some pathological conditions, *extramedullary myelopoiesis* occurs, and the nodes become the site of formation of granular leukocytes.

Because of the phagocytic activity of the reticular cells, particularly in the sinuses, the nodes serve as filters in which various particles, arising locally or brought with the lymph from other regions of the body, are taken up and often destroyed. Even in normal conditions, erythrophagocytosis can be seen in the sinuses of lymph nodes. This

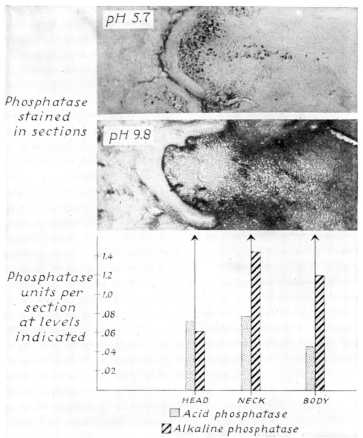

Phosphatase stained in sections

pH 5.7

pH 9.8

Phosphatase units per section at levels indicated

HEAD   NECK   BODY
⊞ Acid phosphatase
▧ Alkaline phosphatase

Fig. 11–8.   Quantitative analyses of amounts of acid and alkaline phosphatase were made on sections taken at the levels indicated in rabbit appendix. The qualitative distribution of the enzymes in the lymphatic tissue is shown in the photomicrographs made with the methods of Gomori. (After Doyle.)

process is much more prominent when great numbers of erythrocytes are brought to the nodes as a result of hemorrhage into the nearby tissues. Particles of coal dust inhaled into the lungs finally enter the bronchial lymph nodes, where they are taken up by the reticular cells and often accumulate in such quantities that the organ becomes black. Pathogenic bacteria brought to the lymph nodes are frequently ingested and sometimes destroyed by the macrophages. Just like all the other tissues and organs containing many macrophages and lymphoid cells, the lymph nodes probably elaborate *antibodies*.

Histogenetic Remarks. In the mammalian embryo the lymphatic system is laid down much later than the blood vascular system. The lymphatic vessels arise first, and the lymphatic organs develop in connection with them somewhat later.

Lymphatic Vessels. Although there are many unsettled details in the question of the mode of develop-

ment of the lymphatic system, most observers believe that the primordia of the lymphatic sacs and vessels arise independently of the veins, although often close to them, as isolated small clefts in the mesenchyme, which are filled with tissue fluid and surrounded by mesenchymal cells. The latter, owing to the pressure exerted by the fluid, acquire a flattened appearance and the character of endothelium. These spaces gradually fuse, forming in certain places large cavities, the *lymphatic sacs,* as well as vessels of more or less cylindrical shape. The sacs later communicate with the adjacent veins.

The vessels elongate rapidly in all directions owing to a continued addition of new cavities arising in the mesenchyme. The presence of blood in the early lymphatic vessels is explained as being due in part to a flow of blood from the veins and in part to the appearance of local hemopoietic islands in the mesenchyme together with the lymph sacs. These blood cells become included in the latter and are carried with the lymph into the veins.

After a certain stage the further development of the lymphatic system takes place mainly by budding of the endothelium of existing lymphatic vessels. These outgrowths may be observed directly in the tail of living amphibian larvae and in chambers in the rabbit's ear. They agree closely with the outgrowths from blood vessels (p. 249).

As in the blood vascular system, the developing lymphatic system does not retain all the parts laid down in the beginning; its constituents continue to change and become reconstructed. The main parts of the primary lymphatic system, the *sacs*, spread irregularly in various directions, and change their form; they develop in part into networks of lymphatic vessels and in part into complexes of lymphatic nodes. The student is referred to Zimmermann's monograph for the latest survey of the field.

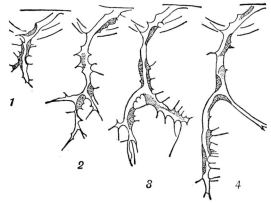

Fig. 11–9. Successive stages (*1–4*) during three days of growth of bud of a lymphatic capillary of frog tadpole. 180 ×. (Redrawn after E. R. Clark.)

Valves. Valves appear in the lymphatic vessels several weeks before they develop in the blood vessels. They appear first in the lymphatics near the jugular sacs and the upper part of the thoracic duct, then in the lymph vessels of the appendages, and finally in the remainder of the thoracic duct. They consist of a connective tissue base and a covering of endothelium.

Lymphatic Nodes. The development of the lymph nodes begins after the formation of the primary lymphatic vascular system. The earliest or primary nodes develop by a transformation of the lymphatic sacs. Each sac disappears as such and separates into a group of connected networks of lymphatic vessels which become nodes of various sizes; portions of the primary cisterna chyli and of the jugular sacs remain as cavities. As the sacs are at first the centers of development of the lymphatic vessels in a given region of the body, so in the future all the lymph collected from that region is finally carried into the corresponding group of deep primary nodes, as the deep jugular nodes, retroperitoneal, and so on. The secondary nodes, such as the peripheral, the inguinal, and the like, appear later along the course of lymphatic vessels; many smaller nodes are apparently formed after birth.

The transformation into a primary node is carried out by an invagination, into the lumen of the sac, of the surrounding mesenchyme, which grows through the sac in thick or thin bars. The mesenchyme forming the bars or partitions between the cavities at first does not contain wandering cells.

According to the newer investigations, the lymphatic sinuses arise as irregular, blind and anasto-

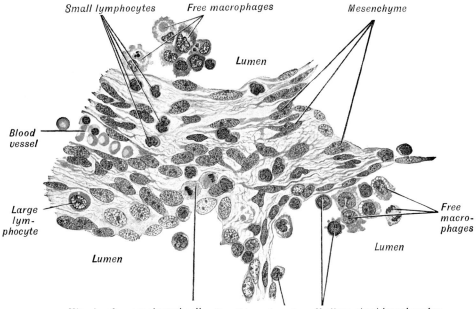

Fig. 11–10. Primordium of lymph node in the wall of cervical lymph sac of a human embryo of 37 mm. Lumen of the sac is divided into cavernous spaces by partitions of mesenchyme. Eosin-azure stain. About 400 ×. (A.A.M.)

mosing spaces, lined from the beginning by flattened mesenchymal cells, and only later do they come in contact with the endothelium-lined afferent and efferent vessels.

The primary node is a common primordium for the lymphatic tissue of the cortex and medulla, from which the medullary substance arises first. The true cortical substance appears much later as the medullary cords on the periphery of the node gradually develop club-shaped thickenings which bulge into the marginal sinus. The development of the lymphatic nodules is completed late, in the majority of cases after birth.

The lymphocytes develop *in situ* by the isolation and rounding up of mesenchymal elements and later through their own multiplication. They accumulate mainly in the marginal sinus and are carried away by the lymph stream. Among these cells, at first the small ones always predominate, but large lymphocytes and macrophages also occur. Granulocytes and megakaryocytes appear temporarily with the lymphocytes, but soon disappear. The mesenchymal elements, which did not transform into lymphoid cells, either remain as undifferentiated elements (primitive reticular cells) or give rise to the fixed macrophages of the stroma. Fibers appear rather late in the stroma of lymphatic tissue.

Regenerative Capacity of Lymphatic System.

When the adult human body is incised or otherwise injured, lymphatic vessels, and sometimes lymphatic organs, are injured. Regeneration of the vessels begins in the lymphatic capillaries and proceeds by vascular budding. In some cases, however, for reasons not known, regeneration of the lymphatic vessels does not take place.

The tissue of the lymphatic nodes responds to local injury at first by the rounding up of reticular cells and their transformation into macrophages, which multiply by mitosis. The lymphocytes, which at first are unchanged, then begin to multiply and hypertrophy into polyblasts. But this attempt at regeneration is limited, and healing is usually brought about by the development of ordinary scar tissue.

After excision in young rabbits, lymph nodes may regenerate from local cells. With advancing age the regenerative ability decreases markedly.

REFERENCES

Clark, E. R., and Clark, E. L.: Further observations on living lymphatic vessels in the transparent chamber in the rabbit's ear—their relation to the tissue spaces. Am. J. Anat., *52:*263, 1933.

Conway, E. A.: Cyclic changes in lymphatic nodules. Anat. Rec., *69:*487, 1937.

Downey, H.: The structure and origin of the lymph sinuses of mammalian lymph nodes and their relations to endothelium and reticulum. Haematologica, *3:*31, 1922.

Downey's Handbook of Hematology. New York, 1938.

Doyle, W. L.: The distribution of phosphatases in the rabbit appendix after x-irradiation. Am. J. Anat., *87:*79, 1950.

Furuta, W. J.: An experimental study of lymph node regeneration in rabbits. Am. J. Anat., *80:*437, 1947.

Hellman, T.: Lymphgefässe, Lymphknötchen und Lymphknoten. Handb. d. mikr. Anat. (v. Möllendorff), 1930, Vol. 6, Pt. 1, p. 233.

Johnson, V., and Freeman, W.: The adaptive value of absorption of fats into the lymphatics. Am. J. Physiol., *124:*466, 1938.

Kampmeier, O.: The genetic history of the valves in the lymphatic system of man. Am. J. Anat., *40:*413, 1928.

Latta, J.: The histogenesis of dense lymphatic tissue of the intestine (Lepus): A contribution to the knowledge of the development of lymphatic tissue and blood-cell formation. Am. J. Anat., *20:*159, 1921.

McClure, C. W. F.: The endothelial problem. Am. J. Anat., *22:*219, 1921.

McMaster, P. D., and others; Lymph. Ann. New York Acad. Sci., *46:*679, 1946.

Recklinghausen, F. v.: Das Lymphgefässsystem. Stricker's Handb. d. Lehre von den Geweben, 1871, Vol. 1, p. 214.

Webb, R. L.: The lymphatic system. Ann. Rev. Physiol., *14:*315, 1952.

Webb, R. L., and Nicoll, P. A.: Behavior of lymphatic vessels in the living bat. Anat. Rec., *88:*351, 1944.

Yoffey, J. M., and Courtice, F. C.: Lymphatics, Lymph and Lymphoid Tissue. Cambridge, Harvard University Press, 1956.

Zimmermann, A. A.: Origin and Development of the Lymphatic System in the Opossum. University of Illinois Press, (3), 7, 1940.

CHAPTER 12

The Spleen

THE SPLEEN, one of the blood-forming and destroying organs, plays important roles in the metabolism and defense mechanisms of the body. It is the largest mass of lymphatic tissue in the body. But unlike the other collections of this tissue which are interposed in the lymph stream, the spleen is inserted in the blood stream. Owing to a peculiar type of blood vessel which allows the circulating blood to come into close contact with the macrophages of this organ, the spleen acts in many respects as a filter for the blood; this property becomes greatly accentuated in immune reactions.

The spleen, much like the lymph node, has a collagenous framework within which is suspended a reticular framework. As in the lymph node, the collagenous framework consists of a *capsule,* thickened at the hilus of the organ, where it is attached to folds of the peritoneum and where arteries enter and veins leave the viscus. Branching and anastomosing continuations of the capsule, called *trabeculae,* penetrate the organ and form part of its framework.

The reticular framework fills the spaces between the capsule, hilus and trabeculae and forms, together with the cells present, the splenic tissue. This is composed of typical lymphatic tissue (*white pulp*) and an atypical lymphatic tissue (*red pulp*). The red pulp is a pastelike, dark red mass which can be scraped from the cut surface of the organ. On a freshly sectioned surface of the spleen the white pulp is seen as irregular long or rounded gray areas, 0.2 to 0.7 mm. in diam-

eter, scattered throughout the red pulp. These white areas are often called malpighian bodies, after the anatomist who first described them. They consist of diffuse and nodular lymphatic tissue, which varies considerably in its finer structure from time to time. It is inadvisable to use the term "malpighian body," since it has been interpreted to mean different structures by various histologists.

The structure of the spleen and the relations between the red and white pulp depend on the distribution of the blood vessels, and change markedly in certain infections, intoxications and disturbances in blood cell formation (anemias, leukemia). The arteries are closely connected with the white pulp and the veins with the red pulp.

Capsule and Trabeculae. The capsule and the trabeculae of the spleen consist of dense connective tissue and a few smooth muscle cells. The collagenous fibers of the trabeculae are continuous with the reticular fibers of the pulp. Elastic fibers form a network between the collagenous bundles. In man, the network of the thickest elastic fibers is located in the deep layers of the capsule. The external surface of the capsule is covered by a layer of flattened mesothelium which is part of the peritoneum.

In the trabeculae the elastic fibers are more numerous than in the capsule and sometimes replace most of the collagenous fibers. Muscle fibers are present in small groups (in man) or in long cords. The slow rhythmical changes in the volume of the organ are due to the

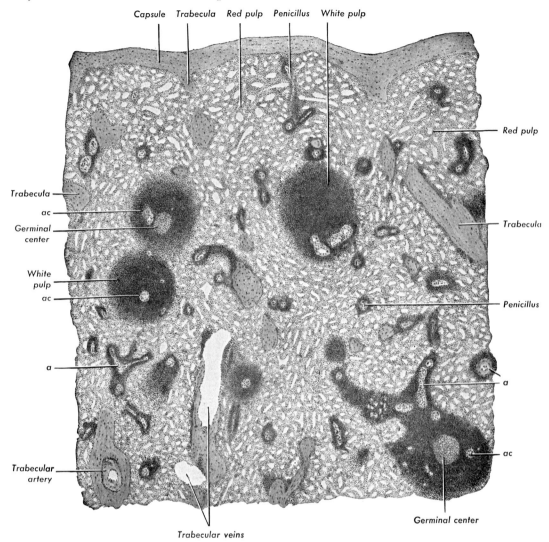

Capsule   Trabecula   Red pulp   Penicillus   White pulp

Red pulp

Trabecula
ac
Germinal
center

White
pulp
ac

a

Trabecular
artery

Trabecula

Penicillus

a

ac

Germinal center

Trabecular veins

Fig. 12–1.   Section of lumen of spleen. The arterial branches are covered with a thick layer of white
pulp (lymphatic tissue) at *ac* and a thin layer at *a*. 32 ×. (A.A.M.)

smooth muscle in the capsule and trabeculae
(in those species in which smooth muscle is
prominent) and to the vascularly controlled
changes in the amount of blood in the organ.

White Pulp. The white pulp (lymphatic
tissue) forms a sheath about the arteries. The
stroma is a network of reticular fibers closely
joined to the primitive reticular cells and
phagocytic reticular cells or fixed macrophages (p. 90). As in all lymphatic tissue,
the meshes of the framework are filled with
free lymphocytes of various sizes, distributed
to form diffuse and nodular lymphatic tissue.
In the center of the lymphatic nodules of the
spleen, as in the nodules of lymph nodes,

the framework consists of thin, scattered
threads, while at the periphery it is coarser
and much denser. A few elastic fibers are
interspersed among the reticular fibers of the
white pulp close to the artery and its capillaries.

The absolute and relative amounts of
dense and nodular lymphatic tissue vary continuously and reflect the reaction of the
lymphatic tissue to various generalized stimuli. The lymphatic tissue of the spleen undergoes the same changes described on pages
92 to 95 for the lymphatic tissue in general. That is, diffuse lymphatic tissue may become nodular, and vice versa. The centers of

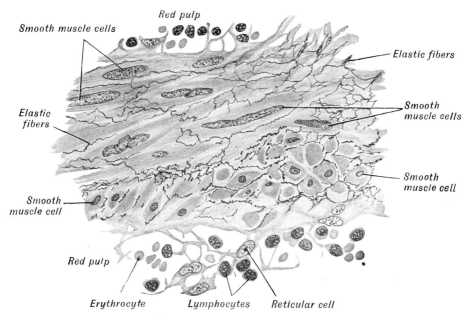

Fig. 12–2.   Portion of a trabecula from spleen of a cat. Elastic fiber stain. 750 ×. (A.A.M.)

the nodules undergo the same cyclic changes as described on page 92. The volume and number of the nodules decrease progressively with age. In myeloid leukemia the red pulp is greatly increased in amount (besides changing qualitatively), while the white pulp almost disappears. In lymphatic leukemia, on the contrary, the white pulp hypertrophies and the red pulp atrophies. The amount of lymphatic tissue is said to diminish during starvation. Lymphocytopoietic centers in the nodules appear and disappear in connection with the general condition of the organism. In the young they are numerous, while in the aged they are usually absent (especially in man). "Reaction centers" are common in certain infections and intoxications.

Red Pulp. This tissue consists of the "venous sinuses" and the tissue filling the spaces between them, the "splenic" or "Billroth cords." The venous sinuses will be discussed in the section on the veins of the spleen, of which they form an integral part. The splenic cords form a spongy network. Their tissue is a modified lymphatic tissue which merges gradually into the tissue of the white pulp. Outside the latter, there is a band of tissue looser than the white pulp and containing some erythrocytes, but devoid of venous sinuses. It constitutes the so-called "marginal zone" of the periarterial lymphatic tissue.

A framework of reticular fibers forms the foundation of the red pulp. At the boundary between the white and red pulp, it is evident that the fibers of the former continue into those of the latter. The collagenous fibers of the trabeculae continue directly into the reticular fibers of the red pulp. The fibrous stroma of the latter is accompanied by fixed macrophages and primitive reticular cells.

In the meshes of this framework are many lymphocytes, free macrophages and all the elements of the circulating blood. The nongranular leukocytes are the most numerous of these free cells. Among them small, medium-sized and large lymphocytes and monocytes are present in great numbers, intermingled without order. The various types of lymphocytes which arise in the white pulp spread by ameboid movement throughout the red pulp, where they continue to multiply.

The free macrophages are similar to those of the lymphatic tissue and are in close genetic relation with the fixed macrophages. They are round or irregularly shaped cells with large vesicular nuclei and much cytoplasm, which often contains engulfed particles, mainly erythrocytes in different stages of digestion, and yellow and brown granules, some of which give an iron reaction. Free macrophages can sometimes be found in blood filling the venous sinuses.

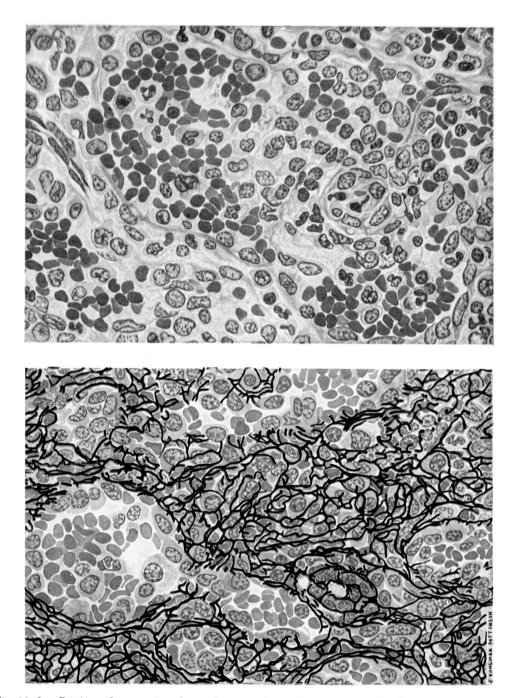

Fig. 12–3.   Portions of two sections from a human spleen, the upper stained with H + E, the lower with H + E after the Bielschowsky impregnation method for reticular fibers. 600 ×.

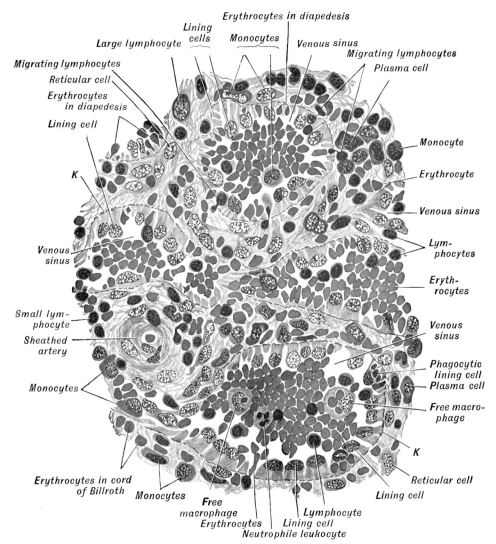

Fig. 12–4.   Red pulp of a human spleen. *K,* condensed cytoplasm of lining cells. Eosin-azure stain.
750 ×. (A.A.M.)

In many mammals (mouse, guinea pig and hedgehog) and in human embryos the red pulp of the spleen contains varying sized groups of myelocytes, erythroblasts, megakaryocytes and plasma cells.

In infections, in some of the anemias and leukemias, in poisoning with certain blood-destroying agents, and in local inflammations of the organ, the splenic tissue undergoes a *myeloid metaplasia* (p. 112). Myelocytes, megakaryocytes and erythroblasts develop within the red pulp; only myelocytes have been described as arising in the germinal centers. This indicates that both white and red

pulp are composed primarily of the same lymphatic tissue, which also has myeloid potencies. The myeloid elements may develop from typical lymphocytes as well as from primitive reticular cells. The old idea of an "antagonism" between the red and white pulp is obviously untenable. The *red pulp is merely a modified lymphatic tissue heavily infiltrated with all the cells of the circulating blood.*

Arteries. The branches of the splenic artery enter the hilum and pass along the trabeculae, with which they branch repeatedly, becoming smaller in caliber. They are

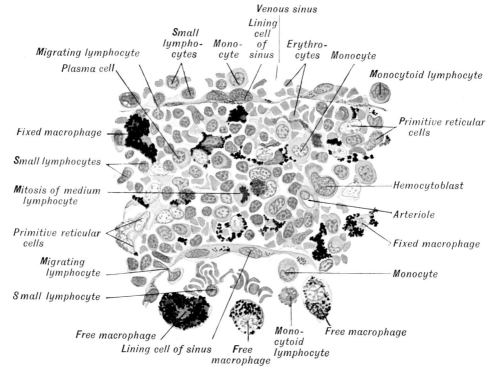

Venous sinus
Lining cell of sinus
Small lympho-cytes
Mono-cyte
Erythro-cytes
Monocyte
Migrating lymphocyte
Plasma cell
Monocytoid lymphocyte
Fixed macrophage
Primitive reticular cells
Small lymphocytes
Mitosis of medium lymphocyte
Hemocytoblast
Primitive reticular cells
Arteriole
Migrating lymphocyte
Fixed macrophage
Small lymphocyte
Monocyte
Free macrophage
Lining cell of sinus
Free macrophage
Mono-cytoid lymphocyte
Free macrophage

Fig. 12–5. Cross section of cord of Billroth lying between two venous sinuses from spleen of a rabbit injected with lithium carmine and India ink. Hematoxylin-eosin-azure II. 460 ×. (A.A.M.)

muscular arteries of medium caliber and have a loose tunica adventitia surrounded by the dense connective tissue of the trabeculae.

When the arterial branches have reached a diameter of approximately 0.2 mm., they leave the trabeculae (Fig. 12–7). At this place the tunica adventitia is replaced by a cylindrical sheath of lymphatic tissue (the white pulp) which accompanies the arteries almost to the point where they break up into capillaries. In many places along the course of the arteries the lymphatic sheath contains lymphatic nodules. The artery, although called "central artery," practically never passes through the nodules.

Throughout its course within the white pulp, the artery gives off numerous capillaries which supply the lymphatic tissue of the sheath. The endothelial wall of these capillaries is supported externally by a thick network of reticular fibers. These arterial capillaries pass into the red pulp. Their terminations are uncertain (p. 270).

The small arteries in the white pulp continue to branch and become thinner; on reaching a caliber of 40 to 50 microns they leave the lymphatic tissue and enter the red pulp. Here they branch into small, straight vessels called *penicilli,* which show three successive parts. The first portion is the longest (0.6 to 0.7 mm.) and is called the *artery of the pulp,* which rapidly becomes narrow and divides (the caliber now is about 10 microns). Each branch (0.15 to 0.25 mm. long) is provided with a characteristic spindle-shaped thickening of its wall, the *Schweigger-Seidel sheath,* but has a narrow lumen (6 to 8 microns)—the so-called *sheathed artery;* this portion may ramify into two or three branches. These—forming the third portion—are the shortest (60 to 90 microns with a lumen up to 10 microns) and represent simple arterial capillaries (Fig. 12–7), which either do not divide or split into only two branches. Their terminations are unknown and will be discussed after the veins have been described.

The artery of the pulp has a tunica media consisting of one layer of smooth muscles surrounded by a thin, discontinuous envelope of lymphatic tissue which contains a few elastic fibers. In man the Schweigger-Seidel sheaths

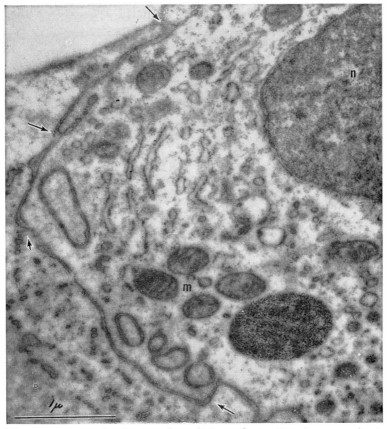

Fig. 12–6. Electron micrograph of macrophage lining splenic sinus in a rat. An infolding of the plasma membrane continues for some distance (arrows). Along its course there are suggestions of tiny vesicles arising from it. *m,* mitochondria; *n,* nucleus. The granular oval body is probably phagocytosed material. Buffered osmic acid fixation. (Courtesy of G. Palade.)

are only slightly developed. The tunica media is lost, so that the sheath is external to the endothelium (Fig. 12–8). The sheath is a compact mass of concentrically arranged, elongated nuclei (probably reticular cells) and longitudinal fibers which continue into the reticular fibers of the red pulp. The arterial capillaries consist of the endothelium, supported externally by a few longitudinal fibers and elongated cells.

In the dog, hedgehog and pig, and in the lower vertebrates, the sheaths are thick, oval bodies; they may be seen in the red pulp with low magnification. Red corpuscles are always present in large or small numbers inside the sheath.

Veins. The veins of the spleen begin as networks of *venous sinuses* which penetrate all the red pulp and are especially numerous outside the marginal zone surrounding the white pulp. These vessels are called *sinuses* because they have a wide (12 to 40 microns)

irregular lumen whose size varies with the amount of blood in the organ. The sinuses, even when moderately expanded, occupy more space than the splenic cords between them.

Unlike the veins, the walls of the venous sinuses do not contain common vascular endothelium, but are lined by long narrow cells arranged parallel to the long axis of the vessel. The middle of each of these rod-shaped cells is distended by a nucleus. These lining cells are fixed macrophages identical in origin and properties with those of the adjacent splenic cords, although normally less phagocytic.

Outside these cells, the wall of the sinus is supported by a system of circular, occasionally branching, reticular fibers which continue into the reticular fibers of the splenic cords. The sinus wall is thus a network of longitudinal, rod-shaped fixed macrophages and circular reticular fibers. Some

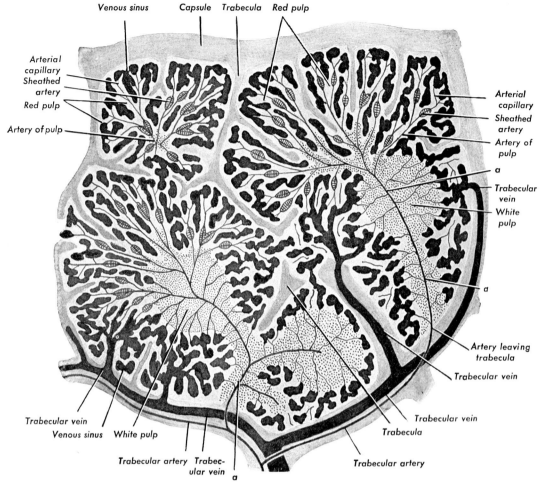

Fig. 12–7. Diagram of spleen. Two complete lobules (right and left) and portions of two lobules (above and below) are shown. *a,* artery surrounded by lymphatic tissue (white pulp).

hold that the meshes of this framework are closed by a thin, homogeneous membrane or by the edges of the phagocytes. Others claim that the presence of such a membrane has not been clearly proved and that the wall of the venous sinuses of the spleen is perforated by many permanent openings. The solution of this problem will do much to solve the riddle of the blood circulation in the spleen.

The venous sinuses empty into the veins of the pulp, whose wall consists of endothelium supported externally by a condensed stroma of the red pulp and a few elastic fibers. These pulp veins coalesce to form the veins of the trabeculae. These vessels consist only of endothelium supported by the connective tissue of the trabeculae. The trabecular veins form the splenic veins, which leave

the organ at the hilum and empty into the portal vein.

Union of the Arteries with the Veins. In almost all the other organs of the body the connection between the arterial and venous systems is accomplished by a direct passage of the arterial capillaries into the venous, in which the endothelium retains its continuity and the vascular lumen is completely closed. In the spleen, however, the connection is different, and its details are still subject to dispute. There are three main theories as to how blood gets from the arteries to the venous sinuses: (1) The arterial capillaries open directly into the spaces between the reticular cells of the splenic cords, and the blood gradually filters into the venous sinuses —the "open" circulation theory. (2) The ar-

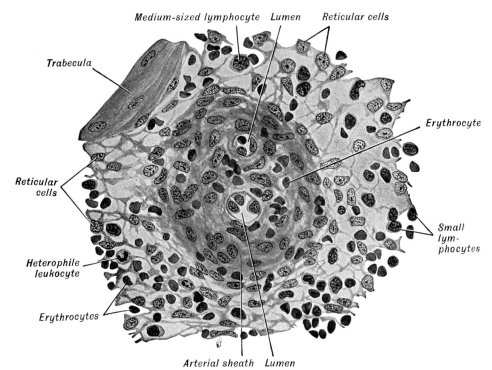

Medium-sized lymphocyte   Lumen   Reticular cells

Trabecula

Erythrocyte

Reticular
cells

Small
lym-
phocytes

Heterophile
leukocyte

Erythrocytes

Arterial sheath   Lumen

Fig. 12–8.   Cross section of sheathed artery which has divided into two lumens. Spleen of a dog. Eosin-azure stain. 500 ×. (A.A.M.)

terial capillaries communicate directly with the lumen of the venous sinuses—the "closed" circulation theory. (3) The compromise view holds that both types of circulation are present at the same time. One of the latest aspects of this theory is that a "closed" circulation in a contracted spleen may become an "open" circulation when the organ is distended (Fig. *12–9*).

The opposing theories are based on the following observations: (1) There are always many erythrocytes scattered irregularly between the fixed cells in the splenic cords. As there is no evidence of erythropoiesis in the cords, the conclusion is that the red blood cells have come from the circulating blood through gaps in the vascular connection between the arterioles and the venous sinuses. Those who maintain that the circulation is "closed" hold that the number of erythrocytes in the splenic cords is much smaller than it should be if the arterial capillaries opened directly into the pulp. They point out that if the capillaries were open, the red pulp should be completely filled with blood, as in hemorrhages in the spleen.

(2) When the splenic arteries are injected

even at low pressures with stained fluids, India ink or avian erythrocytes, the foreign materials readily gain access to the spaces between the fixed cells of the splenic cords, particularly in the red pulp about the white pulp. Only later do they reach the venous sinuses. When the splenic vein is injected, the venous sinuses and the meshes of the stroma can be filled easily, but the arteries cannot.

Those who hold for a closed circulation believe that this injection of the red pulp by foreign materials is artificial and results from the rupture of the delicate vascular walls.

(3) In every freshly fixed spleen, granulocytes, lymphocytes with greatly constricted nuclei, and erythrocytes can be found passing through the walls of the venous sinuses. It is difficult to reconcile this finding with either the "closed" or the "open" circulation theories, for these views hold that there are open connections between the sinuses and the arterial terminals or the meshes of the cords of Billroth, respectively. It is of course possible that such pictures are artefacts due to the collapse of the spleen after it is incised before being fixed.

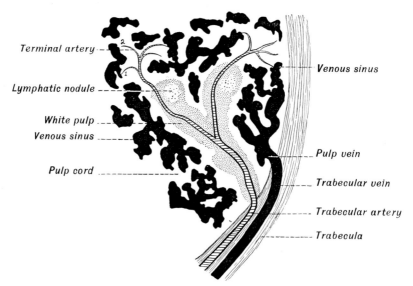

Terminal artery

Lymphatic nodule

White pulp

Venous sinus

Pulp cord

Venous sinus

Pulp vein

Trabecular vein

Trabecular artery

Trabecula

Fig. 12–9. Diagram to show closed (1) and open (2) circulation through the spleen.

The problem of circulation in the spleen would seem to be an ideal one for solution by direct observation of the living organ. Unfortunately, the technique available for this is difficult, and the few reports made with it are contradictory. According to one group, the circulation in the spleen is closed, there is a marked intermittence of circulation, there is extensive filtering of the liquid portion of the blood from the sinuses into the cords of Billroth, and diapedesis of erythrocytes from the sinuses may occur normally and especially during death of the animal. These conclusions are contradicted by another group, which finds that the circulation is open, that is, without preformed connections between the arterial and venous systems, so that the blood from the terminals of the arterial tree passes between the reticular cells (fixed macrophages) of the cords of Billroth and finds its way through openings into the sinuses. According to these observations, erythrocytes may be stored in the spaces between the reticular cells, and it is here that the separation of the blood cells from the plasma occurs. The channels in the cords of Billroth vary from time to time with the degree of engorgement of that part of the organ, so that a channel which previously had been a tortuous passage between reticular cells may appear as a direct communication to the lumen of a venous sinus when the spleen is contracted. From the foregoing it is

obvious that the manner of connection of arterioles and venules in the spleen requires further investigation.

If the splenic veins are tied for a few moments, the splenic artery ligated and the entire organ fixed and sectioned, one can easily trace columns of erythrocytes from the meshes of the cords of Billroth into the venous sinuses. The pictures seen in spleens prepared by this old method correspond more with those seen in the living organ than do the usual preparations made by cutting thin slices from the fresh organ before fixation.

Lymphatic Vessels and Nerves. In man, lymphatic vessels are poorly developed and are found only in the capsule of the spleen and in the thickest trabeculae, particularly those in the vicinity of the hilus. In some mammals true lymphatic vessels follow the arteries of the white pulp to the hilus. Nervous networks, which originate from the celiac plexus and which consist almost entirely of nonmedullated fibers, accompany the splenic artery and penetrate into the hilus of the spleen. In the sheep and ox these nerves form trunks of considerable thickness. The nerve bundles follow mainly the ramifications of the arteries and form networks which can be followed up to the central arteries of the white pulp and even along the branches of the penicilli. The terminal branches usually end with button-like thickenings in the smooth muscles of the arteries and of the trabeculae. Apparently many branches penetrate into the red as well as the white pulp, but their endings here are not definitely established.

Functions of the Spleen. The spleen is closely related to the lymphatic and hemal nodes and the bone marrow, and is an important hemopoietic organ. Lymphocytes are produced in it, mainly in the white pulp and in particular in its nodules. From the white pulp they migrate into the red pulp, where some of them perhaps become monocytes. Lymphocytes and monocytes actively enter the venous sinuses through the reticular wall.

Although in the embryo the spleen is a hemopoietic organ of some importance, the red corpuscles of the splenic tissue of the *normal adult man* are never formed in the white or the red pulp. In certain mammals (but not in man) a few myelocytes and erythroblasts are found normally in the red pulp. Megakaryocytes occur regularly in the red pulp in rats and mice.

In some pathological conditions, especially in *myeloid leukemia,* the red pulp of the spleen undergoes *myeloid metaplasia.* In this case a large number of erythroblasts, megakaryocytes and myelocytes appear in the tissue, so that the red pulp acquires a structure similar to that of red bone marrow.

After the removal of the spleen the number of lymphocytes in the blood increases (lymphocytosis); this is explained by an excessive compensation on the part of lymph nodes. Then, there is an increase in the number of eosinophile leukocytes. Both phenomena soon disappear.

The spleen also acts as a store for red blood cells. From time to time large numbers of them are retained in the red pulp and then given up to the blood stream as they are needed in the circulation.

The destruction of erythrocytes occurs in the spleen, with a varying intensity in different species, for they are phagocytosed by the macrophages in the splenic cords and sometimes by those lining the sinuses. Disintegrating erythrocytes and granules of hemosiderin are often found in the cytoplasm of these phagocytes. After poisoning with substances which destroy the red blood cells (pyrogallol), the red pulp becomes filled with large macrophages containing the debris of erythrocytes. The destruction of erythrocytes also proceeds extracellularly, for particles of disintegrating erythrocytes may be encountered among the cells of the red pulp (p. 106). After splenectomy the erythrolytic

function is carried out by the macrophages of the bone marrow, lymph nodes and liver.

Closely connected with erythrocyte destruction by the spleen is its function in iron metabolism. The iron-containing component of hemoglobin is freed from the disintegrating erythrocytes and stored in the reticular cells of the spleen. This accumulated iron is again utilized in the formation of hemoglobin.

The spleen is thought by some to regulate the formation and destruction of erythrocytes by the production of a hormone which decreases the erythropoietic capacity of the bone marrow. Others think that a hormone is produced by the spleen which inhibits the formation of leukocytes in the other hematopoietic organs. Shielding of the spleen during total body irradiation with x-rays greatly enhances the resistance of mice and accelerates regeneration of bone marrow.

In many animals, splenectomy is often followed by a recrudescence of a latent or low grade infection, as is strikingly exemplified by Bartonella infections of rats, piroplasmosis of dogs and sheep, and malaria of monkeys. Similarly, splenectomy often temporarily depresses antibody formation. This effect is greatly enhanced if combined with so-called "blockade" by the intravenous injection of colloidal dyes or particulate matter.

The spleen possesses a combination of phagocytic, cytopoietic and antibody-forming activities which are of great importance in immunity to organisms or antigens which get into the blood (see review by Taliaferro, 1956). These functions are shared with the other filter organs, chiefly the liver and bone marrow which contain macrophages strategically placed for contact with substances in the blood. The macrophages of the spleen are the most active individually, but the liver, because of its size, is the most important from the standpoint of total phagocytic activity. In the cytopoiesis of phagocytes, the spleen is the most important in producing macrophages and the bone marrow in producing granulocytes. The spleen is probably the most active in antibody formation although evidence is incomplete for the bone marrow. The liver, although it synthesizes serum globulins, forms very little antibody except when lymphatic tissue increases in the periportal spaces, as during long-continued infection or immunization.

The exact cell involved in antibody formation is unknown. Increasing evidence indicates that the process is associated with the mobilization of reticular cells into the very large, basophilic or pyroninophilic lymphocyte or hemocytoblast and its subsequent development into plasma cells.

As macrophages in contact with the blood stream are not restricted to the spleen, it is not surprising that the effects of splenectomy largely disappear as the splenic functions are assumed by the macrophages of other organs, particularly the liver and bone marrow. This makes improbable the view of a few authors that the spleen has peculiar powers of defense in addition to those referable to its content of macrophages and lymphoid cells.

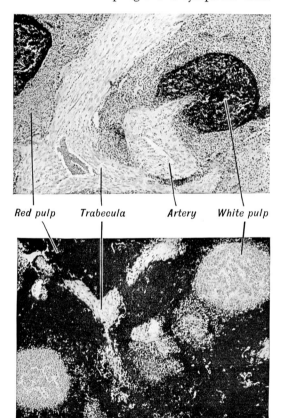

Red pulp   Trabecula   Artery   White pulp

Fig. 12–10. Photomicrographs of sections of spleen of a dog, showing distribution of alkaline phosphatase as the black-stained material in the white pulp of the upper figure and of acid phosphatase as the black-stained material in the red pulp of the lower figure. The thick trabeculae are characteristic of the dog's spleen. 30 ×. (Courtesy of G. Gomori.)

When the lipids in the blood are increased in amount, the reticular cells of the spleen, like the other macrophages of the body, have the capacity to remove the lipids from the blood and to store them. During this process these macrophages increase greatly in size, are filled with lipoid droplets and acquire a foamy appearance; this is observed in man in diabetic lipemia and in Niemann-Pick disease, and in the experimental hypercholesterolemia of rabbits.

During digestion, the spleen increases in size. The reason for this is not known. Relations between the spleen and the various glands of internal secretion have not been established.

Histogenesis and Regeneration of the Spleen. The primordium of the spleen appears, in human embryos of 8 to 9 mm., as a small thickening of the dorsal mesentery, consisting of a closely aggregated mass of energetically multiplying mesenchymal elements.

The mesenchymal cells which compose this first primordium of the spleen multiply independently by mitosis, and the primordium grows. It has been supposed that it also increases in size by apposition of new cells from the mesothelium of the body cavity covering the primordium. After the embryo (pig) has reached a length of 15 mm., it receives no more cells from the mesothelium.

The elements of the primary mesenchymal primordium differentiate in two directions. Some remain connected with one another by means of processes and form the reticular framework of the white as well as the red pulp. Some of the mesenchymal elements soon become isolated from the rest and become free cells, located in the meshes of the framework. At first they all have the character of basophile wandering elements—lymphocytes. Later on, they give origin to red corpuscles, granular myelocytes and leukocytes, and megakaryocytes, as well as to more lymphocytes. In the lower vertebrates up to the urodele amphibians, this erythropoietic function is retained throughout life in the spleen; in the higher vertebrates the myeloid function stops sooner or later and is replaced by an erythrolytic function, although the formation of lymphocytes persists throughout life.

In mammals (pig) the mesenchymal primordium contains a capillary vascular network connected with the afferent arteries and efferent veins. Meanwhile, irregular spaces, the precursors of the venous sinuses, appear (embryo pigs of 4 to 6 cm.) and become connected, in 6- to 7-cm. embryos, with the afferent and efferent vessels.

The tissue of the embryonic mammalian spleen has at first a myeloid character and cannot be compared with either the red or white pulp. At the end of fetal life (in the rat) the adventitia of the arteries begins to be infiltrated with large numbers of lymphocytes, and in this manner the white pulp originates; typical lymphatic nodules are found after birth. Simultaneously, the myeloid elements which had reached their maximum development three weeks after birth (in the rat) begin to disappear gradually, and the tissue of the spleen located between the accumulations of white pulp then may be called the red pulp.

When the spleen is removed, its functions are taken over by other organs, and the formation of a new spleen has never been observed, although a compensatory hypertrophy of the so-called "accessory spleens" has been described. Local injuries and wounds of the spleen are accompanied by a temporary myeloid metaplasia of the red pulp and heal with a simple scar. In the amphibians, particularly in larval stages, a certain degree of regeneration is possible, while in birds the spleen shows marked regenerative powers.

REFERENCES

Coons, A. H., Leduc, E. H., and Connolly, J. M.: Studies on antibody production. I. A method for the histochemical demonstration of specific antibody and its application to a study of the hyperimmune rabbit. J. Exp. Med., *102*:49, 1955.

Hartmann, A.: Die Milz. Handb. d. mikr. Anat. (v. Möllendorff), 1930, Vol. 6, Pt. 1, p. 397.

Jacobson, L. O., Marks, E. K., Robson, M. J., Gaston, E., and Zirkle, R. E.: The effect of spleen protection on mortality following x-irradiation. J. Lab. & Clin. Med., *34*:1538, 1949.

Klemperer, P.: The Spleen. Downey's Handbook of Hematology. P. Hoeber, New York, 1938.

Knisely, M. H.: Spleen studies. I. Microscopic observations of the circulatory system of living unstimulated mammalian spleens. Anat. Rec., *65*:23, 1936.

Leduc, E. H., Coons, A. H., and Connolly, J. M.: Studies on antibody production. II. The primary and secondary responses in the popliteal lymph node of the rabbit. J. Exp. Med., *102*:61, 1955.

MacKenzie, D. W., Jr., Whipple, A. O., and Wintersteiner, M. P.: Studies on the microscopic anatomy and physiology of living transilluminated mammalian spleens. Am. J. Anat., *68*:397, 1941.

Mall, F. P.: On the circulation through the pulp of the dog's spleen. Am. J. Anat., *2*:315, 1903.

Mollier, S.: Ueber den Bau der Kapillaren der Milzvene (Milzsinus). Arch. f. mikr. Anat., *76*:1910, 1911.

Peck, H. M., and Hoerr, N. L.: The intermediary circulation in the red pulp of the mouse spleen. Anat. Rec., *109*:447, 1951.

Robinson, W.: The vascular mechanism of the spleen. Am. J. Path., *2*:341, 1926.

Snook, T.: A comparative study of the vascular arrangements in mammalian spleens. Am. J. Anat., *87*:31, 1950.

Solnitzky, O.: The Schweigger-Seidel sheath (ellipsoid) of the spleen. Anat. Rec., *69*:55, 1937.

Taliaferro, W. H.: Functions of the spleen in immunity. Am. J. Trop. Med. and Hygiene, *3*:391, 1956.

Taliaferro, W. H., and Taliaferro, L. G.: The role of the spleen in hemolysin production in rabbits receiving multiple antigen injections. J. Infect. Dis. *89*:143, 1951.

Thiel, G. A., and Downey, H.: The development of the mammalian spleen, with special reference to its hematopoietic activity. Am. J. Anat., *28*:279, 1921.

Weidenreich, F.: Das Gefässsystem der Milz des Menschen. Arch. f. mikr. Anat., *58*:247, 1901.

CHAPTER 13

Thymus

In MAN the thymus is an unpaired organ situated in the anterior mediastinum, in close connection with the pericardium and the great veins at the base of the heart. The thymus presents marked variations in its structure which depend on the age and condition of the organism as a whole. The organ is closely related to lymphatic tissue, but its specific function other than the production of lymphocytes is unknown, although it has been the subject of much experimentation.

In relation to body weight, the thymus is largest during embryonic life and in childhood up to the period of puberty. After this it begins to involute –a process which pro ceeds gradually and continuously throughout life under normal conditions. This change in its structure is spoken of as *age involution*. During the course of infectious and cachetic diseases the normal slow involution may be greatly accelerated. This is called *accidental involution* and explains many of the contradictory reports on the size of the thymus, since the organ did not have a chance to regenerate in those persons who died as a result of severe infections. At birth the thymus weighs 12 to 15 gm. This increases to about 30 to 40 gm. at puberty, after which it begins to decrease in weight, so that at sixty years it weighs only 10 to 15 gm.

The thymus consists of two main lobes, one on each side of the median line, which are closely joined by connective tissue, but are not actually fused. Each of these lobes is divided into a number of macroscopic lobules varying from 0.5 to 2 mm. in diameter. The lobules are separated from one another by the interlobular connective tissue and are divided into a darkly staining, peripheral cortical area and an inner, lighter staining, medullary portion (Fig. *13–1*). With the study of serial sections one can trace a continuity of the medullary tissue from one lobule to another. That is, the medulla consists of a central stalk from which arise projections of medullary tissue; these are almost completely surrounded by a zone of cortical tissue.

The difference between the cortex and medulla is the fact that the cortex consists mainly of densely packed small lymphocytes with their dark nuclei and in between them only a relatively few reticular cells, with pale-staining nuclei. In the medulla it is the reverse. As one proceeds from the cortex toward the medulla, the number of lymphocytes drops rather abruptly, but there is no sharp line of demarcation between the two zones. The medulla is more vascular than the cortex.

Cells. As mentioned, the cells of the thymus are lymphocytes and reticular cells. The reticular cells are elongated and have pale, round or oval nuclei. In most cases their nuclear membrane is smooth; the nucleus contains a few small chromatin particles and one or two small nucleoli. In the cortex it is difficult to follow the outlines of the cytoplasm, since the surrounding lymphocytes are closely packed around them. However, in the medulla, where the lymphocytes are less numerous, it can be seen that the reticular cells form a network with its meshes filled with lymphocytes. Most of the reticular cells are

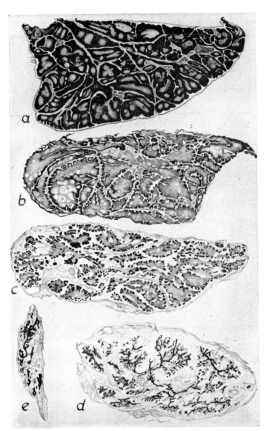

Fig. 13–1. Sections of human thymuses, showing age and accidental involution. *a,* from a newborn (15-gm. gland); *b,* from a 7-year-old boy (35-gm. gland); *c,* from a seventeen-year-old boy (35.2-gm. gland), showing beginning age involution; *d,* from a seventeen-year-old boy (8.8-gm. gland), high grade accidental involution; the dark parenchyma is surrounded by fat and connective tissue; *e,* from a seventeen-year-old boy (1.65-gm. gland), extensive accidental involution. (Redrawn and slightly modified after Hammer, 1906.)

of endodermal origin, although there are a few reticular cells of mesenchymal origin around the blood vessels.

In the embryo the epithelial nature of many of the reticular cells is quite obvious (Fig. 13–4); but as the organ becomes more and more heavily infiltrated with lymphocytes, these epithelial cells become flattened, and it is difficult to distinguish them from the nuclei of connective tissue reticular cells. A peculiarity of the thymic cellular reticulum is the fact that in vitally stained animals these cells in the thymus do not take up any of the dyestuff, while in certain diseases of malnutrition in infants, these reticular cells store large quantities of iron and fat, and in lipoid histiocytosis (Niemann-Pick disease) they become swollen with lipoid droplets. In experimental accidental involution the epithelial cells become loaded with dead lymphocytes.

The epithelial nature of the great mass of reticular cells becomes prominent when the lymphocytes have been destroyed by x-ray and the epithelium begins to develop. It becomes even more prominent in transplants and tissue cultures of the thymus (Fig. 13–3). Certain tumors of clearly epithelial nature arise in this gland.

The lymphocytes of the thymus are morphologically identical with the small lymphocytes in the lymph node and other lymphatic tissues. Some of them are identical with medium-sized and large lymphocytes. Some authors deny their lymphocytic nature and call them *thymocytes,* believing that they have an epithelial origin. However, most workers agree that they arise from the mesenchyme and are lymphocytes which have wandered into the epithelium (see p. 278). In addition, these small cells show the same susceptibility to x-ray injury as do ordinary lymphocytes. Both are cytolyzed by sera obtained by the injection of thymus cells into rats, and both show the same type of ameboid motion and ability to transform into macrophages. Transplants of the thymus consist only of epithelium if lymphocytes are prevented from migrating into them by mechanical means. Further, the transformation of the small thymocytes into plasma cells and eosinophile myelocytes is generally admitted. The mitochondria have the same appearance in both types of cells.

In addition to lymphocytes and reticular cells, eosinophile myelocytes and plasma cells occur not infrequently in the medulla. Exceptionally, the thymus may contain lymphatic nodules.

Fibers. Most of the reticular fibers are concentrated around the blood vessels, and the great masses of epithelial reticular cells do not contain any of these fibers. Further study of the fiber content of the organ, particularly during involution, is necessary.

Hassall's Bodies. The medulla contains the bodies of Hassall, which are characteristic of the thymus. They are rounded acidophile structures which vary from 30 to over 100

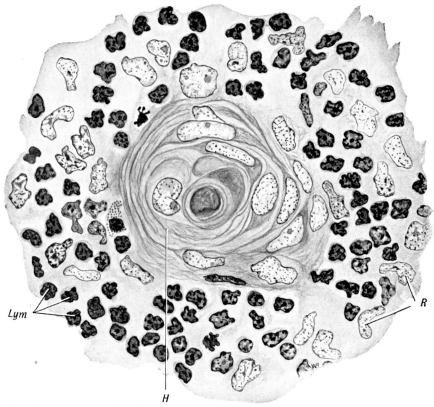

Fig. 13–2. Portion of medulla of thymus of an eight-year-old boy. *H,* Hassall's body; *R,* epithelial reticular cells; *Lym,* lymphocytes; an eosinophile myelocyte is just outside the left-hand margin of the Hassall's body. Eosin-azure stain. 970 ×. (W. B.)

microns in diameter. They are composed of concentrically arranged cells, many of which show evidences of degeneration and hyalinization. Reticular cells are connected at one or more places with the periphery of each Hassall's body. The cells of the central part of a Hassall's body may degenerate completely, so that small cysts may develop in the center. In other cases calcium may be deposited in them.

Involution of the Thymus. The description of a clear-cut separation of the thymus into cortex and medulla obtains normally in the later embryonic periods and in childhood. Normally, involution begins as a gradual thinning out of the lymphoid cells of the cortex; at about four years the epithelial reticular cells become compressed, and the area occupied by them is gradually replaced by adipose tissue, which is thought to arise in the interlobular connective tissue. The medulla begins to atrophy at puberty. This process continues throughout life. The last elements to be replaced are the Hassall's bodies, but even in very old persons there are scattered Hassall's bodies surrounded by a few reticular cells and lymphocytes. This process of normal or age involution may be complicated by the rapid changes of "accidental involution" (Fig. 13–1).

Vessels and Nerves. The arteries supplying the thymus arise from the internal mammary and the inferior thyroid arteries and are first distributed to the cortical tissue. Large venules arise in the medulla and combine into larger veins which empty into the left innominate and thyroid veins. The lymphatics run mainly in the interlobular connective tissue and empty into the anterior mediastinal and tracheobronchial lymph nodes. The thymus receives a few branches from the vagus and sympathetic nerves; these are probably mainly of vasomotor nature.

Histogenesis. In man the primordium of the thymus is an outgrowth of the third branchial pouch on each side of the median line; the fourth branchial pouch often gives rise to some thymic tissue. It has a cleft-like lumen and a wall of several layers of cylindrical epithelium. The surrounding mesenchyme, in the earliest stages, contains many lymphoid cells which arise from mesenchyme cells. The

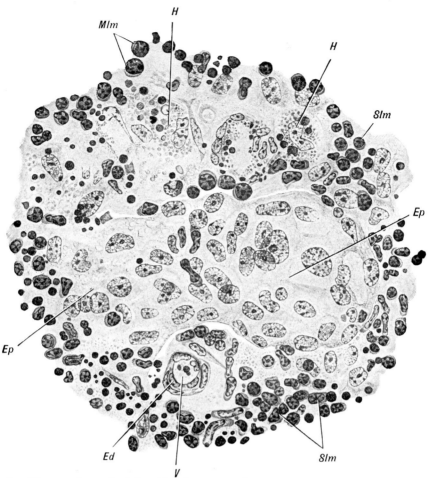

Fig. 13–3.   Tissue culture of adult rabbit thymus, 24 hours *in vitro*, in a medium containing lithium carmine. The epithelial reticulum is contracting into a solid epithelial island (*Ep*); *Ed*, endothelium; *H*, macrophages with carmine granules and cellular debris; *Mlm*, medium-sized lymphocytes; *Slm*, small lymphocytes; *V*, vessel. 870 ×. (After Popoff.)

epithelial bud proliferates, the lumen disappears, and anastomosing strands extend into the mesenchyme. The future lobules arise at the ends of these branches.

In an embryo of about 20 mm., small thymocytes appear. A few authors derive them from the epithelial cells, but most believe that the thymocytes develop from the inwandering of lymphoid cells. Some of them are large, others are small, and there are numerous transitions between the two. The number of lymphocytes increases greatly, partly from inwandering and in part through their own proliferation. The small lymphocyte type gradually predominates. The epithelium is converted into a reticular cell mass whose meshes are occupied by the lymphocytes and are penetrated here and there by blood vessels.

The definitive medulla arises late in the main stem and deeper portions of the lobules by hypertrophy of the epithelium, while most of the lymphocytes move from these areas or degenerate. Later, the Hassall bodies arise.

In later stages of embryonic life some of the lymphocytes turn into granulocytes, but much larger numbers wander into the blood and lymph streams. The thymus in the embryo is thus a blood-forming tissue even though few or no erythrocytes are produced in it. The embryonic thymus bears some points of similarity to the embryonic liver: in both organs the epithelial cells are separated by mesenchymal cells and lymphocytes. In both organs the lymphocytes produce granulocytes, although in the liver they produce vast numbers of erythrocytes.

Most investigators ascribe the regeneration of the small thymocytes in transplants of the gland to immigration of lymphocytes (see Jolly, 1932).

Function of the Thymus. The functions of the thymus are unknown, except for its ability to form lymphocytes and a few plasma cells and myelocytes. But the change from a large organ in the embryo, infancy and childhood into a gradually disappearing organ

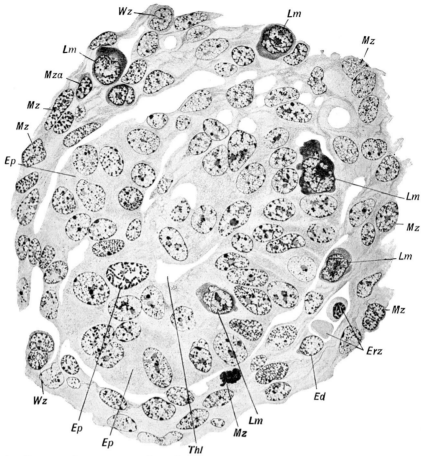

Fig. 13–4.   Portion of cross section through the right thymus of a 14.5-mm. rabbit embryo. The organ appears as an epithelial island (*Ep*) surrounded by mesenchyme (*Mz*); *Ed,* endothelium of a vessel containing a nucleated erythrocyte (*Erz*); lymphocytes (*Lm*) originate from the mesenchyme and wander into the epithelium; *Thl,* lumen of the thymus; *Wz,* histioid wandering cell. 900 ×. (A.A.M.)

with the development of sexual maturity has led many authors to ascribe an endocrine function to this gland.

Purified adrenocorticotrophic hormone causes a striking reduction in weight and size of the thymus in male rats. Repeated injections of horse gonadotrophic hormone cause atrophy of the thymus, but this does not occur in castrated rats. On the contrary, castration causes hyperplasia of the involuted gland in the rat. Selye has found that fasting, toxins and morphine cause a rapid atrophy of the thymus and enlargement of the adrenal cortex in rats, and that atrophy of the thymus does not take place in adrenalectomized rats; hypophysectomy hastens thymic atrophy. The claims that the injection of extracts of the thymus into parent rats causes a precocious growth of their progeny which

is cumulative in succeeding generations and that thymectomy causes a retardation in growth of the progeny have not been substantiated.

Experimental Lymphosarcoma and Lymphatic Leukemia (by H. S. Kaplan). Malignant lymphoid tumors, morphologically indistinguishable from human lymphosarcoma and lymphatic leukemia, occur in fowl and in several mammalian species, of which mice are the most susceptible. The tumor cells usually resemble medium-sized lymphocytes, less often the small or very large ones. In many inbred mouse strains, they tend to arise in the cortex of the thymus as foci of proliferating cells which gradually replace much or all of the cortex and permeate the medulla. They later disseminate to the mediastinal connective tissues, lungs, abdominal viscera, widely distributed lymph nodes, and ultimately the bone marrow and peripheral blood. Incipient tumors may be detected in a preinvasive stage when their rate of growth tends to be slow. Their autonomy, as measured by capacity for progressive growth after isologous transplantation, appears at first to be distinctly limited but increases during the life of the tumor in its primary host.

These tumors may develop spontaneously or in response to treatment with ionizing radiations, hydrocarbon carcinogens, or estrogens. Viruses have also been established as causative agents of mouse leukemia by the inoculation of cell-free filtrates from "spontaneous" lymphatic leukemic tissues into newborn mice of ordinarily resistant strains. The possibility of viral "activation" by the other agents mentioned has not been adequately studied experimentally.

The development of the lymphoid tumors in irradiated mice may be strikingly inhibited by normal isologous bone marrow which has either been shielded in situ during irradiation or which has been injected intravenously after irradiation. Injection of marrow also promotes regeneration of the radiation-injured thymus gland. Tumor incidence is affected by genetic, age, and nutritional factors and by the endocrine environment. Thus, it may be depressed by administration of thymus-involuting hormones or augmented by removal of those endocrine glands which secrete thymolytic hormones. Lymphoid tumors also arise in nonirradiated isologous thymic grafts implanted subcutaneously into thymectomized, irradiated mice of appropriate strains; it has been shown that the cells of these tumors are descendants of the cells of the thymic implants, which had never been exposed to the inciting agent. Accordingly, it appears that indirect mechanisms play an important part in the induction process.

It should be stressed that these findings on the thymic origin of the lymphoid tumors have not been found to apply to a few strains of mice and to other mammals including man.

REFERENCES

Bargmann, W.: Der Thymus. Handb. d. mikr. Anat. d. Menschen (v. Möllendorff), *6*, pt. 4, 1943.

Grégoire, Ch.: Recherches sur la symbiose lymphoépithéliale au niveau du thymus de mammifère. Arch. de Biol., *46:*717, 1935.

Hammar, J.: Ueber Wachstum und Rückgang, über Standardisierung, Individualisierung und bauliche Individualtypen im Laufe des normalen Postfötallebens. Leipzig, Akad. Leipzig Verlagsges., 1932.

Kaplan, H. S., Hirsch, B. B., and Brown, M. B.: Indirect induction of lymphomas in irradiated mice. IV. Genetic evidence of the origin of the tumor cells from the thymic grafts. Cancer Research, *16:*434, 1956.

Law, L. W.: Recent advances in experimental leukemia research. Cancer Research, *14:*695, 1954.

Murray, R. G.: Pure cultures of rabbit thymus epithelium. Am. J. Anat., *81:*369, 1947. The Thymus: in Histopathology of Irradiation from External and Internal Sources. National Nuclear Energy Series, New York. McGraw-Hill, 1948, Vol. 22–I. Chap. 9.

Smith, C., and Ireland, L. M.: Studies on the thymus of the mammal. I. The distribution of argyrophil fibers from birth through old age in the thymus of the mouse. Anat. Rec., *79:*133, 1941.

Van Dyke, J. H.: On the origin of accessory thymus tissue, thymus IV: The occurrence in man. Anat. Rec., *79:*179, 1941.

CHAPTER 14

Glands

WE HAVE seen that the cells forming the connective tissues and the nervous, muscular, and vascular systems have completely lost the arrangement of the cells of the primitive epithelial sheets from which they were derived.

It was pointed out in the chapter on epithelium that the most important and general function of the epithelium is its participation in the metabolism of the body through the absorption of substances from the outside medium, their modification in the body, and the elimination of other materials to the outside. Practically all substances which are normally received and given off by the body must pass through an epithelium.

In the organs to be described in the following chapters the epithelium persists as such or as special structures called *glands*. When glands secrete, they usually produce an aqueous fluid which differs from blood plasma or tissue fluid. This product of cellular activity is called the *secretion*. This difference in the composition of the secretion and the tissue fluid may manifest itself in the production of new substances present only in traces in the tissue fluid (insulin and other hormones, trypsin and other enzymes, mucin, milk).

By contrast, when no new substances are present in the secretion, their concentrations may be significantly different (sweat, cerebrospinal fluid, hydrochloric acid in the stomach). All glands perform work in producing such secretions, in addition to that which is expended in maintaining cellular

integrity. The glomerular filtrate in the kidney is the only fluid produced from plasma which does not involve the expenditure of energy by the structure involved. For this reason, some authors call it an *excretion*.

Classification of Glands. Glands have been classified in many ways to emphasize differences (1) in the mode of secretion (*exocrine*, or to an external surface; *endocrine*, or to the blood or lymph vessels; or *mixed*); (2) in the nature of the secretion product (*cytogenous*, i.e., containing cells; or *noncellular*, i.e., free of cells); (3) in gland cell behavior during secretion (*merocrine*, which does not involve cell destruction; *holocrine*, which is accompanied by cell death; and *apocrine*, which takes place with a loss of some cytoplasm only); and (4) in the organization of the epithelial component of glands (*unicellular, simple* or *compound multicellular*).

Despite the great variety of schemes and elaborate interlocking classification of glands, it is not always possible to characterize them all adequately. This may be seen best in the difficulty of distinguishing clearly between exocrine and endocrine glands (see p. 288). It may be observed also in an attempt to categorize the various kinds of noncellular producing glands. This difficulty appears also in the distinction between merocrine and apocrine glands. The inadequacy of the classification systems used for glands is common to many biological systems, and is due primarily to the lack of fundamental data on histophysiology and histochemistry of the organs.

Most of the glands elaborate an *external secretion* (*exocrine glands*). In these the glandular cavities open freely on the surface of the epithelium from which they have developed, and the secretion is poured out on this surface. Other glands have an *internal secretion* (*endocrine glands*). In the embryo the latter originate in the same way as the exocrine glands through the invagination of an epithelial sheet. Later, however, the connection with the sheet is severed, and the secretion passes into the blood or lymph vessels of the gland and is distributed in this way all over the body. In the majority of endocrine glands, the original simple epithelial arrangement of cells is completely lost.

The ovary and testis, and perhaps the hematopoietic organs, are *cytogenous* glands. The most characteristic parts of their secretion consist of living germ cells and blood cells. The presence of living cells in the secretion of all other glands is only incidental or a result of pathological processes, and is unrelated to their essential secretory products.

The type of secretion in which the glandular cell remains intact throughout a cyclic process of formation and discharge, and then formation again, followed by discharge, and so on, of secretory products is called *merocrine* secretion. In *holocrine* secretion the products accumulate within the cell body; the cell finally dies and is discharged as the secretion of the gland, new cells having arisen in the meantime to repeat the same cycle. The intermediate type of secretion is the so-called *apocrine* type. Here the secretion accumulates within the free end of the cell; after a time, this portion of the cytoplasm is pinched off, but the nucleus and most of the cytoplasm are undamaged, and, after a recovery period, the cell passes through the same process again. The details of these various types of secretion will be considered with the descriptions of specific organs: merocrine secretion with the salivary gland and pancreatic glands, holocrine secretion with the sebaceous glands, and apocrine secretion with the mammary gland.

Unicellular Glands. In mammals practically the only type of unicellular gland is the *mucous* or *goblet* cell, which secretes *mucin*, a polysaccharide protein which forms with water a lubricating solution called *mucus*. These cells are scattered on many mucous membranes, especially those covered with columnar or ciliated epithelium. A fully developed mucous cell has an oval apical, and a slender basal, end; it resembles a goblet. The dilated part consists of a thin protoplasmic wall, the *theca*, and a "cavity" which is filled with an almost homogeneous clear mass of cytoplasm containing a multitude of pale droplets of *mucigen*. These are well preserved by freezing and drying and are stained selectively by a method which visualizes the polysaccharide component of the mucigen. Less specific stains may also be used. The stalk of the goblet cell contains a more or less compressed and disfigured nucleus.

The droplets of mucigen leave the goblet cell from its free surface, and dissolve at once as mucin. The elimination of mucigen may proceed gradually, and the cell may keep its goblet form for a long time. In other cases the whole content is thrown out, and the emptied cell collapses and is compressed between the neighboring cells. After a while a new accumulation of mucigen may begin in the same cell. Small granules appear above the nucleus; they gradually enlarge, acquire the character of mucigen, and cause a new swelling of the apical part. A goblet cell seems to pass many times through the successive phases of secretory activity until it finally perishes and is shed.

Multicellular Glands. The simplest form of multicellular gland is an epithelial secretory sheet, consisting only of secreting cells (Fig. *14–1*). In mammals the epithelium of the choroid plexuses and the surface epithelium of the gastric mucosa are of this type. The epithelium of the mucous membrane of the uterus and oviducts, at certain stages, also belongs to this category. *Intraepithelial glands* are a special form of secretory epithelial sheet. They are small accumulations of glandular cells (usually mucous) which lie wholly within the epithelium and contain their own small lumen (Fig. *14–2*). They are found in the human body in the pseudostratified columnar epithelium of the nasal mucosa and adjoining areas of the caruncula lacrimalis, of the ductuli efferentes and of the urethra.

All other multicellular glands arise as invaginations of the epithelial sheet into the underlying connective tissue (Fig. *14–3*). The gland cells are gathered in the *secretory* or *terminal* portions. The secretion elaborated by the gland cells reaches the surface directly, or through an *excretory duct* consisting of less specialized cells. In many glands the secreting surface is further increased by many extremely fine canals, the *secretory capillaries,* which arise from the lumen of the terminal portion and penetrate between the glandular cells. They are *extracellular,* often branched, and end blindly before reaching the basement membrane. They have no wall of their own, but are formed by groovelike excavations in adjoining cells (Figs. 14–6, 14–7). Exceptionally, glandular cells may contain an *intracellular* system of fine canaliculi which seem to drain the secretion (parietal cells of the gastric glands, Fig. 23–10).

The free surface of the glandular cells is usually provided with *terminal bars.* They are stained black with iron hematoxylin, which shows them to extend along the secretory capillaries and gives them a characteristic aspect in sections (Fig. 2–22).

In the great majority of glands the epithelium lining the glandular cavities is separated by a basement membrane from the connective tissue with its blood vessels. In a few cases, however, the glandular epithelium

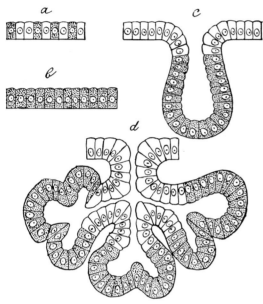

Fig. 14–1. Diagram of unicellular and multicellular glands. *a,* granular, glandular cells are scattered singly among clear, common epithelial cells; *b,* glandular cells arranged in a continuous sheet—secretory epithelial surface; *c,* simplest type of multicellular gland: the area lined with glandular cells forms a saclike invagination into the subjacent tissue; *d,* multicellular gland of greater complexity: the glandular spaces are lined partly with glandular cells (terminal portions), partly with common epithelium (excretory ducts).

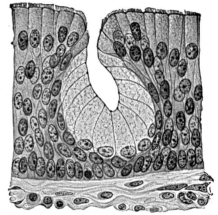

Fig. 14–2. Intra-epithelial gland from the pseudostratified ciliated epithelium of the laryngeal surface of the epiglottis, of a woman of seventy-two years. 534 ×. (After V. Patzelt, from Schaffer.)

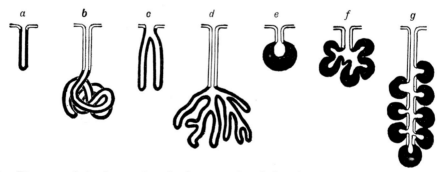

Fig. 14–3. Diagrams of simple exocrine glands. *a,* simple tubular; *b,* simple coiled tubular; *c, d,* simple branched tubular; *e,* simple alveolus; *f, g,* simple branched acinous. The secretory portions are black.

is intimately associated with or penetrated by networks of blood vessels accompanied by connective tissue, as in the thyroid gland.

Simple exocrine glands consist of a secretory unit connected to the surface epithelium of origin directly or by an unbranched duct. The simple glands of man are classified as *tubular, coiled tubular, branched tubular,* and *acinous* or *alveolar* (Fig. *14–3*).

1. *Simple Tubular Glands.* There is no excretory duct, and the terminal portion is a straight tubule which opens directly on the epithelial surface. Such are the intestinal glands (crypts) of Lieberkühn.

2. *Simple Coiled Tubular Glands.* The terminal portion is a long coiled tubule which passes into a long excretory duct. The sweat glands belong to this category. In the large axillary sweat glands of apocrine type, the terminal portions branch.

3. *Simple Branched Tubular Glands.* The tubules of the terminal portion are split forklike into two or more branches which sometimes are coiled near their ends. An excretory duct may be absent, as in the glands of the stomach and uterus, or there may be but a simple short excretory duct, as in some of the small glands of the oral cavity, the tongue and the esophagus, and in some of the glands of Brunner.

4. *Simple Branched Acinous Gland.* If the terminal portion has the form of a spherical or elongated sac, the gland is called *acinous* or *alveolar*. If only one acinus is present with one excretory duct, it is a simple acinous gland; this type does not occur in mammals. If the acinus is subdivided by partitions into several smaller bodies, or if several acini are arranged along a duct, it is a *simple branched*

acinous gland (sebaceous glands of the skin, glands of Meibom in the eyelids).

Compound Exocrine Glands. A compound gland may consist of larger subdivisions called *lobes,* which are further subdivided by connective tissue into smaller parts. The smallest which can be observed easily with the naked eye is called a (*macro*)-*lobule.* This in turn consists of smaller, frequently incompletely separated *microscopic lobules* which contain the glandular units. Glands of each order of complexity may be found in the body. A compound gland consists, then, of a varying number of simple glands whose small excretory ducts join to form ducts of a higher order, which in turn combine with other ducts of the same caliber to form larger ducts of a still higher order.

The compound exocrine glands are sometimes classified by the secretion they furnish. Thus *mucous, albuminous,* and *mixed* glands are distinguished. This classification can be applied with partial success chiefly to the glands of the oral cavity. Another classification is based on the form of the terminal portions.

1. In *compound tubular glands* the terminal portions of the smallest lobules are more or less coiled, usually branching tubules (Fig. *14–4*). To this category belong the pure mucous glands of the oral cavity, glands of the gastric cardia, some of the glands of Brunner, the bulbo-urethral glands, and the renal tubules.

In special cases, as, for instance, in the testis, the terminal coils anastomose with one another.

2. In the *compound acinous* or *alveolar* glands the terminal portions are supposed to

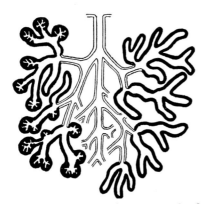
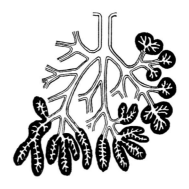

Fig. 14–4. Diagram of compound exocrine glands. Secretory portions black; ducts double contoured.

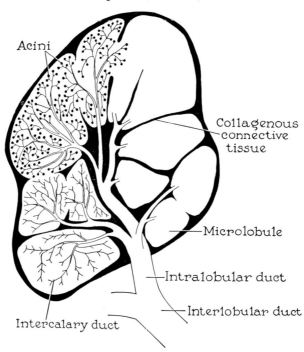

Acini

Collagenous connective tissue

Microlobule

Intralobular duct

Interlobular duct

Intercalary duct

Fig. 14–5. Diagram to show branches of duct system and relations to secretory portion in a (macro)-lobule. Collagenous stroma separates (often incompletely) the microscopic lobules. The main duct shown is a branch of the interlobular duct. The interlobular duct branches into intralobular ducts of several orders. These are continuous with the fine terminal intercalary ducts which end in the secretory portion. (Modified after Heidenhain.)

have the form of oval or spherical sacs. However, as a rule, the form is that of irregularly branched tubules with numerous saccular outgrowths on the wall and on the blind ends (Fig. 14–4). These glands should be designated compound *tubulo-acinous.* To this group belong most of the larger exocrine glands—the albuminous and mixed glands of the oral cavity and respiratory passages, and the pancreas.

In some cases the excretory ducts do not all join into a single main duct, but open independently on a restricted area of a free epithelial surface (lacrimal, mammary and prostatic glands).

Organization of Glands. While glands are recognizably different, it is important to emphasize similarities in the general plan of organization which is shared by all. These may be discussed under four general headings: (1) connective tissue elements, (2) blood vessels, lymphatics, and nerves, (3) ducts, (4) secretory cells.

Connective tissue constitutes 20 per cent or more of the total volume of glands. While

the pattern of connective tissue cells and fibers varies in different glands, the kinds of cells and of fibers are the same in all. In compound exocrine glands and most endocrine glands, the connective tissue is disposed as a condensation of loose connective tissue, in which the gland has developed and which comes to be the largely collagenous capsule. This extends in the gland proper as strands or sheets which separate the lobes and, on further subdivision, the lobules. These separations are not complete, since ducts, blood vessels and lymphatics, and nerves in the connective tissue, connect the glandular portions of the lobes and lobules. The collagenous connective tissue usually penetrates the lobule only slightly, where it frequently continues as reticular connective tissue (Fig. 14–5). This is in intimate contact with the terminal secretory and duct elements, where it becomes continuous with the basement membrane, and also bears the capillaries, lymphatics and nerves. This important part of the connective tissue is common to all glands, unicellular or multicellular, exocrine

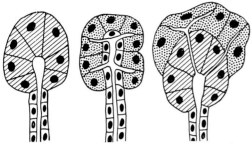

Fig. 14–6. Diagram to show relations of terminal portions of duct system (intercalary duct) and intercellular canaliculi to secreting cells. Crosshatched portion generally mucous; stippled portion serous. (Modified after Zimmermann.)

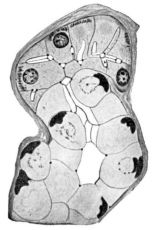

Fig. 14–7. Section of terminal portion of mandibular gland of man with clear mucous and darker albuminous cells. Between the latter are secretory capillaries and systems of terminal bars, stained black with iron hematoxylin. (Redrawn after Zimmermann.)

or endocrine. It consists of the tissue fluid, which is important in the exchange of substances between cells and plasma, and the ground substance and fibrillar components of connective tissue; it contains blood and lymph capillaries and nerve fibers, as well as cells of the connective tissue.

Blood vessels, lymphatics and *nerves* of glands usually show a similar gross distribution. They penetrate the capsule and are subdivided in the collagenous connective tissue septa or strands between the lobules. Within the lobule they are ultimately enclosed by reticular connective tissue. The blood and lymph capillaries form networks about gland cells or terminal ducts, and are separated from them by ground substance and reticular fibers (which may form a basement membrane) and tissue fluid. The major vascular supply is supplemented in most glands by a collateral circulation mediated through capsular vessels of small caliber. The terminal nerve fibers branch, and their final divisions end in a multitude of small enlargements on the surface of capillaries and frequently of gland cells and ducts.

The *duct system* of complex exocrine glands effects an economy of space and organization, and conducts the product of gland cells to the secreting surface. It may also modify the secretion during its passage. The secretory duct divides in the collagenous connective tissue to form the lobar ducts, whose further branchings are named with reference to the lobular structure (Fig. 14–5). The main duct of the gross lobule is the *lobular* duct, while the ducts of the microscopic lobule are called *intralobular* ducts; both are connected by ducts of intermediate caliber. The intralobular ducts are continuous with the *intercalary* duct, whose branches are connected with the secretory acini or tubules by apposition, through the mediation of intercellular canaliculi, or by modifications or combination of both these methods. The epithelium of the largest ducts may be stratified squamous or columnar-cuboidal. As the duct becomes smaller, the epithelium may be simple columnar, cuboidal, and finally squamous.

Gland cells frequently have specific granules, vacuoles and chromophile substance in their cytoplasm, in addition to mitochondria and Golgi apparatus. Although not many gland cells have shown visible indications of secretory activity, reversible changes take place in others which are emphasized to an exaggerated, possibly pathological, degree by excessive stimulation (Fig. 14–8). The number of specific granules decreases, water vacuoles increase, the chromophile substance appears to be more prominent, the mitochondria become larger and more numerous, and the Golgi apparatus hypertrophies. The cytoplasmic volume is decreased. Coincident nuclear changes include an increase in volume with an apparent decrease in stainability and a displacement toward the lumen surface. The nucleolus is increased in size and deeply stained. Gland cells, like others, must be considered to be in a state of con-

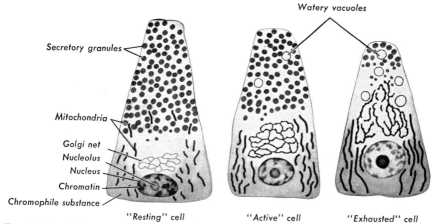

Fig. 14–8. Diagram of serous type of secretory cell in different stages of secretion to illustrate changes in cytoplasmic and nuclear structures which may take place during marked activity.

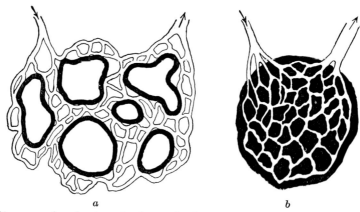

Fig. 14–9. Diagrams of endocrine glands. *a*, gland composed of irregular sacs (heavy black lines) surrounded by connective tissue and blood vessels. This type includes the thyroid and ovary. *b*, in this type the epithelium (black) has no lumen and is penetrated by dense networks of blood vessels (white). To this group belong most of the endocrine glands: suprarenals, parathyroids, hypophysis, corpus luteum, and others.

tinual activity. Even "resting" cells are performing work in maintaining their integrity and internal organization, and in synthesizing and secreting their specific substances or secretions at minimal levels.

The cytological changes in secretion have called forth a massive literature on relations of mitochondria, Golgi apparatus and chromophile substance to the secretion precursor. The current view is that none of these structures is transformed directly into secretory products and that their morphological changes reflect states of activity.

Endocrine Glands. As the endocrine glands develop in the embryo, their connection with the surface epithelium is lost. In some cases the gland consists of sacs lined with epithelium and surrounded by connective tissue (Fig. 14–9, *a*). In most cases the invagination of the epithelium loses its lumen or is solid from the very beginning. It is also effectively separated from the epithelial surface, and its cells form a compact mass thoroughly penetrated by a dense network of blood vessels and connective tissue (Fig. 14–9, *b*). As there are no excretory ducts, all secretions find their way into the general circulation.

Other endocrine glands which are not entirely dissociated from the excretory duct system are called *mixed glands*. In the liver, for example, the hepatic cells which secrete bile into the duct system also eliminate internal secretions directly into the blood ves-

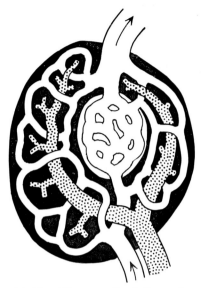

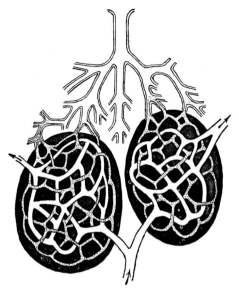

Fig. 14–10. Diagram of relations of secretory portions of a mixed endocrine and exocrine gland (pancreas) to blood vessels and duct system. Endocrine portion white, exocrine portion black, blood vessels white, duct stippled.

Fig. 14–11. Diagram of mixed exocrine and endocrine gland (liver), showing secretory portion in black, blood vessels in white, secretory capillaries stippled, and excretory ducts with double contours.

sels (Fig. 14–11). On the other hand, in the testis and pancreas, one group of cells secretes into the external duct system, while another group passes its internal secretion into the blood (Fig. 14–10).

The endocrine glands secrete their specific products, called *hormones,* directly into the blood stream. The endocrine glands are all circumscribed, with minor exceptions. They are thus set aside from numerous other structures believed to produce internal secretions and also important in coordination and integration within the organism. The circumscribed endocrine glands of man are the *adrenal, hypophysis, thyroid, parathyroid, islets of Langerhans,* and *portions of the testis* and *ovary.* Other glands which resemble these morphologically in some respects, but do not produce any known secretion, are the pineal body and the paraganglia.

Internal secretion by nerve cells is reviewed in detail by the Scharrers (1954) and is discussed in Chapter 15 in connection with the neurohypophysis.

General Properties of Endocrine Glands. There are three main integrative mechanisms which appear phylogenetically as well as ontogenetically. The earliest to appear is a group of substances which diffuses in the intercellular spaces and influences cells in a limited region. This is supplemented in coelenterates and in embryos of higher forms by a nervous system, including in the latter the autonomic and central nervous systems. Demarcated endocrine glands appear at a later time (in arthropods, and in older embryos of higher forms) and are found in all vertebrates. The first system of integration through diffusion is poorly defined and slow, and has a limited extent in animals. The nervous system effects a coordination of slow effectors also, but reaches its highest development in dealing with highly complicated integrated patterns and in delicate, precise and rapid motor patterns. These systems are supplemented by the endocrine glands, which secrete substances which have a longer latent period (since they are distributed by the circulating blood) and produce sustained, persistent results.

The endocrine glands are specialized, generally circumscribed glands or tissues which secrete specific substances called hormones into the circulation. Their primary morphological orientation is not toward the ducts, but toward the vascular system, and it is not surprising that they are all characteristically highly vascular (see Figs. 15–6, 16–6). Endocrine glands are subject to control by the central nervous system, by other endocrine

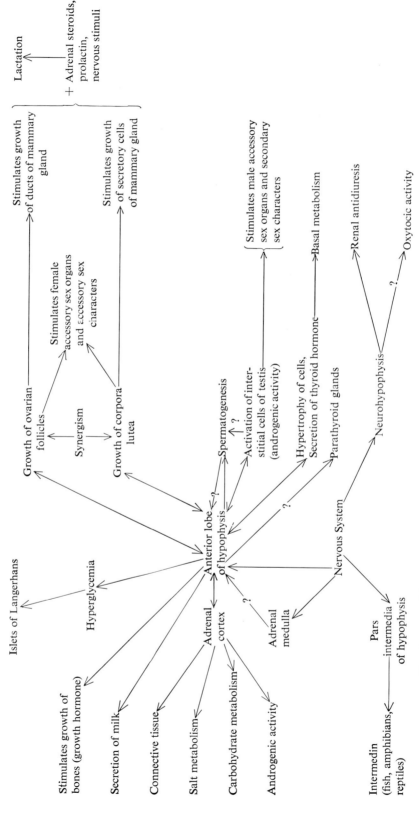

Fig. 14-12.   Schematic diagram of major interrelationships of some endocrine and nervous regulatory organs.

glands, by certain metabolites, or by a combination of these factors. There is, then, a complicated series of *endocrine interrelationships* which are highly important. Some of them are indicated in Figure *14–12*.

Hormones as Integrators. Hormones have been defined as products of specialized tissues which are carried by the blood system to influence other cells, tissues or organs, or the organism as a whole. The integrative action of hormones consists in the depression, activation or maintenance of cells other than, as well as, themselves, as, for example, thyrotrophic hormone of the anterior lobe of the hypophysis and thyroglobulin. Some hormones affect certain organs and tissues almost specifically, under certain conditions, and these are called *target organs;* other hormones have a more general effect which probably influences some basic cell reactions about which little is known. The hormones may be secreted almost as rapidly as they are formed (adrenal cortex), or they may be stored intracellularly or extracellularly in the gland while the blood level is maintained (insulin in the pancreatic islets, thyroglobulin in the thyroid gland colloid). Hormones differ greatly in chemical composition, and include proteins, polypeptides, modified amino acids, and steroids. Like certain drugs, vitamins and trace elements, they may be effective in minute concentrations.

Other Kinds of Integrators. The definition of hormone as given here arbitrarily excludes a wide range of other chemical integrators which may be transmitted by diffusion, which may be intracellular, or which may arise either outside the body or as metabolites from all cells. The first class of integrators, which are transmitted by diffusion, includes *embryonic inductors* (such as are involved in differentiation of the central nervous system, and of the optic lens) and *epinephrine-like* and *acetylcholine-like* substances which may be involved in transmission of the nerve impulse across the synapse and at nerve endings. The second class of integrators, which remain intracellular, includes *genes* and certain enzymes. The third class of integrators, which arise outside the organism, includes certain *vitamins,* as well as *secretagogues* important in the control of the secretion of certain parts of the gastrointestinal tract. Related to these are the integrators which arise from or during metabolic activity. These include carbon dioxide, which aids in the regulation of respiration, and glycogen of the liver, which plays an important part in maintaining the constancy of the blood sugar level. Except for its general origin, the former so nearly resembles a hormone as to have been classified as a *parahormone.* Further, the release of glycogen from the liver was, in fact, the first instance characterized as *internal secretion.*

REFERENCES

Allen, E. (ed.): Sex and Internal Secretions. Baltimore, 1939.

Bernard, C.: Leçons de physiologie expérimentale au Collège de France. Paris, 1855.

Biedl, A.: Innere Sekretion. Ihre physiologischen Grundlagen und ihre Bedeutung für die Pathologie. Berlin, 1922.

Dawson, A. B.: Some morphological aspects of the secretory process. Federation Proc., *1:*233, 1942.

Heidenhain, M.: Plasma und Zelle. Jena, 1907–11; Ueber die teilungsfähigen Drüseneinheiten oder Adenomeren sowie über die Grundbegriffe der morphologischen Systemlehre. Berlin, 1921.

Laguesse, E.: Trois leçons sur les glandes à sécrétion interne en général, et en particulier sur la gland endocrine du pancréas. L'Echo Médical du Nord, 1925.

Möbius, P. J.: Ueber das Wesen der Basedowschen Krankheit. Zentralbl. f. Nervenheilk., 8, 1887.

Schaffer, J.: Das Epithelgewebe. Handb. d. mikr. Anat. (v. Möllendorff), (2), 1927.

Scharrer, E., and Scharrer, B.: Neurosekretion. Handb. d. mikr. Anat. d. Menschen (v. Möllendorff u. Bargmann), Berlin, *6:*953, 1954.

Turner, C. D.: General Endocrinology. 2nd ed. Philadelphia, W. B. Saunders Company, 1955.

Zimmermann, K.: Beiträge zur Kenntniss einiger Drüsen und Epithelium. Arch. f. mikr. Anat., (52), 1898.

CHAPTER 15

Hypophysis

THE HYPOPHYSIS is one of the most important organs of the body with a multiplicity of reciprocal interrelations with other structures and functions which are essential for the regulation of the normal metabolic patterns. The anterior, intermediate and tuberal parts form the *adenohypophysis* which originates from the buccal lining; the *neurohypophysis* develops from the floor of the diencephalon. The organ is intimately related to its innervation, derived in large part from a portion of the brain, the hypothalamus. The cell population of the gland is extremely variable throughout life and the number of cell types is smaller than the number of purified hormones.

The relations of the parts of the hypophysis are tabulated below, shown diagrammatically in Figure *15–2*, and illustrated in Figure *15–1*.

The human gland measures about 1 cm. in length, 1 to 1.5 cm. in width and about 0.5 cm. in height and weighs about 0.5 gm. in men and slightly more in women. The anterior lobe forms about three fourths of the gland, the neural lobe most of the remainder,

the pars intermedia and the pars tuberalis each about 2 per cent. The increased weight during pregnancy is due to enlargement of the anterior lobe.

The hypophysis is lodged in a deep depression of the sphenoid bone, the sella turcica, and is covered by a tough diaphragm. Through it pass the hypophyseal stalk and, with few exceptions, some pia-arachnoid membrane which extends between the diaphragm and the capsule of the gland. Elsewhere the dense collagenous capsule is separated from the periosteum of the sphenoid bone by a looser layer of connective tissue containing numerous veins. This layer appears to be separate from the pia-arachnoidal tissue. In mammals other than man, the diaphragm is commonly incomplete.

The *nerve supply* of the hypophysis is derived from the cervical sympathetic carotid plexus, sphenopalatine ganglion or petrosal nerves (parasympathetic), and the hypothalamo-hypophyseal tract. The last originates chiefly from the supraoptic nucleus, close to the optic chiasma, and to some extent from the paraventricular nucleus in the wall of the third ventricle. Other hypothalamic and tuberal nuclei may also contribute to the tract. Its fibers, rarely

	Divisions		Subdivisions
Adenohypophysis....Lobus glandularis		{	Pars distalis (anterior lobe)
			Pars tuberalis
			Pars intermedia } Posterior lobe
Neurohypophysis {	Lobus nervosus equivalent to infundibular process (neural lobe)		
	Infundibulum (neural stalk)	{	Infundibular stem Median eminence of tuber cinereum } With pars tuberalis to form hypophyseal stalk

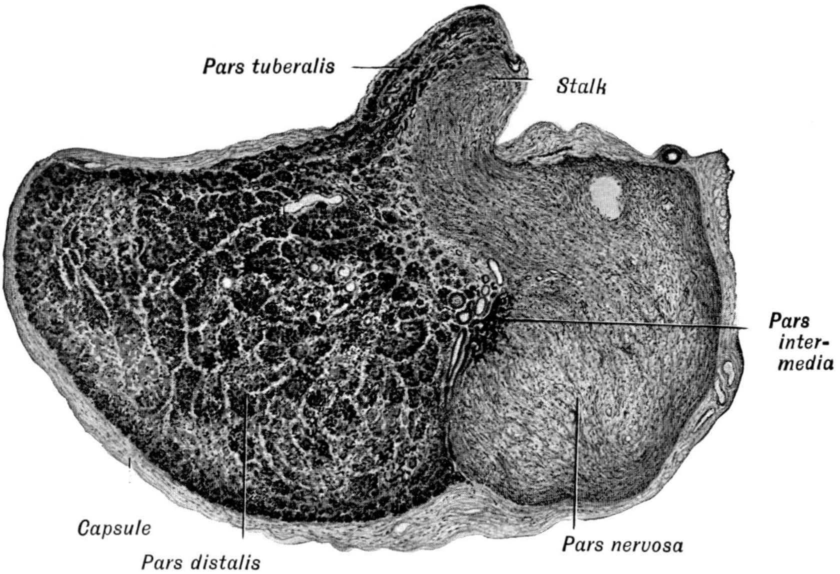

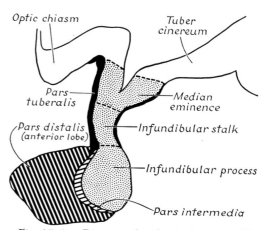

Fig. 15–1. Median section through hypophysis of a forty-five-year old man. 16 ×. (After Schaffer.)

myelinated, course down the infundibular stalk and reach the infundibular process. The ultimate distribution of the nerve fibers will be discussed with each subdivision of the gland.

The *blood supply* of the hypophysis consists of two inferior hypophyseal arteries and a series of twenty or more superior hypophyseal arteries. The former arise from the internal carotid arteries and arborize in the vascular layer of the capsule. The branches supply chiefly the posterior lobe, but also extend to the anterior lobe and anastomose with branches of the superior arteries. The latter arise from the internal carotid artery and the posterior communicating arteries of the circle of Willis and anastomose freely in the region of the stalk. Many continue, chiefly in the pars tuberalis, as vessels of a diameter of about 100 microns, and pass into the anterior lobe. Some break up into a wide capillary plexus in the pars tuberalis and neural stalk. The capillaries join to form venules which course together with the arteries into the substance of the anterior lobe, where they empty into its sinusoids. The venules thus constitute a *portal system* similar to the hepatic portal system. The capillaries of the hypophysis will be described with each subdivision of the gland. The venous drainage of the hypophysis is chiefly through veins which run in the vascular layer of the capsule toward the diaphragm into adjacent dural sinuses. Some of the venous blood enters sinuses in the sphenoid bone.

Pars Distalis. The anterior lobe, or pars distalis, is the largest subdivision of the hypophysis. It is largely enclosed by the dense collagenous capsule. Collagenous bundles, which surround branches of the superior hypophyseal arteries and the portal venules, penetrate the lobe at the pole adjacent to the

Fig. 15–2. Diagram of midsagittal section of hypothalamus and hypophysis of man to show relations of major divisions and subdivisions of the gland to the hypothalamus. (Modified after Tilney.)

pars tuberalis and stream bilaterally to a depth of about one third the thickness of the gland. They are continuous with reticular fibers which constitute the major part of the supporting connective tissue of the lobe and enclose the smaller arterial vessels and the *sinusoids*. The widely anastomotic sinusoids (Fig. 15–6) are lined by phagocytes like those of the sinusoids of the adrenal cortex, liver and spleen. Those near the capsule gather to form collecting venules which become progressively larger in the vascular layer of the capsule. The reticular fibers are sepa-

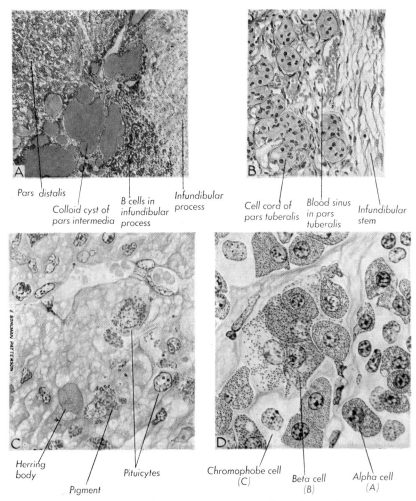

Pars distalis

Colloid cyst of
pars intermedia

B cells in
infundibular
process

Infundibular
process

Cell cord of
pars tuberalis

Blood sinus
in pars
tuberalis

Infundibular
stem

Herring
body

Pigment

Pituicytes

Chromophobe cell
(C)

Beta cell
(B)

Alpha cell
(A)

Fig. 15–3.   Sections of human hypophysis. *A,* pars intermedia and its relations to pars distalis and infundibular process. 60 ✕. *B,* cell cords of pars tuberalis, with numerous small blood vessels, and adjacent infundibular stem. 275 ✕. *C,* cells and intercellular substance of infundibular process. 690 ✕. *D,* cells of pars distalis. 690 ✕. Zenker-formol, H + E.

rated by a homogeneous basement membrane from the gland cells.

The gland cells are arranged as irregular cords and masses which vary from 20 to 180 microns in thickness in man and are intimately related to the sinusoids. There may also be small acinus-like structures with lumina.

There are two major varieties of gland cells, the *chromophile cells* and the *chromophobe cells* (Fig. 15–3). The former are further classified as *alpha* and *beta cells,* according to the staining properties of their specific granules. The chromophobe cells are called *reserve cells, chief cells* or simply *C cells.* In some mammals the alpha or beta cells predominate in the outer or inner portion of the lobe, but in man their distribution is irregular and highly variable. The relative proportion of the gland cells varies markedly in man, and is different from that in other mammals. In general, the beta cells are the least numerous in man. The relative proportions of cells may be markedly influenced by castration or thyroidectomy. In the absence of an appreciable number of mitoses, the conclusion that cells are transformed from one variety to another has led to numerous proposals for cell lineages based on morphological transition stages.

Alpha Cells. Before fixation these appear ovoid or spherical, with the cytoplasm

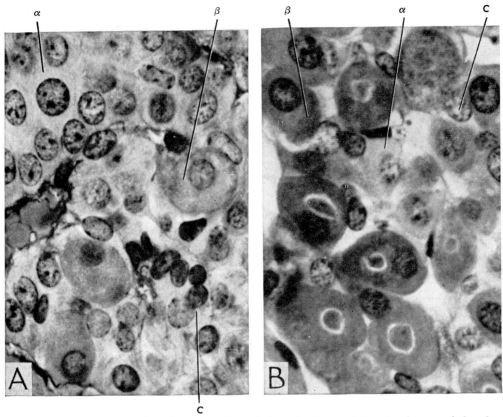

Fig. 15–4. Photomicrographs of anterior lobe of hypophysis of adult rats. *A,* normal female rat; *B,* castrate female rat of same age. Enlarged beta cells with characteristic "signet ring" appearance and reduction in alpha and chromophobe cells follow castration. Zenker-formol, Mallory-azan. 1300 ×.

crowded with small spherical granules. In sections they vary in size from 8 microns to 14 by 19 microns. The spherical or ovoid, eccentrically placed nucleus is about 8 microns in diameter. It has one or two nucleoli, a variable amount of chromatin dispersed on a coarse linin net. The weakly stained cytoplasm contains a centrosome with a diplosome, a Golgi net near the nucleus, and mitochondria distributed throughout the cytoplasm as minute spheres or rodlets. The specific alpha granules vary in size even in the same cell. They are stained by numerous dyes such as eosin, acid fuchsin, Congo red and azocarmine. In some mammals (man, dog, cat, horse) they are coarse; in others (guinea pig, mouse) they are fine. Also present in the cytoplasm are several small lipoid droplets. The reaction for ascorbic acid is strong. The cells vary not only in size, but in form, chromatin content and number of granules. Some cells are degranulated and hyperchromatic; others are stained pale.

Beta Cells. These are round, oval or angular in shape, and vary from about 9 microns to 20 by 25 microns. The nucleus resembles that of alpha cells, but the chromatin masses are larger and more numerous. The cytoplasm contains a centrosome with a rodlike diplosome, a loosely arranged Golgi net somewhat removed from the nucleus, and small mitochondria. The specific beta granules are less numerous than are alpha granules in comparable cells. They vary somewhat in size in different mammals; for example, they are larger in the dog than in rabbits or cats. They are stainable with aniline blue, resorcin fuchsin, hematoxylin and mucicarmine. The lipoid droplets are larger than in alpha cells, though fewer and more variable, and the reaction for ascorbic acid is weaker. Just as for alpha cells, the variants include nongranular or granular hyperchromatic cells as well as pale-stained ones.

C Cells. The reserve, chief or C cells are spherical, angular or elongated and may reach the dimensions of large alpha and beta cells. The nucleus is chromatin-poor. The cytoplasm is devoid of alpha or beta granules, but may contain pale-staining granules. The cytoplasm contains a loosely arranged Golgi net, and numerous mitochondria in the form of granules, rods and filaments. The C cells are rich in lipoid droplets, though this is variable, and the cytoplasmic reaction for ascorbic acid is weaker than in the beta cells. Variants include irregular-shaped cells with pyknotic nuclei and sometimes highly vacuolated cytoplasm.

Hormones of the Anterior Lobe. The anterior lobe of the hypophysis secretes a series of protein hormones which have been separated from one another in nearly pure form.

1. *Growth hormone* plays an important part in the normal growth of the body. Hypophysectomy retards growth of young mammals; in somewhat older animals, growth ceases directly. Growth is restored by the administration of the hormone, and gigantism may be produced experimentally by excessive doses. Dwarfism in certain strains of mice has been traced to a congenital defect in the development of the hypophysis. The hormone has a nearly specific growth effect on epiphyseal cartilage. Simultaneous administration of thyroid extracts augments the action of the growth hormone, while simultaneous administration of adrenocorticotrophic hormone inhibits its action. Certain tumors of the anterior lobe cause *gigantism* in children; this occurs through continued growth in length of the bones if the adenomata become active before closure of the epiphyseal regions. If this occurs after closure of the epiphyseal plate, it causes *acromegaly,* in which the bones become thicker, the hands and feet broader, the mandible heavier, and the calvaria thicker.

2. *Follicle-stimulating hormone* (FSH) promotes growth of ovarian follicles in the female and stimulates spermatogenesis in the male. Hypophysectomy causes atrophy of the sex organs, which may be restored nearly to normal by administration of the hormone. The secretion by the follicles of adequate amounts of estrogen and the complete restoration of spermatogenesis are augmented by subminimal doses of luteinizing hormone.

3. *Luteinizing hormone* (LH) alone has no direct action on the ovary of the hypo-physectomized animal; it causes luteinization of follicles only after ripening by prior treatment with follicle-stimulating hormone. It activates the interstitial cells of the testis, the effect being augmented by the administration of follicle-stimulating hormone.

4. *Prolactin* causes secretion of milk after the ducts and secretory portions of the mammary gland have been developed in response to ovarian hormones. Hypophysectomy abolishes lactation promptly. Prolactin also exerts a *luteotrophic action:* i.e., it maintains existing corpora lutea in an active secretory state. Follicle-stimulating hormone, luteinizing hormone and prolactin together form a *gonadotrophic hormone complex.*

5. *Adrenocorticotrophic hormone* (ACTH) causes growth of the adrenal cortex, particularly the glomerular and fascicular zones, and secretion of its hormones. The atrophic adrenal cortex of hypophysectomized animals is restored to normal by the hormone. Removal of one adrenal is followed by compensatory hypertrophy of the remaining gland, but this does not take place after hypophysectomy. Its curative and ameliorative effects in a great variety of diseases are being evaluated.

6. *Thyrotrophic hormone* has not been as highly purified as the others. It stimulates hypertrophy of the thyroid gland cells and secretion. Hypophysectomy results in atrophy of the thyroid, which may be restored to normal by the administration of hormone extracts.

7. *Other Functions.* The anterior lobe is also involved in some less defined activities reflected in protein, fat and carbohydrate metabolism. Whether some of these are primary activities of the gland, or are mediated by effects on other endocrine glands, is not always clear. Extracts of the anterior lobe have a *diabetogenic action,* which may be ascribed, at least in part, to actions of adrenocorticotrophic hormone (and the adrenal cortex) and growth hormone. Repeated injections of a gland extract in a partially depancreatized dog result in a *diabetes mellitus* which becomes permanent if the treatment is prolonged. However, it may be that the hyperglycemia produced by the extract constitutes such a heavy strain on the pancreatic islet cells that they become exhausted and atrophy. Hypophysectomy

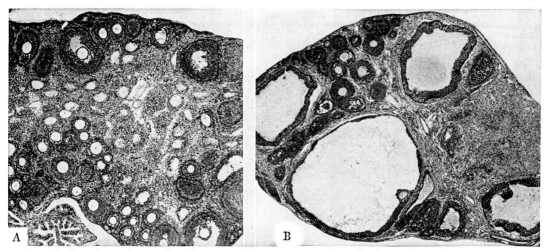

Fig. 15–5. Photomicrographs of ovary of immature rat, *A*, and of rat of similar age, *B*, injected with follicle-stimulating hormone for three days. The hormone caused growth of the follicles and the appearance of a corpus luteum. 38 ×.

results in a low blood sugar and increased sensitivity to insulin. In the depancreatized dog, hypophysectomy diminishes the severity of the diabetes mellitus.

There is some evidence that the anterior lobe exercises some influence over the parathyroid glands. For example, in tadpoles, hypophysectomy is followed by atrophy of the parathyroid glands and a reduced blood calcium level. Again, parathyroid lesions were present in two thirds of hypophysectomized dogs. On the other hand, parathyroid changes following hypophysectomy in the monkey and rat appeared to be negligible.

The anterior lobe also helps to control the number of circulating erythrocytes in rats.

Cells of Origin of Hormones. As the number of hormones in the anterior lobe exceeds the number of principal cell types, more than one function (hormone) has been assigned to each cell type. The evidence associating a cell type in the anterior lobe with the secretion of a hormone is based on considerations which are not altogether consistent or definite. Some examples of the types of evidence utilized will be cited in the following paragraphs.

Growth hormone is generally believed to arise from alpha cells. In a series of acromegalic patients with pituitary adenomata, alpha cells were prominent, while in a series of nonacromegalics with pituitary adenomata, alpha cells were scarce. The outer part of the ox pituitary is richer in alpha cells and has an effect on the growth of tadpoles, while the central part is richer in beta cells and has no effect on their growth. In dwarf mice the alpha cells are lacking, but a good analysis of the beta cells has yet to be made. Contrary to these findings, in the early pig embryo hypophysis there is a stage when the only chromophilic cell present is the beta cell; yet growth hormone is present in such glands despite the absence of alpha cells.

Gonadotrophic hormones are generally believed to arise from beta cells. After castration the rat hypophysis contains more gonadotrophic hormone, and at the same time the beta cells increase in number, some of them becoming markedly enlarged and vacuolated in a characteristic way. The central part of the anterior lobe of the ox hypophysis is rich in beta cells and also in gonadotrophic activity. In the posterior lobe of the human hypophysis, beta cells occur commonly and the lobe has gonadotrophic activity. In the rat and pig, beta granules are most numerous during proestrus, at a time when gonadotrophic activity should be greatest, and decrease rapidly in estrus, when gonadotrophic activity is at its lowest in the cycle. However, some workers associate gonadotrophic hormones with the alpha cells.

Although most of the evidence indicates that thyrotrophic hormone arises from beta cells, some equally good evidence points to the alpha cell or the undifferentiated cell as

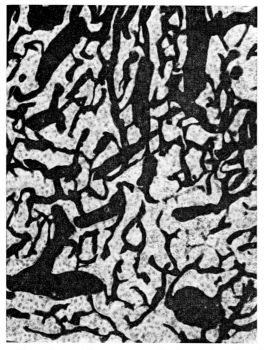

Fig. 15–6. Photomicrograph of anterior lobe of hypophysis of monkey injected with India ink to show the irregular, richly anastomotic sinusoids. 165 ×. Compare with Figure 15–8 of the infundibular process.

the source of the hormone. Evidence on the cells of origin of adrenocorticotrophic hormone is spotty. The administration of the rat hormone is said to cause no changes in the gland cells, or to cause degranulation of alpha and beta cells. Adrenalectomy results in a marked reduction in the beta cells in the dog, less marked changes in the rat. In chronic adrenal insufficiency in man, both alpha and beta cells are reduced in number. Only beta cells combine, in sections, with a fluorescent, dye-tagged antibody specific for ACTH.

Mechanism of Release of Hormones from the Anterior Lobe. Three mechanisms have been proposed to explain how the cells of the anterior lobe are induced to release their hormones into the blood: neural, neurovascular, and humoral.

The anterior lobe contains a number of nerve fibers derived chiefly from the sympathetic chain and from the tract located in the stalk. The former are believed to be confined to the blood vessels along which they enter. The latter are believed to terminate in

the reticular connective tissue or in even more intimate contact with the gland cells as simple end bulbs or pericellular baskets. The cells of origin lie chiefly in the supraoptic and paraventricular nuclei. Stimulation of the hypothalamus along the course of the supraopticohypophyseal tract in the unanesthetized rabbit caused secretion by the gland cells of the hypophysis of sufficient follicle-stimulating hormone to cause ovulation and of sufficient adrenocorticotrophic hormone to stimulate the adrenal gland. The same stimulus was ineffective in influencing the secretion of thyrotrophic hormone. Similarly, transection of the stalk commonly caused disturbances in sexual activities, but did not influence thyroidal activity. It is believed, then, that the secretion of thyrotrophic hormone is not under neural control normally, although under certain conditions of stress the nerve tract originating in the hypothalamus may influence secretion of the hormone.

The neural influence may be direct, through the nerve terminations ending in proximity to the gland cells. It is also possible that the nerve fibers in the stalk, when stimulated, secrete a substance which passes, via the capillaries of the stalk, to the hypothalamo-hypophyseal portal veins, to the anterior lobe of the hypophysis, thence to the sinusoids in intimate contact with the gland cells. Either method requires that the neurons giving rise to the hypothalamo-hypophyseal tract be sensitive to humoral stimuli.

Pars Intermedia. In most human hypophyses, the pars intermedia is poorly delimited (Figs. 15–1 and 15–3, A). But in a small proportion of adults and in many young children, it appears as in most mammals as a *cleft* enclosed by an anterior and posterior wall. In man, the pars intermedia is small (about 2 per cent of the hypophysis); in other animals it is larger, as in the mouse (about 19 per cent), or absent as in some birds, the whale, porpoise, manatee and armadillo. The pars intermedia of most men differs from that of most mammals in several respects: the cleft is rarely complete, cysts occur commonly, and beta cells extend into the neural lobe, sometimes to a surprising extent.

A relatively unmodified hypophyseal cleft persists in a small proportion of adults. The anterior wall comprises an irregular layer, one to two cells thick of undifferentiated alpha, beta and C cells, which blend into the cell cords of the anterior lobe. The posterior wall is thicker, with several layers of small undifferentiated cells among which may be ciliated cells and cells with a cuticular border.

In most men, remnants of the cleft persist as *cysts* 1 to 3 mm. long, chiefly in that portion of the pars intermedia farthest removed from the stalk. At the opposite pole of the pars intermedia, cysts arise as evaginations of the original pouch. The cells enclosing the cyst are largely undifferentiated, small cells without granules and C cells with pale-staining granules. They continue into a zone of chromophobe cells with some beta cells which lie between the anterior lobe and neural lobe and extend to the pars tuberalis. In addition, branched tubules of pale-staining columnar cells and strands of cells which may form cysts extend into the infundibular process. Finally, numerous beta cells somewhat smaller than those in the anterior lobe extend for a variable distance into the same lobe. This beta cell invasion of the neural lobe has been observed in embryos and children. The cystic colloid may vary in consistency from fluid to fairly solid, may be colorless to yellow, and may have free cells suspended in it. It is extremely inert, and in sections stains metachromatically.

Nerve fibers presumably arising from hypothalamic nuclei are rather numerous in the pars intermedia. The rich capillary bed is continuous with that of the neural lobe and with the sinusoids of the anterior lobe. Numerous anastomoses take place between the superior and inferior hypophyseal arterioles in the substance of the pars intermedia. Both nerve fibers and blood vessels are supported by a reticular fiber net which also contains some collagenous bundles.

The pars intermedia secretes *intermedin,* a hormone which causes *melanocytes* to expand and thus darken the skin. The control of the melanocyte expansion in some animals is neural, in others (frog) humoral, in still others both. The secretion of the hormone is controlled by the nerve fibers derived from those which pass down the stalk to the neural lobe. Hypophysectomy in the frog is followed by a blanching of the skin, which may be caused to darken again by the admin-

istration of the hormone. Injury to the hypothalamus results in melanocyte expansion, as do successful transplants. The hormone is effective also in fishes and reptiles.

Though present in birds and mammals, the active substance exerts no known influence.

Pars Tuberalis. Like the pars intermedia, the pars tuberalis constitutes a small part of the hypophysis. Both are continuous with and adjacent to the anterior lobe. The pars tuberalis is 25 to 60 microns thick, the thickest portion being on the anterior surface of the stalk (Fig. 15–2), and is frequently incomplete, especially on the posterior surface of the stalk. The outstanding morphological character is the longitudinal arrangement of cords and balls of epithelial cells, which interdigitate with the longitudinally oriented blood vessels (Fig. 15–3, B).

The pars tuberalis is the most highly vascularized subdivision of the hypophysis, because it accommodates the major arterial supply for the anterior lobe and the hypothalamo-hypophyseal venous portal system. Some nerve fibers terminating on the epithelial cells have been observed. The pars tuberalis is separated from the infundibular stalk by a thin layer of connective tissue continuous with the pia. On the opposite surface, the connective tissue is typical arachnoidal membrane. Between these, the blood vessels and groups of epithelial cells are supported by reticular fibers with some collagenous bundles.

The epithelial cells of the pars tuberalis include undifferentiated cells and some small alpha and beta cells. The main component is a cuboidal-columnar cell, which may reach 12 to 18 microns in size, and contains numerous small granules or sometimes fine colloid droplets. The mitochondria are spheres or short rods, and numerous small lipoid droplets may be present. They are the only cells in the adult hypophysis containing large amounts of glycogen. The cells may be arranged to form a follicle-like structure. Islands 50 to 70 microns in extent of squamous epithelial cells may also be present.

Despite the occurrence of a pars tuberalis in all vertebrates studied, the epithelial cells are not known to have any hormonal function.

Neurohypophysis. The median eminence of the tuber cinereum is included with the

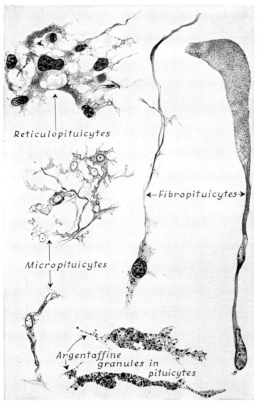

Reticulopituicytes

←Fibropituicytes→

Micropituicytes

Argentaffine
granules in
pituicytes

Fig. 15–7. Three types of pituicytes from the infundibular process of man. Granules may contain pigment, or they may be argentaphilic, or both. All cells 460 ×, except the group of micropituicytes, which are 260 ×. (Redrawn after Romeis.)

The collagenous connective tissue of the capsule of the hypophysis extends somewhat along the blood vessels which penetrate it, and is then replaced by reticular fibers. These form a netlike support for the rich capillary bed and also enclose nests of neuroglial cells. Also enclosed are feltlike whorls of chiefly unmyelinated nerve fibers derived from the hypothalamo-hypophyseal tract. In the stalk and median eminence, they are closely packed and parallel. Some of these fibers extend to the pars intermedia and anterior lobe, but the greater number by far terminate in the neurohypophysis, chiefly the infundibular process.

The cells peculiar to the human neurohypophysis, the *pituicytes,* have been studied most extensively by Romeis, who describes four types in man: *reticulopituicytes, micropituicytes, fibropituicytes,* and *adenopituicytes* (Fig. 15–7). They vary considerably in size and shape and in the extension of their processes which sometimes may be traced for hundreds of microns. They are probably modified glia cells and appear singly or in small or large groups. A characteristic feature of the pituicytes of man and some other mammals is the occurrence of pigment granules (Fig. 15–3, C), which may reduce silver directly or blacken with the methods of Bielschowsky and Hortega. Some of these pigment granules may also contain iron. Glia cells with fibers typical of the central nervous system are also found. All these cell types are also found in the infundibular stem and the median eminence, where their shape and dimensions differ in accordance with the prevailing pattern of nerve fibers and blood vessels, and proximity to the third ventricle. Small beta cells originating in the pars intermedia frequently extend for variable distances into the infundibular process.

In other mammals the specific cells of the neurohypophysis may contain numerous lipoid droplets or visible granules. In the rat these cells are reported to hypertrophy during water deprivation.

Characteristic of the neurohypophysis is the large amount of intercellular substance. During fixation this homogeneous material is precipitated as granules of varying size and tinctorial capacities. These form the larger part of what has been called the Herring bodies (Fig. 15–3, C). Also included in this

infundibular stem and process as a single unit, the neurohypophysis (Fig. 15–2). The vascular pattern of the median eminence and infundibular stem is identical, but differs markedly from that in the rest of the hypothalamus; the connections between the two vascular beds are through capillaries which appear functionally insignificant. All vessels of the neurohypophysis have the property in common of being particularly permeable to certain intravascularly injected dyes such as trypan blue and Evans blue. The cells characteristic of the infundibular process and stem are found in the median eminence, but not elsewhere in the tuber cinereum. After certain hypothalamic lesions, atrophy of the infundibular process and stem is shared also by the median eminence. Finally, the same active substances extracted from the infundibular process are obtained also from the median eminence.

category, probably, are the swellings of fibro-pituicytes and nerve fibers, and some enlarged nerve endings.

Two major substances can be extracted from the neurohypophysis: (1) *vasopressin,* a *blood pressure raising* and *antidiuretic* substance, which counteracts a water diuresis by promoting reabsorption of water chiefly in the thin limb of the loop of Henle; and (2) *oxytocin,* which causes smooth muscle of the uterus to contract. These two substances have been analyzed and synthesized by du Vigneaud and his co-workers. Both of them are cyclopeptides containing 8 amino acids. The antidiuretic substance plays an effective part in the organism; the evidence for the hormonal nature of oxytocin is not as convincing.

When lesions are made in the supraoptic tracts above the median eminence, secretion of the antidiuretic hormone ceases, as indicated by the pronounced polyuria and polydypsia which follow. This condition simulates diabetes insipidus as it occurs sometimes in patients. Urinary elimination of water in patients is restored to normal levels by the administration of antidiuretic extracts. In animals the neurohypophysis atrophies after the lesion, and its content of antidiuretic hormone and oxytocic activity decreases markedly. The same water disturbance follows when the supraoptic tracts are interrupted in the median eminence. But if the tracts are sectioned lower in the stalk, the disturbance may be temporary. It is necessary that the anterior lobe of the hypophysis should be functional for the polyuria to be permanent.

For many years it was believed that the antidiuretic and oxytocic hormones were made in the neural lobe. Owing largely to the work of Ranson and co-workers it seemed that the release of these substances was under the control of certain hypothalamic nuclei via the hypothalamo-hypophyseal nerves. Of late a new trend has been developing in the study of the site of origin of these hormones. According to this view the hormones or their precursors are formed by neurons in the supraoptic and related nuclei and the secretion moves down the nerves of the hypothalamo-hypophyseal tract to the neural lobe where it is stored. Bargmann and Scharrer have produced much presumptive evidence in favor

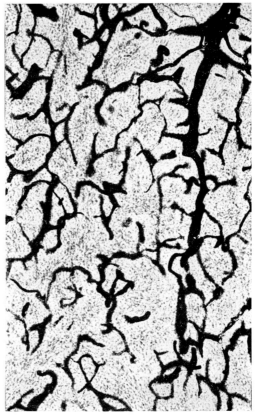

Fig. 15–8. Photomicrograph of infundibular process of monkey injected with India ink to show the pattern of small blood vessels. The arterioles break up into a number of arching, interconnected capillaries. 165 ×. Compare with Figure 15–6 of the anterior lobe.

of this concept. Both views of this problem are summarized as of 1955 in the monograph of G. W. Harris. Irrespective of the question of the site of origin of the hormones, it is assured that electrical stimulation of the hypothalamo-hypophyseal tract results in prompt discharge of the antidiuretic hormone from the infundibular process.

The role of the oxytocic substance has been sought in the mechanism of parturition. The uterine threshold to oxytocin in mice and rabbits is higher at midterm than at term. Destruction of the major part of the supraoptic tract also leads to disturbances in parturition. But attempts at crucial experiments in removing the posterior lobe have led to highly contradictory results both as concerns the mechanism of parturition itself and the significance of the oxytocic substance.

Histogenetic Remarks. The hypophysis arises from two widely separated sources; one of these is an evagination of the ectoderm of the primitive buccal cavity and extends as the *pouch of Rathke* toward the embryonic brain; this constitutes the *pars buccalis.* Kingsbury *et al.* maintain that this is not an active outgrowth and that the hypophyseal part of the ectoderm and infundibular part of the brain are originally close together and that this relation is retained. The most advanced part of this outgrowth comes in contact with a ventral evagination of the diencephalon, the former becoming the pars intermedia, the latter, the *pars nervosa.* The remnants of the pars buccalis divide into two lateral lobes (in embryos of 10.5 mm.) and a large anterior portion. The latter is transformed into the anterior or distal lobe of the definitive gland. In 45-mm. embryos, the two lateral lobes of the pars buccalis fuse at the midline to form the pars tuberalis and begin to grow forward; this portion later grows backward, surrounds the infundibulum, and spreads for a short distance under the tuber cinereum. The pars buccalis in man normally becomes completely separated from the buccal ectoderm. The pars nervosa develops as a downward outpouching of the floor of the diencephalon. Although in some animals it is more or less completely surrounded by the pars buccalis, this is not the case in man. The pars nervosa remains connected, by a stalk of the infundibulum, with the floor of the third ventricle; its cavity disappears in man, but is retained in the cat.

In early embryos and possibly also throughout life, undifferentiated cells are present in the anterior lobe. These may occur as discrete cells which have a nongranular cytoplasm and pale nuclei. In the human embryo, only undifferentiated cells are present at 24 mm. At 30 mm., beta cells are present, and occasionally an alpha cell. At 44 mm., the beta cells have increased in number, alpha cells are common, and some C cells are present. The time of appearance of the specific cells in the anterior lobe has been studied in a number of mammals and also in pigeons and some amphibians.

REFERENCES

Adams, A. E.: Variations in the potency of thyrotrophic hormone of the pituitary in animals. Quart. Rev. Biol., *21:*1, 1946.

Allen, E. (ed.): Sex and Internal Secretions. Baltimore, 1939.

Bailey, P.: The Structure of the Hypophysis Cerebri of Man and of the Common Laboratory Mammals, in Cowdry's Special Cytology. 2d ed. New York, P. Hoeber, (2), 771, 1932.

Bargmann, W.: Weitere Untersuchungen am neurosekretorischen Zwischenhirn—Hypophysensystem. Zeitschr. f. Zellforsch., *42:*247, 1955.

Bargmann, W., and Scharrer, E.: The site of origin of the hormones of the posterior pituitary. Amer. Scientist, April, 1951, p. 255.

Biedl, A.: Innere Sekretion. Ihre physiologischen Grundlagen und ihre Bedeutung für die Pathologie. Berlin, 1922.

Bogdanove, E. M., and Halmi, N. S.: Effects of hypothalamic lesions and subsequent propylthiouracil treatment on pituitary structure and function in the rat. Endocrinology, *53:*274, 1953.

Burrows, H.: Biological Actions of Sex Hormones. 2d ed. Cambridge University Press, London, 1949.

Catchpole, H. R.: Distribution of glycoprotein hormones in the anterior pituitary gland of the rat. J. Endocrinol., *6:*218, 1949.

Dempsey, E. W., and Wislocki, G. B.: Histochemical reactions associated with basophilia and acidophilia in the placenta and pituitary gland. Am. J. Anat., *76:* 277, 1945.

Dougherty, T. F., and White, A.: An evaluation of alterations produced in lymphoid tissue by pituitary-adrenal cortical secretion. J. Lab. & Clin. Med., *32:*584, 1947.

du Vigneaud, V.: Trail of sulfur research from insulin to oxytocin. Science, *123:*967, 1956.

Erdheim, J.: Zur normalen und pathologischen Histologie der Glandula thyroidea, parathyroidea, und Hypophysis. Beitr. z. path. Anat. u. z. allg. Path., *33:*158, 1903.

Everett, J. W., and Sawyer, C. H.: Estimated duration of the spontaneous activation which causes release of ovulating hormone from the rat hypophysis. Endocrinology, *52:*83, 1953.

Friedgood, H. B., and Dawson, A. B.: Physiological significance and morphology of the carmine cell in the cat's anterior pituitary. Endocrinology, *26:*1022, 1940.

Fulton, J. F.: The Hypothalamus. Ass. Res. in Nerv. & Ment. Dis., (20), Baltimore, 1940; see especially Part I.

Furth, J.: Experimental Pituitary Tumors. III. Hormones and Abnormal Growth. Recent Prog. Hormone Research, *XI,* 221, 1955.

Geiling, E. M. K.: The hypophysis cerebri of the finback (*Balaenoptera physalus*) and sperm (*Physeter megalocephalus*) whale. Bull. Johns Hopkins Hosp., *57:*123, 1935.

Gilbert, M. S.: Some factors influencing the early development of the mammalian hypophysis. Anat. Rec., *62:*337, 1935.

Giroud, A., and Leblond, C. P.: Localisations electives de l'acide ascorbique ou vitamine C. Arch. d'Anat. micr., *31:*111, 1935.

Grollman, A.: Essentials of Endocrinology. 2d ed. Philadelphia, 1947.

Halmi, N. S.: Two types of basophils in the rat pituitary: "thyrotrophs" and "gonadotrophs" vs. beta and delta cells. Endocrinology, *50:*140, 1952.

Harris, G. W.: Neural Control of the Pituitary Gland. London (Edward Arnold, Ltd.), 1955.

Houssay, B. A.: Certain relations between parathyroids, hypophysis, and pancreas. Harvey Lectures, *31:*116, 1936.

Hume, D. M.: The neuro-endocrine response to injury: Present status of the problem. Ann. Surg., *138:*548, 1953.

Hunt, T. E.: Mitotic activity in the anterior hypophysis of female rats. Anat. Rec., *82:*263, 1942.

Moore, C. R.: The role of the fetal endocrine glands in development. J. Clin. Endocrinol., *10:*912, 1950.

Peterson, R. R., and Weiss, J.: Staining of the adenohypophysis with acid and basic dyes. Endocrinology, *57:*96, 1955.

Pomerat, G. R.: Mitotic activity in the pituitary of the white rat following castration. Am. J. Anat., *69:*89, 1941.

Rasmussen, A. T.: The morphology of the pars intermedia of the human hypophysis. Endocrinology, *2:* 129, 1928.

Rinehart, J. F., and Farquhar, M. G.: The fine vascular organization of the anterior pituitary gland. An electron microscopic study with histochemical correlations. Anat. Rec., *121:*207, 1955.

Romeis, B.: Hypophyse. Handb. d. mikr. Anat. d. Menschen. (v. Moellendorff), 1940, Vol. 6, Pt. 3.

Scharrer, E., and Scharrer, B.: Neurosekretion. Handb.

mikr. Anat. d. Menschen (v. Möllendorff and Barg-mann), Berlin, 6:953, 1954. Hormones Produced by Neurosecretory Cells. Recent Prog. Hormone Research, 10:183, 1954.

Selye, H.: Textbook of Endocrinology. Montreal, 2nd ed. 1949.

Simpson, M. E., Asling, C. W., and Evans, H. M.: Some endocrine influences on skeletal growth and differentiation. Yale J. Biol. & Med., 23:1, 1950.

Simpson, M. E., Evans, H. M., and Li, C. H.: Bio-assay of adrenocorticotrophic hormone. Endocrinology, 33: 261, 1943.

Simpson, M. E., Evans, H. M., and Li, C. H.: The growth of hypophysectomized female rats following chronic treatment with pure pituitary growth hormone. Growth, 13:151, 1949.

Smith, P. E.: Hypophysectomy and replacement therapy in the rat. Am. J. Anat., 45:205, 1930.

Symposium on The Hypophyseal Growth Hormone, Nature and Actions. Edited by Smith, Gaebler, and Long. The Blakiston Division, McGraw-Hill Book Co., N. Y., Toronto, London, 1955.

Timme, W., Frantz, A. M., and Hare, C. C.: The Pituitary Gland. Assoc. Res. in Nerv. & Ment. Dis., (17), Baltimore, 1938; see especially Sec. I, and Chap. 22.

Turner, C. D.: General Endocrinology. Philadelphia, W. B. Saunders Company, 1955.

Van Dyke, H. B.: The Physiology and Pharmacology of the Pituitary Body. Chicago, 1939.

The references cited were selected primarily for orientation in this rapidly developing subject. Students are referred for the most recent developments to Annual Reviews of Physiology and to Vitamins and Hormones.

CHAPTER 16

Thyroid Gland

THE THYROID gland differs from all other endocrine glands in that hormone storage is developed to the highest degree and reflected morphologically most markedly. It is situated in the anterior middle portion of the neck close to the trachea, and consists of two lateral portions or *lobes* united by a thinner strip, the *isthmus*. Sometimes there is an irregular pyramidal lobe extending toward the thyroid cartilage.

The external connective tissue capsule of the gland continues into the surrounding cervical fascia; it is connected by loose connective tissue with another layer of dense connective tissue which adheres intimately to the organ. This separation of the capsule into two layers permits the organ to be removed easily.

Follicles. Each lobe is incompletely divided by connective tissue into plates, bars, stalks, and bands of gland tissue. These irregular *lobules* consist of spherical follicles 0.02 to 0.9 mm. in diameter lined with an epithelium and containing a stiff jelly called *colloid*. The external surface of the follicles is commonly smooth, and nearly all contain a lumen. Normally in man there is a preponderance of smaller over larger follicles. But in certain conditions they may increase in size, and the external surface may be markedly irregular. In man the size of the follicles varies considerably from region to region, with corresponding differences in the follicular cells and colloid. This has been attributed to cyclic states of activity which take place regionally rather than uniformly. In the thyroid of ani-

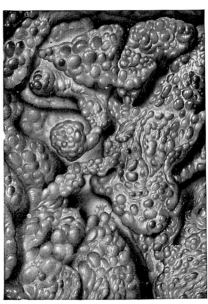

Fig. 16–1. Normal human thyroid. The shape of the parenchymatous regions varies from a triangular or quadrangular area to that of a cube or almost perfect sphere. About 5 ×. (After Reinhoff.)

mals other than man, the follicles are more uniform. In the rat and guinea pigs the follicles on the periphery of the gland are larger than the more central ones, and the colloid of the former is more basophile. Marked irregularity of the follicles may be produced in the rat by prolonged exposure to certain drugs (*allylthiourea, thiourea, and 2-acetyl-amino-fluorene*), a process which may terminate in the formation of benign or malignant tumors.

The follicles are enclosed by a network of

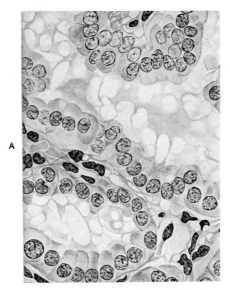
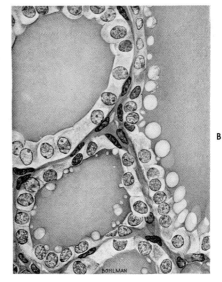

Fig. 16–2. Sections of human thyroid gland in exophthalmic goiter (*A*) and colloid goiter (*B*), from preparations of R. R. Bensley. Note the differences in the height of the epithelium and the amount and depth of staining of the colloid in the two conditions. Hematoxylin and eosin. 570 ×.

reticular fibrils embedded in ground substance. In younger animals the fibers are finer, and the network they form is less dense than in older animals. A basement membrane appears at the base of the follicular cells only in older animals. The connective tissue supports a close net of anastomotic capillaries which surround the follicles like a basket (Fig. 16–6). Outside the capillary layer and between the capillary beds of adjacent follicles are the terminations of the larger-meshed lymphatic vessels. Running along the arteries and their branches in the connective tissue are numerous nerve fibers; these terminate as simple thickenings, chiefly along the blood vessels, and also in direct contact with the base of some thyroid cells.

Gland Cells. Normally, each follicle of the human thyroid consists of an outer shell of gland cells which encloses the colloid. These cells are commonly low cuboidal, and are in close relation with the connective tissue and its network of blood and lymph capillaries. The epithelium of the gland varies in size and arrangement, depending on age, sex, season of the year, diet and certain pathological processes. In general, it is believed that the epithelium is squamous when the gland is underactive, and columnar and folded when it is overactive. There are, however, so many exceptions that it is impossible to determine the functional state of the gland in all cases through histological examination alone.

The gland cells of any one follicle are more or less uniform, though occasionally some columnar cells may be present when most cells are cuboidal. Rarely, there may be *"colloid cells"* of Langendorff with a dark pyknotic nucleus and dense-staining, osmiophilic cytoplasm. They are probably dead or dying cells.

The nucleus of the gland cell is situated centrally or toward the base of the cell. It is commonly spheroidal and poor in chromatin, and contains one or more nucleoli. After stimulation of the gland cells, the nucleus enlarges and stains more lightly.

The cytoplasm is basophile with certain stains; it contains ribonucleic acid as identified by its ultraviolet spectrum. The free border of the cells is provided with numerous fine cytoplasmic projections (microvilli) to be seen only in electron micrographs. Mitochondria, which are usually short, thin and rod-like in the human gland, are more numerous in the apical portion of the cytoplasm. The Golgi apparatus is supranuclear, with a few strands extending sometimes over the sides of the nucleus. Rarely, this apparatus may be situated between the nucleus and the base of the cell. A centrosome is located in the apical cytoplasm—although mitoses are ex-

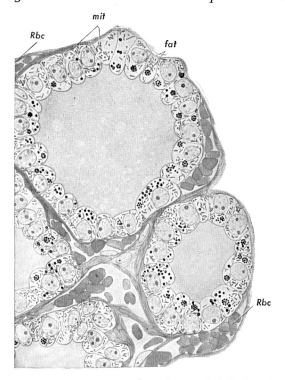

Fig. 16–3. Section through several follicles of human thyroid. *mit,* mitochondria; *fat,* small fat droplets; *Rbc,* red blood corpuscles. Aniline-acid-fuchsin. (Courtesy of R. R. Bensley.)

ceedingly rare—and there are fine terminal bars. Lipoid droplets, *cytochrome-cytochrome oxidase, peroxidase,* and *acid and alkaline phosphatase* have also been described in the cytoplasm. Under certain conditions, organic iodine compounds tagged by I^{131} have been demonstrated in the cytoplasm (Fig. *16–5*). A variety of *inclusions* have been described in the cytoplasm: (1) round droplets of colloid (Langendorff); (2) clear vacuoles possibly related to the colloid vacuoles of Anderson; (3) basal colloid vacuoles (Bensley); (4) minute granules stained supravitally with neutral red (Uhlenhuth); (5) colloid droplets varying in number from cell to cell and preserved only by freezing and drying (De Robertis). The relations of these to one another and to the secretion of colloid are still under discussion. The colloid droplets of De Robertis resemble the follicular colloid in that they stain with aniline blue, contain polysaccharide, and possibly in their ultraviolet absorption curve.

Colloid. The lumen of the follicles is normally filled with a characteristic material called colloid. This is a clear, viscous fluid whose consistency varies when the gland is in different states of activity. It is optically

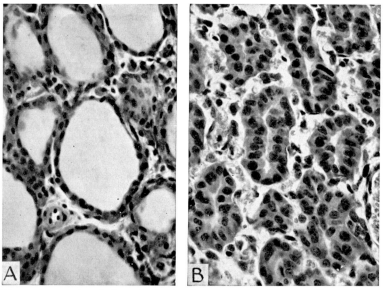

Fig. 16–4. Photomicrographs of thyroid glands of guinea pigs, showing effects of repeated injections of extracts of anterior lobe containing thyrotrophic hormone. *A,* normal acini with low cuboidal epithelium and rich in colloid; *B,* treated, with acini consisting of columnar cells containing small amount of dilute colloid. Fixed by freezing and drying. H + E. 350 ×.

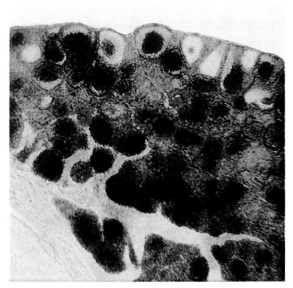

Fig. 16–5. Low power photomicrograph of auto-radiograph of thyroid gland of rat previously injected with I¹³¹. The blackened areas represent sites of deposition of the radioactive material. There is great variability in the content of the isotope in the several follicles. In a few places the epithelium is blackened. (Courtesy of C. P. Leblond, D. Findlay and S. Gross.)

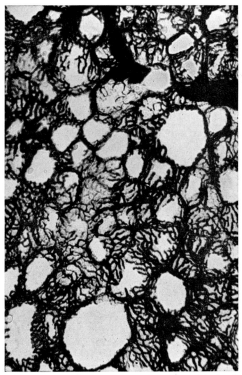

Fig. 16–6. Photomicrograph of thyroid gland of monkey injected with India ink to show pattern of small blood vessels. The richly anastomotic baskets of capillaries intimately enclose the follicles. Some of these are sectioned through the midportion; others are observed from above or below this level. 67 ×.

and probably chemically homogeneous, except for some desquamated cells and, under certain conditions, some macrophages. Irregularities in the colloid are rarely seen in follicles of living animals or after freezing and drying. However, the irregularities in the colloid which are seen after fixation and staining are useful indications of the state of the colloid and probably reflect variations in its protein concentration (Fig. 16–2). In ultraviolet absorption studies, *nucleic* acid was not found in the colloid. However, on the basis of its basophilia and the removal of the basophilic reaction with ribonuclease, it is claimed that ribonucleic acid is probably present in it. After fixatives the colloid in some follicles is more basophile than in others; the former are believed to have a more rapid iodine turnover than the latter.

The colloid has been shown to contain noniodinated and iodinated protein, the proportions of which vary from follicle to follicle. These proteins are presumably identical except for their content of *thyroxine, diiodotyrosine* and *triiodothyronine* which have been demonstrated by microchemical analyses, by ultraviolet absorption and by the use of radio-

active I¹³¹. A second group of proteins present in the colloid is related to the *mucoproteins.* In addition, several enzymes have been identified in colloid—a proteolytic enzyme (probably a *cathepsin*), *peroxidase* and a *mucinase.* All these substances vary from follicle to follicle at any moment, and probably in the same follicle at different times. The colloid is thus an active reservoir, which is in a continual state of flux rather than an inert storage center.

Functional Mechanisms. About one fifth to one tenth of all the iodine of the body is located in the thyroid, nearly all of it in organic form mainly as *iodotyrosines, thyroxine,* and *tri-iodothyronine* which are bound to a globulin. Tri-iodothyronine has also been detected in the blood of euthyroid and hyperthyroid individuals and may be the metabolically active form of the hormone. The mechanism of synthesis, storage and release of the active principle is not well understood. The concentration of administered iodine is very rapid—ten minutes after an injection of inorganic iodide, 40 per cent of the circulating ion is concentrated in the gland. This reaction is partially inhibited by thiocyanates.

Release of the active component may be achieved through the breakdown of the large protein molecule by the action of a proteolytic enzyme, probably cathepsin. The smaller molecules can more readily be absorbed through the gland cell toward the blood stream. The process of hydrolysis and absorption of the smaller moieties is accelerated by the reduction in the viscosity of the colloid through the action of a mucolytic enzyme on its substrate.

Control of the rate of release of the active principle of the thyroid is thought to be mediated largely through other endocrine glands, particularly the anterior lobe of the hypophysis. An excess of thyroid hormone in the blood inhibits the secretion of *thyrotrophic* hormone, which results in reduced thyroid activity. A reduction of thyroid hormone in the blood stimulates the secretion of thyrotrophic hormone, resulting in increased thyroid activity. The accumulation of iodine from the blood, its conversion to the active principle, and its release into the circulation are all affected by thyrotrophic hormone.

Despite the rich innervation of the gland, little or no neural control of thyroid activity is believed to take place. Neural effects may, however, be expressed through the action of nervous impulses directly or indirectly on the pituitary gland, and may occur under unusual stresses.

Functions of the Thyroid Gland. Perhaps the most striking effect of the thyroid secretion is its control over the *metabolic rate* of the body above a minimal value. When a deficiency of thyroid hormone occurs, the metabolic rate is below normal; when there is an excess, the metabolic rate is above normal. When *hypothyroidism* begins in infancy and persists, it leads to *cretinism;* when hypofunction begins in adulthood and persists, it leads to *myxedema.* In both forms the basal metabolic rate is reduced, and in both the symptoms may be removed through timely oral administration of dried thyroid gland. Thyroidectomy may duplicate many of the symptoms of thyroid deficiency in man, but in adults of certain species (monkey) the effects of thyroidectomy are detectable with difficulty.

Hyperthyroidism occurs in persons suffering with *exophthalmic goiter* or with *toxic adenoma.* In both states, follicles become enlarged, with epithelial infoldings, the cells become columnar, the Golgi apparatus hypertrophies, mitochondria increase in number, and the follicular colloid decreases or may be absent (Fig. *16–2, A*). The increased basal metabolic rate and associated symptoms return temporarily toward normal after the administration of iodine or of certain "antithyroid" drugs which are derivatives of thiourea.

Many of the symptoms of hyperthyroidism can be produced in other animals by the administration of an extract of the anterior lobe of the hypophysis containing thyrotrophic hormone. The thyroid of animals treated adequately with this extract shows the same changes as those in human hyperthyroidism. The marked morphological changes are not, however, diagnostic of hyperthyroidism, for they may be duplicated exactly by the administration of certain antithyroid drugs which result in hypothyroidism.

In two other conditions in man, the thyroid enlarges, but the basal metabolic rate is normal: *simple goiter* (Fig. *16–2, B*), due possibly to iodine deficiency, and *nontoxic adenoma.*

As the primary effect of thyroid hormone is on the basal metabolic rate, it is not surprising that it influences carbohydrate metabolism (particularly glycogen storage) and probably also fat and protein metabolism. It is important also in growth of the animal as a whole, especially through its effects on ossification centers, and on the development of certain organs, particularly the genital organs and the thymus. It also influences the functioning of the nervous system. There are certain interrelations with the anterior pituitary gland; thyroidectomy results in hypertrophy of the anterior lobe of the hypophysis, with degranulation of the alpha cells and the appearance of characteristically altered beta cells called thyroidectomy cells. The thyroid hypertrophies during menstruation and pregnancy. Finally, it becomes markedly hypoplastic in vitamin E deficient rats.

Phylogeny. Iodine is found in all marine invertebrates as well as some algae. Diiodotyrosine has been identified in some and may reach high concentrations in certain *sponges*. While there is no agreement on whether the *hypobranchial groove* in the floor of the pharynx of the protochordate *Amphioxus* is homologous with the thyroid gland, there seems to be more reason for homologizing the *endostyle* of the *lamprey* (a cyclostome) with the vertebrate thyroid. Although the endostyle of this animal can concentrate iodine and contains the active thyroid principle, there is nevertheless no evidence that the organ plays any endocrine role in the animal. The thyroid gland appears indisputably as an endocrine gland in certain fishes and remains remarkably constant in all higher animals.

Histogenesis. In man, the primordium of the thyroid gland arises early (embryos of 1.37 mm.) as a medial ventral outgrowth of the entoderm, cranial to that of the trachea. The *foramen cecum* at the base of the tongue of the adult is a vestige of the point from which the diverticulum arose in the embryo. In man there does not seem to be a contribution to the thyroid gland from the fourth branchial pouch.

At first the primordium is a hollow tube which grows caudally and thickens at its end. The connection between the tongue and the thyroid gland usually disappears (embryos of 4 to 7 mm.), but sometimes it persists either as the *thyroglossal duct* or as an irregular mass of thyroid tissue, usually eccentrically located, called the *pyramidal lobe*. The primordium then becomes a solid mass of epithelium, which later splits into ramifying plates and cords of epithelium. Hollows arise within these cords which are then known as *primary follicles*. They later fuse with one another and are invaded by mesenchyme. The walls of these hollows are two cells thick. Then the follicles of the mature organ arise by the repeated constriction of these plates into roughly spherical structures, in which a cavity lined by a single layer of epithelial cells develops; these *definitive follicles* are surrounded by mesenchyme (embryos of 24 mm.). Colloid may be present before birth, but does not become an important constituent of the follicles until after birth. In the pig, calf and rat, thyroid activity appears about the same time as the follicles begin to have stainable colloid. However, in amphibians the thyroid gland has some activity long before the cells appear "glandular" and before colloid formation.

Regeneration. The thyroid gland regenerates rapidly after surgical reduction if iodine is withheld from the diet, but will not regenerate if desiccated thyroid is administered. Autotransplantation is commonly successful, particularly if the animal is thyroid-deficient. Pure cultures of embryonic chick thyroid epithelium have been kept alive for some months.

REFERENCES

Astwood, F. B.: Chemotherapy of Hyperthyroidism. Harvey Lectures, Series 40, 195, 1944–45.

Bargmann, W.: Schilddrüse, in von Möllendorff's Handb. d. mikroskop. Anat. d. Menschen. 1939, Vol. 6, Pt. 2, p. 1.

Bensley, R. R.: Normal mode of secretion in thyroid gland. Am. J. Anat., 19:37, 1916.

Biedl, A.: Innere Sekretion. Ihre physiologischen Grundlagen und ihre Bedeutung für die Pathologie. Berlin, 1922.

Dempsey, E. W., and Singer, M.: Observations on the chemical cytology of the thyroid gland at different functional stages. Endocrinology, 38:270, 1946.

Erdheim, J.: Zur normalen und pathologischen Histologie der Glandula thyroidea, parathyroidea, und Hypophysis. Beitr. z. path. Anat. u. allg. Path., 33:158, 1903.

Furth, J., Burnett, W. T., and Gadsden, E. L.: Quantitative relationship between thyroid function and growth of pituitary tumors secreting TSH. Cancer Research, 13:298, 1953.

Gersh, I., and Baker, R. F.: Total protein and organic iodine in the colloid of individual follicles of the thyroid gland of the rat. J. Cell. & Comp. Physiol., 21:213, 1943.

Goldsmith, DeRobertis, Dempsey, Astwood, Leblond, Chaikoff and Taurog: Thyroid function as disclosed by newer methods of study. Ann. New York Acad. Sc., 50:279, 1949.

Gorbman, A., and Evans, H. M.: Beginning of function in the thyroid of the fetal rat. Endocrinology, 32:113, 1943.

Grollman, A.: Essentials of Endocrinology. Philadelphia, 1947.

Gross, J. and Pitt-Rivers, R.: 3:5:3′—Triiodothyronine. 1. Isolation from thyroid gland and synthesis. 2. Physiological activity. Biochem. J., 53:645 and 652, 1953.

Leblond, C. P., and Gross, J.: Thyroglobulin formation in the thyroid follicle visualized by the "coated autograph" technique. Endocrinology, 43:306, 1948.

Mackenzie, C. G., and Mackenzie, J. B.: Effect of sulfonamides and thioureas on the thyroid gland and basal metabolism. Endocrinology, 32:185, 1943.

Marine, D.: The Thyroid, Parathyroids, and Thymus, in Cowdry's Special Cytology. 2d ed. New York, (2), 797, 1932; The Pathogenesis and Prevention of Simple or Endemic Goiter, Glandular Physiology and Therapy. Chicago, 1935.

Michel, R.: Thyroid. Ann. Rev. Physiol., 18:457, 1956.

Monroe, B. G.: Electron microscopy of the thyroid. Anat. Rec., 116:345, 1953.

Nonidez, J. F.: Innervation of the thyroid gland. III. Distribution and termination of the nerve fibers in the dog. Am. J. Anat., 57:135, 1935.

Purves, H. D., and Griesbach, W. E.: Studies in experimental goitre. VII. Thyroid carcinomata in rats treated with thiourea. Brit. J. Exper. Biol., 27:294, 1946.

Rankin, R. M.: Changes in the content of iodine compounds and in the histological structure of the thyroid gland of the pig during fetal life. Anat. Rec., 80:123, 1941.

Salter, W. T.: The Endocrine Function of Iodine. Cambridge, Mass., 1940.

Selye, H.: Textbook of Endocrinology. Montreal, 1947.

Turner, C. D.: General Endocrinology. Philadelphia, W. B. Saunders Company, 1955.

Students are referred for the most recent developments to Annual Reviews of Physiology.

CHAPTER 17

Parathyroid Glands

THE PARATHYROID glands are small, yellow-brown, oval bodies usually intimately connected with the posterior surface of the thyroid gland. In man there are usually four or five glands, but as many as twelve have been reported. Their total weight varies from 0.05 to 0.3 gm. They may range from 3 to 8 mm. in length, 2 to 5 mm. in width, and 0.5 to 2 mm. in thickness. Most of the glands are in contact with the middle third of the thyroid, some with the anterior third, and the smallest number with the posterior third. About 5 to 10 per cent of the glands are associated with the thymus gland and may be deep in the anterior mediastinum. This association of parathyroid gland and thyroid and thymus stems from their close origin in the embryo.

Most parathyroid glands lie in the capsule of the thyroid, but they may be embedded in it. In either case, the parathyroid glands are separated from the thyroid by a connective tissue capsule. The capsular connective tissue extends into the parathyroid gland, and these trabeculae bear the larger branches of blood vessels, nerves and lymphatics. Between the gland cells is a framework of loose-meshed reticular fibers. These support the rich capillary network (Fig. 17–4) and the nerve fibers which are distributed chiefly along the capillaries, though some may end blindly in the connective tissue, or on or between the gland cells. No basement membrane has been described.

Gland Cells. The parathyroid glands consist of densely packed groups of cells which may form a continuous mass of cells or may

be arranged as anastomosing cords, or less commonly as follicles with a colloidal material in their lumen. Two main types of epithelial cells have been described: *principal cells* and *oxyphile cells* (Fig. 17–2). The *principal cell* is the more numerous and probably the more important. It has a larger, vesicular, centrally placed nucleus embedded in a faintly staining homogeneous cytoplasm which tends to shrink during fixation. The mitochondria are filamentous to granular and sometimes are close to the nucleus. The Golgi apparatus is short and situated close to the nucleus, with no evidence of vascular polarity. The cytoplasm is rich in glycogen and contains numerous fat droplets.

The *oxyphile cell* is larger than the principal cell. The nucleus is smaller and darker-staining, embedded in a deeply staining cytoplasm crowded with granular mitochondria. There is little or no demonstrable glycogen or fat in most oxyphile cells.

Another type of cell, intermediate between the two types, has been described. It has a fine granular cytoplasm which stains faintly with acid dyes, and a nucleus which is smaller and stains darker than that of the principal cells. Also, "water-clear" cells and dark oxyphile cells have been described.

A variety of cytoplasmic droplets, vacuoles and colloid materials have been described as secretion precursors on morphological grounds alone. More detailed cytological studies on experimental material are needed.

The parathyroid glands show certain changes with increasing age: (1) increase

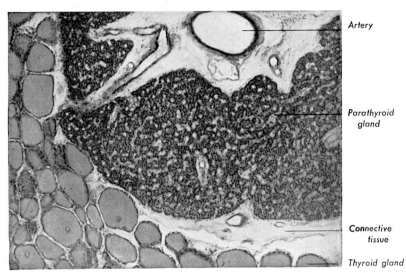

Fig. 17–1. Photomicrograph of section of thyroid and parathyroid glands of *Macacus rhesus.* 80 ×.

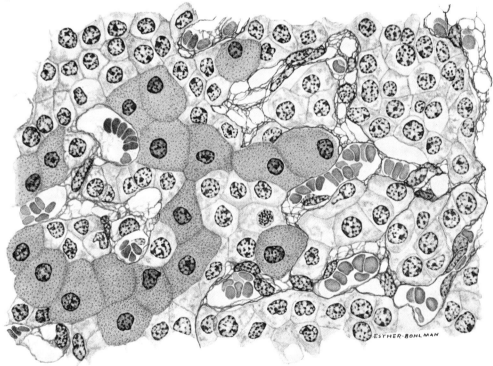

Fig. 17–2. Section through human parathyroid gland showing the small principal cells, often vacuolated, and the large oxyphil cells with fine purplish granules. Mallory-azan stain. Zenker-formol fixation. 960 ×.

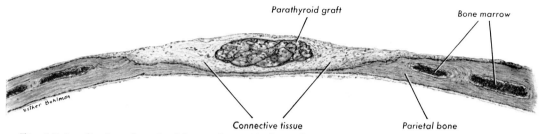

Parathyroid graft   Bone marrow

Connective tissue   Parietal bone

Fig. 17–3. Section of parietal bone of rat 14 days after autogenous transplantation of parathyroid gland. The bone beneath the graft has been nearly completely resorbed. 50 ✕. From a preparation of H. Chang.

in amount of connective tissue, including increased numbers of fat cells as well as mast cells; (2) the oxyphile cells are said to appear at four and one half to seven years, and to increase in number especially after puberty; (3) in the closely packed masses of gland cells, some cords and follicles appear in the year-old infant and increase thereafter; colloid accumulation in the lumen of the follicles shows the same tendency.

When rats are given injections of a large dose of parathyroid extract, the cells of the parathyroid glands become smaller; the Golgi apparatus also becomes smaller and more compact. Both changes are suggestive of hypofunction. After two weeks the cells return to normal both in size and morphology of the Golgi apparatus; these changes are indicative of the resumption of normal secretory activity. During the hypertrophy of the parathyroid glands in rickets, the Golgi apparatus is described as undergoing changes which indicate great secretory activity as compared with normal cells. It is not possible to extend these conclusions to the human gland, for it has to be shown which cells in man are equivalent to those in laboratory animals. Of all mammalian parathyroid glands examined cytologically thus far, those of the horse seem most nearly to resemble those of man.

Function. The function of the parathyroid glands is closely linked with the states of *calcium* in the organism. The maintenance of a physiologically constant concentration of *calcium ions* in the blood plasma appears to be accomplished largely by regulation, by the parathyroid hormone, of the movement of calcium from bone to blood. The mechanism of the influence of the parathyroids upon movement of calcium from bone is but poorly understood. As a result of study of grafts of parathyroid gland to bone, it seems clear that a hormone from the gland acts directly on the bone and causes its absorption (Barnicot; Chang. See Fig. *17–3*).

There is some evidence that the action of parathyroid extract may not be on bone salt primarily, but rather on the ground substance of bone and perhaps on that of other connective tissues. In bone, after large doses, it causes a breakdown of the organic components prior to their absorption. The mobilization of calcium, and its solution and removal, occur coincidentally with this process. This seems to occur around all osteocytes in affected zones, and is not limited to the outer surface of bone spicules (see p. 151).

The parathyroid glands become large in rickets through increase in size and especially in number of their cells. The hypertrophy is greater in low calcium than in low phosphate rickets. Hypertrophy is also observed in nephritis with uremia, and has resulted from the experimental production of renal insufficiency and is associated with extensive bone changes (*renal rickets, renal osteitis fibrosa*) similar to those of primary hyperparathyroidism. It is probably a response to a lowered calcium ion concentration in the plasma resulting from phosphate retention. In birds deprived of sunlight, the parathyroid glands hypertrophy.

Tumor or hyperplasia of the parathyroids may lead to *hyperparathyroidism* associated with high plasma calcium, extensive bone resorption (*osteitis fibrosa*, see p. 151) and pathological calcification in soft tissues. Similar effects may be produced in susceptible animals by the administration of toxic doses of *parathyroid extract.*

Extirpation of the parathyroid glands or atrophy due to some pathological process is followed by *hypoparathyroidism,* character-

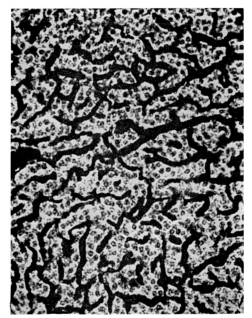

Fig. 17–4. Photomicrograph of parathyroid gland of monkey injected intravenously with India ink to show the extensively anastomotic capillary network in intimate contact with the gland cells. 165 ×.

ized primarily by a decrease in the concentration of calcium in the plasma, and *tetany.* The symptoms may be alleviated by the administration of calcium, an extract of parathyroid glands, or dehydrotachysterol, or by dietary control. A condition of *latent tetany* which occurs in man, with low plasma calcium but without symptoms, may be produced experimentally in dogs.

There is some evidence that a hormone of the pars distalis of the hypophysis affects parathyroid secretion.

Regeneration. The parathyroids have but insignificant powers of regeneration. The glands "take" readily in autotransplants, and may be maintained successfully in tissue culture.

Histogenesis. The parathyroid glands develop from thickenings of the third and fourth branchial pouches on each side. The primordium on the third arch is close to the bud of the thymus. This proximity of origin of the two organs is a probable explanation of the frequent occurrence of aberrant parathyroid bodies in or near the thymus.

Phylogenesis. Parathyroid glands are absent from invertebrates and fishes and are found in all higher orders of vertebrates.

REFERENCES

Bargmann, W.: Epithelkörperchen in von Möllendorff's Handb. d. mikroskop. Anat. d. Menschen. 1939, Vol. 6, Pt. 2, p. 1.

Barnicot, N. A.: The local action of the parathyroid and other tissues on bone in intracerebral grafts. J. Anat., 82:233, 1948.

Bensley, S. H.: The normal mode of secretion in the parathyroid gland of the dog. Anat. Rec., 98:361, 1947.

Biedl, A.: Innere Sekretion. Ihre physiologischen Grundlagen und ihre Bedeutung für die Pathologie. Berlin, 1922.

Bobeau, G.: Recherches cytologiques sur les glandules parathyroïdes du cheval. J. de l'Anat., 47:371, 1911.

Chang, Hwei-ya: Grafts of parathyroid and other tissues to bone. Anat. Rec., 111:23, 1951.

Collip, J. B.: The parathyroid glands. Harvey Lectures, 21:113, 1925–6.

DeRobertis, E.: The cytology of the parathyroid gland of rats injected with parathyroid extract. Anat. Rec., 78:473, 1940.

Erdheim, J.: Zur normalen und pathologischen Histologie der Glandula thyroidea, parathyroidea, und Hypophysis. Beitr. z. path. Anat. u. z. allg. Path., 33:158, 1903.

Gaillard, P. J.: Parathyroid gland tissue and bone *in vitro.* Exp. Cell Research, Suppl. 3:154, 1955.

Marine, D.: The Thyroid, Parathyroids, and Thymus, in Cowdry's Special Cytology. 2d ed. New York, (2), 797, 1932.

Morgan, J. R. E.: The parathyroid glands. Arch. Path., 21:10, 1936.

Norris, E. H.: The parathyroid glands and the lateral thyroid in man: their morphogenesis, histogenesis, topographic anatomy and prenatal growth. Contrib. Embryol., Carnegie Inst., 26:249, 1937.

Sandström: On a New Gland in Man and Several Mammals, (trans. by C. M. Seipel.) Bull. Inst. Hist. Med., 6, No. 3, 1938.

Selye, H.: Textbook of Endocrinology. Montreal, 1948.

Shelling, D. H.: The Parathyroids in Health and in Disease. St. Louis, 1935.

Thompson, D. L., and Collip, J. B.: The parathyroid glands. Physiol. Rev., 12:309, 1932.

Turner, C. D.: General Endocrinology. 2nd ed. Philadelphia, W. B. Saunders Company, 1955.

CHAPTER 18

Adrenal Glands and Paraganglia

THE PAIRED adrenal or suprarenal glands of man are roughly triangular, flattened bodies, one at the cranial pole of each kidney. The glands together average about 10 to 12 gm. in the healthy adult, and measure approximately 5 by 3 by less than 1 cm. An indentation on the anterior surface, the hilus, admits an artery and emits the suprarenal vein. The surface made by cutting through the gland presents a bright yellow cortex in its outer part and a reddish-brown zone adjacent to the thin gray medulla.

Cortex. The cortex, which occupies the greater part of the gland, is disposed in three vaguely defined layers: a thin, outer *zona glomerulosa,* contiguous with the capsule; a middle, thick *zona fasciculata;* and an inner, moderately thick *zona reticularis,* which abuts on the medulla (Fig. *18–1*). The transition from one zone to another is gradual, but may appear sharper in preparations injected to show the vascular pattern.

The *zona glomerulosa* consists of short columnar cells closely packed in ovoid groups or in columns which may form arcs. The nuclei stain deeply, and the rather scanty cytoplasm contains basophilic material which may be diffuse or, as in man, disposed in clumps. Lipid droplets, when present, are scarce and small in most animals, and may be numerous in others. Mitochondria may be filamentous (in man), rodlike (in the guinea pig and cat), or spherical (in the rat). The compact Golgi apparatus is juxtanuclear and may be polarized toward the capillary surface in some animals.

The *zona fasciculata* consists of polyhedral cells considerably larger than those of the zona glomerulosa. They are arranged as anastomosing "cords" of cells with a marked radial orientation, extending between the zona glomerulosa and the reticularis. The nuclei are centrally placed in the cells, and often there are two in one cell. The cytoplasm is basophile or contains basophile masses, more so in the peripheral portion than in the inner portion of the zone. Lipid droplets are numerous. In the outer portion, where they are commonly most numerous, the cytoplasm is reduced to thin films between them; consequently in stained sections from which the lipids have been removed, the cytoplasm appears vacuolated. The lipid droplets are small in some cells, larger in others, but of about equal size in any given cell. There may be a thin transitional region between the zona glomerulosa and zona fasciculata which is relatively free of lipid droplets. This is the region which may contain mitotic figures. The mitochondria appear generally to be less numerous than in the outer cortical zone. The Golgi apparatus is juxtanuclear, and in some animals appears to be somewhat less compact than in the zona glomerulosa.

In the *zona reticularis* the cells are arranged as clearly anastomosing cords. The transition between this zone and the zona fasciculata is gradual, the cells differing little. The cytoplasm contains fewer lipid droplets. Toward the medulla there is a variable number of "light" cells and "dark" cells which

Page 314

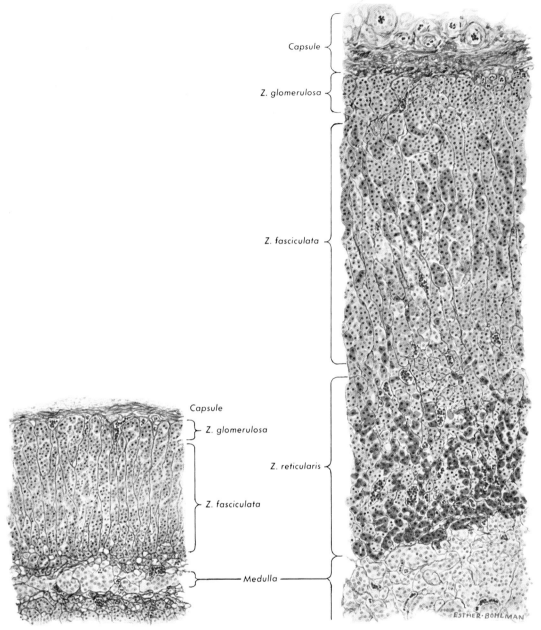

Fig. 18–1. Sections through adrenal gland of man, right, and of a six month infant, left. Mallory-azan stain. 110 ×.

differ in their staining affinities. The nuclei of the light cells are pale-staining, while those of the dark cells are shrunken and hyperchromatic. Mitochondria are few in the former and numerous in the latter. The Golgi apparatus is compact or fragmented. The dark cells contain clumps of yellow or brownish pigment. Both the light and dark cells are regarded by some as degenerating cells.

Medulla. The boundary between zona reticularis and medulla in man is usually irregular in the adult, since columns of cortical cells project into the medulla. In other animals (e.g., mouse) the boundary may be sharp. The irregular cells of the medulla are arranged in rounded groups or short cords surrounded by venules and blood capillaries. When the tissue is fixed in a fluid containing

Medullary vein

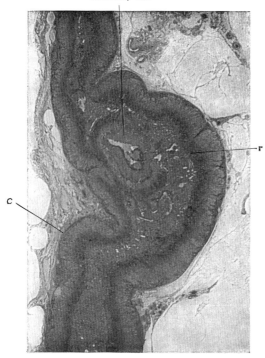

Fig. 18–2. Cross section of human adrenal. The cortico-medullary junction is indicated at *r* and the capsule at *c*. Both medulla and medullary vein are unusually thick. Photomicrograph H + E. 4 ×. (After von Herrath and Abramow.)

potassium bichromate, fine brown granules are seen throughout these cells (Fig. *18–3*). This is the *chromaffin reaction,* probably caused in large part by the presence of epinephrine. The medulla appears green with ferric chloride for the same reason. In addition to the chromaffin cells, there are frequent, single or grouped, sympathetic ganglion cells whose axons end around the chromaffin cells (Fig. *18–3*). The medulla also contains collections of small round cells with deeply staining nuclei and little cytoplasm. These are probably lymphocytes. In the fetal adrenal, similar small round cells occur which are the *sympathochromaffin* cells, the forerunners of the sympathetic and medullary cells.

Connective Tissue and Vascular System of Adrenal Gland. The connective tissue of the adrenal gland consists of a thick collagenous capsule which extends through the cortex to varying depths as trabeculae, and a prominent reticulum. The capsule contains a dense network of branches of the main arteries of the gland, some capillaries and

venules, a nerve plexus and lymphatics. Major branches of arteries, nerves and lymphatics penetrate the cortex, often in the trabeculae. The arteries and nerves continue almost exclusively into the medulla, while the lymphatics are confined to the trabeculae in the cortex. Most of the supporting framework of the cortex consists of reticular fibers which lie between the capillaries and the gland cells and to some extent between the latter. The reticular fibers also enclose the medullary cell cords and support capillaries, veins and nerves. Collagenous fibers appear around the larger tributaries of the veins and merge with the capsular connective tissue.

The vascular pattern is nearly uniform in man, dog, cat and rat. The cortical vessels arise from terminal branches of the network of capsular arteries. These penetrate the zona glomerulosa as sinusoids, where they form arcuate anastomoses, and then traverse the cortex radially from the capsule, as the relatively straight, anastomosing network of the zona fasciculata, passing between the similarly arranged gland cell cords. Those from a given region converge in the zona reticularis toward a collecting vein at the medullary boundary (Fig. *18–5*). There are some small venules in the capsule. There is no venous system in the cortex.

From the capsule, some major arterial branches penetrate the cortex in trabeculae with few or no branches until they reach the medulla. In the medulla, they branch repeatedly to form its rich capillary net around the cords and clumps of cells. An arterial vessel which penetrates at the hilus, branches to form capillaries in a similar way. The capillaries empty into the same venous system which drains the cortex, uniting to form the central veins, which emerge as the suprarenal vein. The central vein and its larger tributaries are lined by endothelium. They have abundant smooth muscle fibers arranged mainly in longitudinal bundles.

The cells lining the capillaries of the smaller vessels in the medulla are endothelial. On the other hand, the lining cells of the sinuses in the cortex are littoral cells of the macrophage system, much like those lining the sinusoids of the liver and hypophysis. They store lithium carmine, and in heavily stained animals their number is greatly increased.

Capsule

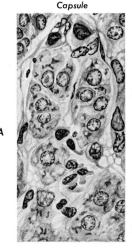

Zona glomerulosa

A

Beginning of zona
fasciculata

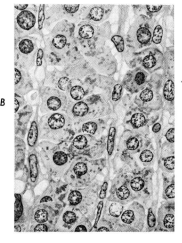

Z. fasciculata

B

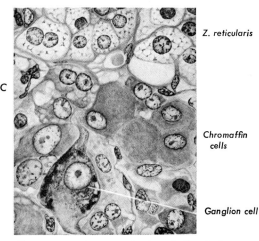

Z. reticularis

C

Chromaffin
cells

Ganglion cell

Fig. 18–3. Sections of adrenal gland of a man. A, from the zona glomerulosa; B, zona fasciculata, showing columns of cells separated by collapsed sinusoids; C, cortico-medullary junction. The medullary portion contains a sympathetic ganglion cell

Lymphatics and Nerves. Lymphatics are limited to the capsule and its cortical trabeculae, and to the connective tissue of the large veins.

The rich nerve plexus in the capsule includes some sympathetic ganglion cells. Branches penetrate the cortex in the trabeculae and are distributed with few exceptions to the medulla. They end mainly in clawlike terminations around individual cells of the medulla. The fibers are preganglionic.

Functions of Cortex. *Hormones and Other Substances in Cortex.* The cortex is essential for life. Its removal or destruction (in man, leading to *Addison's disease*) is fatal. The cortex affects an extensive series of functions: (1) Maintenance of *electrolyte and water balance* in the body. After ablation of the cortex there is excessive excretion of sodium in the urine, resulting in decreased plasma sodium concentration, with corresponding decline of the plasma chloride and bicarbonate levels. The tissues are dehydrated, and eventually concentration of the blood appears. Potassium, magnesium, urea, uric acid and creatinine in the plasma are all lowered. Water changes seem to be accompanied by a shift from extracellular spaces to tissue cells and by abnormal renal function. (2) Maintenance of *carbohydrate balance*. Adrenalectomy results in a *hypoglycemia* with reduced glycogen stores in liver and muscle. Adrenalectomy in the diabetic animal tends to reduce the high blood sugar to normal levels, comparable to the well-known effect of hypophysectomy. There appears to be a concomitant disturbance of protein and fat metabolism. (3) Maintenance of *connective tissue* of the body. This has been indicated by the as yet unexplained and often dramatic effects of cortisone (a steroid from the adrenal cortex) on human beings suffering from a wide variety of diseases. A common feature of these effects seems to be related to some property or properties of the connective tissues. (4) The intense destruction of lymphocytes and subsequent atrophy of lymphatic tissue which results from the action of a variety of noxious agents (part of the *"alarm reaction"* of Selye) is believed by

with Nissl substance and several greenish-brown-stained chromaffin cells. The cells of the zona reticularis are vacuolated. Hematoxylin-eosin-azure II. 730 ×. (Drawn by Miss Esther Bohlman.)

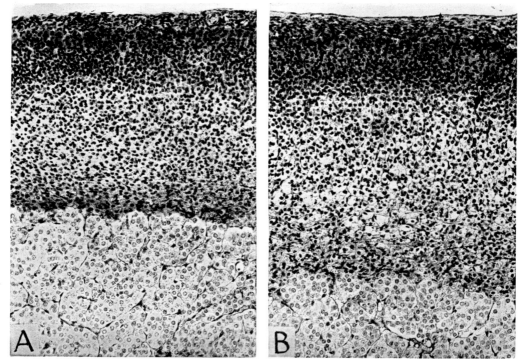

Fig. 18–4. Photomicrographs of adrenal gland of rats, showing effects of injection of adrenocortico-trophic hormone. *A,* atrophic cortex of young hypophysectomized rat; *B,* hypophysectomized rat which had an injection for four days of purified adrenocorticotrophic hormone. The hypertrophy of the zona fascicu-lata is most marked. Zenker-formol, H + E. 165 ×.

some to be due to the liberation of adrenal cortical hormone; it does not occur if the adrenal cortex is removed. (5) Cortical de-ficiency results in *hypotension* (low blood pressure), anorexia, diarrhea, vomiting, as-thenia, lassitude, interference with normal sexual libido, and altered vascular "permea-bility."

Disturbed functions of cortical deficiency are restored by appropriate treatment with suitable extracts or synthetic products. The most notable of these are (1) the *mineralo-corticoids* (*desoxycorticosterone* and *aldo-sterone*) which help regulate the metabolism of some electrolytes and water balance, and (2) the *gluco-corticoids* (*cortisone* and *hydro-cortisone*), which participate in carbohydrate, fat and protein metabolism; they also affect electrolyte exchange and the connective tis-sues.

Thirty steroids have been crystallized from the adrenal cortex; six of these have marked corticoid activity, and several others have sex hormone activity. No one of them exhibits all the physiological effects of a crude extract. In addition, the cortex yields cholesterol,

cholesterol esters, neutral fats and phospho-lipids, ascorbic acid, carotene, choline and glutathione.

Histochemistry of Adrenal Cortex. Numer-ous studies, particularly in recent years, have centered around the distribution of the first four compounds in this series and the 17-*ketosteroids.* Some workers claim that sub-stances are present in the cortex which show all the following properties: (1) a positive test with phenylhydrazine, Schiff reagent and semicarbazide; (2) reduction of silver ions; (3) a positive Liebermann-Burchardt reac-tion; (4) birefringence; (5) yellow or green-ish-white fluorescence; (6) solubility in ace-tone. A uniformly positive result is taken to be a specific identification for 17-ketosteroids. This view has been challenged, and it seems doubtful that the battery of tests is as spe-cific as claimed. Nevertheless, with all the tests described as a "collective stain," some useful information has been obtained. The lipids have been studied by the use of Sudan stains and osmic acid. Tests used for choles-terol, cholesterol esters and ascorbic acid have certain limitations.

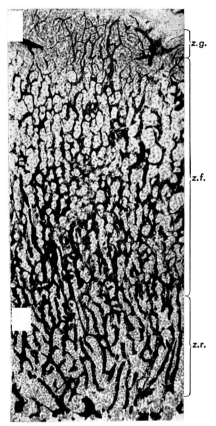

z.g.

z.f.

z.r.

Fig. 18–5. Photomicrograph of adrenal cortex of monkey injected intravenously with India ink to show the vascular pattern. The arcuate sinusoids of the zona glomerulosa (*z.g.*) empty into the more longitudinally oriented sinusoids of the zona fasciculata (*z.f.*). These are joined in the zona reticularis (*z.r.*), where they flow into veins in the medulla. 85 ×.

It is not known whether the variegated functions of the adrenal cortex are mediated equally by all parts of the cortex, or whether different layers have separate functions. It seems that the zona glomerulosa is more involved in the secretion of a desoxycorticosterone-like compound than other zones, and that the zona fasciculata participates in the secretion of cortisone more than other zones. The evidence is the following: (1) Hypophysectomy, which affects glucose metabolism more markedly than electrolyte metabolism, is said to be accompanied by atrophy of the zona fasciculata, with no marked effect on the zona glomerulosa. (2) The administration of desoxycorticosterone in small doses is claimed to result in atrophy of the zona glomerulosa, with no marked effect on the zona fasciculata. The administration of 11-oxysteroids (which affect glucose metabolism) has no marked effect on the zona glomerulosa, but leads to atrophy of the zona fasciculata. The atrophic changes are accompanied in each zone by reduction in lipid content of the cells and in the "ketosteroid" reactions.

Stress. With the exceptions just noted, the cortex appears to respond in a nonspecific manner to a wide variety of stresses which induce adrenal hyperfunction. The cortex enlarges with hypertrophy and hyperplasia, coincidentally with an extensive increase in the capillary bed. There may be an increase in the number of lipid droplets, which in late stages may revert to less than normal. It has been claimed that the cortical cholesterol and ascorbic acid also decline during stress. The "ketosteroid" reactions in the zona fasciculata increase. In general, the same morphological changes can be induced by the administration of adrenocorticotrophic hormone in certain dosages.

Effects of Hyperfunction of Cortex. The metabolic functions of the adrenal cortex are made manifest chiefly as effects of deficiency of cortical activity. Effects of hyperfunction (as in thyroid gland, for example) are lacking except for permeability and *spreading action* under certain experimental conditions. Adrenogenital (androgenic) tumors are characterized by masculinization (in women) or by premature development of male sex characters in children.

Age Change and Growth in Cortex. Marked age changes take place in the human adrenal cortex. Soon after birth, the inner or *boundary zone* of the cortex begins to involute and is largely gone after the first few weeks. The remaining smaller *subcapsular* portion of the cortex contracts upon the medulla (Fig. *18–1*). Accordingly, for some time the infant's adrenal is smaller than at birth. Too rapid involution of the boundary zone may lead to fatal hemorrhage into the adrenals. The zona fasciculata appears early, and by the end of the third year the zona reticularis has developed.

The pigment in the zona reticularis is present after puberty and increases in amount with age. It is similar to the "lipochrome" pigment found in cardiac muscle and nerve cells in old age.

It is commonly believed that new cells are produced by mitosis in the capsule or the transitional zone between the zona glomerulosa and zona fasciculata, and that these are gradually moved into the zona fasciculata and eventually the zona reticularis, where they become "dark" cells or "light" cells and degenerate. The appearance of mitotic figures in certain circumstances in all zones has thrown doubt on this concept.

Relations with Other Endocrine Glands. It is doubtful if the nerve fibers in the adrenal cortex have any important role in the regulation of its activity. Control seems to be mediated almost entirely by the anterior lobe of the hypophysis through secretion of the adrenocorticotrophic hormone. During stress, as part of the "alarm reaction," the rate of secretion of the pituitary hormone appears to be proportional to the intensity of stress. Whether this reaction is mediated by fluctuations in the level of cortical hormones in the blood, or by an intermediate influence by the tissues of the body, is not known. Pituitary ablation leads to cortical atrophy. After unilateral adrenalectomy, compensatory hypertrophy by the remaining adrenal does not occur after hypophysectomy. In Addison's disease, or after adrenalectomy, there appears to be a decrease in the number of basophile cells in the anterior lobe of the pituitary.

There appears to be some relation between the adrenal cortex and the sex glands. Adrenalectomy is followed by loss of libido in male rats, and abnormal estrous cycles or diestrus in females. Orchidectomy in the male mouse delays the normal atrophy of the X-zone (reticularis) of the adrenal cortex. Certain natural and synthetic estrogens exert adrenal steroid effects on metabolism. Removal of the adrenal interrupts lactation. To what extent these effects are mediated through the anterior lobe of the hypophysis, or are direct, is not known.

Certain interrelations of adrenal and thyroid gland are also indicated by several contradictory reports: In rabbits the adrenal glands hypertrophy, sometimes to two or three times the normal size, after removal of the thyroid. Sublethal adrenal injury results in hyperthermia and increased basal metabolic rate. The administration of thyroid powder may be followed by adrenal cortical hypertrophy.

Functions of Medulla. The medulla is not essential for life; it is not certain that it plays any important part in the normal organism.

The medulla elaborates *epinephrine.* Unlike the cortex, the medulla stores high concentrations of its specific product. The compound is readily oxidized, because of its phenolic and alcoholic groupings. For this reason, the medulla can be recognized by the chromaffin reaction and the color reactions with ferric salts and other compounds. It is auto-oxidizable, and may itself give a brown color through the subsequent polymerization of the reaction products. The same reactions are given by paraganglia (see p. 321). An epinephrine-like material is increased in the blood of the adrenal vein after stimulation of the splanchnic nerves and decreased after they are sectioned. Epinephrine appears to be re-formed rapidly in the gland after partial depletion following stimulation. A great variety of conditions (generally the same which cause adrenal cortical hyperactivity) cause an increased rate of secretion by the medulla. This may be due to the suggested stimulation of the cortex by adrenocorticotrophic hormone through release of epinephrine from the adrenal medulla. Epinephrine is rapidly destroyed in the blood and is measurable only in that of the adrenal vein.

Epinephrine has a powerful *sympathomimetic* action; its effect on clotting time of the blood, blood pressure, carbohydrate metabolism, and gastrointestinal tract is essentially the same as that produced by stimulation of sympathetic nerves alone.

The adrenal medulla is unessential for normal activity, even in sympathectomized animals, since no physiological disturbances are produced. There is no deficiency disease of the adrenal medulla. Some believe it to be important in sensitizing the nerve endings of sympathetic nerve fibers, and others to be important in emergencies. Hyperfunction of the adrenal medulla in man occurs rarely, with certain tumors of the medulla or of extramedullary chromaffin tissues containing epinephrine. In such cases there may be attacks of sweating, mydriasis, hypertension and hyperglycemia terminating suddenly in death. The paroxysmal hypertension of adrenal medullary tumors is decreased or abolished by intravenous administration of a series of compounds which have an epinephrine-inhibiting action.

Histogenesis of Adrenal Gland. The cortex develops from the celomic mesoderm on the median side of the wolffian ridge, and the medulla from the ecto-dermal tissue, which also gives rise to sympathetic ganglion cells. In a six weeks' embryo the cortical primordium consists of a rounded bud of cells cranial to the kidney. Strands of sympathochromaffin cells grow ventrally and penetrate the cortical bud in its medial side. At this stage they begin to exhibit the chromaffin reaction characteristic of adrenal medulla, and the cortical cells may already contain fine lipid droplets. At three months, the fetal cortex consists of a narrow outer zone of small cells with deeply staining nuclei, and an inner zone consisting almost entirely of large granular cells lying between capillaries. The outer zone develops into the defini-tive cortex, while the inner zone forms the zone which is destined to atrophy.

Phylogenesis of Adrenal Gland. Chromaffin tissue which yields adrenalin-like activity is present in the central nervous system of leeches; it is present also in the mantles of certain molluscs. In cyclostomes and teleosts the *interrenal bodies* (which are homol-ogous with the cortex) are separate from the discrete chromaffin bodies. In amphibians the two compo-nents are in juxtaposition, or they may be inter-mingled; in reptiles and birds they are commonly intermingled. The well-known cortex and medulla relationship appears in mammals, in which this is the predominant form of organization.

Regeneration of Adrenal Gland. Cortical cells are particularly susceptible to injury. They are replaced by mitosis probably throughout the cortex, with a greater tendency for this to take place in the transi-tion zone between zona glomerulosa and zona fascic-ulata. Successful transplantation seems to require the presence of a capsule. It is more successful also in totally adrenalectomized animals. The medulla does not survive transplantation readily.

THE PARAGANGLIA (CHROMAFFIN SYSTEM)

Under this term are grouped several widely scattered accumulations of cells which seem to have much in common with the medullary cells of the adrenal glands. These paragan-glia include widespread, small accumulations of cells in the retroperitoneum—the organs of Zuckerkandl, and collections of similar cells in the kidney, ovary, liver, testis and heart. Most, but not all, authors believe that they arise from sympathogonia. The paragan-glia all contain chromaffin cells. The chro-maffin cells are clear in the fresh condition or after most fixatives, but stain positively with chromic and osmic acids and contain iron. These cells are usually arranged more or less as cords and have a rich blood supply.

It has not been proved that these para-ganglia have an endocrine function. The as-sumption that they elaborate epinephrine, just like the chromaffin cells of the medulla of the adrenal, has not been established.

Some authors include the medullary cells of the adrenal in this group and speak of them all as the chromaffin system. The advisability of this must be questioned until it has been shown that all the chromaffin organs have the same internal secretion.

Carotid, Aortic and Coccygeal Bodies. These structures are often erroneously in-cluded with the endocrine glands. The ca-rotid and aortic bodies are described on page 248, and the coccygeal body on page 243.

REFERENCES

Bachmann, R.: Die Nebenniere. Handb. mikr. Anat. d. Menschen (v. Möllendorff and Bargmann) Berlin, 6, pt. 5:1, 1954.

Bennett, H. S.: Cytological manifestations of secretion in the adrenal medulla of the cat. Am. J. Anat., 69:333, 1941.

Biedl, A.: Innere Sekretion. Ihre physiologischen Grundlagen und ihre Bedeutung für die Pathologie. Berlin, 1922.

Deane, H. W., and Greep, R. O.: A morphological and histological study of the rat's adrenal cortex after hypophysectomy, with comments on the liver. Am. J. Anat., 79:117, 1946.

Dempsey, Gaunt and Eversole, Greep and Deane, Sayers and Sayers: The adrenal cortex. Ann. New York Acad. Sc., 50:1949.

Flexner, L. B., and Grollman, A.: The reduction of osmic acid as an indicator of adrenal cortical activity in the rat. Anat. Rec., 75:207, 1939.

Flint, J. M.: The blood vessels, angiogenesis, organogene-sis, reticulum, and histology of the adrenal. Johns Hopkins Hosp. Rep., 9:153, 1900.

Hartroft, P. M., and Hartroft, W. S.: Studies on renal juxtaglomerular cells. II. Correlation of the degree of granulation of juxtaglomerular cells with width of the zona glomerulosa of the adrenal cortex. J. Exp. Med., 102:205, 1955.

Hechter, O., and Pincus, G.: Genesis of the adrenocortical secretion. Physiol. Rev., 34:459, 1954.

Hoerr, N.: The cells of the suprarenal cortex in the guinea-pig. Their reaction to injury and their replace-ment. Am. J. Anat., 48:139, 1931.

Iwanow, G.: Das chromaffin und interrenale System des Menschen. Ergeb. d. Anat., 29:87, 1932.

Knigge, Karl M.: The effect of acute starvation on the adrenal cortex of the hamster. Anat. Rec., 120:555, 1954.

Lever, J. D.: Electron microscopic observations on the adrenal cortex. Am. J. Anat., 97:409, 1955. Electron microscopic observations on the normal and de-nervated adrenal medulla of the rat. Endocrinology, 57:621, 1955.

Parkes, A. S.: The adrenal-gonad relationship. Physiol. Rev., 25:203, 1945.

Rogoff, J. M.: The Suprarenal Bodies, in Cowdry's Spe-cial Cytology. 2d ed. New York, (2), 869, 1932.

Selye, H.: Thymus and adrenals in the response of the organism to injuries and intoxications. Brit. J. Exper. Path., 17:234, 1936.

Selye, H.: Textbook of Endocrinology. Montreal, 1947.

Turner, C. D.: General Endocrinology. 2nd ed. Philadel-phia, W. B. Saunders Company, 1955.

The references cited were selected primarily for orienta-tion in this rapidly developing subject. Students are re-ferred for the most recent developments to Annual Reviews of Physiology.

CHAPTER 19

The Pineal Body

THE PINEAL body (conarium, epiphysis cerebri) is a somewhat flattened, conical, gray body measuring 5 to 8 mm. in length, and 3 to 5 mm. in its greatest width. It lies above the roof of the posterior extremity of the third ventricle, to which it is attached by the pineal stalk. The cavity of the third ventricle extends for a short distance into the stalk as the pineal recess; this is lined with ependyma.

Except where it is attached to the habenular and posterior commissures of the midbrain, the pineal body is invested by pia mater. Connective tissue scpta, containing many blood vessels, arise from this layer, penetrate the pineal body and separate its specific elements into cords of cells. In hematoxylin-and-eosin-stained sections the pineal body is seen to consist of cords of epithelioid

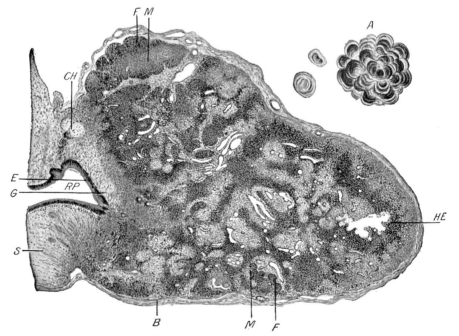

Fig. 19–1.   Median section through pineal body of a newborn child. B, connective tissue sheath (pia mater); CH, superior habenular commissure; E, ependyma; F, group of cells with little protoplasm; G, neuroglia; HE, posterior end of the pineal body; M, cells with much protoplasm; RP, pineal recess; S, connection with posterior commissure. Blood vessels empty. 32 ×. A, acervulus from the pineal body of a woman sixty-nine years old. 160 ×. (After Schaffer.)

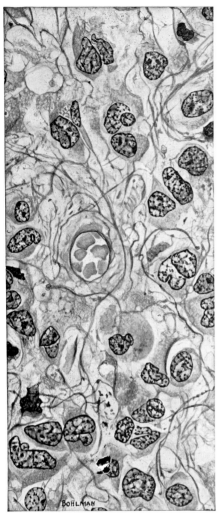

Fig. 19–2. Section of pineal body of man stained with hematoxylin and eosin, showing irregularly shaped cells and their processes. Note blood vessel in the center. Compare with Figure 19–3.

Fig. 19–3. Specifically impregnated section of pineal body of a young boy, showing, C, interlobular tissue, and, D, vessel with club-shaped processes of specific cells in its adventitia. Note parenchymatous cells and their claviform processes bordering on C. (After del Río-Hortega.)

cells with dark nuclei and little cytoplasm, embedded in a reticular framework. With advancing age, some of the small dark cells gradually develop into larger cells with much cytoplasm and paler nuclei.

Besides the presence of neuroglial cells—on which all authors are agreed—five types of cells have been described: (1) chief cells, which are large and have small processes and no vacuoles in their homogeneous protoplasm; (2) smaller cells with fine acidophile granules; (3) cells with large basophile granules; (4) cells with lipoid granules; and (5) nerve cells. Some authors claim that the vari-

ous granules are evidences of a secretory process.

According to the detailed studies of del Río-Hortega on the pineal body, the parenchymatous cells of the organ are specific cells with a characteristic structure. They have long processes which extend for considerable distances and end in bulblike swellings in the interlobular connective tissue. In the center of the lobules, these processes radiate in all directions from the cells, while toward the periphery of the lobules the cells tend to become polarized in one or two processes. Occasionally, there are as many club-shaped ends of fibers in the center of the lobules as in the periphery; these may be considered evidences of atrophy. The specific elements hypertrophy greatly about the *sand granules* (Fig. *19–1, A*) which develop in the pineal body. These parenchymatous cells arise from the same source as the neuroglia and nerve cells, but seem to be an intermediate cellular form.

It is generally believed that the pineal body increases in size until about seven years of age. At this time involution is said to begin and to continue to fourteen years of age. It is manifested by an increase in the amount of neuroglia and by the development of hyaline changes in both the septa and the lobules. The so-called "brain-sand granules" (corpora arenacea) also begin to appear. These are laminated structures consisting mainly of phosphates and carbonates of calcium and magnesium.

The pineal body first appears at the beginning of the second month of gestation as a fold arising from the roof of the diencephalon before which is a collection of rounded cells. By the end of the sixth month, these have differentiated into neuroglia cells and pineal cells.

There are contradictory opinions on the function of the organ. Some authors regard it as a vestigial organ homologous to the pineal sense organ of the lower vertebrates. Others hold it is a gland of internal secretion affecting the gonads. The best evidence for this belief has been found in rabbits and rodents. After reviewing the extensive literature on experimentation in animals and on disease in man, Kitay and Altschule conclude: "Although the available physiologic and clinical data justify the presumption that the gland is functional, its functions cannot yet be defined."

REFERENCES

Bargmann, W.: Die Epiphysis cerebri. Handb. d. mikr. Anat. d. Menschen. von Möllendorff, 6, pt. 4, 1943.
Gladstone, R. J., and Wakeley, C. P. G.: The Pineal Organ. London, 1940.
Kitay, J. I., and Altschule, M. D.: The Pineal Gland. A Review of the Physiologic Literature. Cambridge, Mass., Harvard University Press, 1954.

CHAPTER 20

The Skin

THE SKIN covers the surface of the body and consists of two main layers, the surface epithelium or *epidermis* and the subjacent connective tissue layer—the *corium* or *derma*. Beneath the latter is a looser connective tissue layer, the superficial fascia or *hypodermis*, which in many places is transformed into subcutaneous fatty tissue. The hypodermis is connected with underlying deep fasciae, aponeuroses or periosteum.

The skin is continuous with several mucous membranes through *mucocutaneous junctions*, the most important of which are the vermilion border of the lip, the vulva and the anus.

The skin protects the organism from injurious external influences, receives sensory impulses from the outside, excretes various substances and, in warm-blooded animals, helps to regulate the temperature of the body. The skin is provided with hairs, nails, and glands of various kinds.

On the free surface of the skin, in man, numerous ridges can be seen with the naked eye, which pass in various directions, cross one another in the form of a network, and frequently unite. On the soles, palms and undersurfaces of the fingers and toes, in man and the primates, there is a regular pattern of parallel ridges which form complicated figures. This pattern undergoes marked individual variations, so that it is different in every person.

There is a sharp boundary between the epithelial and the connective tissue portions of the skin, but not between the derma and the hypodermis; here the fibers of one layer pass directly over into the other.

The surface of contact between the epidermis and the derma is uneven in most places. It appears as a straight line on the midline of the perineum and scrotum, and the external ear. In most of the skin of the body the outer portion of the derma is provided with a series of irregular finger-like processes called *papillae*, between which are the epidermal ridges.

EPIDERMIS

The epidermis is a stratified squamous epithelium, the external layer of which hornifies. The nonhornified portion of the epidermis contains 70 per cent water. Excessive loss of water to the outside is hindered by a subcorneally situated, relatively water-impermeable membrane. The horny layer contains only about 10 per cent water. In a humid environment it may take up much water from the outside.

The epidermis varies from 0.07 to 0.12 mm. in thickness on most parts of the body, although on the palms and the palmar surface of the fingers it may reach a thickness of 0.8 mm. and on the sole and toes of 1.4 mm. Continuous rubbing and pressure and other physical agents such as ultraviolet light cause a great thickening of the horny layer anywhere on the body surface. External mechanical causes are not the only factors, since it is well developed in the palms and soles of the fetus.

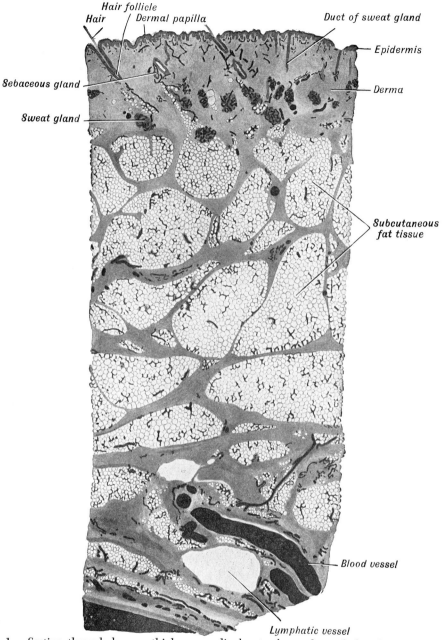

Hair follicle
Hair / Dermal papilla
Duct of sweat gland
Epidermis
Sebaceous gland
Derma
Sweat gland
Subcutaneous fat tissue
Blood vessel
Lymphatic vessel

Fig. 20–1. Section through human thigh perpendicular to the surface of the skin. Blood vessels are injected and appear black. Low magnification. (A.A.M.)

Epidermis of the Palms and Soles. The structure of the epidermis is most typical in those places where it is thickest. Here, in sections perpendicular to the surface, four main layers can be distinguished: (1) the deep layer of Malpighi (*stratum germinativum* or *spinosum*) touching the derma; (2) the granular layer (*stratum granulosum*); (3)

the clear layer (*stratum lucidum*); and (4) the horny layer (*stratum corneum*).

The deepest or basal layer of cells, adjacent to the derma, are cylindrical and placed perpendicular to the surface of the skin; mitotic figures occur rather frequently. The cells above these become polyhedral, and under the granular layer they are flattened.

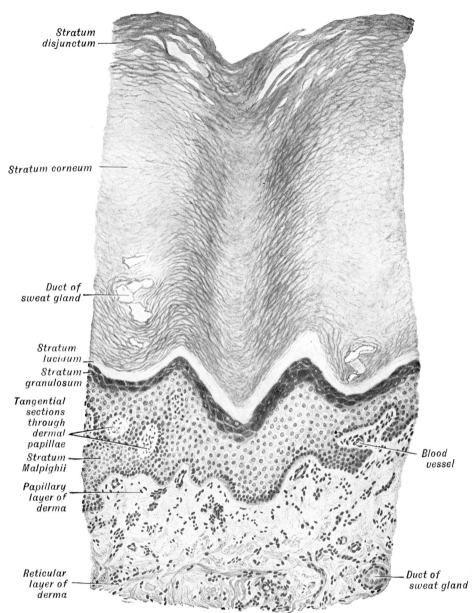

Stratum disjunctum

Stratum corneum

Duct of sweat gland

Stratum lucidum

Stratum granulosum

Tangential sections through dermal papillae

Stratum Malpighii

Papillary layer of derma

Reticular layer of derma

Blood vessel

Duct of sweat gland

Fig. 20–2. Section of human sole; perpendicular to the free surface. 100 ✕. (A.A.M.)

The surface of these cells is covered with thin spines which connect with similar spines of adjacent cells to form intercellular bridges (Fig. 20–3, *y*). The spines at the lower surface of the cylindrical layer of cells are finger-like processes which project into the connective tissue of the derma. The cytoplasm has a few mitochondria near the nucleus and numerous parallel bundles of fibrils. With the electron microscope these fibrils are seen to be composed of great numbers of tiny filaments which do not pass through the intercellular bridges into adjacent cells (Fig. 2–20). These findings thus disagree with the old observations made with the light microscope that the fibrils pass through the intercellular bridges and penetrate rows of cells without interruption. At each intercellular bridge the fibril is thickened into a round or spindle-shaped granule.

The granular layer (Fig. 20–2) consists of three to five layers of flattened cells. Their

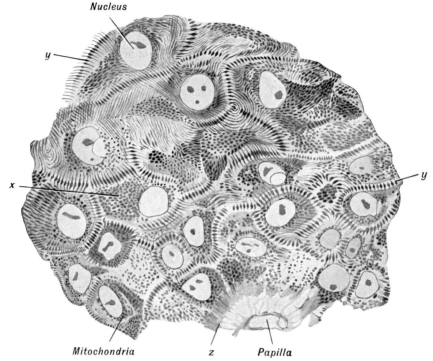

Nucleus

y

x

Mitochondria   *z*   *Papilla*

Fig. 20–3.   Section, tangential to the surface, of the malpighian layer of epidermis of human palm, showing fibrils and intercellular bridges; *z,* scalloped, lower surface of epithelial cells connected with the derma. Intercellular bridges with swellings, in longitudinal section (*y*) and in cross section (*x*). Fixation Champy; Kull's stain (oil immersion). (See also Figure 2–20.) (A.A.M.)

cytoplasm, particularly in the vicinity of the nucleus, contains irregularly shaped granules of *keratohyalin.* Their origin has not been clearly established. With the gradual increase in size and number of the granules, the nucleus disintegrates and becomes pale. At the same time the intercellular spaces become narrow and the bridges shorter and rather indistinct.

The *stratum lucidum* (Fig. 20–2) is formed by several layers of flattened, closely packed cells; in a section it appears as a pale, wavy stripe, with refractile droplets, called *eleidin,* instead of the keratohyalin granules. Usually little remains of the nucleus in such cells.

The thick *stratum corneum* (Fig. 20–2) on the palms and soles consists of many layers of flat, elongated, cornified cells. The material forming these cells is keratin, a transformation product of cellular proteins. Intercellular bridges are absent, and the spinous margins of the densely packed cells are in close contact.

The most peripheral layers of the stratum corneum are dried, horny plates which are constantly being desquamated (*stratum disjunctum*). The cells lost in this way are replaced by new ones from the lower layers.

The electron microscope reveals that the tonofilaments of the cells of the basal layer (Figs. 20–5 and 20–6 A) become compressed into dense irregular masses in the granular layer (20–6, B).

In the lucid layer (lower part of Fig. 20–6 C) all nuclear and cytoplasmic structures have disappeared except the densely packed fibrils which are now fibrils of keratin and some soluble interfibrillar material. In the horny layer the soluble materials are gone and, upper part of Fig. 20–6 C, all the keratin is condensed into a solid amorphous mass except for indications of the former cell outlines and bridge corpuscles.

The number of mitotic figures in the malpighian layer corresponds with the intensity of desquamation in a given region. Against the general view that mitosis in the skin occurs mainly in the basal layer of cells, Thuringer found that in the skin of the scalp and pre-

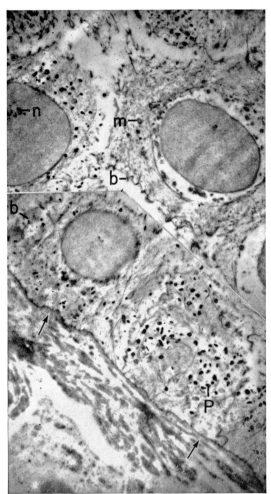

Fig. 20–4. Montage of two adjacent electron micrographs of a section through the connective tissue and two cell layers of the epidermis of human breast skin. The dermo-epidermal junction is indicated by the arrows. Intercellular bridge (*b*), mitochondria (*m*), pigment granules (*P*), and a portion of a nucleolus (*n*) are indicated. Cytoplasmic tonofilaments run toward the derma in basal cells and toward cytoplasmic bridges in prickle cells. Basal cell filaments also are closely associated with the nuclear membranes. 4400 ×. (Courtesy of C. Selby.)

puce only 12 per cent of the mitoses were in the basal layer, with 30 per cent in the lower third, 46 per cent in the middle third and 12 per cent in the outer third of the spinous layer. In the palmar and plantar skin of the cat he found mitoses slightly more numerous in the lower third of the spinous layer than in the basal layer. Both layers respond rapidly with an increased number of mitoses to mechanical stimulation of the skin in these areas.

Epidermis of the Body. On the rest of the body the epidermis is thin and has a simpler structure. Two layers are always present— the stratum Malpighii and the stratum corneum. The granular layer usually consists of two or three layers of cells (Fig. 20–7).

The epidermis, entirely devoid of blood vessels, is nourished by the tissue fluid which penetrates the intercellular spaces of the malpighian layer from capillaries in the underlying connective tissue. Human skin, unlike that of practically all other vertebrates, blisters after exposure to thermal and certain chemical stimuli, such as the "blister" gases. This reaction is apparently made possible by the many layers of cells in human epidermis.

The color of the skin depends on three factors: its inherent color is predominantly yellow; the vascular bed gives a reddish hue; *melanin* is responsible for varying shades of brown. This pigment, formed in melanocytes (see below), accumulates in varying amounts as fine granules within the cells of the stratum germinativum, particularly in its basal, cylindrical layer (Fig. 20–8, *Pb*). As these cells move toward the surface, the granular pigment becomes a finely distributed dust, sometimes seen in the stratum corneum. The pigmentation of the skin of the Negro is due to the greater amount of pigment in all the layers of the epidermis.

At the junction of the layer of pigmented basal epithelial cells with the derma, and projecting slightly into the latter, are branched pigment cells, melanocytes, formerly called "melanoblasts" (Fig. 20–8, *Mel*). The long axis of their nucleus is usually perpendicular to that of the basal cells, and their pigment-containing processes extend for great distances between the epidermal cells. These melanocytes contain a specific *tyrosinase* which oxidizes tyrosin to melanin; the *dermal chromatophores* do not. Exposure to x-rays and ultraviolet light increases the enzymatic activity of the melanocytes. It is now well established that the melanocytes are specific cells that normally elaborate melanin for the epidermal cells.

With the electron microscope a thin homogeneous basement membrane is seen between epidermis and derma.

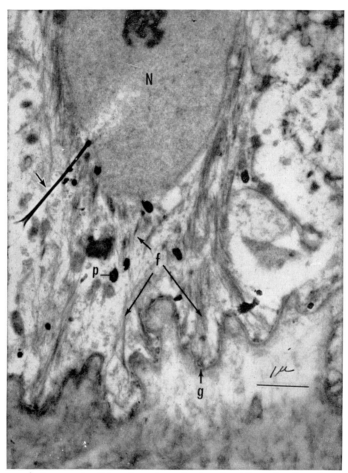

Fig. 20–5. Electron micrograph of basal portion of a basal epidermal cell in human breast skin illustrating the manner in which bundles of tonofilaments (*f*) extend from the nucleus (*N*) to granules (*g*) at the dermo-epidermal junction. Pigment granules (*p*) are indicated. A fold in the section is shown at arrow. (Courtesy of C. Selby.)

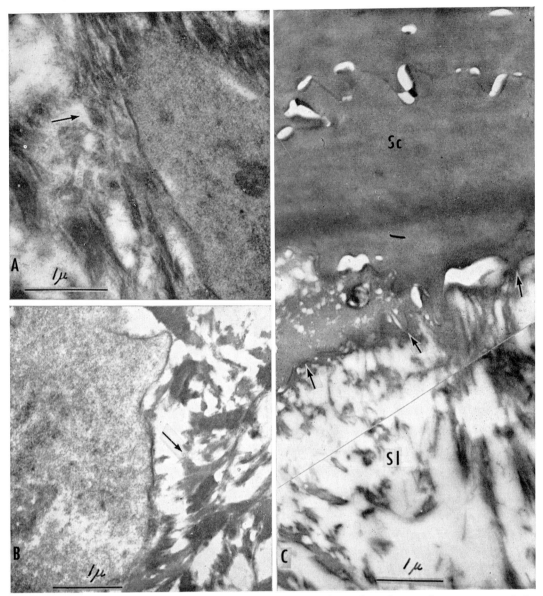

Fig. 20–6. Electron micrographs of sections of human footpad epidermis showing some of the changes in the cells as they move from the basal layer and become the keratinized cell residues of the stratum corneum. A, Malphigian layer cell. Nucleus (including a small section of nucleolus) occupies the right-hand side of this micrograph. Tonofilaments are distributed loosely throughout the cytoplasm and are more tightly packed into tonofibrils around the nucleus (arrow). Mitochondria are primarily localized around the nuclear membrane. Note that the concentration of filaments and their organization into fibrils is greater than in the Malphigian layer of breast epidermis (Figure 20–4). B, cell of granular layer. Although the nuclear contours have become crenated, a portion of the nucleolus is still evident and the nuclear matrix appears unchanged from that of a Malphigian cell. Cytoplasmic particulates and mitochondria have disappeared and dense irregular conglomerates (keratohyalin granules?) have appeared. Tonofilaments are all grouped into bundles of tonofibrils (arrow). C, composite of two adjacent electron micrographs showing details in the S. lucidum (S.l.) and S. corneum (S.c.). In the "glassy" layer all the filaments are condensed into bundles which show a decreased electron density (which begins in the granular layer). Between the S. lucidum and the S. corneum, cell membranes and intercellular bridges are still evident (arrows). In the cornified layer all the dense material (keratin) is condensed into a homogeneous mass with no evident filamentous substructure: cell membranes are still evident enclosing a much smaller cell domain than in the S. lucidum. (Courtesy of C. Selby.)

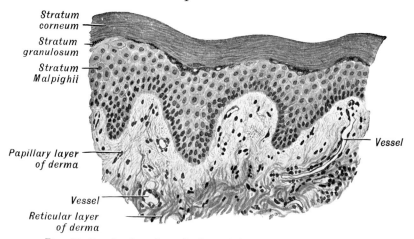

Fig. 20–7.   Section through skin of human shoulder. 125 ×. (A.A.M.)

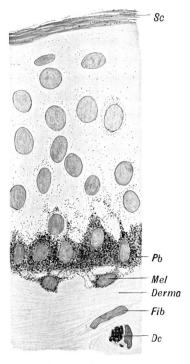

Fig. 20–8.   Section through skin of human mammary papilla. *Sc,* stratum corneum; *Pb,* pigmented basal cells of epidermis; *Mel,* melanocyte; *Fib,* fibroblast; *Dc,* dermal chromatophore. Silver nitrate, faintly counterstained with pyronin methyl green. 650 ×. (W. B.)

Throughout the epidermis, but more frequently in its upper layers, peculiar black, star-shaped figures can be seen in gold chloride preparations. They are provided with long, irregular processes which penetrate the intercellular spaces and follow the intercellu-

lar outlines. They are the so-called *cells of Langerhans.* They have been considered, probably erroneously, as melanoblasts, nerve cells or lymphoid wandering cells by different investigators. It is not at all clear, however, that they are cells. No structural details can be seen in them in gold-impregnated sections, and no traces of them can be found in the usual histologic preparations.

Mucocutaneous Junctions. These are transitions between the mucous membranes and skin to which they are joined. Their epithelium is thicker than that of the adjacent skin and is more like that of the mucosa. They may have a thin rudimentary horny layer. Normally they do not contain sweat glands, hair follicles, hairs or sebaceous glands but are moistened by mucous glands within the orifices. Since the horny layer is thin or may even be absent, the underlying blood shines through and gives the junction a red color as in the case of the vermilion border of the lips.

THE DERMA

The thickness of the derma cannot be measured exactly, because it passes over without sharp borders into the subcutaneous layer. The average thickness is approximately 1 to 2 mm.; it is less on the eyelids and the prepuce (up to 0.6 mm.), but reaches a thickness of 3 mm. or more on the soles and palms. On the ventral surface of the body and on the underside of the appendages it is generally thinner than on the dorsal and upper sides; it is thinner in women than in men.

The surface of the derma fused with the epidermis is usually uneven and covered with projecting papillae. This surface of the derma is soft and is called the *papillary layer.* The main dense portion of the derma is called the *reticular layer.* The two layers cannot be clearly separated (Fig. 20–2).

The reticular layer consists of bundles of collagenous fibers which form a dense felt-work; the bundles run in various directions (Fig. 4–22), but mainly more or less parallel to the surface; less frequently, approximately perpendicular bundles are found. In the papillary layer and its papillae the collagenous bundles are much thinner and more loosely arranged.

The elastic fibers of the derma form abundant, thick networks between the collagenous bundles and are condensed about the hair follicles and the sweat and sebaceous glands. In the papillary layer they are much thinner and form a continuous fine network under the epithelium in the papillae. The cells of the derma are the same as those of the subcutaneous layer except for fat cells and are more abundant in the papillary than in the reticular layer.

Under the epithelium, a few connective tissue pigment cells, *dermal chromatophores,* are scattered (Fig. 20–8, Dc). Their pigment granules are much larger and more irregular than those in the melanocytes and epidermal cells. The dermal chromatophores are normally rare and are numerous only in definite places, as around the anus. Whether these pigmented cells of the derma are related to the pigment in the epidermis is not established. These chromatophores do not elaborate the pigment which they contain. In the skin of the ape, in the so-called "Mongolian spots" and in certain tumors, called "blue nevi," *dermal melanoblasts* appear.

Within the deep parts of the reticular layer in the mammary papillae, the penis, perineum and scrotum, numerous smooth muscle fibers are collected into a netlike layer. Such portions of the skin become wrinkled during contraction of these muscles. Smooth muscles are also connected with the hairs (p. 335). In many places in the skin of the face, cross-striated muscle fibers terminate in the derma. At various levels of the derma are the hair follicles, sweat and sebaceous glands, as well as blood vessels, nerves and many nerve endings.

Hypodermis. The subcutaneous layer consists of loose connective tissue and is a continuation of the derma. Its collagenous and a few elastic fibers pass directly into those of the derma and run in all directions, mainly parallel to the surface of the skin. Where the skin is flexible, the fibers are few; where it is closely attached to the underlying parts, as

on the soles and palms, they are thick and numerous.

Depending on the portion of the body and the nutrition of the organism, varying numbers of fat cells develop in the subcutaneous layer (Fig. 20–1). These are also found in groups in the deep layers of the derma. The fatty tissue of the subcutaneous layer on the abdomen may reach a thickness of 3 cm. or more, while in the eyelids and penis the subcutaneous layer never contains fat cells.

The subcutaneous layer is penetrated everywhere by large blood vessels and nerve trunks and contains many nerve endings.

HAIRS

The hairs are horny threads which develop from the matrix cells of the follicular epithelium. They vary in length from several millimeters to 1.5 meters and from 0.005 to 0.6 mm. in thickness. They are distributed in varying density and in variable strength and length on the whole surface of the skin, except on palms, soles, the sides of fingers and toes, side surfaces of feet below the ankles, the lip, the glans penis, the prepuce, the clitoris and the internal surface of the labia majora.

Each hair arises in a tubular invagination of the epidermis, the *hair follicle,* the walls of which are composed of epithelial and connective tissue. Into the bottom of the follicle projects the connective tissue *papilla.* It is covered all along its convexity with the epithelial matrix cells of hair and root sheath. The matrix cells on the dome of the convexity form the hair *root* which develops into the hair *shaft,* the free end of which protrudes beyond the surface of the skin (Fig. 20–9).

The shaft of most hairs is roughly cylindrical. The cross section can be circular, oval or angulated.

One or more sebaceous glands are connected with each hair. Through a short duct they empty their excretion product into the follicular canal in the upper third of its length. A smooth muscle is attached to the connective tissue sheath of the follicle. The other end of this muscle, which if contracting erects the hair, separates into fine fibrils which disappear in the papillary layer of the dermis.

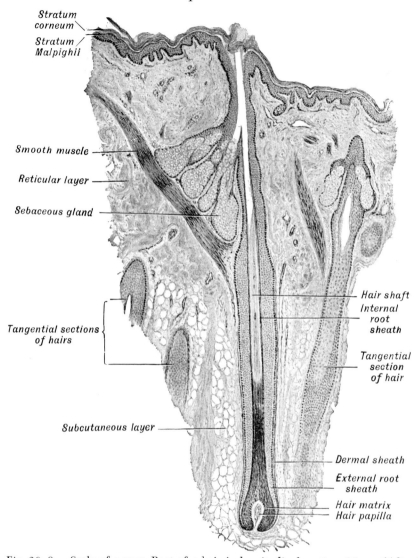

Stratum corneum

Stratum Malpighii

Smooth muscle

Reticular layer

Sebaceous gland

Tangential sections of hairs

Subcutaneous layer

Hair shaft
Internal root sheath

Tangential section of hair

Dermal sheath

External root sheath

Hair matrix
Hair papilla

Fig. 20–9.   Scalp of a man. Root of a hair in longitudinal section. 32 ×. (After Schaffer.)

The follicular epithelium is derived from the embryonic epidermis and differentiates into a specific organ. Its matrix cells covering the hair papilla are undifferentiated cells in which mitoses are frequent. In follicles of thick hairs the central matrix cells, on top of the papillary convexity, develop into the medulla of the hair shaft. This central part of the hair shaft, which is not demonstrable in thinner hairs, consists of loosely connected, relatively soft, horny cells with air between them. The next concentric circle of matrix cells develops into the cortex of the hair, the main constituent of the hair shaft. Its horny cells are hard and tightly woven. The cortex

carries most of the pigment of the hair. Peripheral to the matrix cells of the cortex lie those of the *cuticle of the hair.* This outermost layer of the hair shaft consists of the hardest horny cells, quite solidly connected by serrate edges. More peripheral concentric rows of matrix cells on the slopes of the papilla produce the subsequent layers of the internal and external root sheaths, viz., the cuticle of the root sheath, Huxley's layer, Henle's layer and finally two rows of epithelial cells with a surrounding tough homogeneous "glassy membrane" sending shelflike processes in between the cells of the outermost epithelial layer.

The *cuticle of the internal root sheath,* like

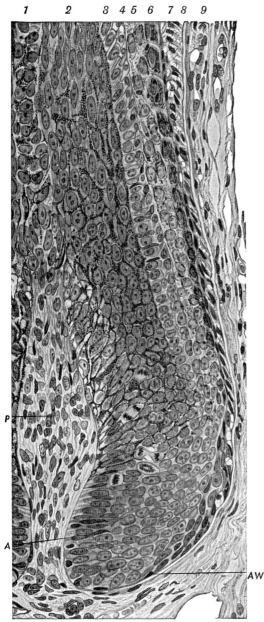

1   2   3 4 5 6   7 8   9

Fig. 20–10. Longitudinal section through a hair from head of a man twenty-two years old. *1*, medulla; *2*, cortex; *3*, hair cuticle; *4*, inner sheath cuticle; *5*, Huxley's layer; *6*, Henle's layer; *7*, external root sheath; *8*, glassy membrane; *9*, connective tissue of the hair follicle; *AW*, external root sheath at the bulb; *A*, matrix; *P*, papilla. 350 ×. (After Hoepke.)

the cuticle of the hair, consists of thin, horny scales which overlap, so that their free margins are toward the bottom of the hair sac.

The cells of *Huxley's layer* are connected with one another by bridges. At the level of

the summit of the papilla they develop trichohyalin granules which remain for a distance of forty to fifty cells, but disappear as the cells cornify. At the middle third of the follicle, the layer of Huxley consists of one to three layers of cornified cells.

The outermost layer (*of Henle*) consists of a single layer of elongated, horny bodies connected by intercellular bridges and welded to the external sheath. In this layer trichohyalin appears about the middle of the papilla, but disappears at the level of its summit.

The external root sheath at the neck of the papilla is one layer of flat cells. It becomes two layered at the level of the middle of the papilla, and further on stratified.

The glassy membrane separates the epithelial from the connective tissue portion of the follicle. The latter portion is made up of two layers, a third internal layer formed by circular fibers and an external, poorly outlined layer consisting of longitudinal collagenous and elastic fibers.

The hair matrix cells are analogous to the germinative cells of the epidermis insofar as the life cycle of both end with formation of horny cells. However, the epidermis produces a relatively soft horny material which is steadily shed in small invisible particles while the cornified product of the matrix cells, the hair, has a hard cohesive nonshedding keratinous structure.

Muscle of the Hair. The hair muscle, the *arrector pili,* is a band of smooth muscle cells connected with its attachment by networks of elastic fibers. When this muscle contracts (from cold, and the like) it moves the hair into a more vertical position and depresses the skin, while the region around the hair is lifted. This is responsible for the so-called "goose flesh."

Replacement of Hairs. Throughout life, even in the embryo, hairs undergo replacement. The hair of every part of the body has a definite period of growth—the hairs of the head two to four years, the eyelashes three to five months. In man this change goes on continuously and passes unnoticed; in those mammals which renew their hair twice a year the process of replacement is rapid.

When the period of growth of the hair approaches its end, multiplication of the undifferentiated cells at the bottom of the hair sac in the matrix slows down and finally stops. The base of the shaft and the root gradually become thinner. The growth from below of the layers of the internal sheath stops. The elements which cover the summit of the papilla all become cornified spindles, and the hair becomes club-shaped. The root separates from the papilla,

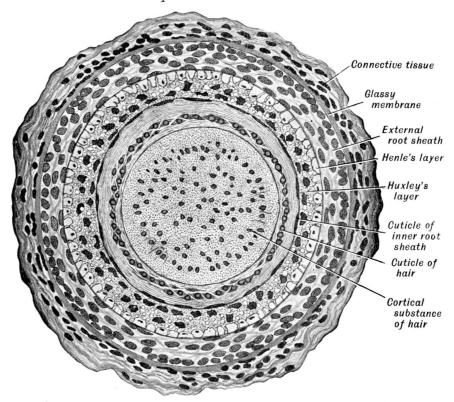

Fig. 20–11.   Cross section through hair follicle, in the skin of a pig embryo, at the level where Henle's
layer is completely cornified and Huxley's layer contains granules of trichohyalin. 375 ×.

moves toward the neck of the follicle, and either falls or is pulled out. The papilla becomes smaller and, according to some, atrophies and disappears.

Usually, even before the old hair drops out, the primordium of a new one is formed in the same hair sac. The epithelium of the matrix begins to multiply; the lower portion of the follicle becomes thicker and longer. The papilla enlarges, or, as some believe, a new one is formed, and invaginates the epithelium at the bottom of the follicle. The cavity of the follicle is soon filled with a mass of young epithelial elements. Inside this mass a layer of hornified cells, filled with trichohyalin, becomes visible; this has the shape of a hollow cone opened in the direction of the papilla. This layer represents the internal root sheath of the new hair. The cells beneath this then form the substance of the hair proper.

NAILS

The nails are horny plates on the dorsal surface of the terminal phalanges of the fingers and toes. The surface of the skin covered by them is the *nail bed*. It is surrounded laterally and proximally by a fold of skin, the *nail wall*. The slit between the wall and the bed is the *nail groove*. The proximal edge of

the nail plate is the *root* of the nail. The visible part of the nail plate is surrounded by the nail wall and is called the *body of the nail*; the distal portion comes forward freely and is gradually worn off or cut off. The nail is semitransparent and shows the underlying tissue rich in blood vessels. Near the root the nail has a whitish color; this portion, the *lunula*, is usually covered by the proximal portion of the nail fold.

The nail plate consists of closely welded, horny scales: cornified epithelial cells so arranged that in section the nail appears striated.

The *nail fold* has the structure of skin with all its layers. Turning inward into the nail groove, it loses its papillae, and the epidermis loses its horny, clear and granular layers. Under the proximal fold, the horny layer spreads onto the free surface of the nail body as the eponychium (Fig. 20–12). The stratum lucidum and the stratum granulosum also reach far inside the groove, but do not continue along the lower surface of the

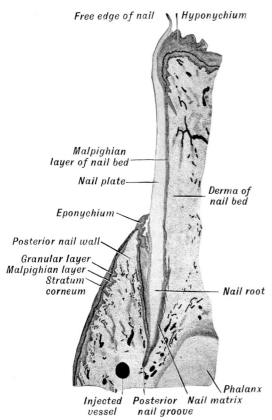

Fig. 20–12. Longitudinal section of nail of a newborn infant. Very low power. (A.A.M.)

nail plate. On the surface of the nail bed only the malpighian layer of the epidermis is present.

In the nail bed the derma is directly fused with the periosteum of the phalanx. The surface of the derma under the proximal edge of the nail is provided with rather low papillae, but under the distal half of the lunula this surface is quite smooth. At the distal margin of the lunula, longitudinal, parallel ridges project instead of papillae. The boundary between the epithelium and the derma of the nail bed in a perpendicular section is, therefore, scalloped (Fig. 20–13), while it is smooth in longitudinal sections. Beyond the free edge of the nail the dermal ridges are replaced by cylindrical papillae.

The epithelium of the nail bed distal to the lunula retains the typical structure of the malpighian layer. The epithelium is thicker between the ridges of the derma than over them. The upper layer of cells which touches the substance of the nail is separated from it in places by an even line, while in others it is jagged. Under the free edge of the nail the usual horny layer again begins; it is thickened at this place and is called *hyponychium* (Fig. 20–12).

The epithelium which lines the proximal portion of the nail bed and corresponds roughly with the lunula is particularly thick; distally and upward it gradually passes over into the substance of the nail plate. Here the new formation of the nail substance proceeds; accordingly, this region of the epithelium is called the *nail matrix* (Fig. 20–

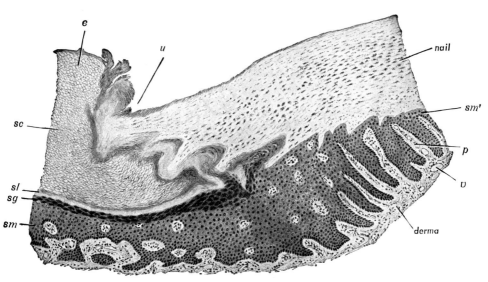

Fig. 20–13. Cross section of lateral edge of a nail and its surrounding parts: *d*, derma of nail bed; *e*, lateral nail wall; *n*, nail plate; *p*, dermal papilla; *sc*, stratum corneum of epidermis; *sg*, stratum granulosum; *sl*, stratum lucidum; *sm*, malpighian layer of epidermis; *sm'*, malpighian layer of nail bed; *u*, lateral nail groove; *v*, vessel. Higher power than in Figure 20–12. (A.A.M.)

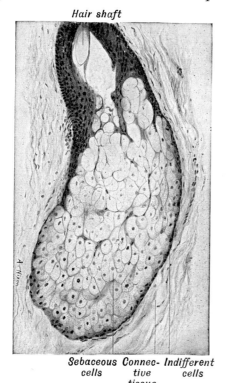

Hair shaft

Sebaceous Connec- Indifferent
cells   tive   cells
            tissue

Fig. 20–14. Section of human sebaceous gland.
120 ×.

12). The cells of the deepest layer are cylindrical, and mitoses can be observed frequently in them. Above these are six to ten layers of polyhedral cells joined by five to twelve layers of flatter cells; this entire mass is penetrated by parallel fibrils of a special "onychogenic" substance. On passing into the proximal edge of the nail plate, these cells cornify and become homogeneous.

As the new formation of the nail takes place in the matrix, the nail moves forward. Most authors deny the participation of the epithelium of the other portions of the nail bed in the formation of the nail substance, and believe that the nail simply glides forward over this region.

GLANDS OF THE SKIN

In man the glands of the skin include the sebaceous, sweat and mammary glands. The last are described in a separate chapter.

Sebaceous Glands. The sebaceous glands are scattered over the surface of the skin (except in the palms, soles and the sides of the

feet where there are no hairs). They vary from 0.2 to 2 mm. in diameter. They lie in the derma, and their excretory duct opens into the neck of the hair follicle. When several glands are connected with one hair, they lie at the same level. On the lips, about the corners of the mouth, on the glans penis and the internal fold of the prepuce, on the labia minora, and on the mammary papilla the sebaceous glands are independent of hairs and open directly on the surface of the skin; to this category also belong the meibomian glands of the eyelids. The sebaceous glands in mucocutaneous junctions are more superficial than those associated with hairs.

The secretory portions of the sebaceous glands are rounded sacs (alveoli). As a rule, several adjacent alveoli form a mass like a bunch of grapes, and all of them open into a short duct; in this way a simple branched gland results. Much less frequently, only one alveolus is present. In the meibomian glands of the eyelids there is one long, straight duct, from which a row of alveoli projects.

The wall of the alveoli is formed by a basement membrane supported by a thin layer of fibrillar connective tissue. Along the internal surface is a single layer of thin cells with round nuclei. Toward the center of the alveoli a few cells cornify, but most of them become larger, polyhedral, and gradually filled with fat droplets. The central portion of the alveoli is filled with large cells distended with fat droplets. The nuclei gradually shrink and then disappear, and the cells break down into fatty detritus which mixes with horny scales. This is the oily secretion of the gland, and it is excreted onto the hair and upon the surface of the epidermis. The ducts of sebaceous glands are lined by stratified squamous epithelium continuous with the external root sheath of the hair and with the malpighian layer of the epidermis.

In sebaceous glands, the secretion results from the destruction of the epithelial cells and is, therefore, of the *holocrine* type; it is followed by a regenerative multiplication of epithelial elements. In the body of the gland, mitoses are rare in the cells lying on the basement membrane; they are numerous, however, in the cells close to the walls of the excretory ducts, whence the new cells move into the secretory regions.

Sweat Glands. The ordinary sweat glands

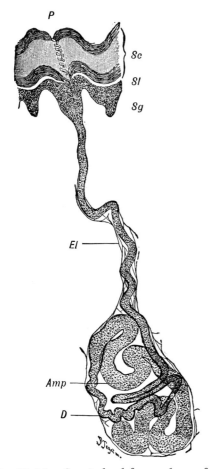

Fig. 20–15. Sweat gland from volar surface of an index finger. The drawing was combined from sections and a teased preparation; *P,* sweat pore; *Sc,* stratum corneum; *Sl,* stratum lucidum; *Sg,* stratum germinativum; *El,* elastic tissue surrounding the duct; *Amp,* ampulla; *D,* sudoriferous duct. 45 ×. (Slightly modified after von Brunn.)

The walls of the secretory portion rest on a thick basement membrane. Directly inside it are spindle-shaped cells 30 to 90 microns in length, with their long axis tangential to that of the glandular tube. They have an elongate nucleus, and fibrils. It is supposed that these "myo-epithelial" cells, by contracting, help to discharge the secretion. They are particularly numerous and are highly developed in the large sweat glands of the axillary and perianal regions.

The truncated pyramidal cells which excrete sweat form a single layer upon the myo-epithelial cells. At the base is a rather large round nucleus; the cytoplasm contains mitochondria and, near the lumen, a number of secretory vacuoles, varying with the functional state of the cell. Sometimes there are also fat droplets, glycogen and pigment granules. Glycogen disappears in functioning cells. The pigment appears in the secretion of certain sweat glands, as in the axilla. The free surface of the cells in the apocrine glands often shows protrusions of protoplasm which are believed to separate and become a part of the secretion.

Between these glandular cells are typical secretory capillaries. The caliber and the shape of the free lumen of the secretory portion fluctuate greatly with the functional state of the gland.

The glandular tube, in passing over into the excretory duct, suddenly becomes much narrower, the lumen acquires a simple, slit-like or starlike shape, while the myo-epithelial and glandular cells on the basement membrane are replaced by a double-layered, thin epithelium. The cells of the external layer have comparatively large nuclei and rather abundant mitochondria; the free surface of the cytoplasm of the cells of the internal layer is condensed and refractile. As it passes through the derma toward the epidermis the duct is slightly twisted and curved.

In the epidermis the lumen of the excretory duct is a spirally twisted, intercellular channel surrounded by concentrically arranged epidermal cells which, in the malpighian layer, have fine, keratohyalin granules in their cytoplasm (Fig. 20–17). On the palms and soles and on the ventral surface of the fingers, the rows of ducts open on the ridges with funnel-shaped openings which can be seen easily with a magnifying glass.

(eccrine type) are distributed along the surface of the skin, with the exception of the margins of the lips, the glans penis and the nail bed. They are simple, coiled, tubular glands; i.e., the secretory portion is a simple tube folded by several unequal twists into a ball, and the excretory duct is a narrow, unbranched tube (Fig. 20–15).

The mass of the secretory portion is located in the derma and measures 0.3 to 0.4 mm. in diameter. In the armpit and about the anus the bodies of some of the sweat glands may reach 3 to 5 mm. in diameter and are of *apocrine type* (see below). In these regions they are red and are located deep in the subcutaneous layer.

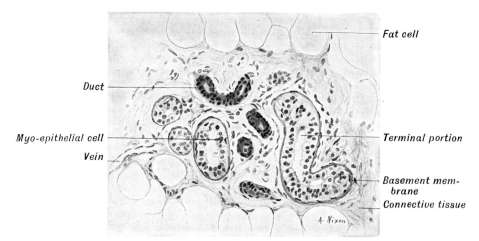

Fig. 20–16.   Section of human sweat gland. 120 ✕.

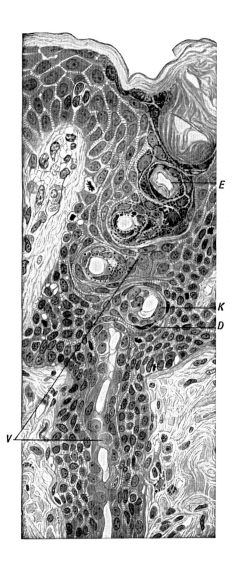

In certain parts of the skin the sweat glands have a peculiar arrangement and function. Such are the *glands which produce cerumen* in the external auditory meatus. They reach a considerable size and extend up to the perichondrium; their secretory portions branch, and the excretory ducts, which sometimes also branch, may open together with the ducts of the adjacent sebaceous glands into the hair sacs of the fine hairs. In the terminal portions are highly developed smooth muscle cells; the glandular cells located upon them are particularly rich in lipid-containing pigment granules.

Moll's glands of the margin of the eyelid are also a special kind of sweat gland with terminal portions which do not form a ball, but are only irregularly twisted and provided with a wide lumen. The excretory ducts open freely or into the hair sacs of the eyelashes.

The secretion of the sweat glands is not the same everywhere. The true sweat, a transparent, watery liquid, is excreted mainly by the small sweat glands, while a thicker secretion of complex composition is produced by those of the axilla and about the anus. In women the apocrine sweat glands of the axilla show periodic changes with the menstrual cycle. These changes consist mainly in enlargement of the epithelial cells and of the lumens of the glands in the premenstrual period, followed by regressive changes during the period of menstruation (Fig. 20–18).

Blood and Lymphatic Vessels of the Skin. The arteries which supply the skin are located in the sub-

Fig. 20–17.   Section through skin from the head of a man twenty-two years old. The end of the excretory duct of a sweat gland: *E*, eleidin; *K*, keratohyalin; *D*, degenerating cells; *V*, hypertrophic cells. 600 ✕. (Drawing by Vierling, after Hoepke.)

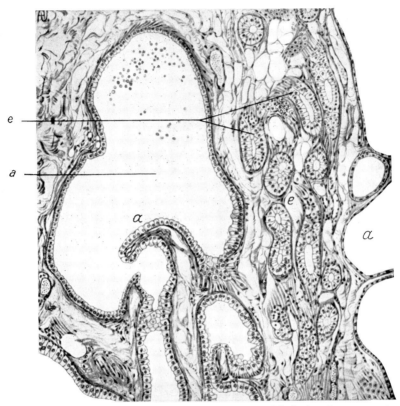

Fig. 20–18. Axillary glands, from a woman thirty-seven years old, during the premenstruum. *a*, greatly enlarged glands which change with the menstrual cycle and, *e*, glands which do not change. Resorcin-fuchsin stain for elastic fibers. (Preparation of Loescke.) 110 ×. (After Hoepke.)

cutaneous layer. Their branches, reaching upward, form a network (rete cutaneum) (Fig. 20–19) on the boundary line between the derma and the hypo-dermis; this is parallel to the surface. From one side of this network, branches are given off which nour-ish the subcutaneous stratum with its fat cells, sweat glands, and the deeper portions of the hair sacs. From the other side of this network, vessels enter the derma; at the boundary between the papillary and reticular layers they form the denser, subpapillary network or the rete subpapillare (Fig. 20–19). This gives off thin branches to the papillae. Each papilla has a single loop of capillary vessels with an ascend-ing arterial and descending venous limb.

The veins which collect the blood from the capil-laries in the papillae form the first network of thin veins immediately beneath the papillae. Then follow three flat networks of gradually enlarging veins on the boundary line between the papillary and reticu-lar layers. In the middle section of the derma and also at the boundary between the derma and the sub-

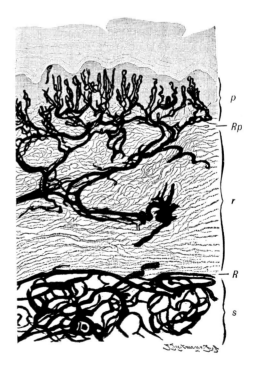

Fig. 20–19. Distribution of blood vessels in the skin. *s*, subcutaneous tissue; *r*, reticular layer of derma; *p*, papillary layer of derma; *R*, rete cutaneum; *Rp*, rete subpapillare. (Modified slightly after von Brunn.)

cutaneous tissue, the venous network is on the same level as the arterial rete cutaneum. Into this network the veins of the sebaceous and the sweat glands enter. From the deeper network the large, independent, subcutanous veins pass, as well as the deep veins accompanying the arteries.

Each hair sac has its own blood vessels. It is supplied with blood from three sources: from a special small artery which gives off a capillary network into the papilla, from the rete subpapillare toward the sides of the hair sac, and from several other small arteries which form a dense capillary network in the connective tissue layer of the follicle.

There is a dense network of capillaries outside the basement membrane of the sebaceous and, particularly, of the sweat glands.

The skin is rich in lymphatic vessels. In the papillary layer they form a dense, flat meshwork of lymphatic capillaries. They begin in the papillae as networks or blind outgrowths which are always deeper than the blood vessels. From this peripheral network, branches pass to the deeper network, which lies on the boundary between the derma and the hypodermis, under the rete cutaneum; it has much wider meshes, and its vessels are provided with valves. From the deeper network large, subcutaneous lymphatic vessels originate and follow the blood vessels. Lymphatic vessels are not connected with the hairs or glands of the skin.

Nerves of the Skin. The skin, with its accessories, serves as an organ for receiving impulses from the external environment; it is accordingly abundantly supplied with sensory nerves. In addition, it contains nerves which supply the blood vessels, sweat glands and arrector muscles.

In the subcutaneous stratum are rather thick nerve bundles which form networks composed mainly of myelinated and some nonmyelinated fibers. The branches given off by this reticulum form, in the derma, several new thin plexuses. Among them the network on the boundary between the reticular and papillary layers stands out clearly, as does also the subepithelial one.

In all the layers of the hypodermis, derma, and epidermis are many different kinds of nerve endings. These are discussed in the section on the Nerve Endings. Among them, the sensory endings probably are all connected with the craniospinal myelinated fibers; the nonmyelinated fibers lead to the blood vessels, smooth muscles and glands. There are also free endings of unmyelinated sensory fibers in or close to the epidermis. The abundant nerves of the hair undoubtedly play an important part in the reception of tactile stimuli.

Histogenesis of the Skin and of Its Accessories. The epidermis develops from the ectoderm, while the derma arises from the mesenchyme.

Epidermis. The epidermis in the human embryo, during the first two months, is a double-layered epithelium. The basal layer, which lies on the mesenchyme, consists of cuboidal or cylindrical cells which multiply energetically. The peripheral layer consists of flat cells which are constantly formed anew from the elements of the deeper layer.

Beginning with the third month, the epidermis becomes three-layered. The new intermediate layer above the basal cells consists of polygonal cells which increase in number and become interconnected by intercellular bridges. At the end of the third month, in the peripheral portions of the intermediate layer, cornification begins and leads to the formation of the layers found in the adult. The horny scales are desquamated and form part of the vernix caseosa.

The irregularities on the lower surface of the epidermis arise at the end of the third month on the inner surfaces of the fingers, palms and soles as parallel ridges protruding into the derma; from the beginning they show a characteristic pattern. From them sweat glands develop. Protruding, longitudinal cushions corresponding to the ridges are formed on the external free surface of the epidermis.

Derma. The derma and hypodermis consist during the first month and a half of mesenchyme with wandering cells. From the second month on, the fibrillar interstitial substance appears. Elastic fibers appear later. In still later stages, the mesenchyme divides into a peripheral dense layer with a compact arrangement of its elements—the derma—and the deep loose layer, the future subcutaneous layer. In the derma, in turn, the peripheral papillary layer differentiates.

Hair. In man, hair first appears in the eyebrows and on the chin and upper lip, at the end of the second month. At first, in the deep layer of the epidermis, a group of cylindrical, dividing cells appear. These grow into the underlying connective tissue and produce a gradually elongating epithelial cylinder. This is the primordium of a hair follicle, the so-called "hair germ"; it is rounded and slightly flattened on its end. Under the latter an accumulation of condensed connective tissue appears early. From it the hair papilla forms and protrudes into the epithelial mass of the bulb (or germ). The epithelial cells at the surface of the connective tissue papilla represent the matrix of the future hair. The connective tissue which surrounds the bulb later forms the connective tissue portions of the hair sac. On the surface of the epithelial hair bulb, two projections arise. The upper represents the primordium of the sebaceous gland; its central cells early undergo a fatty transformation. The lower protuberance becomes the insertion of the arrector pili muscle on the hair sac.

In the mass of the epithelium which forms the hair primordium, there differentiates a layer of rapidly cornifying cells. This layer has the shape of a hollow cone open toward the papilla; it is the primordium of the internal root sheath, in which Henle's layer is the first to appear. The mass of the cells on top of the papilla represents the primordium of the shaft itself and becomes cornified a little later. The layer of epithelium which remains on the outside of the sheath of Henle becomes the external root sheath. The shaft of the new hair elongates, owing to the multiplication of cells of the matrix on the summit of the papilla, and perforates the top of the hollow cone of Henle's sheath. The tip of the hair moves upward, pierces the epidermis, and protrudes above the surface of the skin.

Nails. The development of the nails begins in the third month by the formation, on the back of the terminal phalanx of each finger, of a flat

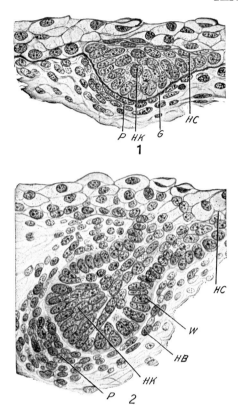

Fig. 20–20. Two early hair primordia of the frontal skin of a three month embryo. *1,* first primordium; *G,* border of the derma; *HC,* hair canal cells; *HK,* hair germ; *P,* primordium of the papilla. *2,* slightly later stage; *HB,* primordium of the dermal hair sheath; *W,* external root sheath. 740 ×. (After Schaffer.)

area, the *primary nail field*. This is surrounded by a fold of the skin. In the region of the nail the epithelium has three or four layers. The true nail substance is laid down during the fifth month, and without the participation of keratohyalin, in the portion of the nail bed near the proximal nail groove. Here the deep layer of the epidermis is transformed into the nail matrix, and its cells are penetrated by the fibrils of onychogenic substance; they become flat, adjoin one another closely, and give rise to the true nail plate. In the beginning it is still thin and is entirely buried in the epidermis of the nail field or bed. It gradually moves in the distal direction. The layers of epidermis which cover the plate eventually desquamate.

Sweat Glands. The development of the ordinary

(i.e., eccrine) sweat glands in man proceeds independently of the hairs. The first primordia appear during the fifth month on the palms and soles and the lower surface of the fingers. At first they are similar to the primordia of the hairs. An epithelial shaft with a terminal thickening grows into the underlying connective tissue. But, unlike that about the hairs, the connective tissue here does not condense about the epithelium. The shaft gradually elongates and becomes cylindrical, and its lower portion curls in the form of a ball. Beginning with the seventh month, an irregular lumen forms in this lower portion which constitutes the secretory part; along the course of the future excretory duct another lumen develops and later unites with the former. In the secretory portion the epithelium around the lumen forms two layers, which differentiate into an external layer of myo-epithelial elements and into an internal layer of glandular cells.

REFERENCES

Becker, S. W.: Melanin pigmentation. Arch. Dermat. & Syph., *16:*259, 1927.

Becker, S. W., and Zimmermann, A. A.: Further studies on melanocytes and melanogenesis in the human fetus and newborn. J. Invest. Dermatol., *25:*103, 1955.

Chase, H. B.: Growth of the hair. Physiol. Rev., *34:*113, 1954.

Cowdry, E. V., and Thompson, H. C. Jr.: The localization of maximum cell division in epidermis. Anat. Rec., *88:*403, 1944.

Danforth, C. H.: Physiology of human hair. Physiol. Rev., *19:*94, 1939.

Felsher, Z.: Studies on the adherence of the epidermis to the corium. J. Invest. Dermatol., *8:*35, 1947.

Hoepke, H.: Die Haut. Handb. d. mikr. Anat. (v. Möllendorff). Berlin, 1927, Vol. 3, Pt. 1.

Kneberg, M.: Improved technique for hair examination. Am. J. Phys. Anthropol., *20:*51, 1935.

Masson, P.: Les glomus cutanés de l'homme. Bull. Soc. française de Dermatol. et de Syphil., *42:*1174, 1935.

Montagna, W.: The Structure and Function of Skin. New York, Academic Press, 1956.

Pinkus, F.: Die normale Anatomie der Haut. Handb. d. Haut- u. Geschlechtskrankheiten, (1), 77, 1927.

Rothman, S.: Physiology and Biochemistry of the Skin. University of Chicago Press, Chicago, 1954.

Selby, C. C.: An electron microscope study of the epidermis of mammalian skin in thin sections. I. Dermo-epidermal junction and basal cell layer. J. Biophys. Biochem. Cytol., *1:*429, 1955.

Stoughton, R. B., and Lorincz, A. L.: The action of collagenase and the anticollagenase factor in human serum. J. Invest. Dermatol., *16:*43, 1951.

Thuringer, J. M.: The mitotic index of the palmar and plantar epidermis in response to stimulation. J. Invest. Dermatol., *2:*313, 1939.

Trotter, Mildred: The Hair, in Cowdry's Special Cytology. 2d ed. New York, (1), 41, 1932.

Zimmermann, A. A., and Cornbleet, T.: The development of epidermal pigmentation in the Negro fetus. J. Invest. Dermatol., *11:*383, 1948.

CHAPTER 21

The Oral Cavity and Associated Structures

GENERAL REMARKS ON THE DIGESTIVE SYSTEM

THE DIGESTIVE system is a long, winding tube which begins with the lips and ends with the anus. On its way through this tract the food undergoes complex mechanical and chemical changes. It is minced and ground by the teeth, is forwarded through the tube by the contraction of its muscular walls, and is digested by the secretions of the various parts of the alimentary system and its auxiliary glands. A part of the digested food is absorbed by the walls of the intestine and passes into the circulation, which carries it into the tissues of the organism; the residue is eliminated as feces.

The digestive tract consists of the following successive parts: mouth, pharynx, esophagus, stomach, small intestine, large intestine, and rectum. The functional condition of one segment causes certain functional changes in the following; thus the regular sequence of the processes necessary for the digestion of food is assured.

In the embryo the entoderm is transformed into the epithelial structures of the alimentary canal; the visceral mesoderm gives rise to its connective and muscular tissues. In the adult the inner surface of the wall of the digestive tube is lined by a *mucous membrane*. It consists of a superficial layer of epithelium and of a layer of connective tissue, the *lamina propria*. The wall of the tube contains smooth muscles which form the *muscularis externa* (see Fig. 21–1).

In most parts of the digestive tube the outer limit of the mucous membrane is marked by a thin, muscular layer, the *muscularis mucosae*. Between it and the muscularis externa is a layer of loose connective tissue, the *tela submucosa*. Where the muscularis mucosae is absent, the lamina propria gradually passes into the submucosa.

In the adult the mucous membrane forms numerous outgrowths which increase the surface of the epithelium. The mucous membrane of the mouth forms the teeth. The mucous membrane is provided with many invaginations, the *glands* or *crypts*. They are lined by epithelium which continues into them from the surface. Some of them elaborate liquids which split the food into its simple chemical constituents—digestion—while others produce mucus which lubricates the surface of the mucous membrane. Some of the glands remain confined to the thickness of the mucous membrane. Others grow to such an extent that they become separate organs, connected with the epithelial surface from which they originated by long excretory ducts. In the oral cavity, esophagus and rectum, the wall of the digestive tube is surrounded by a layer of dense connective tissue which attaches it to the neighboring organs. The outer surface of the stomach and intestines, which are suspended in the peritoneal

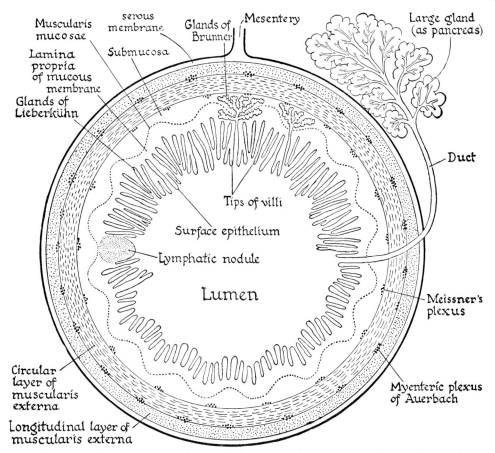

Fig. 21–1. Diagram of cross section of intestinal tract. In the upper half of the drawing the mucous membrane is provided with glands and villi; in the lower half it contains only glands.

cavity by the mesenteries, is covered with a serous membrane which permits these viscera to move freely in the cavity. The wall of the digestive tube is richly provided with blood vessels which bring nutritive materials and oxygen, as well as the raw materials necessary for the secretory activity. These vessels carry a large part of the absorbed products of digestion from the mucous membrane of the small intestine to the rest of the body. The remainder of the absorbed products enter the lymphatics of the intestines. The wall of the digestive tract contains an intricate system of sympathetic nervous ganglia and plexuses which regulate the movements of the tube.

THE ORAL CAVITY

The mucous membrane in the mouth is similar to the skin. The epithelium is strati-fied squamous, and in its deeper layers is more or less distinctly fibrillated. In man, under physiological conditions, it does not undergo cornification. The nucleus of the cells of the superficial layers shrinks and degenerates, but does not disappear, and the cell body does not reach the same degree of flatness as in the epidermis. These superficial cells are always shed in large quantities and are found in the saliva. In some places they contain granules of keratohyalin. In the cells of the middle and superficial layers there is usually some glycogen. In many animals the epithelium of the oral cavity undergoes extensive cornification.

The *lamina propria* is provided, in most places, with papillae similar to those of the skin. The structure is, however, more delicate, and the collagenous and elastic fibers thinner than in the derma. In the posterior section of the oral cavity, it contains many

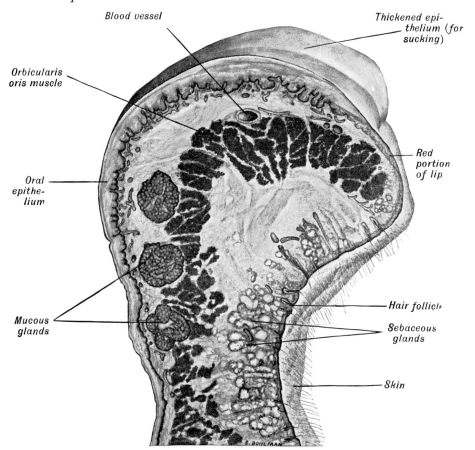

Fig. 21–2. Camera lucida drawing of sagittal section through lip of newborn infant. Stained with hematoxylin. 10 ×. (Drawn by Miss E. Bohlman.)

lymphocytes which are often found migrating into and through the epithelium. The arrangement of the blood vessels is similar to that of the skin. There is a deep submucous plexus of large vessels, from which branches arise and form a second plexus in the lamina propria, which in turn sends small branches into the papillae. The lymphatics also show an arrangement similar to that in the skin, and begin with blind capillary outgrowths in the papillae.

The *oral mucous membrane* is very sensitive and is provided with many nerves belonging to the sensory branches of the trigeminal nerve (lingual nerve). It also contains the specific end organs of the sense of taste.

In most places under the lamina propria, especially in the cheeks, and on the soft palate, there is a fat-containing, loose *submucosa* into which the dense connective tis-sue of the mucosa gradually merges. In such places the mucous membrane can be easily lifted into folds. In those places against which the food is crushed and rubbed, as on the hard palate, there is no submucosa, and the mucous membrane is firmly connected with the underlying periosteum or muscles.

The inner zone of the lip margin in the newborn is considerably thickened and covered with hairless sebaceous glands and contains many high papillae. This seems to facilitate the process of sucking.

The *soft palate* consists of layers of striated muscle and fibrous tissue on both surfaces and on the posterior margin. It is covered with a mucous membrane. On the oral surface the latter has the structure typical of the oral cavity—a stratified squamous epithelium, high interepithelial papillae, and glands of the pure mucous type. These are surrounded by adipose tissue and are scattered in a loose submucous layer separated from the lamina propria by dense elastic networks. This oral type of mucous membrane also covers the posterior margin of the soft palate and continues upon the nasal surface. On this surface, at varying distances from the margin, the stratified epithelium is substituted by pseudostratified, ciliated columnar epithelium which rests on a thickened basement membrane. The lamina propria contains small glands of the mixed type, but no adipose tissue, and is infiltrated with lymphocytes. A dense layer of elastic fibers is found between the glands and the muscles. A submucosa is not present (Fig. 21–3).

THE TONGUE

The tongue consists of interlacing bundles of striated muscle which run in three planes and cross one another at right angles; the muscular mass is covered by a tightly adherent, mucous membrane. The dense lamina propria is fused with the interstitial connective tissue of the muscle, and a submucous layer is present only on the under surface. The lower surface of the tongue is smooth. The uneven dorsal surface in its anterior part is covered by a multitude of small excrescences—the *papillae*—while in its posterior part it presents only irregular bulgings. The boundary line between the two regions is **V**-shaped, with the opening of the angle directed forward. This is the gustatory region of the tongue. At the head of the angle is a small invagination, the *foramen caecum*. It is the rudiment of the thyroglossal duct, which in early embryonic stages connects the thyroid gland primordium with the epithelium of the oral cavity.

Papillae. Three types of papillae are present on the body of the tongue: (1) the filiform, (2) the fungiform and (3) the circumvallate. The first are arranged in more or less distinct rows diverging to the right and left from the middle line and parallel to the **V**-shaped gustatory region. The fungiform papillae are scattered singly between the filiform and are especially numerous near the end of the tongue. The circumvallate papillae, numbering ten to twelve in man, are arranged along the gustatory lines.

The *filiform papillae* are 2 to 3 mm. long. Their core is a connective tissue ridge beset

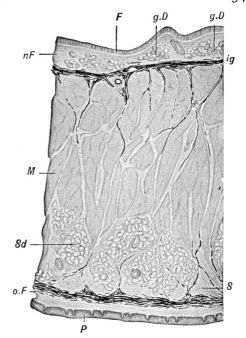

Fig. 21–3.   Portion of sagittal section through the soft palate of a girl nine years old. *nF*, nasal surface; *F*, ciliated epithelium with goblet cells; *g.D.*, mixed glands; *ig*, infraglandular layer of elastic fibers; *M*, musculature; *o.F*, oral surface; *P*, stratified squamous epithelium with papillae; *Sd*, mucous glands; *S*, submucosa. Resorcinfuchsin stain. 12 ×. (After Schumacher.)

with secondary papillae with pointed ends. The epithelium covering these connective tissue outgrowths also forms short papillae which taper into pointed processes (Fig. 21–5). In man the superficial squamous cells are transformed into hard scales containing shrunken nuclei, but no true keratin. The axial parts of the scales at the point of the papilla are connected with its solid axial strand, and their lower edges project from the surface of the papilla like the branches of a fir tree. When digestion is disturbed, the normal shedding of these scales is delayed. They then accumulate, in layers mixed with bacteria, on the surface of the tongue, which thus is covered with a gray film—the "coated" tongue.

The *fungiform papillae* have a short, slightly constricted stalk and a spherical, slightly flattened upper part. The connective tissue core forms secondary papillae; the epithelium covering them has a smooth free surface (Fig. 21–6). On many of the fungiform papillae the epithelium contains taste buds in

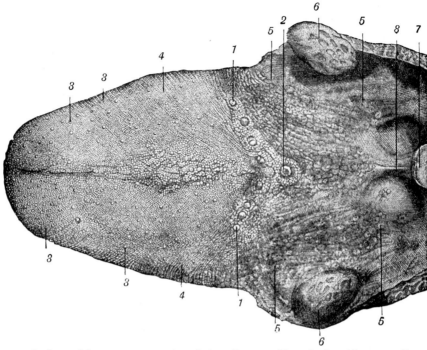

Fig. 21–4. Surface of human tongue. *1* and *2,* vallate papillae; *3,* fungiform papillae; *4,* rows of filiform papillae; *5,* lingual tonsils; *6,* palatine tonsils; *7,* epiglottis; *8,* median glosso-epiglottic fold. (After Sappey, from Schumacher.)

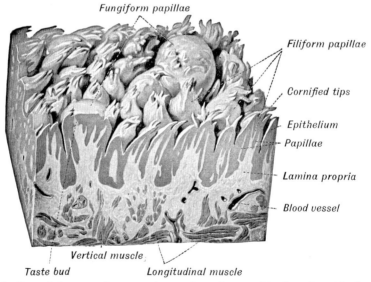

Fig. 21–5. Surface of dorsum of tongue, drawn through a combined study with the binocular microscope and of sections. The anterior cut surface corresponds with the long axis of the tongue—the tip of the tongue being to the reader's left. 16 ×. (After Braus.)

the secondary papillae. As the core is rich in blood vessels, the fungiform papillae have a marked red color.

The *circumvallate papillae* are sunk into the surface of the mucous membrane, and each is surrounded by a deep, circular furrow. The connective tissue core forms secondary papillae only on the upper surface. The covering epithelium is smooth, while that of the lateral surfaces of the papillae contains many taste buds (Figs. 21–7, 21–9).

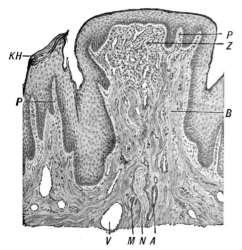

Fig. 21–6.   Perpendicular section through a fungiform papilla from the tongue of a man. *A*, artery; *B*, connective tissue stroma of the fungiform papilla; *KH*, keratohyalin granules in the superficial cells of a filiform papilla; *M*, cross-striated muscle fibers; *N*, nerve; *P*, secondary papillae; *V*, vein; *Z*, cellular stroma with lymphatic and blood vessels. 46 ×. (After Schaffer, from Schumacher.)

In a vertical section, ten to twelve of them can be seen on the lateral surface of the papilla. In the outer wall of the groove surrounding the papilla a few taste buds may be present. The number of taste buds in a single papilla is subject to great variations. On the average it has been estimated at 250.

Connected with the circumvallate papillae are glands of albuminous type (*glands of von Ebner*) whose bodies are embedded deep in the underlying muscular tissue and whose excretory ducts open into the bottom of the furrow.

On the lateral surface of the posterior part of the tongue the paired *foliate papillae* may be found. In man they are rudimentary, although in many animals they represent the main peripheral organ of taste. The fully developed foliate papillae (in the rabbit) are oval bulgings on the mucous membrane, consisting of parallel ridges with grooves between them. The epithelium of the sides of the ridges contains many taste buds. Small albuminous glands open into the bottom of the furrows.

Taste buds are also found on the glosso-palatine arch, on the soft palate, on the posterior surface of the epiglottis, and on the posterior wall of the pharynx as far down as the inferior edge of the cricoid cartilage.

The bulgings on the root of the tongue are caused by lymphatic nodules, the *lingual tonsils* and *follicles* (Fig. 12–8). On the free surface of each lingual tonsil a small opening leads into a deep invagination lined with

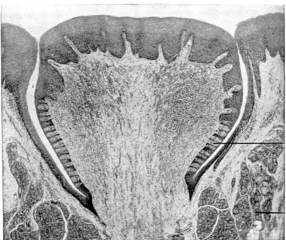

Stratified squamous epithelium

Lamina propria

Taste bud

Gland of v. Ebner

Fig. 21–7.   Section through circumvallate papilla of *Macacus rhesus*. Photomicrograph. 42 ×.

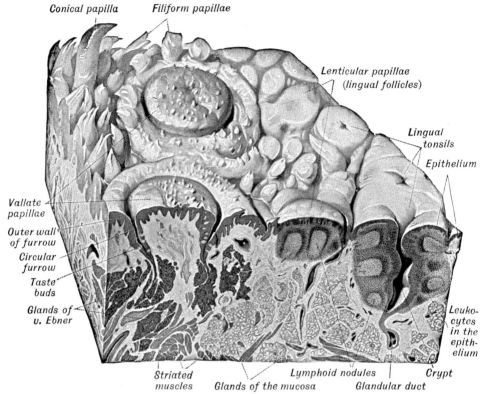

Fig. 21–8. Surface of tongue at the border between the root and the dorsum; prepared as Figure 21–5. 16 ×. (After Braus.)

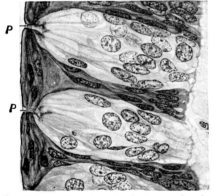

Fig. 21–9. Two taste buds from side of circumvallate papilla of *Macacus rhesus,* showing taste pores at *P.* (Drawn by Miss E. Bohlman.)

stratified squamous epithelium—the *crypt.* The epithelium of the crypt is surrounded by lymphatic tissue; innumerable lymphocytes infiltrate the epithelium and assemble in the lumen of the crypt, where they degenerate and form masses of detritus with the desquamated epithelial cells and bacteria. The lingual tonsils are often connected with mucous glands embedded in the underlying muscle tissue; their ducts open into the crypt or on the free surface.

Taste Buds. The taste buds under low power are seen in sections as pale, oval bodies in the darker stained epithelium. Their long axis averages 72 microns. They extend from the basement membrane almost to the surface. The epithelium over each taste bud is pierced by a small opening—the *outer taste pore* (Fig. 21–9).

Two cell types are usually distinguished among the constituents of a taste bud: the *supporting cells,* and the *neuro-epithelial taste cells.* The first are spindle-shaped, and their ends surround a small opening, the *inner taste pore,* which leads into a pitlike excavation. The taste cells distributed between the supporting cells vary from four to twenty per taste bud. They have a slender, rod-shaped form with a nucleus in the middle and on the free surface a short *taste hair,* which projects freely into the lumen of the pit.

There are only four fundamental taste sensations: sweet, bitter, acid, and salty. It has been shown by the application of substances to individual fungiform papillae that they differ widely in their receptive properties. Some do not give any taste sensations, while others give sensations of one or more taste qualities. No structural differences in the various taste buds have been found, in spite of the differences in sensation mediated. There is, moreover, a general chemical sensitivity in regions of the mouth where there are no taste buds.

Nerves. The anterior two thirds of the tongue is innervated by the lingual nerve, which contains trigeminal fibers of general sensibility and facialis fibers of gustatory sensibility. The latter enter the lingual nerve from the chorda tympani. The posterior third of the tongue is innervated by the glossopharyngeal nerve for both general and gustatory sensibility. Taste buds of the epiglottis and lower pharynx are innervated by the vagus. These nerve fibers are lightly myelinated. They branch profusely under the basement membrane, lose their myelin, and form a subepithelial plexus, from which fibers penetrate the epithelium. Some terminate as intergemmal fibers by free arborization between the taste buds; others, the perigemmal fibers, closely envelop the taste buds; and still others, the intragemmal fibers, penetrate the taste buds and end with small terminal enlargements in intimate contact with the taste cells. The functional significance of these different nerve endings is unknown.

GLANDS OF THE ORAL CAVITY

General Description. Numerous *salivary glands* open into the oral cavity. Many of them are small glands in the mucosa or submucosa and are named according to their location. They seem to secrete continuously and furnish a liquid, the *saliva,* which moistens the oral mucous membrane. In addition, there are three pairs of large glands which constitute the salivary glands proper. They are the *parotid,* the *mandibular* (*submaxillary*), and the *sublingual* glands. They secrete only when mechanical, thermal or chemical stimuli act upon the nerve endings in the oral mucous membrane, and as the result of certain psychic or olfactory stimuli. The saliva secreted by the large glands may be abundant and helps prepare the food for digestion in the stomach and intestine.

The *saliva* collected from the oral cavity is a mixture of the secretions of the various salivary glands. It is a viscous, colorless, opalescent liquid which contains water, mucin, some proteins, mineral salts, and an enzyme (*ptyalin*) which splits starch into water-soluble, less complex carbohydrates. Saliva always contains a number of desquamated squamous epithelial cells and *salivary corpuscles;* most of the latter originate in the follicles of the tongue and in the tonsils, and are degenerated lymphocytes or granulocytes.

The quality of the saliva collected from the oral cavity varies with the predominant participation of one or the other of the glands in its formation. But even the secretion of one gland may change considerably with variations in the stimuli acting upon the oral mucous membrane, as, for instance, with different kinds of food.

These glands may be classified in three categories according to the type of their secretory cells. The glands containing only *mucous* cells elaborate a viscid secretion which consists almost exclusively of mucin. In glands with only *albuminous* cells the secretion is a "serous" or "albuminous," watery liquid which lacks mucus, but contains salts, proteins and ptyalin. In the *mixed glands*—containing serous and mucous cells—the secretion is a viscid liquid containing mucin, salts and ptyalin.

All glands of the oral cavity have a system of branching excretory ducts. The secretory portions in the pure mucous glands are usually long, branching tubules. In the pure albuminous and mixed glands the secretory portions vary from oval to tubulo-acinar forms provided with irregular outpocketings.

The initial intralobular ducts are thin, branched tubules called the *necks* or *intercalated ducts.* The next larger order of branches, also located in the interior of the smallest lobules, has a striated epithelium; these ducts are called "striated" tubules. Then follow the larger branches; among them (in the large glands) lobular, sublobular, interlobular, and primary ducts may be distinguished.

Mucous Cells. In the pure mucous glands the cells are arranged in a layer against the basement membrane and have an irregularly cuboidal form. In fresh condition their cytoplasm contains many pale droplets of *mucigen,* the antecedent of mucin, while the nucleus is invisible. In fixed and stained sections the droplets of mucigen are usually destroyed, so that the cell body appears clear and contains an artificial network of cytoplasm and precipitated mucigen. This network stains like mucin, that is, red with mucicarmine, or metachromatically purple with thionine. The nucleus is at the base of the cell and usually appears angular and compressed by the accumulation of mucigen. Between the droplets of mucigen a few mitochondria and fragments of a Golgi net can be found. The free surface of the mucous cells is usually provided with a network of terminal bars. Secretory canaliculi are absent. Usually the lumen of the terminal portions is large and filled with masses of mucin.

When the secretion leaves the cell, it collapses, its cytoplasm increases relatively in amount, and only a few granules of mucigen may remain confined to its free surface. The nucleus rises from the base of the cell and becomes round. In this condition the mucous cells may be mistaken for albuminous cells. The absence of secretory capillaries always distinguishes them from albuminous cells. The demonstration of these capillaries requires special staining methods. Under physio-logical conditions, the mucous cells rarely discharge all their granules.

The most reliable criterion for separating mucous and serous cells is the positive staining of mucus in the former. The staining reactions of the mucin elaborated by different mucous cells is not the same even in the same gland. Sometimes the mucous cell contains fat droplets. The mucous cells, as a rule, do not show any signs of degeneration; mitoses have occasionally been observed in them.

Albuminous Cells. These elements, when filled with secretion in a resting gland, in fresh condition, contain a multitude of small, highly refractile *secretion granules* in a homogeneous cytoplasm. The cell boundaries are not distinct. The roughly cuboidal cells surround a small tubular lumen.

The secretory granules of the albuminous cells accumulate between the nucleus and the free surface. After the gland has secreted for a certain time, the albuminous cells diminish in size; their granules become less numerous and are confined to the free sur-

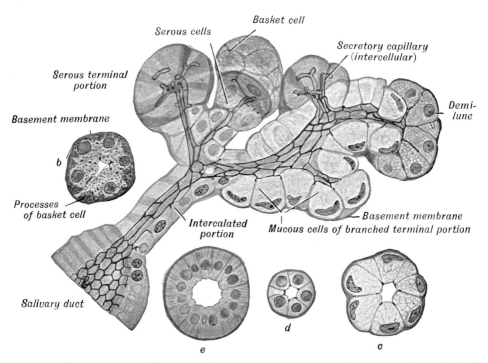

Fig. 21–10. Reconstruction of a terminal portion, with its duct, of a submaxillary gland. *b,* cross section of a purely serous terminal portion, showing basal lamellae; *c,* cross section through a purely mucous terminal portion; *d,* cross section through an intercalated portion; *e,* cross section through a salivary duct. (Redrawn and modified after a reconstruction by Vierling, from Braus.)

face of the cells. In extreme, nonphysiological cases, all the granules may disappear. As the albuminous cells are probably the source of ptyalin, the granules are to be looked upon as zymogen granules, the antecedents of the enzyme. Before leaving the cell they are transformed into secretory vacuoles.

In cells crowded with secretion the nucleus is spherical, small and darkly staining; it occupies a position at the base of the cell and may show irregular indentations. Besides the secretory granules, the cytoplasm contains rod-shaped mitochondria and a Golgi net above the nucleus. A cytocentrum near the free surface is distinct only in empty cells.

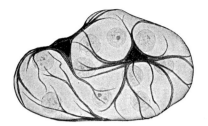

Fig. 21–11. Branching basal (basket or myoepithelial) cells with dark fibrils; from an albuminous terminal portion of human submaxillary gland. Iron-hematoxylin stain. Oil immersion. (After Zimmermann.)

At the base of the cell around the nucleus, and sometimes above it, is an accumulation of chromophile substance, apparently ribose nucleoprotein, which stains darkly with basic dyes and, owing to its arrangement in parallel lamellae, causes a vertical striation. By appropriate technique, mitochondria can be demonstrated between the lamellae. The albuminous cells often contain fat or glycogen. On their free surfaces the albuminous cells are provided with a system of terminal bars; between their lateral surfaces there are always secretory capillaries. Mitoses occur occasionally.

The albuminous cells of the different glands of the mouth are not identical functionally, although they may seem to have the same structure. They are combined into one group and given a general name, because histological methods are not sensitive enough to make the differences visible microscopically. In many cases their secretory granules give a more or less distinct staining reaction for mucus with mucicarmine; such cells are called "muco-albuminous" or "mucoserous."

Cells in the Mixed Glands. The relative number of the two kinds of glandular cells in the mixed glands varies within wide limits. In some cases the albuminous cells are far more numerous than the mucous cells, while in other cases the reverse is true; in still other instances both cell types are present in about equal numbers. The mucous and albuminous cells line different parts of the terminal portion. In those mixed glands in which the albuminous cells predominate, some of the terminal portions may be exclusively albuminous. In others a part of the secretory portion is lined with mucous, and a part with serous cells. In sections the mucous portions can often be recognized by their clear aspect, but more certainly by their color after specific staining of the mucus.

As a rule, the mucous cells are near the excretory ducts, while the serous cells are confined to the blind end of the secretory portion. It is quite probable that the mucous cells in mixed glands arise through the mucous transformation of the cells in the smallest excretory ducts, the *necks* or intercalated ducts. Sometimes single mucous cells are scattered between the unchanged cells of the neck. In other cases the part of the neck directly adjoining the terminal portion is lined exclusively with mucous cells. If the mucous transformation affects all the cells in the neck, this part of the ducts ceases to exist as such. If the mucous cells are not numerous, the secretory portion of the gland will show an irregular mixture of pale mucous, and dark albuminous cells.

If the mucous cells are much more numerous, the albuminous cells are pushed to the blind ends of the terminal portion or into saccular outpocketings. Here they form small groups which in sections appear as darkly staining crescents surrounding the mucous tubules (*demilunes* of Gianuzzi). In them the albuminous cells are small and of irregular shape, and often seem to be entirely separated from the lumen by the large mucous cells. However, there are always secretory capillaries which lead the secretion through the clefts between the mucous cells into the lumen (Fig. 21–10).

Basal (Basket) Cells. In all the glands of

the oral cavity the epithelium in the terminal portion, as well as in the excretory ducts, is provided with basal cells. They lie between the glandular cells and the basement membrane, and appear as slender spindles; usually only their nuclei can be discerned. When seen from the surface, they exhibit a stellate cell body with an angular nucleus and processes containing darkly staining fibrils.

The basal cells are supposed to act as smooth muscle cells and to facilitate the movement of the secretion into the excretory

Fig. 21–12. Cross sections of two isthmuses from human submaxillary gland, each showing three basal cells. *a,* thin and, *b,* thicker canal belonging to purely albuminous terminal portions. In *b* a fixed connective tissue cell is adhering to the basement membrane. (After Zimmermann.)

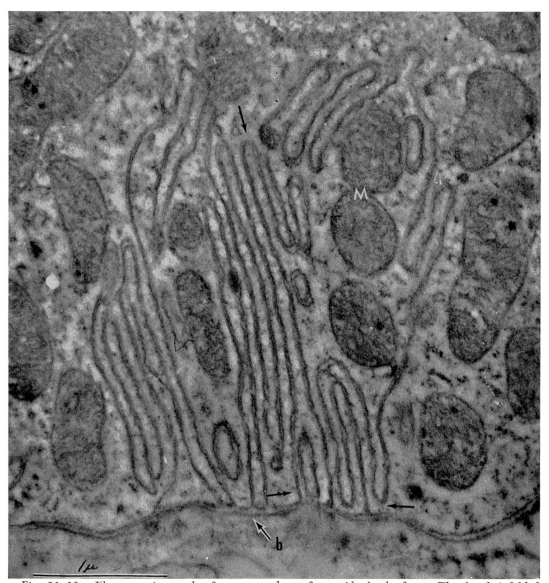

Fig. 21–13. Electron micrograph of secretory duct of parotid gland of rat. The basal infolded membranes (arrows) are shown sectioned at right angles to the base. *b,* basement membrane; *M,* mitochondria. Buffered osmic acid fixation. (Courtesy of D. C. Pease and B. Scott.)

ducts; they are sometimes called "myo-epithelial cells." They are like the myo-epithelial cells of the sweat glands.

Excretory Ducts. The necks, of variable length and branching, have a low cuboidal epithelium. Between its cells and the basement membrane are scattered basal cells. The epithelium of the necks often shows a mucoid transformation.

In the columnar epithelium of the striated tubules the lower parts of the cell bodies show a parallel striation, caused by parallel rows of mitochondria (Fig. 21–10, *e*). As in other epithelia where there is intense exchange of water, numerous infoldings of the basal surface of the cells in the striated ducts are visible with the electron microscope (Fig. 21–13).

The epithelium of the striated tubules is believed by some to contribute water and calcium salts to the secretion. These tubules (as well as the larger ducts) sometimes present a succession of constricted and dilated sections. In the larger ducts the epithelium is columnar and pseudostratified, and occasionally contains goblet cells. Nearing the opening on the mucous membrane, it becomes stratified for a short stretch and is then succeeded by stratified squamous epithelium.

CLASSIFICATION OF ORAL GLANDS BY LOCATION

A. Glands which open into the vestibule of the mouth:
    1. Parotid gland, with a duct opening into the vestibule
    2. Labial glands, scattered in the mucous membrane of the upper and lower lips
    3. Buccal glands, a continuation of the labial glands in the mucous membrane of the cheek
B. Glands which open on the bottom of the oral cavity, between the tongue and the mandible:
    1. Mandibular (submaxillary) gland—a large gland with a duct opening at the side of the frenulum of the tongue
    2. Sublingual glands, situated beneath the mucous membrane at the side of the frenulum of the tongue. Among them:
        (*a*) The large sublingual gland with a duct opening into the duct of the mandibular gland
        (*b*) Several small glands varying in number and size. Their ducts open in many places along a fold of the mucous membrane, the plica sublingualis. At the posterior end of this group are the small glosso-palatine glands.
C. Glands of the tongue:
    1. Anterior lingual gland (gland of Blandin or Nunn), situated at the side of the median line under the apex of the tongue
    2. Posterior lingual glands:
        (*a*) Albuminous or gustatory glands (of von Ebner) connected with the circumvallate papillae and opening into the circumvallate groove
        (*b*) Mucous glands of the root of the tongue.
D. Glands of the palate.

In the various mammals the glands of the oral cavity show great structural differences.

The following descriptions hold only for man:

The *parotid* is a pure albuminous gland. The necks are long and may branch several times. Their cells never undergo a mucous transformation. The striated tubules are fairly numerous. In the parotid gland of the newborn, however, the glandular cells often give a distinct staining reaction for mucus with mucicarmin.

In the *mandibular gland* the majority of the secretory portions are purely albuminous, while some are mucous with albuminous cells in the blind ends. Typical demilunes are rare. In some persons many of the albuminous cells show a slight mucoid reaction. The mucous cells are smaller than in the sublingual or the pure mucous glands. Some of the necks are short; others are long and branching. The striated tubules are numerous and long, and have many branches.

The *sublingual glands* are mixed glands with a markedly varying structure in their different parts. The mucous cells are far more numerous than in the mandibular gland, while the albuminous cells are in the minority and have a pronounced muco-albuminous character. For the most part they are arranged in thick demilunes, and the isthmuses are extremely variable in length; many undergo a complete mucous transformation, so that the terminal portions abut directly on the striated tubules. The latter are scarce and short and are sometimes represented by small groups of irregular, striated cells in the epithelium of the interlobular ducts.

In the *posterior lingual glands* the secretory portions are long-branching, sometimes anastomosing tubules. They contain only albuminous cells, which sometimes show a

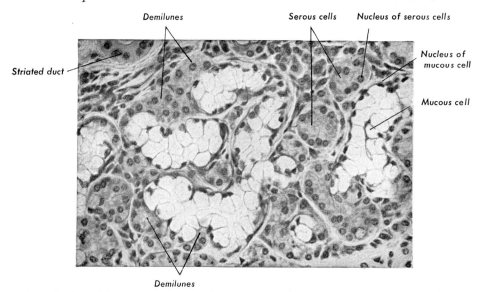

Fig. 21–14.   Section of human mandibular gland with mucous, serous and mixed terminal portions, and demilunes. Photomicrograph. H + E. 240 ×. (After von Herrath and Abramow.)

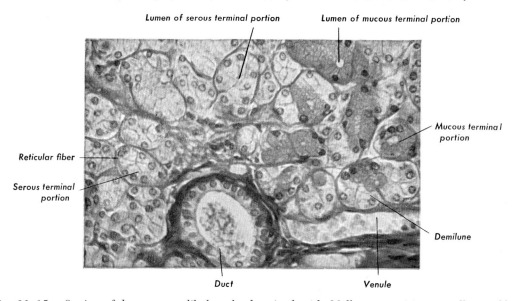

Fig. 21–15.   Section of human mandibular gland stained with Mallory-azan. Mucous cells are blue stained. Photomicrograph. 240 ×. (After von Herrath and Abramow.)

slight reaction for mucus. These glands are rarely of mixed character. The system of the excretory ducts is poorly developed; isthmuses and short tubes are absent. These glands form a thin, serous secretion, which is found only on the furrows of the circumvallate papilla and evidently serves to wash out the taste buds.

The *glossopalatine glands* are pure mucous glands.

The *anterior lingual gland,* in its posterior part, consists of mixed branched tubules, which contain mucous cells and, on their blind ends, thin demilunes of muco-albuminous cells. The anterior part contains secretory portions with muco-albuminous cells only.

The *labial* and *buccal glands* are of the mixed type. The secretory portion sometimes contains only muco-albuminous cells, but in most cases the latter are confined to the blind end, while the rest of the cavity is lined with mucous cells. Some of the secretory parts may contain only mucous cells. As the necks are short and branch but little, the mucous secretory portions often pass directly into striated tubules.

The *glands of the root of the tongue* and the *palatine glands* are of the pure mucous variety. Short isthmuses have been found in the latter group.

Interstitial Connective Tissue; Blood and Lymphatic Vessels. In the interstitial reticular connective tissue of the salivary glands are fibroblasts and macrophages, with fat cells scattered singly or in small groups; plasma cells are of common occurrence. Occasionally, small lymphocytes are also found. The larger blood vessels follow the excretory ducts; the loose capillary networks surround the ducts and the terminal portions. The lymph vessels are said to be scarce.

Nerves. Each salivary gland is provided with sensory nerve endings and two kinds of efferent secretory nerves, parasympathetic (cerebral) and sympathetic fibers. The cerebral preganglionic fibers for the mandibular and sublingual glands run in the chorda tympani nerve to the submaxillary ganglion; the sympathetic preganglionic fibers reach the superior cervical ganglion. From here the postganglionic fibers follow along the carotid artery. The vasodilators are believed to be included in the chorda tympani, the vasoconstrictors in the sympathetic nerves.

The parotid gland receives its secretory fibers from the glossopharyngeal nerve. In the interstitial tissue along the course of its blood vessels, plexuses of myelinated (preganglionic and sensory) and nonmyelinated fibers, and, close to the larger excretory ducts, groups of sympathetic multipolar nerve cells are found. On the outer surface of the terminal portions, nonmyelinated fibers form a network which sends small branches through the basement membranes. These branches form a second network on the inner surface of the membrane, and from this plexus small, final branches penetrate between the glandular cells, branch, and end on their surfaces with small, budlike thickenings.

Stimulation of the cerebral nerves of the mandibular gland causes the secretion of an abundant, thin saliva rich in water and salts, but poor in organic substances. Stimulation of the sympathetic nerve, on the contrary, yields a small quantity of thick saliva, with a high content of organic substances. The mechanism of the action of the nerves upon the glandular cells and the role of the vasodilators in the secretion are not known, and the presence of different kinds of nerve endings has not been proved. It is even doubtful whether the secretory fibers in the chorda tympani and in the sympathetic are of different nature.

After sectioning of the chorda tympani nerve in the dog, the so-called "paralytic" secretion in the

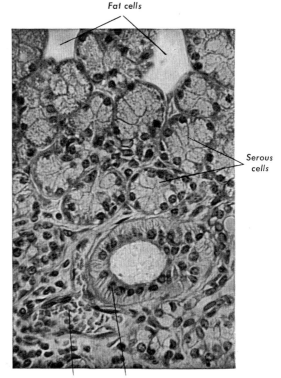

Fat cells

Serous cells

Venule   Striated duct

Fig. 21–16. Section of human parotid gland, showing serous terminal portions and a striated duct. Photomicrograph. H + E. 300 ×. (After von Herrath and Abramow.)

corresponding submaxillary and retrolingual glands occurs. This secretion is accompanied by intense degeneration and atrophy of the gland cells, especially the mucous elements in the retrolingual gland.

Histogenesis of the Glands of the Oral Cavity. Each gland arises at a certain time of fetal life, at a particular place in the wall of the embryonic oral cavity, through the growth of a solid epithelial bud into the subjacent mesenchyme. The large glands, such as the submaxillary and the parotid, appear in embryos of six and eight weeks respectively; the smaller ones later. The epithelial bud grows and ramifies into a branched, treelike structure with club-shaped ends. It consists of undifferentiated polyhedral or cuboidal epithelial cells with many mitoses. Gradually a lumen appears in the older parts of the primordium, and this canalization proceeds distally, but does not reach the terminal branches as long as these continue to grow and to form additional buds. When the lumen reaches the terminal bud, the latter ceases to grow, and only specific differentiation and enlargement of its cells occur. Mucigen appears in the mucous cells and zymogen granules in the serous ones. The histogenetic development of the glands continues after birth.

TONSILS

The aperture by which the oral cavity communicates with the next section of the digestive tract, the pharynx, is called the *fauces*. In this region the mucous membrane of the digestive tract contains accumulations of lymphatic tissue. Besides small infiltrations with lymphocytes, which may occur anywhere in this part of the mucous membrane, well-outlined organs are formed by the lymphatic tissue. The surface epithelium invaginates them, and they are called "tonsils." The lingual tonsils have been described (p. 349).

Between the glossopalatine and pharyngopalatine arches are the *palatine tonsils*. These are two oval, prominent accumulations of lymphatic tissue in the connective tissue of the mucous membrane, with ten to twenty deep *crypts*. The stratified squamous epithelium of the free surface overlies a thin layer of fibrous connective tissue with papillae. The *crypts* almost reach the connective tissue *capsule* and are of simple or branching form.

The nodules with their prominent centers are embedded in a diffuse mass of dense lymphatic tissue 1 to 2 mm. thick, and are usually arranged in a single layer under the epithelium. The crypts with their surrounding sheaths of lymphatic tissue are partially separated from one another by thin partitions of loose connective tissue which invaginate from the capsule. In this connective tissue there are always lymphocytes of various sizes, and mast and plasma cells. The presence of large numbers of heterophile leukocytes indicates inflammation, which is common in mild degree. Frequently there are islands of cartilage or bone, which probably indicate a pathological process. In the deeper portion of the crypts, the limit between the epithelium and the lymphatic tissue is effaced in most places by an intense infiltration of the epithelium with lymphocytes. The epithelial cells are pushed aside and disfigured, so that sometimes only a few remain on the surface. Heterophile leukocytes are always present in small numbers. Plasma cells are common here.

The lymphocytes which pass through the epithelium are found in the saliva as the *salivary corpuscles*. They appear here usually

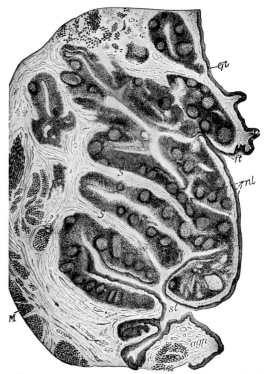

Fig. 21–17.   Section through palatine tonsil of man. *agp,* glossopalatine arch; *ep,* stratified squamous epithelium; *ft,* crypt; *M,* striated muscle; *nl,* lymphoid nodules; *S,* connective tissue septa; *st,* remains of tonsillar sinus. 6½ ×. (After Sobotta.)

as degenerating vesicular elements with a more or less constricted nucleus and granules which show brownian movement. The salivary corpuscles which originate from heterophile leukocytes are recognized by the remnants of the granules and the polymorphous nucleus.

The lumen of the crypts may contain large accumulations of living and degenerated lymphocytes mixed with desquamated squamous epithelial cells, granular detritus and microorganisms. These masses may increase in size and form cheesy plugs which are gradually eliminated. If they remain for a long time, they may calcify. The microorganisms are sometimes the cause of inflammation and suppuration; they may be responsible for some general infections.

Many small glands are connected with the palatine tonsils; their bodies are outside the capsule, and their ducts open for the most part on the free surface. Openings into the crypts seem rare.

In the roof (fornix) and somewhat to the

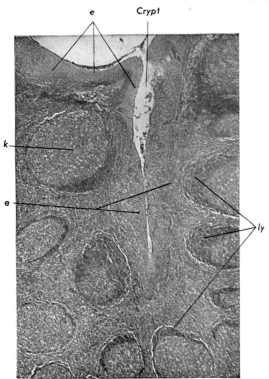

Fig. 21–18. Section of human tonsil. *e,* stratified squamous epithelium of surface; *k,* germinal center; *ly,* concentration of lymphocytes toward the epithelium. H + E. 12 ×. (After von Herrath and Abramow.)

posterior wall of the nasal part of the pharynx is the unpaired *pharyngeal tonsil.* In this region the mucous membrane shows numerous folds, but no crypts. The epithelium on its surface is the same as in the rest of the respiratory passages—pseudostratified, ciliated columnar epithelium with many goblet cells. Small patches of stratified squamous epithelium are common, however. The epithelium is abundantly infiltrated with lymphocytes, especially on the crests of the folds. A 2-mm. thick layer of diffuse and nodular lymphatic tissue is found under the epithelium and participates in the formation of its fold; it is separated from the surrounding parts by a thin capsule which contains many elastic networks and sends thin partitions into the core of the folds. Outside the capsule are small glands of mixed character. Their ducts—often markedly dilated—traverse the lymphatic tissue and empty into the furrows or on the free surface of the folds.

Other small accumulations of lymphatic tissue occur in the mucous membrane of the pharynx, around the orifices of the eustachian tube behind the pharyngopalatine arches, and in the posterior wall.

Unlike the lymph nodes, the tonsils do not have lymphatic sinuses, and lymph is not filtered through them. However, netlike plexuses of blindly ending lymph capillaries surround their outer surface.

The tonsils generally reach their maximal development in childhood. The involution of the palatine tonsils seems to begin about the age of fifteen, while the follicles of the root of the tongue persist longer. The pharyngeal tonsil in the adult is usually found in an atrophic condition, with its ciliated epithelium in great part replaced by stratified squamous epithelium.

The participation of the tonsils in the new formation of lymphocytes is the only established function that can be ascribed to them. It is generally believed, but not proved, that the infiltration of its epithelium with lymphocytes has something to do with the protection of the organism against the penetration of noxious agents and especially of microorganisms into the body. Pathogenic bacteria have been found in the lymphatic tissue of the tonsils (and the nodules of the intestine) as an apparently normal phenomenon. It has been suggested that the bacteria penetrating the lymphatic tissue are made less virulent, and that they then act as antigens and instigate the production of antibodies. On the other hand, the tonsils (and the nodules of the intestine) have been shown to be the portals of entry for pathogenic microorganisms, and general infections have been traced from them.

The palatine tonsils develop from the rudiments of the dorsal part of the second gill pouch. During the fourth month of fetal life the epithelium pushes solid outgrowths into the subjacent connective tissue; these later become hollow. Around these epithelial growths, lymphatic tissue gradually develops through isolation and mobilization of mesenchyme cells which are transformed into lymphocytes, while the cells which remain fixed furnish the reticular framework.

THE PHARYNX

The posterior continuation of the oral cavity is the pharynx. In this section of the

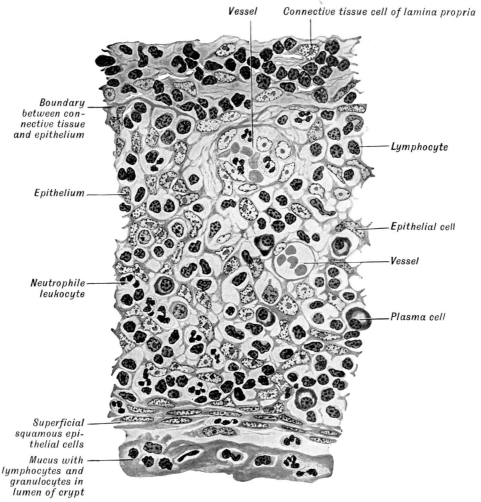

Vessel   *Connective tissue cell of lamina propria*

Boundary between con- nective tissue and epithelium

Lymphocyte

Epithelium

Epithelial cell

Vessel

Neutrophile leukocyte

Plasma cell

Superficial squamous epi- thelial cells

Mucus with lymphocytes and granulocytes in lumen of crypt

Fig. 21–19. Human tonsil; infiltration of the epithelium of the crypt with lymphocytes, neutrophile (heterophile) granular leukocytes and plasma cells. Hematoxylin-eosin-azure stain. 520 ×. (A.A.M.)

digestive tract the respiratory passages and the pathway for the food cross and fuse with each other. The upper part of the pharynx is the nasal, the middle the oral, and the lower the laryngeal portion. In the upper part it approaches the structure of the res- piratory system, while in the lower it cor- responds more to the general plan of the digestive tube.

Instead of a muscularis mucosae, the mu- cous membrane is provided with a thick, dense, netlike elastic layer. A loose submu- cous layer is well developed only in the lat- eral sides of the nasal part of the pharynx and where the pharynx continues into the esophagus; here the elastic layer becomes thinner. In all other places the mucous mem-

brane is directly adjacent to the muscular wall, which consists of an inner longitudinal and an outer oblique or circular layer of striated muscle. The elastic layer fuses with the interstitial tissue of the muscle and sends strands of elastic fibers between the muscular bundles. In the fornix it is fused with the periosteum of the base of the skull.

The lamina propria mucosae consists of dense connective tissue containing fine elas- tic networks; those places covered with strati- fied squamous epithelium are provided with small papillae. In the area covered with pseudostratified ciliated columnar epithelium there are no papillae.

The two lower sections of the pharynx and a part of the nasal region have stratified

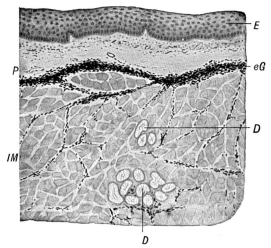

Fig. 21–20. Cross section through posterior pharyngeal wall of human adult. *E*, stratified squamous epithelium; *P*, lamina propria mucosae; *eG*, elastic boundary layer separating the lamina propria from the longitudinal muscular layer, *lM*; *D*, mucous glands deep in the muscle. Resorcinfuchsin and hematoxylin stains. 50 × .(After Schumacher.)

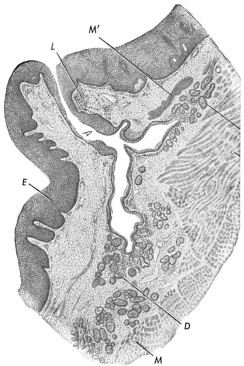

Fig. 21–21. Wall of the pharynx, of an eleven-year-old girl, in longitudinal section. *A*, opening of a mucous gland, *D*, at the apex of a fold of the mucosa; *E*, stratified squamous epithelium; *L*, accumulation of leukocytes around the orifice of the gland; *M*, muscular layer; *M′*, muscle fibers pushed aside by the body of the gland. 27 ×. (After Schaffer.)

squamous epithelium; toward the roof (fornix) of the pharynx its epithelium first becomes stratified columnar and then pseudostratified columnar ciliated, with many goblet cells. On the lateral sides of the nasal part this ciliated epithelium continues downward beyond the aperture of the eustachian tube. With age the ciliated epithelium may be replaced by stratified squamous epithelium over large areas.

Glands of a pure mucous type are found in those places lined with stratified squamous epithelium. They are always located under the elastic layer, sometimes deep in the muscle. Glands of mixed type, similar to those of the dorsal surface of the soft palate, are confined to the regions covered with ciliated epithelium.

REFERENCES

Arey, L. B.: On the development, morphology and interpretation of a system of crypt analogues in the pharyngeal tonsil. Am. J. Anat., *80*:203, 1947.

Becks, H., and Wainwright, W. W.: Rate of flow of resting saliva of healthy individuals. J. Dent. Research, *22*:391, 1943.

Bensley, R. R.: Observations on the salivary glands of mammals. Anat. Rec., *2*:105, 1908.

Kolmer, W.: Geschmacksorgan, in von Möllendorff's Handbuch der mikr. Anat. des Menschen. Berlin, 1927, Vol. 3, Pt. 1, p. 154.

Langley, O.: On the changes in serous glands during secretion. J. Physiol., *2*:1880.

Maximow, A. A.: Beiträge zur Histologie und Physiologie der Speicheldrüsen. Arch. f. mikr. Anat., *58*:1, 1901.

Rawlinson, H. E.: The changes in the cells of the striated ducts of the cat's submaxillary gland after autonomic stimulation and nerve section. Anat. Rec., *63*:295, 1935.

Schumacher, S.: Die Mundhöhle, in von Möllendorff's Handbuch der mikr. Anat. des Menschen. Berlin, 1927, Vol. 5, Pt. 1, p. 1; Die Zunge, ibid., 35, 1927; Der Schlundkopf. ibid., 290, 1927.

Stormont, D. L.: The Salivary Glands, in Cowdry's Special Cytology. 2d ed. New York, (1), 151, 1932.

Zimmermann, K. W.: Die Speicheldrüsen. Handb. d. mikr. Anat. (von Möllendorff), (5), 1927.

CHAPTER 22

The Teeth

THE TEETH are derivatives of the oral mucous membrane. They may be considered modified papillae whose surface is covered by a thick layer of calcified substance originating in part from epithelium, and in part from connective tissue. The most primitive type of teeth, in which the character of cutaneous papillae is quite evident, is found in the placoid scales scattered all over the surface of the body of the selachians. Similar structures develop in many parallel rows in the mucous membrane of the oral cavity of the fishes, where they are subject to continuous renewal during life.

Two sets of teeth have to be distinguished in man and most mammals. The first set forms the *primary* or *deciduous teeth* of childhood; their eruption starts about the seventh month after birth, and they are shed between the sixth and thirteenth years. They are gradually replaced by the *permanent teeth*. The microscopic structure of both kinds of teeth is similar in principle, but the permanent tooth reaches a higher development. Each of the various types of teeth in each set has a different form adapted to its specific functions, i.e., the incisors for biting and the molars for grinding and pounding the food.

All teeth consist of the same two portions, the *crown,* projecting above the gingiva (gum), and the tapering *root,* which fits into an excavation, the *alveolus,* of the maxillary or mandibular bone. Where the crown and the root meet is sometimes called the *neck.* The lower molars have two, the upper molars three, roots. The tooth contains a

small cavity which corresponds roughly with the outer form of the tooth. It is called the *pulp cavity* and continues into each root as a narrow canal that communicates through one or more openings at the apex of the root with the *periodontal membrane.*

The *hard portions of a tooth* consist of three different tissues: dentin, enamel, and cementum. The bulk of the tooth is formed by the *dentin,* or ivory, which surrounds the pulp cavity. It is thickest in the crown and tapers down to the points of the roots. Its outer surface is covered, in the region of the crown, by a layer of enamel, which reaches its greatest thickness on the exposed part of the crown and thins down toward the neck. In the region of the root the dentin is covered by a thin layer of *cementum* which leaves the opening of the canal free. The edge of the enamel meets the cementum at the neck.

The *soft parts* associated with the tooth are (1) the pulp, which fills the pulp cavity; (2) the periodontal membrane, which connects the cementum-covered surface of the root with the bone of the alveolus; (3) the gingiva, that portion of the oral mucous membrane surrounding the tooth. In young persons the gingiva is attached to the enamel; with increasing age it gradually recedes from the enamel, so that in old people it is attached to the cementum.

Dentin. The dentin is yellowish and semi-transparent in fresh condition; when dried, it acquires a silky appearance because air has entered its tubules. It is harder than compact

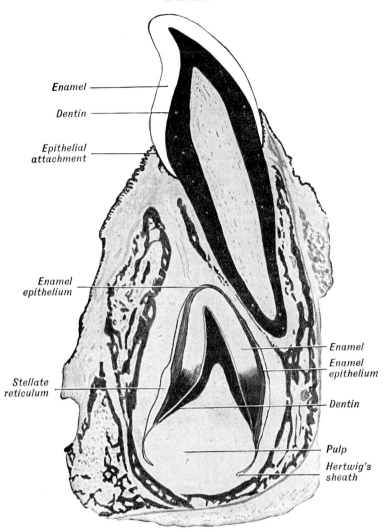

Fig. 22–1. Diagram of deciduous tooth and its corresponding permanent tooth germ (below). Note the surrounding alveolar bone. Retouched photomicrograph. 8 ×. (Courtesy of B. Orban.)

bone, although it resembles bone in its structure, chemical nature, and development.

As in bone, the substance of macerated dentin consists of an organic (28 per cent) and an inorganic (72 per cent) part. They can be separated by decalcification in acids, when the organic part remains and the substance becomes soft, or by incineration when only the inorganic material remains. The latter is much the same as in bone except that it is denser and less soluble. The organic part contains a glycoprotein, dissolves in boiling water, and yields a solution of gelatin.

In a ground section passing through the axis of a macerated tooth, the dentin has a radially striated appearance. This is caused by the presence of innumerable, minute canals, the *dentinal tubules,* which diverge from the pulp cavity toward the periphery and penetrate every part of the dentin. Near the pulp in the innermost part of the dentin, their diameter is 3-4 microns; in the outer portions they become narrower. On their way from the pulp cavity most of the tubules describe an **S**-shaped curve. The tubules branch and, especially in the outer layers of dentin, frequently form loop-shaped anastomoses.

The layer of dentin which is immediately adjacent to the tubules and surrounds them as a sheath of Neumann differs from the rest of the dentin by its high refringence and distinct staining in decalcified specimens.

Between the dentinal tubules are systems of collagenous fibrils arranged in bundles 2 to 4 microns thick and kept together by a cementing substance, containing glycoprotein; they correspond to the ossein fibrils of bone.

The course of the fibrillar bundles is, in general, parallel to the long axis of the tooth

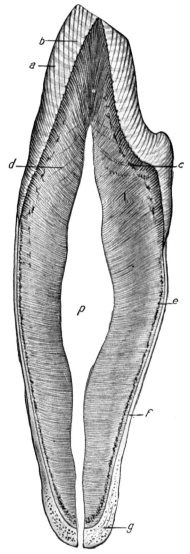

Fig. 22–2. Longitudinal ground section of human cuspid. The top of the crown has been abraded. *a,* parallel stripes of Retzius; *b,* Schreger's lines of the enamel; *c,* large interglobular space (of Owen); *d,* dentin; *e,* Tomes' granular layer of the dentin; *f,* cell-free and, *g,* cellular cementum of root; *p,* pulp cavity. 7 ×. (After von Ebner, from Schaffer.)

and perpendicular to the dentinal tubules. They also run obliquely and around the tubules; in the crown they are tangential to the free surface. The fibrils in the adjacent layers form angles of varying degrees— smaller in the outermost portions of the dentin and larger in the proximity of the pulp cavity.

Some investigators distinguish a peripheral layer of *cover dentin,* with coarser fibers, from the *circumpulpar dentin,* which forms the inner mass and consists of thinner fibrils.

The calcification of the developing dentin is not always complete and uniform. The deposits of calcium salts which appear during development in the organic ground substance have the form of spheres which gradually gain in size and finally fuse. In incompletely calcified regions, between the calcified spheres, there remain angular "interglobular" spaces which contain only the organic matrix of the dentin. The dentinal tubules continue without interruption through the spheres and interglobular spaces. In a macerated tooth, from which all organic parts have disappeared, the tubules as well as the interglobular spaces are filled with air and appear dark in transmitted light. In many otherwise normal teeth there are layers of large, interglobular spaces in the deeper parts of the enamel-covered dentin of the crown—

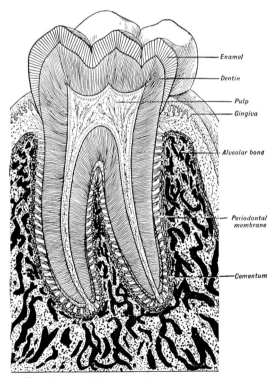

Fig. 22–3. Diagram of sagittal section of adult human lower first permanent molar. (Courtesy of I. Schour.)

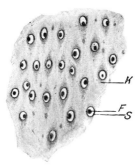

Fig. 22–4. Tangential section through the root of a molar of an ape. *F*, shrunken dentinal fiber; *S*, margin of the tubules (Neumann's sheath); *K*, matrix. 740 ×. (After Schaffer.)

the *lines of Owen*. Immediately under the dentino-cemental junction, in the root there is always a layer of small interglobular spaces, the *granular layer of Tomes* (Fig. 22–2, *e*).

In sections through a decalcified tooth fixed with its soft parts, each dentinal tubule contains a protoplasmic fiber (of Tomes) which in life probably completely fills the lumen of the tubule, but which in fixed preparations appears shrunken. When the tubules are seen in cross section, each small oval contains a dark dot. These fibers of Tomes are processes of the *odontoblasts*, which are arranged on the wall of the pulp cavity and send their protoplasmic processes into the dentinal tubules.

The dentin is sensitive to touch, to cold, to acid-containing foods, and the like. Only occasional nerve fibers penetrate the dentin and extend for short distances. It is believed that the fibers of Tomes transmit the sensory stimulation to the pulp, which contains many nerves.

With the aid of radioactive phosphorus it has been shown that there is an active interchange of calcium and phosphorus between dentin and enamel on one hand and the blood on the other. The interchange persists on a diminished scale via the dentino-cemental junction in teeth in which the pulp cavity has been filled.

In bone the cells are evenly distributed in the hard intercellular substance and send their processes out in all directions, while the cells of dentin remain on the surface of the intercellular substance and only send their processes into it. Although the odontoblasts undoubtedly play a role in the nutrition of the dentin, the latter does not become

Fig. 22–5. Ground cross section of crown of a human cuspid. *D*, dentin; *G*, wavy boundary between enamel and dentin; *O*, surface of the tooth; *RL*, parallel stripes of Retzius; *SB*, enamel tuft. 80 ×. (After Schaffer.)

necrotic after the removal of the pulp and the "filling" of a tooth.

In old age the dentinal tubules are often obliterated through calcification; the dentin then becomes transparent. When the dentin is denuded because of extensive abrasion of the crown, or when the outside of the tooth is irritated, a production of new or "secondary" dentin of irregular structure may often be observed on the wall of the pulp cavity. This may be so extensive as to fill the cavity completely.

Enamel. This cuticular formation of epithelial origin is the hardest substance found in the body; it gives sparks with steel. It is bluish-white and transparent in thin-ground sections. When fully developed, enamel consists almost entirely of calcium salts in the form of large apatite crystals, while only 3 per cent of it is organic substance which contains a glycoprotein. Consequently, after decalcification of a fully developed tooth, the enamel is completely dissolved as a rule.

The enamel consists of thin prisms or rods

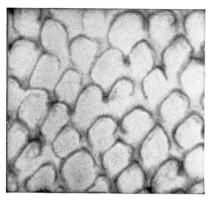

Fig. 22–6.   Cross section of human enamel rods. The dark lines are the cementing substance between the pale rods. Photomicrograph. High magnification. (Courtesy of B. Orban.)

which stand upright on the surface of the dentin, usually with a pronounced inclination toward the crown. They are kept together by a small amount of cement substance. Every rod runs through the whole thickness of the enamel layer. This, however, cannot be seen in sections of the enamel, because the rods are twisted.

The substance of a rod in its longitudinal section seems homogeneous in a ground preparation. But after acid acts upon such a section, a distinct cross striation appears in the rods; this indicates that the calcification probably proceeds by layers.

In the human tooth most of the rods in cross section have the form of fluted semicircles. The convex surfaces of all rods face the dentin, and their cross sections show a scalelike formation (Fig. 22–6).

This form and arrangement are explained by calcification beginning earlier on the side of the rods which lies nearest the dentin. This inner, harder side is supposed to press into the softer side of the adjacent rod, compressing it and leaving one or two groovelike impressions.

The exact course of the enamel rods is extremely complicated and seems to be perfectly adapted to the mechanical requirements connected with the grinding and pounding of food. Starting from the dentin, the rods run perpendicularly to the surface; in the middle zone of the enamel they bend spirally and in the outer zone again assume a direction perpendicular to the surface. In addition, the rods show numerous, small,

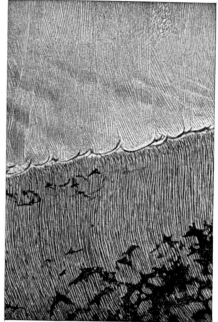

Fig. 22–7.   Dentino-enamel junction of a tooth of a man; ground section. The enamel prisms appear as a fine, wavy striation. The interglobular spaces in the dentin are black (air filled). Between these lacunae are the dentinal tubules. 80 ×. (After Braus.)

wavy curves. On the lateral surfaces of the crown the rods are arranged in zones which encircle the tooth in horizontal planes. The bends of the rods in two neighboring zones cross one another. In axial, longitudinal, ground sections, the crossing of groups of rods appears in reflected light as light and dark lines, more or less perpendicular to the surface—the lines of Schreger (Fig. 22–2).

In a cross section of the crown the enamel shows concentric lines which are brown in transmitted light and colorless in reflected light. In longitudinal, axial sections they are seen to run obliquely inward from the surface and toward the root. They are called the *lines of Retzius* and are connected with the circular striation on the surface of the crown.

The free surface of the enamel is covered by two *membranes.* The inner is about 1 micron thick and is the last product of the activity of the ameloblasts before they disappear. It is somewhat more resistant to acid than is the rest of the enamel. A second membrane, external to the first, is formed of a carbohydrate-containing protein. It is 2 to 10 microns thick and resistant to acids as well as to alkalies. In the adult both membranes are gradually worn off.

In an axial section of the tooth the line of junction between the dentin and the enamel (*dentinoenamel junction*) is uneven and scalloped. Pointed processes of dentin penetrate the enamel and are separated from one another by excavations. Some dentinal tubules penetrate the enamel and end blindly. The spindle-shaped processes of the dentinal matrix penetrating a short distance into the enamel are called *enamel spindles*.

Local disturbances of the enamel during development cause the so-called *enamel lamellae* and *tufts*. These lamellae are organic material extending from the surface of the enamel toward and sometimes into the dentin. The tufts extend from the dentinoenamel junction into the enamel for one third of its thickness. The tuftlike shape, however, is an optical illusion due to the projection of fibers lying in different planes into one plane. They are groups of poorly calcified, twisted rods with abundant cementing substance between them.

Cementum. The cementum covering most of the root is coarsely fibrillated, interstitial bone substance. Near the apex *cementocytes* are embedded in it. Canaliculi, haversian systems and blood vessels are normally absent. The layer of cementum increases in thickness with age, especially near the end of the root, and then haversian systems with blood vessels may appear. Coarse collagenous bundles from the periodontal membrane penetrate the cementum. These fibers of Sharpey remain uncalcified, and in ground sections of the macerated tooth appear as empty canals.

Unlike the high resistance of the dentin, which may remain unchanged even after the destruction of the pulp and odontoblasts and after the "filling" of the pulp cavity, the cementum readily undergoes necrosis when the periodontal membrane is destroyed and may be resorbed by the surrounding connective tissue. On the other hand, new layers of cementum may be deposited on the surface of the root. If this deposition becomes extensive, it may be called *cementum hyperplasia* and is a favorable reaction to irritation.

Pulp. The pulp of the tooth fills the pulp cavity and is the connective tissue which formed the dental papillae during embryonic development. In the adult tooth it has an abundant, gelatinous, basophile ground substance similar to that of mucoid tissue. It contains a multitude of thin collagenous fibrils running in all directions and not combined into bundles. The spindle- or star-

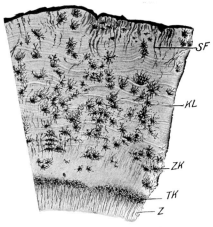

Fig. 22–8. Portion of a ground cross section through the lower part of a root of a macerated human tooth. Air has filled the lacunae. *KL*, refractile boundary between the apparently lamellated layers; *SF*, uncalcified Sharpey's fibers; *TK*, Tomes' granular layer; *Z*, dentin; *ZK*, cementum corpuscles. 80 ×. (After Schaffer.)

shaped cells suggest embryonic mesenchymal elements; macrophages and lymphoid cells are also present. The cells of the pulp adjacent to the dentin are large, elongated, and radially arranged in the fashion of an epithelium; they are called *odontoblasts* and contain mitochondria and a Golgi net in their central part. The odontoblasts send one or more processes into the dentinal tubules; these are called *odontoblastic processes* or the fibers of Tomes.

The pulp continues into the narrow canal of the root, where it surrounds the blood vessels and nerves, and continues through the openings in the apex into the periodontal membrane. The pulp contains many blood vessels. Several small arteries enter each root and are accompanied by veins. The arteries give rise to a dense network of wide capillaries whose loops reach the layer of the odontoblasts and then continue into the veins which occupy a more central position. True lymphatic capillaries have been found by some investigators. Numerous bundles of myelinated nerve fibers, which arise from small cells in the gasserian ganglion, enter the pulp cavity through the canals of the root. They form a plexus in the pulp from which a finer plexus of nonmyelinated fibers in the peripheral layers arises; nerve endings have been described between the odontoblasts.

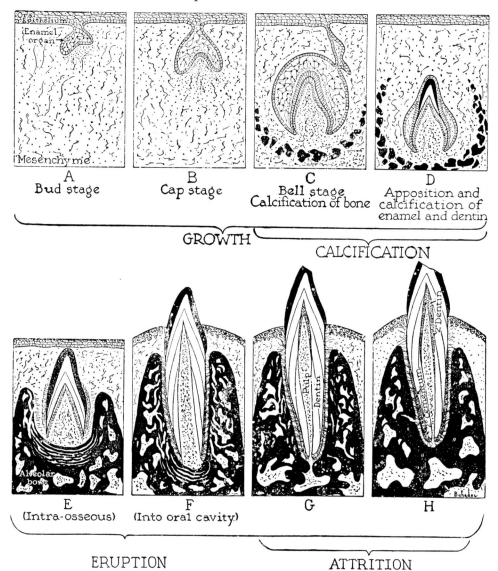

Fig. 22–9.   Diagram of life cycle of a human deciduous incisor. The normal resorption of the root is not indicated. Enamel and bone are drawn in black. (Slightly modified after Schour and Massler.)

Periodontal Membrane. The periodontal membrane, which also serves as periosteum to the alveolar bone, furnishes a firm connection between the root and the bone. It differs from the usual periosteum by the absence of elastic fibers. It consists of thick collagenous bundles, which generally run obliquely from the alveolar wall to the cementum. At the bottom of the alveolar cavity they are thinner, and the softer tissue continues into the pulp. At the neck of the tooth the fibers are especially prominent, are firmly attached to the cementum, and are called the "horizontal groups of fibers" of the tooth. Nearer the surface they run from the bone upward to the edge of the cementum. The fiber bundles of the periodontal membrane have a slightly wavy course; when the tooth is not functioning, they are relaxed and permit it to move slightly on the application of stress.

In many places in the periodontal membrane, blood and lymph vessels and nerves embedded in a small amount of loose connective tissue, and small islands of epithelium are scattered, especially near the surface of the cementum. These islands are vestiges of the epithelial sheath of Hertwig. The epithelial rests frequently degenerate and undergo calcification, giving rise to the *cementicles.*

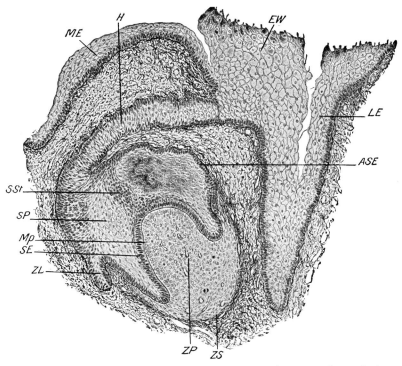

Fig. 22–10. Primordium of the right lower central incisor of a human embryo of ninety-one days, in sagittal section. Collagenous fibers black. *ASE,* external enamel epithelium; *EW,* epithelium of the dental lamina; *H,* neck of the enamel organ; *LE,* labial epithelium; *ME,* epithelium on the floor of the mouth; *Mp,* preformed membrane; *SE,* internal enamel epithelium; *SP,* enamel pulp; *SSt,* enamel cord; *ZL,* internal end of the dental lamina; *ZP,* dental papilla; *ZS,* dental follicle. Mallory's connective tissue stain. 80 ×. (After Schaffer.)

The Gingiva (Gum). The gingiva is that part of the mucous membrane which is firmly connected with the periosteum at the crest of the alveolar bone. It is also linked to the surface of the tooth by the *epithelial attachment of Gottlieb,* which gradually approaches the apex of the tooth with advancing age. The gingiva has high papillae. The epithelial attachment is devoid of papillae except when chronically inflamed. Between the epithelium and the enamel there is a small furrow surrounding the crown, the *gingival crevice.* No glands are found in the gingiva.

Histogenesis of the Teeth. The enamel is a product of the ectodermal epithelium; all the other parts are derivatives of the connective tissue.

In human embryos of the fifth week the ectodermal epithelium lining the oral cavity presents a thickening along the edge of the future upper and lower jaws. The thickening consists of two solid epithelial ridges which extend into the subjacent mesenchyme. Of these, the labial ridge later splits and forms the space between lip and alveolar process of the jaw. The lingual ridge, nearer the tongue, produces teeth and is called the *dental lamina.* According to most investigators, both ridges are independent from the beginning.

The edge of the dental lamina extends into the connective tissue of the jaw and shows at several points budlike thickenings—the primordia of the teeth, the *tooth germs.* There are ten tooth germs in each jaw, one for each deciduous tooth. In each germ a dense group of epithelial cells becomes conspicuous as the *enamel knot;* it is a temporary structure that later disappears. The cells of the mesenchyme under the enamel knot form a dense group, the primordium of the papilla.

The dental lamina then extends beyond the last deciduous tooth germ and slowly forms germs of the permanent molars, which are not preceded by corresponding deciduous teeth.

Beginning with the tenth to twelfth week, the remainder of the dental lamina again produces solid epithelial buds—the *germs for the permanent teeth* —one on the lingual side of each deciduous tooth germ. After the formation of the permanent tooth germs the dental lamina disappears. The transformations of the permanent tooth germ are the same as in the deciduous germ.

The papilla enlarges and invaginates the base of the epithelial tooth germ (Fig. 22–10). The latter, while still connected by an epithelial strand with the dental lamina, becomes bell-shaped and caps the convex surface of the papilla. From now on it is

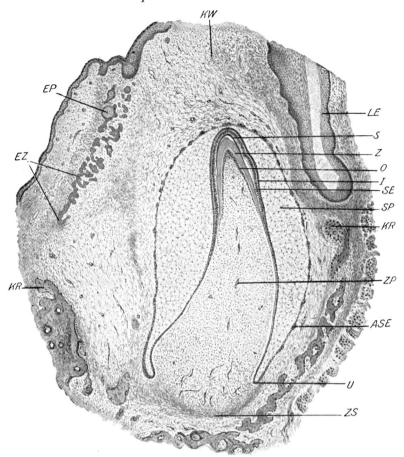

Fig. 22–11. Primordium of lower central incisor of a five months' embryo; sagittal section. *ASE,* external enamel epithelium; *EP,* epithelial pearls in the rests of the permanent dental lamina, *EZ; I,* stratum intermedium; *KR,* alveolar bone; *KW,* gum wall; *LE,* stratified squamous epithelium of the lip; *O,* primordium of the odontoblasts; *S,* enamel cap; *SE,* internal enamel epithelium; *SP,* enamel pulp; *U,* transition of the external into the internal enamel epithelium; *Z,* dentin; *ZP,* dental pulp; *ZS,* dental follicle. 30 ×. (After Schaffer.)

called the *enamel organ,* because it produces the enamel in its further development. Both the papilla and the enamel organ gradually gain in height, and the latter soon acquires approximately the shape of the future organ.

A concentric layer of connective tissue, the dental sac, develops around the tooth primordium and interrupts its epithelial connection with the oral cavity. Around the sac and at a certain distance from it the bone of the jaw develops.

The peripheral cells of the enamel organ are arranged in a regular, radial fashion. On the convex surface the outer enamel epithelium remains small and cuboidal. On the invaginated base the cells of the inner enamel epithelium become tall and regular. They help in the elaboration of the enamel and are called *ameloblasts* or *ganoblasts.* Their attachments are provided with a system of terminal bars. In the inner mass of epithelial cells a clear liquid accumulates between the cell bodies, which remain connected with one another by long processes. The epithelium thus acquires a reticular connective tissue-

like appearance—the *stellate reticulum* (enamel pulp).

When the formation of the hard tooth substances begins (embryos of about twenty weeks), the mesenchyme of the papilla contains numerous blood vessels and a few reticular fibrils between its cells. The cells adjacent to the layer of ameloblasts become transformed into odontoblasts (Fig. 22–11 O).

The dentin first appears as a thick limiting line between ganoblasts and odontoblasts, sometimes called the *membrana preformata.* Some believe that the odontoblasts do not form the dentin, but are probably concerned in its nourishment and possibly with the deposition of calcium in it. In any event, just before the dentin is formed, the odontoblasts develop large amounts of glycoprotein, which may be related to the ground substance.

The layer of dentin extends down the slopes of the papillae. It gradually grows thicker and is transformed into a solid cap of dentin through the apposition of new layers on its concave surface. As the odontoblasts recede from the dentin, thin processes

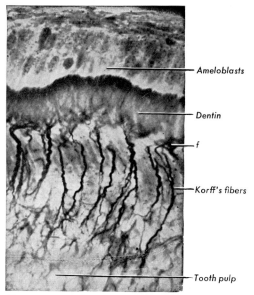

Ameloblasts

Dentin

f

Korff's fibers

Tooth pulp

Fig. 22–12. Continuation of Korff's fibers of the pulp into the matrix of the dentin at *f*. Photomicrograph. 700 ×. (Courtesy of B. Orban.)

of their cytoplasm remain in the mass of deposited dentin as the dentinal fibers.

When the dentin first appears, it is a soft fibrillar substance—the *predentin*. The fibrils are continuations of the fibrils of the papilla. They are of the argyrophile type and are generally called *Korff's fibers*. They enter the dentin, spread out fanlike, and change into the collagenous, fibrillated matrix of the dentin (Fig. 22–12).

In dentin formation, calcification follows closely the deposition of the fibrillar soft substance. But during the whole process there is always a thin layer of uncalcified dentin near the odontoblasts.

The process of dentin formation is much the same in nature as the formation of bone. Almost immediately after the appearance of the first calcified dentin on the convexity of the papilla, the ameloblasts begin the elaboration of enamel. It is deposited layer by layer on the surface of the calcifying dentin.

The ameloblasts grow into tall and regular columnar cells; in the earlier stages each cell contains a cytocentrum and a Golgi net above the elongated, oval nucleus. The attached part of the cell contains granular material which stains brown with osmic acid. In vitally stained animals this part stores the dyes in granular form. On the slopes of the papilla the ganoblasts become lower, and at the base of the papilla they continue into the outer enamel epithelium.

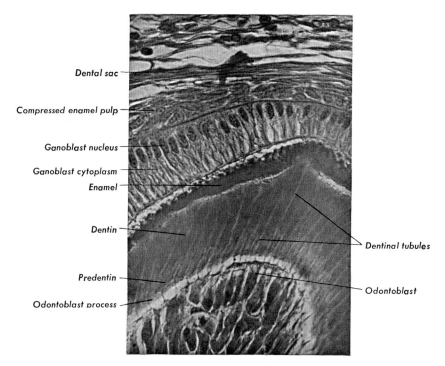

Dental sac

Compressed enamel pulp

Ganoblast nucleus

Ganoblast cytoplasm

Enamel

Dentin

Dentinal tubules

Predentin

Odontoblast

Odontoblast process

Fig. 22–13. Section of incisor of human fetus of five months, showing formation of enamel and dentin. Photomicrograph. Mallory-azan stain. 500 ×. (After von Herrath and Abramow.)

As the mass of enamel increases, the ameloblasts recede, and their basal surfaces remain covered by thin, cuticular plates and connected with one another by terminal bars. The most recent investigations demonstrate the development of the enamel rods from their beginning as individual rods and not from a homogeneous mass. Thus the *Tomes' processes* are the primordia of the enamel rods; each corresponds to a separate ganoblast and remains connected with it until the enamel is complete. It is probable that the processes of Tomes are a cuticular secretion of the basal ends of the ameloblasts.

Calcification starts at the periphery of each row and proceeds toward its interior. When the cementing substance finally calcifies, so little organic material remains in the enamel that it is completely dissolved in decalcification. Complete calcification is not reached until late, and for a long time dyes and other substances may penetrate the partly calcified enamel. That the calcification is seldom absolutely uniform has been mentioned. One of the most striking causes of hypocalcification is parathyroidectomy.

Schour (1936) studied the rate of deposition of enamel with sodium fluoride and of dentin with vital injections of alizarine. He found that the daily thickening of dentin is about 4 microns and that unusual increments (*neonatal lines*) appear in the enamel and dentin formed in the deciduous teeth at the time of birth.

The disturbances in the development of the teeth due to vitamin deficiencies are described by Mellanby.

When the definitive thickness and extension of the enamel capsule are reached in the neck region, the ameloblasts become small cuboidal cells and then atrophy. Before they disappear, they elaborate the inner cuticle of the enamel which covers the ends of the rods.

At the end of the enamel organ, the outer and inner enamel epithelium form a fold, the *epithelial sheath of Hertwig*. The *development of the root* begins shortly before the eruption of the tooth, continues after the crown has emerged from within the mucous membrane, and is not completed until much later; the epithelial sheath disappears when the root development is finished.

When the germ of the permanent tooth begins to develop, its growth pressure causes resorption, first of the bony partition between the two teeth, then of the root, and eventually even of a part of the enamel of the deciduous tooth. Osteoclasts are prominent in this process of destruction just as in the resorption of bone. The crown of the permanent tooth moving upward gradually takes the place of the former deciduous crown.

REFERENCES

Becks, H., Collins, D. A., Simpson, M. E., and Evans, H. M.: Changes in the central incisors of hypophysectomized female rats after different postoperative periods. Arch. Path., *41:*457, 1946.

Bélanger, L. F.: Autoradiographic visualization of the entry and transit of S[35] methionine and cystine in the soft and hard tissues of the growing rat. Anat. Rec., *124:*555, 1956.

Engel, M. B.: Glycogen and carbohydrate-protein complex in developing teeth of the rat. J. Dent. Res., *27:*681, 1948.

Greulich, R. C., and Leblond, C. P.: Radioautographic visualization of the formation and fate of the organic matrix of dentin. J. Dental Research, *33:*859, 1954.

Hampp, E. G.: Mineral distribution in the developing tooth. Anat. Rec., *77:*273, 1940.

Hoffman, M. M., and Schour, I.: Quantitative studies in the development of the rat molar. II. Alveolar bone, cementum, and eruption (from birth to 500 days). Am. J. Orthodontics, *26:*854, 1940.

Kitchin, P. C.: Some observations on enamel development as shown in the mandibular incisors of the white rat. J. Dent. Res., *13:*25, 1933.

Lehner, J., and Plenk, H.: Die Zähne. Handb. d. mikr. Anat. d. Menschen (v. Möllendorff), (5)[3], 449, 1937.

Mellanby, M.: Influence of diet on structure of teeth. Physiol. Rev., *8:*345, 1928.

Orban, B.: Oral Histology and Embryology. 3rd ed. St. Louis, 1953.

Saunders, J. B. de C. M., Nuckolls, J., and Frisbie, H. E.: Amelogenesis. A Histologic Study of the Development, Formation and Calcification of the Enamel in the Molar Tooth of the Rat. J. Am. Coll. Dentists, 1, 1942.

Schour, I.: The Teeth, in Cowdry's Special Cytology. 2d ed. New York, (1), 69, 1932. The neonatal line in the enamel and dentin of the human deciduous teeth and first permanent molar. J. Am. Dent. A., *23:*1946, 1936.

Schour, I., Editor: Noyes' Oral Histology and Embryology. 8th ed. Lea & Febiger, Philadelphia, 1953.

Schour, I., and Massler, M.: The effects of dietary deficiencies upon the oral structures. Physiol. Rev., *25:*442, 1945.

Stahl, S. S., Weinmann, J. P., Schour, I., and Budy, A. M.: The effect of estrogen on the alveolar bone and teeth of mice and rats. Anat. Rec., *107:*21, 1950.

Symposium on "Recent advances in the study of the structure, composition and growth of mineralized tissues. (Ed. R. O. Greep). Ann. New York Acad. Sci., *60:*541, 1955.

Watson, M. L., and Avery, J. K.: The development of the hamster lower incisor as observed by electron microscopy. Amer. J. Anat., *95:*109, 1954.

Weidenreich, F.: Ueber den Bau und die Entwicklung des Zahnbeines in der Reihe der Wirbeltiere. Zeit. f. Anat. u. Entwicklungsgesch., *76:*218, 1925.

Wislocki, G. B., and Sognnaes, R. F.: Histochemical reactions of normal teeth. Am. J. Anat., *87:*239, 1950.

Wolbach, S. B., and Howe, P. R.: The incisor teeth of albino rats and guinea-pigs in vitamin A deficiency and repair. Am. J. Path., *9:*275, 1933.

CHAPTER 23

Esophagus and Stomach

THE ESOPHAGUS

THE ESOPHAGUS is a muscular tube which conveys the food rapidly from the pharynx to the stomach. Its wall presents all the layers characteristic of the digestive tube in general.

The mucous membrane is 500 to 800 microns thick. The stratified squamous epithelium continues into the esophagus from the pharynx. At the transition of the esophagus into the stomach in the cardia, it is abruptly succeeded by the simple columnar epithelium of the stomach. On macroscopical examination the boundary line between the smooth white mucous membrane of the esophagus and the pink surface of the gastric mucosa appears as a jagged line.

In man the flattened cells of the superficial layers of the epithelium contain a small number of keratohyalin granules, but do not undergo true cornification. The lamina propria is bent by numerous longitudinal ridges which fuse with one another in many places and carry high conical papillae. These ridges and the papillae penetrate the epithelium, but do not cause any prominences on its free surface.

The lamina propria consists of loose connective tissue with relatively thin collagenous fibers and a few fine elastic networks; the latter do not penetrate the papillae. Besides the usual connective tissue cells, numerous lymphocytes are scattered throughout the tissue. Around the excretory ducts of the mucous glands, small lymphatic nodules are found.

At the level of the cricoid cartilage the elastic boundary layer of the pharynx is succeeded by the *muscularis mucosae*. It consists of longitudinal smooth muscle fibers and thin elastic networks. Toward the stomach the muscularis mucosae attains a thickness of 200 to 400 microns.

The dense connective tissue of the *submucous layer* consists of thick collagenous and elastic networks, and small infiltrations of lymphocytes about the glands. Together with the muscularis mucosae, it forms numerous longitudinal folds which cause the irregular form of the lumen in cross section. During the swallowing of food these folds are smoothed out. This is made possible by the elasticity of the connective tissue which forms the submucous layer.

The *muscularis externa* of the human esophagus is 0.5 to 2.2 mm. thick. In the cranial quarter of the esophagus both its layers consist of striated muscle; in the second quarter the striated muscle is gradually substituted by bundles of smooth muscles; in the caudal third only the latter are found. The relations between the two types of muscular tissue are subject to individual variations. The two layers of the muscularis externa are not regularly circular and longitudinal, respectively: in the inner layer there are many spiral, elliptical or oblique bundles; the longitudinal muscular bundles of the outer layer in many places are irregularly arranged.

The outer surface of the esophagus is connected with the surrounding parts by a layer

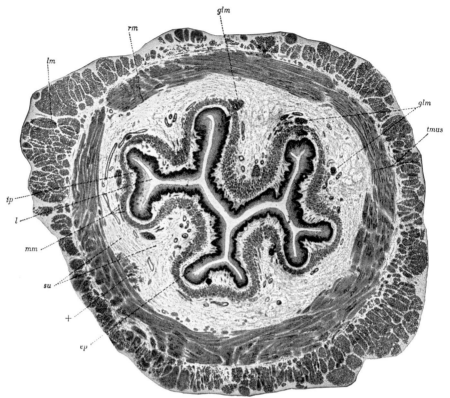

Fig. 23–1. Cross section from the middle third of the esophagus of a twenty-eight year old man. *ep,* epithelium; *glm,* mucous glands; *l,* lumen; *lm,* longitudinal muscle; *mm,* lamina muscularis mucosae; *rm,* circular muscle; *su,* submucosa; *tmus,* tunica muscularis; *tp,* lamina propria mucosae; +, inner longitudinal muscle. 8 ×. (After Sobotta.)

of loose connective tissue called the *tunica adventitia.*

Glands of the Esophagus. Two kinds of small glands occur in the esophagus: *esophageal glands proper* and *esophageal cardiac glands.* The esophageal glands proper are unevenly distributed, small, compound glands with richly branched tubulo-alveolar secretory portions containing only mucous cells. They are located in the submucous layer and can just be recognized with the naked eye as elongated white granules. The branches of the smallest ducts are short and fuse into a cystically dilated main duct which pierces the muscularis mucosae and opens through a small orifice. The epithelium in the smallest ducts is low columnar; in the enlarged main duct stratified squamous epithelium is found. The mucous glands often give rise to cysts of the mucous membrane.

The *esophageal cardiac glands* closely resemble the cardiac glands of the stomach.

Two groups of them can be distinguished: one is in the upper part of the esophagus at the level between the cricoid cartilage and the fifth tracheal cartilage; the other is in the lower part of the esophagus near the cardia. They show great individual variations and sometimes are entirely absent.

Unlike the esophageal glands proper, they are always confined to the lamina propria mucosae. Their terminal portions are branched and curled tubules that contain columnar or cuboidal cells with a pale granular cytoplasm, which sometimes seems to give the mucin reaction; secretory canaliculi are present. The smallest ducts fuse into a large duct, which is sometimes cystically dilated and always opens on the summit of a papilla. Its columnar epithelium often gives a distinct reaction for mucin and more or less resembles the mucous epithelium of the gastric foveolae.

In the regions of the mucous membrane which contain the upper and lower cardiac glands, the

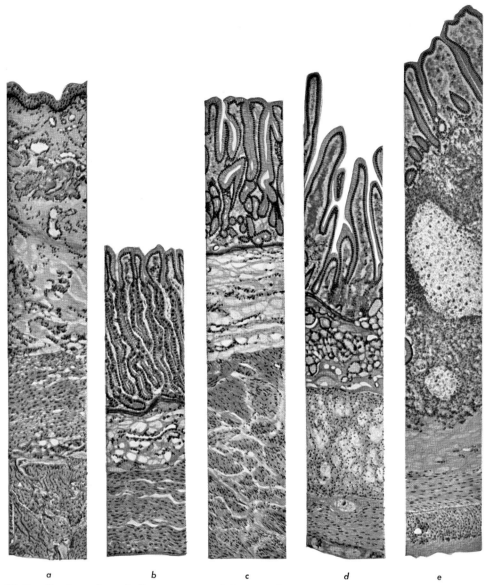

Fig. 23–2.   Sections through five segments of human alimentary canal. *a,* esophagus; *b,* fundus of
stomach; *c,* pylorus of stomach; *d,* duodenum; *e,* appendix. H + E. 35 ×.

stratified squamous epithelium may be substituted in
places by a simple columnar epithelium of the same
aspect as in the gastric pits. Such patches suggest
erosions, that is, places denuded of epithelium.
Sometimes the patches lined with mucous gastric
epithelium are of considerable size and are provided
with pitlike invaginations and even with tubular
glands like those of the fundus; they may even contain typical zymogenic and parietal cells.

The number and development of the cardiac
glands as well as of the islands of gastric mucosa
in the esophagus are subject to great individual
variations. According to some investigators, the presence of this ectopic gastric epithelium may be of
some importance for the origin of diverticula, cysts,
ulcers and carcinomas of the esophagus.

In many mammals, especially those which con-
sume coarse vegetable food (rodents, ruminants and

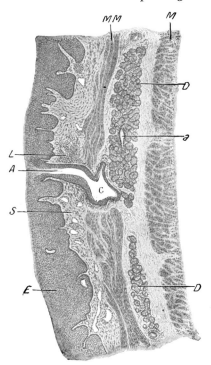

Fig. 23–3. Esophagus of man; lower third; longitudinal section. *A,* excretory duct of a mucous gland, *D; a,* smaller excretory duct which passes over into the secretory portion; *C,* ampulla-like dilatation; *E,* stratified squamous epithelium; *L,* collection of leukocytes in the lamina propria mucosae, *S; MM,* muscularis mucosae; *M,* circular muscle layer of the muscle coat. 27 ×. (After Schaffer.)

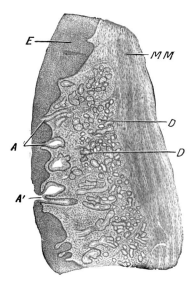

Fig. 23–4. Longitudinal cross section through upper end of esophagus with glands of the cardiac type, *D,* in the mucosa. *A, A',* openings of the glands at the apex of papillae; *E,* stratified squamous epithelium; *MM,* muscularis mucosae. From an eleven year old girl. 27 ×. (After Schaffer.)

the horse), the stratified squamous epithelium of the esophagus undergoes cornification. The esophageal glands are present in most of the mammals, but instead of being purely mucous, as in man, they have a mixed character. In some species no glands are found (rodents, horse, cat).

Histogenetic Remarks. The histogenesis of the epithelium of the esophagus in man presents certain peculiarities, which are especially important in connection with the question of metaplasia, *i.e.,* of the transformation of one epithelial type into another. At first the entodermal layer is a simple, low columnar epithelium. It then becomes two-layered, and in the ninth week the superficial cells become ciliated. In the eleventh week, vesicle-like, glycogen-containing elements appear between the ciliated cells, soon outnumber them, and later are transformed into squamous cells. Finally, all the ciliated cells disappear, and the epithelium becomes stratified squamous. In embryos of the other mammals the epithelium does not seem to contain any ciliated cells.

THE STOMACH

In the stomach the food is thoroughly moistened, softened and partly dissolved by the gastric juice, ground by the contractions of the muscular wall, and transformed into a pulplike mass—the *chyme.* When the chyme has attained the necessary softness, it is transferred to the intestine in small portions. Thus the function of the stomach is in part mechanical and in part chemical. The first is taken care of by the external muscular coat, whose different parts work in perfectly regulated coordination, the second by the glands of the mucous membrane.

The cavity of the empty stomach in its living condition is not much larger than that of the intestine. The trumpet-shaped opening which leads from the esophagus into the stomach is called the *cardia.* To the left of the cardia the wall of the stomach forms a bulging which is directed upward—the *fundus* (or *fornix*); it continues down the right concave and the left convex margins, which are called the *lesser* and the *greater curvatures.* The transition of the stomach into the duodenum, the first part of the small intestine, is called the *pylorus.* Some investigators believe that the wall of the stomach is constricted in its middle part into the *isthmus.* The wall of the stomach consists of the usual layers of the digestive tube.

The mucous membrane of the stomach in the living condition is grayish-pink, except for narrow, pale, ring-shaped areas at the pylorus and cardia. The surface of the filled stomach is stretched evenly. In the empty, contracted stomach it forms numerous high, mostly longitudinal folds. This is made possible by the loose consistency of the submucous layer and the action of the muscularis mucosae. Another much finer and more constant relief is brought about by a system of furrows which subdivide the surface of the mucous membrane into small, slightly bulging, gastric areas 1 to 6 mm. in diameter. With a magnifying lens the surface of each area is seen to be further subdivided by tiny grooves into irregularly convoluted ridges. In a perpendicular section through the mucous membrane the furrows, which are cut across, appear as invaginations, the so-called *gastric pits* or *foveolae gastricae*.

The thickness of the mucous membrane in all parts of the stomach is occupied by a multitude of glands which open into the bottom of the gastric pits. The epithelium which lines the gastric pits and covers the free surface of the mucosa between them has everywhere the same structure. On the basis of differences in the glands, three portions are distinguished in the stomach.

The first zone, which forms a narrow (5 to 30 mm.) ring-shaped area around the cardia, is called the *cardiac area* and contains glands of the same name. The second zone comprises the *fundus and proximal two thirds* of the stomach and contains the gastric glands proper or the *glands of the fundus*. The third part, the *pyloric region*, occupies the distal ninth of the stomach and extends for a greater distance on the lesser curvature than on the greater; it is characterized by the presence of *pyloric glands*. These zones are not separated by sharply drawn limits; along the borderline the glands of one mix to a certain extent with those of the other. According to some, between the second and third zones is a narrow strip, some millimeters in width, occupied by a fourth type of glands, the *intermediate glands*. In the dog, the animal especially used for physiological experimentation, this intermediate zone reaches a high development and a width of 1 to 1.8 cm.

In various other mammals the subdivisions of the stomach are much more sharply pronounced and are marked by deep constrictions which separate the organ into chambers. The esophageal, stratified squamous, sometimes cornified epithelium may invade a smaller or larger part of the stomach; this first esophageal part, as a rule, has few or no glands. In the ruminants the three first chambers—the rumen, the reticulum, and the omasus (or psalterium)—are all of esophageal nature; only in the fourth portion, the abomasus, are gastric glands found, and

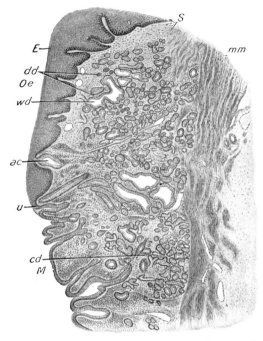

Fig. 23–5. Longitudinal section through the junction of esophagus and stomach of man. *E*, stratified squamous epithelium of the esophagus; *M*, stomach; *Oe*, esophagus; *S*, lamina propria mucosae; *ac*, esophageal cardiac glands; *cd*, cardiac glands; *dd*, glandular tubes; *mm*, muscularis mucosae; *u*, transition of stratified squamous epithelium into cylindrical epithelium of the stomach; *wd*, dilated glandular duct. 120 ×. (After Schaffer.)

here only does digestion occur. In the monotremes and marsupials the whole stomach is occupied by the esophageal region, and the stratified squamous epithelium reaches as far as the glands of Brunner. In the pig the second, or cardiac, region, with mucus-secreting gastric epithelium and cardiac glands, is highly developed; the third, physiologically most important portion is the region of the corpus or fundus, while the fourth portion is the pyloric region.

Surface Epithelium. The ridges between the gastric pits and their walls are lined by a tall (20 to 40 microns), regular columnar epithelium. At the cardia it begins abruptly under the overhanging edge of the stratified squamous epithelium of the esophagus. In

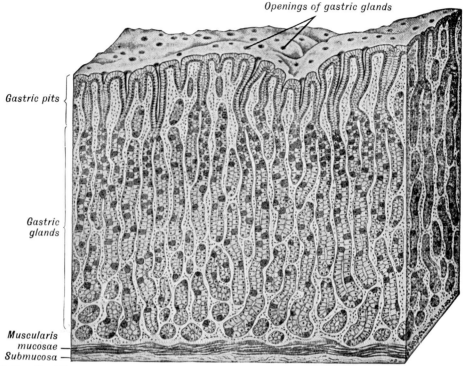

Fig. 23–6.   Semidiagrammatic view of a portion of the gastric mucosa. (From a reconstruction by Kaunhoven and Stein. After Stöhr-von Möllendorff.)

the pylorus it is replaced by the intestinal epithelium. In the cells on the free surface round granules fill the supranuclear part of the cells. Downward into the foveolae they become more and more confined to the free surface. In the bottom of the pits only a thin layer of granules lines the surface; these elements continue down into the neck of the glands. The granules consist of mucigen or of mucin of a peculiar type. After proper fixation it can be stained with some of the dyes which are elective for typical mucus, as mucicarmine. With other mucin dyes the result is negative. Having left the cells, the granules furnish the layer of alkaline mucus which lubricates the surface of the mucosa. Unlike the mucus secreted by the mucous glands of the oral cavity, it is not precipitated by acetic acid.

In sections in which the granules of mucigen have not been preserved, the supranuclear parts of the cells appear clear and transparent and only faintly granular; the free surfaces are covered with thin terminal bars. In the midst of the clear substance a diplosome is located. A Golgi net is also present above and sometimes around the nucleus. The cytoplasm in the basal part of the cell contains threadlike mitochondria. Fat droplets and glycogen granules have been found in these cells. The introduction of glucose into the stomach does not influence the amount of glycogen in its epithelium.

Even under physiological conditions many of the surface cells are desquamated and perish. Signs of regeneration are seen only in the deeper part of the foveolae, where mitoses are frequent in the less differentiated cells which contain but a small quantity of mucigen granules under their free surface. The newly formed cells are slowly pushed upward through growth pressure and replace the lost ones.

Gastric Glands. These glands, which are the most important contributors to the secretion of the gastric juice, are simple, branched tubules. They are densely arranged, perpendicularly to the surface of the mucosa, and penetrate its whole thickness, which measures from 0.3 to 1.5 mm. They open in small groups through a slight constriction into the bottom of the foveolae. The diameter of the glandular tubule is 30 to 50 microns, but the lumen is narrow. The blind ends are slightly thickened and coiled and sometimes divide into two or three branches; they almost reach the muscularis mucosae. The number of these glands is estimated at 35,000,000.

There are four types of cells in these glands. Many different names have been proposed for them, so that the nomenclature is rarely alike in any two descriptions. The four types are: (1) body chief, or zymogenic cells, (2) parietal cells, (3) mucous neck cells, and (4) argentaffine cells (of Heidenhain).

Zymogenic Cells. The zymogenic cells are arranged in a simple layer on the inner surface of the basement membrane and line the lumen in the lower half or third of the glandular tubule. After death they begin to disintegrate almost immediately unless there was no acid in the stomach, when they may remain for some time. In fresh condition, especially after a period of fasting, the cells are full of coarse, brilliant granules. After intense secretory activity the cells are smaller and contain but few granules near their surface. The granules are believed to contain pepsinogen, the antecedent of the enzyme pepsin. Only some osmic-sublimate and formalin mixtures preserve the granules; in most cases they dissolve, and the fixed cytoplasm shows an alveolar structure. The spherical nucleus does not show any peculiarities. Under the nucleus in the basal part of the cell the cytoplasm contains radially striated accumulations of chromophile substance; the zymogenic cells contain mitochondria and a Golgi net.

The free surfaces of the cells are provided with terminal bars. True secretory capillaries are not present. It is not clear whether the zymogenic cells under physiological conditions are subject to degeneration and renewal, or not. Mitoses are never found in them. It is possible that they may arise from the mucous neck cells, although in the adult, transitions between them—zymogenic cells with a slight mucin content near the free surface—are rare.

Parietal Cells. Between the zymogenic cells, but more numerous toward the neck, parietal cells are scattered singly. They are of spherical, sometimes slightly triangular form

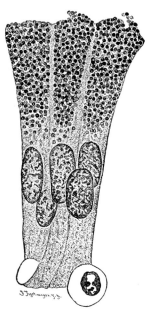

Fig. 23–7. Surface epithelium of the human stomach; fixed with sublimate-osmic acid and stained with gentian to show the mucous droplets. (After Heidenhain.)

and occupy a peripheral position between the zymogenic cells and the basement membrane. Sometimes they even cause bulgings on the outer surface of the glands, especially after prolonged activity when the zymogenic cells are small.

The parietal cell contains a large round nucleus; sometimes two or even more nuclei are present in one cell. The cytoplasm stains readily with acid aniline dyes. The cell contains a diplosome and numerous short rod-shaped mitochondria, but no distinct secretory granules. The most typical features of the parietal cells are secretory canaliculi which occupy an intracellular position and form a loose network between the surface and nucleus. They communicate, through a small cleft between the adjacent zymogenic cells, with a branch of the main lumen. Through this canal the secretion of the parietal cells enters the lumen. The parietal cells do not seem to undergo any morphological changes with the various stages of functional activity.

Mucous Neck Cells. These are found in the neck of the glands, where they are arranged in one layer and fill the spaces between the parietal cells. In passing toward the bottom of the gland they are abruptly

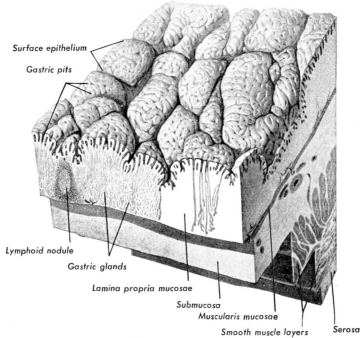

Surface epithelium

Gastric pits

Lymphoid nodule

Gastric glands

Lamina propria mucosae

Submucosa

Muscularis mucosae

Smooth muscle layers   Serosa

Fig. 23–8.   Surface of gastric mucosa of a man; drawn with a binocular microscope. The cut surfaces are slightly diagrammatic. At the left, the normal distribution of the gastric glands; to the right, only a few are indicated. Glands, gray; gastric pits, black. 17 ×. (After Braus.)

succeeded by the zymogenic cells. In fresh condition they are filled with pale, transparent granules.

In sections in which the secretory granules are not preserved and which are stained only with nuclear dyes, they are similar to the zymogenic cells and were overlooked by many investigators. Their nuclei, however, are different from those of the zymogenic cells because they are usually flat, sometimes concave, and occupy the base of the cell. In sections stained with mucicarmine or mucihematein, the cytoplasm is filled with brightly stained granules, while the zymogenic cells remain colorless. This indicates that the mucous neck cells are mucus-secreting elements. Their mucus, however, gives staining reactions different from that of the mucus of the gastric surface epithelium and from that of the glands of the oral cavity.

Where the necks of the glands open into the narrow bottoms of the foveolae, the mucous neck cells are connected with the surface epithelium by a series of gradual transitional forms. As mitoses are not found in the mucous neck cells of the adult, it is probable that new ones arise through a gradual transformation of the undifferentiated

epithelium in the bottom of the foveolae.

In many gastric glands the mucous neck cells advance far toward the bottom and are sometimes scattered singly between the zymogenic cells. This is especially prominent in the glands near the pyloric region. According to some, the glands of the narrow intermediate zone may contain only mucous neck and parietal cells and be devoid of zymogenic cells.

Argentaffine Cells. Argentaffine cells, like those in the intestine, are moderately abundant in the fundic glands and are less frequent in the pyloric glands. These cells are scattered singly, between the basement membrane and the zymogenic cells, and have a somewhat flattened form. Their cytoplasm is filled with small granules which can be stained with silver or chromium salts. They are more numerous in the duodenum.

Pyloric Glands. In the pyloric region the foveolae reach deeper into the mucous membrane (to one half of its thickness) and have more branches than in the body of the stomach. The glands here are also of the simple, branched tubular type, but the lumen is larger, and the tubules are coiled, so that in perpendicular sections they are seldom seen

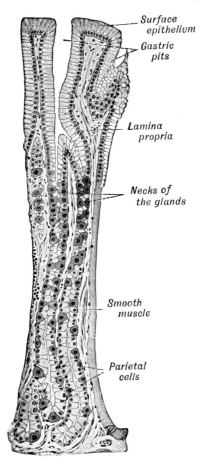

Fig. 23–9. Fundic glands of human stomach. Zymogenic cells gray; parietal cells dark gray. 130 ×. (After Braus.)

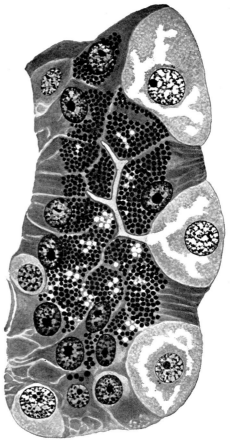

Fig. 23–10. Blind end of gastric gland of monkey. Zymogenic cells with black secretory granules; between them, secretory capillaries; three parietal cells with intracellular canaliculi. Iron-hematoxylin stain. 1000 ×. (A.A.M.)

as longitudinal structures. The pyloric glands contain only one type of cell; its cytoplasm is pale and contains an indistinct granulation (Fig. 23–12). Secretory capillaries have been described between them. The nucleus is often flattened against the base of the cell. In sections stained with hematoxylin and eosin, they sometimes resemble the mucous neck cells or even the zymogenic cells, or the cells of the glands of Brunner of the duodenum. Some investigators believe that the pyloric glandular cells are identical with the mucous neck cells, since both give similar staining reactions for mucus. Certain dyes (cresyl violet, Giemsa mixture), however, seem to stain them in a specific way; they may be compared, perhaps, only with the cells of the cardiac glands. In the human stomach, the pyloric glands in the region of

the sphincter may contain parietal cells. Argentaffine cells have also been described in the pyloric glands.

Cardiac Glands. These are compound tubular glands much like the cardiac glands of the esophagus. The terminal portions open directly into the gastric pits and show enlargements in many places. The clear glandular cells are found either alone or alternating with numerous parietal cells.

Ectopic Intestinal Epithelium and Glands in the Stomach. In the cardiac as well as in the pyloric region of the gastric mucosa, patches of intestinal epithelium and glands may be found among the gastric foveolae. Some believe them to be signs of chronic inflammation. The intestinal epithelium may be identified at once by its striated border and by the scattered goblet cells. The cardiac glands may open into these glands of Lieberkühn (see Chap. 24).

Lamina Propria. The scanty connective

tissue of the lamina propria fills the narrow spaces between the glands and the muscularis mucosae and forms larger accumulations only between the necks of the glands and between the foveolae. It consists of a delicate network of collagenous and argyrophile fibrils and is almost devoid of elastic elements. Its cells have not been investigated satisfactorily. Besides oval pale nuclei which seem to belong to fibroblasts or reticular cells, the meshes of the fibers contain numerous small lymphocytes, and some plasma cells, eosinophile leukocytes, and mast cells. Sometimes, cells with coarsely granular acidophile inclusions are found between the epithelial cells of the glands; these are *Russell's bodies,* which may develop under physiological conditions, but are common in pathological cases. In the lamina propria, especially in the pyloric region, small, spherical accumulations of lymphatic tissue occur normally. Strands of smooth muscle also occur.

Other Layers of the Wall. The *muscularis mucosae* consists of an inner circular and an outer longitudinal layer of smooth muscle; in some places there is a third, outer circular layer. From the inner layer strands of smooth muscle cells run between the glands toward the surface. The contraction of these strands compresses the mucous membrane and probably facilitates the emptying of the glands.

The *submucous layer* consists of dense connective tissue which contains fat cells and is rich in mast cells, lymphoid wandering cells and eosinophile leukocytes. This layer contains the large blood and lymph vessels and venous plexuses.

The *muscularis externa* consists of three layers—an outer, mainly longitudinal, a middle circular, and an inner oblique. The outermost layer is formed by the continuation of the longitudinal fibers of the esophagus. They keep their longitudinal course only along the two curvatures, while on the anterior and posterior surfaces they gradually bend toward the larger curvature. In the pyloric region the longitudinal fibers are assembled in a layer which continues into the same layer of the intestinal wall.

The middle layer is the most regular and continuous of the three. In the pylorus it forms a thick, circular sphincter which helps control the evacuation of the stomach. The emptying of the stomach depends primarily

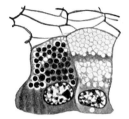

Fig. 23–11.   Two cells from the boundary between neck and body of a gastric gland of *Macacus rhesus.* A zymogenic cell with black-stained secretory granules, and a mucous neck cell with pale vacuoles, previously occupied by mucous droplets. On the free surface, a net of terminal bars. Iron-hematoxylin stain. 1000 ×. (A.A.M.)

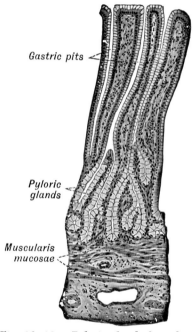

Gastric pits

Pyloric glands

Muscularis mucosae

Fig. 23–12.   Pyloric glands from human stomach. Slightly diagrammatic. 75 ×. (After Braus.)

on the contraction of the gastric musculature.

The work of all the parts of the muscular coat just described is regulated with marked precision. The wall of the stomach adapts itself to the volume of its contents without raising the pressure in its cavity.

The *serous membrane* is a thin layer of loose connective tissue attached to the muscularis externa and covered with mesothelium. It continues into the large and small omentum.

Histophysiological Remarks. The quantity of *gastric juice* secreted during twenty-four hours by the human stomach is estimated at 1000 to 1500 cc. It is a clear, colorless liquid which contains, besides water and salts, 0.4 to 0.5 per cent hydrochloric acid and enzymes. *Pepsin,* which digests protein in acid medium and clots milk, is the most important of these; it is a protein and has been crystallized by Northrop. He finds it probable "that the various pepsins vary from species to species, as do the hemoglobins." The other ferments are *rennin,* which has a stronger clotting action on milk than pepsin and is present mainly in infancy, and small amounts of a *lipase* (which splits fat). In the dog it is possible to obtain the secretion of the two main parts of the stomach separately. Whereas the body of the stomach secretes only when certain stimuli act upon the mucous membrane (for instance, the ingestion of food or psychic impressions), the pyloric region secretes continuously. The secretion of the body contains both pepsin and hydrochloric acid. It is also possible to distinguish two kinds of secretion furnished by the gastric glands—the secretion of the ordinary acid gastric juice, rich in pepsin, and of a juice which is also rich in pepsin, but contains a mucin-like substance and has only a weakly acid or even an alkaline reaction.

It is generally believed that pepsin is secreted by the zymogenic cells and that their granules are transformed into active pepsin only when acted upon by the hydrochloric acid. Analyses show that the pepsin content is higher, the more zymogenic cells in a given location (Linderstrøm-Lang and Holter). Injection of histamine causes the secretion of large amounts of acid gastric juice low in pepsin, while stimulation of the vagus nerve results in a great increase in the pepsin content of the juice. Bowie has shown that this is accompanied by an extensive discharge of zymogen granules. It has been observed that, if a small fragment of the fresh mucous membrane with gastric glands is treated with hydrochloric acid, the zymogenic cells disintegrate rapidly, while the parietal cells remain unchanged for a while. According to Ivy, the pyloric fluid does not contain enzymes in significant amounts.

Physiological and histological evidence supports the idea that the parietal cells are the source of the hydrochloric acid of the gastric juice, although the mechanism of forma-

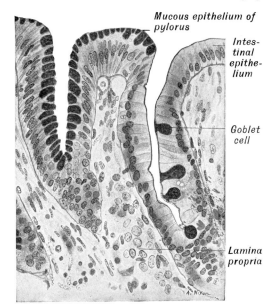

Fig. 23–13. Section through junction of the pyloric and duodenal epitheliums of an eight year old child. Stained with hematoxylin and for mucus with mucicarmine. 220 ×.

tion of the acid is unknown. Earlier histologists tried to locate hydrochloric acid itself within or at the surface of the parietal cells. The problem is particularly difficult, since the acid is highly diffusible. It was realized in the course of time that no cell could tolerate the free acid in its cytoplasm, and attempts were then made to locate the chloride. The bulk of evidence favors the view that the process is similar to that of acidification of the urine which occurs in the distal convolution of the nephron. According to current theory, it is probable that neutral salt is excreted by the parietal cells and then follows reabsorption of the base in combination with bicarbonate, the process involving carbonic anhydrase and possibly urease. The over-all mechanism is an *ion exchange procedure.* In the actively secreting stomach, chloride is concentrated in the connective tissue of the submucous and, to a lesser extent, of the subepithelial layers. Chlorides have not been demonstrated in any of the epithelial cells except the zymogenic ones, and in them in only small amounts.

The mucous neck cells and the surface epithelium secrete *mucus.* The gastric mucus forms a layer on the surface of the mucous membrane which is supposed by some to

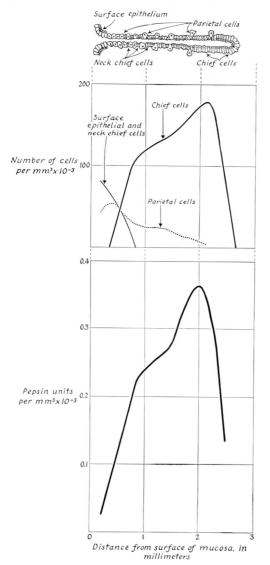

is prevented by an antiterment elaborated by the mucous membrane. Immediately after death autodigestion begins.

The gastric mucosa also contains a substance necessary for the production of erythrocytes.

Blood Vessels and Lymphatics of the Stomach. See page 395.

Nerves. The nerves of the stomach are of the same types and distribution as those of the intestine (see p. 397).

Histogenetic Remarks. In the young embryo the stomach is lined by an even layer of pseudostratified columnar epithelium. In embryos of 22.8 mm., groups of tall and low cells alternate, so that small pits arise, although the basement membrane remains even. In later stages (42 mm.) the pits begin to project into the underlying mesenchyme, while the tall cells between them begin to elaborate mucus. In embryos of 90 mm., at the bottom of the crypts, solid buds of granular cells appear—the primordia of the glands. In the 120-mm. stage the glandular primordia establish two kinds of cells. Some of them stain intensely with eosin and are accumulated at the blind ends and later assume a peripheral position they are the future parietal cells; others remain pale—the future zymogenic cells.

At birth the length of the glands equals one half of the thickness of the mucosa. Their number gradually increases, partly through division of the blind ends of the tubes, partly through the formation of new buds of undifferentiated cells. The pyloric and cardiac glands seem to arise from the very beginning as structures different from the gastric glands.

Fig. 23–14. In the upper part of the figure is a schematic disposition of cells in a single fundic gland. Upper graph shows the numbers of each cell type in sections at different levels, and the lower graph shows the pepsin activity in sections adjacent to those from which the cell counts were made. (After Linderstrøm-Lang).

protect it against autodigestion by delaying the diffusion of pepsin and hydrochloric acid, by inhibiting the action of pepsin, and by combining with the acid, for the mucosa is neutral during periods of inactivity. According to another opinion, autodigestion in life

REFERENCES

Bensley, R. R.: The Gastric Glands, in Cowdry's Special Cytology. 2d ed. New York, (1), 197, 1932.

Bowie, D. J., and Vineberg, A. M.: The selective action of histamine and the effect of prolonged vagal stimulation on the cells of gastric glands in the dog. Quart. J. Exper. Physiol., *25*:247, 1935.

Dawson, A. B.: Argentophile and argentaffin cells in the gastric mucosa of the rat. Anat. Rec., *100*:319, 1948.

Heinz, E., and Öbrink, K. J.: Acid formation and acidity control in the stomach. Physiol. Rev., *34*:643, 1954.

Holter, H., and Linderstrøm-Lang, K.: Beiträge zur enzymatischen Histochemie; die Verteilung des Pepsins in der Schleimhaut des Schweinemagens. Ztschr. physiol. Chem., *226*:149, 1934.

Landboe-Christensen, E.: Extent of the pylorus zone in the human stomach. Acta path. Microbiol. Scand., Suppl. 54, 671, 1944.

Langley, J. N.: On the histology of the mammalian gastric glands and the relation of pepsin to the granules of the chief cells. J. Physiol., *3*:269, 1880–82.

Müller, E.: Drüsenstudien. II. Ueber die Fundusdrüsen des Magens. Ztschr. f. wiss. Zool., *64*:624, 1898.

Oppel, A.: Schlund und Darm. Lehrbuch der vergl. mikr. Anat. der Wirbeltiere. Jena, 1897.

Plenk, H.: Der Magen, Handb. d. mikr. Anat. (v. Möllendorff), 1932, Vol. 5, Pt. 2, p. 1.

CHAPTER 24

The Intestines

THE SMALL INTESTINE

THE SMALL intestine is a tube about 7 meters long and divisible into three portions, the *duodenum,* the *jejunum,* and the *ileum,* which gradually pass into one another. Their structure, although showing some differences, is everywhere the same in principle, so that one description applies to all. The main functions of the small intestine are (1) the forwarding of the chyme along its course, (2) continued digestion of the chyme by means of special juices secreted by its walls and by the accessory glands, and (3) absorption of the liquefied nutritive material into the blood and lymph vessels.

Surface of the Mucous Membrane. In the small intestine, from which the organism receives all its food material, the surface is enormously increased through the formation of circular folds, or *valves of Kerkring,* and the villi.

The folds are constant structures and do not disappear even when the intestinal wall is distended. They begin 2 to 5 cm. from the pylorus and reach their maximal develop-

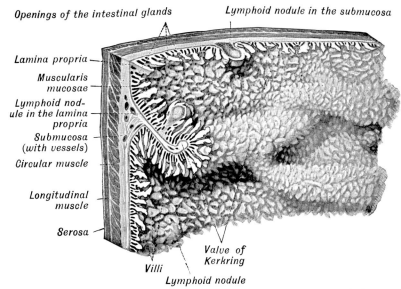

Openings of the intestinal glands
Lymphoid nodule in the submucosa
Lamina propria
Muscularis mucosae
Lymphoid nodule in the lamina propria
Submucosa (with vessels)
Circular muscle
Longitudinal muscle
Serosa
Valve of Kerkring
Villi
Lymphoid nodule

Fig. 24–1. Portion of small intestine; drawn with binocular microscope and from sections. 17 ×. (After Braus.)

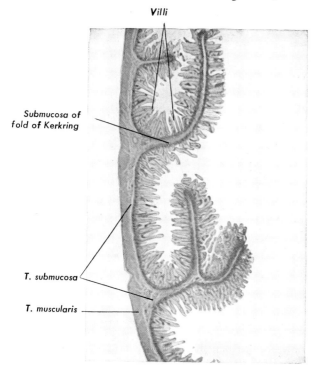

Villi

Submucosa of
fold of Kerkring

T. submucosa

T. muscularis

Fig. 24–2. Longitudinal section of human jejunum, showing three folds of Kerkring. Photomicrograph. H + E. 3 ×. (After von Herrath and
Abramow.)

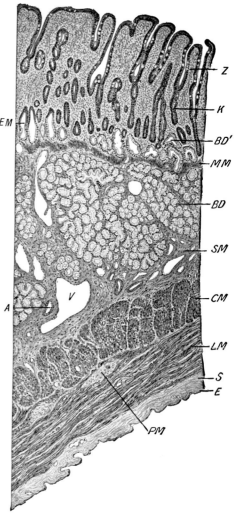

Fig. 24–3. From longitudinal section of human
duodenum. *A,* artery; *BD,* Brunner's glands in the
submucosa; *BD',* Brunner's glands in the mucosa;
CM, circular muscle cut across; *E,* mesothelium of
serosa; *EM,* emptying of a Brunner gland into a
crypt; *K,* crypt of Lieberkühn; *LM,* longitudinal
muscle layer; *MM,* muscularis mucosae; *PM,* plexus
myentericus with a ganglion cell in cross section;
S, serosa; *SM,* submucosa; *Z,* villus. 30 ×. (After
Schaffer.)

ment in the distal half of the duodenum
and the proximal part of the jejunum; in the
ileum they become smaller and less numerous and disappear in its middle. In the lower
duodenum they reach a height of 8 mm. and
usually extend over two thirds of the circumference. Often the folds branch; folds which
run uninterruptedly around the whole intestinal tube are rare. The folds are formed
by all the layers of the mucosa, including the
muscularis mucosae; their core is submucosa.

The *villi* are outgrowths of the mucous
membrane and have a length of 0.5 to 1.5
mm. They cover the entire surface of the
mucosa and give it a typical velvety appearance; they vary from ten to forty to the
square millimeter. In the duodenum they are
broad, leaflike structures arranged with their
long diameter in the transverse direction and
in alternating, longitudinal rows; in the ileum
they gradually become more finger-like.

Many villi, especially in the infant, are
divided on their summits into two or more
lobes by slits which extend for varying distances into the villi. In this way the villi are

supposed to increase in number during the
growth of the intestine. The innumerable
openings of the glands, or *crypts of Lieberkühn,* may be seen between the bases of the
villi with a magnifying lens. They are simple
tubes 320 to 450 microns long, which penetrate the thickness of the mucous membrane
and almost reach the muscularis mucosae.
The spaces between them are wider than
those between the glands in the stomach.

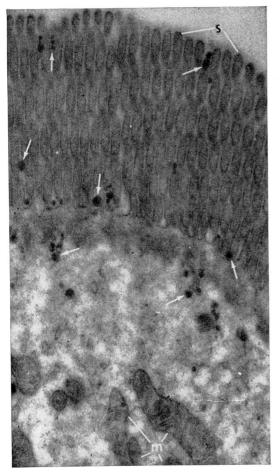

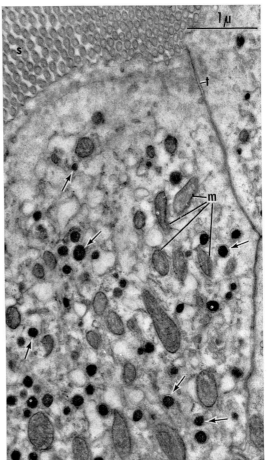

Fig. 24–4. Electron micrograph of striated border (s) and apex of a jejunal epithelial cell 22 minutes after corn oil had been instilled into the stomach of the rat. Droplets of fat (arrows) are seen in the intermicrovillous spaces as well as in the immediately subjacent cytoplasm. m, mitochondria. Buffered osmic acid fixation. 36,000 ×. (Courtesy of S. Palay and L. Karlin.)

Fig. 24–5. Electron micrograph of striated border and apical cytoplasm of a jejunal epithelial cell from a rat 70 minutes after corn oil had been instilled into the stomach of the animal. Fat droplets (arrows) appear throughout the apical cytoplasm except in the striated border (s) and immediately subjacent zone. A terminal bar (t) appears at the right upper margin of the picture. m, mitochondria. Buffered osmic acid fixation. (Courtesy of S. Palay and L. Karlin.)

Epithelium. The epithelium, which covers the free surface of the mucous membrane, is simple columnar. Three types of cells can be distinguished in it: (1) columnar cells with a striated border, (2) goblet cells, (3) argentaffine cells.

The columnar cells have a prismatic form and a height of 22 to 26 microns; their outlines change considerably with the movement of the villi. The free surface is covered with a striated border rich in phosphatase. With the electron microscope the striated appearance is found to be due to countless numbers of closely packed processes called micro-

villi (Figs. 24–4 and 24–5). Under the striated border there is always a thin layer of homogeneous cytoplasm. Under this layer longitudinally arranged, wavy mitochondria are accumulated. The Golgi net occupies the space between these mitochondria and the nucleus. Beneath the nucleus the cytoplasm contains a group of granular mitochondria.

The bases of the cells are connected with the surface of the lamina propria. This close connection of the epithelium with the connective tissue condition withstands successfully the strain arising from the movements of the villi and the mechanical action of the

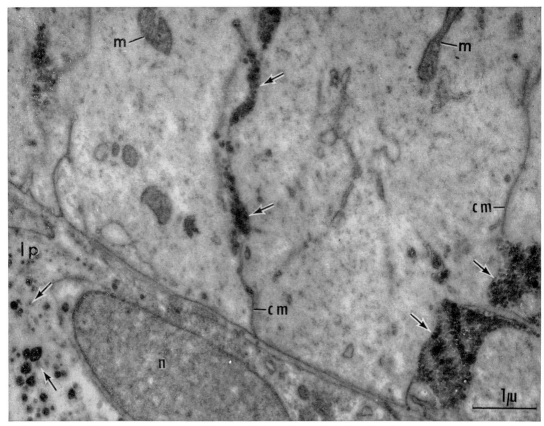

Fig. 24-6. Electron micrograph of bases of jejunal epithelial cells of a rat 60 minutes after a meal of Purina laboratory chow (containing protein as well as fat). The fat droplets (arrows) lie between the cells of the epithelium as well as free in the lamina propria (*lp*). A fibroblast lies beneath the epithelium. *cm,* intercellular membrane; *m,* mitochondria; *n,* nucleus of fibroblast. Buffered osmic acid fixation. (Courtesy of S. Palay and L. Karlin.)

passing food material. After fixation the epithelium often appears detached from the stroma on the summit of the villi, and a cavity is seen between the two tissues. This free space is an artefact, caused especially by the agonal contraction of the smooth muscles in the core of the villi.

Goblet cells are scattered between the cylindrical epithelial cells. The *argentaffine cells* are more common in the glands of Lieberkühn. Everywhere in the small intestine, irregularly distributed lymphocytes can be seen penetrating from the lamina propria into the epithelium of the villi.

The epithelium of the villi, under physiological conditions, is shed in considerable quantities and, together with the mucus, forms a part of the feces. In experimental animals a short section of the small intestine may be separated from the rest of the gut and its ends connected to form a loop, while its attachment to the mesentery remains unaltered and the remaining ends of the intestine are sewed together. After a time the isolated loop is found greatly distended with digestive juices, masses of mucus and desquamated epithelium. This explains why a certain amount of feces is formed even in a starving organism. It is clear that such extensive losses require a corresponding regeneration.

Crypts of Lieberkühn. The epithelium covering the villi continues into the glands of Lieberkühn. Above the bottom of the crypt, their walls are lined with a low columnar epithelium which contains numerous mitoses. Here regeneration takes place, and the new cells moving upward differentiate into goblet cells and into the columnar cells with striated borders. All the stages in this process are to be seen in the upper half of the crypt.

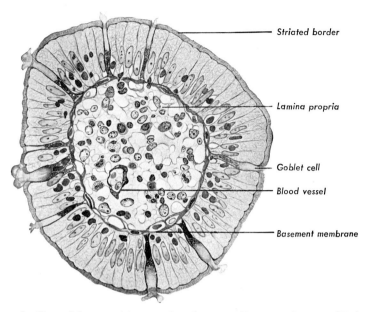

Fig. 24–7. Cross section of villus of human jejunum. Iron-hematoxylin-azan. 514 ×. (Redrawn and slightly modified after V. Patzelt.)

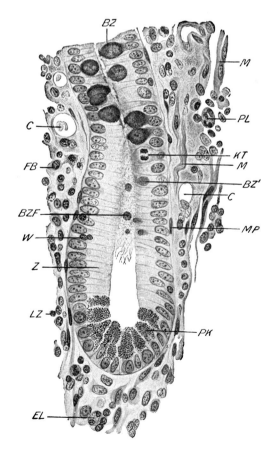

In the bottom of the glands of Lieberkühn in the small intestine, the large *cells of Paneth* occur regularly. The base of these cells is occupied by chromophile substance. Around the large, spherical nucleus are a few mitochondria. Above the nucleus the cytoplasm is filled with large, round, acidophile, secretory granules. Sometimes each granule is surrounded by a clear vacuole; a discharge into the lumen is rarely seen except under the influence of pilocarpine. The granules dissolve in acids and in mineral salts, but are resistant to alkalies. Their nature is not clear.

Argentaffine Cells. Between the cells lining the glands of Lieberkühn (rarely in the epithelium of the villi) are found the argentaffine cells, which differ from the rest of the epithelium by their form and by the presence of specific granules in their cytoplasm. They are scattered singly, and their

Fig. 24–8. Crypt of Lieberkühn with surrounding lamina propria. *BZ*, goblet cells; *BZ'*, goblet cells at end or beginning of secretion; *BZF*, goblet cells cut tangentially; *C*, capillary; *EL*, eosinophile leukocyte; *FB*, reticular cells; *KT*, mitosis in an epithelial cell; *LZ*, lymphocyte; *M*, smooth muscle cells; *MP*, reticular cells beneath basement membrane; *PK*, Paneth cells; *PL*, polymorphonuclear leukocytes; *W*, wandering cells in the epithelium; *Z*, epithelial cells of the gland. 380 ×. (After Schaffer.)

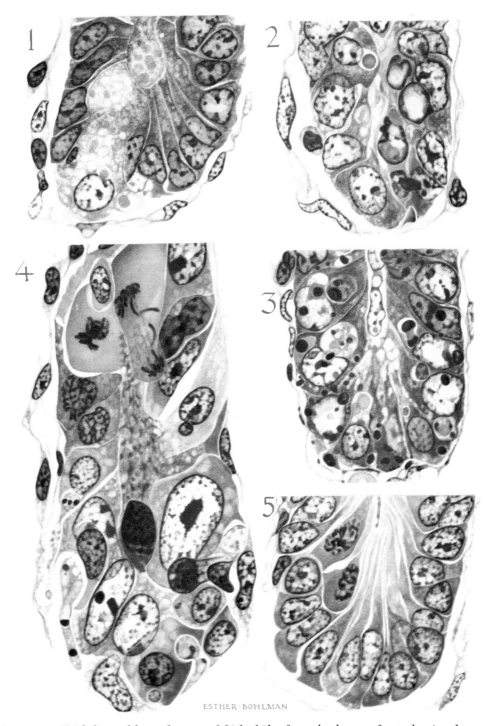

ESTHER·BOHLMAN

Fig. 24–9.   Epithelium of base of crypts of Lieberkühn from duodenum of rat, showing degenerative and regenerative changes after total body exposure to 600 roentgens of x-rays. *1,* normal; *2,* one-half hour; *3,* three hours; *4,* twenty-eight hours, and *5,* five days after irradiation. (After M. Pierce, in Histopathology of Irradiation from External and Internal Sources. Courtesy of Atomic Energy Commission.)

number varies greatly. Moderate numbers are found in the stomach. In the jejunum and ileum they are relatively rare; they are more common in the duodenum and particularly in the appendix. Their body, as a rule, adheres closely to the basement membrane and even bulges into its outer surface. The cytoplasm of the base of the cells is filled with small granules which stain easily with eosin. They are electively stained black by solutions of silver ammonium oxide, and acquire a brownish-yellow color after the action of chromates. They vary from species to species; they give positive tests for polysaccharides in some. Their nature and function are obscure.

Lamina Propria. The lamina propria of the mucous membrane fills the spaces between the glands of Lieberkühn and forms the core of the villi. It is a peculiar type of connective tissue and contains a stroma of argyrophile fibers similar to that of the lymphatic tissue. Close to the fibers are fixed cells with oval, pale nuclei; these are perhaps comparable with the primitive reticular elements of the lymphatic tissue stroma. Some of them become macrophages which may contain pigment inclusions; sometimes they react positively to tests for iron. In vitally stained animals, however, they contain, as a rule, only few dye granules. The dye storing is more pronounced in the macrophages of the lower ileum and cecum.

The argyrophile framework of the lamina propria at the epithelium-covered surface is condensed to a reticular basement membrane. Fine elastic networks extend from the muscularis mucosae along the blood vessels; they also surround the glands of Lieberkühn and take part in the formation of their basement membrane. The argyrophile framework in many places contains strands of smooth muscle which arise from the inner surface of the muscularis mucosae, run toward the surface, and are especially prominent in the core of the villi. Here they are arranged parallel to the axis of the villus, around the central lacteal.

The meshes of the argyrophile framework contain large numbers of free cells. The most numerous are small lymphocytes; medium-sized forms also occur; large lymphocytes are rare. Plasma cells are numerous in all stages of development. They are said to increase greatly in number during digestion.

Many of them degenerate and produce Russell's bodies. The lamina propria always contains granular leukocytes, mainly eosinophils, most of which migrated from the blood vessels. Sometimes, especially in the guinea pig, a few eosinophile myelocytes of local origin, with occasional mitoses, can be found. Mast cells are infrequent in the human intestine. Among them are small, young cells with but a few granules.

Many lymphocytes and a few granular leukocytes penetrate the epithelium on the villi or the glands of Lieberkühn, and occasionally even pass into the lumen. This phenomenon increases in intensity in the caudal direction and reaches its highest development in the large intestine.

Another peculiar type of wandering cell found in the epithelium of the crypts in many animals is a cell with a small, round, dark nucleus and a large, swollen body containing a number of large, round granules or droplets which stain bright red with eosin — the *globular leukocyte*. Sometimes they divide mitotically; they are also found in a degenerating condition with a pyknotic nucleus.

Lymphatic Tissue. The lamina propria of the small intestine contains great numbers of isolated lymphatic nodules ("solitary follicles") varying from 0.6 to 3 mm. in diameter. They are scattered all over the intestine, but are more numerous and larger in the distal part (Fig. 24–12); in the ileum they may be found on the surface of the *valvulae conniventes* or between them. If they are small, they occupy only the deeper layer of the mucous membrane above the muscularis mucosae. The larger ones occupy the whole

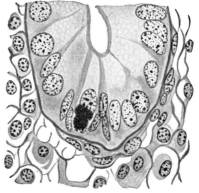

Fig. 24–10. Bottom of a gland of Lieberkühn, with an argentaffin cell. (Redrawn from Masson.)

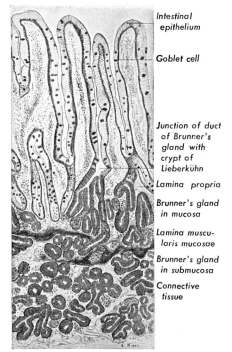

Intestinal
epithelium

Goblet cell

Junction of duct
of Brunner's
gland with
crypt of
Lieberkühn

Lamina propria

Brunner's gland
in mucosa

Lamina muscu-
laris mucosae

Brunner's gland
in submucosa

Connective
tissue

Fig. 24–11. Section of duodenum of a child of eight years. Mucicarmine and hematoxylin stains. 65 ×.

thickness of the mucosa, bulge on its surface, and may even extend through the muscularis mucosae into the submucous layer. They are visible to the naked eye, and their surface is free from villi and usually also from crypts.

Groups of many solitary nodules massed together are called *patches of Peyer* or *aggregated nodules.* They occur, as a rule, only in the ileum, but occasionally may be found even in the duodenum; their number is estimated at thirty to forty. They always occur on the side of the intestinal wall opposite to the line of attachment of the mesentery; they are elongated, oval, slightly prominent areas. Their long diameter varies from 12 to 20 mm., the short from 8 to 12 mm. They consist of dense lymphatic tissue with large lymphocytopoietic or reaction centers in their interior. Their periphery is marked by a thin layer of condensed reticular fibers.

The lamina propria and the submucosa in the vicinity of the nodules are always infiltrated with lymphocytes. Large numbers of them penetrate the epithelium and finally reach the cavity of the intestine. In old age the follicles and the patches of Peyer undergo involution.

Muscularis Mucosae. This layer averages 38 microns in thickness and consists of an inner circular and an outer longitudinal layer of smooth muscle and of elastic networks.

Other Coats of the Wall. The submucous layer consists of dense connective tissue with numerous elastic networks and occasional lobules of adipose tissue. In the duodenum it is occupied by a thick layer of duodenal glands.

The external and internal layers of the muscular coat are well developed and regular in the small intestine. Carey (1921) showed that these are not arranged as in the conventional descriptions, in an inner circular and an outer longitudinal layer, but that the outer layer is wound as an open spiral (one turn in 200 to 500 mm.), and the inner as a close spiral (one turn in 0.5 to 1 mm.). Between them is the sympathetic myenteric nerve plexus. Some strands of muscular cells pass from one layer into the other. The external coat consists of a layer of mesothelial cells resting on loose connective tissue. At the attachment of the mesentery, the serous layer of the intestines continues onto the surface of the mesentery.

Duodenal Glands (of Brunner). The glands of Brunner appear in the region of the sphincter of the pylorus with the first glands of Lieberkühn. Sometimes they extend into the pyloric region for several centimeters. They are arranged in lobules 0.5 to 1 mm. in diameter. Their terminal portions are richly branched and coiled tubules. These fuse into branching ducts which open into the bottom or side of a crypt of Lieberkühn. The gland is located for the most part in the submucosa, while the ducts pierce the muscularis mucosae. The cuboidal glandular cells contain fine granules, which stain with mucihematein after fixation in alcohol. After fixation and staining in aqueous solutions they present the usual aspect of a mucous cell—a pale, irregular cytoplasmic network with large, empty meshes and a flattened dark nucleus at the base. The cells of the terminal portions gradually pass into the cells of the ducts. They become smaller and contain less of the mucous secretion. The transition into the crypts of Lieberkühn is abrupt.

In the distal two thirds of the duodenum the glands of Brunner gradually diminish in size and finally disappear. They show a tendency to occupy the core of the circular folds and are separated by increasing, free intervals. In some cases they extend into the upper part of the jejunum.

THE APPENDIX

The appendix is a blindly ending evagination of the cecum in man and many animals. Its wall is thickened by an extensive development of lymphatic tissue which forms an almost continuous layer, with many large and small lymphatic nodules. The small lumen in cross section has an angular form. Sometimes it contains masses of dead cells and detritus; in other cases it is obliterated. It is difficult to draw a distinct line between the normal and certain pathological conditions in this organ. The glands of Lieberkühn radiate from the lumen; they have an irregu-

lar shape and variable length and are embedded in the lymphatic tissue. The epithelium of the surface of the glands contains only a few goblet cells and consists mostly of columnar cells with a striated border. The zone of undifferentiated cells with mitoses is shorter than in the small intestine. In the bottom of the glands, besides occasional cells of Paneth, argentaffine cells are regularly present. They are more numerous than in the small intestine and average five to ten to a gland; they also occur in the upper part of the glands. Villi are absent.

The lymphatic tissue of the appendix is similar to that of the tonsils. Often it presents chronic inflammatory changes. The muscularis mucosae of the appendix is poorly developed. The submucosa forms a thick layer with blood vessels and nerves, and occasional fat lobules. The muscularis externa

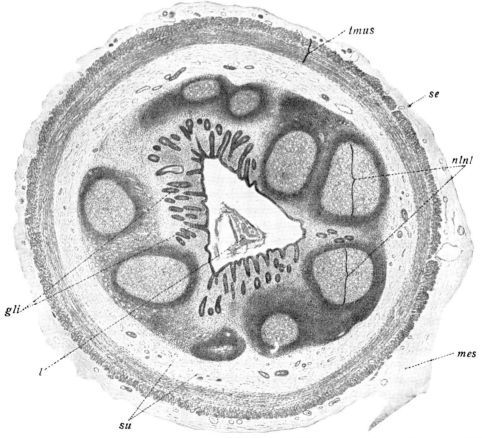

Fig. 24–12. Appendix from a twenty-three year old man. *l*, lumen with feces; *gli*, crypts of Lieberkühn; *nlnl*, centers of lymphatic nodules; *su*, submucosa; *tmus*, muscularis externa; *se*, serosa; *mes*, mesentery. 22 ×. (After Sobotta.)

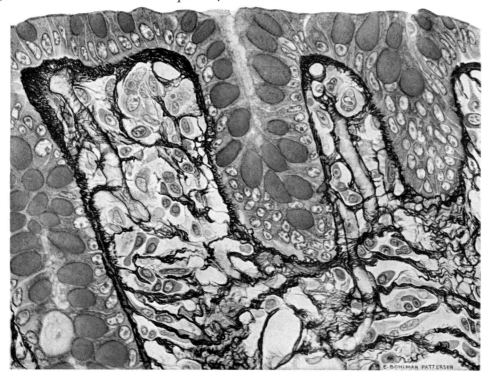

Fig. 24–13.   Slightly tangential section through mucous membrane of human colon. The reticular fibers are condensed beneath the epithelium and about the blood vessels. The mucigen of the goblet cells stains blue. Bielschowsky-Foot and Mallory-azan stains. 600 ×.

is reduced in thickness, but always shows the two usual layers. The serous coat is similar to that covering the rest of the intestines.

THE LARGE INTESTINE

The mucous membrane of the large intestine does not form folds except in its last portion, the rectum. Being devoid of villi, it has a smooth surface. The villi cease, as a rule, above the ileocecal valve.

The *glands of Lieberkühn* are straight tubules and attain a greater length than in the small intestine—up to 0.5 mm., and in the rectum to 0.7 mm. Their structure differs from that in the small intestine by the richness in goblet cells. The free surface, between the openings of the glands, is lined with simple columnar epithelium with a thin striated border. At the bottom of the crypts are the usual proliferating, undifferentiated epithelial cells and occasionally argentaffine cells; as a rule there are no cells of Paneth.

The structure of the *lamina propria* is essentially the same as in the small intestine; eosinophile leukocytes are abundant, often penetrating the epithelium of the crypts. Scattered lymphatic nodules are always present in varying numbers and are also found in the rectum. They reach far into the submucous layer.

The *muscularis mucosae* is well developed and consists of longitudinal and circular strands. It may send slender bundles of muscle cells toward the surface of the mucosa. The submucous layer does not present any peculiarities. The muscularis externa differs from the same coat in the small intestine by the arrangement of its outer longitudinal layer, which is massed into three thick, longitudinal strands—the *taenia coli.* In the rectum it again becomes continuous all around the periphery of the wall. The serous coat of the colon in its free portion forms the *appendices epiploicae;* these protuberances consist of adipose tissue and accumulations of cells similar to those in the omentum.

In the anal region the mucous membrane is thrown into longitudinal folds, the *rectal columns of Morgagni.* The crypts of Lieberkühn suddenly become short and disappear, while on the surface, along a jagged line

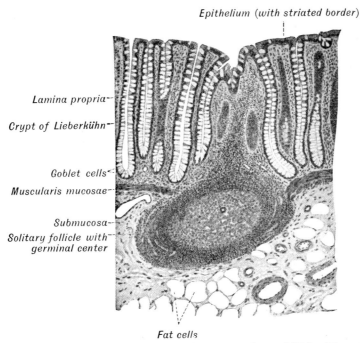

Epithelium (with striated border)

Lamina propria

Crypt of Lieberkühn

Goblet cells

Muscularis mucosae

Submucosa

Solitary follicle with germinal center

Fat cells

Fig. 24–14. Mucosa of human transverse colon, showing a solitary follicle. 70 ×. (After Braus.)

about 2 cm. above the anal opening, stratified squamous epithelium appears with superficial, flattened cells. This is a transition zone between the mucous membrane and skin. At the level of the external sphincter the surface layer assumes the structure of the skin, and here sebaceous and large apocrine, circumanal glands appear. The lamina propria here contains convolutes of large veins, which, when abnormally dilated, appear as hemorrhoidal nodes.

Blood Vessels. The arrangement of the blood and lymph vessels in the wall of the stomach and intestine is similar in principle. As the important differences depend mainly on the presence of villi, the small intestine shows significant peculiarities.

In the stomach the arteries arise from the two arterial arches along the lesser and greater curvatures and are distributed to the ventral and dorsal surfaces. The arteries reach one side of the intestine with the mesentery. They run in the serous coat and break up into large branches which penetrate the muscularis externa and enter the submucous layer, where they form a large submucous plexus.

In the stomach and colon the submucous plexus gives off branches directed toward the surface. Some break up into capillaries supplying the muscularis mucosae; others form capillary networks throughout the mucosa and surround the glands with dense meshes. The capillary net is especially prominent around the foveolae.

From the superficial, periglandular capillary networks, veins of considerable caliber arise. They form a venous plexus between the bottom of the glands and the muscularis mucosae. From this plexus, branches run into the submucosa and form a venous plexus. From this submucous plexus, the large veins follow the arteries and pass through the muscularis externa into the serous membrane. The veins of the submucous plexus (in the stomach) are provided with valves and a relatively thick, muscular coat.

In the small intestine the submucous arterial plexus gives off two kinds of branches which run toward the mucosa. Some of these arteries ramify on the inner surface of the muscularis mucosae, and break up into capillary networks which surround the crypts of Lieberkühn in the same way as about the glands of the stomach. Other arteries are especially destined for the villi, each villus receiving one or sometimes several such small arteries. These vessels enter the base of the villus and form a dense capillary network immediately under its epithelium. Near the tip of the villus one or two small veins arise from the superficial capillary network and run downward, anastomose with the glandular venous plexus, and pass into the submucosa, where they join the veins of the submucous plexus. These veins in the intestine have no valves. Their continuations which pass through the muscularis externa with the arteries are provided, however, with valves. Valves disappear in the collecting veins of the mesentery.

Lymph Vessels. In the stomach the lymphatics begin as an extensive system of large lymphatic capillaries in the superficial layer of the mucous membrane between the glands. They are always deeper

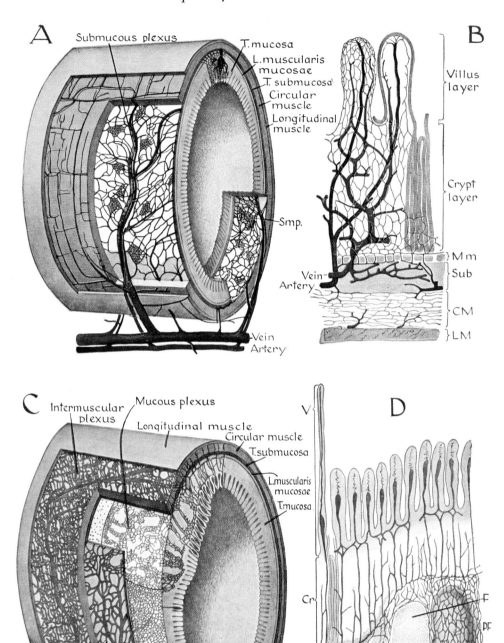

Fig. 24–15.   Diagrams of distribution of blood vessels, *A* and *B*, and of lymphatics, *C* and *D*, in the small intestine of the dog. *B* and *D* are drawn on a larger scale to show details. *CM*, circular muscle; *Cr*, crypt; *LM*, longitudinal muscle; *Mm*, lamina muscularis mucosae; *Sub*, tunica submucosa; *V*, villus; *F*, follicle; *PF*, perifollicular plexus. (Redrawn and slightly modified after Mall.)

than the blood capillaries. They anastomose everywhere throughout the mucous membrane, surround the glandular tubules, and take a downward course to the inner surface of the mucous membrane, where they form a plexus of fine lymphatic vessels. Branches of the plexus pierce the muscularis mucosae and form a plexus of lymphatics provided with valves in the submucosa. From this submucous plexus larger lymphatics run through the muscularis externa; here they receive numerous tributaries from the lymphatic plexus in the muscular coat and then follow the blood vessels into the retroperitoneal tissues. In the wall of the colon the lymphatics show a similar arrangement.

The lymphatic vessels of the intestine are important in the absorption of fat from the small intestine. During digestion, all their ramifications are filled with milky white lymph—a fine emulsion of neutral fats. This white lymph, drained from the intestine, is called *chyle,* and the lymphatics which carry it, *lacteals.*

In the small intestine the most conspicuous parts of the lymphatic system are the *central lacteals* in the core of the villi. Each conical villus has one lacteal which occupies an axial position and ends blindly near the tip. The broader villi of the duodenum may contain two or perhaps more lacteals which intercommunicate. The lumen of these lacteals, when distended, is considerably larger than that of the blood capillaries. The wall consists of thin endothelial cells and is everywhere connected with the argyrophile reticulum and surrounded by thin, longitudinal strands of smooth muscle.

The central lacteals at the base of the villi anastomose with the lymphatic capillaries between the glands, which have a similar arrangement as in the stomach and also form a plexus on the inner surface of the muscularis mucosae. Branches of this plexus, provided with valves, pierce the muscularis mucosae and form on its outer surface, in the submucosa, a loose plexus of larger lymphatics. The latter also receives tributaries from the dense network of large, thin-walled lymphatic capillaries which closely surround the surface of the solitary and aggregated follicles. The large lymphatics which run from the submucous plexus through the muscularis externa into the mesentery receive additional branches from a dense, tangential plexus located between the circular and longitudinal layers of the muscularis externa.

Nerves. The nerve supply seems to be similar in principle in all parts of the gastrointestinal tube and consists of an intrinsic and an extrinsic part. The first of these is comprised of nerve cells and their fibers located and originating in the wall of the intestine. The extrinsic nerves are represented by the preganglionic fibers of the vagus and the postganglionic fibers of the sympathetic. The latter run to the intestine from the celiac plexus. They enter the intestinal wall through the mesentery along the branches of the large vessels.

Numerous groups of nerve cells and bundles of

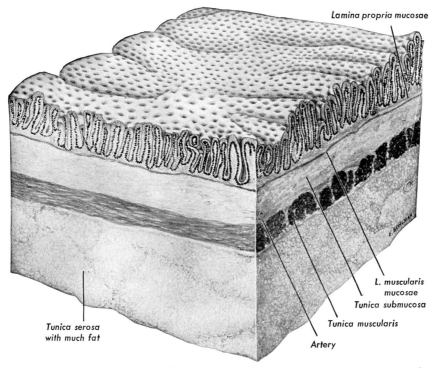

Fig. 24–16. Camera lucida drawing of block from human colon stained with hematoxylin. Note the single muscle layer. The openings of the glands of Lieberkühn are clearly shown. 24 ×. (Drawn by Miss E. Bohlman.)

nerve fibers are seen in the narrow space between the circular and the longitudinal layers of the muscularis externa. This is the *myenteric plexus of Auerbach.* In the submucosa similar elements form the *submucous plexus of Meissner.* These plexuses form the intrinsic nervous mechanism of the intestinal wall.

The nerve cells of the enteric ganglia are connected with one another by strands of nonmyelinated nerve fibers of both extrinsic and intrinsic origin. These nerve cells appear in two principal forms, which may present differences in their secondary characters. The first type occurs exclusively in the myenteric plexus. It is a multipolar cell with short dendrites which terminate in brushlike arborizations on the bodies of cells of the second type in the same ganglion. The axon can be traced for a considerable distance through neighboring ganglia and is supposed to form connections with cells of the second type in other ganglia. These neurons are associative.

The cells of the second type are far more numerous and show great variations in their forms. Their dendrites vary in number and are often missing. They begin as diffuse receptive endings in relation with nerve cells of the first and second types in the ganglia of origin or in other ganglia. The axon enters a fiber bundle and divides; its branches terminate in the circular or longitudinal layer of the muscularis externa in connection with individual smooth muscle cells. Thus the neurons of the second type are motor. Those in the myenteric plexus supply the muscularis externa; those of the submucous plexus supply the muscularis mucosae and the muscles of the villi.

A third cell type occurs in the enteric plexuses and also scattered in the submucosa and in the interior of the villi. This is the "interstitial cell," with a finely vacuolated protoplasm and short, branching processes which interlace with other processes to form an irregular feltwork. It does not contain neurofibrils, and may possibly be of microglial nature.

Most of the nonmyelinated fibers of the bundles which connect the ganglia and the fibers in the ganglia are processes of the enteric neurons. The rest is formed by extrinsic fibers, mainly of vagal, and to some extent of sympathetic origin.

The vagal fibers terminate as pericellular arborizations on cells of the second type in the enteric ganglia. The sympathetic fibers cannot be distinguished from the axons of the motor cells in the fiber bundles. They do not seem to enter into synaptic relationship with the nerve cells of the ganglia but take part, together with axons of intrinsic neurons, in the formation of the intramuscular plexuses and terminate in connection with the muscular cells. The sympathetic fibers supply the blood vessels, too. Some of them have also been described as forming a plexus in the subserous coat and ending freely in the connective tissue.

If the intestine is detached from the mesentery and placed in warm Tyrode solution, it will show normal peristaltic movements if the mucous membrane is stimulated by objects introduced into the lumen. This shows that the intestine is an automatic organ whose movements are determined by the local neuromuscular mechanism and that they are only regulated through the extrinsic nerves. Numerous nerve endings of sensory nature have been found under and in the epithelial layers of the villi.

Some investigators believe that the enteric plexuses mediate complete reflex arcs, the sensory component being enteric, a cell of the plexus, with dendritic endings in contact with the epithelium of the villi or the glands of Lieberkühn, while the axons transmit the impulse to another enteric neuron whose axon ends in the smooth muscles. Most authors hold, however, that all neurons of the enteric plexuses are of efferent nature and that therefore the sensory nerve endings in the mucous membrane must be of extrinsic nature. The local reflexes in the intestine are explained as "axon reflexes." The axons of the enteric neurons are supposed to divide into two branches, one of which receives stimuli transmitted to the other branch without passing through the cell body.

Histophysiological Remarks. An important role in the digestion of the chyme in the small intestine is played by the two large glands attached to the duodenum; the *liver,* which secretes the bile, and the *pancreas,* which secretes the pancreatic juice. The wall of the intestine itself adds an important secretion, the *intestinal juice.*

The glands of Brunner, like the pyloric glands, secrete continuously. Their secretion is a viscid, mucous, alkaline liquid. It contains a proteolytic enzyme activated by hydrochloric acid and closely resembles pepsin. It is supposed to be especially active in the digestion of the collagen of adipose tissue, and thus makes the fat of the latter easily accessible to the action of fat-splitting enzymes.

The intestinal juice proper is secreted by the portions of the small intestine which do not contain glands of Brunner. It is a yellow, alkaline liquid which always contains small flakes of mucin mixed with desquamated epithelial cells and many microorganisms. There are several important enzymes in the juice: *erepsin,* which breaks down the proteins to amino acids, a *lipase,* a *nuclease,* several *enzymes for splitting carbohydrates,* and *enterokinase,* which activates trypsinogen. The mucin of the intestinal juice is important in the formation of feces. *Secretin,* a hormone formed in the duodenal mucosa, is absorbed by the blood and stimulates the pancreas.

The surface of the villi serves primarily for absorption, while the intestinal juice is secreted by the glands of Lieberkühn. What cells of the latter are instrumental in the secretion of the enzymes is not known. The mucus obviously originates from the goblet cells in the crypts and on the villi.

The *secretion of the large intestine* contains small quantities of enzymes. Its main constituent, the mucus, plays a mechanical role in providing the necessary consistency to the feces and lubricating the mucous membrane.

The nutritive components of the chyme are converted into soluble, easily diffusible substances so that they can be absorbed. The partially digested proteins coming from the stomach are broken down into their constituent amino acids by the action of trypsin and erepsin. The neutral fat is split into glycerol and fatty acids. The carbohydrates are transformed into simple sugars, mainly glucose. These substances are absorbed by the surface epithelium of the intestine, especially by that of the villi. The total surface is estimated at 4 to 5 square meters.

The absorptive process cannot as yet be explained on known laws of diffusion and osmosis. After passing through the outermost layer of the epithelium, the different substances undergo complex transformations whose nature is for the most part obscure.

The description of the intestinal epithelium, as given earlier, applies to the resting epithelial cells. During absorption, especially of proteins, changes in the mitochondria have been described. Some believe the Golgi net to be the first part of the cell to show changes in connection with absorption; the lacunae are said to enlarge and to contribute to the formation of vacuoles.

Proteins can rarely be seen on their way through the epithelium, since they are absorbed in the form of soluble amino acids and probably carried at once by the blood of the portal vein to the liver. However, in young, especially in suckling animals, the striated border of the epithelium seems to be much more permeable to foreign substances than in the adult. It is possible that even unchanged protein, including some antibodies, may enter by the intestinal epithelium of the young. In suckling mice the epithelium of the small intestine, especially in its lower part, contains many large granules apparently of protein nature. They may be compared with the meconium corpuscles found in human fetuses (Fig. 24–18). Even

microscopically visible particulate matter, as granules of India ink, when fed to suckling mice penetrate the epithelium, a phenomenon never observed in adults.

Of all the nutritive substances, the transformation of fat is the easiest to follow, because it appears as sharply outlined droplets which give characteristic staining reactions, among which is the blackening with osmic acid. As seen in osmicated preparations under the electron microscope, during early stages of absorption of fat, tiny droplets may be seen between the microvilli and in the subjacent cytoplasm (Fig. 24–4). A little later, the droplets have left these regions and have coalesced into larger droplets which move toward the region of the Golgi apparatus and the nucleus (Fig. 24–5) and then into the space between adjacent cells. Via this space they reach the lamina propria whence they move into the lacteals (Fig. 24–6).

The *amino acids* and *glucose* enter the blood of the subepithelial capillaries and with it are brought through the portal vein into the liver, where they undergo further transformations. The largest part of the absorbed fat is carried away from the intestine with the chyle.

An important mechanism for the transmission of substances absorbed by the epithelium into the blood and lymph is the movement of the villi. This can be observed

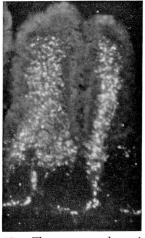

Fig. 24–17. Fluorescence photomicrograph of small intestine of rat during absorption of vitamin A concentrates. The vitamin A fluorescence is imparted by the epithelium, by the lamina propria of the villi, and by the contents of the lacteals. (After Popper and Greenberg.)

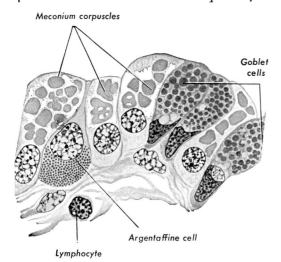

Fig. 24–18. Epithelium from tip of villus in small intestine of 4½ month human fetus; Hematoxylin-eosin-azure II. 1040 ×. (A.A.M.)

in a living animal if a loop of the intestine is split open and the surface of the mucous membrane is watched with a binocular microscope. There seems to be no relation between the movements of the individual villi. Every villus contracts independently, approximately six times a minute. Here and there a villus suddenly becomes shorter by about one half its length, while its thickness remains unchanged; then it expands again. Thus, during the contraction, the volume of the villus is greatly reduced and the contents of its capillaries and especially of the central lacteal are forwarded into the submucous plexus. When the villus expands, the liquid which penetrates the epithelium is believed to reach the central lacteal and the blood capillaries. The expansion calls forth another contraction, and so on. The contraction is obviously due to the shortening of the longitudinal muscular strands of the core of the villus. The movement is believed to be regulated by the submucous plexus of Meissner. Direct mechanical stimulation of the base of a villus with a bristle also calls forth a contraction; the stimulus radiates from the affected villus to the surrounding ones.

Histogenetic Remarks. The histogenesis of the mucous membrane of the intestine resembles that of the stomach. At first the boundary between the epithelium and the connective tissue is even. The development of villi begins in embryos of 20 mm. in the duodenum and gradually extends downward. In the

duodenum, jejunum and the upper part of the ileum they arise as isolated epithelial outgrowths. In the remaining parts of the intestine, longitudinal ridges develop which later are subdivided by the transverse furrows into single villi. The number of the villi in a given stretch increases through the appearance of new outgrowths in the hollows between the older villi. In a fetus of 100 mm. villi are found all along the intestine, including the colon, although they disappear from the latter in the later stages. This is due either to a fusion of the villi from their base upward or to their shortening through the stretching of the growing wall. In an embryo of 55 mm. the supranuclear protoplasm of the epithelial cells on the tips of the villi acquires a transparent aspect, while on the free surface a condensed cytoplasmic layer develops. Between these elements, scattered goblet cells appear.

In a fetus of four months, the epithelium of the villi has a manifold appearance. In the lower parts of the small intestine the common epithelial cells with the clear supranuclear parts contain a multitude of coarse, yellow granules. They are called *meconium corpuscles* and are similar to those seen in the lumen of the intestine. Their yellowish color is due to adsorption of bile pigment.

Between the common epithelial cells are many typical goblet cells. Beginning with the fourth month, argentaffine cells make their appearance. During the seventh month the cells of Paneth appear. In the human fetus they seem to occur not only in the crypts, but also on the villi.

The development of the glands of Lieberkühn also starts in the duodenum and proceeds downward. In a fetus of the fourth month the excavations between the villi are lined with small crowded cells with a cytoplasm darker than that of the epithelium of the villi. From these cells, evaginations arise which penetrate the subjacent connective tissue. In the seventh month, besides the formation of glands from new invaginations, a dichotomous division of the blind ends of the glands contributes largely to the continuing increase of the number of glands. Bifurcation of the crypts proceeds in the newborn.

The glands of Brunner make their appearance during the sixth month as massive, epithelial ingrowths in the depth of the duodenal crypts. In a fetus of 290 mm. they are numerous in the upper part of the duodenum and consist of branching tubules. Farther downward they are smaller, and the intervals between them larger.

REFERENCES

Bensley, R. R.: The Structure of the Glands of Brunner. The Decennial Publ., University of Chicago, *10*:279, 1903.

Dempsey, E. W., and Deane, H. W.: The cytological localization, substrate specificity, and *p*H optima of phosphatases in the duodenum of the mouse. J. Cell. & Comp. Physiol., *27*:159, 1946.

Emmel, V. M.: Alkaline phosphatase in the Golgi zone of absorbing cells of the small intestine. Anat. Rec., *91*:39, 1945.

Florey, H. W., Wright, R. D., and Jennings, M. A.: The secretions of the intestine. Physiol. Rev., *21*:36, 1941.

Granger, B., and Baker, R. F.: Electron microscope investigation of the striated border of intestinal epithelium. Anat. Rec., *107*:423, 1950.

Hill, C. J.: A contribution to our knowledge of the enteric plexuses. Phil. Tr. Roy. Soc., London, S. B., *215*:355, 1927.

Landboe-Christensen, E.: The Duodenal Glands of Brunner in Man, Their Distribution and Quantity, an Anatomical Study. Ejnar Munksgaard, Copenhagen; London, Oxford University Press, 1944.

Macklin, C. C., and Macklin, M. T.: The Intestinal Epithelium. Special Cytology (Cowdry). 2d ed. New York, (1), 231, 1932.

Mall, F. P.: Die Blut- und Lymphwege im Dünndarm des Hundes. Abh. sächs. Ges. Wiss., math.-physikal. Kl., *14*:153, 1888.

Möllendorff, W. von: Ueber die Anteilnahme des Darmepithels an der Verarbeitung enteral und parenteral zugeführter saurer Farbstoffe. Münch. med. Wochenschr., *18*:569, 1924.

Patzelt, V.: Der Darm. Handb. d. mikr. Anat. d. Menschen (v. Möllendorff), (5)³, 1, 1937.

Zetterqvist, H.: The Ultrastructural Organization of the Columnar Absorbing Cells of the Mouse Jejunum. Stockholm, Aktiebolaget Godvil, 1956.

CHAPTER 25

Liver, Bile Ducts and Gallbladder

THE LIVER

THE LIVER plays an indispensable part in the metabolism of the body, and elaborates bile. It is the largest gland of the organism, weighing about 1.5 kilograms in men and slightly less in women. It occupies the upper right quadrant of the abdominal cavity, a part of its surface being attached to the diaphragm. It arises in the embryo as an evagination of the intestine, and develops into a compound gland whose secretory portions are branching and anastomosing tubules. In the lower vertebrates this condition remains throughout life, but in the mammals the original architecture undergoes a complete remodeling.

Lobule of the Mammalian Liver. The mammalian liver is made up of polygonal prisms, each representing an architectural unit or lobule, 0.7 to 2 mm. in diameter. The periphery of each lobule is translucent and gray, while its center is brown. In man the outlines of the lobules are usually indistinct, because the connective tissue partitions between them are poorly developed. In the pig, on the contrary, each lobule is completely surrounded by a layer of connective tissue, and the lobulation is obvious. When a freshly sectioned surface of such a liver is scraped with a knife, the soft tissue is squeezed out of the lobules and the remaining partitions give the impression of a honey-combed structure. In cirrhosis of the liver in man, the connective tissue is greatly increased and the lobulation completely distorted.

In the salivary and pancreatic glands each lobule represents a mass of glandular tissue drained by a duct of a certain order and size. The liver lobule, however, is best conceived as depending not on the duct system, but as centering on the hepatic vein. This is clearly seen in microscopic sections of a liver whose blood vessels have been injected with colored masses.

The liver lobule has also been described as the amount of liver tissue which surrounds and is drained by the smallest interlobular bile ducts. According to this idea, the center of the liver lobule would be the structures in the periportal areas, and the lobule would extend into the parenchyma of the several surrounding anatomical lobules. This theory considers only the bile excretory function of the liver and overlooks entirely the fact that the liver is predominantly an endocrine gland. It also disregards the structure of this organ as seen in such species as the pig, in which the liver lobule is demarcated by a continuous connective tissue layer. (See Pfuhl, Arey, Opie for discussions of this point.)

The lobule of the liver in cross section has five, six or seven sides. The diameter of the cross section is decidedly smaller than the height of the lobule. Running through the center of the lobule, in its long axis, is the central vein, while at the periphery are the branches of the portal vein (intralobular vein), the interlobular bile ducts, branches of the hepatic artery, and the lymphatics which form a network about the portal vein and its branches.

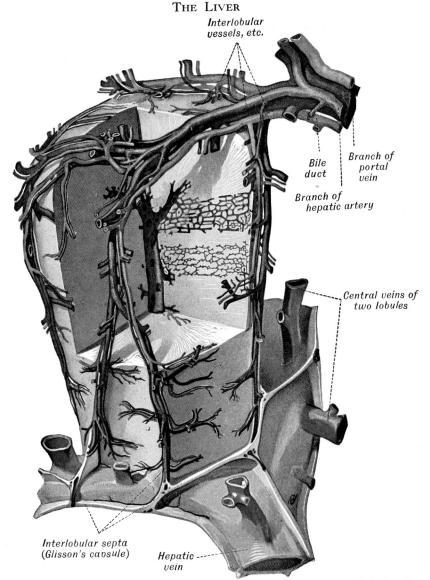

Fig. 25–1.   Lobule of liver of a pig. Wax reconstruction by Vierling. A portion of the lobule is cut away to show the bile capillaries and sinusoids. 400 ×. (After Braus.)

Blood Vessels. The principal afferent blood vessel of the liver is the portal vein. It collects the blood from the viscera of the digestive tract and from the spleen and enters the liver at the porta together with the hepatic artery. The liver of mammals receives a smaller part of its blood supply from the hepatic artery. This relatively small vessel supplies the interlobular connective tissue and its contained structures and helps to nourish the parenchyma of the gland. In the living frog liver, numerous anastomoses have been seen between the terminals of the hepatic

artery and those of the portal vein. The blood is drained from the liver by the two or more *hepatic veins;* these enter the inferior vena cava as it passes through the fossa for this vessel.

Throughout the liver the terminal branches of the portal vein and the radicles of the hepatic vein are about equal distances apart. Each radicle of the hepatic vein is surrounded by a layer of liver tissue of uniform thickness, and this mass constitutes the *hepatic lobule* (Fig. 25–4). Because of their central position in the long axis of the lobules,

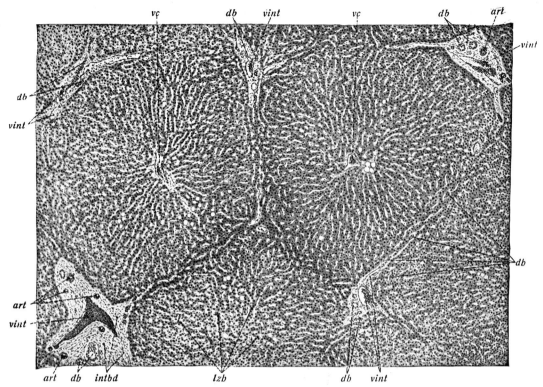

Fig. 25–2. Low power view of a portion of liver from a twenty-two year old man. Two complete lobules are surrounded by portions of other lobules. *db*, bile duct; *vint*, interlobular vein; *art*, branch of hepatic artery; *vc*, central vein; *intbd*, interlobular connective tissue; *lzb*, liver cell cords. 70 ×. (After Sobotta.)

the intralobular branches of the hepatic vein are called *central veins.* Several central veins join to form an *intercalated vein*—the sublobular vein of the older literature. Several of these veins unite to form a *collecting vein;* these in turn join to form the hepatic veins, which pursue a course through the liver independent of the portal venous system.

Hepatic Sinusoids. The plates of liver cells (p. 406) are separated from one another by the sinusoids of the liver. These are irregular tortuous blood spaces which pursue a radial course in the lobule and connect the ends of the interlobular portal veins with the intralobular central veins. They also receive blood from the branches of the hepatic artery. Although the direct connections of the sinusoids with both interlobular and intralobular (central) veins can be traced in sections, the connection between the hepatic artery and the sinusoids can be seen only in injection preparations and in the living animal. The finest branches of the hepatic artery empty into the sinusoids at the periphery of the

lobule. The contraction or dilatation of these vessels determines the amount of arterial blood reaching a sinusoid at any given time.

The sinusoids must be distinguished from capillaries (see p. 233). As seen in living animals, the lining of the hepatic sinusoids appears as a continuous refractile line. As seen in sections, the lining is composed of an irregular alternation of two kinds of cells connected by many intermediate forms. One of these, the *undifferentiated lining cell,* has a small dark nucleus so compact that practically no structural details can be made out within it (Fig. 25–6, *a*). Its cytoplasm extends as a thin film along the sinusoid. The other lining cells are fixed macrophages—the phagocytic stellate cells of von Kupffer. They are distinctly larger than the cell type just described. In sections their cytoplasm often extends into well-defined processes, and one often gets the impression that these cells project into the lumen. They have large oval nuclei with a small, prominent nucleolus. Frequently these cells contain granules of

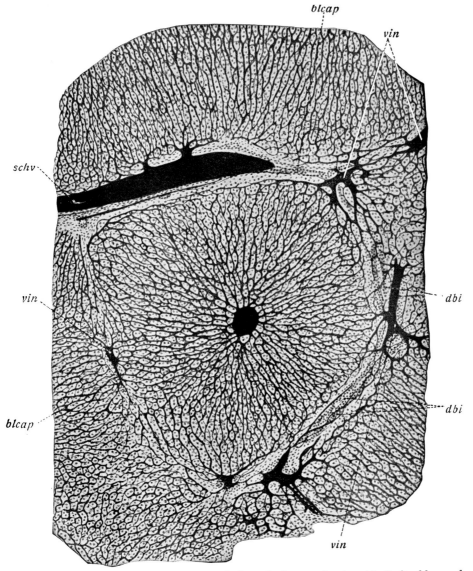

Fig. 25–3.   Portion of liver of a rabbit injected through the portal vein with Berlin blue and gelatin. A complete lobule surrounds the central vein. *blcap*, hepatic sinusoids; *vin*, interlobular veins; *dbi*, interlobular bile ducts; *schv*, large interlobular vein. 54 ×. (After Sobotta.)

green waste pigment, or engulfed erythrocytes in various stages of disintegration, and iron-containing granules. In animals vitally stained with lithium carmine or trypan blue they store large amounts of these dyes in granular form. The undifferentiated lining cells of the first type do not store vital dyes. When, however, finely divided particulate matter such as Higgins' India ink is injected intravenously, the relatively large carbon particles are deposited in the Kupffer cells and in the indifferent lining cells of the liver

sinusoids. The Kupffer cells take up more of the ink. Numerous transitional forms connect the two cell types (Fig. 25–6, *a, b, c, d*). The more vital dye introduced, the more numerous and larger are the phagocytes. The increase is thought to be due to mobilization of the undifferentiated lining cells.

Smooth muscle cells have been described at the junction of the sinusoids with the central veins. Marked changes occur continuously in the caliber of the sinusoids and in the rate of flow of blood through them. For the frog these changes have been explained as resulting from the activity of sphincters controlling the inflow and outflow of the blood of the sinusoids. This mechanism permits the storage and release of blood from the liver.

Hepatic Cells. As seen in sections, the liver cells are arranged more or less regularly in columns or plates extending radially from the central vein to the periphery of the lobule. It is claimed that this appearance in sections is due to the fact that the liver is made of a mass of hepatic cells penetrated at close intervals by the sinusoids and that only one hepatic cell separates adjacent sinusoids (Elias). This disagrees with the conventional description of the epithelium arranged in cords which in section are two cells thick. The plates may branch slightly and anastomose with nearby ones, but in spite of this their general direction is perpendicular to that of the central vein. Between them are broad, irregular, thin-walled sinusoids. The liver

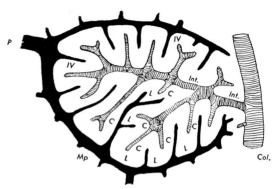

Fig. 25–4.   Diagram showing that the branches of the portal vein (black) are separated from the radicles of the hepatic veins (cross hatched) by a uniform layer of hepatic tissue (white). *P,* large branch of portal vein; *Mp,* medium-sized branch of portal vein; *Iv,* interlobular veins; *C,* central veins; *Int,* intercalated vein; *Col,* collecting vein; *L,* hepatic lobules. (Redrawn and slightly modified after Pfuhl.)

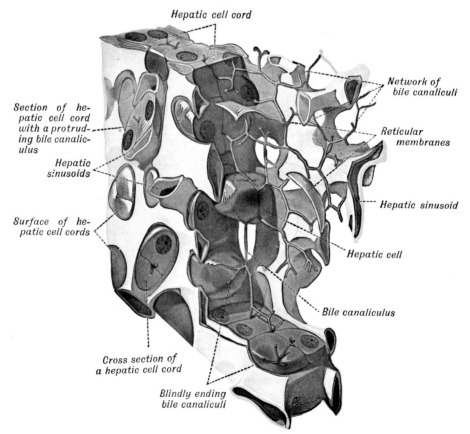

Fig. 25–5.   Reconstruction (by A. Vierling) of a portion of a lobule of a human liver. Hepatic cell cords in yellow, with red nuclei; sinusoids, blue; bile capillaries, green. 1000 ×. (After Braus.)

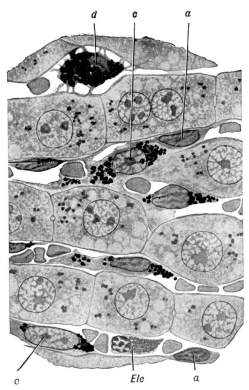

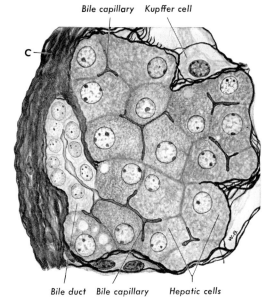

Fig. 25–7. Section through margin of lobule from human liver, showing the connection between liver cells and an interlobular bile duct. The latter is surrounded by collagenous tissue, *C*. Bielschowsky silver impregnation and Mallory-azan stain. 480 ×.

Fig. 25–6. Liver of rabbit, injected intravenously with India ink. *Elc,* eosinophile leukocyte; *a,* cells of wall of sinusoid in resting condition; *d,* stellate cell of Kupffer; *b* and *c,* transitions from *a* to *d.* Note absence of carbon in liver cells. Hematoxylin-eosin-azure II stain. (A.A.M.)

cells are polygonal in shape and have six or more surfaces. Most liver cells have one large round nucleus, although binucleated cells are not uncommon. The nucleus is quite vesicular; it has a smooth membrane and one or more prominent nucleoli and a few small chromatin dots.

The cytoplasm of the liver cell presents an extremely variable appearance which reflects to some extent the functional state of the cell. Both glycogen and fat are dissolved in the preparation of the usual sections, but by appropriate methods both types of inclusion are readily demonstrable (Figs. *1–12,* 3, 1; *1–9*). Their actual content of these constituents shows great variations under normal conditions. Sometimes the liver cells may be almost completely filled with glycogen, while at other times they may contain a large number of fat droplets. There are great variations in the protein inclusions in the liver cell. They are often intensely basophile and presumably contain ribonucleic acid. The relative amounts of these substances demonstrable in the liver cells depend primarily on the amounts of carbohydrate, fat and protein in the diet and on the stage of digestion.

The liver cells contain a cytocentrum which may be obscured in the large cytoplasm, mitochondria of extremely variable appearance, and a Golgi net sometimes close to the nucleus, but usually near the bile capillary. There are also vacuoles in the liver cells which stain supravitally with neutral red. Many attempts have been made to correlate the Golgi net and the mitochondria with the various functional states of the liver.

The liver lobule in the white mouse may be divided into three zones of activity which are reflected in differences in the mitochondria (Fig. 25–9). In the zone of permanent repose (*A*) surrounding the central vein, the fine, long mitochondria forming irregularly curving threads of uniform thickness do not change during normal alimentation or in starvation. This zone probably constitutes a region of reserve, which becomes active only when feeding is excessive or when the adjoining parenchyma is injured. The zone of permanent function (*C*), at the periphery of the lobule, contains more granular or rounded

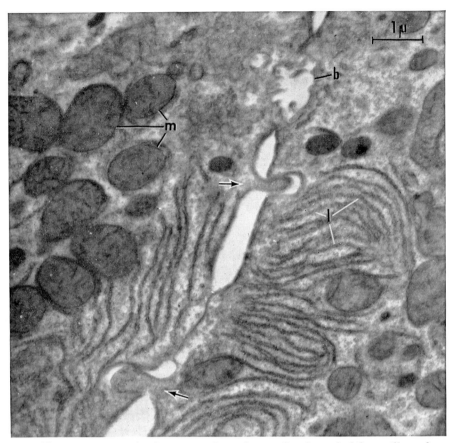

Fig. 25–8.   Electron micrograph of junction of two liver cells of rat. *b,* bile capillary; *l,* cytoplasmic lamellae; *m,* mitochondria. Two interlocking processes on the surface of contact between the liver cells are indicated by arrows. The partial separation of these cells is presumably an artefact. Buffered osmic acid fixation. (Courtesy of D. Fawcett.)

mitochondria, and rarely filaments. In the intermediate zone between these two (*B*), the mitochondrial morphology changes with the activity of the liver. This zone is at rest during starvation; its mitochondria begin to change with digestion and activity proceeds from the periphery to the center of the lobule during the course of digestion.

On feeding fat, the liver cells become somewhat larger and full of fat droplets. The mitochondria decrease as the fat increases. On feeding carbohydrates the cells become pale, and between the glycogen granules, small, iron-containing particles and some fat droplets appear. On feeding proteins the cells become large and full of protein inclusions.

In spite of the manifold functions which the liver cells perform, there is a marked similarity in appearance in all of them. This is at variance with what is seen in other organs, in which highly specialized functions are carried on by cells which morphologically are highly differentiated. It would appear that all the liver cells are equally endowed with the same functional capacities, but that their active participation in these processes under normal conditions depends on the location of the cell in the lobule.

Bile Canalicules. In adult man the thin bile canalicules run between the hepatic cells. They are a condensation of the membrane of the hepatic cells and require special methods for their demonstration. The bile canalicules run through the liver cell plates and receive short lateral branches which extend between the sides of adjoining liver cells. In planes running parallel to several adjacent plates the bile canalicules of adjoining masses of liver cells anastomose with one another. The canalicules are always inter-

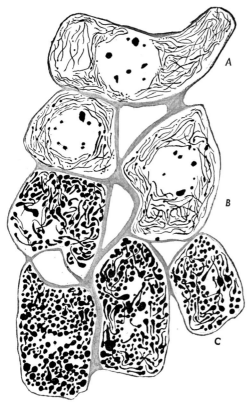

Fig. 25–9. Cells from the liver of white mouse fed proteins two hours previously, showing differences in mitochondria. *A*, cell from the zone of permanent repose; *B*, cells of the variable zone; *C*, cells from the zone of permanent function. 1200 ×. (After Noel.)

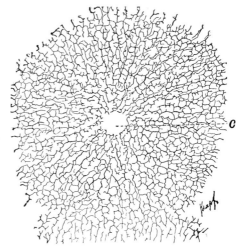

Fig. 25–10. Human bile capillaries. The capillaries of one lobule anastomose with those of the adjoining lobule (below in the figure). C, central vein. Chrome silver method. 110 ×. (After Böhm, Davidoff and Huber.)

cellular; this has been verified by studies on the liver of living frogs and rats. In some species the canalicules are stained by the methods for demonstrating phosphatase.

Connective Tissue of the Liver. The lobules of the liver are partially separated by the thin strands of dense connective tissue called periportal connective tissue. This is a part of *Glisson's capsule,* the dense connective tissue sheathing the intrahepatic portions of the portal vein, bile duct and hepatic artery, and is also continuous with the thin layer of connective tissue of the peritoneum covering the liver. In the human liver it is normally small in amount and barely suffices to form a framework for the interlobular artery, portal vein, bile ducts and lymphatics (see Fig. *11*–3). In chronic inflammatory conditions the connective tissue may be increased in amount and may show an accumulation of lymphoid cells and macro-

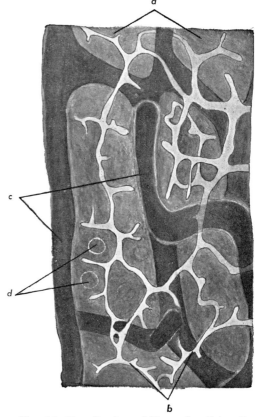

Fig. 25–11. Portion of liver of a living frog. Natural injection with fluorescein, as seen by ultraviolet light. *a*, liver cells; *b*, bile capillaries; *c*, sinusoids; *d*, indications of nuclei of hepatic cells. 600 ×. (Redrawn and slightly modified after Ellinger and Hirt.)

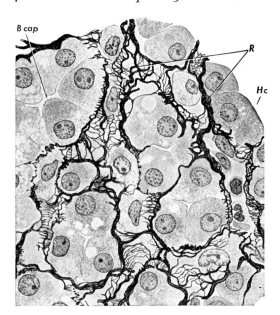

Fig. 25–12.   Section of human liver. *Hc,* hepatic cell; *B cap,* bile capillaries; *R,* reticular fibers forming a continuous membrane on the surface of the hepatic cells facing the sinuses. Bielschowsky-Foot stain. 840 ×. (A.A.M.)

phages. In sections stained for collagenous and reticular fibers by Mallory's aniline blue mixture or with one of the silver impregnation methods, the intralobular reticular fibers become visible. The periportal collagenous connective tissue continues directly into the dense network of reticular fibers which surrounds the sinusoids. Of the latter fibers, the larger ones, as a rule, run parallel to the long axis of the sinusoid, while the smaller ones form a dense interlacing network of cross fibers. This network of fibers supports the liver parenchyma.

It is quite likely that the reticular fibers with their ground membrane, together with the lining and Kupffer cells, form a complete wall for the sinusoids (Fig. 25–12). This lining completely separates the blood from direct contact with the liver cells, and the space between this membrane and the hepatic cells is available in the interior of the lobule for the transfer of lymph.

Lymph Spaces. In the liver the site of origin of the lymph and its mode of entry into the periportal lymphatics are unknown. As seen in ordinary sections, the liver cells are in intimate contact with the thin lining of the sinusoids on one side and the bile capillaries

on the opposite side. According to some estimates, one third to one half of all the lymph of the body originates in the liver, and yet the lymphatic vessels begin in the periportal connective tissue about the terminal ramifications of the portal vein. Lymphatic capillaries have not been demonstrated within the liver lobule. Accordingly, it has been assumed that there is a *potential lymphatic space* between the sinusoidal lining and the liver cells. This space cannot be demonstrated by injection methods.

Regeneration. If portions of the liver are removed from a rat or dog so that only a small part of its substance remains, most of the tissue lost will be re-formed in a few days. The increase in the number of hepatic cells takes place by mitosis of liver cells, and the new tissue will soon look like that from a normal liver. Partial hepatectomy with the ensuing regeneration has become an important method for studying a great variety of biological problems.

Histophysiological Remarks. No structural characteristics of the liver cells have been correlated constantly with the excretion of any of the biliary constituents. All the hepatic epithelial cells seem to have the same abilities.

The liver plays an important part in the intermediate metabolism and storage of carbohydrates, in the metabolism of fats and of amino acids, and in the synthesis of proteins. It serves as a depository for numerous vitamins, enzymes and hormones. The number of chemical syntheses carried out by the liver is large. It secretes bile into the bile passages, synthesizing the bile salts and excreting the bile pigments elaborated elsewhere from the hemoglobin of destroyed red blood cells. It is rich in fixed macrophages— the Kupffer cells—which have functions similar to those of macrophages elsewhere in the body. Changes in the caliber of its vessels make the liver an important storehouse and regulator of the circulating blood.

When the liver is removed by ordinary surgical methods, the animals die in a few minutes. However, when a collateral circulation has developed as a result of preliminary operations, dogs may survive hepatectomy for thirty-six to forty hours if they are given frequent injections of sugar solutions.

In contrast to the other glands of internal

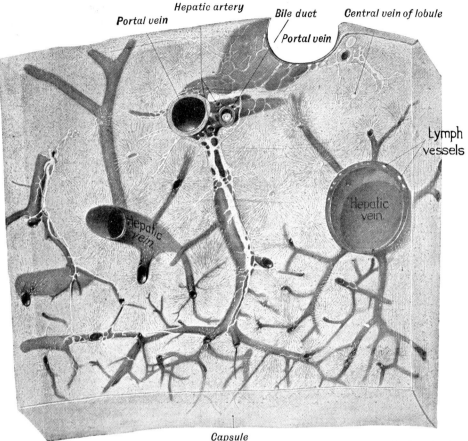

Fig. 25–13. Thick section of liver of adult cat; cleared in oil of wintergreen. The lymphatic network appears pale and the blood vessels dark. The lymphatic vessels are confined to the interlobular connective tissue, where they surround the branches of the larger blood vessels and bile ducts. 16 ×. (After F. C. Lee.)

secretion which elaborate potent hormones, the endocrine functions of the liver are concerned with the storage of various foodstuffs and of the anti-anemic factor necessary for red blood cell formation. Heparin is stored and perhaps made in the liver. Fibrinogen is made in the liver and given off to the passing blood.

One of the most important functions of the liver is the *formation of glycogen.* It increases in the liver after meals and decreases during fasting, and may even disappear completely. It is present in submicroscopic particles; the granular appearance in sections is due to the fixation. When stored in increasing amounts in the liver cells, it is seen at first in those around the central vein; when sufficient carbohydrate food is eaten, all the liver cells may take up glycogen. The liver gives up its glycogen in the reverse order; that is, the cells at the periphery of the lobule are the first to lose it. It is claimed that in mice the first site of deposition and removal of glycogen is about the central vein.

Another important function of the liver is the *formation of urea* by deamination of arginine.

The liver cells contain much fat, but an estimate of the amount present cannot be determined by staining methods, for a good deal of it may be present in a masked form in the liver. Under some pathological conditions the liver cells may take up so much fat that most of the other constituents of their protoplasm are obscured.

Bile, the external secretion, is apparently elaborated continuously. It contains water, bile pigments, bile acids, cholesterol, lecithin, neutral fats and soaps, inorganic salts and traces of urea. The bile receives, from the epithelium of the bile ducts and possibly from the neck of the gallbladder, a mucinous nucleo-albumin. Bile pigment (from broken-down erythrocytes) is formed outside the liver cells. The *bile acids* are formed in the liver cells, for, if the liver is extirpated, no trace of bile acids can be found in the blood or urine. It is probable that cholesterol is not formed in the liver. When the excretion of bile is interrupted by mechanical obstruction of the bile ducts, bile continues to be formed and is absorbed from the liver at first through the lymphatics and later also by the blood vessels of the liver. Hanzon, studying the elimination of the sodium salt of fluorescein by fluorescence microscopy in living rats, reports leakage of the dye from bile capillaries into the sinusoids in the early stages of obstructive jaundice. When bile pigment reaches a concentration in the blood and tissues sufficient to stain the entire body yellow, the condition is known as *jaundice.* It may also be produced through the action of certain blood-destroying agents. Occlusion of the common bile duct causes a great disturbance in the digestion and absorption of fats, owing to the absence of bile acids from the intestine.

After certain dyes are introduced into the organism, they may be found in the bile. If a bit of liver be teased at an appropriate time after the injection of sodium sulfindigotate, the bile capillaries will be beautifully demonstrated.

BILE DUCTS

The constituents of the bile are emptied into the bile canalicules, which communicate with the interlobular bile ducts by the canals of Hering. The finest radicles of the bile ducts are 15 to 20 microns in diameter and have a small lumen surrounded by cuboidal epithelial cells. They do not have a cuticular border, and their cytoplasm rarely contains fat droplets. The cells show an occasional mitosis. These small ducts lie on a basement membrane immediately surrounded by dense collagenous bundles.

The interlobular bile ducts form a richly anastomosing network which closely surrounds the branches of the portal vein. In progressing toward the porta, the lumen of the ducts becomes gradually larger, while the epithelium becomes taller (the ducts of the

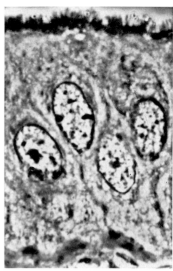

Fig. 25–14. Epithelium of human gallbladder, showing striations like cilia on free border. Phase contrast photomicrograph of a section. 2000 ×. (Courtesy of P. H. Ralph.)

second order) and has a layer of mitochondria at the base of the cell and another near the free border. These cells contain large numbers of fat droplets and, when these are numerous, cholesterol crystals. Although a faint thickening of the periphery of these cells may be seen in some animals, it is not found in man. Lymphocytes are frequently seen migrating through the epithelium into the lumen. As the ducts become larger, the surrounding layers of collagenous connective tissue become thicker and contain many elastic fibers. At the transverse fossa of the liver, the main ducts from the different lobes of the liver fuse to form the common hepatic duct, which, after receiving the cystic duct, continues to the duodenum as the common bile duct.

The epithelium of the extrahepatic ducts is tall columnar. The mucosa is thrown into many folds and is said to yield an atypical variety of mucus. The scanty, subepithelial connective tissue contains large numbers of elastic fibers, some lymphoid cells and occasional leukocytes; many of these penetrate the epithelium and pass into the lumen. Scattered bundles of smooth muscles first appear in the common bile duct; they run in the longitudinal and oblique directions, and form an incomplete layer around the wall of the duct. As it nears the duodenum, the

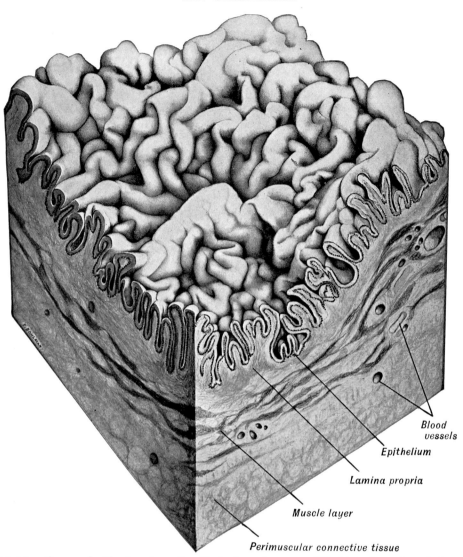

Blood vessels

Epithelium

Lamina propria

Muscle layer

Perimuscular connective tissue

Fig. 25–15. Camera lucida drawing of a block from human gallbladder. Stained with hematoxylin. 32 ×. (Drawn by Miss E. Bohlman.)

smooth muscle layer of the ductus chole-dochus becomes more prominent, and its in-tramural portions function as a sort of sphinc-ter in regulating the flow of bile.

THE GALLBLADDER

The gallbladder is a pear-shaped, hollow viscus closely attached to the posterior sur-face of the liver. It consists of a blindly end-ing fundus, a body, and a neck which con-tinues into the cystic duct. Normally it meas-ures approximately 10 by 4 cm. in adult man and has a capacity in most animals of 1 to 2

cc. per kilogram of body weight. It shows marked variations in shape and size, and is frequently the seat of pathological processes which change its size and the thickness of its wall. The mucosa is easily destroyed, so that in most specimens removed even a short time after death, large areas of epithelium are found to be desquamated or disintegrating.

The wall consists of the following layers: (1) a mucous layer consisting of a surface epithelium and a lamina propria, (2) a layer of smooth muscles, (3) a perimuscular con-nective tissue layer, (4) a serous layer, cover-ing a part of the organ. The *mucous layer* is

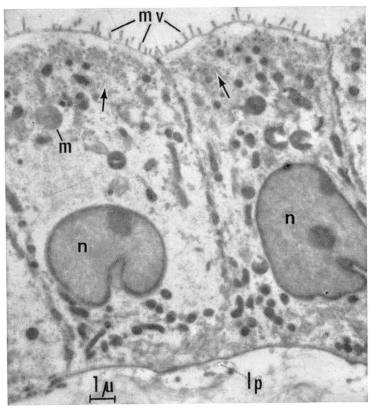

Fig. 25–16.   Electron micrograph of epithelium of gallbladder of mouse. *lp,* lamina propria; *mv,* micro-villi; *m,* mitochondria; *n,* nuclei. The arrows point to small granules, perhaps absorbed material. Buffered osmic acid fixation. (Courtesy of E. Yamada.)

thrown into frequent *folds.* The major folds are subdivided by many smaller folds; they are easily seen in the contracted or even par-tially distended organ. But when the viscus is greatly distended, its wall becomes much thinner and most of the folds disappear, al-though some of them can always be seen.

The epithelium consists of tall columnar cells with oval nuclei, containing a few scat-tered chromatin granules, toward the base of the cell. The cytoplasm stains faintly with eosin. A typical striated border is lacking here, although fine cilia-like processes have been seen with phase contrast microscopy (Fig. 25–14). Occasionally, neutral fat and other lipids may be demonstrated in the cell bodies. Mitochondria occur in two zones of these cells as in the epithelium of the bile ducts. Goblet cells do not occur. Except in the neck of the viscus, there are no glands in its mucosa.

In the lamina propria and in the perimus-cular layer near the neck of the gallbladder

are simple tubulo-alveolar glands. Their epi-thelium is cuboidal and clear, and the dark nuclei are compressed at the base of the cell. They thus stand out sharply against the darker, tall columnar epithelium of the gall-bladder. These glands are said to secrete mucus.

Outpouchings of the mucosa have some-times been confused with glands. These out-pouchings are lined with and are continuous with the surface epithelium and extend through the lamina propria and the muscular layer. These are the *Rokitansky-Aschoff sinuses* and probably are indicators of a path-ological change in the wall of the organ which thus permits an evagination of the mucosa through the enlarged meshes of the muscular network. They are not found in embryonic gallbladders and should not be confused with the "true" ducts of Luschka described later, for the latter never communi-cate with the lumen of the gallbladder.

The next layer of the wall is composed of

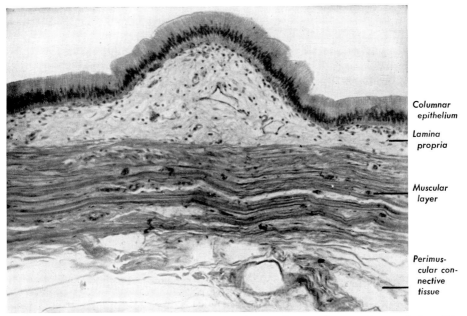

Columnar
epithelium

Lamina
propria

Muscular
layer

Perimus-
cular con-
nective
tissue

Fig. 25–17. Section of wall of gallbladder of *Macacus rhesus*. Fixation by vascular perfusion. Photomicrograph. 142 ×.

an irregular network of longitudinal, transverse, and oblique smooth muscle fibers, accompanied by a network of elastic fibers. The spaces between the bundles of muscles are occupied by collagenous, reticular and some elastic fibers, with a sprinkling of fibroblasts. The blood vessels and lymphatics contained in the perimuscular layer send branches into and through the muscular layer to the mucosa.

Under the muscular layer is a fairly dense *connective tissue layer* which completely surrounds the gallbladder and is in places continuous with the interlobular connective tissue of the liver (Fig. 25–17). It contains many collagenous and a few elastic fibers and scattered fibroblasts with a few macrophages and lymphoid wandering cells, small lobules of fat cells, and the blood vessels, nerves and lymphatics supplying the organ.

Not infrequently, particularly in the hepatic surface and near the neck, are peculiar, ductlike structures. They may be traced for considerable distances in this connective tissue layer, and some of them connect with the bile ducts. They are never connected with the lumen of the gallbladder, and are probably aberrant bile ducts laid down during the embryonic development of the biliary system. They have been called "true" *Luschka*

ducts to distinguish them from epithelial outpouchings of the mucosa.

The portion of the gallbladder not attached to the liver is covered with the peritoneum. Through it the ramifying arteries, veins and lymphatics can be seen with the unaided eye. This *serosal layer* is continuous with that covering the liver.

The gallbladder at its neck continues into the cystic duct. The wall of the latter is thrown into prominent folds which constitute the *spiral valve of Heister*. These are said to contain smooth muscle bundles, and are thought to prevent distention or collapse of the cystic duct when the latter is subjected to sudden pressure.

Blood Vessels. The gallbladder is supplied with blood by the cystic artery. The venous blood is collected by veins which empty primari'y into capillaries of the liver and only secondarily into the cystic branch of the portal vein. A prominent feature of the gallbladder is its rich supply of lymphatic vessels, of which there are two main plexuses: one in the lamina propria (but not within the rugae) and the other in the connective tissue layer. The latter plexus receives tributaries from the liver, thus affording an explanation for hepatogenous cholecystitis. These plexuses are collected into larger lymphatics which pass through the lymph node or nodes at the neck and then accompany the cystic and common bile ducts. They pass through several lymph nodes near the duodenum and finally communicate with the cisterna chyli.

Nerves. The nerves are branches of the splanchnic sympathetic and the vagus nerves. The effects of stimulation of these nerves have given rise to contradictory results in the hands of different investigators. It is probable that both excitatory and inhibitory fibers are contained in each of them. Of greater clinical importance are the sensory nerve endings, since overdistention or spasms of the extrahepatic biliary tract inhibit respiration and set up reflex disturbances in the gut tract.

Histophysiological Remarks. The gallbladder serves as a reservoir for bile, which is probably excreted by the liver continuously, if at different rates. Ingestion of fat or meat automatically discharges this reservoir. After a standard meal of egg yolks, three fourths of its contents are expelled within forty minutes.

The prevalent view that bile is expelled by the gallbladder musculature is supported by much physiological evidence, including the fact that it responds to intravenous injection of *cholecystokinin*—a secretin-like substance extracted from the mucosa of the small intestine.

Of special clinical importance is the in- spissating function of the gallbladder. Its mucous membrane withdraws water and inorganic ions from the bile and it concentrates the x-ray opaque halogen salts of phenolphthalein (Graham-Cole test). Failure to visualize the gallbladder after this test indicates that the organ is diseased or occluded. Whether, under normal conditions, it will absorb more than negligible amounts of other constituents of the bile has never been demonstrated. But if the mucosa be damaged, it may lose its concentrating power or become semipermeable. Undoubtedly, absorption of bile salts under such conditions is an important factor in the precipitation of gallstones. After obstruction of the cystic duct the bile may be resorbed *in toto* or replaced by "white bile," a colorless fluid consisting largely of exudate and mucus.

There is a little evidence in favor of a secretory function of the gallbladder. A variety of mucus is added to the bile as it passes down the larger bile ducts, and mucus-secreting glands are fairly numerous in the neck. In a few animals a gallbladder is never pres-

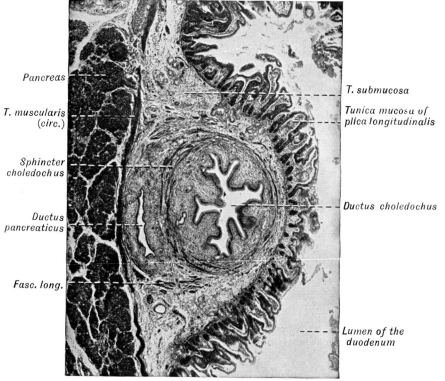

Pancreas

T. muscularis (circ.)

Sphincter choledochus

Ductus pancreaticus

Fasc. long.

T. submucosa

Tunica mucosa of plica longitudinalis

Ductus choledochus

Lumen of the duodenum

Fig. 25–18. Transverse section of plica longitudinalis of a 43-cm. human fetus. 34 ×. (After Boyden: Surgery, 1937.)

ent. Its surgical removal in man is often followed by a marked dilatation of the biliary passages.

THE CHOLEDOCHO-DUODENAL JUNCTION*

In man this zone comprises the portion of the duodenal wall that is traversed by the ductus choledochus and pancreaticus and by the short ampulla into which they usually empty. For most of its length it consists of an oblique passage through the tela submucosa; proximally it is guarded by a contractile "window" in the muscle of the duodenum and distally by the valvules of the ampulla of Vater. From "window" to ostium, associated bile and pancreatic passages are invested by a common musculus proprius, the *sphincter of Oddi.*

In man this may consist of four parts: (1) *the sphincter choledochus* (Fig. 25–18), a

* This section was contributed by E. A. Boyden.

strong annular sheath which invests the common bile duct from just outside the fenestra to its junction with the pancreatic duct; (2) *the fasciculi longitudinales,* longitudinal bundles which cover the interval between the two ducts and extend from the margins of the fenestra to the ampulla; (3) *the sphincter ampullae,* a meshwork of fibers about the ampulla of Vater (if present) and strongly developed in only one sixth of adults; and (4) *the sphincter pancreaticus,* present in one third of adults as a band encircling the pancreatic duct just before it joins the ampulla. The first is so placed as to stop the flow of bile, the second to shorten the intramural portion of the ducts (thus facilitating the flow into the duodenum), and the third, when strongly developed, to create abnormally a continuous channel between bile and pancreatic ducts (thus permitting reflux of bile into the pancreatic duct).

Histophysiological Remarks. The most important part of the musculus proprius is the

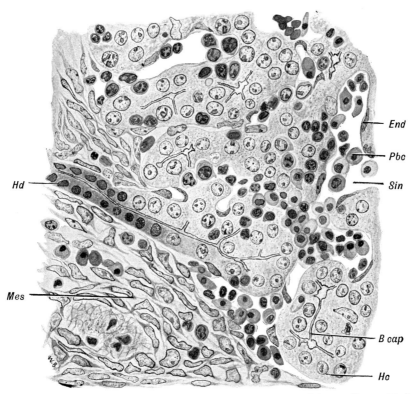

Fig. 25–19. Head of hepatic duct of 16-mm. human embryo. *B cap,* bile capillaries; *End,* lining cells of sinusoids; *Hc,* hepatic cells; *Hd,* hepatic duct; *Mes,* mesenchyme; *Pbc,* primitive blood cells; *Sin,* sinusoids. Note continuity of hepatic duct and its lumen with hepatic cell cords and bile capillaries respectively. Eppinger stain for bile capillaries. 700 ×. (W. B.)

sphincter choledochus. During fasting this muscle retains the bile against the secretory pressure of the liver, causing it to back up into the gallbladder, the mucosa of which then concentrates it. Upon ingestion of food, the sphincter relaxes and the gallbladder contracts, with the result that concentrated bile soon reaches the duodenum, there acting as a cholagogue.

Experimentally the classic studies of Bergh and Layne have shown that the human sphincter can act independently of duodenal musculature and that spasms of the sphincter produce pain resembling biliary colic. Usually such pain is referred to anterior quadrants, but 30 seconds later it may appear in scapular regions.

After resection of the gallbladder a postcholecystectomy syndrome develops in from 5 to 40 per cent of patients, depending upon whether the operation was for typical gallbladder colic and stones or for cholecystitis without pain. The syndrome may be attributable to lesions in organs adjacent to the biliary tract, to stones left in the duct, to hypertrophy or irritability of the sphincter (following inflammation of the tract), to fibrosis of the sphincter, duodenitis, etc. However, it has not yet been proven that psychic stimuli or reflexes can induce physiological spasm of the sphincter (biliary dyskinesia). The sphincter is not relaxed by neuro-mimetic drugs but only by food, certain hydragogue cathartics and antispasmotics.

Histogenesis of the Liver and Its Ducts. The liver arises early in the embryo as a diverticulum of the midgut. It appears as a ventral outgrowth which soon becomes hollow and lined by columnar epithelium; its cavity is continuous with that of the intestine. The hepatic diverticulum then extends into the mesenchyme of the septum transversum. In a 4-mm. embryo the liver consists of a thin stalk capped by a proliferating mass of liver cell cords. In a 10-mm. embryo the stalk has divided into two main branches which go to the right and left lobes of the liver. There is also a caudal diverticulum of the stalk which is the primordium of the future gallbladder and cystic duct. The liver cell cords continue to proliferate and even in embryos of 10 mm. contain bile capillaries. At these stages, the liver cords are distinctly tubular and may have five or six liver cells radiating around each lumen. In embryos of about 20 mm., with the ingrowth of connective tissue about the portal vein into the liver, interlobular bile ducts appear in this connective tissue and accompany the portal vein throughout its future ramifications.

As the connective tissue continues to extend into the liver substance along with the branches of the portal vein, the liver becomes divided into lobules. The exact mechanism by which the small liver of the newborn grows into the large organ of the adult is not known.

Blood formation begins early in the liver and becomes so developed here that for a time it is the main blood-forming organ of the embryo. Blood formation stops in the liver about the seventh month of fetal life, although this potency remains here for the life of the individual and not infrequently is brought into play in the course of certain diseases in extra-uterine life.

Bile capillaries form a continuous system in the youngest human embryos. At first these canalicules are continuous with the main hepatic ducts and, during the progressive embryonic development of the liver, with the finer branches of the interlobular ducts. There are two main theories as to the mode of origin of the ducts. The more probable of these is that the liver cells develop by branching from the head of the embryonic duct primordium and that, with the ingrowth of connective tissue into the liver substance, those liver cords nearest the connective tissue are transformed into ducts.

REFERENCES

Arey, L. B.: On the presence of so-called portal lobules in the seal's liver. Anat. Rec., *51:*315, 1932.

Beams, H. W., and King, R. L.: Effect of ultracentrifuging on the mitochondria of the hepatic cells of the rat. Anat. Rec., *59:*395, 1934.

Bergh, G. S., and Layne, J. A.: A demonstration of the independent contraction of the sphincter of the common bile duct in human subjects. Am. J. Physiol., *128:*690, 1940.

Boyden, E. A.: An analysis of the reaction of the human gallbladder to food. Anat. Rec., *40:*147, 1928.

Boyden, E. A., Bergh, G. S., and Layne, J. A.: An analysis of the reaction of the human gall bladder and sphincter of Oddi to magnesium sulfate. Surgery, *13:*723, 1943.

Buchanan, J. M., and Hastings, A. B.: The use of isotopically marked carbon in the study of intermediary metabolism. Physiol. Rev., *26:*120, 1946.

Bucher, N. L. R., Scott, J. F., and Aub, J. C.: Regeneration of the liver in parabiotic rats. Cancer Research, *11:*457, 1951.

Cole, W. H. and Grove, J.: Persistence of symptoms following cholecystectomy with special reference to anomalies of the ampulla of Vater. Ann. Surg., *136:*73, 1952.

Deane, H. W.: The basophilic bodies in hepatic cells. Am. J. Anat., *78:*227, 1946.

Elias, H.: A re-examination of the structure of the mammalian liver. I. Parenchymal architecture. Am. J. Anat., *84:*311, 1949. II. The hepatic lobule and its relation to the vascular and biliary systems. Am. J. Anat., *85:*379, 1949.

Ellinger, P., and Hirt, A.: Mikroskopische Untersuchungen an lebenden Organen. I. Methodik. Zeit. f. Anat. u. Entwicklungs., *90:*791, 1929.

Fawcett, D. W.: Observations on the cytology and electron microscopy of hepatic cells. J. Natl. Cancer Inst., *15:*1475, 1955.

Fiessinger, N.: La cellule hépatique. Revue générale d'histologie, Fasc. 13, 1911.

Hall, E. M., and MacKay, E. M.: The relation between the mitochondria and glucose-glycogen equilibrium in the liver. Am. J. Path., 9:205, 1933.

Halpert, B.: Morphological studies on the gallbladder. II. The "true Luschka ducts" and "Rokitansky-Aschoff sinuses" of the human gallbladder. Bull. Johns Hopkins Hosp., 41:77, 1927.

Hanzon, V.: Liver cell secretion under normal and pathologic conditions studied by fluorescence microscopy on living rats. Acta Physiol. Scand., 28: suppl. 101, 1952.

Johnson, F. P.: The isolation, shape, size, and number of the lobules of the pig's liver. Am. J. Anat., 23:273, 1918.

Kater, J. McA.: Variations in the mitochondria of the hepatic cells in relation to alterations of the glycogen-glucose equilibrium. Anat. Rec., 49:277, 1931.

Knisely, M. H.: The structure and mechanical functioning of the living liver lobules of frogs and Rhesus monkeys. Proc. Inst. Med. Chicago, 16:286, 1947.

Kupffer, C. von: Ueber die sog. Sternzellen der Säugetier Leber. Arch. f. mikr. Anat., 54:254, 1899.

Lazarow, A.: Particulate glycogen. A submicroscopic component of the guinea pig liver cell; its significance in glycogen storage and the regulation of blood sugar. Anat. Rec., 84:31, 1942.

Lee, F. C.: On the Lymph Vessels of the Liver. Carnegie Inst., Contrib. to Embryol., No. 74, 65, 1925.

Noel, R.: Recherches histo-physiologiques sur la cellule hépatique des mammifères. Arch. d. anat. micro., 19: 1, 1923.

Opie, E. L.: Mobilization of basophile substance (ribonucleic acid) in the cytoplasm of liver cells with the production of tumors by butter yellow. J. Exper. Med., 84:91, 1946.

Petrén, T.: Die Venen der Gallenblase und der extrahepatischen Gallenwege beim Menschen und bei den Wirbeltieren. Stockholm, 1933.

Pfuhl, W.: Die Leber. Die Gallenblase und die extrahepatischen Gallengänge. Handb. d. mikr. Anat. (v. Möllendorff), 1932, Vol. 5, pp. 235, 426.

Schwegler, R. A., Jr., and Boyden, E. A.: The development of the pars intestinalis of the common bile duct in the human fetus, etc. Anat. Rec., 67:441; 68:17, 193, 1937.

Wakim, K. G., and Mann, F. C.: The intrahepatic circulation of blood. Anat. Rec., 82:233, 1942.

Williams, W. L., Lowe, C. U., and Thomas, L.: The effects of cortisone upon the parenchymal cells of the rabbit liver. Anat. Rec., 115:247, 1953.

Wilson, J. W.: Liver. Ann. Rev. Physiol., 13:133, 1951.

Wilson, J. W., and Leduc, E. H.: Abnormal mitosis in mouse liver. Am. J. Anat., 86:51, 1950.

Yamada, E.: The fine structure of the gall bladder epithelium of the mouse. J. Biophys. Biochem. Cytol., 1: 445, 1955.

CHAPTER 26

Pancreas

NEXT TO THE LIVER, the pancreas is the largest gland connected with the alimentary tract. It consists of an *exocrine portion,* which elaborates certain digestive juices, and an *endocrine portion,* whose secretion plays an important part in the control of the intermediate carbohydrate metabolism of the body. Unlike the liver, in which both exocrine and endocrine functions are carried on by the same cells, the exocrine and endocrine functions of the pancreas are carried on by distinctly different groups of cells.

The pancreas is a pink-white organ which lies in the retroperitoneum about the level of the second and third lumbar vertebrae; on the right it is intimately adherent to the middle portion of the duodenum and extends transversely across the body to the spleen. In the adult it measures from 20 to 25 cm. in length and varies in weight from 65 to 160 gm. It is covered by a thin layer of connective tissue which does not, however, form a definite, fibrous capsule. It is finely lobulated, and the outlines of the larger lobules can be seen with the naked eye. It is usually described as having a head, a body and a tail. The head is slightly thicker than the rest and fills the loop formed by the middle portion of the duodenum, to which it is intimately adherent. It partially encircles this viscus and in rare cases may surround it completely. The lower part of the head contains a groove through which the mesenteric vessels pass.

Exocrine Portion. The pancreas is a compound *acinous* gland whose lobules are bound together by loose connective tissue through which run blood vessels, nerves, lymphatics and excretory ducts (Fig. 26–1). The acini which form the external secretion vary from rounded structures to short tubules. They consist of a single row of pyramidal epithelial cells resting on a delicate reticular membrane and converging toward a central lumen. The size of the lumen varies with the functional condition of the organ; thus it is small when at rest, but during active secretion becomes distended with secreted material. Between the acinar cells are fine secretory capillaries connected with the central lumen.

The acinar cells show rather striking differences in the various stages of secretion. In general, the basal part of the cell, when seen in the living condition, is homogeneous or may show a faint longitudinal striation, owing to the presence of filamentous mitochondria in it. The supranuclear portion— the part between the nucleus and the lumen —is filled with a number of highly refractile granules. These are the secretion granules, which vary greatly in number, depending on the stage of secretion. Occasionally, even in the living cell, fine clefts can be observed between these granules. This is probably the canalicular apparatus; if the secretion granules are stained supravitally, these canals become still more prominent. In sections stained with hematoxylin and eosin after Zenker-formol fixation, the basal parts of the acinar cells stain a dark purple, while the secretory granules are a bright orange-red.

The relationships between the basophile homogeneous zone at the base (Figs. 26–2,

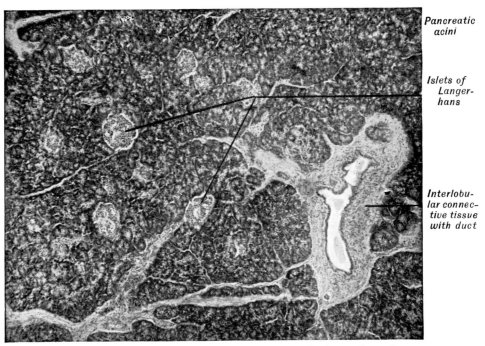

Fig. 26–1.   Photomicrograph of human pancreas, showing several islets and one large interlobular duct. 65 ×.

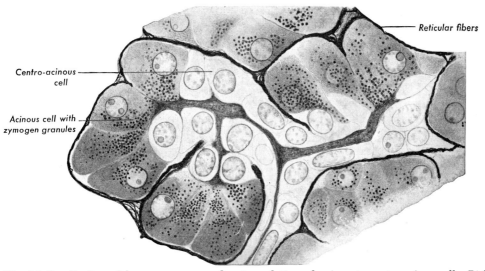

Fig. 26–2.   Section of human pancreas, showing relation of acinar to centro-acinar cells. Bielschowsky-Foot and Mallory-azan stain. 1260 ×. (Drawn by Miss Agnes Nixon.)

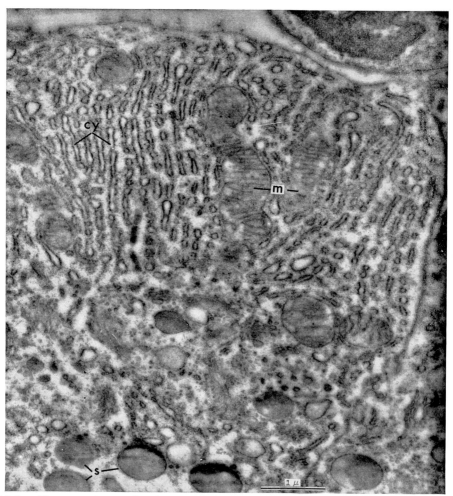

Fig. 26–3. Electron micrograph of portion of acinar cell of guinea pig pancreas, showing mitochondria (*m*), the cytoplasmic membranes (*cy*) with tiny dark granules of RNA, and secretion granules (*s*). The oval appearance of the latter is presumably due to compression during sectioning. Buffered osmic acid fixation. (Courtesy of G. Palade and P. Siekevitz.)

26–5), apparently rich in ribose nucleoprotein, and the amount of secretory granules depend on the state of digestion; these relationships are shown in Figure 26–6, in which the Golgi apparatus is stained black and the secretory vacuoles appear as paler dots. In *B,* an acinus from a resting gland, the proximal portion of the cells is homogeneous, while the distal portion contains a moderate number of secretion granules, more or less separated from the remainder of the cell by the network of the Golgi apparatus. In *A,* from a starving animal, the number of secretion granules has increased greatly; in several places these have extended into the basal or proximal zone of the cell, and the Golgi ap-

paratus is much more diffuse than in *B.* In *C,* an acinus from a mouse into which pilocarpine had been injected three hours previously, the amount of homogeneous protoplasm is greatly increased, and all the secretory granules have been discharged into the lumen, about which the Golgi apparatus forms a limiting network.

The nucleus is spherical and it contains much chromatin, and one or two prominent oxyphile nucleoli. In some animals the cells frequently contain two nuclei, but this is relatively infrequent in man. Mitotic figures are rarely found in the acinar cells of a normal, active gland in the adult.

Between periods of active secretion the

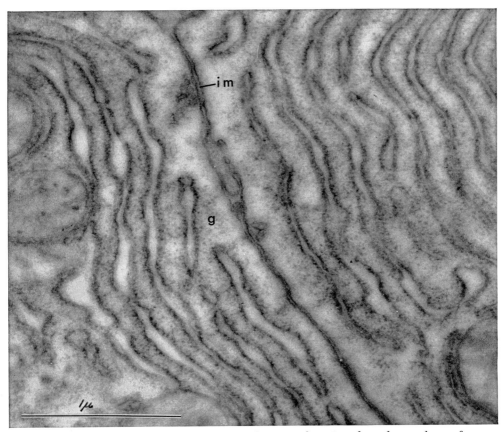

Fig. 26–4. Electron micrograph, at high magnification, of section through cytoplasm of pancreatic acinar cells of guinea pig, showing the lamellated cytoplasmic membranes and the fine RNA granules (g) on and between them. *im,* Intercellular membrane. Buffered osmic acid fixation. (Courtesy of G. Palade and P. Siekevitz.)

resting cells accumulate secretory granules, apparently at the expense of the homogeneous basal cytoplasm, but, as with secretion granules in general, the chemical precursors of the granules are unknown.

Islets of Langerhans. In addition to these external secreting portions of the gland, the pancreas also contains islands of Langerhans. These are irregular structures, more or less completely delimited from the acini by a thin reticular membrane and provided with an extensive blood supply. Indeed, their great vascularity early suggested the possibility of their being endocrine organs. After staining the islets differentially by the arterial injection of the gland with neutral red or Janus green the number of islands of Langerhans in adult man was found to vary from about 200,000 to 1,800,000. The number in the tail is slightly higher than in the body or head.

As seen in the usual preparations stained

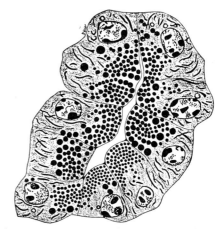

Fig. 26–5. Section of pancreatic acinus of a guinea pig, showing mitochondrial filaments embedded in the homogeneous basal substance. Secretion granules are rounded and in distal parts of the cytoplasm. Acid fuchsin methyl green stain, 1000 ×. (After Bensley.)

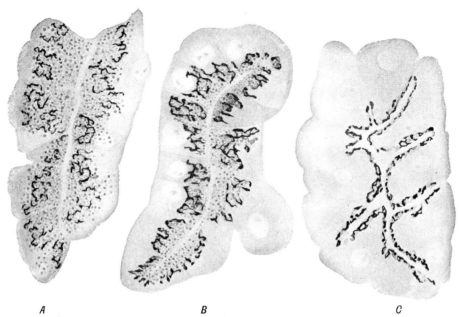

A   *B*   *C*

Fig. 26–6.   Sections through three pancreatic acini of mice, showing changes in the zymogen granules and Golgi apparatus. *A*, during starvation; *B*, normal pancreas; *C*, three hours after the injection of pilocarpine. Method of Kolatschew. 950 ×. (Redrawn after Nassonow.)

by hematoxylin and eosin, the islands of Langerhans seem to be composed of almost syncytium-like cords of irregularly prismatic cells distinctly paler than the surrounding acinar cells. With such a technique, no secretion granules are to be seen in the cells of the islets. By special methods, however, it can be shown that several types of granular cells are present which stain quite differently from those of the acini and accordingly must have a different constitution. One of these is found in a small number of cells, called *alpha* or *A cells;* these granules are insoluble in alcohol. Other cells, the *beta* or *B cells,* constitute the bulk of the island. The granules in these cells are soluble in alcohol. In the guinea pig some of the cells in the islands do not contain granules; these are called *C cells.*

In sections of the mammalian pancreas freshly fixed in Zenker-formol and stained with the Mallory-azan or Masson method, three types of granular cells are found in the islands. The *A* cells have granules which are large and stain a brilliant red; the *B* cells have smaller, brown-orange granules; while a third type of cell, called *D,* is filled with small, blue-stained granules. In the dog, Hunt found the *A, B* and *D* cells to constitute 20, 75 and 5 per cent of the cells, respectively.

Several cases of a rare disease in man have been associated with small tumors of the pancreas. Most of the cells composing some of these tumors are considered to be atypical *B* cells because of the staining reactions of their granules. Curiously, these tumor cells often contain chromophile substance like that in the acinar cells.

The mitochondria of the islands resemble those of the duct cells; that is, they are usually small rods or delicate filaments, and thus contrast sharply with the heavier, granular or filamentous mitochondria of the acinar cells. The acini contain chromophile substance and zymogen granules; the islets do not contain either of these, but do have their several kinds of specific granules. The Golgi net in the islets is much smaller than in the acini.

Ducts. The pancreas usually communicates with the duodenum by a large and a small duct. The large, or main, duct (of Wirsung) begins in the tail and runs through the substance of the gland, receiving throughout its course numerous accessory branches, so that it gradually increases in size as it nears the duodenum. In the head of the organ, it runs parallel with the ductus choledochus, with which it may have a common opening, or it may open independently in the ampulla of

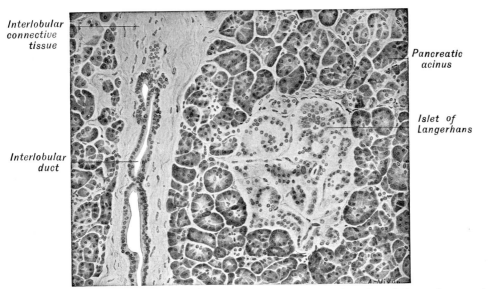

Fig. 26–7. Section of human pancreas, showing contrast between the islet of Langerhans and the surrounding acinous tissue. 470 ×. (Drawn by Miss A. Nixon.)

Vater. The opening and closing of these ducts are controlled by the sphincter of Oddi (p. 417). The accessory duct (of Santorini) is about 6 cm. long. It is practically always present and lies cranial to the duct of Wirsung.

The ducts represent two separate primordia. They are lined by a columnar epithelium in which goblet cells and occasional argentaffine cells are interspersed. At times small mucous glands bulge slightly from the ductal epithelium. The primary ducts are surrounded by a layer of dense, collagenous connective tissue which contains a few scattered elastic fibers. The intralobular ducts are of low columnar epithelium and rest on a reticular basement membrane. The terminals of the intralobular ducts continue into the acini as the *centro-acinous cells*. In sections stained with the Mallory-azan technique, the pale orange stained centro-acinous cells are in sharp contrast to the purple stained acinar cells with their bright red zymogen granules.

In addition to these ducts, the pancreas contains a system of anastomosing small *tubules* which arise from the large ducts and run in the connective tissue surrounding them. These tubes have a diameter of 12 to 27 microns; they are connected with both the islets of Langerhans and the small mucous glands and only occasionally with the acini. These structures, although studied most extensively in the guinea pig, are also said to be present in man. The epithelium of these tubules is of a low, irregularly

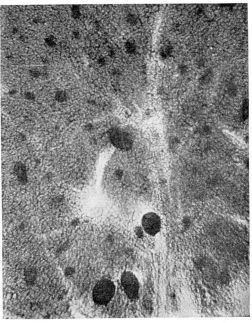

Fig. 26–8. Photomicrograph of portion of guinea pig pancreas, in which the islands of Langerhans have been stained differentially by injection of neutral red into the vessels. Note the variations in size of the islands. 38 ×. (After Bensley.)

cuboidal type. They contain occasional mitoses. The cytoplasm is homogeneous in most cases. Occasional goblet cells and a few cells with true mucous granules may be found within them.

Some of the projections in these tubules consist of island cells, singly or in groups, but the most

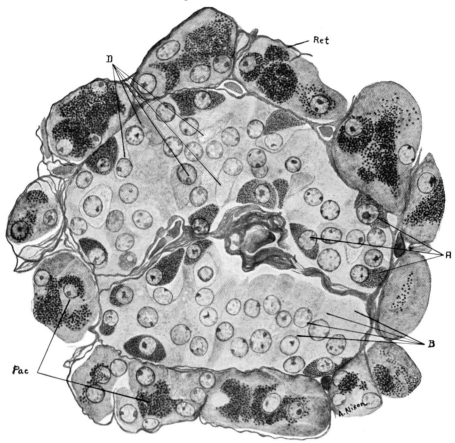

Fig. 26–9. Section of human pancreas. The central part of the figure is an islet of Langerhans with granular cells of types *A, B* and *D; Pac,* pancreatic acini; *Ret,* reticular fibers. Mallory-azan stain. 960 ×. (After Bloom, 1931.)

striking feature of these tubules is their connection, by one or more short stalks, with large islands of Langerhans. These ductules are composed of undifferentiated epithelium, and from them new islands, and probably also new acini, arise from time to time, particularly after injury to the pancreas. They do not carry any secretion.

Blood Vessels, Lymphatics and Nerves. The arterial supply of the pancreas is from branches of the celiac and superior mesenteric arteries. From the celiac it receives branches through the pancreaticoduodenal and the splenic arteries; it also receives small branches from the hepatic artery. The inferior pancreaticoduodenal artery is a branch of the superior mesenteric. The vessels run in the interlobular connective tissue and give off fine branches which enter the lobules. Veins accompany the arteries throughout and lead the blood either directly into the portal vein or indirectly through the splenic vein.

The exact lymphatic supply of the gland has not been worked out in detail. The lymphatic drainage is mainly into the celiac nodes about the celiac artery.

The nerve supply is mainly of unmyelinated fibers arising from the celiac plexus. These fibers accompany the arteries into the gland and end about the acini with fine terminals. There are many sympathetic ganglion cells in the interlobular connective tissue. The organ also receives myelinated fibers from the vagus nerves; it has been suggested that these are of secretory nature.

Histogenesis. The pancreas arises from two diverticula of the duodenum close to the hepatic diverticulum. The two primordia of the pancreas are known as the *ventral* and *dorsal pancreases;* these fuse, and the duct of the ventral pancreas becomes part of the main pancreatic duct. The great mass of the organ is formed by the dorsal pancreas, which gives rise to the body and tail and part of the head. The duct of this primordium becomes the future accessory duct. Most of the main pancreatic duct of the adult is formed from the remainder of the duct of the dorsal primordium which fuses with the duct of the ventral primordium.

At first the primordium consists of a network of anastomosing tubules lined by a single layer of cells. These differentiate into acini, in which the characteristic secretion granules appear, and also into islands. It is said that specific granules are to be found in human embryos 31 cm. long. Although the question has not been finally settled, it is probable that the acini do not develop into islands, but

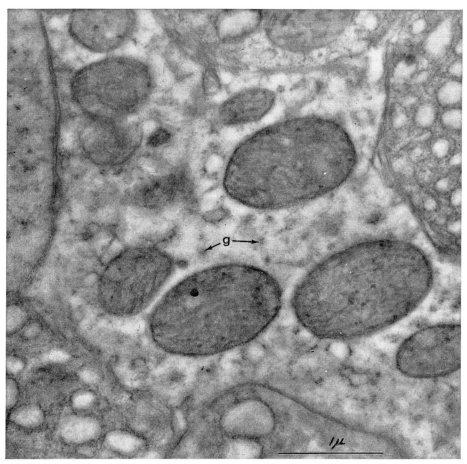

Fig. 26–10. Electron micrograph of centro-acinar cell of pancreas of guinea pig showing mitochondria and few dense granules (g) in contrast to the large numbers of these granules in the adjacent acinar cells. Compare with Fig. 26–4. Buffered osmic acid fixation. (Courtesy of G. Palade.)

that the latter come directly from the embryonic tubules of the duct.

Regeneration. If the great mass of the pancreas is removed experimentally, the organ regenerates but slightly. If a portion of the tissue be injured by a wound, mitotic figures appear in the ductal epithelium, and many new islands are formed, but few, if any, new acini develop as a result of the injury. If the main pancreatic ducts be ligated, there is at first a rapid disintegration of the pancreatic acini followed by a much slower disintegration of the original islands, but at the same time ducts begin to proliferate and give rise to many new islands and to some new acini. This process extends over a period of months and even years. One week after the ligation, in the guinea pig and rabbit, most of the acini have regenerated; after one month, there is considerable regeneration of new islands and some acini from the ducts; then, most of the acini degenerate (year and a half). After nearly three years, it is said that only the main duct is present as a blindly ending structure, that there are no acini left, and that a few new islands have arisen by sprouting from the ducts. It seems fairly well assured that the

pancreas, even in the adult, is provided with undifferentiated cells which can give rise to new acini and, to a great extent, to new islands.

Histophysiological Remarks. *Internal Secretion.* Extirpation of the pancreas in animals results in severe *diabetes,* a disturbance in carbohydrate metabolism in which the concentration of glucose in the blood rises and the excess is excreted in the urine. Such a condition results shortly in the death of the animal, but is delayed if the pituitary gland is also removed.

If the pancreatic ducts are ligated, the animals do not suffer diabetes, although the acinar tissue degenerates, and the islands persist and may even increase in number. One of the great achievements in modern therapeutics, the *insulin* treatment of diabetes, rests upon the demonstration that extracts of pancreas tissue, in which degeneration of the

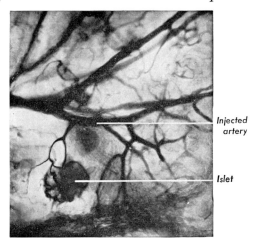

Injected
artery

Islet

Fig. 26–11.   Photomicrograph of vascular injection of pancreas of guinea pig, showing blood supply to an islet of Langerhans. From a preparation of R. R. Bensley. 95 ×.

acinar tissue had been induced by ligation of the ducts, relieved the symptoms of diabetes. Insulin was subsequently obtained from the whole or intact pancreas by preventing the destructive effect of the acinar secretion upon the internal secretion of the islets of Langerhans. Insulin is the first protein of which the structure has been completely determined. The smallest subunit of the hormone possessing biological activity has a molecular weight of 11,500 and consists of four long chains of amino acids cross-linked by disulfide bridges. A combination of insulin with protamines is used to extend the activity of the preparation over longer periods of time. There are many indications that the *B* cells are concerned with the production of insulin, although the proof of this is not certain.

When glucose is administered continuously intravenously in guinea pigs, the *B* cells at first lose their granules and later become more numerous, through mitosis and through transformation of acinar cells, and loaded with granules. If the injection of glucose is continued for several days, many of the *B* cells lose their granules and become vacuolated (exhaustion). Cells like these also occur after removal of large parts of the pancreas.

The exact mode of action of insulin is not known, but it is an important factor in the endocrine balance which determines the level of the blood sugar. There are also cases of pituitary diabetes and even of thyroid or adrenal cortical diabetes, since all these endocrine glands are also concerned with the regulation of carbohydrate metabolism, transport or storage.

Animals injected with alloxan suffer a severe hyperglycemia and die, owing to degeneration of the *B* cells. The diabetogenic action of alloxan can be prevented by a prophylactic injection of 1,2-dimercaptopropanol.

Accompanying the tumors of the pancreas composed of atypical *B* cells, there is a great decrease in the concentration of sugar in the blood. The symptoms of hypoglycemia in these cases may be relieved temporarily by administration of glucose, and some patients have been cured by removal of the tumors.

Glucagon, the hyperglycemic-glycogenolytic factor, is a distinct protein hormone found in the pancreas and present in most insulin preparations in small amounts. Although the known actions of this agent appear to oppose those of insulin, its role as a physiological antagonist of insulin has not been established. It has been claimed that this hormone originates in the *A* cells.

External Secretion. The external secretion of the pancreas follows a rhythmical cycle seemingly dependent on the fact that, in certain stages of digestion, the acid content of the stomach, on reaching the duodenum, produces there a substance called *secretin.* This substance, carried to the pancreatic cells by the blood, induces them to secrete. Then the alkaline secretion in the duodenum neutralizes the acid material from the stomach and inhibits the formation of secretin until new acid is brought from the stomach. The nature of secretin and how it acts upon the pancreatic cells are not known.

The *zymogen granules* in the pancreatic acini decrease in number after the injection of pilocarpine or stimulation of the vagus nerve, and during digestion. It is claimed, however, that in normal secretion there is not an extensive diminution of zymogen granules; accordingly, the formation of pancreatic juice, rich in ferment, does not remove all granules. The pancreatic juice contains several types of pro-enzymes. One of these when activated becomes trypsin, a proteolytic enzyme; another, an amylase or sugar-splitting enzyme; a third, lipase, a fat-splitting enzyme; and, finally, an enzyme like the rennet of gastric juice.

As these enzymes are present as inactive precursors, they cannot injure the pancreas. In certain pathological conditions, however, these pro-enzymes may be converted into the active enzymes which destroy the pancreatic tissue itself.

REFERENCES

Andrew, W.: Senile changes in the pancreas of Wistar Institute rats and of man with special regard to the similarity of locule and cavity formation. Am. J. Anat., 74:97, 1944.

Babkin, B. P., Rubaschkin, W. J., and Ssawitch, W. W.: Ueber die morphologischen Veränderungen der Pankreaszellen unter der Einwirkung verschiedener Reize. Arch. f. mikr. Anat., 74:68, 1909.

Banting, F. G., and Best, C. H.: The internal secretion of the pancreas. J. Lab. & Clin. Med., 7:251, 1922.

Bast, T. H., Schmidt, E. R., and Sevringhaus, E. L.: Pancreatic tumor with hypoglycemic status epilepticus. Acta Chirurgica Scandinavica, 71:82, 1932.

Beams, H. W.: Golgi apparatus, canalicular apparatus, vacuome, and mitochondria in the islets of Langerhans of the albino rat. Anat. Rec., 46:305, 1930.

Bensley, R. R.: Studies on the pancreas of the guinea pig. Am. J. Anat., 12:297, 1911.

Bensley, S. H., and Woerner, C. A.: The effects of continuous intravenous injection of an extract of the alpha cells of the guinea pig pancreas on the intact guinea pig. Anat. Rec., 72:413, 1938.

deDuve, C.: Glucagon. Lancet, 2:99, 1953.

Diamare, V.: Studii comparativi sulle isole di Langerhans del pancreas. Internat. Monatschr. f. Anat. u. Physiol., 16:155, 1899.

Dunn, S. J., Sheehan, H. L., and McLetchie, N. G. B.: Necrosis of islets of Langerhans produced experimentally. Lancet, 1:484, 1943.

Gomori, G.: Pathology of the pancreatic islets. Arch. Path., 36:217, 1943.

Laguesse, E. L.: Le pancréas. La glande exocrine. La glande endocrine. Revue générale d'histologie, 1 and 2, 1906.

Lane, M. A.: The cytological characters of the areas of Langerhans. Am. J. Anat., 7:409, 1907.

Latta, J. S., and Harvey, H. T.: Changes in the islets of Langerhans of the albino rat induced by insulin administration. Anat. Rec., 82:281, 1942.

Lazarow, A.: Protection against alloxan diabetes. Anat. Rec., 97:37, 1947.

McHenry, E. W., and Patterson, J. M.: Lipotropic factors. Physiol. Rev., 24:128, 1944.

O'Leary, J. L.: An experimental study on the islet cells of the pancreas in vivo. Anat. Rec., 45:27, 1930.

Opie, E. L.: The relation of diabetes mellitus to lesions of the pancreas. Hyaline degeneration of the islands of Langerhans. J. Exper. Med., 5:527, 1902. Cytology of the pancreas, in Special Cytology (Cowdry). 2d ed. New York, (1), 373, 1932.

Sanger, F., and Thompson, E. O. P.: Amino-acid sequence in the glycyl chain of insulin. Biochem. J., 53:353, 1953.

Sanger, F., and Tuppy, H.: Amino-acid sequence in the phenylalanyl chain of insulin. Biochem. J., 49:481, 1951.

Sjöstrand, F. S., and Hanzon, V.: Membrane structures of cytoplasm and mitochondria in exocrine cells of mouse pancreas as revealed by high resolution electron microscopy. Exp. Cell Res., 7:393, 1954. Ultrastructure of Golgi apparatus of exocrine cells of mouse pancreas. Exp. Cell Res., 7:415, 1954.

Soskin, S., and Levine, R.: Carbohydrate Metabolism. 2nd ed., Chicago, University of Chicago Press, 1952.

Staub, A., Sinn, L., and Behrens, O. K.: Purification and crystallization of glucagon. J. Biol. Chem., 214:619, 1955.

Thompson, E. O. P.: The insulin molecule. Scientific American, 192 (5):36, 1955.

Warren, Shields, and Le Compte, P. M.: The Pathology of Diabetes Mellitus. 3rd ed., Philadelphia, Lea & Febiger, 1952.

Zimmermann, K. W.: Die Speicheldrüsen der Mundhöhle und die Bauchspeicheldrüse, in von Möllendorff's Hand. d. mikr. Anat. des Menschen. Berlin, 1927, Vol. 5, Pt. 1, p. 61.

CHAPTER 27

The Respiratory System

THE RESPIRATORY system serves mainly for the intake of oxygen by the body and the elimination of carbon dioxide. It may be divided into *conducting* and *respiratory portions*. The former are air-conducting tubes connecting the external air with that portion of the lungs where the exchange of gases between blood and the air takes place. These tubes are the hollow passages of the nose, the pharynx, the larynx, the trachea, and bronchi of various sizes. The ends of the smallest branches of the air-conducting passages are capped by the respiratory portion of the lungs, formed by many small air vesicles, called *alveolar sacs* and *alveoli*. The pharynx also connects the mouth with the esophagus; the larynx contains the vocal organ.

THE NOSE

The nose is a hollow organ composed of bone, cartilage, muscles and connective tissue. Its skin is provided with unusually large sebaceous glands and a few small hairs. The integument continues into the vestibule through the anterior nares. The epithelium here is stratified squamous, and there are some hairs which are believed to help in removing particles of dust from the inspired air. The remainder of the nasal cavity is lined with ciliated epithelium, with a specialized, nonciliated epithelium in the olfactory area.

The nose, like the larynx and trachea, is lined with pseudostratified, ciliated, columnar epithelium in which goblet cells are richly interspersed. A basement membrane separates the epithelium from the underlying connective tissue layer with its mixed mucous glands. The mucus from these glands keeps the walls of the nasal cavity moist. In the lower nasal conchae are rich venous plexuses which warm the air passing through the nose. These plexuses differ from erectile tissue by the absence of septa containing smooth muscle.

Leukocytes and lymphocytes migrating through the epithelium, and collections of lymphatic tissue beneath it, are characteristic of the respiratory epithelium of the nose, especially near the nasopharynx.

After leaving the nasal cavity, the inspired air passes by way of the nasopharynx and pharynx to the larynx. The nasal part of the pharynx is lined by ciliated columnar epithelium. In its oral part, it is lined by stratified squamous epithelium which is continuous with that of the mouth above and the esophagus below. The structure of the pharynx is described on page 359.

The Organ of Smell. The receptors for the sense of smell are located in the *olfactory epithelium*. In fresh condition it is yellowish-brown in contrast to the surrounding pink mucous membrane. The olfactory area extends from the middle of the roof of the nasal cavity some 8 to 10 mm. downward on both sides of the septum and on the surface of the upper nasal conchae. The surface of these areas of both sides is about 500 sq. mm. The outlines of the olfactory area are irregular.

The olfactory epithelium is pseudostrati-

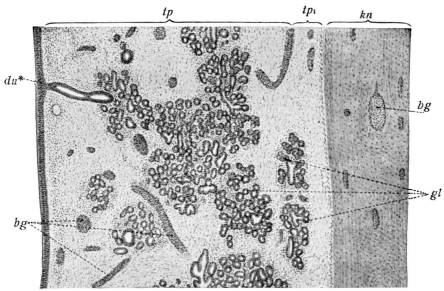

Fig. 27–1. Respiratory mucosa of osseous portion of nose of a twenty-two year old man. *du**, opening of duct; *tp,* lamina propria, with glands (*gl*) and blood vessels (*bg*), which acts as a periosteum (*tp₁*) for the bone (*kn*). 45 ×. (After Sobotta.)

fied columnar and about 60 microns thick. Unlike the ciliated epithelium, it lacks a distinct basement membrane. It consists of three kinds of cells: (1) supporting cells, (2) basal cells, and (3) olfactory cells.

The *supporting cells* are tall, slender elements with an axial bundle of tonofibrils. At the free surface they form small cuticular plates kept together by a system of thin terminal bars. Small, round openings for the sensory cells remain between the borders of the cuticles. Under the cuticle each cell contains a diplosome, from which a tiny flagellum emerges. The upper part of the cell contains a small Golgi net and pigment granules which cause the brown color of the olfactory area.

Between the bases of the supporting cells, the *basal cells* form a single layer of small conical elements with dark nuclei and branching processes.

The *olfactory cells,* evenly distributed between the supporting cells, are bipolar nerve cells. Their round nuclei occupy a zone between the nuclei of the supporting cells and the connective tissue. The periphery of the cell, a modified dendrite, extends as a cylindrical process from the nucleus to the surface. The proximal end tapers into a thin, smooth filament about 1 micron thick. It is an axon—a fiber of the olfactory nerve. It

passes into the connective tissue and, with similar fibers, forms small nerve bundles. These are collected into about twenty macroscopically visible *fila olfactoria.*

The cytoplasm of the olfactory cell contains a network of neurofibrils which are especially distinct around the nucleus. The head of the olfactory cell protrudes freely through the opening of the cuticular membrane. It enlarges slightly to the so-called *olfactory vesicle,* which contains at its surface six to eight tiny granules similar to the basal bodies of the ciliated cells; each granule sends out a fine olfactory cilium 2 microns long.

The unmyelinated fibers of the olfactory nerve are kept together by a delicate connective tissue rich in macrophages. The fila olfactoria pass through openings of the cribriform plate of the ethmoid bone and enter the olfactory bulb of the brain, where the primary olfactory center is located. The olfactory mucous membrane is also provided with myelinated nerve fibers originating from the trigeminal nerve. After losing their myelin they enter the epithelium and end with fine arborizations under its free surface between the supporting cells. These endings are receptors for stimuli other than odors.

The *lamina propria* of the olfactory mucous membrane is fused with the periosteum. Among its cells are numerous pigment cells, and some lymphoid cells which migrate into the epithelium.

Beneath the epithelium the lamina propria contains a rich plexus of blood capillaries. In its deeper layers it contains a plexus of large veins and dense networks of lymph capillaries. The latter continue into large lymphatics which course toward the lymph nodes on the sides of the head. A colored mass injected into the subarachnoid spaces of the brain can penetrate into the lymph capillaries of the olfactory region as well as into the sheaths of the fila olfactoria. This indicates a possible pathway for infec-

tions to spread from the nasal mucous membrane to the meninges.

The lamina propria in the olfactory area contains the *olfactory glands* of Bowman of branched, tubulo-alveolar type. The secretory portions are mainly parallel to the surface, while the narrow duct assumes a perpendicular course and opens on the surface. Immediately under the epithelium the duct is often considerably enlarged. The low pyramidal cells of the secretory portions are serous, containing secretory granules.

Histophysiological Remarks. The olfactory stimuli are probably of chemical nature. The secretion of the glands of Bowman keeps the surface of the olfactory epithelium moist and furnishes the necessary solvent. As most odoriferous substances are much more soluble in lipids than in water, and as the olfactory cells and their cilia contain a considerable amount of lipids, odoriferous substances, even if present in extreme dilution, may become concentrated in these structures. The continuous stream of the secretion of the olfactory glands, by removing the remains of the stimulating substances, keeps the receptors ready for new stimuli. In this respect the olfactory glands doubtless have a function similar to that of the glands connected with the taste buds.

The olfactory epithelium in man is easily

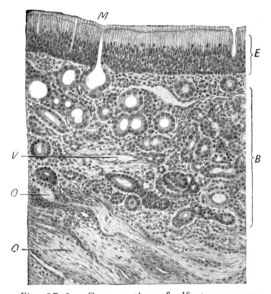

Fig. 27–2. Cross section of olfactory mucous membrane on the medial surface of the middle concha, from a man. *B,* glands of Bowman; *E,* olfactory epithelium; *M,* opening of a gland on the surface; *O,* bundle of olfactory fibers; *V,* vein. 70 ×. (After Schaffer.)

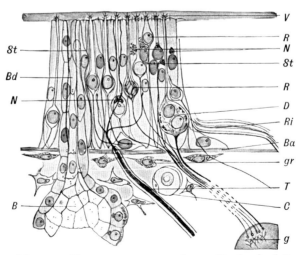

Fig. 27–3. Diagram of human olfactory mucous membrane. *B,* gland of Bowman, with diplosomes in its cells, and with its excretory duct, *Bd; Ba,* layer of basal cells; *C,* capillary; *D,* large binucleated olfactory cell; *g,* olfactory glomerulus; *gr,* connective tissue cells; *N,* Golgi net in the supporting and in the olfactory cells; *R,* olfactory cells with neurofibrils and the olfactory vesicles, *V; Ri,* olfactory fibers; *St,* supporting cells with tonofibrils; *T,* myelinated fibers of the N. Trigeminus. (After Kolmer.)

affected by inflammation of the mucous membrane of the nose and is often more or less altered and replaced by atypical epithelium.

Histogenetic Remarks. The olfactory region appears in the embryo a little later than the primordia of the eye and ear. In embryos of 4.9 mm. it is a paired, thickened, ectodermal area at the anterior edge of the medullary plate. The plate is later gradually invaginated and recedes from the surface. Some of the epithelial cells are transformed into olfactory elements, which send out axons growing toward the anterior part of the brain vesicle.

Nasal Sinuses. Connected with the nasal cavity, and forming cavities in the respective bones, are the frontal, ethmoidal, sphenoidal, and maxillary sinuses—the *accessory sinuses of the nose.* They are lined with an epithelium similar to that of the nasal cavity, but containing fewer and smaller glands. The mucosa of all the sinuses is delicate and cannot be differentiated as a separate layer from the periosteum of the bones, to which it is usually tightly adherent.

THE LARYNX

The larynx is an elongated, irregularly tubelike structure, whose walls contain hyaline and elastic cartilages, connective tissue, striated muscles, and a mucous membrane with glands. It serves to connect the pharynx with the trachea. As a result of changes in its shape resulting from the contraction of its muscles, it produces variations in the opening between the vocal cords. The size of this opening conditions the pitch of the sounds made by the passage of air through the larynx.

The main framework of the larynx is made of several cartilages. Of these the thyroid and cricoid cartilages and the epiglottis are unpaired, while the arytenoid, corniculate, and cuneiform are paired. The thyroid and cricoid and the lower parts of the arytenoids are hyaline cartilages. The *extrinsic* muscles of the larynx connect it with surrounding muscles and ligaments and facilitate deglutition. The *intrinsic* muscles connect the cartilages of the larynx; by their contraction they give different shapes to the laryngeal cavity and thus are active in phonation.

The anterior surface of the *epiglottis* and the upper half of its posterior surface, the *aryepiglottic folds,* and the *vocal cords* are covered with stratified squamous epithelium.

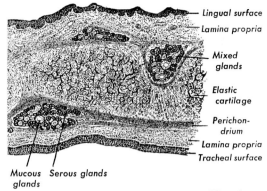

Fig. 27–4. Cross section through middle of epiglottis of a twenty-two year old man. 27 ×. (After von Ebner.)

In the adult, ciliated epithelium usually begins at the base of the epiglottis and extends down the larynx, trachea and bronchi.

The cilia are 3.5 to 5 microns long and beat toward the mouth; thus they move foreign particles, bacteria and mucus from the lungs toward the exterior of the body. After death, the cilia have been seen to beat for fifty to seventy hours; in tissue cultures of rabbit lung they may beat for twelve days or more.

A centriole has not been demonstrated in the ciliated epithelium of the respiratory tract. Evidences of regeneration of the tracheal epithelium are rare; this may be associated with the absence of a centriole. Goblet cells in varying numbers are scattered between the cylindrical cells. The glands of the larynx are of the tubulo-acinous, mixed mucous variety. Some of the ducts secrete mucus; the alveoli secrete mucus and may have crescents. A few taste buds are scattered on the under surface of the epiglottis.

The *true vocal cords* enclose the vocal or inferior thyro-arytenoid ligaments. Each of these (one on each side) consists of a band of elastic tissue bordered on its lateral side by the thyro-arytenoid muscle and covered medially by a thin mucous membrane with a stratified squamous epithelium. The space between the vocal cords is usually given as 23 mm. long in men, and 18 mm. in women. Its shape undergoes great variations in the phases of respiration and in the production of different sounds in talking and singing. Contraction of the thyro-arytenoid muscle approximates the arytenoid and thyroid cartilages, and this relaxes the vocal cords.

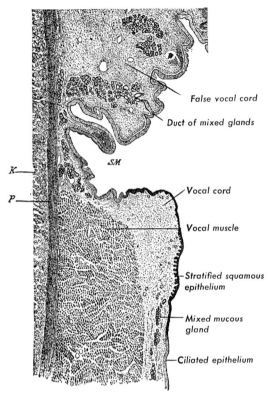

Fig. 27–5. Frontal section through middle of glottis of a boy of nine years. *K*, thyroid cartilage with its perichondrium, *P*; *SM*, laryngeal ventricle. 15 ×. (After von Ebner.)

The larynx is supplied by the upper, middle and lower laryngeal arteries, which, in turn, arise from the superior and inferior thyroid arteries. The veins from the larynx empty into the thyroid veins. The larynx contains several rich plexuses of lymphatics which lead into the upper cervical lymph nodes and to those about the trachea. The superior laryngeal nerve sends sensory nerves, and the inferior laryngeal, motor nerves to the larynx.

TRACHEA

The trachea is a thin-walled, fairly rigid tube about 11 cm. long and 2 to 2.5 cm. in diameter. It is continuous with the larynx above and ends by dividing into the two main bronchi below.

The epithelium of the trachea is ciliated pseudostratified columnar and rests on a distinct basement membrane. Numerous goblet cells are scattered throughout the epithelium. The lamina propria contains many elastic fibers and numerous small glands like those of the larynx. These glands, most of which

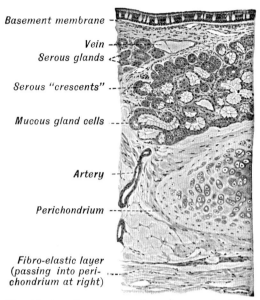

Fig. 27–6. Cross section through part of a human trachea. 60 ×. (After Braus.)

are external to the elastic fibers, open by short ducts on the free surface of the epithelium. In the posterior portion of the trachea, the glands extend through the muscular layer. Stimulation of the recurrent laryngeal nerve activates secretion in these glands. The lamina propria also contains accumulations of lymphatic tissue.

The most characteristic part of the trachea is its framework of sixteen to twenty hyaline cartilages. These are **C**- or **Y**-shaped and encircle the tube except in its posterior part. Because of the spaces between them they give the tube much more pliability and extensibility than if they formed a continuous sheet. The cartilages pass obliquely down the trachea. With advancing age they become fibrous, but do not ossify as the thyroid cartilage does. They are surrounded by dense connective tissue which contains many elastic and reticular fibers.

The posterior wall of the trachea, close to the esophagus, is devoid of cartilages. Their place is taken by a thick layer of smooth muscle bundles which run mainly transversely. They are inserted into the dense, elastic fiber bundles surrounding the trachea and especially its cartilages, and are joined to the mucous membrane by a layer of loose connective tissue, some adipose tissue, and mucous glands.

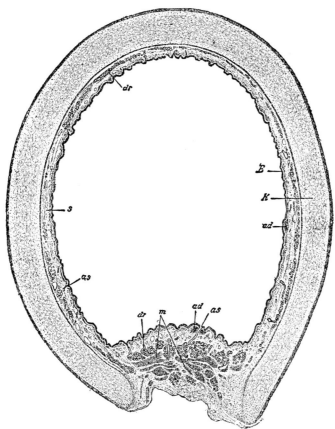

Fig. 27–7. Cross section through trachea of a boy of nine years. *E*, ciliated epithelium; *K*, cartilage; *ad*, lymphoid tissue; *dr*, glands with a duct, *as; m,* smooth muscle of the membranous portion of the wall; *s*, mucosa. 8 ×. (After Kölliker-von Ebner.)

A delicate network of lymphatics is found in the mucosa, and a much coarser plexus occurs in the submucosa. These lead into the lymphatic nodes which accompany the trachea along its entire length. The arteries for the trachea are mainly from the inferior thyroid. The nerves supplying the trachea arise from the recurrent branch of the vagus nerve and from the sympathetic. The sympathetic nerves of the trachea contain small ganglia, from which fibers lead to the muscle of the organ. Myelinated sensory nerves are also found.

THE LUNGS

The lungs constitute a paired organ occupying a great part of the thoracic cavity and constantly changing in form with the different phases of respiration. The right lung consists of three lobes and the left lung of two, and each lobe receives a branch of the primary bronchi. The outer surface of the lungs is closely invested by a serous membrane, the *visceral pleura.*

In children the lungs, because of their great blood supply, are a pale pink. With advancing age they become gray, owing to the inhalation of carbon particles, particularly in city dwellers.

Each of the five lobes of the lungs is divided by thin connective tissue septa into great numbers of roughly pyramidal portions of pulmonary tissue, the *lobules.* These are so arranged that the apex of each points toward the hilus and the base toward the pleura. In the adult lung, these gross lobules are not so easily seen, except under the pleura, as in the embryonic lung. Under the pleura, however, the progressive deposition of carbon from the inspired air marks the outlines of these lobules distinctly. Each lobule is supplied by a small bronchiole.

Bronchial Tubes. The trachea divides into two main branches called *bronchi.* These tubes enter the substance of the lungs at the

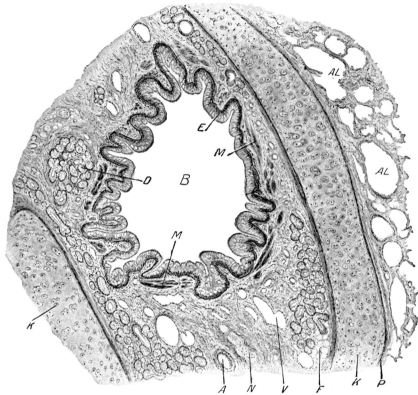

Fig. 27–8.   Cross section through small bronchus of a man. *A,* artery; *AL,* alveoli; *B,* bronchus; *D,* mixed glands; *E,* ciliated epithelium with globlet cells; *F,* fat tissue; *K,* cartilage; *M,* circular muscle; *N,* nerve; *P,* perichondrium; *V,* vein. Mallory's connective tissue stain. 30 ×. (After Schaffer.)

hilus, one on each side, and, maintaining a downward and outward direction, divide into two smaller bronchi on the left side and three on the right. These give rise to smaller bronchi from which *bronchioles* of several orders originate. With the development of lung surgery, knowledge of the segmental distribution of the secondary bronchi in the lobes has become important. According to Boyden, the right lung is made up of ten principal bronchopulmonary segments, while the left lung can be divided into eight segments. The basic pattern of the secondary bronchi appears, however, to be subject to considerable variation. It has been estimated that there are from fifty to eighty terminal bronchioles in each lobule. This number is probably somewhat high. Each *terminal bronchiole* continues into one, two or more respiratory bronchioles. These break up into two to eleven *alveolar ducts,* from which arise the *alveolar sac* and *alveoli.* Thus the main successive divisions of the bronchial

tree are primary bronchi, secondary bronchi, bronchioles, terminal bronchioles, respiratory bronchioles, alveolar ducts, alveolar sacs, and alveoli. An *atrium* has been described as connecting the alveolar sacs and the alveolar ducts (see p. 439).

Before the bronchi enter the lungs their structure is practically identical with that of the trachea. But as soon as they enter the lungs, the *cartilage rings* disappear and are replaced by irregularly shaped *cartilage plates* which completely surround the bronchus. As a result, the intrapulmonary bronchi and their branches are cylindrical and not flattened on one side like the trachea and the extrapulmonary portions of the bronchi. At the same time as the cartilage plates become irregularly distributed around the tube, the muscular layer completely surrounds the bronchus. The cartilages disappear when the diameter of the bronchiole reaches 1 mm.

The innermost layer of the bronchi is a mucous membrane continuous with that of

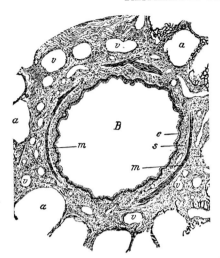

Fig. 27–9. Cross section through a bronchiole (*B*) 0.7 mm. thick. *a,* alveoli; *e,* epithelium; *s,* lamina propria with cross sections of elastic fibers; *m,* circular muscle; *v,* veins. Lung fixed by filling it with alcohol. 55 ×. (After von Ebner.)

the trachea and lined by the same type of epithelium. The lamina propria consists of a small amount of reticular and collagenous connective tissue and many elastic fibers; it contains a few lymphoid cells and is delimited from the epithelium by a basement membrane. The mucosa of the bronchi, in histologic sections, shows a marked longitudinal folding due to the contraction of the muscle. It is claimed that these folds disappear when the lung is distended.

Next to the mucosa is a layer of smooth muscles which run in all directions around the tube, but never form a closed ring as in the blood vessels and intestines. The muscles form an interlacing feltwork whose meshes become larger in the smaller bronchioles. Numerous elastic fibers are intimately associated with the smooth muscle cells. As will be discussed later, the elastic fibers and smooth muscles throughout the lung play an important part in the changes in its structure which occur during respiration. A dense network of blood vessels accompanies and penetrates this myo-elastic layer.

The outermost layer of the bronchial wall consists of dense connective tissue which contains many elastic fibers. It surrounds the plates of cartilage and continues into the connective tissue of the surrounding pulmonary tissue and into that accompanying the large vessels.

Mucous and mucoserous glands are found, as in the trachea, as far out in the bronchial tree as the cartilage extends. The glands are usually under the muscular layer, through which their ducts penetrate to open on the free surface.

Lymphatic tissue, diffuse and often with nodules, occurs regularly in the mucosa and in the fibrous tissue around the cartilage, especially where the bronchi branch.

With the progressive decrease in the size of the bronchi and bronchioles as they proceed from the trachea, the layers of their walls become thinner, and some of them fuse into one layer. The smooth muscle, however, is distinct up to the end of the respiratory bronchioles and even continues in the walls of the alveolar ducts.

RESPIRATORY STRUCTURES OF THE LUNGS

The *unit* of the lung is composed of all the structures, beginning with a respiratory bronchiole and extending to and including the alveoli with all the blood vessels, lymphatics, nerves and connective tissue. In the newborn, the pulmonary lobule (unit) is small. The respiratory bronchiole has not yet developed, and the alveoli are represented as shallow pouches on the walls of the alveolar ducts (Fig. 27–14).

In a thin section of a lung the respiratory portion of the organ appears as a lacework of large spaces separated from one another by thin-walled septa (Fig. 27–11). Here and there this lacework is traversed by the thick-walled bronchi and various-sized arteries and veins. But a different picture is seen in a thick section with the binocular microscope. Here the lung appears as an irregular honeycomb in which the polyhedral alveoli and alveolar sacs form the "cells" (Figs. 27–10, 27–12). These form a honeycomb traversed by the system of bronchioles and the alveolar ducts into which the atria, alveoli and alveolar sacs open.

The lungs should be fixed, for histological purposes, either by way of the trachea or by injection through the pulmonary artery, with the lungs still in the body to prevent over-distention. The usual method of dropping a bit of lung into fixing fluid gives highly distorted pictures, for the lung shrinks greatly when the reduced pressure of the pleural cavity is raised and the air in the organ prevents the

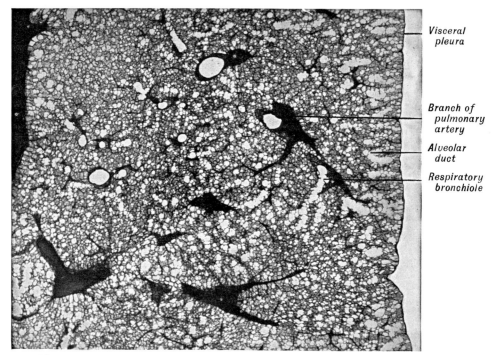

Fig. 27–10. Photomicrograph of a thick (120 microns) section of lung of *Macacus rhesus.* 10 ✕.

penetration of the fixative. Some aspects of the structure of this organ may be seen best in sections of 60 to 120 microns. Hematoxylin and eosin staining gives but a poor idea of the constitution of the lung; special staining and injection methods are necessary. Further, the lung changes its form continuously with every inspiration and expiration (Fig. 27–20).

Respiratory Bronchioles. In the adult the respiratory bronchioles begin with a diameter of about 0.5 mm. They are short tubes, lined in their first part with a ciliated columnar epithelium devoid of goblet cells. A short distance down the bronchiole, the ciliated columnar epithelium loses its cilia and becomes low cuboidal. These bronchioles have walls composed of collagenous connective tissue in which bundles of interlacing smooth muscles and elastic fibers course. They lack cartilage. A few alveoli bud off from the side of the respiratory bronchiole opposite that along which the branch of the pulmonary artery runs. A thin process of the cuboidal epithelium of the bronchiole extends over the alveolar wall according to the electron microscopic observations of Low and Sampaio. These alveoli are the first of the respiratory structures of the lung and are responsible for the term "respiratory bronchiole." The

bronchioles soon branch and radiate conelike into two to eleven alveolar ducts which extend for relatively long distances. They are surrounded by alveoli which have arisen from adjacent ducts.

Alveolar Ducts. The structure of the alveolar ducts is hard to visualize in thin sections of the distended lung. In thick sections, particularly when studied with the binocular microscope, the alveolar ducts are seen as thin-walled tubes. They usually follow a long, tortuous course and give off several branches which in turn may branch again. They are closely beset with thin-walled outpouchings, the alveolar sacs (and single alveoli). These blind, polyhedral sacs open only on that surface which faces the alveolar duct. As the alveolar sacs are closely packed against one another, their openings form the greatest part of the wall of the alveolar duct. The wall of the alveolar duct between the mouths of the alveolar sacs consists of strands of elastic and collagenous fibers and smooth muscle cells. In thin sections of the lung, only small portions of these fibers and muscles are seen; they appear as short knobs parallel to the long axis of the alveolar duct.

In thick sections it becomes evident that

Labels on figure:
Visceral pleura
Branch of pulmonary artery
Alveolar duct
Respiratory bronchiole

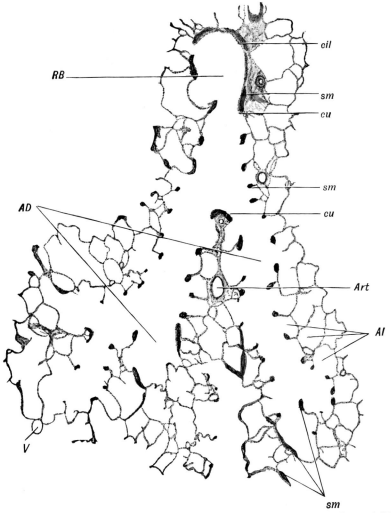

Fig. 27–11. Section through respiratory bronchiole (*RB*) and two alveolar ducts (*AD*) of human lung, showing the smooth muscle, *sm* (in black), in the walls of the alveolar ducts; *cil,* ciliated epithelium; *cu,* cuboidal epithelium; *Art,* arteriole; *Al,* alveolar sacs; *V,* vein. (Slightly modified from Baltisberger.)

the short knobs seen in the thin sections are merely tangentially cut, small portions of the long connective tissue fibers and muscle bundles which interweave in three planes between the mouths of the alveolar sacs.

Alveolar Sacs and Alveoli. From the alveolar ducts arise single alveoli and alveolar sacs containing two to four or more alveoli.

It has been suggested that the space between the alveolar duct and the alveolar sacs be termed the *atrium,* especially at the ends of the alveolar ducts. The structures described under this term have not been generally accepted as forming a distinct entity,

for some authors consider them parts of the alveolar ducts.

The alveoli are thin-walled polyhedral formations, one side of which is always lacking, so that air may diffuse freely from the alveolar ducts into the alveolar sacs and thus into the cavities of the alveoli. The most conspicuous feature of the alveolar walls is a dense, single network of capillaries which anastomose so freely that many of the spaces between them are smaller than the diameter of the vessel lumina. The alveolar walls contain a close meshed network of branching reticular fibers. These, along with the less

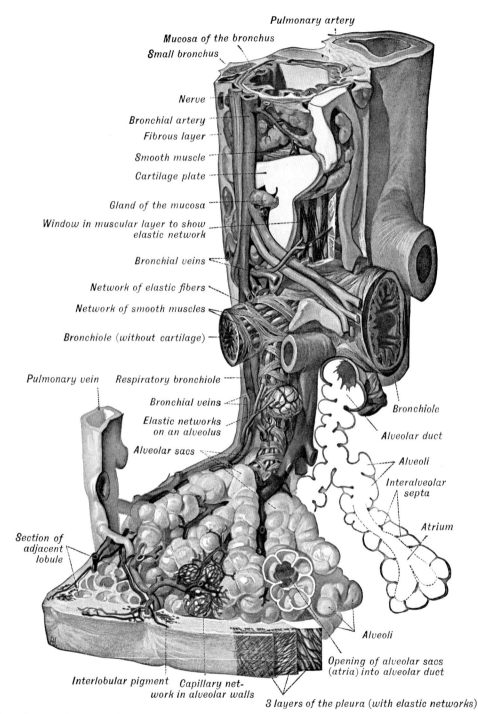

Pulmonary artery

Mucosa of the bronchus
Small bronchus

Nerve

Bronchial artery

Fibrous layer

Smooth muscle

Cartilage plate

Gland of the mucosa

Window in muscular layer to show
elastic network

Bronchial veins

Network of elastic fibers

Network of smooth muscles

Bronchiole (without cartilage)

Pulmonary vein   Respiratory bronchiole

Bronchial veins

Elastic networks
on an alveolus

Alveolar sacs

Section of
adjacent
lobule

Interlobular pigment   Capillary network in alveolar walls

Bronchiole

Alveolar duct

Alveoli

Interalveolar
septa

Atrium

Alveoli

Opening of alveolar sacs
(atria) into alveolar duct

3 layers of the pleura (with elastic networks)

Fig. 27–12.   Portion of a pulmonary lobule from the lung of a young man. Free reconstruction by
Vierling, somewhat foreshortened. Mucosa and glands, green; cartilage, light blue; muscles and bronchial
artery, orange; elastic fibers, blue-black; pulmonary artery, red; pulmonary and bronchial veins, dark
blue. 32 ×. (After Braus.)

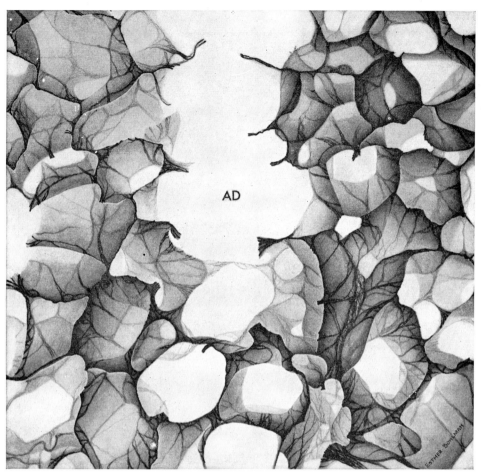

Fig. 27–13.   Portion of 120 μ thick section of lung of *Macacus rhesus* stained with orcein for elastic fibers and light green. *AD*, alveolar duct and the honeycomb of alveoli connected with it. 200 ×.

numerous elastic fibers, form the supporting framework for the thin-walled air vesicles and their numerous capillaries. The capillaries are so situated that the greater portion of their surface is toward the alveolar air. The larger reticular and elastic fibers occupy a central position in the septa, with the anastomosing capillaries weaving back and forth in the meshes of the fibers to jut into the adjacent alveolar spaces. This relationship of supporting fibers to capillaries is best seen in the lung of the newborn, in which the interalveolar septa have a thick, cellular central stroma that becomes less conspicuous with advancing age, owing to the thinning and stretching of the alveolar walls.

The mouths of the alveolar sacs are completely surrounded by a wavy wreath of collagenous fibers. These continue from one sac to the next and help to give thickness to the wall of the alveolar duct. These curled wreaths probably straighten out with deep inspirations. Elastic fibers accompany the collagenous fibers. The dense networks of reticular fibers within the walls of the alveoli and alveolar sacs are continuations of these collagenous fibers, which, in turn, are connected with the collagenous fibers in the walls of the arteries, veins and bronchioles. The elastic fibers are likewise continuations of those of the bronchioles.

Cells Lining the Alveoli. For many decades, one of the most controversial problems in histology concerned the structure of the covering of the alveolar wall. At one extreme was the belief that the alveoli are covered by epithelial cells irregularly interspersed among exceedingly thin, non-nucleated plates.

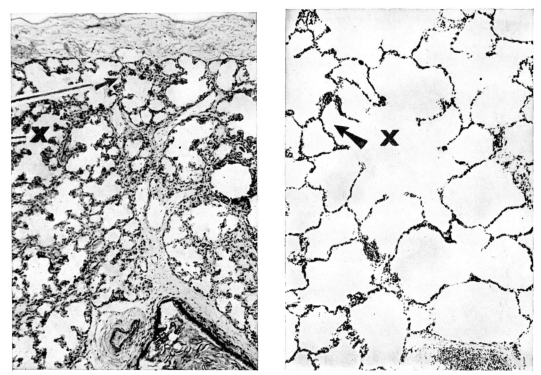

Fig. 27–14.   Section of lung of human newborn (*left*) and of twelve year old girl (*right*). Both specimens fixed immediately after death by the intratracheal injection of Zenker-formol solution. Note increase in size of alveolar ducts (*x*) and alveoli (arrowhead). Mallory-azan stain. Photomicrographs. 82 ×. (Courtesy of C. G. Loosli.)

At the other extreme was the claim that the capillaries lie in a connective tissue framework and are not separated by cells from the air space. The electron microscopic studies of Low and later of Van Breemen and of Karrer show that there is a thin, apparently continuous, cellular covering of the alveolar wall (Fig. 27–17). This thin cellular layer, often just at or below optical microscopic visibility, is thicker than the endothelium in most places. Separating this epithelium from the endothelium is a thin, continuous, homogeneous basement membrane.

Low and Sampaio instilled thorium oxide into the trachea of rats and half an hour later found that the continuous epithelial lining of the alveoli is not phagocytic in contrast to the macrophages free in the alveoli and resting on the attenuated epithelium. They noted that the cytoplasm of some epithelial cells closely resembles that of the macrophages, but they incline to the view that the alveolar epithelium is of entodermal and the macrophages of mesodermal origin. They sum-

marize the problem of the fine structure of the respiratory portion of the lung: "If the disagreements of the past regarding the entodermal or mesodermal origin of the alveolar walls are viewed in retrospect, particularly with reference to the new facts listed at the beginning of this discussion, it is not difficult to see reasons for the discord. The tendency of some investigators to assign mesodermal origin to the alveolar wall is logically traceable to three factors, namely (1) doubt that any epithelium existed at all since it was largely invisible with available technical methods, (2) the obviously mesodermal characteristics of the macrophages and (3) the close resemblance of some cells now known to be epithelial to these macrophages. If the epithelium had been demonstrated then as it is today no one would have thought of assigning it a mesodermal origin."

In practically every section of lung, free macrophages (alveolar phagocytes) can be found in the alveoli. They are indistinguishable from the macrophages in other parts of

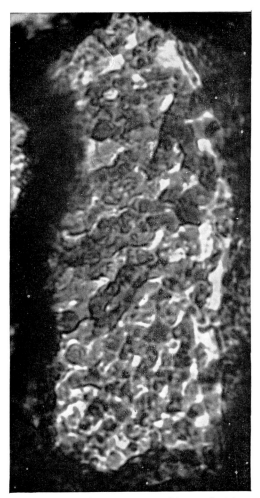

Fig. 27–15. Thick section of lung of eighteen year old man, showing surface view of alveolar septum. Specimen fixed immediately after death by intratracheal injection of Zenker-formol solution after pulmonary veins and artery had been ligated to keep blood in capillaries. Note close network of capillaries. Mallory-azan stain. Photomicrograph. 625 ×. (Courtesy of C. G. Loosli.)

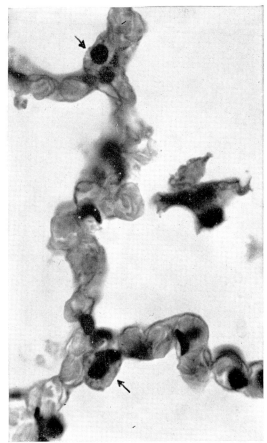

Fig. 27–16. Photomicrograph of alveolar wall of lung of eighteen year old man. From same specimen as that in Figure 27–15. Note the thin membrane between the lumina of the capillaries and the air spaces. Arrowheads point to "septal cells" in their characteristic location on the alveolar walls. Hematoxylin-eosin-azure II stain. 1000 ×. (Courtesy of C. G. Loosli.)

the body. When they contain particles of dust, they are called "dust cells." In certain cardiac diseases they become filled with granules of hemosiderin.

In tissue cultures of the lungs and in certain *in vivo* experiments, inconspicuous cells in the septa mobilize in a few hours and assume the appearance and function of typical macrophages. The name "septal cells" has been suggested for them. In acute pneumococcal infections of the lungs of dogs and monkeys, the principal reaction of the "septal cells" appeared to be one of enlargement without detachment from the alveolar walls. No phagocytic properties are observed in them; the chief source of the macrophages is from hypertrophy of the hematogenous lymphocytes and monocytes after they enter the air spaces in the early stages of the disease. Whatever the origin of the alveolar phagocyte, it acts in defense of the lung, including the removal of the dust particles, as a typical macrophage.

In certain strains of mice, nonmetastasizing pulmonary tumors arising from cells on the alveolar walls have been produced by the subcutaneous injection of carcinogenic

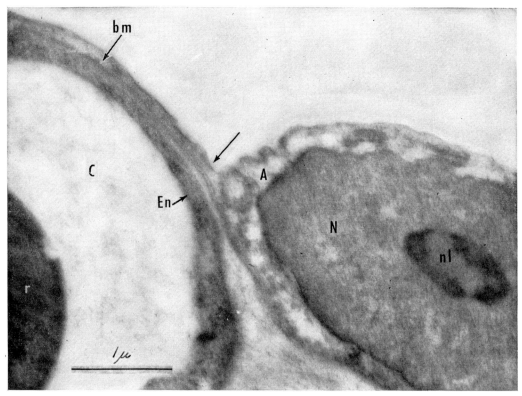

Fig. 27–17. Electron micrograph of section of alveolar wall of human lung showing the thin extension (arrow) of the alveolar epithelial cell (*A*) over the capillary, *C; En,* endothelium; *bm,* basement membrane; *N,* nucleus; *nl,* nucleolus; *r,* erythrocyte. Buffered osmic acid fixation. (Courtesy of F. Low.)

agents. On serial transplantation, some of these tumors change from an epithelial pattern to that of a fibrosarcoma.

In some pulmonary diseases, air spaces develop which are lined by cuboidal epithelium and have thick connective tissue walls poor in capillaries. They do not resemble normal alveoli. The lining cells are probably a downgrowth of epithelium from the terminal bronchioles, secondary to destruction of the normal architecture of the alveolar walls by the disease process. Evidence to support this view is found in studies of the pathogenesis of certain experimental virus infections in animals and "alveolar cell tumors" in man.

Openings or "pores" in the interalveolar septa connecting adjacent alveoli are much more numerous in some species of mammals than in others. There is no doubt of their normal occurrence. In certain pathological conditions, such as lobar pneumonia, threads of fibrin pass through the alveolar walls and connect the inflammatory exudate in adjacent alveoli. The pores permit the spread of bacteria from one alveolus to its neighbors in pneumonia. They also provide a collateral air circulation, which aids in preventing *atelectasis* when secondary bronchi become obstructed.

Blood Vessels. The lungs receive most of their blood from the pulmonary arteries. These are of large caliber and of elastic type. The branches of these arteries in general accompany the bronchi and their branches as far as the respiratory bronchioles. The arterial paths in the lung, however, are subject to considerable variation. It would appear that the rather easily resectable bronchopulmonary segment should not be considered a morphological bronchovascular unit (Boyden). From the respiratory bronchioles they divide, and a branch passes to each alveolar duct and is distributed in a capillary network over all the alveoli which communicate with this duct. The venules arise from the capillaries of the pleura and from the capillaries of the alveolar septa and portions of the alveolar ducts and run in the intersegmental

pleura

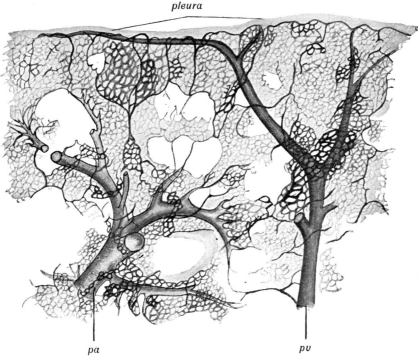

pa   *pv*

Fig. 27–18. Section through lung of a dog, perpendicular to the pleura, showing relation of the pulmonary artery (*pa*) and the pulmonary vein (*pv*) to the pleura. Artery gray, veins black. About 100 ×. (Redrawn and slightly modified after W. S. Miller.)

connective tissue, independently of the arteries, and fuse to form the pulmonary veins. In passing through the lung, the pulmonary artery is usually above and behind its accompanying bronchial tube, while the vein is below and in front of it.

The bronchial arteries and veins are much smaller than the pulmonary vessels. These arteries arise from the aorta or the intercostal arteries and follow the bronchi. They are distributed to the walls of the bronchi, their glands, and the interlobular connective tissue beneath the pleura. Most of the blood carried by the bronchial arteries is brought back by the pulmonary veins. In the alveoli which arise from the respiratory bronchioles, there is a capillary anastomosis between the terminations of both the pulmonary and bronchial arteries.

Lymphatics. There are two main divisions of the lymphatics of the lungs. One set is in the pleura, and the other in the pulmonary tissue. They communicate infrequently; both of them drain into the lymph nodes at the hilum of the lung. The lymphatics of the pleura form a dense network with large and small polygonal meshes. The large meshes are surrounded by large vessels and demark the lobules; the small meshwork is formed of smaller vessels which mark out the anatomical unit. There are many valves in these lymphatics which control the flow of lymph, so that it passes to the hilum and not into the pulmonary tissue. These pleural lymphatics combine into several main trunks which drain into the lymph nodes at the hilum.

The pulmonary lymphatics may be divided into several groups which include those of the bronchi, of the pulmonary artery, and of the pulmonary vein. The lymphatics in the bronchi form an anastomosing network. They terminate in the alveolar ducts, and their end branches join the lymphatic radicles of the plexuses about the pulmonary artery and vein. There are no lymphatic vessels beyond the alveolar ducts. The pulmonary artery is accompanied and drained by two or three main lymphatic trunks. The lymphatics associated with the pulmonary vein begin with its radicles in the alveolar ducts and in the pleura. All the lymphatics of the pulmonary tissue drain toward the hilus nodes. Efferent trunks from the hilar nodes anastomose to form the right lymphatic duct, which is the principal channel of lymph drainage from both the right and left lungs. There are no valves in the intrapulmonic lymphatics except in a few vessels, in the interlobular connective tissue near the pleura, which accompany the branches of the pulmonary veins. These lymphatic vessels connect the pulmonary and pleural lymphatic plexuses. As their valves point only toward the pleura, they provide a mechanism whereby lymph can flow from the pulmonary tissue into the pleural lymphatics if the normal flow of lymph in the former toward the hilum is interrupted.

As has been mentioned, the mucous membrane of the bronchi is infiltrated with lymphocytes and often contains lymphatic follicles. There are other accumulations of lymphatic tissue in the adventitia of the pulmonary arteries and veins, but these, as a rule, do not form nodules in the normal lung.

Nerves. The pulmonary plexuses at the root of the lung are formed by branches of the vagus and from the thoracic sympathetic ganglia. The bronchoconstrictor fibers are from the vagus nerve, while the bronchodilator fibers are from the sympathetic and arise mainly from the inferior cervical and first thoracic ganglia. The pulmonary vessels are supplied with both sympathetic and parasympathetic nerve fibers. Their effect on these vessels is not understood, as the experimental evidence is contradictory. The sympathetic fibers act as vasoconstrictors for the bronchial arteries.

The Pleura. The serous membrane lining the pleural cavities is reflected over the lungs as the *visceral pleura.* It consists of a thin layer of collagenous tissue containing some fibroblasts and macrophages, and several prominent layers of elastic fibers running at various angles to the outer surface. It is covered by a layer of mesothelial cells like those of the peritoneum. A similar serous layer lines the wall of the thoracic cavity and is called the *parietal pleura.* A prominent feature of the pleura is the great number of blood capillaries and lymphatic vessels distributed in it. The few nerves of the parietal pleura are connected with the phrenic and intercostal nerves. The nerves to the visceral pleura are believed to be branches of the vagus and sympathetic nerves supplying the bronchi.

Histogenetic Remarks. The lung arises in the embryo as a medial diverticulum of the foregut, caudal to the branchial clefts; it extends caudally and divides into two branches. The medial diverticulum is the primordium of the future larynx and trachea, and the first two lateral branches will form the two main bronchi of the adult lung. These two branches divide repeatedly; they become surrounded by a relatively dense mass of mesenchyme, so that throughout most of the embryonic period, up to six months, the lung has a suggestive glandlike structure (Fig. 27–19, *A*).

The primitive bronchi are lined with cuboidal epithelium. They branch dichotomously and are capped by end buds lined with cylindrical epithelium. The lumen of the end knobs is distinctly larger than that of the ducts. The knobs continue to branch perpendicularly to the axis of their ducts. In the three- to four-month stage the connective tissue cells and fibrils become prominent, and the connective tissue contains many blood vessels. The lymphatics at this time are large and divide the pulmonary tissue into fairly distinct lobules. The end knobs now begin to branch irregularly.

In the eighteen- to twenty-week stage the lobulation becomes decidedly less prominent as the connective tissue diminishes in amount and the lymphatics become much narrower. The end knobs become much smaller.

At six to seven months, in a 35-cm. fetus, the small bronchi are lined in part with ciliated epithelium, which flattens toward the peripheral ends of the bronchi. These branch and end in the terminal ducts capped with the end knobs. The latter

finally become alveoli, according to most authors. This view is probably incorrect.

About the beginning of the sixth month of gestation, the lung undergoes rapid structural alterations. It loses its glandlike appearance and becomes a highly vascular organ. The factors responsible for these morphological changes are not known. Although the human fetus begins a pattern of respiratory activity early in intra-uterine life, such activity is not necessary for the normal development of the lungs.

In human embryos and in pig embryos the cuboidal epithelial membrane becomes attenuated and blood capillaries come close to the surface of the walls of the future air space, as seen with the light microscope. The details of the transformations in the walls and the important question of the manner in which the lung grows await further studies including use of the electron microscope. The few thus made in newborn mammals indicate that there is a continuous, thin epithelial covering of the walls of the future air spaces.

The majority of investigators consider the initial respiratory air spaces to be alveoli similar in size to those seen in the adult lung. In man it would seem that these saccular spaces correspond more correctly to alveolar ducts and that definitive alveoli are absent. At term, the alveoli are shallow indentations on the respiratory channels. According to Dubreuil and co-workers, the adult type of respiratory unit does not become apparent until several years after birth. One has only to compare in Figure 27–14 the inflated lung of the newborn with the expanded lung of a twelve-year-old, to note the marked increase in size of the alveolar ducts and the alveoli. Whether growth of the lung takes place only by an increase in size and distention of existing ducts and alveoli or by some other process needs further study.

Repair of the Lung. The lung is frequently the seat of inflammatory conditions which leave it unimpaired or healing. There are certain infections, however, notably tuberculosis, in which large masses of pulmonary tissues are destroyed. In this case healing is always attended by connective tissue scar formation; there is no evidence to show that the pulmonary tissue can regenerate after destruction.

Histophysiological Remarks. The primary function of the lungs is to serve as a means for the assimilation of oxygen from the air and for the removal of carbon dioxide from the body. The network of blood capillaries in the wall of the air vesicles is separated from the air by a thin, moist membrane which permits the ready diffusion of oxygen into the blood and carbon dioxide out of it. The question whether the passage of the gases is to be looked upon as a secretion or as a simple process of diffusion must be decided in favor of the latter view for the present, except that liberation of carbon dioxide from carbonic

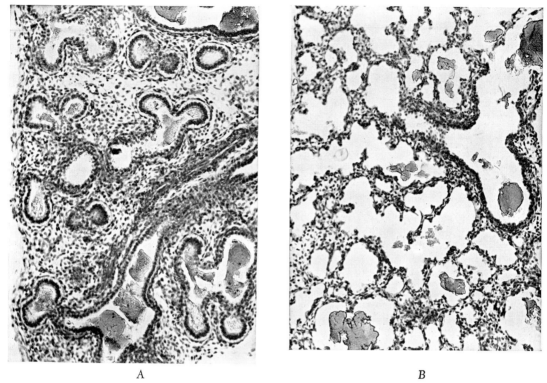

A
B

Fig. 27–19. Photomicrographs of section of lung, *A,* of 147-gm. (4 months') fetus, and, *B,* of a 440-gm. (6½ months') fetus. Both specimens show thorotrast aspirated by intra-uterine respirations. The lung of the 6½ months' fetus was expanded by extra-uterine respiration. Note change in character of lung structure from glandular type (previable) to respiratory type (viable). Respiratory portion of lung of older fetus consists essentially of alveolar ducts; alveoli are absent or are represented only by shallow indentations on duct walls. Hematoxylin and eosin stain. 45 ×. (After Davis and Potter.)

acid by dehydration is now known to be greatly accelerated by *carbonic anhydrase.* The capillaries in the respiratory portions of the human lung are estimated to have a surface area of 140 square meters. The lung also eliminates approximately 800 cc. of water a day in the expired air; under abnormal conditions it may also remove certain other substances from the blood, such as alcohol.

The lung has a large margin of reserve; that is, the body at rest uses but a small portion—about one-twentieth—of the pulmonary aerating surface.

The alveoli probably change but little during inspiration, and the flow of blood is actually faster then. It is becoming more and more probable that the great increase in the volume of the lungs in inspiration takes place mainly through a great distention of the alveolar ducts. The smaller bronchi and bronchioles also distend with inspiration.

The pressure within the lung is that of the atmosphere. The lungs are maintained in a partially distended position by the reduced pressure of the potential space between the two layers of the pleura. An increase in the size of the thorax, such as occurs with every inspiration, still further decreases pressure in the pleural cavity; consequently the lung sucks in more air and becomes larger, and its elastic and reticular fibers are put under still greater tension. This is a purely passive activity on the part of the lung. In expiration, as the thoracic cavity becomes smaller, the pressure in the pleural cavity rises slightly (although it is still below atmospheric pressure). This decreases the tension on the elastic and reticular fibers, and they pull the lung into a more contracted state, thus forcing some of the air out of it. It is probable that the smooth muscles of the alveolar ducts and the bronchioles also help force the air out of the lung by their contraction.

When the pleural cavity is connected with

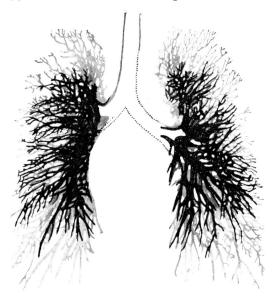

Fig. 27–20. Tracings from x-ray shadows of human lungs in deep inspiration (gray) and forced expiration (black). (Redrawn and slightly modified after Macklin.)

the outside air, either by accident or by surgical intervention, the pressure in the lungs and the pleural cavity becomes equalized at that of the atmosphere. The lung in this side of the chest collapses immediately, because the force which normally opposes the contraction of its elastic elements has been removed. This condition is known as *pneumothorax.* Such a lung remains collapsed until pressure in the pleural cavity is reduced by absorption of the air contained in it.

With each inspiration the descent of the diaphragm enables the bronchi in the lower lobes of the lungs to extend. Since the main bronchi are not fixed in the thorax, but descend on inspiration, a mechanism is provided whereby the bronchi of the upper lobes of the lungs extend at the same time.

The lung of a normal adult who has lived in the vicinity of a large city is usually greatly blackened by a pigment which, on chemical analysis, has been found to be carbon. This material has been inhaled with the air. Part of it is returned to the exterior by the action of the cilia in the bronchi; part of it is expelled in the so-called "dust cell"; and part of it is accumulated in the interstitial lymphoid tissue of the lung or in the peribronchial and peritracheal lymph nodes. The particles of dust in the alveoli are taken up by the ameboid "dust cells." It is probable that these cells, by their own motion, reach the ciliated epithelium in the terminal bronchioles or enter the finer lymphatic radicles. Carbon-containing macrophages may be seen frequently in the lymphatics, but the manner in which they enter these vessels has not been described.

REFERENCES

Bargmann, W.: Die Lungenalveole. Handb. d. mikr. Anat. d. Menschen (v. Möllendorff), (5)[3], 799, 1936.

Barnard, W. G., and Day, T. D.: The development of the terminal air passages of the human lung. J. Path. & Bact., *45:*67, 1937.

Bell, E. T.: Hyperplasia of the pulmonary alveolar epithelium in disease. Am. J. Path., *19:*901, 1943.

Bloom, G.: Studies on the olfactory epithelium of the frog and the toad with the aid of light and electron microscopy. Zeitschr. f. Zellforsch., *41:*89, 1954.

Boyden, E. A.: Segmental Anatomy of the Lungs. A Study of the Patterns of the Segmental Bronchi and Related Pulmonary Vessels. McGraw-Hill Book Co. Inc. (Blakiston Div.), New York, 1955.

Bremer, J. L.: Postnatal development of alveoli in the mammalian lung in relation to the problem of the alveolar phagocyte. Contrib. Embryol., Carnegie Inst., *25:*85, 1935.

Clements, L. P.: Embryonic development of the respiratory portion of the pig's lung. Anat. Rec., *70:*575, 1938.

Dubreuil, G., Lacoste, A., and Raymond, R.: Observations sur le développement du poumon humain. Bull. d'Histologie Appliquée à la Physiol. et à Path., *13:*235, 1936.

Fried, B. M.: The lungs and the macrophage system. Arch. Path., *17:*76, 1934.

Grady, H. G., and Stewart, H. L.: Histogenesis of induced pulmonary tumors in strain A mice. Am. J. Path., *16:*417, 1940.

Hartroft, W. S., and Macklin, C. C.: The Size of Human Lung Alveoli Expressed as Diameters of Selected Alveolar Outlines as Seen in Specially Prepared 25 Micron Microsections. Tr. Roy. Soc. Canada, Sec. V.: 63, 1944.

Herbut, P. A.: "Alveolar cell tumor" of the lung. Further evidence of its bronchiolar origin. Arch. Path., *41:* 175, 1946.

Karrer, H. E.: The ultrastructure of mouse lung. General architecture of capillary and alveolar walls. J. Biophys. Biochem. Cytol., *2:*241, 1956.

Kolmer, W.: Geruchsorgan. Handb. d. mikr. Anat. (v. Möllendorff), 1927, Vol. 3, p. 192.

Lang, F. J.: Ueber die Alveolarphagozyten der Lunge. Virch. Arch., *275:*104, 1930.

Larsell, O., and Dow, R. S.: The innervation of the human lung. Am. J. Anat., *52:*125, 1933.

Loosli, C.: The rabbit's lung after phrenicotomy and pneumothorax. Anat. Rec., *62:*381, 1935. Interalveolar communications in normal and in pathologic mammalian lungs. Arch. Path., *24:*743, 1937. The pathogenesis and pathology of experimental type I pneumococci pneumonia in the monkey. J. Exper. Med., *76:*79, 1942.

Low, F. N.: The pulmonary alveolar epithelium of laboratory mammals and man. Anat. Rec., *117:*241, 1953.

Low, F. N., and Sampaio, M. M.: The pulmonary alveolar epithelium as an entodermal derivative. Anat. Rec., Vol. 127, No. 1, 1957.

Macklin, C. C.: The musculature of the bronchi and

lungs. Physiol. Rev., *9:*1, 1929. Residual Epithelial Cells on the Pulmonary Alveolar Walls of Mammals. Tr. Roy. Soc. Canada, Sec. V: 93, 1946.

Miller, W. S.: The Lung. 2d ed. Springfield, Ill., Charles C Thomas, 1947.

Ogawa, G.: The finer ramifications of the human lung. Am. J. Anat., *28:*315, 1920.

Oppel, A.: Atmungsapparat. Lehrbuch der vergl. mikrosk. Anat. der Wirbeltiere, (6), 1905.

Palmer, D. W.: The lung of a human foetus of 170 mm. C. R. Length. Am. J. Anat., *58:*59, 1936.

Potter, E. H., and Bohlender, G. P.: Intrauterine respiration in relation to development of the fetal lung. Am. J. Obst. & Gynec., *42:*14, 1941.

Robertson, O. H.: Phagocytosis of foreign material in the lung. Physiol. Rev., *21:*112, 1941.

Ross, I. S.: Pulmonary epithelium and proliferative reactions in the lungs. Arch. Path., *27:*478, 1939.

Schaeffer, J. P.: The mucous membrane of the nasal cavity and the paranasal sinuses, in Cowdry's Special Cytology. 2d ed. New York, (1), 105, 1932.

Wearn, J. T., and others: The normal behavior of the pulmonary blood vessels, with observations on the intermittence of the flow of blood in the arterioles and capillaries. Am. J. Physiol., *109:*236, 1934.

Willson, H. G.: The terminals of the human bronchiole. Am. J. Anat., *30:*267, 1922.

CHAPTER 28

Urinary System

THE KIDNEY

The mammalian kidney is a compound tubular gland which elaborates the urine. Its glandular tubules are called uriniferous tubules and are provided with a peculiar filtration apparatus, a tuft of capillaries, the glomerulus.

The human kidney is a paired, bean-shaped body situated in the posterior part of the abdominal cavity, one on either side of the vertebral column. From the excavated edge, or *hilus,* a large excretory duct, the *ureter,* leads to the *urinary bladder,* the reservoir for the urine. The *urethra,* the last section of the excretory passages of the kidneys, conveys the urine outside the body. The male urethra also serves for the discharge of semen.

The kidney is loosely invested by a *capsule* of dense collagenous bundles and a few elastic fibers. The glandular part of the kidney surrounds a large cavity, the *sinus,* adjacent to the hilus. The sinus contains the *renal pelvis* and is filled with loose connective and fat tissue through which the vessels and nerves pass to the renal tissue.

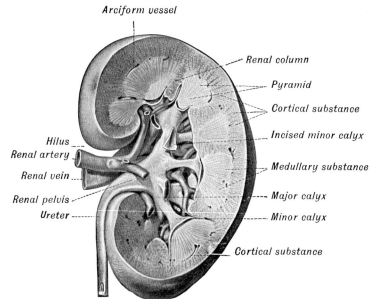

Fig. 28–1.   Human kidney, seen from behind after removal of part of the organ, three-fifths natural size. (After Braus.)

The pelvis is an enlargement of the excretory passages of the kidney. Distally, it is continuous with the ureter; toward the renal tissue, it forms two or more outpocketings, the *major calyces*. These again are subdivided into a varying number of smaller outpocketings, the *minor calyces*.

The glandular substance consists of an outer mass—the cortex—which covers the medullary substance composed of eight to eighteen *renal pyramids (of Malpighi)*. These are roughly conical bodies placed with the base outward and with the apex, or *papilla,* projecting into the lumen of each minor calyx. The tip of the papilla is perforated by ten to twenty-five small openings —the *area cribrosa.*

The gray substance of each pyramid is radially striated by brownish lines which converge toward the apex of the papilla. This striation is caused by the straight parts of the uriniferous tubules and the blood vessels which parallel them.

Owing to the different character of the straight tubules in its various levels, each pyramid can be subdivided into an inner and an outer zone. In the latter, again, a darker and thicker inner, and a lighter and thinner outer layer can be distinguished on macroscopic examination of the fresh section.

Where the dark brown cortex separates the lateral surfaces of the pyramids it forms the *renal columns (of Bertin)*. From the bases of the medullary pyramids, thin, radially directed processes arise which enter the cortical substance, but do not reach the surface of the organ. They show the same striation as the substance of the pyramid and are called *medullary rays (of Ferrein)*.

The pyramids can be considered the lobes of the kidney. In the fetal period they are separated from each other by connective tissue, and fuse only in later stages, although in the ox, and sometimes in man, the lobated condition remains throughout life.

Each pyramid can be subdivided into smaller structural units, the *renal lobules,* on the basis of the branching of the excretory ducts. Adjoining lobules are not separated from one another by connective tissue partitions.

Uriniferous Tubules. As in most other glands, the kidney contains two kinds of tubules: the first are the secretory portions

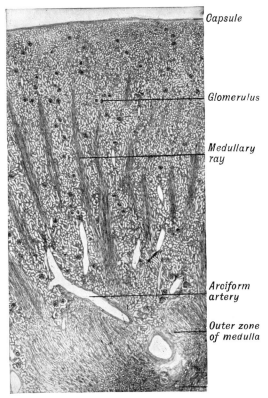

Fig. 28–2. Low power view of section of kidney of *Macacus rhesus*. Fixation by vascular perfusion— hence the empty blood vessels. Photomicrograph (slightly retouched). 13 ×.

which help form the urine; the second are excretory ducts which convey the urine to the ureter. In contrast to other glands, which arise from a single primordium, the secretory portions of the kidney tubules develop from the metanephrogenic blastema and unite secondarily with the excretory ducts which arise from the wolffian duct. The secretory portions are long, tortuous simple tubes, each of which ends in a saclike enlargement, the *capsule of Bowman.* As the uriniferous tubules follow a tortuous course, the form and relation of the tubules can be elucidated only by teasing the tissue after maceration or by reconstructing the tissue in wax from serial sections.

Secretory Portion, the Nephron. Each tubular secretory portion, beginning with the capsule of Bowman and ending at the junction with the excretory ducts, is the structural and functional unit of the kidney—the nephron (Fig. 28–3). Each part of the nephron has a peculiar configuration, occupies a

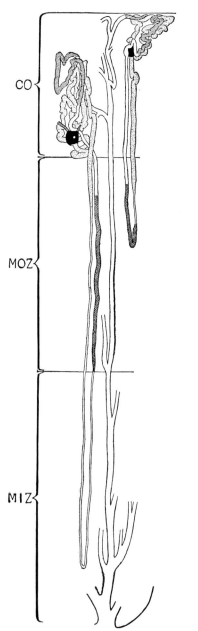

definite position in the cortex or medulla, and is lined with a specific type of epithelium. The successive parts of the nephron are renal corpuscle with its capsule of Bowman, the proximal convolution, descending and ascending limbs of Henle's loop, and distal convolution. A short connecting tube joins the collecting tubule or excretory duct with the nephron.

Renal Corpuscle. The capsule of Bowman arises in the embryo as a spherical epithelial vesicle which is later invaginated by a tuft of blood capillaries, the *glomerulus,* and thus is transformed into a double-walled cup. The capsule and the glomerulus together form the roughly spherical renal corpuscle (of Malpighi). The original cavity of the capsule of Bowman is transformed into a cleftlike space. At one pole of the corpuscle the outer or "parietal" layer of the wall continues into the next section of the nephron. On the opposite side the glomerulus is connected with its afferent and efferent arterioles. Here the parietal wall is reflected onto the surface of the glomerulus as the "visceral" layer of the capsule. The glomeruli are scattered throughout the cortical tissue between the medullary rays.

Estimates of the number of glomeruli vary from 1,000,000 or less to about 4,500,000 in one human kidney. Since the glomerulus is essentially a filtration apparatus, the size of its free surface is important. The values given by various investigators (e.g., 0.78 square meter for all the glomeruli of one kidney) cannot be considered reliable.

As seen with the optical microscope the "visceral" epithelial cells covering the surface of the glomerulus adhere closely in a continuous layer to the capillary loops. They contain a few mitochondria and a Golgi net. The claim that the visceral epithelium consists of isolated perivascular mesenchymal cells or pericytes has not been generally accepted. The "parietal" epithelium is usually of the simple squamous type, and the limits of its polygonal cells can be demonstrated fairly well.

Much of the old controversy on detailed glomerular structure is being cleared up by the electron microscope. The "visceral" epithelial cells have processes from which arise still finer ones (called pedicels). These interdigitate with similar, adjacent processes

Fig. 28–3. Diagram of two nephrons and their connection with collecting tubules. *CO,* cortex; *MOZ,* outer zone of medulla; *MIZ,* inner zone of medulla; Malpighian corpuscles, black; proximal convolution, stippled; thin limb of Henle, white; limb of Henle, crosshatched and then white (to indicate the opacity and clearness seen in macerated preparations, but not in sections); distal convolution, obliquely striated; collecting tubules white. (Redrawn and slightly modified after Peter.)

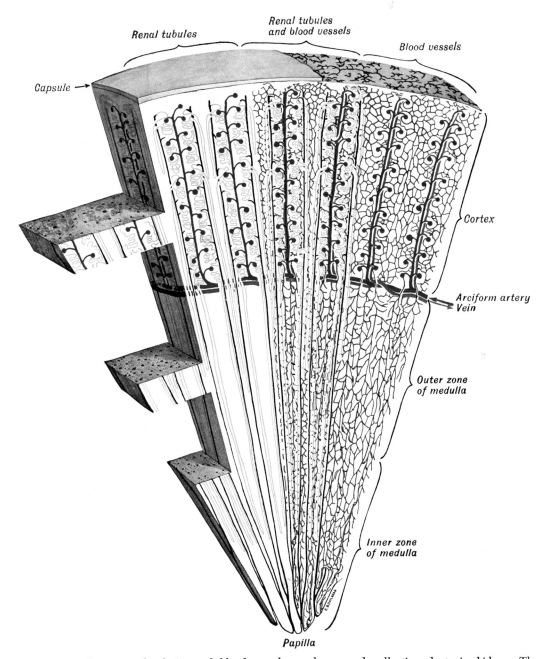

Renal tubules

Renal tubules
and blood vessels

Blood vessels

Capsule →

Cortex

Arciform artery
Vein

Outer zone
of medulla

Inner zone
of medulla

Papilla

Fig. 28–4. Diagram of relations of blood vessels, nephrons and collecting ducts in kidney. The actual structures are much more complicated than those indicated here. *Arteries,* red; *veins,* blue; *glomeruli,* red dots; *nephrons,* green; *collecting ducts,* black. Six interlobular arteries and attached glomeruli are shown. The right-hand pair shows their relation to the veins, the left-hand pair their relation to nephrons, and the central pair shows their relations to both nephrons and veins. (Extensively modified from the diagrams of Peter, Braus, and von Möllendorff.)

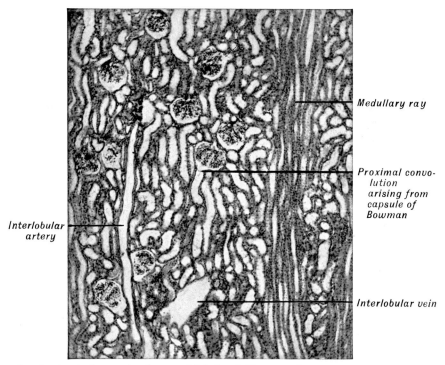

Fig. 28–5.   Section in long axis of a renal lobule of *Macacus rhesus*. Photomicrograph. 58 ×.

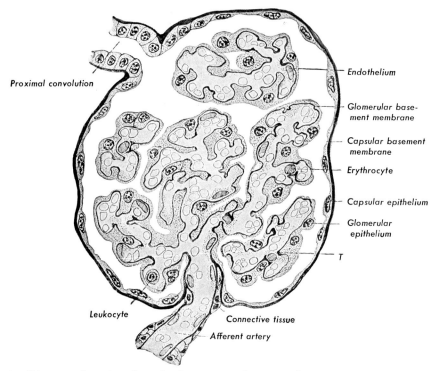

Fig. 28–6.   Diagram of section through the greatest diameter of a normal human glomerulus: *T*, thickening of glomerular basement membrane—often seen at orifice into another loop. (Slightly modified after McGregor.)

from which they seem to be separated by narrow slits. All of them rest on the basement membrane separating the epithelium from the endothelium of the glomerular capillaries (Figs. 28–8 and 28–9). The epithelium extends over the exposed surface of the capillaries and the spaces between them. The endothelium seems to be either exceedingly attenuated or discontinuous, for there are frequent round openings or thin areas 500 to 1000 A in diameter according to most electron microscopists, all of whom are using similar fixation and ultramicroscopic techniques. If the slits between the finest processes of the visceral epithelium on one side of the basement membrane and the fine fenestrations of the endothelium on the other actually exist in the living animal, then the formation of the glomerular filtrate depends on the basement membrane as the filter.

The glomerulus is a convolute of tortuous capillaries interposed in the course of an artery.

The afferent arteriole lacks a distinct adventitial coat; its media consists of circularly arranged smooth muscle cells. Near the entrance of the vessel into the glomerulus, the smooth muscle cells of the vas afferens become large and pale-staining, an appearance which gave them the name "epithelioid." They suggest the cells in the carotid body. They form a cuff extending for 25 to 85 microns along the arteriole and, because of their position, have been called the *juxtaglomerular cells*. They are absent from children below the age of two years. Unlike the cells in the carotid and aortic bodies, which have a rich supply of nerves, the innervation of the juxtaglomerular cells is not different from that of the unchanged smooth muscle cells of the vas afferens. The internal elastic lamella is well developed, but ceases with the branching of the vessel.

The vas afferens, entering the renal corpuscle, divides into two to four, rarely up to ten, primary branches, each of which branches to form an individual vascular lobule. Within each lobule there are a few large communicating vessels which, on their way to join and form the efferent arteriole, give rise to large numbers of cross-connecting capillaries (Fig. 28–10).

Although silver nitrate fails to bring out all the cellular outlines in the endothelium of the glomerular capillaries, the outlines are clearly demonstrated with the electron microscope. Each capillary loop is covered by a basement membrane on which rest the visceral epithelial cells. The epithelial nuclei are believed to be ten times as numerous as the endothelial nuclei. A few reticular fibers have been found in the glomerulus, and, according to some, a few fibroblasts.

The efferent arteriole has a layer of circular smooth muscle fibers, but is devoid of an elastic membrane. Its diameter is distinctly smaller than that of the afferent vessel. It is probable that the contractility of the vas efferens helps regulate the pressure in the glomerulus.

Proximal Convolution. The short transition from the capsule to the following part of the tubule is sometimes referred to as the "neck," although a marked constriction is by no means typical. The next part of the tubule, the *proximal convolution,* averages 14 mm. long and 60 microns in diameter, has a tortuous course, and constitutes most of the cortical substance. In it begins the transformation of the glomerular filtrate into urine by reabsorption of some constituents and addition of others by secretory processes. In addition to many small loops, it always forms a large loop directed toward the periphery, then returns to the vicinity of its renal corpuscle, approaches the nearest medullary ray, and runs toward the medulla. In the outer zone of the pyramid, the proximal convolution tapers down into its terminal portion, which continues into the U-shaped *loop of Henle.*

The epithelium of the proximal convolution consists of one layer of truncated pyramidal cells. Their cytoplasm is abundant and stains deeply with eosin; each cell contains a large, pale, spherical nucleus. Only three or four nuclei are usually seen in a transection of the tubule. The limits between the cells are rarely seen, because the sides of the cells are provided with grooves and ridges perpendicular to the basement membrane and interdigitating with the same structures of the adjacent cells.

In fresh condition the cells appear opaque and granular. They undergo postmortem changes rapidly, and it is not easy to preserve them satisfactorily in fixed material. After suitable fixation and staining, the basal parts

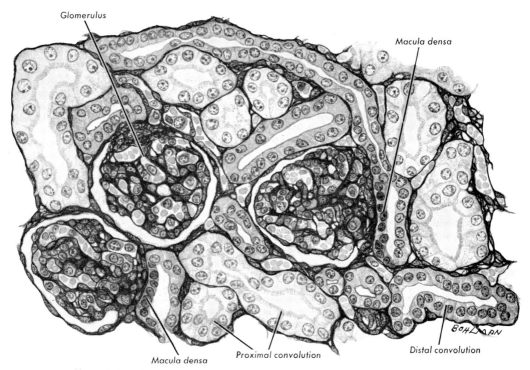

Fig. 28–7.   Section of cortex of kidney of an infant of six months. 410 ×.

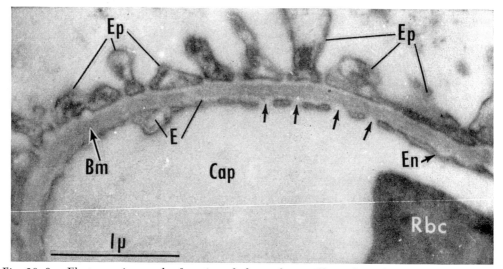

Fig. 28–8.   Electron micrograph of section of glomerular capillary of rat showing interrupted nature of the fine processes (pedicels) of visceral epithelium (*Ep*), the endothelium (*En*) interrupted at arrows, and the continuous basement membrane (*Bm*); *Rbc,* red blood corpuscle. (Courtesy of Vincent Hall.)

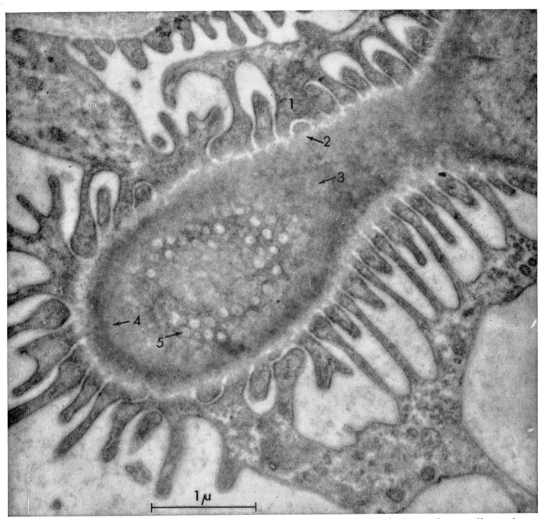

Fig. 28–9. Electron micrograph of tangential section through wall of glomerular capillary of rat. This is an especially clear view of what seem to be perforations or exceedingly thin areas (5) in the endothelial lining of the capillary. 4, 3, and 2 are successive layers of the basement membrane. The finest interdigitating processes, pedicels, (1) of the epithelial cells covering the basement membrane are shown as forming an incomplete layer. Buffered osmic acid fixation. (Courtesy of D. Pease.)

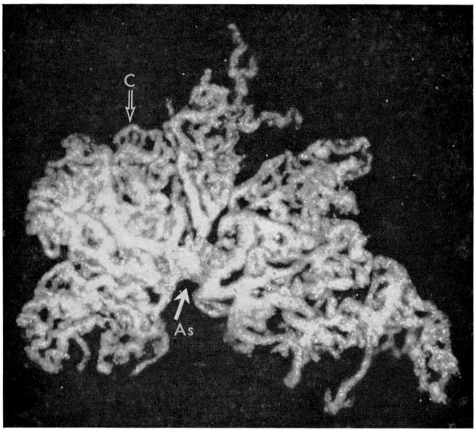

Fig. 28–10.   Photomicrograph by incident light of rat glomerular vessels. Vascular injection with latex. After dissecting the glomerulus the lobules were teased and flattened. The arteriolar branches form five separate lobules. *As,* stalk of the afferent arteriole. The arrow at C points to the lateral branching of a communicating vessel into short anastomosing capillaries. 295 ×. (Courtesy of Vincent Hall.)

of the cells are occupied by parallel rod-like mitochondria perpendicular to the basement membrane and reaching the level of the nucleus. In poorly fixed slides this typical striation of the epithelium is invisible, because the rods disintegrate into granules. This also occurs during life as a degenerative process in pathological conditions. The superficial part of the cell body contains granular mitochondria and often small vacuoles which stain supravitally with neutral red.

The free surface of the cells lining the lumen is covered by a *brush border* (Fig. 28–11). The limit between the latter and the cytoplasm is marked by a layer of granules which in section appear as a darkly staining line. Under this line, above the nucleus, are a pair of centrioles and a Golgi net; in compensatory hypertrophy of the kidney this organoid recedes to the infranuclear region. The edges of the free surfaces of the cells,

under the brush border, are provided with a system of terminal bars.

In the normal human kidney the epithelium of the proximal convolution does not contain lipoid inclusions. In pathological conditions, as well as in postmortem autolysis, droplets of neutral fat and of phosphatids readily appear. In some animals (cat) they are of normal occurrence.

During diuresis the lumen of the proximal convolution is large, the cells are low and flattened, and the brush border high. In the resting condition the cells are high and provided with a bulging surface which transforms the lumen into an irregular, star-shaped cleft. Other structural changes, such as vacuolization of the apical parts, bulging of drops of the superficial cytoplasm through the brush border into the lumen, as well as the formation of vacuolated or foamy masses in the lumen, all seem to be artefacts.

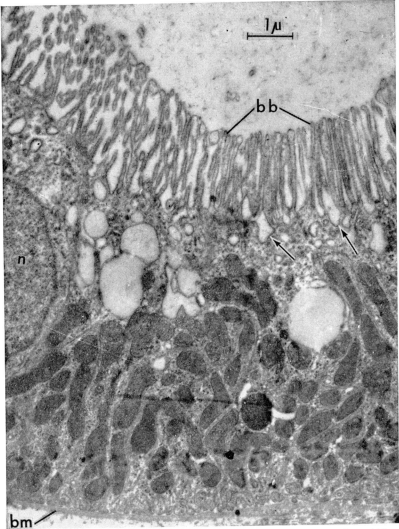

Fig. 28–11. Electron micrograph of section through proximal convolution of rat kidney showing the microvilli forming the brush border (*bb*), the basement membrane, *bm*, nucleus, *n*. Much of the cell is filled with closely packed mitochondria. The arrows show vesicles communicating with spaces between microvilli. Buffered osmic acid fixation. (Courtesy of D. C. Pease.)

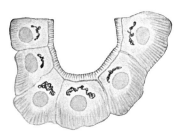

Fig. 28–12. Transection of proximal convolution of guinea pig under high magnification. Between nucleus and brush border the Golgi net is seen. (Redrawn after Brugnatelli.)

Although the whole length of the proximal convolution seems to have essentially the same structure, certain experiments (vital staining, poisoning with uranium, chromium, bichloride of mercury, and others) allow a subdivision of this tubule into three or four successive stretches, which show specific reactions to the different noxious factors. Similar conclusions on functional differentiation within this segment of the nephron have been drawn from histochemical studies in a variety of vertebrates.

Loop of Henle. The proximal convolution continues into the loop of Henle. This has two straight limbs running parallel to each other in the radial direction and connected by a sharp bend or crest. The descending limb of the loop is a thin, straight tubule with an outer diameter of 14 to 22 microns. The ascending limb is thicker (33 microns). The transition from the thin descending to the thick ascending limb is usually abrupt and rarely occurs at the crest of the loop.

The loops of Henle are of different lengths, depending on the level they reach in descending into the pyramid and on the position of the renal corpuscle to which they belong. In the human kidney the short ones are about seven times as numerous as the long ones. They belong to those renal corpuscles located nearer to the surface of the kidney; their crest is always formed by the thick ascending limb and is located in the outer zone of the medulla. The thin, descending limb may be short or even absent. In the latter case the proximal convolution continues directly into the thick ascending limb. In the longer loops which belong to the deeper renal corpuscles the crest is formed by a thin limb. These loops sometimes extend nearly to the apex of the papilla. In this case the length of the thin limb may vary from 4.5 to 10 mm. or even more.

The ascending thick limb of the loop of Henle has, on the average, a length of 9 mm. It occupies a position nearer to the corresponding collecting tubule than the descending limb. This part of the nephron is usually located in the outer zone of the medulla.

As the proximal convolution passes into the descending thin limb of the loop, the caliber of the lumen tapers gradually, but the epithelium changes abruptly. The cells with the brush border are suddenly replaced by thin, squamous epithelial cells with a pale-staining cytoplasm containing a slightly flattened nucleus which causes a bulging of the central part of the cell body into the lumen. The cell outlines are also sometimes distinctly festooned, e.g., in the cat. The edges of the free surfaces are provided with terminal bars. At the free surface, above the nucleus, a pair of centrioles with a central flagellum is present; a Golgi net has also been described; mitochondria are scarce.

Owing to the thinness of the epithelium, the descending limbs of the loops can be easily mistaken for blood capillaries (Fig. 28–15).

The change from the descending limb to the ascending limb is usually also fairly sudden. The epithelium becomes cuboidal and stains darker. Rod-shaped mitochondria cause a distinct perpendicular striation of its

basal part, where the cell boundaries are not clearly seen. The superficial parts of the cells, where granular mitochondria occur, are, on the contrary, sharply outlined. The nucleus is spherical or slightly flattened. A pair of centrioles occupies the free surface and seems to be provided with a central flagellum.

The ascending limb of Henle's loop enters the cortical tissue, returns to the renal corpuscle of its nephron and attaches itself to its vascular pole, particularly to the vas afferens with its juxtaglomerular cells. That side of the tubule in contact with the vas afferens forms an elliptical disk of tall thin cells measuring 40 by 70 microns in man. This area, called the *macula densa,* has been reported to be significant in the hemodynamics of the kidney. From here the loop gradually passes into the *distal convolution.*

Distal Convolution. This portion of the tubule has many outpocketings and zigzag contortions; it usually forms a loop directed toward the periphery and above the corresponding renal corpuscle. Its length is estimated at 4.6 to 5.2 mm., its diameter at 20 to 50 microns.

In the distal convolution the epithelium is lower and the lumen is larger than in the proximal convolution. The free surfaces of the cells show microvilli with the electron microscope. In the basal parts of the cells a more or less distinct striation can be seen; the limits of the cells are fairly distinct. The electron microscope makes visible lengthy infoldings of the basal surface of the cells. They run for considerable distances between the mitochondria (Figs. 28–13 and 28–14). Pease interprets these infoldings as functioning in water transport, just as he interprets similar basal infoldings in the striated salivary gland ducts (Fig. 21–13) and in the choroid plexus (Fig. 9–60). The cytoplasm stains less intensely with acid dyes than in the proximal convolution. In a cross section the cells are more numerous than in the latter; instead of three to four, five to eight nuclei can usually be counted. Each distal convolution continues by a short connecting tubule into one of the initial branches of the collecting tubules.

Excretory Ducts or Collecting Tubules. The connections of the collecting tubules with the nephrons are located in the cortex along a medullary ray and are called the

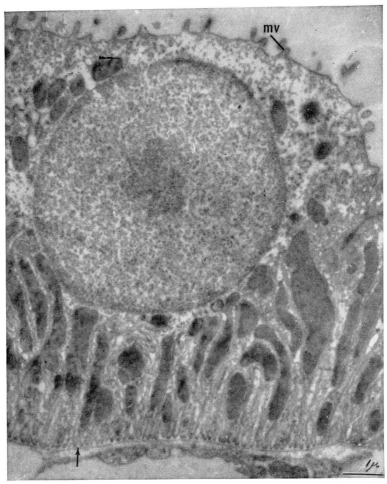

Fig. 28–13. Electron micrograph of section through distal convolution of rat kidney. Relatively scattered microvilli (*mv*) are seen on the free surface. The basal surface shows the prominent infoldings of the plasma membrane (arrow). They frequently seem to surround the mitochondria. Buffered osmic acid fixation. (Courtesy of D. Pease.)

"peripheral branchings" of the collecting ducts. From the medullary ray the collecting tubules pass radially inward through the outer zone of the medulla without further fusions. When they reach the inner zone, they fuse at acute angles with other similar tubules, and this is repeated seven times. These fusions or branchings are in the medulla near the pelvis and are called the "central branchings (or fusions)." Through the central fusions large, straight collecting tubules are formed, the so-called *papillary ducts* (of Bellini), with a lumen measuring 100 to 200 microns. They open on the area cribrosa on the apex of the papilla.

The system of the intrarenal excretory ducts has a typical epithelium, quite different from that of the various parts of the nephron. In the smallest collecting tubules the cells are cuboidal, sharply outlined, contain a darkly staining round nucleus, and have a clear cytoplasm. The latter contains a few fine mitochondria and, at the surface, a pair of centrioles with a central flagellum.

As the collecting tubules grow larger, the cells also grow higher, and finally acquire in the ducts of Bellini a tall columnar form. They are always arranged in a regular, single layer, with all the nuclei at one level and with the free surfaces bulging slightly into the lumen. The cytoplasm keeps its pale appearance. The centrioles remain at the free bulg-

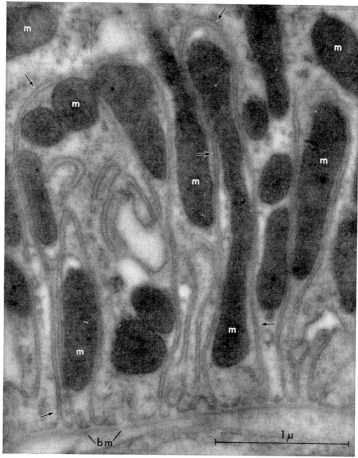

Fig. 28–14.   Electron micrograph of basal surface of distal convolution of rat kidney. Above the basement membrane (*bm*) are the prominent basal infoldings of the plasma membrane indicated by arrows. *m*, mitochondria. Buffered osmic acid fixation. (Courtesy of D. Pease.)

ing surface. In the area cribrosa the simple columnar epithelium of the ducts of Bellini continues onto the surface of the papilla.

The length of the collecting tubules is estimated at 20 to 22 mm.; the length of the nephron at 30 to 38 mm.

Renal Lobule. Each renal lobule is composed of the glandular tissue surrounding a medullary ray. The slender, pyramidal form of the renal lobule and the presence of a medullary ray forming its core are the results of the straight, radial course of the collecting tubules, of the gradual increase of their branchings toward the capsule and of the accumulation of nephrons in the cortex. Each medullary ray contains several straight collecting tubules, the loops of Henle, and the terminal portions of the proximal convolution. It is surrounded by the convoluted portions of the tubules and by the renal corpuscles. At the apex of the lobule, which reaches far into the papilla of the pyramid, the collecting tubules begin to fuse with one another and finally open, as

the ducts of Bellini, on the area cribrosa. A large number of lobules form the malpighian pyramid.

A few authors prefer to consider that the renal lobules center about the radial branches of the arciform artery extending toward the capsule of the organ. According to this view, the interlobular arteries are really *intralobular* arteries. In view of the embryonic development of the organ from a series of branching ducts, it seems best to consider the lobule as centering about these ducts rather than about the arterial tree. A similar problem is found in the determination of the hepatic lobule.

Interstitial Connective Tissue. The interstitial connective tissue in the normal kidney is small in amount and is of the reticular type. Its branching fibers, accompanied by a few fibroblasts and fixed macrophages, form networks in the narrow spaces between the convoluted and straight tubules. The fibers are especially numerous and thick in the apex of the pyramids, where most of them are arranged concentrically around the ducts of Bellini and are embedded in an abundant, amorphous ground substance.

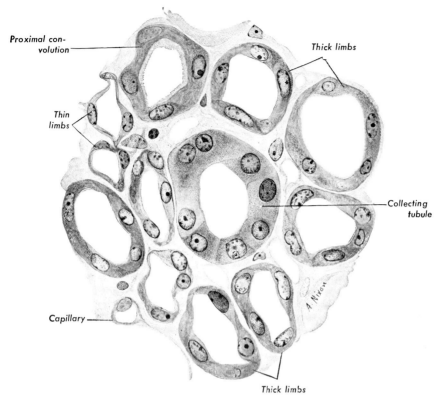

Proximal con-
volution

Thin
limbs

Thick limbs

Collecting
tubule

Capillary

A. Nixon

Thick limbs

Fig. 28–15.   Section of medullary ray from kidney of *Macacus rhesus*. The organ was fixed by perfusion—hence the slightly dilated condition of the tubules. Iron-hematoxylin stain. About 800 ×.

Thick, collagenous fibers are found only in the adventitia of the larger blood vessels. A few collagenous fibers surround the capsules of Bowman and the larger papillary ducts. Elastic fibers are absent except in the walls of the blood vessels. In old age the amount of collagenous tissue in the kidney may increase considerably through a transformation of the reticular fibers.

Basement Membrane. The epithelium of the nephron and of the excretory ducts rests upon a well-developed basement membrane which is hyaline in its central part. It is found in the renal corpuscle, where it separates the endothelium of the capillary loops from the "visceral" epithelial layer, and also lies beneath the parietal epithelium. In the proximal convolution the hyaline membrane is particularly thick. Its inner surface, to which the bases of the epithelial cells are attached, is provided with numerous, small circular ridges. The interstitial reticular fibers fuse with the outer surface of the membrane.

Blood Vessels of the Kidney. Roughly, one quarter of the cardiac output enters the kidney and passes through the glomeruli before being distributed to the rest of the organ (see Figs. 28–4, 28–16). The renal artery enters the hilus of the kidney and divides

into two sets of principal branches, a ventral and a dorsal. The first set has a wider distribution in the organ than the second. These principal branches of the renal artery are "end arteries" and are not connected by large anastomoses. In the fat tissue surrounding the pelvis they branch into *interlobar arteries;* these are in the columns of Bertin between the malpighian pyramids or lobes of the kidney.

The interlobar arteries break up into branches which run approximately parallel to the surface of the kidney at the limit between the bases of the pyramids and the cortex. They have a more or less arched course (arterial arcades) with the convexity directed toward the periphery of the organ. They are called *arciform* or *arcuate arteries.* At more or less regular intervals they give off smaller branches which run radially to the surface of the kidney. Since these radial branches are located in the cortical substance between the medullary rays, they are called *interlobular arteries.*

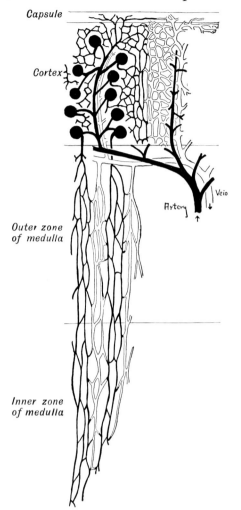

Capsule

Cortex

Outer zone
of medulla

Inner zone
of medulla

Artery   Veio

Fig. 28–16.   Diagram of blood supply to kidney.
Arteries and arterial capillaries, black; veins and
venules, double-contoured.

The interlobular arteries give off numerous
smaller branches, each of which is the afferent vessel of a glomerulus. From the glomerulus the blood is carried away by the
efferent vessel. The vas efferens breaks up
into a network of arterioles which supply the
convoluted uriniferous tubules of the cortex
with blood. Direct observation in living amphibians and some mammals shows that the
circulation may cease from time to time in
particular glomeruli.

It is probable that the efferent artery of
a glomerulus supplies much of the nephron
belonging to the same renal corpuscle. The
tissues of the medulla and the medullary rays
also receive their blood supply from the effer-

ent glomerular arterioles. The medullary rays
are supplied by the efferent vessels of the
nearest glomeruli. The pyramids of Malpighi
are supplied by the *arteriolae rectae spuriae,*
which arise as efferent vessels from the glomeruli near the medulla. The arteriolae rectae
spuriae assume a straight course toward the
pelvis. This arrangement causes a radial
striation of the outer zone of the malpighian
pyramid. Having entered the medullary substance, they branch profusely at acute angles
and form a capillary network with radially
elongated meshes about the straight tubules.

The existence of the so-called "arteriolae rectae
verae," which are supposed to arise directly from
the arcuate or the interlobular arteries and to enter
the medulla, is denied by most investigators. It has
been claimed that apparently direct communications
between arterioles and venules may arise through
partial obliteration of glomeruli.

The veins of the cortex arise from the capillary
networks in the outermost layers of the cortex
through the confluence of radially arranged branches,
which form the so-called *stellate veins.* These continue into interlobular veins, which follow the corresponding arteries and everywhere receive additional capillaries from the labyrinth. The interlobular veins fuse to form the large arcuate or arciform
veins which run beside the arteries of the same
name. In the medulla straight, radially arranged
veins arise (*venulae rectae*) which join the arciform veins directly. The latter fuse and form interlobar veins which accompany the large arteries and
finally give rise to the renal vein.

Lymphatics. Networks of lymphatic capillaries are
found in both the capsule of the kidney and in the
glandular tissue. Both groups are connected by occasional anastomoses. The lymphatics of the capsule
join the lymph vessels of the neighboring organs.
The lymph capillaries in the glandular tissue form
dense networks between the uriniferous tubules, especially in the cortex. They pass into lymphatics which
accompany the larger blood vessels, and leave the
kidney at the hilus. They are not present in the
glomeruli or medullary rays.

Nerves. Macroscopic dissection shows that the
sympathetic celiac plexus sends many nerve fibers
into the kidney. Their distribution in this organ has
not been worked out satisfactorily. It is relatively
easy to follow nonmyelinated and myelinated fibers
along the course of the larger blood vessels. They
provide the adventitia with sensory nerve endings
and the muscular coat with motor endings. Along
with the afferent arterioles, nerve fibers may reach
the renal corpuscles, and some of them seem to form
end branches on their surface. The nerve supply of
the uriniferous tubules, however, has not been clearly
demonstrated. Some investigators describe plexuses
of fine nerve fibers which surround and seem to penetrate the basement membrane. On its inner surface
they are supposed to form another plexus from which
terminal branches arise to end with minute end
knobs between the epithelial cells.

Histophysiological Remarks. The kidneys, in elaborating the urine, eliminate water and some of the substances dissolved in the blood. With minor exceptions they do not produce new material. In addition to their *excretory functions,* by which they dispose of waste products and substances foreign to the organism, the kidneys have equally important *conservative* functions, by which they retain the necessary amounts of water, electrolytes and other chemical substances in the body, while permitting any excess of these substances to be eliminated. They thus play a large part in the maintenance of the constancy of composition of the internal environment of the organism. It may be inferred from the structure of the kidney that the malpighian corpuscle acts as a filtration apparatus with pressure supplied in the capillaries and that differences in structure of the several parts of the tubule reflect secretory and conducting functions.

Before considering the complex processes in the kidney, it is necessary to recall that the transport of substances across cell membranes may occur by simple diffusion or may take place in the opposite direction, in which case work is done. The concentration of substances despite an opposing osmotic force is an example of secretion. In other circumstances the substance which is accumulated arises as a result of specific synthesis. Secretion proceeds only when the diffusion is offset by hydrostatic or electrical pressures. The translation of energy is often indirect, with the energy initially derived from chemical transformations appearing as muscular work, membrane potentials and ionic exchange mechanisms.

Glomerulus. Fluid aspirated from the glomerular space (with the rest of the nephron blocked) in the living frog is similar in composition to the plasma, except for the absence of fats, plasma proteins and substances combined with these large molecules. This fluid contains water, phosphates, reducing substances, creatinine, uric acid, urea and chloride; certain dyes are also found in it after being introduced into the animal.

That the glomerulus functions as an ultrafilter in mammals, including man, is supported by less direct but no less convincing evidence. The passage of fluorescein and esculin from the blood stream into the cap-

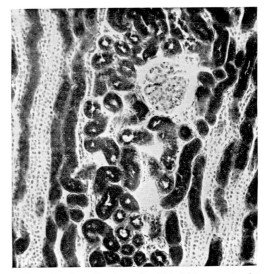

Fig. 28–17. Section of rabbit kidney stained to show alkaline phosphatase as black material, apparently limited to the proximal convolutions. 100 ✕. (Courtesy of G. Gomori.)

sular space has been observed with the aid of ultraviolet light. Intravenously injected potassium ferrocyanide and uric acid are found in the capsular space, but, when injected into rabbits whose blood pressure had been lowered beneath the osmotic pressure of the blood, neither of these substances is found within the nephron.

The trend in study of renal secretion has been toward a more quantitative evaluation of the process. Urine formation is energetically costly and is rendered extremely inefficient by the presence of the glomerulus in the nephron. It has been calculated that in man about 1300 ml. of blood pass through the kidneys per minute, and that, with normal blood pressures, all the glomeruli form about 125 ml. of filtrate of plasma per minute, and that the cells of all the renal tubules reabsorb 124 ml. of this and return it to the blood, leaving a volume of 1 ml. to be excreted. This fraction (remainder) is not simply derived by absorption of water, but its contents have been modified by (1) passive diffusion back into the blood (urea), (2) absorption by osmotic work, and (3) excretion into the lumen of other substances.

The origin of this state of affairs has been explained by some on the premise that fishes evolved, not in the sea, but in fresh water. With their tissues hypertonic to the milieu, there was a copious urine to be excreted, and a glomerulus was of real value. Those fishes which returned to the sea (elasmobranchs) became adapted to a hypertonic milieu, retaining large amounts of urea in the blood and tissues by reducing the number and size of glomeruli or by losing their glomeruli. Unfortunately, man has retained the glomerulus, although it would be far more efficient to excrete all the water and wastes by secretory activity.

The transport of certain substances into and out of the nephron is capable of rather precise measurement in healthy people and is the basis of a variety of measures of their kidney function. Inulin is a nonmetabolized carbohydrate which, when injected intravenously, does not appear in the urine of aglomerular fish; it has been found in glomerular filtrate, and is not secreted or absorbed by the tubules. It has been used as a measure of the amount of plasma filtered by the combined glomeruli. This is calculated from the concentrations of inulin in the urine and in the plasma during the experiment. The volume of plasma containing the same amount of inulin as that found in the urine is the amount of plasma which has been "cleared" of this substance by filtration. The inulin clearance furnishes a standard from which it may be estimated what proportions of other substances are reabsorbed or excreted by cells in various parts of the tubule.

In rats, mice and some other mammals there is evidence for intermittency of function of individual glomeruli. This is most readily observed in immature specimens. While not demonstrated in dogs or man, the possibility of intermittent function of glomeruli has profound implications for all quantitative studies on kidney function.

Proximal Convolution. It is also well established for a wide variety of animal forms that the renal tubules have both excretory and absorptive functions. Various segments of the tubules have been studied by direct methods in the frog and salamander. Tubules were punctured at various levels and fluid removed for analysis, and fluid of known composition was perfused through a part of the tubule between two micropipettes. It was found that sodium and chloride are absorbed in the distal portions of the tubule, where acidification of the urine also takes place. Absorption of

glucose takes place in the proximal portion in Necturus. As a result of this system of filtration and absorption, nearly $\frac{1}{2}$ pound of glucose and more than 3 pounds of sodium chloride per day must be recovered from the glomerular filtrate in man. When the level of glucose in the blood is raised experimentally above a definite level, it is not completely absorbed from the glomerular filtrate, and it appears in the urine. The *tubular maximum for reabsorption of glucose (glucose Tm)* is thus an index of reabsorptive capacity of the kidney tubules.

In current research it is considered that in the proximal convolution, in addition to glucose, amino acids, vitamin C and other constituents are absorbed by osmotic work.

As certain poisons more or less selectively affect particular portions of the proximal convolution, and as certain dyes and iron salts are eliminated in greater amounts in some parts of this segment of the nephron than in others, it is probable that different parts of the proximal convolution have different functions.

Substances such as phenol red, Diodrast (an organic iodine compound), para-amino-hippuric acid (P.A.H.) and creatinine are added to the glomerular filtrate by secretory work. Phenol red has been seen to be eliminated by the proximal convolution in living frogs; the same part of the nephron in cultures from a human fetus of three and a half months secretes this indicator if it is added to the medium, while the epithelium of the rest of the tubules does not.

There is now adequate evidence that tubular excretion plays an important part in the excretion of phenol red, Diodrast and creatinine in man.

Certain substances, when introduced into the blood in moderate concentrations, are entirely removed during a single passage of blood through the kidneys. Among these are Diodrast and para-aminohippuric acid. Since it is impossible to remove all the substances dissolved in the plasma by filtration and have any fluid plasma left, the complete removal of a substance in one passage of blood through the kidney must occur in part by filtration and in part by excretory work. Knowing the concentration of such substances in the blood and the amount found in the urine produced in a given period of time, one can calculate the blood flow through the kidney. The blood flow is equal to the plasma flow plus the cell volume found by hematocrit. From the values for Diodrast (or P.A.H.) clearance, and for inulin clearance one can determine the fraction of renal plasma flow which is filtered by the glomeruli. Thus

$$\text{Filtration fraction} = \frac{\text{Inulin clearance}}{\text{P.A.H. clearance}}$$

If now one raises the concentration of Diodrast or para-aminohippuric acid in the blood, a point is reached at which the kidney fails to remove all the material from the blood. The maximum concentration which is completely cleared of the substance is taken as a measure of the *excretory capacity of the tubule* (*Tm—tubular maximum*). If the values are known for renal plasma flow and inulin clearance, the measurement of other substances—e.g., urea, uric acid, phosphate and bicarbonate buffers—in the blood and urine may be related to the activities of the total number of nephrons with regard to these substances. In this fashion it has been calculated which substances are secreted, which are reabsorbed, and which diffuse passively from the glomerular filtrate. The localizations of these specific events in various portions of the tubule are less well known.

Loop of Henle and Distal Convolution. The loop of Henle seems to be primarily concerned with the reabsorption of water and sodium. Perhaps for this reason the antidiuretic hormone of the posterior pituitary appears to be effective only in animals having a loop of Henle. With respect to water regulation, the kidney is working hardest when there is minimal urine flow.

A different sort of mechanism is postulated to account for excretion of acid of the urine. Although the evidence is physiological and biochemical without a close correlation with histology, the process has been ascribed to the distal region of the nephron. It must be borne in mind that, in the elimination of acid in the urine, there is a maximum gradient of acidity (hydrogen ion concentration) possible in the kidney, so that the urine is limited in acidity to pH 4.5, the blood being pH 7.4. The elimination of additional acid therefore requires the simultaneous elimina-

tion of additional base. If the acidity achieved makes too drastic demands upon the alkaline reserve of the body, it is neutralized by ammonia derived from glutamine and by oxidative deamination of some amino acids.

In general, the processes of secretion and reabsorption have been considered to be completed when the urine has passed the distal convolution. There is however increasing evidence from studies on rats that the collecting tubule plays an active role in chloride reabsorption and other ion exchange.

Relations to Disease. It would appear that knowledge of the absorptive and excretory capacities of the kidneys for various substances should be particularly informative in renal disease in which nephrons may be altered or obliterated both morphologically and functionally. Such is indeed the case, but the diseased kidney is much more complex than the normal. The calculations given earlier are based on the knowledge or assumption of a definite blood flow moving diffusely through the kidney with certain hydrostatic pressures operating at the glomeruli. The hemodynamics of the kidney are complicated, and its vascular system is particularly responsive to systemic changes. Thus, with lowered blood pressure, as in shock, the kidney may shut down, becoming *ischemic*. In other circumstances some of the nephrons may degenerate structurally or functionally throughout their length or in part.

The substance *renin* has been extracted from mammalian kidneys and found to have the property of raising the general arterial blood pressure. The relation of this material, and of substances which inactivate it, to hypertension is the subject of active study. It is claimed that the juxtaglomerular cells of the vas afferens undergo a rapid hyperplasia and elaboration of granules after partial clamping of the renal artery in rabbits and dogs, a procedure which results in an increased blood pressure. It has been suggested that these cells secrete a substance concerned with the maintenance of the increased arterial tension. But Selye and Stone believe that the hypertensive materials are secreted by the tubular epithelium, since the juxtaglomerular apparatus often disappeared completely in the kidney of rats after partial clamping of the renal artery.

EXCRETORY PASSAGES OF THE KIDNEY

The excretory passages convey the urine from the parenchyma of the kidney to the outside. No appreciable changes in the composition of the urine occur in these passages except a slight admixture of mucus. The walls of the excretory passages are provided with a well-developed coat of smooth muscle; its contractions move the urine forward.

The calyces, the pelvis, the ureter and the bladder all have a similar structure, although the thickness of the wall gradually increases in the sequence indicated. The inner surface is lined with a mucous membrane. There is no distinct submucosa in man, and the lamina propria of the mucosa is attached to the smooth muscle coat, which is covered by an adventitial layer of connective tissue. The upper part of the bladder is covered by the serous membrane of the peritoneum.

Although of mesodermal origin in the ureter and of entodermal in the bladder, the lining of the mucous membrane in all the parts just mentioned is the same "transitional" epithelium. In the calyces it is two to three cells thick, in the ureter four to five; in the empty bladder six to eight cell layers are seen. In the contracted condition of the wall of the viscus, the epithelium is thick and its cells are round, or even columnar or club-shaped. In the distended condition the epithelium is thin, and the cells are greatly flattened and stretched parallel to the surface. Scattered lymphoid cells migrate between the epithelial cells. Owing to the similarity of the epithelial structure in these parts of the excretory tract, no conclusions can be drawn on the exact origin of epithelial cells found in the urine.

The epithelium lining the excretory passages seems to be impermeable to the normal, soluble substances of the urine. If the viscus is damaged, this property may, of course, be greatly altered. *Intra-epithelial cysts*—round or oval cavities filled with a peculiar colloidal substance—often develop in the epithelium of the ureter and bladder. No true glands are present in the calices, the pelvis and the ureter; glands may be simulated here by small, solid nests of epithelial cells located in the thickness of the epithelial sheet. In the urinary bladder, however, and in the vicinity of the internal urethral orifice, small, sometimes branched invaginations of the epithelium into the subjacent connective tissue can be found. They contain numerous clear mucus-secreting cells and are similar to the glands of Littré in the urethra.

No distinct basement membrane between the epithelium and the lamina propria can be discerned. The connective tissue of the latter, especially in the ureter, forms thin folds which may penetrate deep into the epithelium. The blood capillaries which they contain sometimes lie deep in the epithelial sheet.

The dense connective tissue of the mucous membrane generally does not form any papillae. It contains elastic networks and sometimes small lymphatic nodules. Its deeper layers have a looser arrangement; therefore the mucous membrane in the empty ureter is thrown into several longitudinal folds, which cause a festooned appearance of the edge of the lumen in cross sections. In the bladder the deep, looser layer of connective tissue is especially abundant, so that in the contracted condition of the organ the mucous membrane forms numerous, thick folds. In some places a thin layer of smooth muscle fibers seems to divide the connective tissue into a superficial lamina propria and a deeper submucous layer.

The muscular coat of the urinary passages generally consists of an *inner* longitudinal and an *outer* circular layer. Beginning with the lower third of the ureter, a third external longitudinal layer is added, which is especially prominent in the bladder. In contrast to the intestine, the smooth muscles in the urinary passages do not form regular layers, but appear as loose, anastomosing strands, separated from one another by abundant connective tissue and elastic networks, which continue into the lamina propria mucosae.

In the small calyces, which are hollow cones capping the papillae of the pyramids, the strands of the inner longitudinal muscle layer end at the attachment of the calyx to the papilla. The outer circular strands reach higher up and form a muscular ring around the base of the papilla.

The calyces show periodic contractions moving from their base to their apex. This muscular activity helps to move the urine out of the papillary ducts into the calices. The muscular coat of the ureter also performs

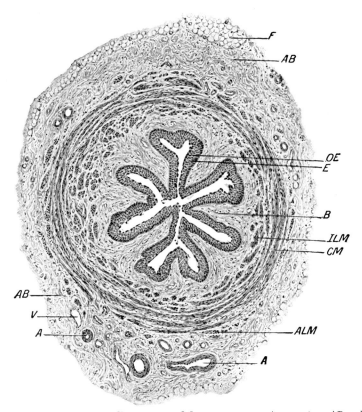

Fig. 28–18.   Cross section of markedly contracted human ureter. *A*, arteries; *AB*, adventitial connective tissue; *ALM*, external longitudinal muscle bundles; *B*, lamina propria; *CM*, circular muscle bundles; *E*, deep layer of the epithelium; *F*, fat tissue; *ILM*, internal longitudinal muscle bundles; *OE*, superficial epithelial cells; *V*, veins. 30 ×. (After Schaffer.)

slow peristaltic movements. The waves of contraction proceed from the pelvis toward the bladder.

As the *ureters* pierce the wall of the bladder obliquely, their openings are usually closed by the pressure of the contents of the bladder and are open only when the urine is forced through them. A fold of the mucous membrane of the bladder acts as a valve and usually prevents the backflow of the urine. In the "intramural" part of the ureters, the circular muscular strands of their wall disappear, and the connective tissue of the mucous membrane is occupied by longitudinal muscular strands whose contraction opens the lumen of the ureter.

The muscular coat of the *bladder* is very strong. Its thick strands of smooth muscle cells form three layers which, however, cannot be distinctly separated from each other. The outer longitudinal layer is developed best on the dorsal and ventral surfaces of the viscus, while in other places its strands may be wide apart. The middle, circular or spiral layer is the thickest of all. The innermost layer consists in the body of the bladder of relatively rare, separate longitudinal or oblique strands. In the region of the trigone, thin, dense bundles of smooth muscle form a circular mass around the internal opening of the urethra—the internal sphincter of the bladder.

Blood Vessels and Nerves. The blood vessels of the excretory passages penetrate first through the muscular coat and provide it with capillaries; then they form a plexus in the deeper layers of the mucous membrane. From here small arteries mount to the surface and form a rich capillary plexus immediately under the epithelium.

The deeper layers of the mucosa and the muscularis in the pelvis and the ureters contain a well-developed network of lymph capillaries. In the bladder they are said to be present only in the muscularis.

In the adventitial and muscular coats of the ureter, nerve plexuses, small ganglia and scattered nerve cells can be found. Most of the fibers supply the muscles; some fibers of apparently efferent nature have been traced into the mucosa and the epithelium.

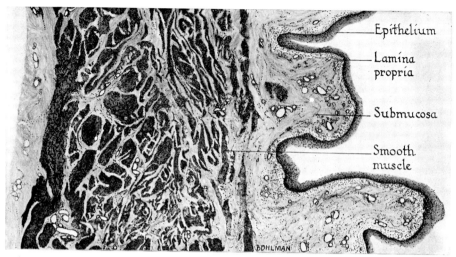

Fig. 28–19. Low power view of contracted urinary bladder of *Macacus rhesus.*

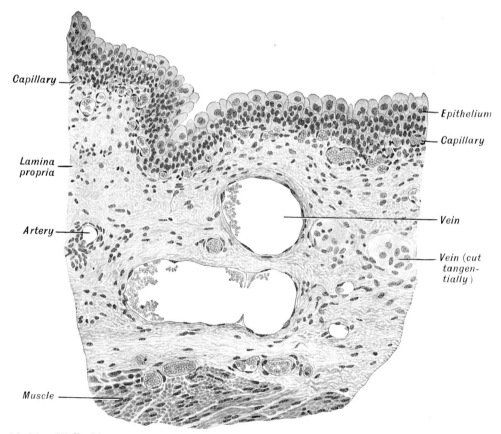

Fig. 28–20. Wall of human urinary bladder in contracted condition; capillaries penetrate the epithelium.
150 ×. (A.A.M.)

A sympathetic nerve plexus, the plexus vesicalis, in the adventitial coat of the bladder is formed in part by the pelvic nerves which originate from the sacral nerves, and in part by the branches of the plexus hypogastricus. The vesical plexus sends numerous nerves into the muscular coat. A continuation of the nerve plexus, seemingly without nerve cells, however, is found in the connective tissue of the mucous membrane. Here the sensory nerve endings are located. Many fibers penetrate into the epithelium, between the cells of which they form free end branchings provided with varicosities.

URETHRA

Male Urethra. The male urethra has a length of 18 to 20 cm. Three parts can be distinguished in it. The proximal, short part, surrounded by the prostate, is the *pars prostatica.* Here the posterior wall of the urethra forms an elevation, the colliculus seminalis. On its surface in the middle line the *vesicula prostatica* opens; to the right and to the left of this the two slitlike openings of the ejaculatory ducts and the numerous openings of the prostatic gland are located. The second, also very short part (18 mm. long), the *pars membranacea urethrae,* stretches from the apex of the prostate to the bulb of the corpus cavernosum penis. The third stretch, the *pars cavernosa,* about 15 cm. long, passes length-wise through the corpus cavernosum of the urethra.

The prostatic part is lined by the same "transitional" type of epithelium as the bladder. The pars membranacea and the pars cavernosa are lined by a stratified or pseudostratified columnar epithelium. Patches of stratified squamous epithelium are common in the cavernous parts; in the terminal enlarged part of the canal, the fossa navicularis, stratified squamous epithelium occurs as a rule. In the surface epithelium occasional mucous goblet cells may be found. Intraepithelial cysts containing a colloid-like substance are common. Lymphocytes migrating through the epithelium are rare.

The lamina propria mucosae is a loose connective tissue with abundant elastic networks; no separate submucous layer can be distinguished. This connective tissue contains numerous scattered bundles of smooth muscle, mainly longitudinally directed. In the outer layers, however, circular bundles are also present. The lamina propria has no distinct papillae; the latter appear only in the fossa navicularis. The membranous portion of the urethra is surrounded by a mass of striated muscle, a part of the urogenital diaphragm.

The surface of the mucous membrane of

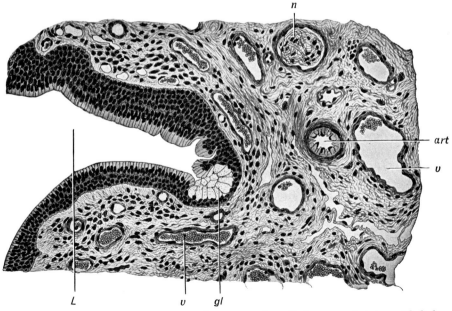

Fig. 28–21.   Section of cavernous part of male human urethra. *L,* lacuna; *gl,* intra-epithelial group of glandular cells; *v,* veins; *art,* artery; *n,* encapsulated sensory nerve ending. 165 ×. (A.A.M.)

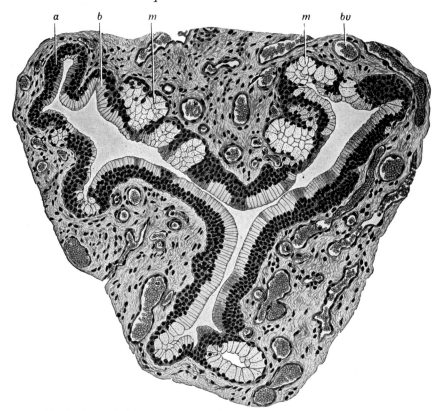

Fig. 28–22. Urethral gland (gland of Littré) from human pars cavernosa urethrae. *a,* darkly staining, stratified columnar epithelium; *b,* epithelium with clear cells; *m,* outpocketings with clear mucous
cells; *bv,* blood vessels. 165 ×. (A.A.M.)

the urethra shows many recesses, the *lacunae
of Morgagni.* These outpocketings continue
into deeper, branching tubules, the *glands of
Littré;* the larger ones among them are found
especially on the dorsal surface of the cavernous portion of the urethra. They run
obliquely in the lamina propria and are directed with their blind end toward the root
of the penis; they sometimes penetrate far
into the spongy body. The glands of Littré
are lined with the same epithelium as the
surface of the mucous membrane, but in
many places this epithelium is transformed
into compact intra-epithelial nests of clear
cells, which give the reaction of mucus. In
old age some of the recesses of the urethral
mucosa may contain concretions similar to
those of the prostate.

The deeper venous plexuses of the urethral mucosa in the pars cavernosa gradually merge into the
cavernous spaces of the spongy body (p. 501). Numerous sensory nerve endings are present in the
urethral mucous membrane.

Female Urethra. The female urethra is 25
to 30 mm. long. The mucous membrane
forms longitudinal folds and is lined with
stratified squamous epithelium; in many
cases, however, pseudostratified columnar
epithelium can be found. Numerous invaginations are formed by the epithelium; the
outpocketings in their wall are lined in many
places with clear mucous cells, as in the
glands of Littré of the male urethra. The
glands may accumulate colloid material in
their cavities or may even contain concretions.

The lamina propria, devoid of papillae, is
a loose connective tissue with abundant elastic networks. It is provided with a highly
developed system of venous plexuses and has,
therefore, a cavernous character (corpus
spongiosum).

The mucous membrane with its veins is
surrounded by a thick mass of smooth muscles; the inner layers of the latter have a
longitudinal, the outer layers a circular, ar-

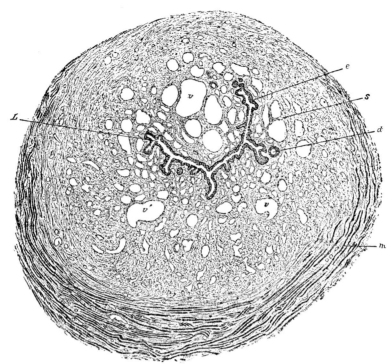

Fig. 28–23. Cross section through urethra of a woman. *L*, lumen; *d*, glandlike lacuna; *e*, epithelium; *m*, cross-striated muscle bundles of the urethral muscle; *s*, lamina propria with small and large veins, *v* (corpus spongiosum). The darker portions of the lamina propria are smooth muscle bundles. 10 ×. (After von Ebner.)

rangement. Distally, the smooth muscles are strengthened by a striated muscle sphincter.

Histogenesis of the Kidney. The independent origin of the nephrons and the collecting tubules in the embryo has been mentioned. The nephrons develop through differentiation of a compact, mesenchyme-like tissue, the *metanephric blastema,* which arises from the mesoderm. The system of excretory ducts arises as a hollow outgrowth of the wolffian duct, in much the same manner as other epithelial glands develop. This outgrowth grows forward in the mesenchyme as the primordium of the ureter and of the renal pelvis. It forms four branches—the primordia of the calices, which end blindly in club-shaped dilatations, each of which forms secondary, tertiary, and so on, branches—the collecting tubules of various orders.

In human embryos of 7 mm. the metanephric blastema adheres to the wall of the dilated pelvis primordium and appears in sections as a semilunar *cap.* As the branches of the pelvis form, the metanephric cap separates into a piece for each branch (human embryos of 9.5 mm.), so that the ampullar dilatation of each branch carries its own metanephric cap.

In human embryos 13 to 19 mm. in length, the edges of the cap covering each blind end of the collecting tubules swell and glide down its sides. As the ampulla divides dichotomously, the metanephrogenic cap is divided equally between the two new ampullae.

The roundish, compact metanephric body soon acquires an eccentric lumen around which its cells become radially arranged; it is now called the metanephric vesicle. Next it stretches and is transformed into an S-shaped tubule which grows rapidly in length and becomes tortuous. It is the future nephron. One end of it coalesces with, and opens into, the neighboring collecting tubule. The other end enlarges, flattens slightly, and is invaginated by a tuft of capillaries from a branch of the renal artery. In this way the malpighian or renal corpuscle is formed with its capsule and glomerulus. In the meantime the collecting tubules continue to grow toward the periphery and to branch dichotomously, still keeping their metanephrogenic caps.

Succeeding generations of nephrons with their renal corpuscles are added to the branching tree of the collecting tubules, until the whole metanephric blastema is exhausted. This continues in the human fetus throughout the latter period of intra-uterine life and comes to its end six or eight days after birth.

When the glomerulus invaginates the wall of the capsule of Bowman, the visceral epithelium is much thicker than the parietal. Later, both layers become simple squamous epithelia. Soon after the S-shaped tubule of the nephron becomes connected with the collecting tubule, the histological differentiation of the different parts of the nephron begins. The proximal part, adjacent to the capsule, becomes tortuous, and its epithelium develops a glandular character, increases in height, and its cytoplasm stains with

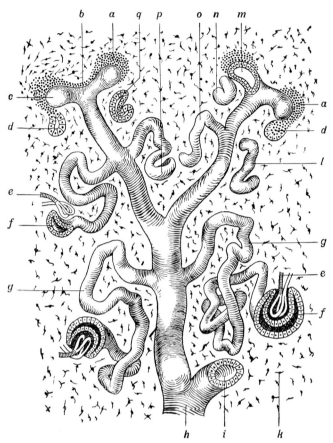

Fig. 28–24. Diagram of development of metanephros. *a,* metanephrogenic tissue capping ampulla of collecting tubule; *b,* ⊤-shaped branching of growing end of collecting tubule; *c,* enlarged blind end of same (ampulla); *d,* primordium of uriniferous tubule just formed from metanephrogenic tissue; *e,* vessel which forms the glomerulus; *f,* capsule of Bowman cut open; *g,* uriniferous tubule in later stage of development; *h,* collecting tubule; *i,* cross section of same; *k,* connective tissue; *l,* uriniferous tubule before establishment of a connection with the collecting tubule; *m,* ampulla of collecting tubule cut open; *n,* primordium of uriniferous tubule just separated from metanephrogenic tissue; *o,* newly formed uriniferous tubule which has just become connected with collecting tubule (stage immediately following *l*); *p,* spoon-shaped enlargement of blind end of uriniferous tubule—capsule of Bowman; *q,* primordium of uriniferous tubule just separated from metanephrogenic tissue (same as *n*), cut open. (Modified after Corning.)

acid dyes. The following stretch of the tubule forms a loop, which slips out of the coils formed by the convoluted tubule and extends toward the renal pelvis. It is forced out of the tubular convolute surrounding the renal corpuscle, because the initial part of the future distal convolution early becomes attached to the glomerulus and consequently cannot be removed from this place as the nephron grows in length. The epithelium of the collecting tubules soon acquires its typical clear appearance; this differentiation begins in the deeper parts, which are nearer to the pelvis, and gradually extends peripherally.

The terminal branches of the collecting tubules and the nephrons may sometimes miss each other and remain disconnected. In such cases the convoluted tubules with their renal corpuscles continue for some time to elaborate urine and, having no outlet, are gradually transformed into cysts. The cystic kidney is a not uncommon abnormality of development.

REFERENCES

Abell, R. G., and Page, I. H.: The effects of renal hypertension on the vessels of the ears of rabbits. J. Exper. Med., *75:*673, 1942.

Bensley, R. R., and Bensley, R. D.: The structure of the renal corpuscle. Anat. Rec., *47:*147, 1930.

Chambers, R., and Kempton, R. T.: Indications of function of the chick mesonephros in tissue culture with phenol red. J. Cell. & Comp. Physiol., *3:*131, 1933.

Christensen, K.: Renal changes in the albino rat on low choline and choline-deficient diets. Arch. Path., *34:*633, 1942.

Edwards, J. G.: Studies on aglomerular and glomerular kidneys. Am. J. Anat., *42:*75, 1928. The vascular pole of the glomerulus in the kidney of vertebrates. Anat. Rec., *76:*381, 1940.

Ellinger, R., and Hirt, A.: Mikroskopische Untersuchungen an lebenden Organen. II. Zur Funktion der Froschniere. Arch. f. exp. Path., *145:*193, 1929.

Flexner, L. B.: Biochemical changes associated with onset of secretory activity in the metanephros of the fetal pig. The cytochrome oxidase-cytochrome system and oxidation-reduction potentials. J. Biol. Chem., *131:*703, 1939.

Gersh, I.: Histochemical studies on the mammalian kidney. II. The glomerular elimination of uric acid in the rabbit. Anat. Rec., *58:*369, 1934. The correlation of structure and function in the developing mesonephros and metanephros. Contrib. Embryol., Carnegie Inst., *26:*35, 1937.

Goormaghtigh, N.: Existence of an endocrine gland in the media of the renal arterioles. Proc. Soc. Exper. Biol. & Med., *42:*688, 1939.

Hall, V.: Further Studies of the Normal Structure of the Renal Glomerulus. Proc. 6th Annual Conf. on The Nephritic Syndrome. J. Metcoff, Editor, 1955.

Heidenhain, R.: Physiologie der Absonderungsvorgänge. Hermann's Hand. der Physiologie, Leipzig. 1883.

Höber, R., and Briscoe-Woolley, P. M.: Conditions determining the selective secretion of dyestuffs by the isolated frog kidney. J. Cell. & Comp. Physiol., *15:*35, 1940.

Huber, G. C.: Renal Tubules, in Cowdry's Special Cytology. 2d ed. New York, *2:*933, 1932.

Kirkmann, H., and Stowell, R. E.: Renal filtration surface in the albino rat. Anat. Rec., *82:*373, 1942.

Longley, J. B., and Fisher, E. R.: Alkaline phosphatase and the periodic acid Schiff reaction in the proximal tubule of the vertebrate kidney: a study in segmental differentiation. Anat. Rec., *120:*1, 1954.

Ludwig, C.: Von der Niere. Stricker's Handbuch der Gewebelehre, 1871, Vol. 1, p. 489.

MacCallum, D. B.: The bearing of degenerating glomeruli on the problem of the vascular supply of the mammalian kidney. Am. J. Anat., *65:*69, 1939.

Möllendorff, W. v.: Der Exkretionsapparat. Handb. d. mikr. Anat. (v. Möllendorff), (7)[1], 1, 1930.

Noll, A.: Die Exkretion (Wirbeltiere). Handb. d. vergl. Physiol. (Winterstein), (2)[2], 760, 1924.

Oliver, J.: New Directions in Renal Morphology: A Method, Its Results and Its Future. Harvey Lectures, Series 40, 102, 1944–45.

Pease, D. C.: Electron microscopy of the vascular bed of the kidney cortex. Anat. Rec., *121:*701, 1955. Electron microscopy of the tubular cells of the kidney cortex. Anat. Rec., *121:*723, 1955.

Peirce, E. C.: Renal lymphatics. Anat. Rec., *90:*315, 1944.

Peter, K.: Untersuchungen über Bau und Entwickelung der Niere. Jena, 1909, 1927.

Piel, C. F., Dong, L., Modern, F. W. S., Goodman, J. R., and Moore, R.: The glomerulus in experimental renal disease in rats as observed by light and electron microscopy. J. Exp. Med., *102:*573, 1955.

Policard, A.: Le tube urinaire des mammifères. Rev. gén. d'histologie, Lyons, 1908.

Rhodin, J.: Correlation of Ultrastructural Organization and Function in Normal and Experimentally Changed Proximal Convoluted Tubule Cells of the Mouse Kidney. Stockholm, Aktiebolaget Godvil, 1954.

Richards, A. N., and Walker, A. M.: Methods of collecting fluid from known regions of the renal tubules of amphibia and of perfusing the lumen of a single tubule. Am. J. Physiol., *118:*111, 1937, and following papers; Processes of Urine Formation. Proc. Roy. Soc., London, S. B., No. 844, *126:*398, 1938.

Schloss, G.: The juxtaglomerular E-cells of rat kidneys in diuresis and antidiuresis, after adrenalectomy and hypophysectomy, and in avitaminosis A, D and E. Acta Anatomica, *6:*80, 1948.

Sjöstrand, F. S., and Rhodin, J.: The ultrastructure of the proximal convoluted tubules of the mouse kidney as revealed by high resolution electron microscopy. Exp. Cell Research, *4:*426, 1953.

Smith, H. W.: The Kidney. New York, Oxford University Press, 1951.

Spargo, B.: Kidney changes in hypokalemic alkalosis in the rat. J. Lab. & Clin. Med., *43:*802, 1954.

Symposium: Histochemistry and kidney structure. J. Histochem. & Cytochem., *3:*243, 1955.

Walker, A. M., Bott, P. A., Oliver, J., and MacDowell, M. C.: The collection and analysis of fluid from single nephrons of the mammalian kidney. Am. J. Physiol., *134:*580, 1941.

Yamada, E.: The fine structure of the renal glomerulus of the mouse. J. Biophys. Biochem. Cytol., *1:*551, 1955.

Zimmermann, K. W.: Ueber den Bau des Glomerulus der Säugetiere, Weitere Mitteilungen. Zeit. f. mikr.-anat. Forsch., *32:*176, 1933.

CHAPTER 29

Male Genital System

THE MALE reproductive system consists of the testes, a complex system of excretory ducts with their auxiliary glands, and the penis.

THE TESTIS

The testis is a compound tubular gland surrounded by a firm, thick white capsule, the albuginea testis—a typical fibrous membrane. At the posterior edge of the organ, the thickening of the capsule projects into the gland as the *mediastinum testis*. From the mediastinum thin partitions, the *septula testis*, extend radially to the capsule and divide the organ into about 250 conical compartments, the *lobuli testis*, which converge with their apices toward the mediastinum. As the septula are interrupted in many places, the lobules intercommunicate, especially in their peripheral portions.

The cavity of each lobule contains the terminal portions of the seminiferous tubules. These are 30 to 70 cm. long and 150 to 250 microns in diameter. Their combined length in man is estimated at 250 meters. One to three of them occupy a lobule. They have an extremely tortuous course, rarely branch, and are called the *convoluted seminiferous tubules* (Fig. 29–22). The tubules in adjacent lobules may be connected by loops. The spermia are formed in the convoluted tubules. The testes are suspended in the scrotum by the spermatic cords. Each of these contains the excretory duct (*ductus deferens*), blood vessels and nerves supplying the testis on that side of the body. The *epididy-mis,* an elongated body attached to the posterior surface of the testis, contains the proximal parts of the excretory duct system of this organ.

The anterior and lateral surfaces of each testis and epididymis are surrounded by a cleftlike serous cavity, a detached part of the peritoneal cavity, in the dorsal wall of which the testes develop in the embryo before descending into the scrotum. The wall of this cavity, the *tunica vaginalis propria testis,* comprises an outer parietal, and an inner visceral, layer. At the posterior edge of the testis, where the epididymis is attached and the blood vessels and nerves enter the organ, the parietal layer is reflected into the visceral layer. After removal of the parietal layer, the *visceral coat* covering the testis appears as a free, smooth surface, lined with mesothelium. This is the remnant of the germinal epithelium which covers the primordium of the gonad in the embryo and gives rise to the glandular tissue of the testis. The *tunica vaginalis propria* enables the testis, which is sensitive to pressure, to glide freely in its envelopes. Obliterations of the serous cavity of the tunica vaginalis may cause atrophy of the testis.

SEMINIFEROUS EPITHELIUM

In the adult the convoluted seminiferous tubule is lined by the complex seminiferous epithelium with its two kinds of cells. The first are nutrient and supporting elements— the *sustentacular cells* (*of Sertoli*). The others, forming the vast majority, are the *sex* (*germ* or *spermatogenic*) cells, which, through proliferation and complex transformations, furnish the mature spermia.

Cells of Sertoli. In a tubule with active spermatogenesis the Sertoli cells are slender, pillar-like elements perpendicular to the base-

Page 476

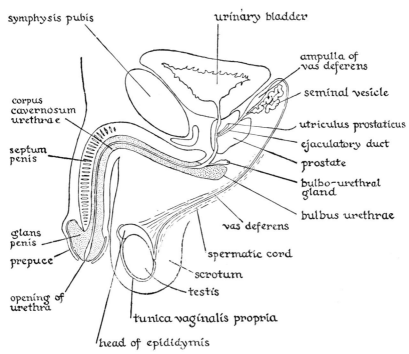

symphysis pubis

urinary bladder

ampulla of vas deferens

seminal vesicle

corpus cavernosum urethrae

utriculus prostaticus

ejaculatory duct

septum penis

prostate

bulbo-urethral gland

bulbus urethrae

vas deferens

glans penis

prepuce

spermatic cord

scrotum

testis

opening of urethra

tunica vaginalis propria

head of epididymis

Fig. 29–1. Diagrammatic median section of male sexual apparatus. (Redrawn from Eberth, slightly modified.)

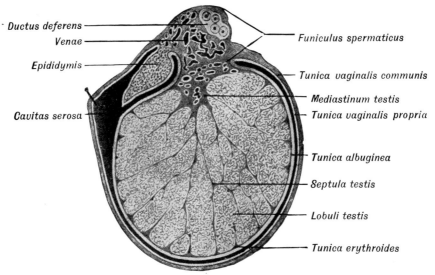

Ductus deferens

Venae

Funiculus spermaticus

Epididymis

Tunica vaginalis communis

Mediastinum testis

Tunica vaginalis propria

Cavitas serosa

Tunica albuginea

Septula testis

Lobuli testis

Tunica erythroides

Fig. 29–2. Cross section of human testis with its envelopes. 2 ×. (After Eberth.)

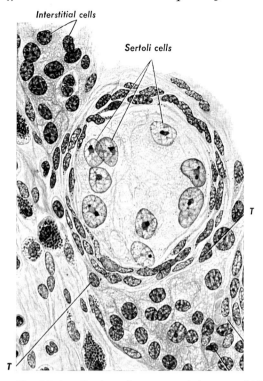

Interstitial cells

Sertoli cells

T

T

Fig. 29–3. Portion of seven months' cryptorchid testis of an adult guinea pig stained vitally with lithium carmine several days before death. The spermatogenic cells have disappeared, and the tubules are filled with a syncytium of Sertoli cells; the interstitial cells do not store carmine, in contrast to the dye-storing macrophages; *T*, transition from mesenchymal cells to interstitial cells. Hematoxylin stain. 490 ×. (After Esaki.)

ment membrane, to which they are attached. They are separated from one another at fairly regular intervals by the densely crowded spermatogenic cells.

The outlines of the sustentacular cells cannot be seen distinctly, and there is a widespread opinion that the spermatogenic cells are embedded in a continuous "Sertolian syncytium." However, in sections parallel to the basement membrane, the bases of the Sertoli cells are sometimes seen as distinctly outlined, polygonal areas. In pathological conditions, when the spermatogenic cells degenerate and disappear to a large extent, the lumen of the depleted seminiferous tubules appears surrounded by a loose protoplasmic network with scattered Sertoli nuclei and the few spermatogenic cells which escaped destruction. Occasionally a Sertoli cell may round off and float in the lumen, where it

may phagocytose degenerating spermatogenic cells or spermia.

The characteristic nucleus of the Sertoli cell has an oval shape and an average size of 9 by 12 microns. In the human testis it is usually at some distance from the basement membrane with its long axis directed radially. The membrane of the Sertoli nucleus is usually wrinkled, and the folds often extend deep into the interior of the nucleus (Fig. 29–5). This is probably not a sign of amitotic division. The vesicular nucleus is in striking contrast to the nuclei of the spermatogenic cells. The nucleus contains a large, compound nucleolus which consists of an oval, central acidophile part and of one to three small, round basophile granules.

The cytoplasm of the Sertoli cells in fixed preparations has a loose reticular structure. It contains small mitochondria, wavy fibrils, granules staining with iron hematoxylin, and lipoid droplets which cause the brown color of the sectioned surface of the fresh testis and are supposed to be an evidence of the nutrient activity of these cells. In the human testis each Sertoli cell contains one spindle-shaped crystalloid near the nucleus.

At certain periods during spermatogenesis, the Sertoli cells enter temporarily into an intimate connection with the developing spermatogenic cells.

Under normal conditions the Sertoli cells are never seen to divide either mitotically or amitotically. They are highly resistant to various noxious factors which easily destroy the spermatogenic cells.

Spermatogenesis. *General Remarks.* The testis produces by mitosis large numbers of spermatogonia from which the mature germ cells are derived by two successive processes, the first nuclear and the second primarily cytoplasmic. The first (meiosis) results in cells with half the somatic number of chromosomes in their (haploid) nuclei. In the second process the spermatids formed by meiosis undergo transformation into highly differentiated spermatozoa.

As a rule the earliest generations of spermatogenic cells are near the basement membrane of the seminiferous tubule, while the more mature forms line the lumen. The cells from which spermatogenesis starts are called *spermatogonia.* They divide mitotically in the *period of proliferation.* Some of the sper-

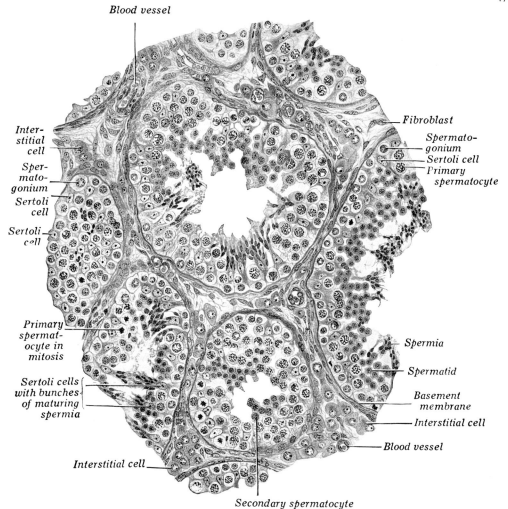

Blood vessel

Fibroblast

Inter-
stitial
cell

Spermato-
gonium

Sertoli cell

Sper-
mato-
gonium

Primary
spermatocyte

Sertoli
cell

Sertoli
cell

Primary
spermat-
ocyte in
mitosis

Spermia

Spermatid

Sertoli cells
with bunches
of maturing
spermia

Basement
membrane

Interstitial cell

Blood vessel

Interstitial cell

Secondary spermatocyte

Fig. 29–4. Human testis (from operation). The transections of the tubules show various stages of spermatogenesis. 170 ×. (A.A.M.)

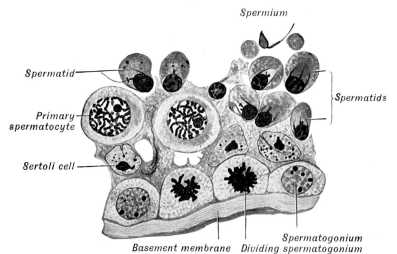

Spermium

Spermatid

Spermatids

Primary
spermatocyte

Sertoli cell

Basement membrane   Dividing spermatogonium

Spermatogonium

Fig. 29–5. Human testis, from young adult; seminiferous epithelium with mitoses of spermatogonia. The spermatids show a caudal sheath. Iron-hematoxylin stain. 750 ×. (A.A.M.)

matogonia persist as such along the inner surface of the basement membrane and by their continued multiplication are the source of the countless spermia produced during the life of the individual.

In the *period of growth* each spermatogonium gradually increases in size, and its nucleus changes markedly. This growth causes a shifting of the cells toward the lu-

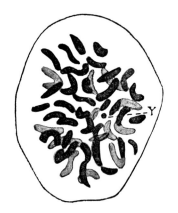

Fig. 29–6. Human spermatogonial plate, showing forty-eight chromosomes. Iron-hematoxylin stain. 3600 ×. (After Evans and Swezy.)

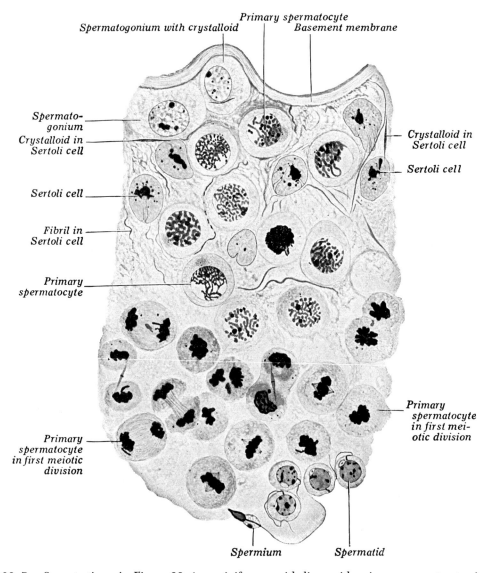

Fig. 29–7. Same testis as in Figure 29–4; seminiferous epithelium with primary spermatocytes in first meiotic division. Iron-hematoxylin stain. 750 ×. (A.A.M.)

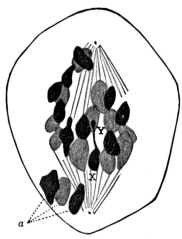

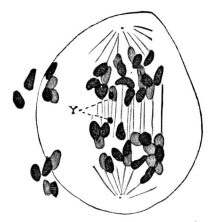

Fig. 29–8. Spindle of human primary sperma-tocyte, showing twenty-four chromosomes. The chromosomes at *a* were behind the others and were drawn outside the spindle for clearness. Iron-hema-toxylin stain. 3600 ×. (After Evans and Swezy.)

Fig. 29–9. Anaphase of human secondary sper-matocyte, showing the two small Y chromosomes—the last to divide. There are twenty-four chromo-somes in each group. Iron-hematoxylin stain. 3600 ×. (After Evans and Swezy.)

men of the tubule. The growing cell is known as a *primary spermatocyte.* When it has reached its full development, the *period of maturation* begins, and the primary sper-matocyte divides into two new cells—the *sec-ondary spermatocytes.* Each secondary sper-matocyte soon divides, giving rise to two *spermatids.* By individual transformations they become *spermia.*

The two divisions leading from one pri-mary spermatocyte to four spermatids differ from the common somatic mitoses and are called maturation divisions or "meiotic divi-sions." Through them the nucleus of each spermatid receives only one half of the so-matic number of chromosomes typical for the respective animal species (forty-eight in man).

Spermatocytogenesis. The nucleus in the earlier generations of mammalian spermato-gonia contains dustlike particles of chromatin and a round body that stains like chromatin. Near the nucleus is a thin *crystalloid body* smaller than that of the Sertoli cells. The later generations of spermatogonia are smaller and are found either at or near the basement membrane. The crystalloid seems to be ab-sent. In the nucleus the chromatin is ar-ranged in darkly staining flakes on the inner surface of the membrane. These differences between the earlier and the later generations of spermatogonia are not distinct in man.

In the human spermatogonium there are

twenty-three pairs of chromosomes of varying sizes and shapes and one pair of hetero-chromosomes (X-Y). The X and Y chromo-somes in man were first accurately figured by Painter (1923).

The changes undergone by a spermato-gonium developing into a primary spermato-cyte (period of growth) represent a gradual preparation for the meiotic divisions and the reduction of chromatin.

The primary spermatocytes occupy the middle zone of the seminiferous epithelium and are large, spherical or oval cells. The nucleus undergoes a series of transformations which lead to the first meiotic division. The chromatin forms long, thin threads which conjugate two by two, probably side by side, and form a haploid number of bivalent chro-mosomes (*parasynapsis*), each consisting of two synaptic mates. Thus in the human pri-mary spermatocyte there are twenty-four bi-valent chromosomes, one of which is X-Y (Fig. 29–8). In mammals the history of their development is not as clear as in many invertebrates.

In the first meiotic division of the human spermatocytes each bivalent chromosome, in-cluding the X-Y chromosome, separates into its two constituent chromosomes along the line of their previous conjugation. As a re-sult, of the two secondary spermatocytes orig-inating from a dividing primary spermato-cyte, one will contain twenty-three ordinary

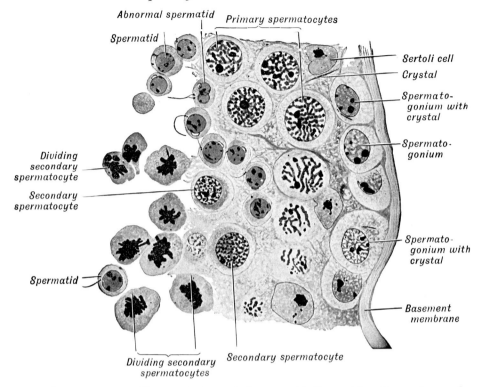

Fig. 29–10. Same testis as in Figure 29–4; seminiferous epithelium with mitoses of secondary spermatocytes—second meiotic division. 750 ×. (A.A.M.)

chromosomes and an X chromosome, while the other will have twenty-three chromosomes and the Y. The secondary spermatocytes are smaller than the primary.

The difference between mitosis and the first meiotic division is essentially this: In a somatic mitosis the individual chromosome splits and the half chromosomes separate, while in the first meiotic division whole chromosomes, the *synaptic mates* (the halves of the bivalent chromosomes), move away from each other toward the poles.

In mammals the interval between the two meiotic divisions is unknown. In the second meiotic division the spindle is more slender than in the first mitosis and extends nearly to the surface of the cell. Each of the twenty-four chromosomes, which are now small and dumbbell-shaped, divides into halves by longitudinal splitting. Thus the second meiotic division corresponds in principle to an ordinary but haploid somatic mitosis. Each of the relatively small daughter cells of the secondary spermatocytes, the spermatids, has a

nucleus about 5 to 6 microns in diameter containing several chromatin granules. Half of the spermatids have the X chromosome and half the Y.

The large attraction sphere (idiozome) is surrounded by the Golgi apparatus. The idiozome separates from the centriole as a darkly staining spherical body with a central clear area—the *acroblast*. The centriole later divides into a distal centriole touching the cell surface and a proximal one deeper in the cytoplasm.

The details of spermatid formation and the phenomena of spermiogenesis are not completely known for human material. For a more general and complete idea of the process and its genetic importance, a comparative study of the testis of various animal species, including invertebrates, is necessary.

Spermiogenesis. The spermatids are the last generation of spermatogenic cells. They do not divide, and each undergoes a long series of peculiar transformations, to form the mature spermium. The following descrip-

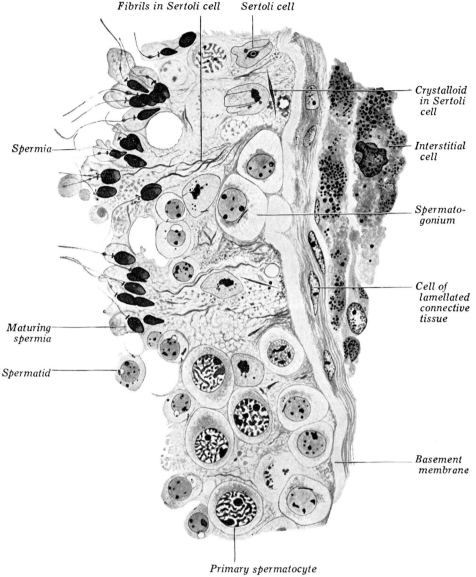

Fig. 29–11.   Same testis as in Figure 29–4; seminiferous epithelium with bunches of maturing spermia, connected with Sertoli cells. Iron-hematoxylin stain. 750 ×. (A.A.M.)

tion is based largely on iron-hematoxylin preparations studied with the light microscope. These observations are being extended and corrected by investigations with the electron microscope. (Compare Figs. 29–12 and 29–13, 29–14 and 29–15.)

The most striking changes at the beginning of spermiogenesis concern the centrioles and the acroblast. From the distal centriole, a thin filament grows out (Fig. 29–12), the primordium of the axial thread of the tail of the spermium. It grows longer and thicker and straightens out. In the interior of the clear central area of the acroblast a small, darkly staining, round body—the *acrosome*—appears. Then the acroblast, flattening against the nucleus, becomes hemispherical, and the acrosome touches the nuclear membrane. The darker peripheral layer of the acroblast (Golgi material) recedes into the protoplasm as the *acroblast remnant* and later disintegrates. The clear layer, covering the acrosome, extends beyond the equator of the nucleus. In the human spermium it forms a delicate

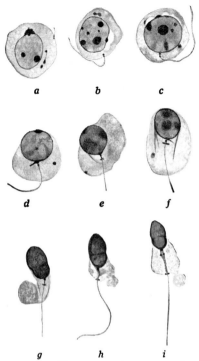

Fig. 29–12. Nine successive stages of spermiogenesis from human testis; explanation in the text (p. 483). Iron-hematoxylin stain. 1500 ×. (A.A.M.)

membrane, the *head cap,* which covers the anterior pole of the nucleus, the head of the future spermium.

The nucleus moves to the periphery of the cell body (Fig. 29–12). Then it assumes a slightly flattened, oval form, while the chromatin condenses into a darkly staining homogeneous mass. In this way the *head of the spermium* is formed.

During these transformations of the nucleus the temporary manchette, or caudal sheath, appears (Figs. 29–12 and 29–13). It is a thin membrane which has the form of a wide tube or funnel. It begins at the equator of the nucleus and extends a short distance backward, where it ends with a free edge in the cytoplasm. Its significance is obscure, and it soon disappears.

The centrioles undergo important transformations. The proximal centriole becomes attached to the posterior pole of the nucleus and is transformed into the anterior knob of the neck of the spermium. The distal centriole divides into two parts. Its anterior part constitutes the posterior knob of the neck.

The axial thread remains connected with this body. The posterior part of the distal centriole becomes a ring surrounding the axial thread (Fig. 29–12). It moves along the axial filament away from the posterior knob until it reaches the surface of the cell body, where it marks the posterior limit of the *middle piece* of the spermium.

During the migration of the centrioles toward the nucleus the extracellular part of the axial filament grows in length and finally reaches the size of the tail of the spermium. On its surface an extremely thin sheath is formed; it is missing on the end section of the tail.

The cytoplasm of the spermatid gradually recedes from the nucleus and acquires an elongated, pearlike shape. It contains, besides some mitochondria, the disintegrating acroblast remnant, fat and lipoid droplets and heavily staining granules of undefinable nature. For some time the cytoplasm remains attached to the middle piece of the young spermium; it probably furnishes an external sheath for this part. Finally, it is sloughed off as an irregular round mass and disintegrates in the lumen of the seminiferous tubule. A part of this is carried into the semen as granular detritus. The major part, however, seems to be absorbed and utilized by the Sertoli cells. A small drop of cytoplasm remains attached to the middle piece of the spermium for a long time.

Mature Spermium. The mature human spermium consists of a head, a connecting or middle piece, and a tail. In ordinary sections the spermia do not show any particular inner structure. For seeing the details, special histological methods, such as iron hematoxylin, and the electron microscope are necessary.

The *head* is a flattened, almond-shaped body measuring 4 to 5 microns in length and 2.5 to 3.5 microns in width. It is a condensed nucleus. The middle piece is of cylindrical or spindle shape and connects the posterior pole of the head with the tail. It has a length of 5 microns and a thickness of 1 micron. The tail has a length of 52 microns. At its anterior end it has the same thickness as the middle piece, but gradually tapers toward the free end. It can be subdivided into the principal part and a short terminal part of extreme thinness.

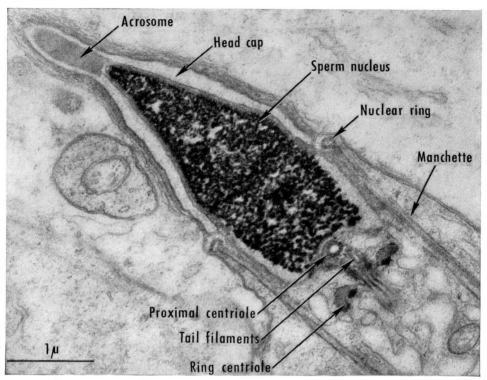

Fig. 29–13. Electron micrograph of late spermatid of cat. Buffered osmic acid fixation. (Courtesy of M. H. Burgos and D. Fawcett.)

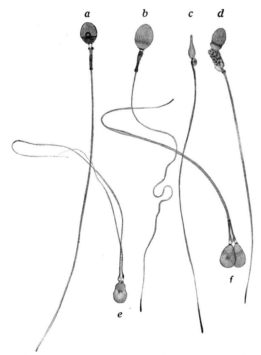

In fresh preparations from the testis the spermia either are motionless or display only a slight motility.

In man, two kinds of spermia are produced in equal numbers—spermia containing in their head the chromatin of twenty-three chromosomes and an X chromosome, and spermia with twenty-three chromosomes and a Y chromosome. All mature egg cells, however, are alike, having twenty-three chromosomes and an X chromosome. The fertilization of an ovum, carrying twenty-four chromosomes—one of which is X—by a spermium with twenty-four chromosomes—one of which is X—results in the formation of a new individual with forty-eight chromosomes (including X-X) in its cells, and is a female. In the case of a spermium with the Y chromosome and an ovum with its twenty-three and X chromosomes, a male individual with forty-six plus X-Y chromosomes in the body

Fig. 29–14. Human spermia (spermatozoa). *a* and *b*, head seen from flat surface; *c*, head seen in profile; in *c* and *d*, a bit of protoplasm remained attached to the middle piece; *e*, abnormal spermium with one head and two tails; *f*, abnormal spermium with two heads and one tail. Iron-hematoxylin stain. 1500 ×. (A.A.M.)

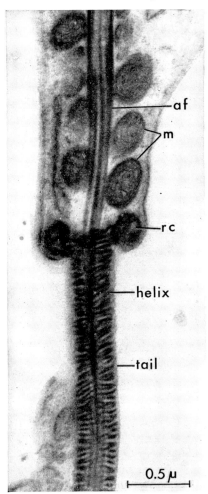

Fig. 29–15. Electron micrograph of mid-piece and beginning of tail of spermium of macaque. Axial filaments (*af*) in the mid-piece continue into the tail. Helix coils around the surface of the tail. *m,* mitochondria, *rc,* ring centriole. Buffered osmic acid fixation. (Courtesy of D. Fawcett.)

cells is produced. Two types of mature, human spermia containing either the X or the Y chromosome have not been described morphologically. In the process of fertilization, the centrioles of the spermium, and especially the anterior knob, are supposed to furnish the egg with the active cytocentrum needed for its cleavage divisions.

Spermatogenetic Wave. The successive phases of spermatogenesis are arranged in the seminiferous tubules according to certain definite rules. The least developed elements are always located nearer the basement membrane, the most developed nearer the lumen. This movement is due to growth pressure.

The spermatogonia remain adjacent to the basement membrane. The primary spermatocytes, in the early stages of the growth period, may keep this position for a while. The larger cells move toward the lumen and form a second, third and even fourth layer of cells. The spermatids form the inner layer of the epithelium and are usually found in large groups, all the cells of which, originating from a single spermatogonium, show the same stage of development. The same typical arrangement in groups is characteristic of the first and second meiotic divisions. The transformations of all cells of one generation occur more or less synchronously.

During spermiogenesis the spermatids become closely connected with the Sertoli cells. When the spermia have reached a certain degree of maturity and their cytoplasm has been sloughed off, the whole group leaves the Sertoli cell. After a period of inactivity the same Sertoli cell receives a fresh crop of spermatids.

In the human testis, spermatogenesis, having started at puberty, continues without interruption during the whole period of sexual activity. This also holds true for domesticated mammals, whose sexual activity is not distinctly regulated by the seasons of the year.

There are, as a rule, four generations in a given cross section—spermatogonia, spermatocytes (one or both types), spermatids, and spermia. But the degree of maturity of each generation varies in the different combinations. As a rule, a cross section of a tubule shows the same combination of generations along its periphery. In following a *longitudinal section* of an isolated and straightened tubule, one can see the epithelium changing continuously. This depends on the fact that spermatogenesis is a wavelike activity proceeding along the tubule in the direction from the excretory ducts (the tubuli recti) to the periphery of the testis. In the rat the length of the spermatogenetic wave has been found to be 32 mm. The time necessary for the development of a spermium from a spermatogonium is estimated at twenty days for the rat.

The regular succession of generations of spermatogenic cells and the definite phases of the spermatogenetic wave has been worked out mainly for the testis of the rat, which is a classical object for studies on spermato-

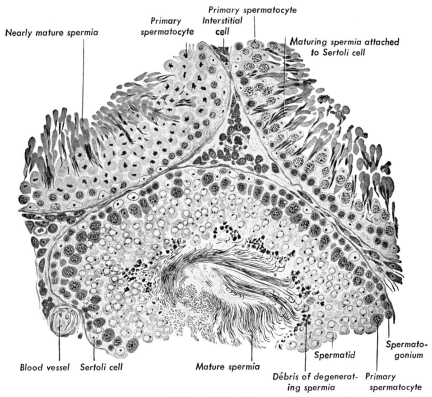

Fig. 29–16. Testis of rat. The transections of the tubules show various stages of spermatogenesis. 190 ×.
(A.A.M.)

genesis. In other mammals and especially in man the succession of the generations and the combinations of the different cell types are much less regular. Shorter or longer stretches in the tubules may be in resting condition and not show any spermatogenesis. They alternate with relatively small patches of active epithelium.

In seasonally breeding mammals active spermatogenesis, having begun at puberty, is repeated and discontinued periodically for the rest of their lives. Each time it continues only during the period of rut, at the end of which the spermatogenic cells degenerate and are cast off. Concomitantly, the seminiferous tubules shrink, and contain only Sertoli cells and some few spermatogonia. In this condition they resemble in structure the tubules of a prepubertal testis. At the beginning of a new period of sexual activity, spermatogonia multiply and rapidly produce the various generations of spermatogenic cells, while the Sertoli cells are compressed and become inconspicuous.

In the lower vertebrates, these cyclic changes of the testis in connection with the seasons are still more prominent.

Degenerative and Regenerative Phenomena. In an active human testis the tubules often contain in their lumen masses of degenerating spermatogenic cells which finally disintegrate into granular and fatty detritus. This is not pathologic unless it exceeds certain limits. The degenerating cells are usually seen close to stretches of active seminal epithelium with normal spermatogenesis in full progress.

Often, abnormal spermatogenic cells can be found. In the spermatogonia this manifests itself usually by an excessive hypertrophy. Among the spermatocytes giant forms are also common, as well as cells with two or more nuclei, sometimes of unequal size. They arise through fusion or abnormal mitosis. The spermatids often fuse to form multinucleated giant cells. Spermatids with two or even more nuclei may continue their development; thus monster spermia with two or many tails

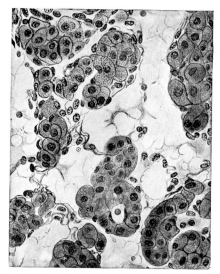

Fig. 29–17. Testis of an eighteen months crypt-orchid guinea pig. Note the groups of interstitial cells, absence of seminiferous tubules. The interstitial connective tissue is slightly edematous. (Drawn by Miss A. Nixon from a preparation of C. R. Moore.)

and sometimes with one tail and two heads may arise.

The degenerating and monster spermatogenic cells are carried, with the mature spermia, into the epididymis, where their substance is perhaps reabsorbed by the epithelium of the excretory ducts.

The sex cells of the seminiferous epithelium are sensitive to noxious factors of various kinds. In pathological conditions of general (infectious diseases, alcoholism, dietary deficiencies) or local (injury, inflammation) character, and under the influence of mental depression, the degenerative changes, especially the formation of multinucleated giant cells by the coalescing spermatids, may become prominent. Exposure of the testis to a sufficient dose of x-rays causes an extensive degeneration of spermatogenic cells and even temporary sterilization. They are also sensitive to high temperature. Even the normal temperature of the body of a mammal is incompatible with their normal development. In the majority of the mammals the testes, in the adult, are lodged in the scrotum, which has a lower temperature than the body. Cryptorchid testes, which remain in the abdomen, never produce mature spermia, and show atrophic tubules containing Sertoli cells with a few scattered spermatogonia. In

experimental cryptorchidism the testis soon shrinks and contains only Sertoli cells and remnants of sex cells; after a long time the tubules may disappear. The seminiferous tubules atrophy in rats fed on a diet lacking vitamin E; they degenerate to a lesser extent in vitamin A deficiency.

In all such cases the Sertoli cells are more resistant than spermatogenic cells. Some of the spermatogonia, however, seem in many cases to remain intact at the basement membrane between the Sertoli elements. Under favorable conditions, when the noxious factor is removed (for instance, on replacing the artificially ectopic testis in the scrotum), a more or less complete regeneration of the seminiferous epithelium from these residual cells may take place. In the seminiferous epithelium regenerating after x-ray sterilization, neoformation of spermatogonia from mitotically dividing Sertoli cells has been described.

In mammals with a short life, spermatogenesis continues until death without change. In man, although spermatogenesis continues far into the senile period, the seminiferous tubules undergo gradual involution with advancing age. A testis of a man older than thirty-five will always show an increasing quantity of scattered atrophic tubules; in the remaining parts of the gland, spermatogenesis may continue without visible alterations. Sometimes in very old persons all the tubules are depleted of spermatogenic cells and contain only atrophic Sertoli cells.

Capsule and the Interstitial Tissue of the Testis. The tunica albuginea, the mediastinum and the septula of the testis consist of dense connective tissue. The mediastinum contains a few smooth muscle fibers. On the inner surface of the albuginea the dense tissue passes into a looser layer containing many blood vessels—the "tunica vasculosa testis." This layer continues into the interstitial tissue which fills the angular spaces between the convoluted tubules.

The seminiferous epithelium rests on the inner surface of a basement membrane which has a faintly fibrillar structure. Externally the basement membrane is strengthened by a layer of lamellated connective tissue. The interstitial tissue contains thin collagenous fibers, blood and lymph vessels, nerves and several types of cells: fibroblasts, macro-

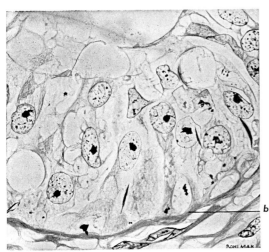

Fig. 29–18. Atrophic seminiferous tubule from otherwise normal testis of thirty-five year old man. *b*, basement membrane. The tubule is lined with Sertoli cells containing crystalloids. Note absence of spermatogenic cells. Formalin. Iron-hematoxylin stain. 615 ×. (From a preparation of H. Okkels.)

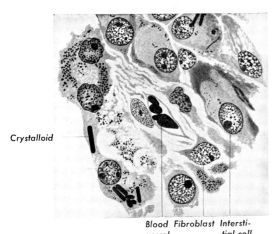

Crystalloid

Blood Fibroblast Interstitial cell
vessel

Fig. 29–19. Human testis from young adult. Groups of interstitial cells with centrioles, darkly stained granular inclusions, and crystalloids. Iron-hematoxylin stain. 650 ×. (A.A.M.)

phages, mast cells and embryonic perivascular elements. The specific interstitial cells (of Leydig) are also present.

Interstitial Cells. These are scattered in the angular spaces between the tubules in compact groups without a definite relation to the blood vessels. Their body, measuring 14 to 21 microns in diameter, is irregularly polyhedral and is often provided with processes. Transitional forms to much smaller, round or elongated cells are common. The

large, spherical or wrinkled nucleus contains coarse chromatin granules, and one or two large nucleoli. Cells with two nuclei are common. Adjacent to the nucleus is a large, clear attraction sphere. It contains centrioles which appear as a group of small round granules or as two rod-shaped bodies. The sphere is surrounded by a Golgi apparatus. The peripheral cytoplasm contains numerous mitochondria. In fresh condition the cytoplasm is filled with refractile granules, many of which react positively to tests for neutral fat and lipids (sometimes cholesterol esters). Some brownish granules are waste pigment (lipofuscin). The most interesting inclusions are rod-shaped crystalloids with rounded or pointed ends (Fig. 29–19). These are characteristic of the human testis, although they are not of constant occurrence and show great variations in size. They are monorefringent, swell in a 10 per cent solution of potassium hydroxide, and are dissolved by hydrochloric acid with pepsin. They are insoluble in 10 per cent hydrochloric, nitric or acetic acid, and in fat solvents.

It seems that the interstitial cells are modified connective tissue cells. In inflammatory lesions of the testis and in tissue cultures they divide mitotically and become fibroblasts. They may increase in number through transformation of spindle-shaped connective tissue elements, probably of embryonic nature, scattered between the tubules and around the blood vessels.

Some authors claim that the interstitial cells of the testis arise from the same source as the elements of the seminiferous epithelium in the tubules; other believe them to be remnants of the epithelium of the tubules of the mesonephros. Groups of interstitial cells may be found in the connective tissue of the epididymis.

The "epithelioid" character of the interstitial cells suggests the possibility of an endocrine glandular function.

Endocrine Function of the Testis. The testis, besides producing spermia, causes the development and maintenance of the "secondary sexual characters" and of the sex impulse. In the developing organism it helps to regulate the growth of the skeleton and of other parts. Castration before puberty delays the cessation of growth of the long bones, and the secondary sexual characters do not

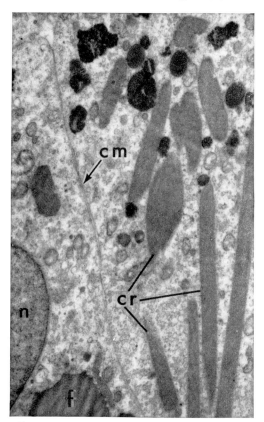

Fig. 29–20. Electron micrograph of section through interstitial cell of testis of cat showing the edge of the nucleus (*n*), fat droplet (*f*), intercellular membrane (*cm*) and characteristic crystals (*cr*). The small dark granules between the crystals are of lipid nature. Buffered osmic acid fixation. 3200 ×. (Courtesy of D. Fawcett.)

Fig. 29–21. Electron micrograph through crystalloid of interstitial cell of testis. Note regularity of the pattern indicating the crystal structure of the large molecules forming the crystal. Buffered osmic acid fixation. (Courtesy of D. Fawcett.)

develop. With castration after puberty, the libido gradually disappears, the secondary sexual characters and the auxiliary sex glands (Figs. 29–31, 29–35) undergo partial involution, and disorders of metabolism eventually appear. The implantation of a testis into such a person may restore normal conditions to a certain extent. In experimental animals the injection of testicular hormone prevents many of these changes, and implantation of a testis may cause the appearance of secondary male characters in a spayed female. This is due to a hormone (testosterone), secreted by the testis. Cancer of the prostate often undergoes marked regression after castration (or treatment with female sex hormones).

Some authors ascribe the production of testosterone to the interstitial cells; others,

to the seminiferous epithelium (spermatogenic and Sertoli cells). A third possibility is, of course, the participation of both elements. Most of the data favor the first hypothesis. Persons with cryptorchid testes display, in most cases, a normal sexual behavior and normal secondary characters; they usually retain their virility, although sterility is the rule. The seminiferous tubules of such males are always atrophic, as a result of the higher temperature in the abdomen. In experimental animals with cryptorchid testes of long duration, the seminiferous tubules seem to disappear completely, leaving large masses of interstitial cells. Such individuals, as a rule, keep their libido, the potentia coeundi, and the secondary sexual characters. Similar results were obtained after ligation of the vas deferens or the ductuli efferentes and after large doses of x-rays. Grafts of testicular tissue into castrated animals are supposed to act through their interstitial cells, which proliferate, while the seminiferous tubules become atrophic. These and many other facts indicate that the male sexual hormone is probably secreted by the interstitial cells rather than by the seminiferous epithelium.

The reciprocal effects of hormones of the hypophysis and testis are discussed in Chapter 15. Here it need be recalled only that the follicle-stimulating hormone (FSH) stimulates spermatogenesis in animals, although not always in man. In the rat, follicle-stimulating hormone has no effect on androgen production. The interstitial cell-stimulating hormone (ICSH or LH) activates the interstitial cells, and this effect is increased if follicle-stimulating hormone is administered at the same time. Hypophysectomy leads to testicular atrophy, which can be restored by the injection of gonadotrophins. Administration of androgen decreases the gonadotrophin level; after castration, gonadotrophin accumulates in the pars distalis of the hypophysis, where the beta cells show characteristic changes, the so-called "castration cells." The influence of the adrenal cortex on the gonads is discussed in Chapter 18.

Blood Vessels, Lymphatics and Nerves of the Testis. The blood supply of the testis is derived mainly from the internal spermatic artery. Some branches penetrate the interior of the gland in the region of the mediastinum, while others run to the anterior side, in or under the albuginea, in the tunica vasculosa. From the mediastinum and from the septula testis, the smaller branches penetrate into the interior of the lobules and break up into capillaries, forming loose networks around the seminiferous tubules. The course of the veins corresponds to that of the arteries. Everywhere in the interstitial tissue between the seminiferous tubules, networks of lymph capillaries can be demonstrated. The nerves, from the plexus spermaticus internus, surround the blood vessels with fine plexuses. The existence of end branches penetrating through the basement membrane into the epithelium of the seminiferous tubules seems doubtful.

EXCRETORY DUCTS

Tubuli Recti and Rete Testis. At the apex of each lobule, its seminiferous tubules join and pass abruptly into the first section of the system of excretory ducts—the *tubuli recti*. These are short and straight and have a diameter of but 20 to 25 microns. They enter the mediastinum testis and form in its dense connective tissue a system of irregular, anastomosing, epithelium-lined cavernous spaces —the *rete testis*.

At the transition of the seminiferous tubules into the tubuli recti the spermatogenic cells disappear and only the Sertoli cells remain. Here they are tall columnar cells, with a cytoplasm containing numerous fat droplets. The cavernous spaces of the rete testis are lined with a cuboidal or squamous epithelium. Its cells are provided with a "central flagellum" and contain fat droplets.

Ductuli Efferentes. At the upper part of the posterior edge of the testis, twelve or more efferent ductules arise from the rete and emerge on the surface of the testis. They measure about 0.6 mm. in diameter and 4 to 6 cm. in length. Through numerous spiral windings and convolutions they form five to thirteen conical bodies about 10 mm. in length—the *vascular cones*. These have their bases toward the free surface of the head of the epididymis and their apices toward the mediastinum testis. They are kept together by connective tissue and constitute part of the head of the epididymis.

The ductuli efferentes have a typical epithelium. Their lumen has a festooned outline, because it is lined by alternating groups of tall and low cells. The latter form "intraepithelial glands," small, cuplike excavations in the thickness of the epithelium, not affecting the basement membrane. The clear cells of these excavations contain pale secretion and pigment granules. There is a brush border and a central flagellum on the free surface. The formation of bleblike outgrowths as a sign of secretory activity has also been described. In animals intravitally stained they contain dye inclusions, presumably by absorption from the lumen. The tall cells usually have a conical form with the broad end toward the lumen. On their free surface are cilia which beat toward the epididymis and move the spermia in this direction. Their cytoplasm stains intensely and contains numerous fat droplets and pigment granules. Often both cell types are distributed irregularly.

Outside the thin basement membrane is a thin layer of circularly arranged smooth muscle cells. In the ducts forming the coni vasculosi, the muscular layer becomes more prominent.

Ductus Epididymis. The winding tubules

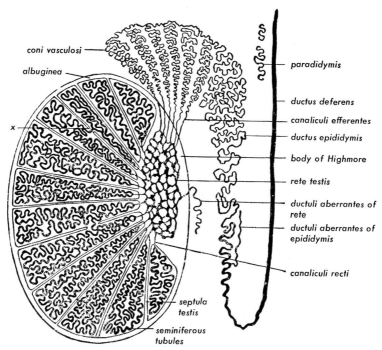

Fig. 29–22. Diagram of arrangement of seminiferous tubules and excretory ducts in the testis and epididymis. *x,* communication between seminiferous tubules of different lobules.

of the vascular cones gradually fuse into the single ductus epididymis (Fig. 29–22). This highly tortuous, long canal (4 to 6 m.) forms, with the surrounding connective tissue, the body and the tail of the epididymis. The duct gradually straightens out and merges into the ductus deferens which has a length of 40 to 45 cm.

In the proximal, convoluted part (the body) the lumen is lined by a tall, pseudostratified columnar epithelium. The cross sections of the duct have a regular, circular outline. On the inner surface of the basement membrane, small angular basal cells containing lipoid droplets form a discontinuous layer. On their free surface the columnar cells carry a tuft of long (30 microns), nonmotile *stereocilia,* kept together by cytoplasm. In the cytoplasm immediately above the nucleus a Golgi apparatus is present. Nearer to the free surface, secretion granules, vacuoles, fat droplets and pigment inclusions are found. They move toward the lumen, leave the cell through the stereocilia, and represent the secretion. In the distal part of the duct the epithelium gradually becomes lower.

The basement membrane is surrounded by a highly developed capillary network and by a circular layer of smooth muscular fibers which probably help to forward the spermia.

Nerves (mostly nonmedullated) form a plexus of fine fibers connected with the muscles of the vessels and of the wall of the duct. Small sympathetic ganglia have also been described.

A number of rudimentary structures are found attached to the testis and epididymis and to the further sections of the excretory duct.

The *appendix testis* (*hydatid Morgagni*) is the remainder of the abdominal end of the duct of Müller. It is located at the upper pole of the testis, near the head of the epididymis, as a small nodule consisting of vascular connective tissue and lined with columnar, sometimes ciliated epithelium. The *appendix epididymis* is believed to be the rudiment of the wolffian body (mesonephros). It is a nodule, 3 by 2 mm., containing a cyst lined with columnar epithelium and connected with the head of the epididymis by a stalk of variable length. The *ductuli aberrantes* are blindly ending epithelial tubules, one in connection with the rete testis, another with the lower part of the ductus epididymis. They are rudiments of the tubules of the mesonephros. The *paradidymis,* also a rudiment of the wolffian body, is a group of coiled epithelial tubules in the connective tissue of the spermatic cord at the level of the head of the epididymis. In some cases, especially in newborn infants, small nodules with the structure of the cortex of the adrenal may be found in the con-

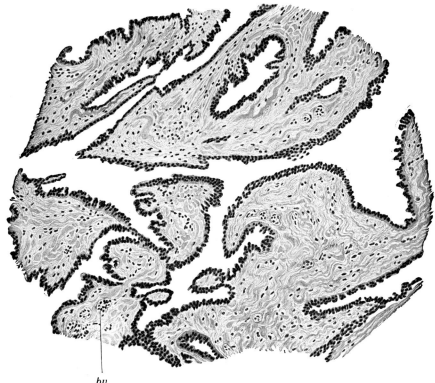

bv

Fig. 29–23. Rete testis, human: *bv*, blood vessel. 140 ×. (A.A.M.)

Ciliated cells   Secreting cells

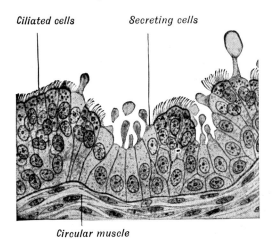

Circular muscle

Fig. 29–24. Part of cross section of human ductus efferens. Groups of ciliated cells alternate with groups of secreting cells. 450 ×. (After Eberth.)

nective tissue of the tail of the epididymis. In the neighborhood of the paradidymis small accumulations of chromaffin tissue have been described.

Ductus Deferens. On passing into the ductus deferens, the duct develops a larger lumen and a thicker wall. Under the basement membrane the lamina propria mucosae

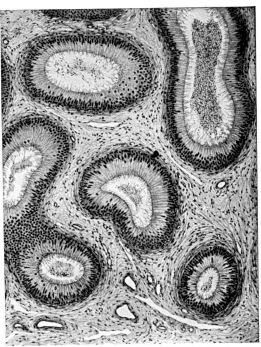

Fig. 29–25. Section of ductus epididymis of a thirty-two year old man. The stereocilia are prominent. The lumens contain spermia. Iron-hematoxylin-chromotrop 2 R. 72 ×. (After Stieve.)

rises in longitudinal folds which cause the deeply festooned outlines seen in cross section. The pseudostratified columnar epithelium is lower than in the epididymis, and the cells usually have stereocilia. The connective tissue of the mucous membrane contains extensive elastic networks. The 1 mm.-thick layer of smooth muscles reaches a high grade of development; it consists of inner and outer longitudinal layers with a powerful circular, intermediate layer. On the periphery there is an adventitial coat of connective tissue. The duct is easily palpable through the thin skin of the scrotum.

The duct is accompanied by loose, longitudinal strands of smooth muscle—musculus cremaster internus—which form a part of the *spermatic cord.* It also contains arteries, the veins of the pampiniform plexus with muscular walls, and nerves of the plexus spermaticus.

The vas deferens, after crossing the ureter, dilates into a spindle-shaped enlargement, the *ampulla.* At the distal end of the latter it forms a large, blind, glandular evagination—the *seminal vesicle.* Then, as the short (19 mm.) and straight *ejaculatory* duct (0.3 mm. in diameter), it pierces the body of another gland, the *prostate,* attached to the bottom of the urinary bladder, and opens by a small slit into the prostatic part of the urethra, on a small thickening of its posterior wall —the *colliculus seminalis* or *verumontanum.*

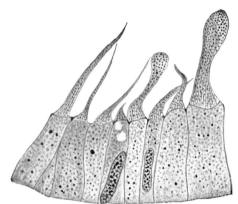

Fig. 29–26.   Section of human ductus epididymis; free surface of epithelium, with stereocilia, discharging secretion. 1000 ×. (Redrawn after M. Heidenhain and F. Werner.)

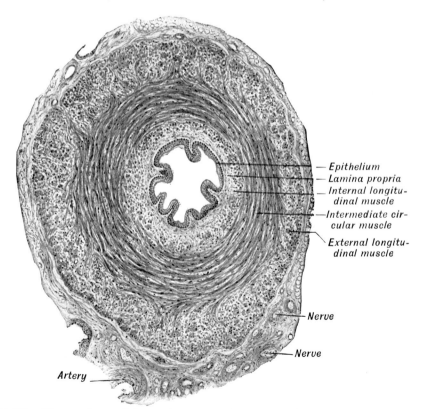

— Epithelium
— Lamina propria
— Internal longitudinal muscle
—Intermediate circular muscle
—External longitudinal muscle
— Nerve
— Nerve
Artery

Fig. 29–27.   Human ductus deferens in cross section. 30 ×. (After Schaffer.)

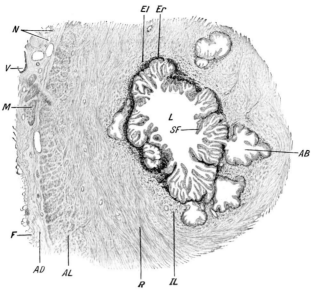

Fig. 29–28. Portion of cross section through ampulla of human ductus deferens. *AB*, glandlike out-pouchings of main lumen; *L*, lumen; *AD*, adventitia; *AL*, external longitudinal muscle layer; *El*, longitudinal and, *Er*, ring-shaped elastic fibers; *F*, fat tissue; *IL*, internal longitudinal muscle layer; *M*, smooth muscle bundles in adventitia; *N*, nerves; *R*, circular muscle layer; *SF*, folds of mucosa; *V*, veins. Orcein stain. 26 ×. (After Schaffer.)

The openings of the ejaculatory ducts are located to the right and to the left of the *utriculus prostaticus,* a blind invagination on the summit of the colliculus.

In the ampulla of the ductus deferens, the mucous membrane with its epithelium is thrown into numerous, thin, irregularly branching folds (Fig. 29–28) which in many places fuse with one another, producing in a section a netlike system of partitions with angular meshes. The epithelium may show signs of secretion. From the excavations between the folds, numerous tortuous, branched outpocketings reach far into the surrounding muscular layer (Fig. 29–28) and are lined with a single layer of columnar, clear cells of glandular nature containing secretion granules. The musculature is much less regularly arranged than in the other parts of the ductus deferens.

Ejaculatory Ducts. The epithelium lining the ejaculatory ducts is a simple or pseudo-stratified columnar epithelium, probably endowed with glandular functions. Its cells contain a large quantity of yellow pigment granules. Near the opening of the ducts the epithelium often assumes the structure of "transitional" epithelium. The mucous membrane of the ducts forms many thin folds reaching far into the lumen; its connective tissue is provided with abundant elastic networks. The dorsomedial wall of the ducts contains a series of outpocketings of glandular nature, which may be accessory seminal vesicles. The ducts proper are surrounded only by connective tissue.

AUXILIARY GLANDS

The glands associated with the excretory duct of the testis are the seminal vesicles, prostate and bulbo-urethral glands.

Seminal Vesicles. The seminal vesicles are tortuous, elongated, hollow bodies with an irregular, branched lumen and numerous outpocketings. They are evaginations of the ductus deferens and are similar to it in structure. Their wall consists of an external connective tissue sheet with elastic nets, of a middle layer of smooth muscle thinner than in the duct and of a mucous membrane resting upon a thin submucous layer. The mucous membrane forms an intricate system of thin, primary folds, which branch into secondary and tertiary folds. These project far into the lumen and anastomose frequently with one another. In this way numerous cavities of different sizes arise, separated

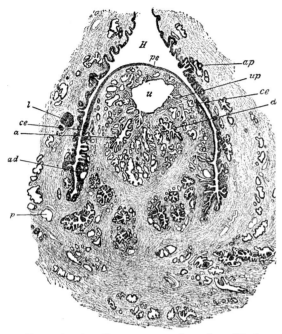

Fig. 29–29. Cross section through colliculus seminalis of a young man. Urethra, *H,* incised above; *a,* ejaculatory canal; *ad,* adenoid tissue; *ap,* accessory prostatic gland; *ce,* stratified cylindrical epithelium; *l,* lacuna in cross section; *p,* prostatic ducts; *pe,* stratified epithelium; *up,* prostatic ducts, which empty into utriculus of prostate, *u.* 10 ×. (After von Ebner, from Schaffer.)

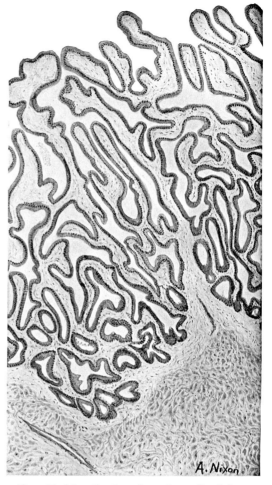

Fig. 29–30. Section through wall of human seminal vesicle, showing the folded tunica mucosa, the pale-staining lamina propria and the darker muscle coat. 85 ×.

from one another by thin, branching partitions; all open into the larger central cavity. In sections, however, many of them seem to be isolated (Fig. 29–30). Some are provided with glandlike invaginations similar to those in the ampulla.

The epithelium shows great individual variations, which probably depend on age and on functional influences. As a rule, it is pseudostratified and consists of a layer of round basal cells and of a layer of larger, superficial, cuboidal or low columnar cells. All basal cells have a pair of centrioles above the nucleus, while in the superficial cells the centrioles are located at the surface and form a central flagellum. Terminal bars have also been described. The cells contain numerous granules or even large lumps of a yellow pigment; it has a fatty nature, reacts negatively to tests for iron, and makes its first appearance at the time of puberty. A similar pigment is also found in the smooth muscles and in the connective tissue of the seminal vesicles. In many places the epithelial cells,

especially in the deeper crypts between the folds and in the glandlike structures, contain secretion granules; on the free surface drops or bleblike formations appear which are cast off into the lumen. The secretion of the seminal vesicles is a yellowish, viscid, sticky liquid containing globulin. In sections it forms coagulated, netlike, deeply staining masses in the lumen. After castration, the epithelium atrophies, but can be restored by injections of testis hormone (Fig. 29–31).

The muscular wall of the seminal vesicles is provided with a plexus of nerve fibers and with small sympathetic ganglia.

Prostate Gland. The prostate is the size of a horse chestnut and surrounds the urethra at its origin from the urinary bladder.

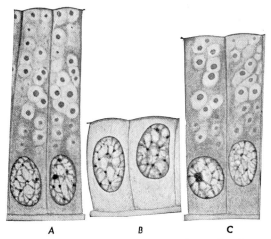

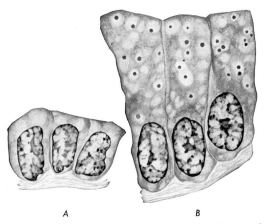

Fig. 29–31. Sections of seminal vesicle of rat. A, from normal animal; B, from twenty-day castrate; C, from twenty-day castrate receiving twenty-nine injections of testis hormone in twenty days. Note absence of secretion granules in B. Bouin; hematoxylin. High magnification. (After Moore, Hughes and Gallagher.)

Fig. 29–32. A, atrophic epithelium of seminal vesicle removed from a rat fed on a diet deficient in vitamin B for thirty-two days. B, epithelium of other seminal vesicle after injection for thirteen days with male hormone. Note the return to normal appearance and compare with Figure 29–31. Bouin, hematoxylin preparations of C. R. Moore. 2000 ×. (Drawn by Miss E. Bohlman.)

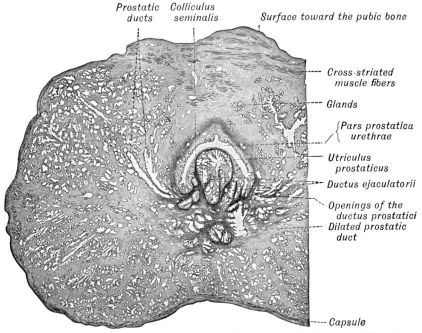

Fig. 29–33. Low power view of human prostate. Elastic fibers appear black. 4 ×. (After Braus.)

It is a conglomerate of thirty to fifty small, compound tubulo-alveolar glands; they give origin to sixteen to thirty-two excretory ducts, which open independently into the urethra on the right and left sides of the colliculus seminalis. The form of the glands is irregular. Large cavities, sometimes cystic, alternate with narrow, branching tubules. The blind ends of the secreting portions are sometimes narrower than the excretory ducts. In many places branching papillae and folds with a thin core of connective tissue project far into the lumen. In sections they may appear as free, epithelium-lined islands in the cavities.

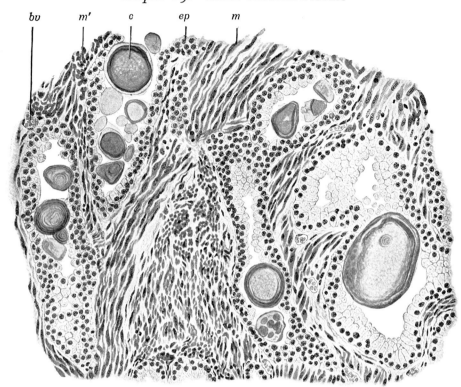

Fig. 29–34.   Human prostate. *ep*, epithelium lining the glandular cavities; *c*, concretions; *m*, smooth muscles in interstitial tissue in longitudinal section; *m'*, same in cross section; *bv*, blood vessels. 190 ×. (A.A.M.)

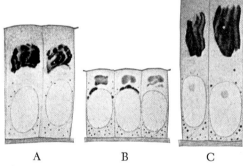

| A | B | C |

Fig. 29–35.   Sections of prostate gland of rat. *A, B, C,* from posterior lobe cells; *B,* from a twenty-day castrate; *C,* from twenty-day castrate receiving twenty-nine injections of testis hormone in twenty days. The changes in the Golgi net are quite striking. Mann-Kopsch technique. High magnification. (After Moore, Price and Gallagher.)

There is no distinct basement membrane, and the glandular epithelium rests upon a layer of connective tissue with dense elastic networks and numerous blood capillaries. In the larger alveolar cavities it may be low cuboidal or even squamous, but in most places it is simple or pseudostratified columnar. The cytoplasm of the cells contains numerous secretory granules. Some of them stain black with iron hematoxylin, but the majority are of lipoid nature. Sometimes, on the free surface of the cells, drops of cytoplasm seem to become detached from the cell body. The epithelial cells become small and lose their secretion granules after castration. Injections of testicular hormone restore the cells quickly to their normal appearance and activity (Fig. 29–35).

The abundant interstitial tissue of the prostate consists of dense connective tissue with collagenous fibers, and elastic networks and many smooth muscles arranged in strands of varying thickness. The connective tissue forms a capsule at the periphery of the organ. Together with the smooth muscles it is arranged in thick, broad septa, widely separating the glands from one another and radiating from the region of the colliculus seminalis to the periphery. Around the urethra the smooth muscles form a thick ring —the internal sphincter of the bladder.

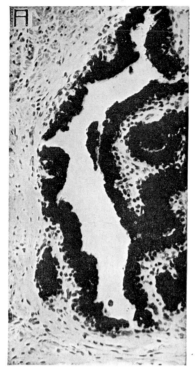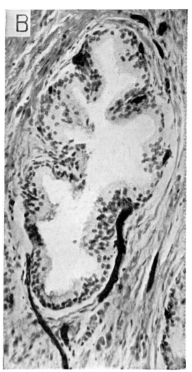

Fig. 29–36. Photomicrographs of sections of human prostate. *A,* black-stained acid phosphatase obscures the epithelium. *B,* black-stained alkaline phosphatase is limited to the blood vessels. 180 ×. (Courtesy of G. Gomori.)

The *secretion of the prostate* is a thin, opalescent liquid with a slightly alkaline re-action and the odor of semen. The liquid contains proteins, fine lipoid granules in sus-pension, but no mucus. In sections the secre-tion in the glandular cavities appears granular. It contains occasional desquamated cells and spherical or oval, often concen-trically striated, bodies—the *prostatic concre-tions* (Fig. 29–34). These originate through condensation of the secretions, may become calcified, and exceed 1 mm. in diameter. The concretions are added to the semen and can be found in the ejaculate; the larger ones sometimes remain in the gland and are lodged in cysts. Their number increases with age.

The prostate is abundantly provided with plexuses of mostly nonmyelinated nerve fibers connected with small sympathetic ganglia. Sensory nerve endings of various kinds (end bulbs, genital corpuscles, and so on), belonging to myelinated fibers, are scattered in the interstitial connective tissue. Free nerve end-ings occur in the epithelium.

The *utriculus prostaticus,* lodged in the mass of the prostate gland and opening on the colliculus seminalis, according to some recent observations, is not a vestigial organ without any function, but is an accessory gland of the male sexual apparatus. It is a blind vesicle of considerable size lined by a mu-cous membrane with many folds and with glandlike invaginations. The epithelium is similar to that of the prostate. Sometimes patches of ciliated co-lumnar epithelium can be found.

Bulbo-urethral Glands. The bulbo-urethral glands (of Cowper), each the size of a pea, are of compound tubulo-alveolar variety and in some respects resemble mucous glands; their ducts enter the posterior section of the cavernous part of the urethra. The ducts as well as the secreting portions are of irregular size and form, and in many places show cystlike enlargements. The terminal portions end blindly or are connected with one an-other by anastomoses. The connective tissue partitions between the glandular lobules measure 1 to 3 mm. in diameter and contain elastic nets and thick strands of striated and smooth muscles. The latter may penetrate with the connective tissue into the interior of the lobules.

The structure of the epithelium in the

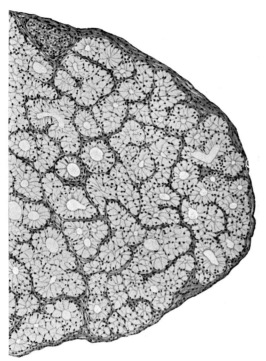

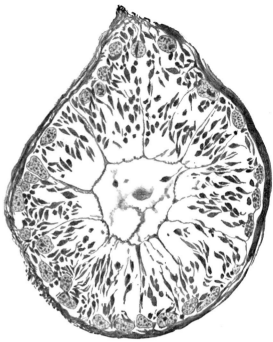

Fig. 29–37. Part of lobule of bulbo-urethral gland of a twenty-three year old man. Zenker. 120 ×. (Slightly modified after Stieve.)

Fig. 29–38. Alveolus of human bulbo-urethral gland (Cowper's gland). Spindle-shaped, darkly stained inclusions in the cells and in the lumen. Mallory stain. 740 ×. (Redrawn after Schaffer.)

secreting portions and in the ducts is subject to great functional variations. In the enlarged alveoli the cells are usually flattened; in the other glandular spaces they are cuboidal or columnar with the nuclei at the base. The cytoplasm contains small mucoid droplets and spindle-shaped inclusions staining with acid dyes (Fig. 29–38). They are supposed to leave the cell body as such and then to dissolve and mix with the mucin. The cells also contain various-sized colloidal spherules. The presence of secretory capillaries is doubtful. The excretory ducts are lined with a pseudo-stratified epithelium resembling that of the urethra and may contain large patches of secreting cells. They are also provided with small accessory glandular outpocketings having the structure of the glands of Littré of the urethra.

After fixation, the secretion appears in the lumen of the glandular spaces and ducts as angular precipitates which stain brightly with eosin. In life it is a clear, viscid and lubricant, mucus-like substance which can be drawn out easily into long thin threads. Unlike true mucus, it does not form a precipitate with acetic acid.

THE PENIS

The penis is formed by three cylindrical bodies of cavernous, erectile tissue—the *two corpora cavernosa penis and* the unpaired *corpus cavernosum urethrae.* The first two are separated from each other in their posterior, divergent parts, but join at the pubic angle and run side by side to their pointed ends. On the upper surface of the penis, along the line of their junction, is a shallow longitudinal groove where the dorsal artery and vein are located. On the lower surface the corpora cavernosa form a deep groove occupied by the corpus cavernosum urethrae (spongiosum). The latter, beginning with the bulbus urethrae between the crura of the corpora cavernosa penis, is pierced throughout its length by the *urethra* and ends with a mushroom-shaped enlargement, the *glans penis,* which caps the conical ends of both corpora cavernosa penis.

The erectile tissue of the corpora caver-

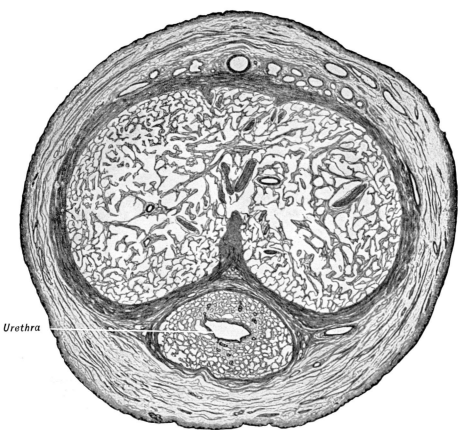

Urethra

Fig. 29–39. Cross section of penis of a twenty-one year old man. The septum in the corpus cavernosum penis is incomplete, since the section is from the distal part of the organ. The penis was fixed by injection of formalin into the corpus cavernosum. 3½ ×. (Slightly modified after Stieve.)

nosa penis is a vast spongelike system of irregular vascular spaces, intercalated between the afferent arteries and the efferent veins. In the relaxed condition of the organ the cavernous spaces contain but little blood and appear as irregular clefts. In erection they are large cavities filled with blood under high pressure. This causes the enlargement and the rigidity of the penis.

Each of the *cavernous bodies* is surrounded by a thick (1 mm.), resistant, fibrous membrane, the *tunica albuginea*. Its collagenous fibers are arranged in an outer, mainly longitudinal, and an inner, circular, layer, and are accompanied by elastic nets. Between the two cavernous bodies the albuginea forms a fibrous partition, which, especially near the end of the penis, is pierced by numerous clefts through which the cavernous spaces of both sides communicate. On the inner surface of the albuginea, especially in the posterior part of the erectile bodies, there is a layer of dense connective tissue containing a multitude of small veins draining the cavernous spaces.

The cavernous spaces are largest in the central zone of the cavernous bodies. In the collapsed condition, they may have a diameter of 1 mm. Toward the periphery they gradually diminish in size. The partitions between them, the *trabeculae,* consist of dense fibrous tissue and contain thick collagenous bundles with fibroblasts, elastic networks, and strands of smooth muscle fibers. Their surface is lined with endothelium, which continues into that of the arteries and of the veins.

The albuginea of the corpus cavernosum urethrae is much thinner than in the corpora cavernosa penis and contains circularly arranged smooth muscle fibers in its inner layer. It also is provided with abundant elastic networks. Unlike those of the corpora cavernosa penis, the blood lacunae here are

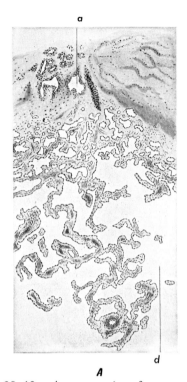

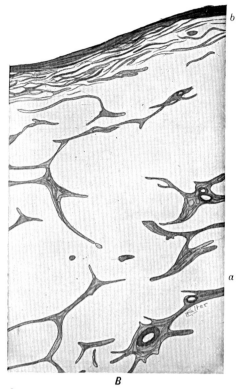

Fig. 29–40.   *A,* cross section of crus penis of a man of twenty-seven. *a,* vena profunda penis; *d,* central cavernous spaces. *B,* crus penis of man; fixed in artificial erection by injection of gelatin. *a,* central zone; *b,* peripheral zone. (Modified and redrawn after Kiss.)

everywhere the same in size. The trabeculae between them contain more numerous elastic fibers, whereas smooth muscles are relatively scarce. The cavernous spaces occupying the axis of the corpus cavernosum gradually pass into the venous plexus of the urethral mucosa.

The *glans penis* consists of dense connective tissue containing nets of large anastomosing veins, with circular and longitudinal smooth muscles in their thick walls. The longitudinal muscle strands often bulge into the lumen of the veins.

The skin covering the penis is thin and is provided with an abundant subcutaneous layer containing smooth muscles, but is devoid of fat tissue. The skin has no hairs on the distal part of the penis and only small sweat glands. The glans is covered by a circular fold of the skin, the *prepuce.* Its inner surface, adjacent to the glans, is moist and has the character of a mucous membrane. On the surface of the glans penis the derma of the skin is fused with the connective tissue

between the veins just described. In this region peculiar sebaceous glands are described (*glands of Tyson*), which are not connected with hairs. They show great individual variations in number and distribution.

Blood Vessels. The erectile tissue of the penis is supplied with blood from the arteria penis. It breaks up into several large branches (arteria profunda penis, dorsalis penis, and so forth) which run to different parts of the organ, but all anastomose with one another. In all these branches, even before they enter the erectile tissue, the intima forms long ridge-like thickenings which project into the lumen. They consist of loosely arranged collagenous and elastic fibers, and contain strands of smooth muscle fibers, mostly arranged longitudinally.

Wherever the arterial branches enter into the corpora cavernosa through the albuginea, they assume a longitudinal, forward course, and give off many new branches. In the quiescent condition of the penis they have a convoluted or curled course—*helicine arteries.* They have a thick media. When they reach 65 to 80 microns in diameter (precavernous arteries), they run in the longitudinal trabeculae of the corpora cavernosa, and open directly into the cavernous spaces.

The intima of the helicine arteries is also provided with longitudinal ridges of connective tissue and smooth muscle, as in the branches of the arteria penis before they enter the erectile tissue. The ridges are located especially at the places of division of the vessel.

The arterial supply of the corpus spongiosum is similar to that of the corpus cavernosa penis.

The major part of the blood leaves the corpora cavernosa penis through the vena profunda penis. Its radicles have a thick muscular wall. They arise under the albuginea, especially in the posterior regions of the erectile bodies, through confluence of a multitude of branched "postcavernous" venules. The latter run parallel to the surface under the albuginea, have a length of 300 to 400 microns or more, and do not have any muscles in their thin walls. They originate from the peripheral cavernous spaces which are in direct or indirect communication with the largest axial blood spaces. The blood from the corpus spongiosum is drained mainly through the vena dorsalis penis. Unlike those of the corpora cavernosa penis, the first radicles of this vein start from the lacunae with large openings and leave the corpus by the shortest way, by piercing the albuginea.

The arrangement and structure of the afferent and efferent blood vessels in the corpora cavernosa penis explain the *mechanism of erection.* The arteries play the active, the veins the passive, role. The erection begins with the relaxation of the tonus of all smooth muscles in the arteries and in the erectile bodies. The blood pressure overpowers the remaining elastic resistance of the tissue, and stretches the media in the arteries. The presence of longitudinal ridges in their intima is believed to enable the lumen in such places to enlarge quickly. The lacunae of the cavernous bodies are filled with arterial blood. As the helicine arteries open especially into the axial, largest spaces, these spaces compress the peripheral, smaller spaces and the thin-walled veins under the albuginea which drain the latter. In this way the outflow of the blood is throttled down, the blood accumulates in the corpora cavernosa under increasing pressure, and the erectile tissue becomes rigid. The helicine arteries during erection are passively stretched, and their convolutions are evened out. Since in the corpus spongiosum there is no difference between axial and peripheral lacunae and the draining veins are not compressed, there is no noticeable retention of blood, and the circulation continues freely. Consequently the corpus spongiosum never attains a great rigidity during erection.

After ejaculation the arterial musculature regains its tonus. The afflux of the arterial blood is reduced to the usual degree. The excess of blood, which has accumulated in the corpora cavernosa penis, is slowly pressed out into the veins through the action of the smooth muscles of the trabeculae and through the retraction of the elastic networks. Owing to the compression of the peripheral small veins and to the valves, the return of the penis to the flaccid condition is accomplished only gradually.

Lymphatics. Dense, superficial networks of lymphatic capillaries are found in the skin of the penis, of the prepuce and of the shaft. They form a dorsal superficial lymph vessel, which runs toward the medial inguinal lymph nodes. Deep nets of lymphatic capillaries collect the lymph from the glans; they form a plexus on each side of the frenulum and continue into a dorsal subfascial lymph vessel.

Nerves. The nerves of the penis belong to the cerebrospinal (nervi pudendi) and to the sympathetic (plexus cavernosus) systems. They first supply the striated muscles of the penis (such as the bulbocavernosus) and also furnish the sensory nerve endings in the skin and the mucous membrane of the urethra. Among these sensory endings, free-branching nerve endings in the epithelium of the glans, the prepuce and the urethra can be distinguished. Besides, there are free nerve endings in the subepithelial connective tissue of the skin and the urethra. Thirdly, numerous encapsulated corpuscles of various types are present: corpuscles of Meissner in the papillae of the skin of the prepuce and the glans, genital corpuscles in the deeper layers of the stratum papillare of the derma of the glans and in the mucous membrane of the urethra, and corpuscles of Vater-Pacini along the dorsal vein in the subcutaneous fascia, in the deeper connective tissue of the glans and under the albuginea in the corpora cavernosa. The sympathetic nervous plexuses are connected with the smooth muscles of the vessels and form extensive, nonmyelinated networks in the smooth muscles of the trabeculae in the corpora cavernosa.

SEMEN

As the spermia pass along the excretory ducts, the secretions of the ducts and accessory glands are added to them; the final product is the semen. The spermia in the seminiferous tubules seem to be nonmotile. They are slowly forwarded into the tubuli recti and the rete testis, perhaps by passive pressure of liquid accumulating in the tubules, which cannot expand because they are surrounded by the firm albuginea. In the ductuli efferentes, the epithelium with cilia beating toward the epididymis takes care of the further transport of the spermia. The glandular cells devoid of cilia undoubtedly add their secretion to the moving mass.

The long, winding duct of the epididymis is slowly traversed by the spermia. They are kept here, especially in the tail, for a long time, sometimes for months. Here the majority of them lose the last remnant of cytoplasm attached to the middle piece.

What forces move them forward in the canal is not quite clear. Capillary forces may play a role, and a part of the way seems to be made through the movements of the spermia themselves. During ejaculation the contractions of the circular smooth muscles surrounding the tubules are of primary importance.

The viscid secretion of the epithelium of the ductus epididymidis adds nutritive material to the spermia. As a rule, spermia taken from the epididymis are more resistant to environmental changes than those from the testis.

The spermia do not accumulate in the ductus deferens. This part of the excretory system with its heavy muscular coat is adapted only to their speedy transportation.

The function of the seminal vesicles seems to be primarily glandular; their thick secretion is added, during ejaculation, to the mass of the spermia, which pass through the vas deferens and the ampulla into the ejaculatory ducts.

In the process of *ejaculation* the muscular tissue of the prostate also contracts and discharges its abundant liquid secretion; it dilutes the thick part of the semen and stimulates the movements of the spermia. The semen, entering the urethra and mixing with the secretion of the glands of Cowper and Littré, is thrown out through the contraction of the bulbocavernosus muscle compressing the bulbus urethrae.

The spermia are believed to number about 60,000 in a cubic millimeter of semen; each ejaculate on the average contains 200 to 300 million spermia. The tail performs whipping, undulatory movements; the spermium, therefore, advances with the head forward and simultaneously rotates around its long axis. Its speed is 14 to 23 microns in a second.

Under suitable conditions the spermia may remain alive outside the body for several days and also in the excretory ducts after death. In the uterus and the fallopian tube, living spermia have been found some days after coitus.

Besides the spermia, the semen contains degenerated cells, probably cast off from the epithelium of the excretory ducts and the urethra. Occasionally, columnar epithelial cells and wandering cells of connective tissue origin may also occur. There are, furthermore, round, hyaline bodies of unknown origin, lipoid granules, at times concretions from the prostate and a multitude of fat, protein and pigment granules. When the semen cools and begins to dry, peculiar crystals of various forms develop—the *spermia crystals of Böttcher.* They are believed to consist of phosphate of spermin.

It has been claimed that the different components of the semen are discharged from the urethra in a certain sequence. With the development of the erection the slimy secretion of the glands of Cowper and Littré lubricates the urethra. At the beginning of the ejaculation the prostatic secretion is discharged first. Being alkaline, it neutralizes the acid reaction of the urethra, where remnants of urine may be present, and the equally acid reaction of the vaginal mucus. Then the masses of spermia accumulated in the vas deferens and the ductus epididymidis are thrown out. The final portion of the ejaculate is probably represented by the thick, alkaline, globulin-containing secretion of the seminal vesicles. In some animals (mouse) the abundant secretion of the seminal vesicles is coagulated in the vagina by an enzyme contained in the prostatic juice, and thus a solid plug is formed in the vagina which temporarily occludes its lumen and prevents the backflow of the semen.

Histogenesis of the Testis. See page 540.

REFERENCES

Allen, E.: Sex and Internal Secretions. Baltimore, 1939.

Burgos, M. H., and Fawcett, D. W.: An electron microscope study of spermatid differentiation in the toad, *Bufo arenarum* Hensel. J. Biophys. Biochem. Cytol., *2:*223, 1956.

Burgos, M. H., and Fawcett, D. W.: Studies on the fine structure of the mammalian testis. I. Differentiation of the spermatids in the cat (*Felis domestica*). J. Biophys. Biochem. Cytol., *1:*287, 1955.

Burrows, H.: Biological Actions of Sex Hormones. 2d ed. London, Cambridge University Press, 1949.

Challice, C. E.: IX. Electron microscope studies of spermiogenesis in some rodents. J. Roy. Micros. Soc., *73:*115, 1953.

Clermont, Y., and Leblond, C. P.: Spermiogenesis of man, monkey, ram and other mammals as shown by the "periodic acid-Schiff" technique. Am. J. Anat., *96:* 229, 1955.

Elftman, H.: The Sertoli cell cycle in the mouse. Anat. Rec., *106:*31, 1950.

Farris, E. J.: Human Fertility and Problems of the Male. White Plains, N. Y. Author's Press, 1950.

Gatenby, J. B., and Beams, H. W.: The cytoplasmic inclusions in the spermatogenesis of man. Quart. J. Microsc. Sc., *78:*1, 1935.

Huggins, C.: The physiology of the prostate gland. Physiol. Rev., *25:*281, 1945.

Macklin, C. C., and Macklin, M. T.: The Seminal Vesicles, Prostate and Bulbo-urethral Glands, in Cowdry's Special Cytology. 2d ed. New York, *3:*1771, 1932.

Metz, C. W.: The Male Germ Cells, in Cowdry's Special Cytology. 2d ed. New York, *3:*1727, 1932.

Moore, C. R.: Biology of the Testes, in Allen, E.: Sex and Internal Secretions. 2d ed. Baltimore, 1939, p. 353.

Moore, C. R., Price, D., and Gallagher, T. F.: Rat prostate cytology as a testis-hormone indicator and the prevention of castration changes by testis extract injections. Am. J. Anat., *45:*71, 1930.

Painter, T. S.: Studies in mammalian spermatogenesis. J. Exper. Zool., *37:*3, 1923.

Price, D.: Normal development of the prostate and seminal vesicles of the rat, with a study of experimental post-natal modifications. Am. J. Anat., *60:*79, 1936.

Rasmussen, A. T.: Interstitial Cells of the Testis, in Cowdry's Special Cytology. 2d ed. New York, *3:*1673, 1932.

Romeis, B.: Hoden, samenableitende Organe und accessorische Geschlechtsdrüsen. Handb. der norm. und pathol. Physiol., etc. Berlin, *14:*693, 1926.

Roosen-Runge, E. C., and Giesel, L. O., Jr.: Quantitative studies on spermatogenesis in the albino rat. Am. J. Anat., *87:*1, 1950.

Scott, W. W.: The lipids of the prostatic fluid, seminal plasma and enlarged prostate gland of man. J. Urol., *53:*712, 1945.

Stieve, H.: Männliche Genitalorgane, in Möllendorff's Handb. der mikr. Anat. des Menschen. Berlin, 1930, Vol. 7, Pt. 2.

Waldeyer, W.: Die Geschlechtszellen. Hertwig's Handb. d. vergl. u. exp. Embryol. Jena, 1901, Vol. 1, Pt. 1.

Young, W. C.: Die Resorption in den Ductuli efferentes der Maus und ihre Bedeutung für das Problem der Unterbindung im Hoden-Nebenhoden System. Zeit. f. Zellforsch. u. mikr. Anat., 1933.

CHAPTER 30

Female Genital System

THE FEMALE genital organs consist of the ovaries, a system of excretory ducts (the oviducts, the uterus and vagina) and the external genitalia. In the sexually mature female, the ovary and its ducts undergo marked cyclic changes.

THE OVARY

The human ovary is a slightly flattened bean-shaped body measuring 2.5 to 5 cm. in length, 1.5 to 3 cm. in width and 0.6 to 1.5 cm. in thickness. One of its edges, the *hilus,* is attached by the mesovarium to the broad ligament, which extends laterally from the uterus. The free surface of the ovary bulges into the peritoneal cavity. Embedded in its connective tissue are the *follicles* in which the female sex cells, the *ova,* develop. When the follicles reach maturity, they rupture on the surface of the ovary, and the ova gain access to the open end of the oviduct.

The thick peripheral layer or cortex of the ovary contains the various-sized follicles and surrounds the medulla (zona vasculosa) except at the hilus. The medulla consists of loose connective tissue and a mass of contorted blood vessels which are large in proportion to the size of the ovary. At the hilus, strands of smooth muscle fibers extend in from the mesovarium.

Germinal Epithelium. The epithelium covering the free surface of the ovary is called the "germinal epithelium," because in the embryo ova appear to arise from it (p. 540). In the infant it is a simple cuboidal or columnar epithelium. In the adult its cells gradually become lower and may be flattened when under tension. A basement membrane is absent. In vitally stained animals the cells of the germinal epithelium store masses of dye granules in the infranuclear zone. Beneath this germinal epithelium is a layer of dense connective tissue—the *tunica albuginea.*

Follicles. The younger the person, the more numerous are the follicles. In the newborn infant the follicles in both ovaries were believed to number 400,000. However, a study of serial sections of the ovaries from a normal mature woman of twenty-two years revealed a total of 420,000. Their number decreases progressively throughout life, and at the menopause they are hard to find. Most of this decrease is due to atresia (p. 515). A few may persist even in old age.

Primary Follicles. The vast majority of the follicles are primary follicles. These are found mainly in the periphery of the cortex, and in young females they form a thick layer immediately beneath the tunica albuginea. They are probably the source of all the other follicles in primates.

They are spheroidal bodies about 45 microns in diameter. The center is occupied by the large, round ovum. Its eccentric nucleus contains a loose network of linin threads with small chromatin granules and a large chromatin nucleolus. The side of the nucleus with the larger amount of cytoplasm contains an accumulation of small mitochondria, the cytocentrum and the Golgi net. The ovum

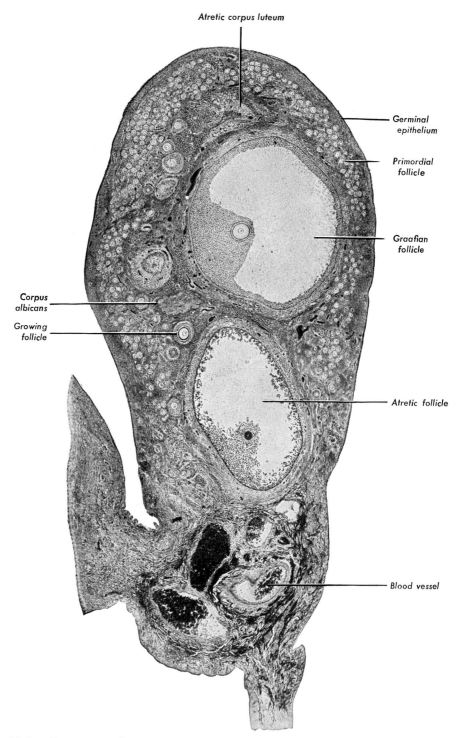

Fig. 30–1.   Transection of ovary of *Macacus rhesus.* Retouched photomicrograph. 42 ✕.

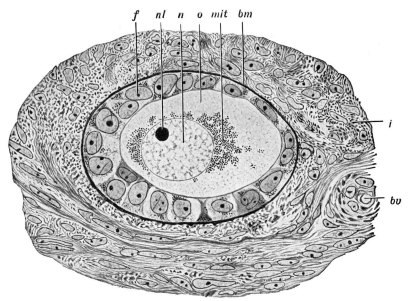

Fig. 30–2. Follicle in first stages of growth from ovary of adult woman. *f*, follicular cells with mitochondria; *nl*, nucleolus of ovum; *n*, nucleus of ovum; *o*, protoplasm of ovum; *mit*, perinuclear accumulation of mitochondria (yolk nucleus); *bm*, basement membrane; *i*, interstitial connective tissue; *bv*, blood vessel. Aniline-acid fuchsin stain. 780 ×. (From a preparation of C. M. Bensley.) (A.A.M.)

in the primary follicle lacks a membrane; it is separated from the adjacent interstitial tissue by a layer of flattened follicular cells, seven to ten of which appear in a section.

Growing Follicles. The progressive development of a primary follicle consists in growth and changes in the ovum, follicular cells, and the adjacent connective tissue. As the egg increases in size, its nucleus enlarges, and the mitochondria become more evenly distributed in the cytoplasm. Later, yolk granules of two kinds appear. When the ovum reaches a diameter of 60 to 80 microns, a refractile, deeply staining cell membrane appears, the *zona pellucida*. It is probably elaborated by both the ovum and the surrounding follicular cells; it gradually becomes thicker.

The growing follicle enlarges mainly through mitotic proliferation of the follicular cells. The few squamous cells of the primary follicle turn first into a layer of columnar cells surrounding the ovum and then into a stratified epithelium which thickens more rapidly on one side of the ovum. The follicle becomes oval, and the ovum eccentric in position. Follicles in the deeper zones of the cortex are the first to develop.

When the follicle is about 0.2 mm. in diameter, several irregular spaces filled with the clear *liquor folliculi* appear between the follicular cells. The increase in amount of this liquid causes a further increase in the size of the follicle, which is now a graafian follicle. In the human ovary the separate cavities usually flow together, and the resulting vesicle has a stratified epithelial lining of follicular cells which is thickened on one side. This is the *cumulus oophorus,* which surrounds the ovum. The follicular cells have a columnar or polyhedral shape; where the liquor accumulates between them they are angular or stellate, and are connected with one another by their processes.

In growing follicles, round, darkly staining bodies (of Call-Exner) surrounded by follicular cells may be found. They probably represent new centers of secretion of follicular liquid. In tissue cultures the follicular epithelium shows both connective tissue and epithelial characteristics.

A follicle 0.4 mm. in diameter has a decided polar structure (Fig. 30–1). The ovum is nearly full grown and is embedded in a solid mass of follicular epithelial cells—the *cumulus oophorus* or *discus proligerus*—which protrudes into the large liquid-filled cavity. On the other side the stratified epithelium forms a continuous, even layer. Meanwhile the connective tissue surrounding

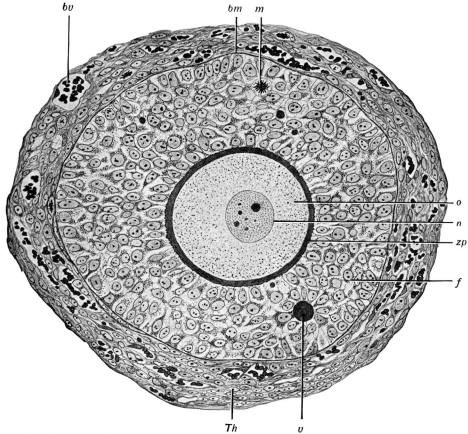

Fig. 30–3.   Growing follicle from human ovary. *o,* ovum already five-sixths of its full size; *n,* its nucleus; *zp,* zona pellucida; *f,* follicular epithelium with mitochondria; *v,* vacuoles of Call-Exner; *Th,* theca folliculi (outer and inner layer not yet differentiated); *bv,* blood vessels with erythrocytes; *bm,* basement membrane; *m,* mitosis of follicular cell. 375 ×. (From same section as Figure 30–2.) (A.A.M.)

the growing follicle differentiates into a capsule, the *theca folliculi,* separated from the follicle by a basement membrane.

At first the spindle-shaped cells and reticular fibers are arranged in several concentric layers around the basement membrane. Later this capsule becomes subdivided into two layers. In the *theca interna,* the layer immediately surrounding the basement membrane, an increasing number of blood capillaries develops. When the follicle has become a vesicle of 2 to 3 mm., the connective tissue cells increase in size and become loosely arranged. The *theca externa,* or outer layer, keeps its dense structure of concentrically arranged, fusiform cells and thick fibers. As the follicle continues to enlarge, these layers become more and more prominent. There is no sharp limit between the two layers of the

theca or between the theca externa and the surrounding stroma.

The follicle continues to grow, owing to the rapid mitotic proliferation of the follicular epithelium and to the progressing accumulation of the follicular liquid. If a follicle is to reach maturity and rupture, it must gradually extend toward the free surface of the ovary. The cause of this is probably the eccentric development of the theca interna, which is thicker and looser on the outer side of the follicle.

Mature Graafian Follicles. The mature follicles are large vesicles which occupy the thickness of the ovarian cortex and bulge on the free surface of the organ. The liquid in the follicular cavity is under considerable pressure, and the outer part of the wall is thin.

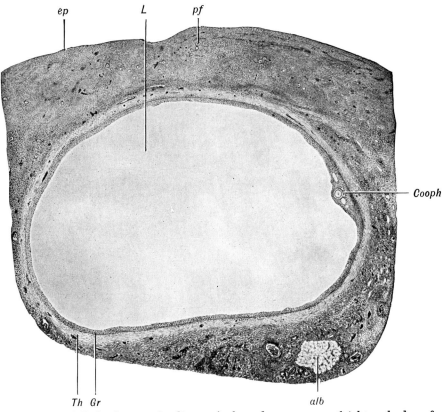

ep   L   pf

Cooph

Th Gr   alb

Fig. 30–4. Large follicle (5 mm. in diameter) from human ovary (eighteenth day of menstrual cycle). *ep,* surface of ovary with germinal epithelium; *L,* follicular liquid; *pf,* primary follicle; *Cooph,* cumulus oophorus with ovum; *alb,* corpus albicans; *Gr,* membrana granulosa; *Th,* theca externa and interna. 20 ×. From same ovary as Figure 30–2. (A.A.M.)

It is believed that a follicle requires about ten to fourteen days to reach maturity. Even with careful study it is somewhat difficult to determine whether a follicle is still growing, has reached maturity, or is beginning to involute. In the human ovary a 10-mm. follicle has been found with a normal ovum developing the first polar body.

The protein-containing follicular liquid appears finely granular in fixed sections. The follicular epithelium lining the cavity is often called the *membrana granulosa* and is intimately adherent to the *glassy membrane* which separates it from the connective tissue capsule (*theca*) of the follicle. Between the polyhedral cells of the inner layers of the membrana granulosa, intercellular vacuoles are common. Mitotic figures gradually decrease in number among the granulosa cells in later stages. The connection of the ovum with the membrana granulosa is further

loosened by the development of new, liquid-filled, intercellular spaces in the cumulus.

A layer of columnar follicular cells remains attached to the ovum; near maturity these cells become tall and conspicuous, forming the *corona radiata,* which probably has protective and nutritive functions similar to those of the Sertoli cells in the testis.

The ovum in the mature follicle reaches a diameter of 120 microns or more. Its surface is immediately surrounded by a thick membrane—the *oolemma,* or *zona pellucida.* A "perivitelline space" between the oolemma and the ovum has not been demonstrated in the mammalian egg prior to polar body formation. The cytoplasm of the human ovum contains some yolk granules, and in fixed material its peripheral layer is quite clear. The eccentric nucleus (vesicula germinativa) measures 25 microns in diameter, and has a thick membrane, a slightly granular linin net-

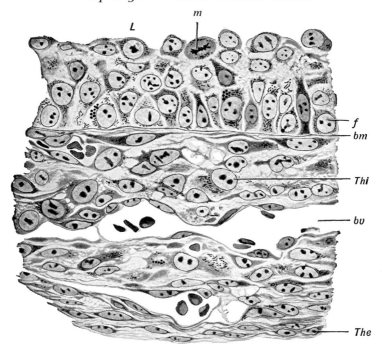

Fig. 30–5. Part of wall of large follicle in Figure 30–4, under higher magnification. *f,* follicular epithelium; *bm,* basement membrane; *Thi,* cells of the theca interna; *bv,* blood vessel; *The,* cells of theca externa; *m,* mitosis of follicular epithelial cells; *L,* cavity of follicle; all cells contain mitochondria. 780 ×, reduced to four-fifths. (A.A.M.)

work, and a large chromatin nucleolus—the *macula germinativa.* A cytocentrum has not been found in the mature ovum. In the living state, yolk granules of various sizes and colors are uniformly distributed through the cytoplasm (Fig. 30–7).

In the mature follicle the connective tissue capsule reaches its highest development. Its theca externa consists of concentrically arranged fibers and fusiform cells and contains large blood vessels. The theca interna is composed of large polyhedral cells with oval nuclei and fine lipoid droplets in their cytoplasm. These are modified connective tissue cells. Between the large cells of the theca interna is a network of thin fibrils continuous with those of the theca externa and the rest of the ovarian stroma. There are many capillaries in the theca interna, close to the basement membrane.

Upon reaching maturity the follicles either rupture or involute, but follicles may degenerate at any stage of development from primordial follicles.

Rupture of Graafian Follicles. Ovulation. The follicular fluid accumulates faster than the follicle grows, and so the superficial part of the follicular wall, bulging on the surface of the ovary, becomes progressively thinner. The follicular fluid which forms just before ovulation is more watery than the rest and appears to be secreted at a rapid rate. The blood vessels are compressed, and the small spot at the apex of the bulging finally opens.

Through the small opening in the wall of the follicle on the free surface of the ovary, the follicular liquid oozes out into the peritoneal cavity. The ovum, whose connections with the cells of the cumulus oophorus were loosened in the last stages of development, is torn away with the corona radiata from the cumulus and is discharged with the liquid. The immediate cause of the rupture of the follicular wall is not known. In women it usually occurs spontaneously in the intermenstrual period.

This process which frees the ovum and enables it to meet the male sex cell for the purpose of fertilization is called "ovulation." Each time one ovum is set free; in some cases, two or, rarely, even more. Sometimes the maturation of a follicle with consequent

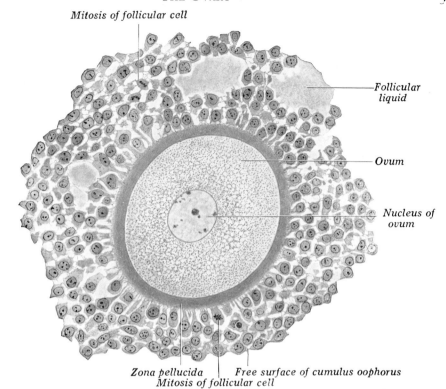

Mitosis of follicular cell

Follicular liquid

Ovum

Nucleus of ovum

Zona pellucida | *Free surface of cumulus oophorus*
Mitosis of follicular cell

Fig. 30–6.   Ovum of follicle in Figure 30–4 with surrounding follicular cells under higher magnification. 375 ✕. (A.A.M.)

ovulation occurs alternately in both ovaries, but the same ovary may develop a follicle several times in succession. In the human female a follicle ripens at intervals averaging twenty-eight days, although variations of a week or more are common. Cycles of typical duration not associated with ovulation may occur.

It is probable that the fimbriae of the tube closely invest the ovary at the time of ovulation.

Maturation of the Ovum. The ova in the ovary of an adult mammal are in the period of growth and are called *primary ovocytes;* they are homologues of primary spermatocytes. The period of growth in ovogenesis is followed by a period of maturation in which the primary ovocyte undergoes two maturation divisions. The resulting four cells have a haploid number of chromosomes (twenty-four in the human species). Only one develops into the mature ovum; the other three are thrown off as rudimentary structures and degenerate (Fig. 30–8).

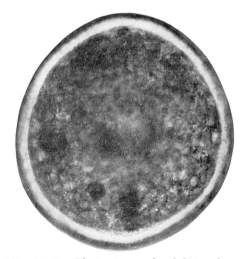

Fig. 30–7.   Photomicrograph of living human ovum. Note yolk granules. The nucleus is not visible. The zona pellucida appears as a bright layer. 450 ✕. (Courtesy of W. H. Lewis.)

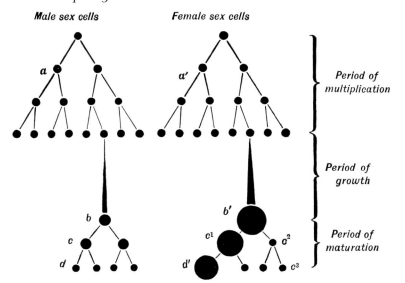

Fig. 30–8.   Diagram of development of the male (left) and of the female (right) sex cells. (Redrawn after Boveri.)

The first maturation division begins shortly before ovulation. The chromatin is equally divided between the daughter cells, but only one of them, the *secondary ovocyte,* receives practically all the cytoplasm of the mother cell; the other becomes the *first polar body*—an abortive secondary ovocyte which degenerates.

Immediately after the expulsion of the first polar body, the nucleus of the secondary ovocyte enters the second meiotic division. The spindle remains at the metaphase, and the division is not completed until fertilization. The chromatin mass is divided equally, but the bulk of the cytoplasm is again retained by one daughter cell—the mature *ovum* (corresponding to the spermatid). The other daughter cell is the small, abortive *second polar body.* In the human subject incomplete observations on the formation of the polar bodies have been published.

Transformation of the Graafian Follicle after Rupture. The Corpus Luteum. After the rupture of the follicle and the discharge of the liquor and the ovum with its corona radiata, the wall of the follicle collapses, and the epithelial membrane granulosa is thrown into folds and appears considerably thickened. The follicular epithelial cells and the cells of the theca interna change into large pale-staining cells, somewhat like those of the suprarenal cortex. The former follicle is now called the *corpus luteum.* The cavity now has an irregular, stellate shape. The theca externa keeps its regular, ovoid outlines (Fig. 30–11), while the theca interna, on the contrary, loses them. At the base of the folds of the granulosa, the cells of the theca interna accumulate in triangular masses,

while between the folds they are scarce or absent.

If the ovum is fertilized, the corpus luteum becomes a *corpus luteum of pregnancy;* if the ovum is not fertilized, menstruation follows about two weeks after ovulation and the corpus luteum becomes a *corpus luteum of menstruation.* Both types of corpora lutea undergo the same changes during the first ten days or so. When menstruation begins, a hemorrhage occurs into the corpus luteum and it begins to involute. During the succeeding months, a hyaline material accumulates between the lutein cells, and the corpus luteum is reduced to a scar, the *corpus albicans* (Fig. 30–13).

The principal role in the formation of the corpus luteum is played by the epithelial follicular cells. They begin at once to hypertrophy and in a few days attain a considerable size. The cell body becomes polyhedral; the nucleus also swells and assumes a spherical form with a coarse chromatin network, and one or two nucleoli. Mitoses may be found, but are rare. Such hypertrophied follicle cells are called *granulosa lutein cells,* although the characteristic lipoid pigment, *lutein,* is at first found only in traces. Simultaneously the spindle-shaped cells of the theca interna, and with them a multitude of capillary sprouts, penetrate radially into the thick layer of follicular cells. When these connective tissue elements reach the inner

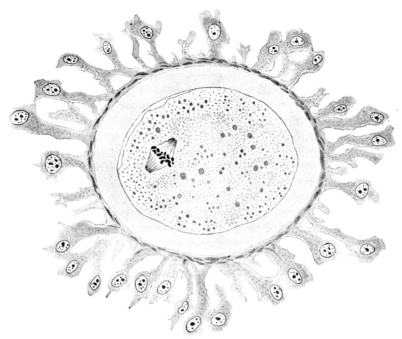

Fig. 30–9. Ovum from mature follicle of guinea pig, with corona radiata, thick zona pellucida and the first polar spindle. 530 ×. (Redrawn after Rubaschkin.)

surface of the folded granulosa layer, they rapidly form a loose, gelatinous connective tissue which covers the inner surface of the wall and leaves a space free in the center. This is filled with the remains of the liquor folliculi, transuded serum, and a varying, usually small number of extravasated erythrocytes. The large, lipid-containing, epithelioid cells of the theca interna remain scattered at the periphery of the folded layer of lutein cells and accumulate in the angle of the folds (Fig. 30–11). Their aspect and their inner structure are similar to those of the granulosa lutein cells. They have therefore been given the name of *theca lutein cells* (*paralutein cells*). There are no transitions between these two types of lutein cells.

The granulosa lutein cells have a clear, slightly vacuolated cytoplasm, and a distinct cytocentrum in the vicinity of the nucleus. The theca lutein cells are smaller and more highly vacuolated in ordinary sections. The granulosa lutein cells contain phosphatides, cerebrosides and lutein pigment. In the peripheral layers, especially in the theca lutein cells, cholesterol esters occur. Active and regressing corpora lutea give a greenish phosphorescence in ultraviolet light, perhaps owing to vitamin A. In vitally stained animals the lutein cells may contain granular dye inclusions in regressive stages of their development.

The polyhedral lutein cells are surrounded by a network of sinusoidal blood capillaries with a thin endothelium. They seem to be arranged in radial cords or strands. Between them networks of reticular fibers can be revealed by appropriate methods (Fig. 30–12).

If the ovum is fertilized, the corpus luteum passes through a period of growth and a period of regression. The corpus luteum of pregnancy grows larger than that of menstruation, and its lutein cells reach a larger size. The lutein and neutral fat content of the lutein cells is much less than in the corpus luteum of menstruation, and the color is not as yellow as in later stages. Involution of the true corpus luteum usually begins at the fifth or sixth month of gestation. After delivery it proceeds rapidly in qualitatively the same way as in the corpus luteum of menstruation; but, as the corpus luteum of pregnancy is larger, it takes a longer time before the stage of the corpus albicans is reached. The final scar is also larger, persists longer, and, through its shrinking, usually causes a distinct retraction of the surface of the ovary.

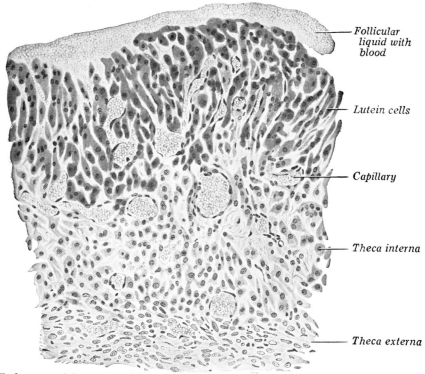

Follicular
liquid with
blood

Lutein cells

Capillary

Theca interna

Theca externa

Fig. 30–10.   Early stage of formation of human corpus luteum. Capillaries invade the granulosa, which is transformed into a layer of lutein cells. (Redrawn from R. Meyer.)

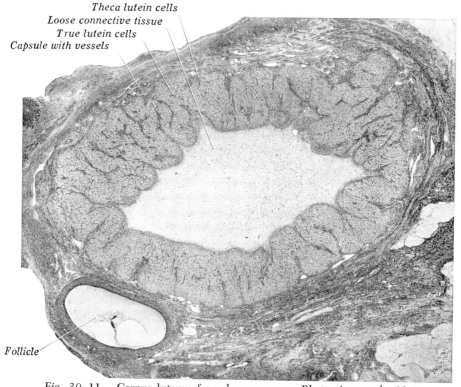

Theca lutein cells
Loose connective tissue
True lutein cells
Capsule with vessels

Follicle

Fig. 30–11.   Corpus luteum from human ovary. Photomicrograph. 11 ✕.

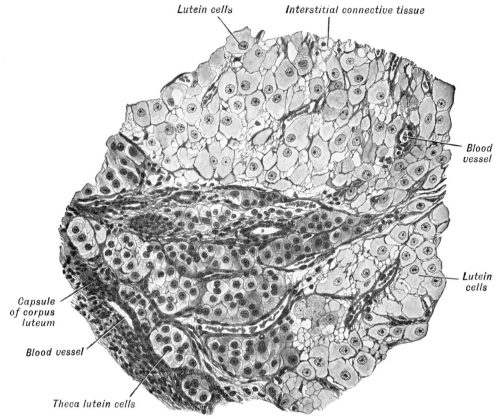

Fig. 30–12. Cross section of peripheral layer of human corpus luteum of pregnancy, stained for reticular fibers by the Bielschowsky method. 235 ×. (A.A.M.)

A considerable effusion of blood into the follicle at the moment of ovulation does not occur in the human subject. In the early stages only an insignificant diapedesis of erythrocytes occurs in the wall of the collapsed follicle.

After regression has begun the granulosa lutein cells show an increasing infiltration with neutral fat in addition to other lipids. As the quantity of pigment increases in the human species, the lutein border assumes a brighter yellow color. If there has been a hemorrhage into the corpus luteum, the connective tissue on the inner surface of the lutein cell layer organizes the blood clot; hemosiderin accumulates in the connective tissue cells; sometimes, extracellular crystals of hematoidin can be found. The theca lutein cells shrink and gradually disappear.

Involution (Atresia) of Follicles. As the period of sexual activity in the human female lasts about thirty years, and since one ovum is not discharged oftener than once a month in ovulation, the number of ova which reach maturity and are discharged from the ovary does not exceed 400. The remainder of the 400,000 or more original follicles gradually degenerate and disappear. This in-

volution of a follicle is called "atresia." It begins in intra-uterine life, becomes prominent at birth and before puberty, continues on a smaller scale throughout the period of sexual life, and is completed after the menopause. Every normal ovary, therefore, contains degenerating follicles. *Atresia may begin at any stage of development of the follicle*— even in apparently mature ones. It is not known why a few follicles reach maturity and rupture, while others degenerate at various stages of development. The ovum always seems to be affected primarily.

If a primary follicle is doomed to destruction, the ovum shrinks and degenerates. The follicular cells may show a tendency to engulf its debris, but they also degenerate quickly, after which the small cavity in the connective tissue stroma is closed without leaving a trace. In the vesicular follicle the ovum and the follicular cells show various signs of degeneration. The connective tissue cells of the theca interna penetrate into the epithelium and absorb it.

With the increase in size of the follicle undergoing atresia, the histological pictures become more

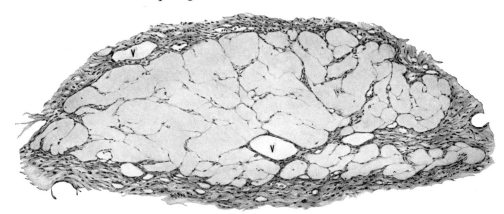

Fig. 30–13. Corpus albicans of human ovary. Fixation by perfusion—hence the empty vessels (*V*). Dense, hyaline material separates the residual cells of the corpus luteum. The whole structure is surrounded by the stroma of the ovary. 135 ×.

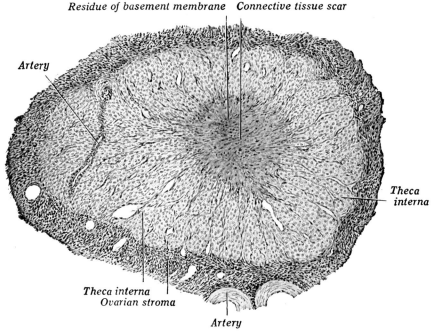

Fig. 30–14. Corpus atreticum with a well-developed theca interna, from the ovary of a thirty-nine year old woman. 85 ×. (After Schaffer.)

complicated and variable. The first signs of retrogression are always noticed in the egg cell. Its cytoplasm is filled with fat droplets, and it becomes coarsely granular and disintegrates. The zona pellucida is highly resistant; it shrinks and collapses, but otherwise seems unchanged. In the substance of the degenerating ovum which has lost its corona radiata and floats freely in the follicular liquid, small cells have often been observed. They were thought to be cells of the follicular epithelium; it is more probable, however, that they are connective tissue wandering cells which actively penetrate the dead ovum and destroy it.

Before undergoing complete degeneration and disintegration, the ovum in an atretic follicle often shows signs of an atypical development. Maturation spindles may appear and lead to the formation of more or less characteristic polar bodies. Amitotic fragmentation of the nucleus and division of the protoplasm also occur. These changes result in the appearance in the interior of the zona pellucida of several cell bodies of varying size and with more or less distinct nuclei. These changes have been considered by some authors as possibly being an attempt at parthenogenetic development. They must, of course, be sharply distinguished from cases of ovarian pregnancy in which an ovum retained in a ruptured follicle is fertilized by a spermium finding its way into the ovary.

The follicular epithelium in an atretic follicle always degenerates. The cells first affected are those near the cavity of the follicle. The peripheral cell adjacent to the basement membrane, as well as the cells of the cumulus, may remain alive for a considerable time and are even said to show mitoses. The retrogressive changes are manifested in chromatolysis of the nucleus and fatty or hyaline degeneration of the cytoplasm. The cells round off, shrink, and float in the liquor folliculi as small, round particles; they contain deeply staining granules of chromatin.

At an early stage of atresia, at a time when the follicular epithelium may still seem normal, but undoubtedly is already changed, the connective tissue elements of the theca and blood vessels penetrate the basement membrane in many places and invade the degenerating epithelium. The cavity of the follicle collapses, its outlines, marked by the basement membrane, become wavy, and the cavity is filled by a large number of fibroblasts, wandering cells and blood capillaries. Some of these elements in vitally stained animals accumulate granular dye inclusions. The remnants of the degenerated, follicular epithelium are rapidly resorbed. The folded and collapsed zona pellucida remains alone amid the connective tissue elements.

Simultaneously, the theca interna undergoes important changes (Fig. 30–15). The folded basement membrane which separates it from the epithelium often increases in thickness, and is transformed into a layer of hyaline substance. The large cells of the theca interna increase further in size and are usually arranged in radial groups or strands, separated from one another by partitions of smaller, fusiform cells, and fibers (Fig. 30–14). The cells acquire a typical epithelioid character and are filled with lipid and fat droplets. They are identical with the theca lutein cells, but reach a higher degree of development in the atretic follicle.

The cavity of the atretic follicle, containing the collapsed zona pellucida and connective tissue, is now surrounded by a broad, festooned layer of epithelioid, lipid-containing theca interna cells, arranged in radial cords and provided with a rich capillary network. The microscopic aspect of such an atretic follicle is similar to that of an old corpus luteum; therefore, such structures have been called corpora lutea atretica. The main differences are, of course, the presence of the degenerated ovum in the center of an atretic follicle, and the degenerate granulosa cells.

The ultimate fate of an atretic follicle is shrinkage. Strands of fibrous connective tissue penetrate, together with blood vessels, through the hyaline membrane into the interior, and compress and destroy the remains of the degenerated elements. The resulting scar with its hyaline streaks sometimes resembles a corpus albicans, but is usually much smaller and sooner or later disappears in the stroma of the ovary.

The layer of hypertrophic theca interna cells, which surrounds the cavity of the atretic follicle, is broken up into separate cell islands of various forms and sizes by the invading strands of fibrous tissue. These islands are irregularly scattered in the stroma and may persist for a time. They constitute the so-called "interstitial gland" of the ovary.

Stroma. The interstitial connective tissue or stroma of the human ovarian cortex consists of networks of reticular fibers and spindle-shaped cells which resemble smooth muscle cells, but do not have fibrils in their cytoplasm. True smooth muscle cells have been described in the theca externa of the follicles of the pig's ovary. The cells of the ovarian stroma are not common fibroblasts, for they may give rise to interstitial cells and, in ovarian pregnancy, to decidual cells. Elastic fibers occur in the cortex only in the walls of the blood vessels. Beneath the "germinal" epithelium the interstitial connective tissue is condensed into the tunica albuginea. The peculiar layer of stroma surrounding the follicles, the theca folliculi, has been described.

The medulla is made of loose connective tissue with many elastic fibers and, accompanying the blood vessels, strands of smooth muscle cells.

Interstitial Cells. Much has been written on the "interstitial cells" of the ovary. In the adult human ovary they are either absent or present in small numbers, as irregular cords of large polyhedral "epithelioid" cells scattered in the stroma. In postembryonic life they arise from the theca interna of atretic follicles. The "interstitial gland" reaches its greatest development in the postembryonic human ovary the first year of life —at a time when atretic follicles are most numerous. It involutes at puberty with the beginning of menstruation and the formation of corpora lutea. During pregnancy, and especially at its end, it may increase slightly for a short time.

In the early stages of atresia, the interstitial cells form a layer around the cavity. When this layer is broken up later into separate cell clusters, the stress of growth changes in the stroma scatters the interstitial cells, and their original relations to the atretic follicles are obscured. In the human ovary they soon degenerate and disappear.

In animals with large litters (rodents) the development of the "interstitial gland," also connected with atresia of follicles, may be enormous. The cell foci originating from the breaking up of the hypertrophied theca interna of atretic follicles persist, enlarge and fuse. Through the continuous addition of new cells, most of the organ is transformed into a diffuse mass of large, closely packed, lipid-containing, interstitial cells, almost identical with true

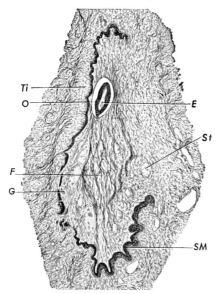

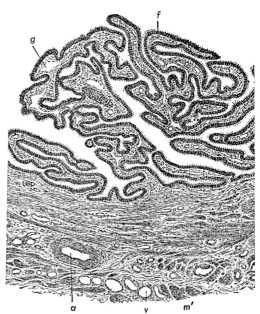

Fig. 30–15. Atretic follicle with highly developed glassy membrane, *SM*, which is partly broken through. *E*, residue of the ovum; *F*, fibrin-like network which is the residue of the follicular cavity; *G*, scattered granulosa cells; *A*, zona pellucida; *St*, invading stroma with vessels; *Ti*, cells of the theca interna. Ovary of a young woman. Mallory's connective tissue stain. 85 ✕. (After Schaffer.)

Fig. 30–16. Portion of cross section through ampulla of tube of a twenty-seven year old woman. *S*, mucosa, passing over without a sharp border into the muscular layer; *a*, artery; *f*, folds of mucous membrane covered with ciliated epithelium and containing blood vessels, *g; m*, smooth muscle bundles cut longitudinally and in cross section at *m'; v*, veins. 50 ✕. (After von Ebner, from Schaffer.)

granulosa lutein cells. The remaining follicles and the corpora lutea are embedded in this huge cell mass, and only a thin albuginea separates the latter from the germinal epithelium on the surface.

In the hilus of the ovary, groups of large, epithelioid cells can be found in connection with bundles of nonmyelinated nerve fibers—*sympathicotrophic cells*. Although they are usually considered chromaffin cells, their chromaffin nature is not certain, since they do not always stain with chromates and since their cytoplasm contains cholesterol esters not typical for these elements.

In the broad ligament and in the mesovarium, small accumulations of "interrenal" tissue (cortex of adrenal) have also been described.

Vestigial Organs. Certain vestigial organs are found in connection with the ovary. The most important of them is the *epoophoron*. It consists of several parallel or divergent tubules, located in the mesovarium, running from the hilus of the ovary toward the oviduct and fusing into a longitudinal canal, which is parallel to the oviduct. All these tubules end blindly; they are lined by a low cuboidal or columnar, sometimes ciliated, epithelium, and are surrounded by a condensed connective tissue layer containing smooth muscle. The lateral end of the longitudinal duct sometimes ends in a cystlike enlargement—the *hydatid of Morgagni*—while its inner end may extend far toward the uterus as the so-called *duct of Gärtner*. Between the epoophoron and the uterus in the tissue of the broad ligament, especially in the fetus, irregular fragments of epithelial tubules—the *paroophoron*—may be found.

The epoophoron is the rudiment of the genital part of the mesonephros and corresponds to the epididymis of the male. The paroophoron is the remnant of the caudal part of the mesonephros and corresponds to the paradidymis in the male.

Vessels and Nerves. Relatively large vessels from the anastomosis of ovarian and uterine arteries enter the hilus and, branching profusely, run through the medulla. Because of their tortuous course, they were called arteriae helicinae. As in the corpora cavernosa penis, they may show longitudinal ridges on their intima. In the periphery of the medulla they form a plexus from which smaller twigs penetrate radially between the follicles into the cortex and break up into capillaries. These form dense networks in the theca of the larger follicles at the surface of the basement membrane. In comparison with such capillary nets, that of the cortex is coarse. The veins accompany the arteries; in the medulla they are large and tortuous and form a plexus in the hilus.

Networks of lymph capillaries arise in the cortex, especially in the theca externa of the large follicles. Lymph vessels with valves are found only outside the hilus.

The nerves of the ovary are derived from the ovarian plexus and from the uterine nerves. They enter the organ through the hilus, together with the blood vessels. They consist for the most part of nonmyelinated fibers; thin myelinated fibers are also present. The presence of sympathetic nerve cells in the ovary has not been confirmed. The majority of

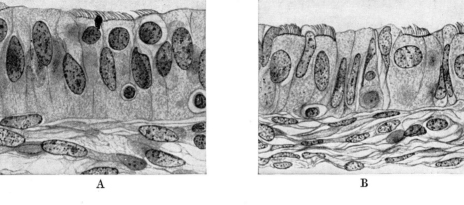

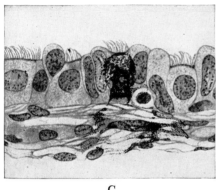
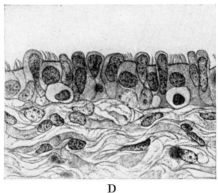

Fig. 30–17. Epithelium of human fallopian tube, showing physiological changes. *A,* midinterval; *B,* late interval; *C,* premenstrual; *D,* pregnancy. 700 ×. (After Snyder.)

the nerves supply the muscular coat of blood vessels. Many fibers penetrate into the cortex and form plexuses around the follicles and under the germinal epithelium on the surface. It seems doubtful whether they penetrate through the basement membrane into the epithelium of the follicles. Sensory fibers ending in corpuscles of Pacini have been described in the stroma.

THE OVIDUCT OR FALLOPIAN TUBE

The oviduct, a muscular tube 1 cm. thick and about 12 cm. long, is attached by the mesosalpinx at the broad ligament to the base and side of the pelvis; it is the proximal part of the müllerian duct of the embryo. Since the uterus arises from the fusion of the two müllerian ducts, the tubal and uterine epithelium are continuous. The myometrial mesenchyme secondarily envelops the uterine end of the tube, and so in the adult the tube pierces the fundus of the uterus. The abdominal part of the tube (ampulla) ends in a funnel-shaped opening, the

infundibulum, whose edge is split into many fringes, the fimbriae, the largest of which extends toward the ovary. The ampulla continues into the narrower isthmus adjoining the uterus. The part of the tube traversing the wall of the uterus is the pars interstitialis.

The wall of the oviduct consists of a mucous membrane, a muscular layer and an external serous coat. The mucous membrane in the ampulla is thick and forms numerous, high, branched folds. In transection the lumen, therefore, looks like a labyrinth of narrow spaces between epithelium-lined partitions. In the pars isthmica the longitudinal folds are much smaller. In the interstitial part they are reduced to low ridges.

The epithelium is of the simple, sometimes pseudostratified, columnar variety. It is highest in the ampulla and diminishes in height toward the uterus. It consists of two kinds of cells. One of these, especially numerous on the fimbriae and ampulla, carries cilia which beat toward the uterus. The other

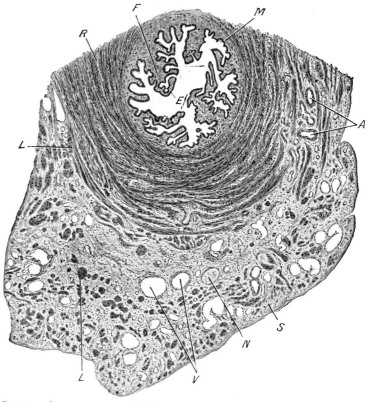

Fig. 30–18.   Portion of cross section of fallopian tube of a thirty-nine year old woman. Uterine portion (isthmus): *A,* arteries; *E,* ciliated epithelium; *F,* longitudinal folds of mucosa in cross section; *L,* longitudinal muscle; *M,* lamina propria; *N,* nerve; *R,* circular muscle; *S,* serosal covering; *V,* veins. 32 ×. (After Schaffer.)

is devoid of cilia, but is of glandular nature and contains granules. The secretion probably provides the ovum with nutritive material and, in some species, with an albuminous envelope. In the marsupials a shell as well as albumen is formed about the ova. The two types of epithelial cells are probably merely different functional conditions of one element. In women the epithelium of the oviduct undergoes slight cyclic changes with the uterine mucous membrane. True glands are absent in the oviduct.

The lamina propria of the mucous membrane of the oviduct consists of a network of thin fibers and of numerous fusiform or angular cells. Wandering cells and mast cells also occur. The fixed cells here seem to have the same potencies as in the uterus. In cases of tubal pregnancy, some of them may be transformed into decidual cells.

No true muscularis mucosae, and therefore no submucous layer, can be distinguished.

The mucous membrane is immediately surrounded by the muscular coat, which consists of two layers of smooth muscle bundles. The inner layer is circular or spiral; the outer is longitudinal. There is no distinct limit between the two, however, because of various spirally directed bundles. Toward the periphery the longitudinal bundles gradually appear in increasing quantities between the circular bundles. They are embedded in an abundant, loose connective tissue with elastic networks, and extend far into the serous layer and into the ligamentum latum. Toward the uterus the muscularis increases in thickness. The peritoneal coat of the fallopian tube has the usual serosal structure.

At the time of ovulation both ovary and oviduct exhibit active movements (Westman). The abdominal opening of the oviduct contains, in its mucosa, a ring of large blood vessels, especially veins, extending into the fimbriae. Between them muscle fibers

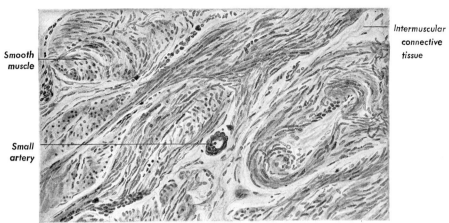

Smooth muscle

Intermuscular connective tissue

Small artery

Fig. 30–19. Section of myometrium of a woman of thirty-six years. Low magnification. Hematoxylin-eosin-azure II stain. (Drawn by Miss A. Nixon.)

form a network. It is a sort of erectile tissue. At the time of ovulation the vessels are filled with blood, and the enlargement and turgescence of the fimbriae, together with the contraction of the muscles, bring the opening of the funnel in close contact with the surface of the ovary.

The rhythmic contractions of the oviduct are probably of primary importance in the transport of the ovum. Contraction waves pass from infundibulum to uterus, and the cilia beat in the same direction.

The mucous membrane and its folds as well as the serous coat contain abundant blood and lymph vessels. Larger nerve bundles are found together with the vessels in the serous layer and in the peripheral parts of the longitudinal muscle. The circular muscle layer contains a dense plexus of thin nerve bundles supplying the muscle fibers and penetrating the mucous membrane.

UTERUS

The uterus is that part of the reproductive passages in which the ovum develops until the time of delivery. In the human subject it is single and represents the parts of the embryonic müllerian ducts which have fused in the midline. Developmental abnormalities range from a deep notch in the fundus to two intact uteri, cervices and vaginae.

The human uterus is a pear-shaped organ flattened in the dorsoventral direction and provided with a correspondingly flattened cavity and a thick muscular wall. Four parts

may be distinguished in it: (1) the body (corpus uteri) with its rounded upper end, the fundus; (2) the isthmus—the middle, slightly constricted part; (3) the cervix—the cylindrical lower part with the cervical canal; and (4) the portio vaginalis—the lower end, protruding into the vagina, and pierced by the cervical canal.

The wall of the uterus consists of three layers: the outer—the serous membrane of the peritoneum which is found only on a part of the viscus; the middle—a thick (2 cm.) mass of smooth muscle, the *myometrium;* the inner—the mucous membrane, the *endometrium.*

The serous membrane has the usual structure of the peritoneum.

Myometrium. The smooth muscle fibers of the muscular layer are arranged in cylindrical or flat bundles separated from one another by interstitial connective tissue containing isolated smooth muscle cells. According to the direction and disposition of the bundles, several layers of muscles can be distinguished in the myometrium, but are not sharply outlined, because fibers frequently pass from one layer into another.

Immediately under the mucous membrane, a thin layer of mostly longitudinal, but some circular and oblique, bundles may be distinguished. This is called the *stratum submucosum.* It forms distinct muscular rings around the intramural parts of the oviducts. The next layer to the outside is the thickest; it is called the *stratum vasculare,* because it contains many large blood vessels, especially veins, which give it a spongy appearance; here circular and oblique muscle bundles predominate. Farther outside, a layer

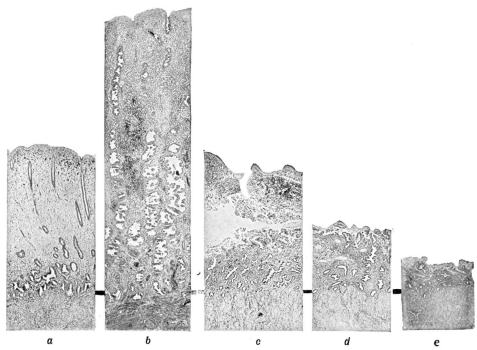

a   *b*   *c*   *d*   *e*

Fig. 30–20.   Sections through human endometrium at stages of the menstrual cycle: *a,* follicular phase, on day eleven of cycle; *b,* lutein phase, on day twenty-three of cycle; *c,* first day of menstruation; *d,* second day of menstruation; *e,* fourth day of menstruation. 18 ×. (Courtesy of G. W. Bartelmez.)

with circular and longitudinal fibers follows, the *stratum supravasculare.* Finally, immediately under the serous coat, there is a thin longitudinal muscle layer, the *stratum subserosum.* The two last-named layers send out their muscular bundles into the wall of the oviducts and into the broad and round ligaments.

The cervix is composed mainly of dense fibrous tissue in which, according to Danforth, a variable number of smooth muscle cells is distributed at random.

The smooth muscle cells of the myometrium have a length of about 50 microns. In the pregnant uterus, when the mass of the organ increases about twenty-four times, they hypertrophy to a length of more than 500 microns. In this condition there seems also to occur an increase in the number of the muscle fibers through division (Fischer-Wasels) and through transformation of the embryonic connective tissue cells and lymphocytes into new muscular elements, especially in the innermost layers of the myometrium (Stieve). In the puerperium the muscle cells show fatty infiltration and rapidly diminish in size. It is possible that some of them degenerate.

The connective tissue between the mus-

cular bundles consists of collagenous bundles, fibroblasts, embryonic connective tissue cells, macrophages and mast cells. There is a typical reticulum continuous with the collagenous intermuscular tissue. Elastic networks are especially prominent in the peripheral layers of the uterine wall, at the limit between the serosa and the muscularis. From here they extend inward between the muscle bundles. The innermost layers of the myometrium do not contain elastic fibers. The latter are, of course, found everywhere in the wall of the blood vessels. In the cervix the collagenous and elastic elements are especially numerous. This is the cause of the firmer consistency of this part of the uterus.

In pregnancy the connective tissue of the uterus becomes more abundant and succulent, which causes a considerable loosening of coherence between the muscle bundles.

Endometrium. In a sexually mature, nonpregnant woman, the uterine mucosa is subject to cyclic menstrual changes closely related to ovarian activity. Beginning with puberty (at the average age of fourteen) and ending with the menopause (usually at the age of forty-five to fifty), every twenty-one

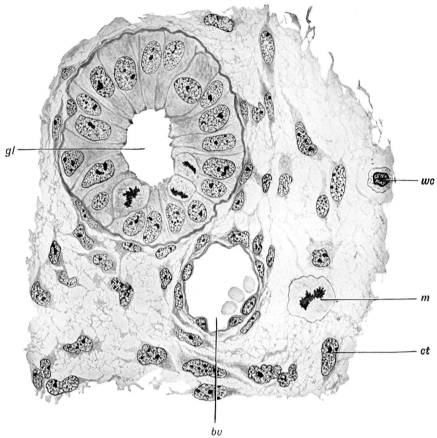

Fig. 30–21. Mucous membrane of human uterus, eleventh day of menstrual cycle. *gl,* cross section of gland with mitotically proliferating epithelium; *bv,* blood vessel; *ct,* connective tissue cell of lamina propria; *m,* mitosis of same; *wc,* wandering cell. 415 ×. (From the same mucous membrane as in Figure 30–20, *a.*) (A.A.M.)

to thirty-five days the mucous membrane of the corpus undergoes marked changes. These culminate in its partial destruction, which is accompanied by a more or less abundant extravasation of blood and appears as a bloody vaginal discharge—the *menstrual flow.* The flow, which marks the beginning of the cycle, lasts for three to five days.

The uterus is lined by a simple columnar epithelium. From fundus to vagina small groups of ciliated cells are scattered among the secreting cells. As far as the beginning of the cervical canal, this surface epithelium is substantially like that of the *uterine glands* which grow out from it in infancy. These are simple tubules slightly branched in a zone adjacent to the myometrium. They are separated from one another by connective tissue, the *stroma,* which resembles mesenchyme. Its irregularly stellate cells have a large, ovoid

nucleus. The cell processes appear to anastomose throughout the tissue and adhere to the framework of reticular fibers, which are condensed as basement membranes under the epithelium. Elastic fibers are absent except in the walls of the arterioles. There is a ground substance at times rich in tissue mucoid; in it are lymphoid wandering cells and granular leukocytes. Macrophages are not uncommon, but for some unknown reason they are not mobilized for phagocytosing extravasated blood. This may perhaps be due to conditions similar to those responsible for the failure of blood to clot after it has been in contact with the endometrial stroma.

The number of uterine glands varies from one person to another and may be rapidly increased by budding and growth toward the surface from the basal zone (O'Leary). Such buds which do not reach the surface become

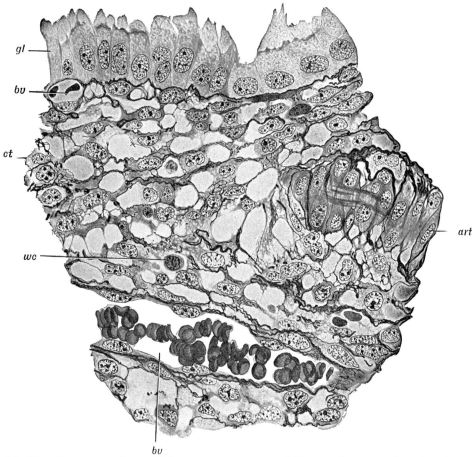

Fig. 30–22. Mucous membrane of human uterus, twenty-fifth day of menstrual cycle. *gl,* glandular epithelium; *bv,* blood vessel; *ct,* connective tissue of lamina propria, with silver-impregnated fibrils; *wc,* wandering cell; *art,* artery. 625 ×. (A.A.M.)

dilated (cystic). The glands seem to vary in their proximity to one another during the cycle, owing largely to changes in the diameter of the glands and in the amount of stromal ground substance (Fig. 30–20).

The uterine mucous membrane is firmly bound to the underlying myometrium. Occasional strands of endometrium extend down among the muscle bundles. Under pathological conditions the myometrium may be extensively invaded in this manner (adenomyosis). In old age, the endometrium, together with the other parts of the genital system, atrophies and becomes thin; the glands may become partly obliterated and form small cysts.

Endometrial Blood Supply. Certain arteries pass through the myometrium and basal endometrium with but few branches, to spread out into a rich capillary bed super-

ficially. These vessels are more or less contorted, and are termed "coiled arteries." During most of the cycle they constrict and dilate rhythmically, so that the surface is alternately blanched and suffused with blood (Markee). The basal half of the endometrium is supplied by arterioles with many branches which supply a dense capillary bed in the endometrium and the adjoining myometrium. The zone of endometrium between the superficial and basal circulations is supplied by vessels intermediate in form and has a coarser capillary mesh. The thin-walled veins form an irregular anastomosing net with sinusoidal enlargements at all levels.

Endometrial Cycle. Four phases of activity can be recognized in the endometrial cycle: (1) The follicular phase comprises the first half of the cycle and is typically associated with a rapidly growing graafian follicle. (2)

Progravid (lutein phase) is usually associated with an active corpus luteum. (3) Ischemic phase, when little blood flows through the coiled arteries. (4) Menstrual phase, associated with endometrial damage and extravasation.

1. The *follicular phase* usually begins at the end of a menstrual flow and is characterized by numerous mitoses in all endometrial tissues. The glands in the superficial two thirds or more are straight with narrow lumina (Fig. 30–20, *a*). The secretion accumulates in the glands, and their lumina widen as they become wavy in form. Glycogen is present in the gland cells, but only a thin mucoid is secreted at this time. The abundant stroma is rich in tissue mucoid. Coiled arteries are not found in the superficial third, which has only capillaries and venules.

The phase of hyperplasia may continue for a day or two after ovulation, which is believed to occur usually between the tenth and sixteenth days after the onset of a menstrual period. There may be a brief halt in the thickening of the endometrium at this time, a diapedesis of erythrocytes may occur under the surface epithelium, and some blood may occasionally enter the uterine lumen and reach the vagina. This has been termed *intermenstrual bleeding.* According to some, it corresponds to the estrous bleeding of the dog.

2. During the *progravid phase* the thickening of the endometrium is due largely to the increase of secretion and edema fluid. The glands become tortuous and then irregularly sacculated, i.e., "progravid" in form, especially in the middle half of the endometrium (Fig. 30–20).

The secretion now contains glycogen, and the mucoid is thicker. The gland cells are lower and wider; in the superficial zone they may contain lipoid granules which, however, do not enter the gland lumen. During this phase the cells readily change their form when immersed in the fixing solution, owing to the presence of much intracellular secretion, and have tongues projecting beyond the terminal bars (Fig. 30–22) (Bartelmez). In poorly preserved material the cells may even appear continuous with the secretion in the lumen.

In pregnancy the "progravid" changes progress for six to eight weeks (p. 528).

3. *Ischemic Phase.* In the nonpregnant cycle extensive vascular changes occur thirteen to fourteen days after ovulation and constitute the ischemic phase. This phase was discovered by Markee in transplants of endometrium to the eyes of monkeys.

A day or more before menstruation the coiled arteries constrict so that the superficial zone is blanched for hours at a time. With this the endometrium shrinks, and in the course of two days or more a transplanted bit of endometrium may decrease as much as 76 per cent in area. This involution is due to a loss of secretion and water (edema fluid). The stroma becomes denser. The closely packed stroma cells, irregularly collapsed glands and coiled arteries are characteristic of this phase. Usually many leukocytes are found in the stroma and between the epithelial cells. Sooner or later the coiled arteries clamp down, so that the superficial zone becomes anemic, while the blood continues to flow in the more basal portion of the endometrium.

4. *Menstrual Phase.* After a variable number of hours, the constricted arteries open up for a short time, the walls of vessels near the surface burst, and blood pours into the stroma and soon discharges into the uterine lumen. Such blood does not clot. Subsequently, patches of blood-soaked tissue separate off, leaving the torn ends of glands and arteries and veins open to the surface. Blood may ooze from such veins, a reflux from the intact basal circulation. The menstrual discharge thus contains altered arterial and venous blood, with normal and hemolyzed, sometimes agglutinated, erythrocytes, disintegrated or autolyzed epithelial and stroma cells as well as the secretions of the uterine, the cervical and the vulval glands. Sometimes there are tissue fragments, but blood clots are abnormal. The average loss of blood is 35 cc. By the third or fourth day of the flow the entire uterus may present a raw wound surface. The superficial gland and stroma cells are normal histologically.

Below the zone of extravasation the endometrium remains intact during menstruation, although it does shrink down. Typical progravid glands may be recognizable as such until the end of menstruation (Fig. 30–20). The surviving zone is accordingly wider than the "basalis" of many authors.

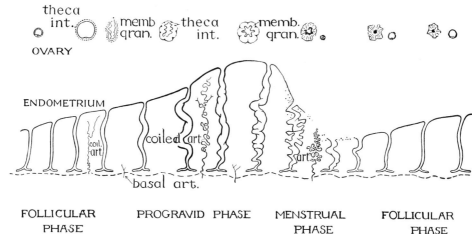

Fig. 30–23.   Diagram of interrelations of ovary and endometrium in a cycle which involves ovulation. Cycles are said to begin with the onset of menstrual bleeding. One complete cycle and the beginning of another are indicated. The ovarian changes involve the growth of a graafian follicle, its rupture, corpus luteum formation and regression. The endometrial development is indicated by changes in thickness, in the form of the glands and the coiled arteries. These changes depend in part on the time between the onset of menstruation and ovulation as well as on the duration of the cycle. Ovulation may occur normally as early as the seventh day or as late as the twenty-second day after the beginning of a menstrual period, but in most instances it probably occurs between the ninth and sixteenth days. The normal variability in cycle length is from twenty-one to forty days. *art,* coiled arteries; *memb. gran.,* membrana granulosa of the graafian follicle and the granulosa lutein cells; *theca int.,* theca interna. (Courtesy of G. W. Bartelmez.)

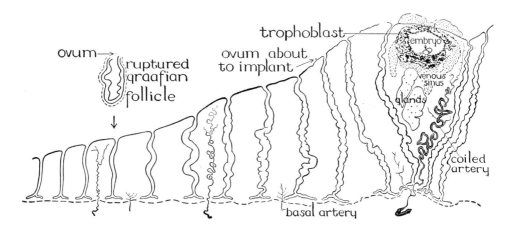

BEGINNING OF A PREGNANT CYCLE

Fig. 30–24.   Diagram showing beginning of a pregnant cycle. It is identical with Figure 30–23 until after implantation, which probably occurs about a week after ovulation. The relation of a recently implanted ovum to the endometrium is from a reconstruction of the ovum described by Brewer and about fourteen days old. It is buried in the endometrium and surrounded by dilated veins which had been opened by the trophoblast. Areas about the ovum with extravasated maternal blood are stippled; two glands below the ovum are dilated with blood. (Courtesy of G. W. Bartelmez.)

Before the vaginal discharge has ceased, epithelial cells glide out from the torn ends of the glands, and the surface epithelium is quickly restored. Then the superficial circulation is resumed, the stroma again becomes succulent, and the follicular phase of the new cycle may begin at once.

The "typical" conditions illustrated in Figures 30–20 and 30–23 are not always realized. In fact, the ovary may not produce a ripe follicle in the course of a cycle, and then the endometrial changes are minimal. Nevertheless, a clinically typical bleeding occurs at the expected time. This has been termed "anovulatory menstruation."

Such variability introduces difficulties in the evaluation of endometrial tissue removed at operation or biopsy. Errors are also introduced when only small fragments of endometrium are available, as in curettings. The various phases of the cycle in "typical" cases are identified by certain characters: (1) follicular phase: endometrium 1 to 5 mm. thick; straight, narrow glands becoming wavy, the epithelium tall, becoming vacuolated (glycogen), many mitoses in all tissues, no coiled arteries in the superficial third, and a subepithelial zone free of reticulum postmenstrually. (2) Progravid phase: endometrium 2 to 6 mm. thick, glands wavy or sacculated with wide lumen, epithelial cells broad with blebs, stroma edematous superficially, mitoses confined to coiled arteries which are present near the surface. (3) Ischemic phase: endometrium 3 to 4 mm. thick, greatly contorted arteries and glands, dense stroma with leukocytosis. (4) Menstruation: endometrium 0.5 to 3 mm. thick, superficially extravasated blood, the glands and arteries appear collapsed, the stroma is dense, and the surface is denuded.

Isthmus and Cervix. The mucous membrane of the corpus passes sometimes gradually, more often abruptly, into that of the isthmus, which remains thin and shows few signs of cyclic change. It lacks coiled arteries and usually does not bleed during menstruation. It has a dense stroma. The glands are sparse and are oblique to the surface.

The mucosa of the cervix has a different structure. It has a firmer consistency, a thickness of 2 to 3 mm., and shows, on its surface, branching folds (plicae palmatae, arbor vitae). The surface is lined by a tall columnar epithelium; in fixed material the oval nuclei are at the base of the cells with mucus in their apical parts. In the mucosa numerous large glands are present which differ from those of the corpus in that they are extensively branched, and are lined with a mucus-secreting, tall, columnar epithelium. Some of its cells, especially on the surface, are ciliated. The canal of the cervix is usually filled with mucus. Often some of the cervical

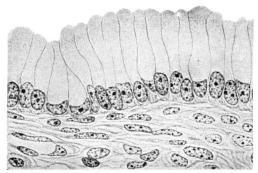

Fig. 30–25. Epithelium of endocervix of a woman of forty-six years, fourteen days after the beginning of the last menstrual period. 540 ×. (After Stieve.)

glands are transformed into cysts which may reach the size of a pea—the so-called *nabothian follicles.*

The mucosa of the cervix does not take part in the menstrual changes. An increase in vaginal mucus (which comes largely from the cervix) has been described about the middle of the cycle (Papanicolaou). In pregnancy the cervical glands enlarge, proliferate, and accumulate large quantities of mucus. The connective tissue between them is reduced to thin partitions.

The outer surface of the portio vaginalis is smooth, covered with a mucous membrane similar to that of the vagina, and consists of a stratified squamous epithelium with glycogen in its cells and a lamina propria with small papillae well separated from one another.

The transition between the columnar mucous epithelium of the cervical canal and the stratified squamous epithelium of the portio vaginalis is abrupt; as a rule the borderline is just inside the external opening of the cervix. In some cases patches of columnar epithelium may extend for short distances upon the outer surface of the portio vaginalis, forming so-called "physiologic erosions"; in others the vaginal end of the cervical canal has stratified epithelium.

Endometrium in Early Pregnancy. Great advances in our knowledge of early stages of placentation in man have been made by Hertig and Rock and in primates by Streeter and his colleagues, Wislocki, Hartman and Heuser, at the Carnegie Institution. Their papers as well as the extensive monograph on the human and monkey placenta by Wis-

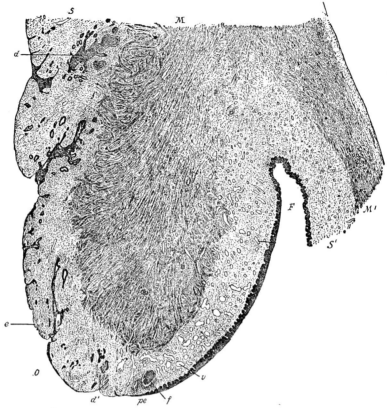

Fig. 30–26. Sagittal section through posterior half of the portio vaginalis uteri and the fornix vaginae of a young woman. *F*, fornix; *M*, muscle coat of the cervix; *M'*, muscle coat of the vagina; *O*, external orifice of the uterus; *S*, mucosa of the cervix; *S'*, mucosa of the vagina; *d, d'*, cervical glands; *c*, cylindrical epithelium; *f*, lymph follicle; *pe*, beginning of stratified squamous epithelium with papillae; *v*, veins. 10 ×. (After von Ebner.)

locki and Bennett should be consulted for the details and peculiarities of human placentation.

After fertilization, segmentation occurs as the ovum moves down the tube and enters the uterus. The human ovum burrows into the endometrium, presumably through the activity of the outer layer of cells of the blastocyst. These cells will also help to form the *placenta,* the organ for the transfer of nutritive materials from the maternal circulation to the embryo and the removal of its waste products. These nourishing cells are therefore called *trophoblasts.*

At the time the ovum enters it, the endometrium may resemble that in Figure 30–20, *b;* the glands are distended with glycogen and a mucoid, there are lipoid granules in epithelium and stroma, and the latter is edematous.

The youngest, embedding, human ovum is believed to be about seven and one-half days old (Fig. 30–27). It shows the blastocyst attached to the endometrium and invading its stroma. The advancing edge of the blastocyst consists of a multinucleated protoplasmic mass, the *syncytial trophoblast.* Closer to the primordium of the embryo proper the trophoblast is made up of distinct cells, the *cytotrophoblast.* In the next older specimen (nine days) found by these authors, the ovum has burrowed deeper into the endometrium and is almost covered with uterine surface epithelium. The syncytial trophoblast has increased in amount, and intercommunicating lacunae have developed in it. Some of these contain blood liberated by the penetration of the trophoblast into the maternal vessels. This is the beginning of the uteroplacental circulation, on which the continued growth of the embryo depends. In all probability the cytotrophoblast is giving rise to syncytial

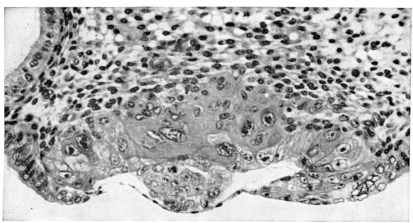

Fig. 30–27. Section of a seven and one-half day human ovum which is just embedding. Note broad layer of trophoblast penetrating endometrium. The faint cleft is probably the future amnion. 300 ✕. Hertig-Rock. (Courtesy of Carnegie Institution of Washington.)

trophoblast externally and has begun to form mesoblastic cells on its inner surface. The embryo proper at this time consists of a well-defined epithelial disk; an amniotic cavity is beginning to develop.

In the eleven-day specimen of Hertig and Rock (Figs. 30–28, 30–29) the trophoblast has increased in amount and, with the primitive mesoblast, forms the *chorion*. There are more frequent communications between the lacunae in the syncytial trophoblast and the maternal vessels.

This invasion of the maternal blood vascular system by trophoblast becomes progressively extensive. The syncytium continues to enlarge the implantation cavity during the earliest weeks of pregnancy. Until term it is concerned with the absorption of nutriment and the excretion of wastes for the embryo and its membranes.

During the next few days the ovum enlarges by the growth of the trophoblast and the accumulation of fluid in the primitive chorionic mesoblast. By the end of the second week the conditions shown in Figure 30–24 are reached, in which a reconstruction of the ovum described by Brewer (1937) is shown. The wide lacunae in the plasmodial trophoblast are in open communication with dilated maternal veins, and there has been considerable extravasation of blood about the ovum. A cap of blood overlies the implantation site. Adjacent to the nutrient-laden maternal tissue, the trophoblast has grown more luxuriantly. The embryo is attached to the chorion on this side by a mass of mesenchymal cells, the future umbilical cord.

At several points on the chorionic wall, mesoblast is beginning to spread out into the trophoblast to produce the first *villi;* these outfoldings of the chorion serve to increase its absorbing surface. Fetal blood vessels develop in the connective tissue core, which is covered by cellular and syncytial trophoblast (Fig. 30–32). The deeply staining syncytium has granular mitochondria and usually droplets of lipid. In the cellular trophoblast, usually called Langhans cells in the villi, the mitochondria are elongate and sparse. The cytoplasm of these cells usually stains feebly and is rich in a labile form of glycogen.

During the third week the cellular trophoblast at the tips of the villi begins to grow rapidly and, mushrooming out, serves to anchor the villus to the decidua basalis. As this process continues, the cellular proliferations of adjacent villi merge, and thus an outer wall of trophoblast is formed through which the maternal vessels communicate with the space between the villi. This *intervillous space,* which has developed from the trophoblastic lacunae and the dilated maternal veins, is bounded throughout pregnancy by normal or degenerated trophoblast except where it communicates with maternal vessels. It contains more or less maternal blood; the villi absorb nutriment from it and excrete wastes into it. The development of a func-

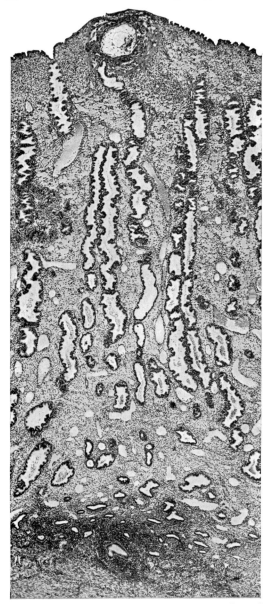

Fig. 30–28. Photomicrograph of section through implantation site of the eleven-day Hertig-Rock ovum. The entire thickness of the endometrium is shown. The glands are progravid, the stroma edematous, and the superficial veins are dilated. 22 ×. (After Hertig and Rock, 1941.)

tional vascular system during the fourth week makes possible the nutrition of the rapidly growing embryo.

Figure 30–30 shows the relations of chorion and endometrium at the end of the fourth week. The implantation site occupies only a small part of the endometrium, all of which, except for a basal zone, is sloughed off after

delivery. During pregnancy it has accordingly been called the *decidua* and is divided into three regions: overlying the ovum is the *decidua capsularis;* underlying it is the *decidua basalis,* which comprises the maternal component of the placenta; the rest of the endometrium as far as the internal os uteri is the *decidua vera.*

The vera continues to thicken during the first eight or ten weeks of pregnancy as the glands become more dilated with secretion and edema fluid accumulates. The stroma cells in the superficial third round up and enlarge, often becoming epithelioid. The superficial zone so formed has narrow glands and is called the *stratum compactum* in contrast to the underlying *stratum spongiosum,* which may extend to the myometrium; or, as in Figure 30–30, there may be an intervening *stratum basale* of narrow tortuous glands and dense stroma.

The villi of the inner wall grow and branch profusely; together with the *chorionic plate* from which they arise, they constitute the *chorion frondosum.* The superficial villi, on the other hand, soon appear stunted and during the third month they degenerate, leaving the chorionic plate smooth; this is the *chorion laeve.*

The amnion closely enswathes the embryo for the first two months, and there is a large cavity between amnion and chorion, the *exocelom.* Early in the third month, the amniotic fluid increases rapidly, and the amnion is soon in contact with the chorion on all sides. As the membranes fuse, the exocelom is obliterated (Fig. 30–31). The uterus begins to enlarge, and chorion laeve as well as all three deciduae is stretched and becomes thinner. But the placental villi are growing, and the margin of the placenta becomes well defined. A section of the placenta from this stage shows, beginning at the fetal surface, first the amniotic epithelium, then the fused connective tissue of amnion and chorionic plate, followed by the villi cut in various planes. Some villi are fused to the decidua basalis, and there are bands of necrotic trophoblast adjoining the decidua basalis. Here there are dilated and stretched glands and greatly modified coiled arteries which carry maternal blood to the intervillous space.

During the second half of pregnancy the terminal branches of the villi grow smaller

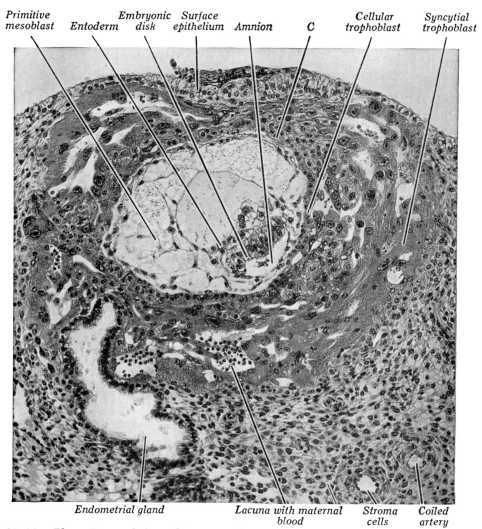

Primitive mesoblast Entoderm Embryonic disk Surface epithelium Amnion C Cellular trophoblast Syncytial trophoblast

Endometrial gland Lacuna with maternal blood Stroma cells Coiled artery

Fig. 30–29.   Photomicrograph from the same section as Figure 30–28, magnified 160 diameters. The bulk of the ovum consists of masses of trophoblast (syncytium) invading the endometrium. Within the syncytial trophoblast is the cellular trophoblast with obvious cell boundaries. The cells are arranged as a simple epithelium except for the clump at C. The cellular trophoblast immediately surrounds the primitive chorionic mesoblast in which the embryo is suspended. (After Hertig and Rock, 1941.)

and more numerous, but the rapid growth of the fetus involves an actual decrease in the thickness of the placenta with an increase in its circumference. By the fifth month most of the cellular trophoblast (Langhans cells) has differentiated into syncytium. The syncytium thins out, and in many spots overlying fetal capillaries it becomes a delicate membrane.

The detailed cytology and histochemistry of the trophoblast at various stages of pregnancy are given by Wislocki and Bennett, who suggest that the steroid hormones of the placenta are produced by the syncytial troph-

oblast and the gonadotrophic hormone by the cellular trophoblast. (See also Dempsey and Wislocki.)

Textbooks of embryology and obstetrics must be consulted for more details on the development of the placenta and its circulation.

Vessels and Nerves. The larger branches of the uterine artery run chiefly in the stratum vasculare of the myometrium. From here radial branches run directly to the mucosa and form "coiled arteries." During progravid stages these vessels grow and become progressively more tortuous, soon reaching the surface and forming a rich capillary net. The basal zone is supplied by arterioles from the adjacent

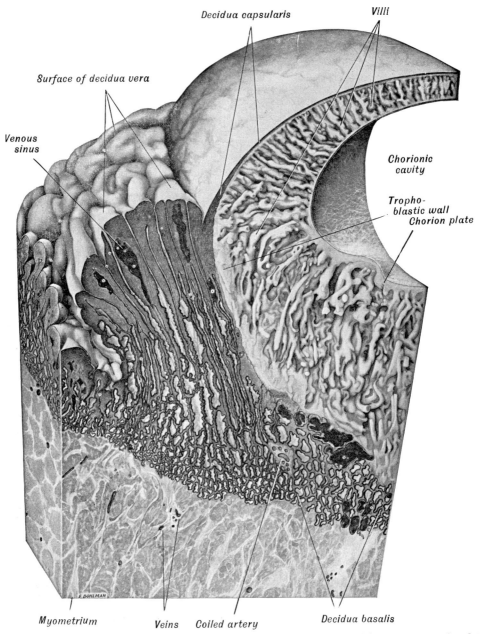

Fig. 30–30.   Margin of implantation site from a four weeks' pregnancy. The ovum is enclosed in the maternal decidua. The villi adjacent to the decidua basalis are long, have many secondary and a few tertiary branches, and are anchored to the decidua by a wall of cytotrophoblast. The decidua vera exhibits three zones: (1) a superficial compact zone with decidual cells; (2) a spongy zone of dilated and sacculated glands; (3) a basal zone of narrow glands, which may be entirely absent. In the implantation site the compact zone has been obliterated by the developing ovum except for the attenuated decidua capsularis. The embryo and the amnion surrounding it are not shown. 17 ×. (Courtesy of G. W. Bartelmez. Drawn by Miss Esther Bohlman.)

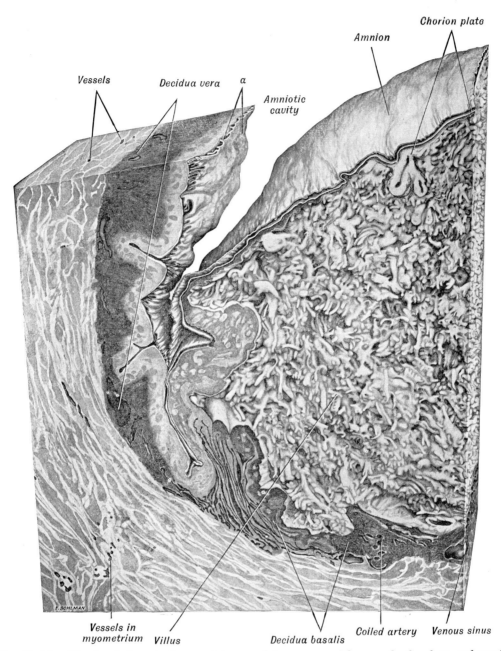

Vessels · Decidua vera · a · Amniotic cavity · Amnion · Chorion plate

Vessels in myometrium · Villus · Decidua basalis · Coiled artery · Venous sinus

Fig. 30–31.   Margin of placenta from a sixteen weeks' pregnancy. The growth of embryo and amnion as well as the enlargement of the uterus as a whole has changed the relations shown in Figure 30–30. The connective tissue of amnion and chorion has fused everywhere, obliterating the exocelom. Decidua capsularis and chorion laeve have fused with the stretched and regressing decidua vera, obliterating the uterine cavity as far as the internal os. The placental villi have grown and branched profusely, increasing the size of the placenta. The end of each villous trunk remains attached to the decidua basalis, and the small twigs float freely in the fluid of the intervillous space. The placenta now has a well-defined margin where the villi are shorter and there are wide communications between intervillous space and maternal veins. *a,* fused amnion and chorion. 7.5 ×. (Courtesy of G. W. Bartelmez. Drawn by Miss Esther Bohlman.)

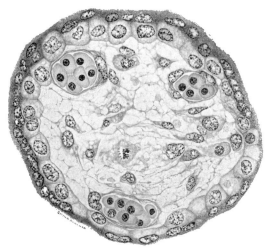

Fig. 30–32. Section through placental villus from a 2-cm. human embryo. The brush border on the syncytial trophoblast is barely visible. Beneath it is the continuous layer of cellular trophoblast. The vessels in the mesenchyme are filled with primitive erythrocytes. One mesenchymal cell in mitosis. 450 ×.

muscle. In the myometrium the capillaries have a peculiarly thick endothelium and sometimes a small lumen. The veins form plexuses in the deeper layer of the lamina propria mucosae. Another plexus of large veins without valves is found in the stratum vasculare of the myometrium.

Pregnancy causes irreversible changes in the vessels. In a uterus which has been pregnant, the wall of the vessels at the placental site shows an irregular thickening of the intima with neoformation of smooth muscle, while in the media the muscle is largely substituted by coarse elastic networks.

The lymph vessels of the myometrium are readily demonstrated, but their presence in the endometrium has been questioned.

The nerves of the uterus are for the most part nonmyelinated, although many fine and some thick, myelinated fibers occur also. They form the plexus uterovaginalis and are connected with a sympathetic "cervical" ganglion, located in the lateral, upper wall of the vagina. The ganglion contains, besides nerve cells, a considerable quantity of chromaffin elements. Inside the myometrium no nerve cells are found. Branching bundles of nerve fibers accompany the blood vessels and supply the muscular elements of the latter and of the myometrium. Some branches run through the mucosa toward the epithelium. The endings of the uterine nerves are not known exactly, but there is good physiological evidence for afferent and efferent fibers to the myometrium. There is, however, no intrinsic coordinating mechanism like that of the gut. The rich innervation suggests an interplay of nervous and hormonal effects normally, even though in transplants the characteristic myometrial and vasomotor responses can be obtained under conditions that appear to rule out the nervous system completely.

VAGINA

The vagina arises from the distal ends of the müllerian ducts, fused in the midline; the outer part develops from the urogenital sinus. Its lower end is marked by a dorsal, transverse, semicircular fold of the wall, the hymen. The wall of the vagina consists of three layers: (1) the mucous membrane; (2) the muscular coat; and (3) the adventitial connective tissue.

The adventitial coat is a thin layer of dense, connective tissue which merges into the loose connective tissue joining the vagina to the surrounding part. In this connective tissue there is a large venous plexus, nerve bundles, and small groups of nerve cells.

The interlacing smooth muscle bundles of the middle layer are arranged circularly and longitudinally; the longitudinal bundles are far more numerous, especially in the outer half of the layer. The interstitial connective tissue contains abundant, coarse, elastic networks. Striated muscle fibers form a ring-shaped sphincter around the introitus of the vagina.

The mucous membrane consists of a lamina propria and an epithelium on the free surface. The lamina propria is a dense connective tissue; toward the muscular layer it becomes looser, and this part may be considered a submucosa. While in the anterior wall of the vagina, papillae are scarce and small, in the posterior wall the lamina propria sends numerous high papillae deep into the covering epithelium. Immediately under the epithelium there is a dense network of fine elastic fibers; from here fine fibers run downward to the muscular layer and become condensed in the walls of the blood vessels. Accumulations of lymphocytes are numerous, and sometimes lymph nodules are found. Lymphocytes are always seen migrating into the epithelium. The deeper layers of the lamina propria contain dense plexuses of small veins.

The epithelium is of the stratified squamous variety and has a thickness of 150 to 200 microns. Under normal conditions the superficial cell layers in primates do not show cornification, although they contain granules of keratohyalin. The nuclei usually remain stainable, and the cells become loaded with glycogen and fat. In a prolapsed vagina, when the mucous membrane is exposed to air, the

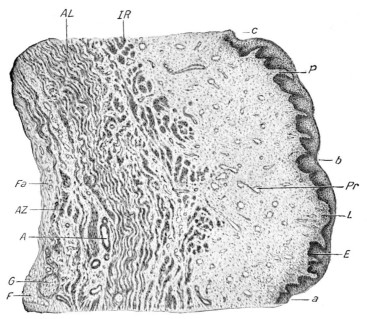

Fig. 30–33.   Anterior wall of vagina of young woman; longitudinal section. *A*, artery in the muscle; *AL*, external longitudinal layer and, *AZ*, external circular bundles of muscular layer; *a*, *b*, *c*, furrows between the rugae, of which two are shown in cross section; *E*, stratified squamous epithelium; *F*, fat lobules; *Fa*, fibrous layer; *G*, ganglion; *IR*, internal circular muscle layer; *L*, papillary layer of the lamina propria; *Pr*, infiltrated with leukocytes; *P*, papilla. 26 ×. (After Schaffer.)

superficial cells are cornified as in the epidermis.

Glands are missing in the vagina; exceptionally, some few glands of the cervical type are found in the fornix. The mucus, lubricating the vagina, originates from the cervix and is made acid by the fermentative action of bacteria on the glycogen from the vaginal epithelium.

The *hymen* is a fold of the mucous membrane with a thin connective tissue core and stratified squamous epithelium on both surfaces.

In spayed animals the vaginal epithelium is low, whereas epithelial proliferation is clearly associated with a high level of the ovarian hormone, estrone. The estrone response of the vaginal epithelium in the spayed rat and mouse remains the best quantitative test for the hormone.

In primates, partly because of the normal presence of bacteria, the vaginal contents vary so greatly as to be of little value in diagnosing ovarian conditions. Sometimes a reduction in the number of leukocytes can be recognized about the middle of the menstrual cycle which corresponds to the preovulatory phase in rodents, and the like. A high estrone level is indicated by the thick epithelium and occasionally by erythrocytes of uterine origin. Usually three zones can be recognized: (*a*) a basal zone of columnar and polyhedral cells with many mitoses;

(*b*) a narrow and variable zone with flattened cells sometimes containing granules that resemble keratohyalin; and (*c*) an outer zone of squamous cells loaded with glycogen and fat. The nuclei of these cells stain readily in most cases. During menstruation the microscopic picture of the vaginal lavage is dominated by erythrocytes, normal and hemolyzed, and leukocytes. Blood-soaked fragments of endometrium may occur in normal women, but blood clots are abnormal.

In sexually inactive states such as childhood and old age, a vaginal proliferation is readily produced by the administration of estrone. This has proved to be a valuable method of clearing up vaginal infections.

In *gestation* the smooth muscle fibers enlarge and recede from one another. The connective tissue elements—the collagenous bundles and the cells—enlarge and are arranged more loosely. The blood vessels, especially the veins, also enlarge, and the capillary endothelium swells. The thickness of the epithelium increases considerably during the first half and then diminishes greatly.

In various mammals (rat, guinea pig, opossum, and others) the cyclic changes in the vaginal epithelium can be correlated with the ovarian and uterine changes, so that it is simply necessary to examine washings from the vagina to make a diagnosis of the stage in the ovarian cycle. The cyclic vaginal changes in the rat and guinea pig are as follows: During the rapid growth period of the graafian follicle the epithelium grows rapidly, so that ten to fifteen layers can be recognized, and leukocytes

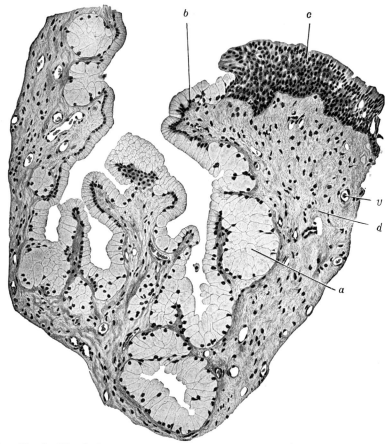

Fig. 30–34.   Gland of Bartholin. A large duct with patches of stratified columnar epithelium (*c*) gives off smaller branches lined with columnar mucous cells (*b*) and continuing into tubulo-alveolar terminal portions; these are lined with large mucous cells (*a*); *d*, interstitial connective tissue; *v*, blood vessel. 185 ×. (A.A.M.)

which were previously abundant disappear from the mucous membrane. A thick layer of squamous cells forms, in which the nuclei can no longer be stained. About the time of ovulation the squamous cell layer is sloughed, and leukocytes swarm through the epithelium in vast numbers. The cheesy mass which fills the lumen is discharged. In the guinea pig the vaginal orifice is sealed by an epithelial proliferation. During the rest of the cycle the epithelium is of the low stratified squamous type, and leukocytes continue to pass through it.

Vaginal lavages can accordingly be assigned to definite stages of the estrus cycle.

I. *Proestrus* associated with rapidly growing follicles. Leukocytes disappear from the lavage, and only nucleated epithelial cells are present.

II. *Estrus* associated with ripe follicles. All nucleated epithelial cells are gradually replaced by squamous "plates" with no visible nuclei. The female will mate only during this stage, rarely during stage I.

III. *Metaestrus.* The vagina is filled with a mass of sloughed epithelial plates; leukocytes begin to appear and rapidly become numerous. Ovulation occurs during this stage or between stages II and III.

IV. *Diestrus.* Until the beginning of the next cycle the lavage has nucleated epithelial cells, squamous plates and large numbers of leukocytes.

EXTERNAL GENITALIA

The outer sexual organs comprise the clitoris, the labia majora and minora, and certain glands which open into the vestibulum vaginae.

The *clitoris* corresponds embryologically to the dorsal part of the penis; it consists of two small, erectile, cavernous bodies, ending in a rudimentary glans clitoridis, which is covered by the mucous membrane of the vestibulum vaginae, the space flanked by the labia minora. Into this space the vagina and the urethra open; it is lined with stratified squamous epithelium. Around the opening of the urethra and on the clitoris are several small glands—*glandulae vestibulares minores;* they resemble the glands of Littré in the male urethra, and contain mucous cells.

Two larger glands, the *glandulae vestibulares majores,* or *glands of Bartholin,* each the size of a bean, are located in the lateral walls of the vestibule. They open on the inner surface of the labia minora. They are of tubulo-alveolar character, closely correspond structurally to the bulbo-urethral glands of men, and secrete a similar lubricating mucus. After the thirtieth year they gradually begin to undergo involution.

The *labia minora* are covered with stratified squamous epithelium and have a core of spongy connective tissue with fine elastic networks and a large quantity of blood vessels, but without fat cells. It forms high papillae penetrating deep into the epithelium; the latter contains pigment in its deeper layer, while on the surface a thin, horny layer is present. Numerous, large sebaceous glands are found on both surfaces; they are devoid of hair.

The *labia majora* are folds of skin with a large amount of fat tissue and a thin layer of smooth muscle, as in the scrotum. The outer surface is covered with hair; the inner is smooth and hairless. On both surfaces sebaceous and sweat glands are numerous.

The outer genital organs are richly supplied with sensory nerve endings. The epithelium contains the usual free nerve endings. In the papillae, Meissner corpuscles, in the subpapillary layer, genital corpuscles are scattered. In the deeper parts of the connective tissue of the labia majora and in the cavernous bodies of the clitoris, pacinian corpuscles have been found.

CORRELATIONS IN THE FEMALE REPRODUCTIVE SYSTEM

Hormones are concerned in the embryonic development of the reproductive tract, but opinion is divided on whether these are exactly the same as the hormones of the adult (see reviews by Jost and by Moore). The changes of puberty are under hormonal control, and estrogens are probably the immediate agents concerned. Excision of both ovaries at an early stage arrests the development of the uterus and the secondary sex characters. During the period of sexual activity the ovarian

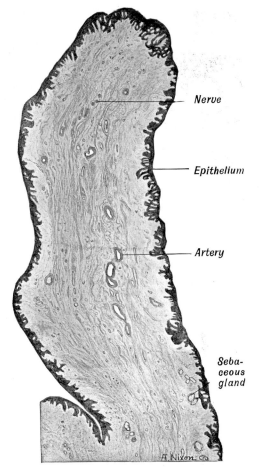

Fig. 30–35.   Cross section of labium minus of a woman of thirty-four years. 10 ×.

hormones, *estrone* and *progesterone,* control the tubal, uterine and vaginal changes. Removal of the ovaries in a sexually mature female abolishes menstruation in women and estrus in animals. This is accompanied by involution of the uterus and is an artificial menopause. Injection of estrogens for a short time into ovariectomized females will produce uterine bleeding. But injection of estrogen over long periods will inhibit menstruation, even if the ovaries are intact.

The follicle-stimulating and luteinizing hormones of the hypophysis together cause the preovulatory growth and rupture of ovarian follicles; the increased secretion of these hormones is caused by the action of estrogen and possibly progesterone on the pituitary. Other endocrines are also involved in the control of pregnant and nonpregnant cycles. Psychic states may influence the men-

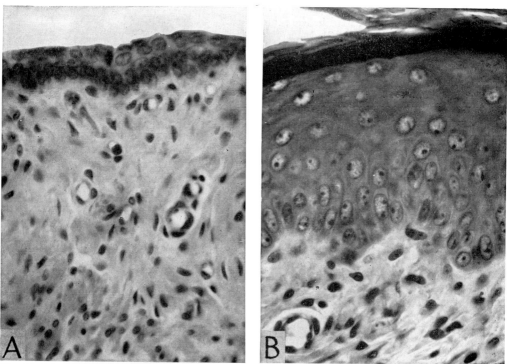

Fig. 30–36. Photomicrographs of vagina of immature rat (*A*), and similar rat injected with follicle-stimulating hormone for three days (*B*). The hypertrophied epithelium is shedding cornified epithelium on the free surface. 510 ×.

strual rhythm in women, and direct relations between the central nervous system and the hypophysis have been demonstrated. The complex interrelationships which control the reproductive organs are reviewed in detail in *Sex and Internal Secretions,* edited by E. Allen, and more recently in books by Burrows and by Turner.

In the vast majority of mammals, mating occurs only when the female is in "heat," or estrus. In primates there is no definite period of heat. In the human species the most obvious external indications of the reproductive cycle are hemorrhages. The menstrual cycle is, however, fundamentally similar to the estrus cycle, if it is divided into preovulation and postovulation phases. Under optimal conditions the correlated ovarian and uterine changes are more or less as indicated in Figure 30–23, which illustrates nonpregnant cycles. Thus ovulation may occur from seven to twenty-two days after the onset of a menstrual flow, and the endometrium will vary accordingly. One cycle may be twenty-four days in length, the next twenty-eight or thirty-two days.

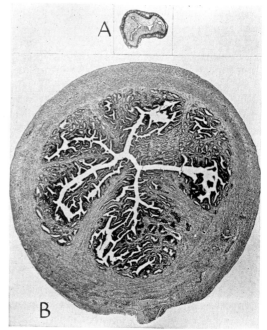

Fig. 30–37. Photomicrographs of uterus, *A,* of immature rabbit, and *B,* of similar rabbit showing hypertrophy of all layers of the uterus after priming with small doses of estradiol for five days, followed by six daily injections of progesterone. 14 ×.

It is believed that secretion of *estrone* by the growing follicle causes regeneration of the endometrium after menstruation, while *progesterone,* secreted by the corpus luteum, causes the progravid changes of the endometrium as a potential nidation site for a fertilized ovum.

Estrone is probably secreted by the follicular cells, although there is some evidence which suggests that it may be formed by the theca interna. The interval between the follicular phase and the lutein phase involves a superficial endometrial hyperemia and sometimes diapedesis of erythrocytes with the appearance of blood in the vagina. If the follicular phase has been produced with estrone in a spayed female, progravid changes will appear on the administration of progesterone. It would seem that the ischemic phase with the associated involution of the endometrium is due to a reduction in the available ovarian hormones, and there is evidence that the corpus luteum is regressing at this time. It has been suggested that the ovarian hormones, having been kept at a definite high threshold for a definite time, inhibit the gonadotrophic activity of the distal hypophysis, and this is the reason for the diminished production by the ovary (Corner). Whether the hemorrhagic changes involve other hormonal mechanisms or not remains to be seen.

If the ovum is not fertilized, the corpus luteum regresses, and the anterior pituitary makes follicle-stimulating hormones; this starts a new ovarian cycle. If the ovum is fertilized, the developing placenta secretes a luteinizing hormone (placental gonadotrophin), which keeps the corpus luteum active and probably inhibits the hypophysis from secreting follicle-stimulating hormone. After several months' pregnancy, the placenta produces large amounts of progesterone, and removal of the ovaries will not interrupt pregnancy.

The estrus state appears at intervals which vary according to the species (four to five days in the rat, fifteen to seventeen days in the guinea pig, about three weeks in the sow, twice yearly in the bitch and ewe). Wild species such as the opossum and ground squirrel, which have a definite breeding season, exhibit several cycles if pregnancy is prevented. In the absence of pregnancy, the cycles in domestic animals continue throughout the year when food and temperature conditions are kept optimal.

During estrus graafian follicles are approaching maturity, the content of estrone in the blood is high, and its action is manifested by the behavior of the animal and the anatomical and physiological reactions of the reproductive tract. In the rat, as the follicles approach maturity, there is a rapid secretion of fluid by the uterine glands, so that the organ is greatly distended. The active proliferation of vaginal epithelium is interpreted by Papanicolaou as an adaptation for mating. The changes of these phases of the cycle (proestrus and estrus) have been produced experimentally by estrogens in spayed animals.

After ovulation the ova pass into the tube and reach the uterus on the fourth day. In the interim the uterus has collapsed and the vaginal epithelium has been sloughed. As the corpora lutea develop, the uterine muscle becomes less active, and then the ova, if fertilized, are regularly spaced along the uterine horns. If mating has not occurred, regressive changes appear in the corpora lutea, uterus and vagina, and a new cycle begins.

In the rabbit, ovulation is not spontaneous. An isolated female in heat has about ten large graafian follicles in the ovaries. After mating, these follicles grow rapidly, and in about ten hours ovulation occurs. The stimulus of coitus involves the portio vaginalis of the cervix and an erogenous area of skin on the flanks. The resulting nervous impulses pass to the spinal cord and brain. Through a center in the hypothalamus the pars distalis of the hypophysis is stimulated to secrete gonadotrophic hormones which activate the ovaries. If one and one quarter hours elapse between mating and hypophysectomy, enough gonadotrophic substance enters the blood stream to induce ovulation. Under these conditions corpora lutea develop, but they promptly regress, and, in the consequent absence of progesterone, the fertilized eggs die. Such corpora can be maintained in a functional state either by gonadotrophins or by estrone.

Comparison of the Structure of Testis and Ovary. The sex cells in the testis and ovary of the embryo arise from the same germinal epithelium. In the testis of the adult it persists as a flattened mesothelium on the outer surface of the albuginea. On the surface of the adult ovary it remains more or less unchanged.

The spermatogenic cells and the ova undergo comparable developmental transformations; both pass through a period of intense mitotic activity of the ordinary somatic type —period of multiplication. After that they both grow without dividing and are transformed into primary spermatocytes and primary ovocytes respectively (Fig. 30–8, *b, b'*) —period of growth. Finally, both spermatogenic cells and ova pass through the period of maturation, characterized by the two "meiotic" divisions. In both cases the result is a sex cell ready for fertilization, with a nucleus containing but one half of the somatic number of chromosomes.

Spermia are produced anew continuously, or at certain intervals, during the whole sexual life of the individual, while the ova in primates probably complete their period of multiplication shortly before birth or in the first weeks of extra-uterine life. Then, slowly, one by one, they undergo the maturation divisions. The vast majority of them degenerate before they reach this stage.

In various rodents, eggs develop from the germinal epithelium throughout infancy and even during sexual maturity.

The embryonic origin of the Sertoli cells in the testis and of the follicular epithelium in the ovary is the same. In the adult, both protect the developing sex cells and furnish them suitable nutritive material. The possibility of production of spermatogenic cells by Sertoli cells has been mentioned; a similar production of new ova by the follicular cells in the mammals has not been observed.

The interstitial cells are far less constant in the mammalian ovary than in the testis. They probably arise from the theca interna of atretic follicles; in the human ovary they may even be absent.

The morphological relations and similarities between the two sex glands are revealed best in their embryonic histogenesis.

Histogenesis of the Sex Glands. The primordia of the gonads arise as thickened strips of mesodermal epithelium on the surface of the urogenital folds—the *genital ridges*. The *germinal epithelium* of the ridge has the same structure at first in both sexes. This is the "indifferent" stage of the gonad, although the sex of the embryo is determined at the time of fertilization.

The excretory ducts of the sexual apparatus develop in close connection with the embryonic urinary system, being laid down as two longitudinal ducts on both sides—the *ducts of Wolff* and of *Müller*. They arise from the mesoderm which lines the celom, and both open into the urogenital sinus. When the thickened germinal epithelium in the male embryo develops into the seminiferous tubules, the wolffian duct comes into connection with them and furnishes the excretory system of the male sexual gland, while the duct of Müller involutes, leaving only small rudiments. In the female the same mesodermal primordium of the gonad is transformed into the ovary. Here the wolffian ducts regress, whereas the müllerian ducts furnish the oviducts, the uterus and the vagina.

The germinal epithelium of the "indifferent" gonad consists of two kinds of cells. The majority are small, cuboidal or columnar elements in a pseudostratified layer or in several layers. They contain threadlike mitochondria and show numerous mitoses. Between them, large spherical elements are scattered—the *primitive sex cells*. They are far less numerous, and their number can be counted in some species. They have a clear cytoplasm, a large vesicular nucleus and granular mitochondria. They show occasional mitotic divisions.

There is a massive penetration of the subjacent mesenchyme by epithelium in which the sex cords develop. They consist of the same two cell types as the germinal epithelium. The deepest parts of the epithelial mass consist of smaller cells arranged in a network which later receives a lumen—the rete. It is present in both sexes.

In the male human embryo the testis becomes recognizable at about seven weeks. The sex cords are transformed into convoluted seminiferous tubules. Their peripheral ends anastomose and open through the rete testis into the tubules of the mesonephros (the future coni vasculosi) and beyond into the wolffian duct (the future vas deferens, Fig. 30–38).

Throughout the prepubertal period, the seminiferous tubules seem to contain the same two apparently independent cell types. The primary sex cells are scattered singly between the small epithelial cells (Figs. 30–39, 30–40).

At the onset of puberty, the sex cells begin to proliferate. They become spermatogonia, and the "follicular" epithelial cells gradually assume the structure of Sertoli cells. Once spermatogenesis starts, it continues without interruption throughout the sexual life.

The beginning of sexual differentiation may be determined in female embryos at eight weeks. Mesenchyme grows into the solid epithelial mass and separates it into thin *medullary cords* (Fig. 30–38), homologues of the seminiferous tubules, and becomes connected with the tubules of the mesonephros. They contain primitive sex cells (*primitive ova*) and may even show transient formation of rudimentary follicles which disappear.

In human embryos of four to five months a new cortical layer of epithelium is formed (Fig. 30–41). This second proliferation period produces the primitive cortex of the ovary. Mesenchymal strands with blood vessels penetrate the epithelial cortex, and subdivide it into cell clusters of irregular form. The ova are surrounded by the smaller epithelial cells—the primary follicles.

The sex cells in the cortex of the embryonic human ovary now show the same nuclear transformations as in the spermatogenic cells (Fig. 30–41). The resting nuclei of the ova have a few large chromatin particles and a nucleolus. Such cells, at the end of the period of multiplication, correspond to spermatogonia and are called *oogonia*.

The older oogonia enter the period of growth and become *primary ovocytes*—homologues of the primary spermatocytes. Their body enlarges, and the chromatin is arranged in thin threads interlacing in the nuclear space (leptotene stage, Fig. 30–41). Later, the threads, often joining one another side by

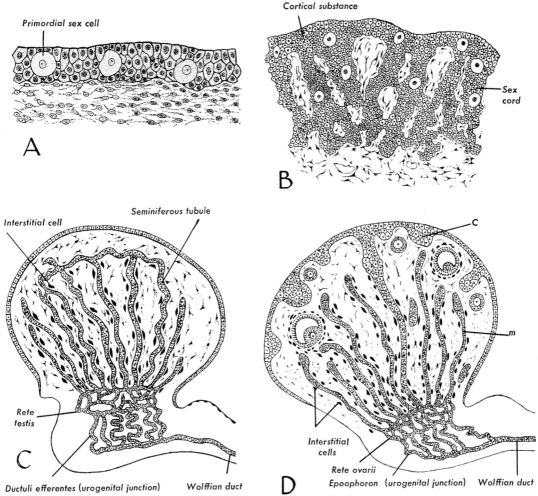

Fig. 30–38. Diagram of development of the sex glands. *A*, Primordium in early indifferent stage (*germinal plate*) with primordial sex cells. *B*, later but still indifferent stage, showing formation of sex cords. *C*, development of testis. *D*, development of ovary; *c*, cortical substance with formation of follicles; the medullary cords (*m*) are homologues of seminiferous tubules (in *C*) and, like them, are derivatives of the sex cords (in *B*). (After Kohn.)

side, are coiled up at one pole of the nucleus (synaptene stage, Fig. 30–41). The pachytene and diplotene stages develop later in the same way as in spermatogenesis.

After the diplotene stage is reached, further transformation of the ovocytes ceases for a long time. Such ovocytes in the follicles contain a large chromatin nucleolus and, near the nucleus, a crescentic accumulation of mitochondria. After birth the ovocytes in the primary follicles gradually undergo the transformations described early in this chapter.

In the ovary of a human embryo of about 180 mm., mesenchyme reaches the surface layer of germinal epithelium and forms the albuginea which separates the definitive cortex from the epithelial sheet on the surface. After this, according to the dominant opinion, additional ova are not formed from the germinal epithelium. Thus the medullary cords of the ovary

are homologous to the seminiferous tubules of the testis.

Interstitial Cells. The interstitial cells of the testis appear first in the human embryo of 19.5 mm. They arise from mesenchymal cells, although some claim that they may come from cells of the sex cords. In the second half of embryonic life, the interstitial cells in the testis are arranged in broad strands between the seminiferous tubules. Toward the end of gestation their number decreases relatively. At the beginning of puberty they again become more conspicuous.

The first interstitial cells of the ovary are found in human embryos of 4 cm. Mesenchymal origin seems clear, but some investigators derive them from germinal epithelium. After a period of numerical increase, they involute or become connective tissue cells. In embryos of 7 cm. another period of develop-

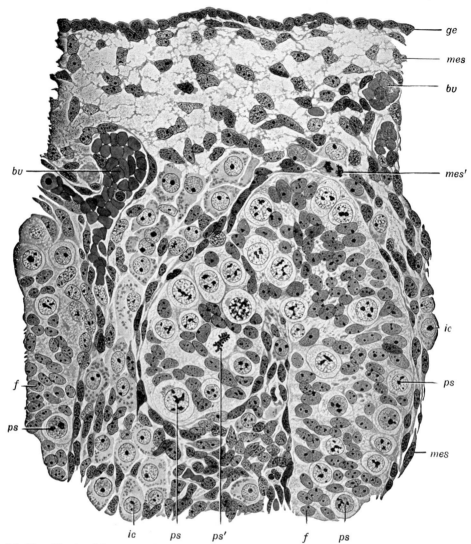

Fig. 30–39. Testis of human embryo of 70 mm. Seminiferous tubules without free lumen, with two kinds of cells. *ps* and *ps'*, primordial sex (spermatogenic) cells and, *f*, follicular (future Sertoli) cells. Between the tubules abundant interstitial tissue, with mesenchymal cells (*mes, mes'*) and interstitial cells (*ic*); *bv*, blood vessels; *ge*, germinal epithelium. 585 ×. (A.A.M.)

ment begins in the medulla of the ovary; hypertrophy of the mesenchymal cells is more pronounced. Involution occurs again shortly after birth. The third generation of interstitial cells appears in the cortex around the follicles before the second has disappeared. In post-embryonic life there are no cells resembling interstitial cells except the theca cells of atretic follicles.

Origin of Definitive Sex Cells. A disputed question is the origin of the definite sex cells.

In some lower invertebrates (Ascaris) the sex cells are separate from somatic cells in early stages of ontogenesis. This continuity of the sex or germ cells throughout innumerable generations is called the "germ track."

Many investigators have tried to establish the ex-

istence of a germ track in mammals. Cells have been found in early stages of development in the guinea pig which have the aspect of ova—the primitive sex cells. They were first found in the mass of undifferentiated cells at the posterior end of the primitive streak and in the entoderm of the posterior part of the intestine. These primitive sex cells were seen to migrate through the mesenchyme to the root of the mesentery and to enter the thickened celomic epithelium of the primordium of the gonad. In the description given they were mentioned as one of the two cell types present in the germinal epithelium.

In many of the lower vertebrates (chick, reptiles, amphibians, fishes) cells with a similar history have been found. If, in young amphibian and chick embryos, the parts containing the primitive sex cells

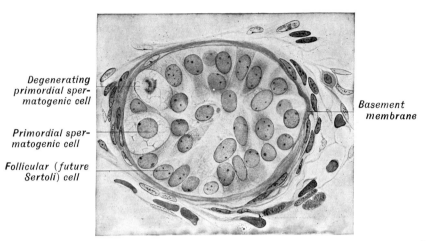

Degenerating primordial spermatogenic cell

Basement membrane

Primordial sper-
matogenic cell

Follicular (future
Sertoli) cell

Fig. 30–40. Section of seminiferous tubule of testis of six months' infant. Iron-hematoxylin. 720 ×.

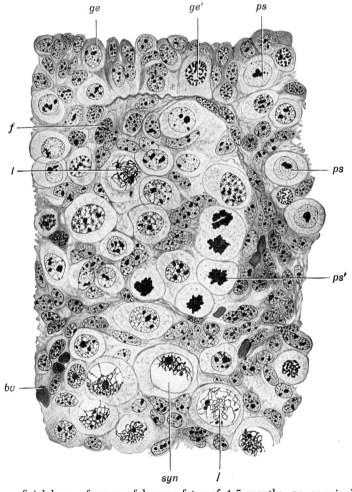

ge   ge'   ps

f

l

ps

ps'

bv

syn   l

Fig. 30–41. Superficial layer of ovary of human fetus of 4.5 months. ge, germinal epithelium with mitosis (ge'); ps, ps', primordial sex cells (ova) with mitosis; l, leptotene nuclei in growing ovocytes; syn, synaptene nuclei; f, follicular cells; bv, blood vessels. 625 ×. (A.A.M.)

are excised on one side, the corresponding gonad does not develop, or remains sterile. Although the primitive sex cells have not been traced back to the earliest stages of ontogenesis, the evidence seems to be in favor of the existence of a germ track in the other mammals and, perhaps, in man.

This conclusion is, however, far from being generally admitted. Numerous investigators point out that the primitive sex cells sooner or later degenerate and disappear among the epithelial cells of the sex cords and follicles, especially in mammalian embryos. They claim that the definitive sex cells of the adult develop secondarily in the germinal epithelium or, later, in the sex cords, through transformation of the common celomic epithelial cells. If this is true, then there is no germ track in the vertebrates. This conception of the nature of the definitive sex cells would gain strong support if certain observations mentioned for the mature sexual glands could be confirmed—the neoformation of spermatogonia from Sertoli cells as described in the regeneration of the seminiferous epithelium after x-raying, the postpubertal neoformation of ova from the germinal epithelium and the regeneration of the ovarian cortex after injuries.

It may be, however, that the apparently undifferentiated cells which give rise to definitive sex cells are primordial sex cells which have de-differentiated during development and do not again differentiate until an adequate stimulus is given.

REFERENCES

Allen, E. (ed.): Sex and Internal Secretions. Baltimore, Williams & Wilkins, 1939.

Bartelmez, G. W.: Some effects of fixation and other insults on uterine epithelial cells in primates. Anat. Rec., 77:509, 1940. Menstruation, Glandular Therapy, Symposium, Chap. 13, Chicago, 1942.

Bartelmez, G. W., and Bensley, C. M.: Human Uterine Gland Cells, in Cowdry's Special Cytology. 2d ed. New York, (3), 1523, 1932.

Burrows, H.: Biological Actions of Sex Hormones. London, 2d ed. Cambridge University Press, 1949.

Chiquoine, A. D.: The identification, origin and migration of the primordial germ cells in the mouse embryo. Anat. Rec., 118:135, 1954.

Corner, G. W.: Cytology of the Ovum, Ovary, and Fallopian Tube, in Cowdry's Special Cytology. 2d ed. New York, (3), 1565, 1932. Influence of the ovarian hormones, oestrin and progestin on the menstrual cycle of the monkey. Am. J. Physiol., 113:238, 1935. Ourselves unborn. Yale University Press, 1945.

Danforth, D. N.: The fibrous nature of the human cervix, and its relations to the isthmic segment in gravid and non-gravid uteri. Am. J. Obst. & Gyn., 53:541, 1947.

Daron, G. H.: The arterial pattern of the tunica mucosa of the uterus in *Macacus rhesus*. Am. J. Anat., 58:349, 1936.

Dempsey, E. W., and Wislocki, G. B.: Histo-chemical reactions associated with basophilia and acidophilia in the placenta and pituitary gland. Am. J. Anat., 76:277, 1945.

Duke, K. L.: The germ cells of the rabbit ovary from sex differentiation to maturity. J. Morphol., 69:51, 1941.

Engle, E. T.: Proceedings of the Conference on Diagnosis in Sterility. Springfield, Ill., Charles C Thomas, 1946.

Engle, E. T., and Smith, P. E.: Some uterine effects obtained in female monkeys during continued oestrin administration, with especial reference to the cervix uteri. Anat. Rec., 61:471, 1935.

Everett, J. W.: Pituitary-Ovarian Relationships. Progress in Clin. Endocrin., Jan., 1950.

Farris, E. J.: Human Ovulation and Fertility. Philadelphia, J. B. Lippincott Co., 1956.

Gruenwald, P.: The development of the sex cords in the gonads of man and mammals. Am. J. Anat., 70:359, 1942.

Hertig, A. T., and Rock, J.: Two human ova of the pre-villous stage, having a developmental age of about seven and nine days respectively. Contrib. Embryol., Carnegie Inst. Wash. Publ. No. 557, 65, 1945.

Hertig, A. T., Rock, J., Adams, E. C., and Mulligan, W. J.: On the preimplantation stages of the human ovum: A description of four normal and four abnormal specimens ranging from the second to the fifth day of development. Contrib. Embryol., Carnegie Inst. Wash. Publ. No. 603, 199, 1954.

Hisaw, F. L.: Development of the graafian follicle and ovulation. Physiol. Rev., 27:95, 1947.

Jost, A.: Le controle hormonal de la differentiation du sexe. Biol. Rev., 23:201, 1948.

Latta, J. S., and Pederson, E. S.: The origin of ova and follicle cells from the germinal epithelium of the ovary of the albino rat as demonstrated by selective intravital staining with India ink. Anat. Rec., 90:23, 1944.

Long, J. A., and Evans, H. M.: The Oestrus Cycle in the Rat and Its Associated Phenomena. Mem. Univ. California, (6), 1922.

Markee, J. E.: Menstruation in intraocular endometrial transplants in the Rhesus monkey. Contrib. Embryol., Carnegie Inst. Wash. Publ. No. 518, 219, 1940.

Moore, C. R.: The role of the fetal endocrine glands in development. J. Clin. Endocrinology, 10:942, 1950.

Papanicolaou, G. N.: Atlas of Exfoliative Cytology. Harvard University Press, Cambridge, Mass., 1954.

Ramsey, E. M.: Circulation in the maternal placenta of the Rhesus monkey and man, with observations on the marginal lakes. Am. J. Anat., 98:159, 1956.

Rock, J., and Hertig, A. T.: Information regarding the time of human ovulation derived from a study of three unfertilized and eleven fertilized ova. Am. J. Obst. & Gyn., 47:343, 1944.

Rossman, I.: On the lipin and pigment in the corpus luteum of the Rhesus monkey. Contrib. Embryol., Carnegie Inst. Wash. Publ. No. 541, 97, 1942.

Sawyer, C. H., Everett, J. W., and Markee, J. E.: A neural factor in the mechanism by which estrogen induces the release of luteinizing hormone in the rat. Endocrinology, 44:218, 1949.

Schmidt, I. G., and Hoffmann, R. A.: Effects of ACTH on pregnant monkeys and their offspring. Endocrinology, 55:125, 1954.

Schroeder, R.: Die weiblichen Genitalorgane. Handb. d. mikr.-Anat. (v. Möllendorff), (70), 329, 1930.

Snyder, F. F.: Changes in the human oviduct during the menstrual cycle and pregnancy. Bull. Johns Hopkins Hosp., 35:141, 1924.

Wislocki, G. B., and Bennett, H. S.: The histology and cytology of the human and monkey placenta, with special reference to the trophoblast. Am. J. Anat., 73:335, 1943.

Wislocki, G. B., and Dempsey, E. W.: Electron microscopy of the human placenta. Anat. Rec., 123:133, 1955.

Witschi, E.: Migration of the germ cells of human embryos from the yolk sac to the primitive gonadal folds. Contrib. Embryol., Carnegie Inst. Wash., 32:67, 1948.

CHAPTER 31

The Mammary Gland

THE MAMMARY gland undergoes extensive structural changes which depend on the age and sex of the person and the functional condition of the sexual apparatus. In its structure and development, the mammary gland suggests somewhat a sweat gland. In man, only one pair develops normally and is laid down in the same manner in the embryos of both sexes. In males the gland involutes after birth. In females it continues to develop; it reaches its final development only at the end of pregnancy and remains in this condition until the end of the period of lactation, when it undergoes a partial involution; it becomes markedly atrophic after the menopause.

Resting Mammary Gland. Each mammary gland of a woman consists of fifteen to twenty-five closely adjoining, irregular lobes radiating from the mammary papilla, or nipple. These are separated from one another by layers of connective tissue and much adipose tissue. Each lobe is provided with an excretory duct 2 to 4.5 mm. in diameter and lined by stratified squamous epithelium. This is the *lactiferous duct,* which runs toward and opens on the nipple and has an irregular, angular form in cross section. Each duct under the areola—the pigmented circular area of skin surrounding the nipple—has a local dilatation, the *sinus lactiferus;* it then becomes constricted again and, curving toward the surface of the skin, opens at the summit of the nipple as an independent opening 0.4 to 0.7 mm. in diameter.

Each lobe is subdivided by layers of connective tissue, rich in lobular masses of adipose tissue, into lobules of various orders. The smallest consist of elongated tubes or sacs, the alveolar ducts, covered by round evaginations, the alveoli.

The interlobular connective tissue is of the dense type. The intralobular connective tissue is much more cellular than the interlobular tissue and contains fewer collagenous fibers and practically no fat (Fig. 31–3). This layer of loose connective tissue about the ducts undoubtedly has a functional significance in providing an easily distensible medium for the hypertrophy of the epithelial portions of the organ during pregnancy and lactation.

The wall of the secretory portions, the alveolar ducts and the alveoli, consists of a basement membrane, a layer of myo-epithelial cells and, on the internal surface, a row of low columnar glandular cells. The myo-epithelial cells are especially prominent near the excretory ducts. These cells serve to associate the mammary gland morphogenetically with the sweat glands.

There has been much discussion as to the presence of *alveoli* in the nonlactating breast. According to most descriptions, the epithelial structures consist, during the resting phase, only of ducts and their branches. Some authors, however, believe that the resting breast always has a few alveoli budded off from the ducts and that these are grouped into small lobules. These pass over without definite boundaries into the primary excretory ducts by a simple constriction. The latter, in turn, gradually unite with similar

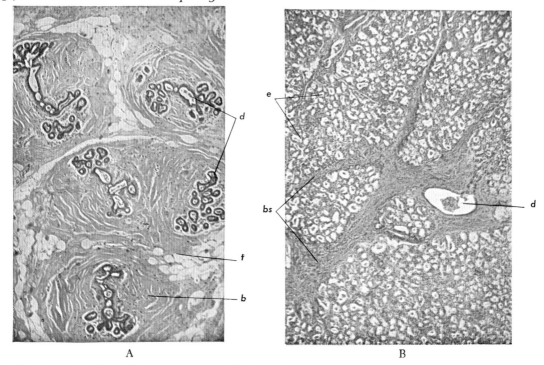

A   B

Fig. 31–1.   Sections of human mammary gland. In the resting gland (A) the scattered lobules consist mainly of ducts (*d*) without terminal portions, and are embedded in dense connective tissue (*b*) and fat cells (*f*). In the lactating gland (B) the lobules with their secreting terminal portions (*e*) are separated by connective tissue septa (*bs*) which contain the ducts (*d*). Photomicrographs. H + E. 6 ×. (After von Herrath and Abramow.)

ducts into larger and larger ducts which finally form the lactiferous duct; along its course the latter receives, directly, small ducts from the alveoli close to the nipple.

Each lobe of the mammary gland is thus an independent, compound alveolar gland. The mammary gland is a conglomeration of a variable number of such independent glands —each with its own excretory or lactiferous duct which has its separate opening on the surface of the nipple.

In a mature mammary gland periodical changes undoubtedly take place in connection with the sexual cycle of the ovaries and the uterus. The exact changes which take place have not been studied thoroughly in women. This is due to the difficulty in obtaining portions of the gland in healthy women and correlating their structure with the functional condition of the ovaries and uterus. To date the few studies made are based mainly on postmortem material. This obviously does not help much in elucidating the changes in normal women. It is probable that the changes in the breast which occur with menstruation consist in a hyperemia and perhaps edema of the interstitial connective tissue. The claim that the ductule and acinar epithelium undergoes a marked cyclic hyper-

plasia—on the order of the progravid changes in the endometrium—is probably unfounded. In laboratory animals, an extensive literature shows quite clearly that the cyclic changes in the breast of the female are intimately bound up with the functional state of the ovaries and uterus.

Nipple and Areola. The skin of the nipple and areola has tall, complex papillae. The epidermis is deeply pigmented, especially after the first pregnancy. Smooth muscles are located both circularly around the papilla mammae and along the length of the lactiferous ducts. In the papillary area are special accessory mammary glands; these are the *areolar glands of Montgomery.* They occupy an intermediate position between the true mammary gland and the sweat glands. Along the margin of the areola are large sweat and sebaceous glands which lack hairs or rudimentary hairs (Fig. 31–2). These glands often open to the exterior by a common opening with the sweat glands.

Mammary Gland during Gestation. From the time of implantation of the ovum in the

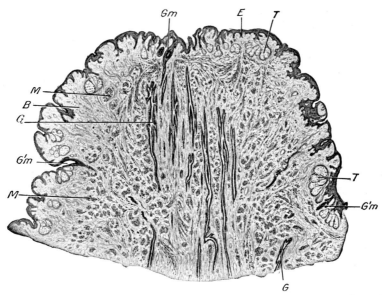

Fig. 31–2. Nipple of female breast in perpendicular section. B, connective tissue stroma; E, epidermis; G, longitudinally cut mammary ducts, which open at the apex, Gm, and the sides of the nipple, G'm; M, cross section of circular smooth muscle bundles; T, sebaceous glands without hairs. 6 ×. (After Schaffer.)

uterus, progressive, deep-seated changes take place in the mammary gland. These develop during the period of gestation and can be separated into two phases. During the first half of pregnancy rapid multiplication of the epithelium is noticed at the ends of excretory ducts, and secretory portions are formed devoid of a lumen, but provided with pocket-like evaginations, the alveoli. The masses of interstitial fatty tissue disappear for the most part and make room for the hypertrophy of the epithelial structures. Parallel to this process, an infiltration with round lymphoid cells begins in the surrounding interstitial tissue. During the second part of the pregnancy the multiplication of epithelial cells gradually decreases in intensity, while the glandular cells gradually begin to produce a secretion; at the end of pregnancy the colostrum appears. During the first days after delivery the colostrum is replaced by milk, and the infiltration of the stroma of the gland by lymphoid elements becomes less intense.

Mammary Gland during Lactation. The different parts of the active mammary gland are usually not in the same functional state at the same time; therefore their histological appearance varies in different parts of the organ. In some places the secretory portions are filled with milk, their lumen is wide, and

the walls are dilated and thin; in others, on the contrary, the lumen is narrow, and the epithelium forms a thick layer; in certain places the glandular elements may be greatly distended with secretion, while in others they may appear more or less free of it.

The shape of the glandular cells fluctuates from cylindrical or conical to flat. The boundary between them is usually indistinct. If the cells are tall, then their distal ends, as in sweat glands, are often definitely separated from one another and project into the lumen of the alveoli as free, rounded, scalloped or star-shaped protrusions. The nucleus may be round or oval and is located at about the middle of the cell. If the cells are short, their free surface is usually more or less smooth; the nucleus here is frequently shrunken.

In the cytoplasm of the glandular cells are short or long rod-shaped or granular mitochondria. In the flattened cells they are few in number; in the tall conical ones they are more abundant. At the base of the cells is some chromophile substance.

The most characteristic expression of the secretory function is the drops of fat, sometimes of considerable size, which accumulate mainly on the free surface of the cell body projecting into the lumen. After the dissolu-

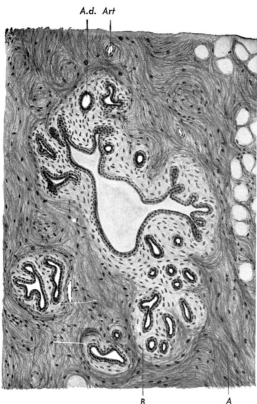

A.d. Art

B   A

Fig. 31–3. Section through mammary gland (resting state) of a thirty-seven year old woman. A, interlobular and, B, intralobular connective tissue; *Art,* artery; *A.d.,* alveolar duct. Hematoxylin-eosin-azure stain. 75 ×. (Drawn by R. L. Mc-Kinney.)

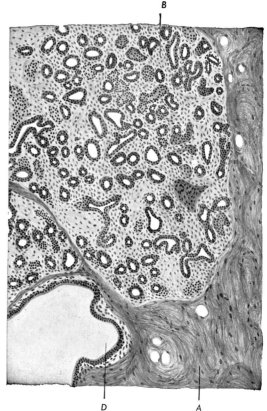

B

D   A

Fig. 31–4. Hypertrophy of lobule of mammary gland from a woman in the fourth month of pregnancy. D, duct; A, interlobular connective tissue; B, intralobular connective tissue. Hematoxylin-eosin-azure stain. 75 ×. (Drawn by R. L. Mc-Kinney.)

tion of the fat in preparing sections, clear vacuoles remain in place of the fat drops. Sometimes, granules of albuminous substance, with which fat had probably been mixed, also can be seen. Some authors have even described the presence of fat droplets in the nucleus, but this has not been confirmed sufficiently. It is unlikely that the mitochondria change into fat droplets. Cyclic changes in the Golgi net during the phases of secretion have been described.

Besides the fat drops in the peripheral portions of cells, round secretory granules and vacuoles of unknown, probably albuminous nature are sometimes seen. The fat drops, which accumulate in the end of the cell protruding into the lumen, pass out of the protoplasm; in preparations treated with osmic acid this can be observed directly, and the free fat drops can also be noticed in the

lumen of the alveoli (Fig. 31–6). In preparations from which the fat has been dissolved, the resulting vacuoles appear in many places to be open to the outside, and the distal end of the cell, therefore, appears torn and uneven. The secretory granules of albuminous character have probably been dissolved previously.

It is possible, however, that the process of secretion may, during strong sucking, be accompanied by a partial disintegration of the glandular cell. The portion of the cell, filled with fat drops, which protrudes into the lumen of the alveolus sometimes becomes constricted off from the remaining, larger portion of the cell body which remains in its place. The detached part flows into the lumen, where the remains of the protoplasm and albuminous granules dissolve and the drops become free. The glandular cell rapidly

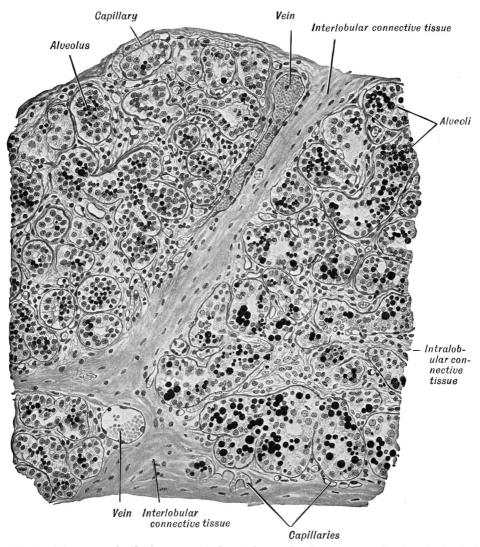

Capillary

Vein

Interlobular connective tissue

Alveolus

Alveoli

Intralobular connective tissue

Vein Interlobular connective tissue

Capillaries

Fig. 31–5. Mammary gland of woman in the sixth month of pregnancy, showing the beginning of secretory activity with osmic acid-stained droplets of fat (black) in the hypertrophic epithelium. 187 ✕. (A.A.M.)

replaces the lost protoplasm and, after having again accumulated secretion, excretes it in the same way. This type of secretion is intermediate between the merocrine and the holocrine types and is called *apocrine*.

The epithelium of the excretory ducts is cubical or even low cylindrical in the small ones. Between it and the basement membrane, elongated, spindle-shaped myo-epithelial cells are ordinarily seen. In the larger ducts the epithelium becomes taller and cylindrical; in the main lactiferous ducts it is stratified and is replaced by a stratified squamous epithelium at some distance from the opening on the nipple.

The interstitial connective tissue of the lactating mammary gland, which separates the lobes and lobules of various orders, is a rather dense connective tissue distributed in stripes of varying widths. In the functioning gland the mass of the connective tissue is much less than that of the glandular elements. In addition to the collagenous fibers, the interstitial substance contains elastic fibers which form dense networks, particularly along the external surfaces of the excretory ducts. Normally, there are no elastic fibers within the lobules.

In certain places, particularly in the peripheral portions of the organ near the nipple, the interstitial tissue is penetrated by peculiar shafts of smooth muscles connected with tendons of elastic networks.

Those portions of the interstitial connective tissue which extend between the small alveoli and directly cover the secretory portions have different properties—here the tissue is rich in blood vessels, is much looser, and contains a much larger number of cells. In addition to fibroblasts and macrophages, lymphocytes of various types and plasma cells are present here in considerable numbers. In man granular leukocytes are rare, and the presence of a noticeable number of them is always an indication of abnormal, inflammatory changes which have induced the migration of these elements from the blood vessels. In abnormal function of the mammary gland, the penetration of a few wandering elements into the glandular epithelium and inside the alveoli can be observed.

Regression of the Mammary Gland. With the end of the nursing period, a regression takes place in the mammary gland. The glandular elements return to a resting state. The production of milk ceases, the secretion remaining in the glands is absorbed rapidly, an apparent increase in the stroma begins, and the alveoli, owing to a decrease in size and the degeneration of the glandular cells, diminish greatly and lose their lumen. The gland, however, does not return to its original state, because many of the alveoli which had formed during the period of pregnancy do not disappear entirely, and the remains of the secretion may sometimes be retained in the mammary ducts for a considerable time. In such a resting condition the gland remains until the following pregnancy, when the same cycle of changes is repeated.

Involution of the Mammary Gland. In old age the mammary gland gradually undergoes involution. The epithelium of the secretory portions, and partly also of the excretory ducts, atrophies, and the gland tends, in a general way, to return to the prepubertal condition in which there are only a few scattered ducts. On the other hand, the epithelium is not infrequently the seat of a pathological growth.

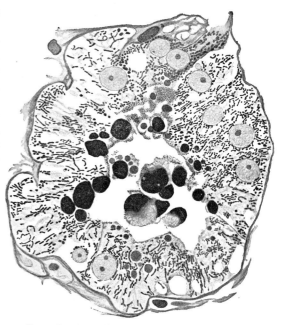

Fig. 31–6. Alveolus of lactating mammary gland of a rabbit. The cells contain mitochondria and droplets of fat (stained black with osmic acid). The latter, with the adjacent protoplasm, are extruded into the lumen. 1000 ×. (A.A.M.)

Equally striking changes occur in the interstitial connective tissue. This becomes decidedly less cellular; the number of collagenous fibrils decreases, and the whole mass becomes more homogeneous and stains much less intensely with eosin. One author has pictured the change as having occurred through a "melting down" of the fibrillar intercellular tissue into a homogeneous mass. When stained with aniline blue, the interstitial substance in such a breast appears finely granular and deep blue.

Blood and Lymphatic Vessels. The blood supply of a functioning mammary gland is much greater than that of a resting gland. The arteries arise from the internal mammary artery, the thoracic branches of the axillary artery and from the intercostal arteries. They pass mainly along the larger ducts and break up into dense capillary networks on the external surface of the basement membrane of the secretory portions (Fig. 31–5). The veins empty into the axillary and internal mammary veins.

The lymphatic vessels begin with capillary networks located in the connective tissue layers surrounding separate alveoli. They collect along the course of the mammary ducts into a subpapillary lymphatic network. From here several large vessels lead the lymph mainly into the lymphatic nodes in the axilla, but also into connection with the lymphatics leading beneath the sternum, and even into those of the other breast.

Nerves. Besides the nerves which supply the smooth muscles of the blood vessels and of the papilla, the mammary gland has also secretory nerve endings closely connected with the glandular elements, as well as rather numerous sensory nerve endings of the nipple; some of the latter have a structure similar to that of the genital bodies.

Histogenesis of the Mammary Gland. The primordium of the mammary gland appears in a human embryo of 8 mm. as a paired thickening of the epidermis, the "milk line," which begins at the root of the upper extremity and proceeds to the inguinal fold. It continues to thicken and becomes the mammary fold; this is retained in man in only a limited region of its cranial portion as a pair of flat, lens-shaped thickenings. These become hemispherical or club-shaped, epithelial thickenings directed toward the underlying connective tissue. This, in turn, thickens and lifts the developing gland slightly above the rest of the surface of the organism (in human embryos 19 to 30 mm. long). In most mammals several pairs of such thickenings are formed.

The cells of this epithelial bud are cylindrical in shape and are arranged radially, while the deeper layers are polyhedral. By continuing to multiply they form, in human embryos of 50 to 60 mm., on the lower convex surface of the body, the primordia of sixteen to twenty-five projections, with swellings at their ends. These projections gradually elongate in the direction of the connective tissue layer and become the mammary ducts. Their number fluctuates with the age of the embryo, since they do not all originate at once; for this reason their lengths, at any given moment, are not equal. The peripheral cells at first maintain their cylindrical shape, while the others are multiangular and have round nuclei. Externally they are gradually covered by a condensing connective tissue. In the course of time each of these cylindrical, epithelial projections or shafts gives rise, by elongation and twisting, to larger and larger numbers of branches; these are also swollen at their ends and are the primordia of the future excretory ducts. A lumen appears in them, except in the terminal swellings, owing to the moving aside and to partial degeneration of the constituent cells. Some of the cells which touch the connective tissue develop into basket cells of so-called "myo-epithelial" nature.

In newborn of both sexes the glands have a diameter of 3.5 to 9 mm., and at this time contain a number of distinct alveolar portions, some of which, however, are rudimentary. At the same time, in the lumen of the developing and branching ducts, a substance is formed which suggests colostrum. This secretion is called witch's milk and contains little but degenerating, fatty epithelial cells; it can be squeezed out of the papilla in newborn infants; it soon disappears.

In males the mammary gland undergoes a regression, and only the nipple remains with the surrounding areola. In females, however, the development, although rather slow, continues, and the slow elongation and branching of the epithelial shaft goes on throughout childhood. With the onset of sexual maturity, the development does not change qualitatively, but increases in intensity and quantity; each original epithelial shaft forms numerous branches through the multiplication of its constituent cells. Having reached a certain degree of development, the organ undergoes but slight changes and remains in a state of functional rest. There is no secretion, and even the secretory portions are missing, according to most authors, who believe that only excretory ducts are present at this time.

Histophysiological Remarks. Milk is an aqueous solution of albumins (mainly casein), lactose and inorganic salts (including small amounts of iron) in which numerous fat drops, the *milk globules,* are suspended. Some of these are at the limit of visibility; most of them are 2 to 5 microns and seldom up to 10 to 12 microns in diameter. These are the same fat drops produced and given off by the glandular cells. Small numbers of milk globules with one-sided caps, free disintegrating nuclei, nucleated or non-nucleated fragments of glandular cells, and transformed leukocytes are also found.

All these constituents of the milk can be

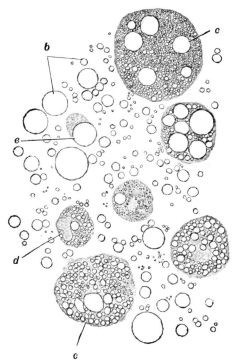

Fig. 31–7. Human colostrum, fresh preparation. *b,* Milk globules of various sizes; *c,* colostrum bodies with fat droplets of various sizes; *d,* colostrum bodies with nuclei; *e,* milk globules with "caps." 1000 ×.

seen in histological preparations in the lumina of the dilated secretory portions and of the excretory ducts; this is particularly clear after fixation with osmic acid, when the milk globules are stained black. The number of the cellular fragments and leukocytes appears to be larger in the alveoli than in the excreted milk; this shows that these structures autolyze during the excretion of milk.

During the last days of pregnancy, the first two or three days after delivery, and at the end of the period of lactation, the secretion of the mammary gland is quite different from milk and is called *colostrum.* It differs from milk by being poor in fat. But it contains numerous globules with particles of cellular fragments, free nuclei and *colostrum bodies* (9 to 40 microns in diameter). These globular bodies are often capable of active ameboid movements. After fixation and staining they appear as free, large cells with usually one constricted nucleus; their cytoplasm is filled with many small and a few large fat drops. A considerable portion of these elements shows indications of degeneration.

Many authors recognize the colostrum bodies as transformed epithelial glandular cells which are filled with the products of secretion and have become detached. But it is more probable that they are wandering lymphoid cells of various kinds, which have escaped from the connective tissue into the epithelium and into the lumen of the glandular spaces, and which ingest fat droplets by phagocytosis. During the periods when colostrum appears, the interstitial connective tissue which surrounds the secretory portions is heavily infiltrated by hematogenous and histogenous lymphocytes. In fixed preparations these elements may often be seen on their way through the basement membrane into the epithelium and thence into the lumen of the alveolus.

The colostrum bodies always appear when the equilibrium between the secretion of the milk and its excretion is upset, that is, either when the feeding of the child has not yet begun, as in the last days of pregnancy, or when it has come to an end. The presence in the colostrum of hematogenous granular leukocytes, particularly of the neutrophile type, is usually an indication of an inflammatory process in the mammary gland.

The proliferative changes in the gland during gestation are due mainly to hormones arising in the ovary (estrone and progesterone) and apparently acting through the pars distalis of the hypophysis, for these hormones have no effect on the mammary gland in hypophysectomized animals. A mammogenic duct growth factor has been extracted from the pars distalis of the hypophysis. The initiation of lactation seems to be due to the lactogenic hormone of the pars distalis of the hypophysis. The factors involved in lactation are discussed by Petersen.

The production of the colostrum in newborn infants probably depends on the same hormones which bring about the production of milk in the mother. Some believe that there are indications of a dependence of this process on the hypophysis of the embryo.

REFERENCES

Dempsey, E. W., Bunting, H., and Wislocki, G. B.: Observations on the chemical cytology of the mammary gland. Am. J. Anat., *81:*309, 1947.

Eggeling, H. von: Die Milchdrüse, in Möllendorff's Handbuch der mikroskopischen Anatomie des Menschen. Berlin, 1927, Vol. 3, pp. 1, 117.

Jeffers, K. R.: Cytology of the mammary gland of albino rat. Am. J. Anat., *56:*257, 279, 1935.

Lewis, A. A., and Turner, C. W.: The Mammogenic Hormones of the Anterior Pituitary. I. The Duct Growth Factor. Research Bulletin 310, University of Missouri, College of Agriculture, 1, 1939.

Loeb, L.: The Cytology of the Mammary Gland, in Cowdry's Special Cytology. 2d ed. New York, *3:* 1631, 1932.

Lyons, W. R. Lobulo-alveolar Mammary Growth Induced in Hypophysectomized Rats by Injections of Ovarian and Hypophysial Hormones. Essays in Biology, University of California Press, 1943.

Petersen, W. F.: Lactation. Physiol. Rev., *24:*340, 1944.

Rawlinson, H. E.: The use of an iron stain for the study of alveolar development in the mouse mammary gland. Canadian J. Res., E, *28:*1, 1950.

Richardson, K. C.: Contractile Tissues in the Mammary Gland, with Special Reference to Myoepithelium in the Goat. Proc. Roy. Soc. London, s. *136:*30, 1949.

Weatherford, H. L.: A cytological study of the mammary gland. Golgi apparatus, trophosporgium, and other cytoplasmic caniliculi. Mitochondria. Am. J. Anat., *44:*199, 1929.

Williams, W. L.: Normal and experimental mammary involution in the mouse as related to the inception and cessation of lactation. Am. J. Anat., *71:*1, 1942.

CHAPTER 32

The Eye

THE ABILITY to react to light is a widespread property of living matter, but in complex animals certain cells are specifically adapted to respond to light. Scattered photoreceptive cells in lower animals probably distinguish only varying intensities of light and only crudely perceive the direction of the light stimuli. In the vertebrates, more efficient organs evolved, the eyes, which not only react to various intensities and qualities of light, but are capable of distinguishing the form, size and minute changes in the position of external objects. The photoreceptor organ, the retina, developed from a bilateral outgrowth of the front end of the brain.

STRUCTURE OF THE EYE IN GENERAL

The anterior segment of the eye, the cornea, is transparent and permits the rays of light to enter. The rest of the wall of the eye is opaque. It has a darkly pigmented inner surface which absorbs light rays, and is to a great extent lined with photosensitive nervous tissue, the retina. The cavity of the eyeball is filled with transparent media arranged in separate bodies. Their surfaces, with those of the cornea, act as a system of convex lenses. These produce an inverted, reduced and real image of the objects of the outside world in the photoreceptive layer of the retina, the rods and cones.

The wall of the eyeball is composed of three coats. The thick and tough outer fibrous tunic gives the organ its form and protects its inner delicate structures. It is subdivided into a large, opaque, posterior portion, the sclera, and a smaller anterior, transparent segment, the cornea. The middle vascular tunic or uvea is concerned with the nutrition of the ocular tissues, and its smooth muscles provide the mechanism for accommodation. Part of the uvea extends anteriorly as far as the ora serrata and is called choroidea. Its anterior portion, the ciliary body, is the muscular instrument for the accommodation of the refraction of the eye; it forms a girdle 5 to 6 mm. wide between the ora serrata and the sclerocorneal junction. The iris, a thin membrane, is a continuation of the ciliary body and projects over the anterior surface of the lens. The diameter of the iris is approximately 12 mm. Its opening, the pupil, can be reduced or expanded through the contraction or relaxation of the constrictor and the dilator muscles of the pupil. In this way the iris functions as an adjustable optic diaphragm regulating the amount of light entering the eye.

The third or innermost tunic, the retina, contains in its functioning or optic part the receptors for light and the first links of the nervous pathways conveying impulses through the optic nerve to the brain. The spot where the nerve inserts into the eyeball, the papilla of the optic nerve, is a pink disk about 1.4 mm. in diameter. It is situated about 3 mm. nasal to the posterior pole of the eye. The portion of the retina lining the inner surface of the ciliary muscle (ciliary

Page 553

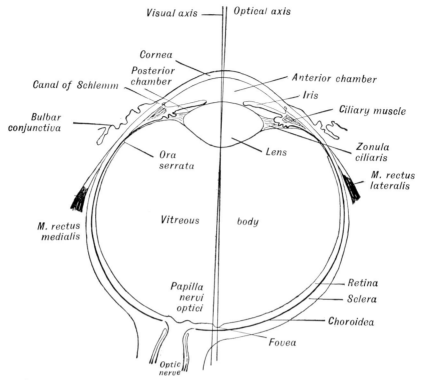

Visual axis ——— Optical axis

Cornea
Posterior chamber
Canal of Schlemm
Bulbar conjunctiva
Anterior chamber
Iris
Ciliary muscle
Ora serrata
Lens
Zonula ciliaris
M. rectus lateralis
M. rectus medialis
Vitreous   body
Papilla nervi optici
Retina
Sclera
Choroidea
Fovea
Optic nerve

Fig. 32–1.   Diagram of horizontal section through the right eye of man.

portion of the retina) and that lining the posterior surface of the iris (*iridial portion of the retina*) are not photosensitive.

The space enclosed by the tunics of the eye is filled with the transparent *dioptric media,* which must also include the *cornea.* Because of the considerable difference between the index of refraction of the cornea (1.376) and of the surrounding air (1.0), the cornea is the chief refractive apparatus of the eye. Of the enclosed transparent media the most anterior is the *aqueous humor.* It is contained in the *anterior chamber,* a small cavity bordered in front by the cornea and behind by the ciliary body, the iris and the central portion of the anterior surface of the lens. The *posterior chamber,* also filled with aqueous humor, is a narrow, circular space enclosed by the iris, the lens, and the ciliary and vitreous bodies.

The next of the transparent media is the *crystalline lens.* This is an elastic biconvex body suspended from the inner surface of the ciliary body by a circular ligament, the *ciliary zonule.* It is placed directly behind the pupil, between the aqueous humor of the

anterior chamber and the cornea anteriorly, and the vitreous body posteriorly. The lens is second in importance to the cornea as a refractive apparatus of the eye, and is the dioptric organ of accommodation.

The large posterior portion of the cavity of the eye, between the posterior surface of the lens, the ciliary body, and the posterior wall of the eyeball, called *vitreal cavity,* is filled with a viscous transparent substance, the *vitreous humor* or *body.* It adjoins the retina and permits light to pass freely to the photoreceptors.

The retina is transparent during life. Only its outermost layer, the pigment epithelium, is opaque and forms the first barrier to the rays of light.

MEASUREMENTS AND LANDMARKS

The adult human eyeball is a roughly spherical body about 24 mm. in diameter and weighing 6 to 8 gm. The center of the cornea is the *anterior pole;* the *posterior pole* is located between the fovea and the optic papilla. The line connecting the two poles is the *anatomical axis.* The *visual axis* is the line drawn from the center of the fovea—the spot of most distinct vision—to the apparent center of the pupil. The

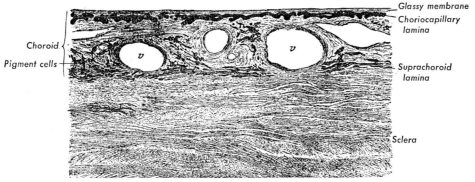

Fig. 32–2. Choroid and sclera of human eye in cross section. 135 ×. (After Schaffer.)

equatorial plate is vertical to the axis and passes through the greatest expansion of the eyeball, the *equator*. Planes passing through the axis subtend the *meridians* of the eye. The two most important are the vertical and the horizontal meridians. The first passes through the fovea and divides the eyeball, including the retina, into nasal and temporal halves. The plane of the horizontal meridian divides the eyeball and retina into an upper and a lower half. These two planes divide the eyeball and the retina into four quadrants, an upper nasal and an upper temporal, a lower nasal and a lower temporal.

The *anteroposterior diameter* along the axis of the eye is 24 mm., or a little more. The *inner axis*, the distance between the inner surface of the cornea and the inner surface of the retina at the posterior pole, measures a little less than 22 mm. The *optical axis* passes through the optical centers of the refractive media, and is almost identical with the anatomical axis. The visual axis, where it touches the retina, is from 4 to 7 degrees lateral and 3.5 degrees below the optical axis.

The *radius of the curvature* of the large posterior segment around the fundus measures somewhat less than 13 mm., and gradually decreases toward the corneoscleral junction. The cornea has the smallest radius of curvature, approximately 7.8 mm. (outer corneal surface).

The eyeball is lodged in a soft cushion filling the bony orbit of the skull and made up of loose connective and fatty tissue, muscles, fasciae, blood and lymphatic vessels, glands and nerves. This permits the eye to move freely around its *center of rotation*. The eye is connected with the general integument by the conjunctiva. The lids are a mechanical protection against external noxious agents.

FIBROUS TUNIC

The Sclera. The sclera is 1 mm. thick at the posterior pole, 0.4 to 0.3 mm. at the equator, and 0.6 mm. toward the edge of the cornea. The sclera consists of flat collagenous bundles which run in various directions parallel to the surface (Figs. 32–2, 32–8, 32–10). The tendons of the eye muscles are attached to its outer surface. Between

these bundles are fine elastic nets. The cells of the sclera are flat, elongated fibroblasts. Melanocytes can be found in the deeper layers, especially in the region of the entrance of the optic nerve.

The outer surface of the sclera is connected with a dense layer of connective tissue—the *capsule of Tenon*—by an exceedingly loose system of thin collagenous membranes separated by clefts—the *space of Tenon*. This arrangement makes rotating movements of the eyeball possible in all directions.

Between the sclera and the choroid is a layer of loose connective tissue with numerous melanocytes, fibroblasts and elastic networks. When these tunics are separated, part of this loose tissue adheres to the choroid and part to the sclera as its *suprachoroid lamina* (Fig. 32–2).

Cornea. The cornea is slightly thicker than the sclera and measures 0.8 to 0.9 mm. in the center and 1.1 mm. at the periphery. In man the refractive power of the cornea, which is a function of the index of refraction of its tissue (1.376) and of the radius of curvature of its surface (7.8 mm.), is twice as high as that of the lens. The *transparency of the cornea* is high, though less than that of the aqueous humor and of glass. It is due partly to the great regularity of its structural composition, and partly to other factors of chemical nature still incompletely understood.

In a vertical section through the cornea, the following layers can be seen: (1) the epithelium, (2) the membrane of Bowman, (3) the stroma or substantia propria, (4) the membrane of Descemet, (5) the corneal mesenchymal epithelium.

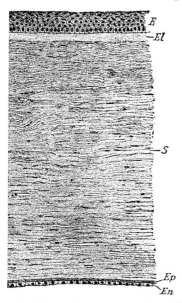

Fig. 32–3. Vertical transection of middle part of human cornea. *E,* epithelium; *El,* Bowman's membrane; *S,* substantia propria; *Ep,* membrane of Descemet; *En,* corneal mesenchymal epithelium. 135 ×. (After Schaffer.)

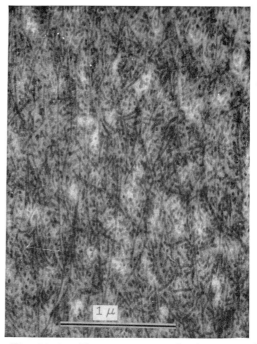

Fig. 32–4. Electron micrograph of section of Bowman's membrane showing the random arrangement of the fibrils. Buffered osmic acid fixation. (Courtesy of M. Jakus.)

Epithelium. The epithelium is stratified squamous with an average thickness of 50 microns and consists, as a rule, of five layers of cells. The outer surface is quite smooth and is composed of large squamous cells. As in other types of stratified squamous epithelium, the cells are connected with one another by thin intercellular bridges. Often lymphoid cells penetrate between the cells and appear as irregular, branched cells of Langerhans; they come from the blood vessels at the periphery of the cornea.

The epithelium of the cornea is extremely sensitive and contains numerous free nerve endings (Fig. 9–33). It is endowed with a remarkable capacity for regeneration. Small defects of the epithelial layer, caused by injuries, heal rapidly by a flattening and gliding movement of the adjacent epithelial cells. Mitoses in the basal epithelial cells set in later and may be found at considerable distances from the wound. In normal conditions a few mitoses can be found in the basal cell layer.

Bowman's Membrane. The corneal epithelium rests upon the 6 to 9 microns thick, indistinctly fibrillated membrane of Bowman. This is a condensed outer layer of the subadjacent substantia propria, from which it cannot be isolated. With the electron microscope the membrane is seen to consist of a feltwork of randomly arranged fibrils, apparently of collagen, (Fig. 32–4). They are about 180 A in diameter and may show a periodic banding of about 500 A. The membrane does not contain elastin and ends abruptly at the periphery of the cornea.

Substantia Propria. This layer forms about 90 per cent of the cornea (Fig. 32–3). It is a transparent, regular connective tissue whose bundles form thin lamellae arranged in many layers. In each layer the direction of the bundles is parallel; in adjacent lamellae the bundles intercross at various angles (Fig. 32–5). The lamellae everywhere interchange fibers and thus are kept tightly together. The fibrils are thicker than those in Bowman's membrane, measuring about 230 A thick on the average. Between the fibrils, the bundles and the lamellae, there is a mucoid cement substance. The substantia propria always contains a number of lymphoid wandering cells which migrate from the blood vessels of the corneal limbus. In inflammation enormous numbers of heterophile leukocytes and lymphoid cells penetrate between the lamellae.

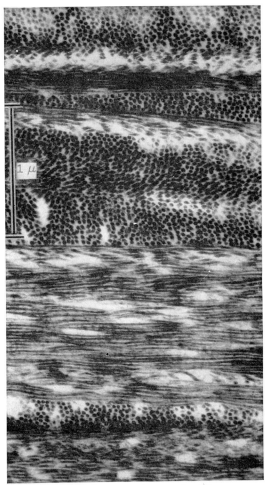

Fig. 32–5. Electron micrograph of human corneal stroma. Note the different directions of the cross striated collagenous fibrils in successive layers. 34,700 ×. (Courtesy of M. Jakus.)

The substantia propria contains fine elastic networks especially abundant in the layers in front of the membrane of Descemet.

Membrane of Descemet. This lamella, 5 to 10 microns thick, can be isolated from the posterior surface of the substantia propria. At the periphery of the cornea the membrane of Descemet continues as a thin layer on the surface of the trabeculae of the iridial angle. It is a basement membrane probably secreted by the corneal mesenchymal epithelium. Although homogeneous under the light microscope, cross sections of the membrane are shown by the electron microscope to have an apparent cross striation of granular bands about 1070 A apart and connected by filaments less than 100 A in width and about

270 A apart (Fig. 32–6, *A*). In tangential sections there is seen a two-dimensional array of nodes, about 1070 A apart, connected by filaments to form hexagonal figures (Fig. 32–6, *B*). The diagram in Figure 32–7 shows the relationship between structures seen in the two planes. On the basis of histochemical data, chemical analyses and x-ray diffraction studies it is concluded that the membrane belongs to the collagen class of fibrous proteins despite its atypical fine structure.

Corneal Mesenchymal Epithelium. The inner surface of the membrane of Descemet is covered by a layer of large, squamous cells.

Sclerocorneal Junction. In a meridional section the boundary between the opaque sclera and the transparent cornea appears as an oblique line (Fig. 32–10). The outer edge of the sclera overlaps the border of the cornea. When the collagenous bundles of the sclera continue directly into those of the cornea, their striation loses its distinctiveness, and the tissue becomes homogeneous and transparent.

At the marginal zone or limbus of the cornea, the epithelium of the cornea gradually changes into that of the conjunctiva of the bulb. Where the membrane of Bowman ends, a subepithelial layer of loose connective tissue begins; it contains the loops of the vessels which furnish the nutritive materials to the cornea and are the source of the wandering cells mentioned earlier. The blood vessels which invade the substantia propria in chronic inflammation also arise from these loops.

On the inner surface of the wall of the eyeball, the sclerocorneal junction is marked by a shallow, ring-shaped furrow, the *internal scleral furrow* or *sulcus.* Its posterior lip forms a small, centrally projecting ridge, the *scleral roll,* to which the ciliary body is fastened (Fig. 32–8). At the bottom of the internal scleral furrow the scleral tissue contains one or several cavities lined with endothelium. They are the cross sections of a circular canal which parallels the border of the cornea and in many places breaks up into several irregular branches which then fuse again. It is the *canal of Schlemm,* or the "venous sinus" of the sclera (Fig. 32–8). It communicates with the venous system and is believed to drain the aqueous humor from the anterior chamber (see p. 577). It is usually

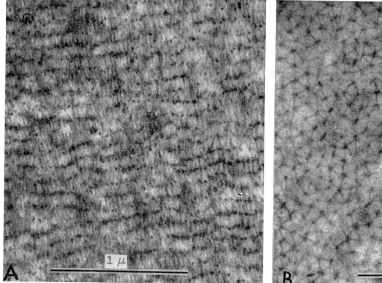

Fig. 32–6.   Electron micrographs: *A,* cross section and, *B,* tangential section of Descemet's membrane. Notice the striate appearance in the cross section and the hexagonal arrangement in the tangential. See text and Figure 32–7. (Courtesy of M. Jakus.)

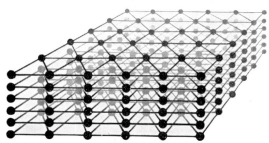

Fig. 32–7.   Diagram of structure of Descemet's membrane based on electron micrographs. See text for explanation. (Courtesy of M. Jakus.)

filled with clear liquid, and contains blood only when there is stasis in the venous system.

THE UVEA (THE VASCULAR TUNIC)

Choroid Membrane. The choroid is a thin, soft, brown membrane adjacent to the inner surface of the sclera (Fig. 32–2). Between the sclera and the choroid is a potential cleft, the perichoroidal space; it is traversed by thin lamellae which run obliquely from the choroid to the sclera and form a loose, pigmented tissue layer—the *suprachoroid layer.* This is composed of fine, transparent membranes with fibroblasts on their surface and with a rich network of elastic fibers (Fig. 32–2). Everywhere between and

in the lamellae large, flat melanoblasts are scattered. In the suprachoroid, as in the rest of the uvea, are scattered macrophages. The lamellae of the suprachoroid pass without a distinct boundary into the substance of the choroid. This tunic can be subdivided into three main layers. From outside inward they are: (1) the vessel layer, (2) the capillary layer, and (3) the glassy or Bruch's membrane.

Vessel Layer. This layer consists of a multitude of intercrossing large and medium-sized arteries and veins (*v* in the lower part of *Choroid* in Fig. 32–2). The spaces between the vessels are filled with loose connective tissue rich in melanocytes. The lamellar arrangement here is much less distinct than in the suprachoroid. According to some, the vessel layer contains strands of smooth muscle independent of the arteries.

Choriocapillary Layer. This is formed by a capillary network arranged in one plane (see Fig. 32–2). In places this layer is connected with the vascular layer. The individual capillaries have a large and somewhat irregular caliber. The net is especially dense and the capillary layer much thicker in the region of the fovea. Anteriorly it ceases near the ora serrata. This layer contains flattened fibroblasts, which have been erroneously described as a separate endothelial layer.

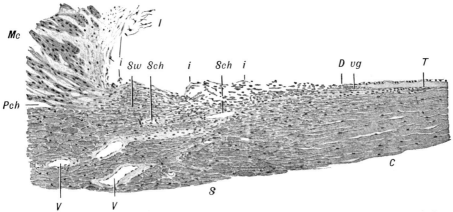

Fig. 32–8. Meridional section through scleral furrow. *C*, cornea; *D*, border of Descemet's membrane; *I*, iris root; *i*, uveal framework; *Mc*, ciliary muscle; *Pch*, beginning of perichoroidal space; *Sch*, canals of Schlemm, with their veins, *V*; *Sw*, scleral roll; *T*, deep root of the scleral framework; *vg*, anterior marginal ring. 96 ×. (After Salzmann.)

Glassy or Bruch's Membrane. This is a brilliant, limiting line 1 to 4 microns thick between the choroid and the pigment epithelium of the retina. It can be divided into two lamellae. The outer one, facing the capillary layer, is a dense plexus of finest elastic fibers which are the continuation of the elastic nets of the capillary interstices. The inner, thicker lamella is homogeneous, and is produced by the pigment epithelium of the retina.

Ciliary Body. If the eyeball is cut across along its equator, and its anterior half, after removal of the vitreous, is inspected from within, a sharply outlined, dentate border is seen running around the inner surface of the wall in front of the equator. This is the *ora serrata* of the retina. The girdle between the ora and the edge of the lens is the *ciliary body,* a thickening of the vascular tunic. Its surface is covered by the darkly pigmented ciliary portion of the retina. In a meridional section through the eye bulb, the ciliary body appears as a thin triangle with its small base facing the anterior chamber of the eye and attached here by its outer angle to the scleral roll. The long narrow angle extends backward and passes into the choroidea (Fig. 32–10). The inner surface of the ciliary body is divided into a narrow anterior zone, the *ciliary crown,* and a broader posterior zone, the *ciliary ring* (Fig. 32–9). The inner surface of the ring has shallow grooves, *ciliary striae,* which run forward from the teeth of the ora. On its inner surface the ciliary crown

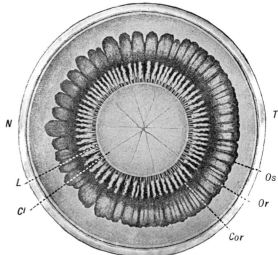

Fig. 32–9. Anterior half of the eye seen from within. *N*, nasal and, *T*, temporal side; *Os*, ora serrata retinae; *Or*, ciliary ring; *Cor*, ciliary crown; *Cl*, circumlental space; *L*, posterior surface of the lens with the lens star. 3 ×. (After Salzmann.)

has seventy radially arranged ridges, the *ciliary processes.*

Ciliary Muscle. The main mass of the ciliary body, exclusive of the ciliary processes, consists of the smooth *ciliary muscle.* It is composed of three portions. Closest to the sclera is the muscle of Brücke, whose bundles are stretched chiefly in the meridional direction. The outer part of the ciliary muscle stretches the choroidea and is also called *tensor muscle of the choroid.* Its role in accommodation is discussed in the section deal-

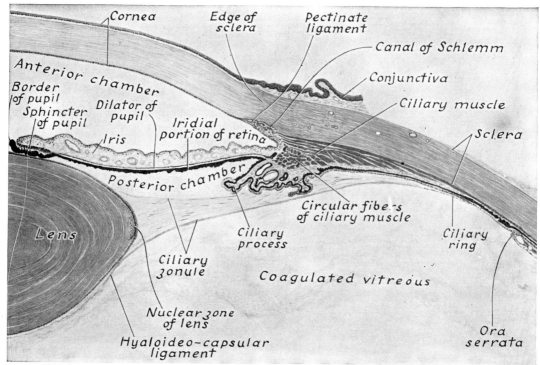

Fig. 32–10. Part of meridional section of human eye. 14 ×. (Modified after Schaffer.)

ing with the lens. In the next inward portion of the ciliary muscle, the bundles of muscle cells radiate fanlike from the region of the scleral roll toward the cavity of the eyeball; this is the *radiated* or *reticular portion of the ciliary muscle.* The third or *circular portion of the ciliary muscle* (of Müller) is usually absent in the newborn, appearing in the course of the second or third year. The meshes between the muscular bundles are filled with a small amount of connective tissue with abundant elastic networks and melanocytes. The latter become especially numerous toward the sclera and where the connective tissue gradually passes into the lamellae of the suprachoroid.

The inner, *vascular layer of the ciliary body* consists of connective tissue with numerous blood vessels. In the ciliary ring it is the direct continuation of the same layer of the choroid. In the region of the ciliary crown it covers the inner surface of the ciliary muscle and forms the core of the ciliary processes. The vessels are almost exclusively capillaries and veins of varying caliber. The corresponding arteries branch in the peripheral layers of the ciliary body. The connective tissue is dense, especially

near the root of the iris, and contains abundant elastic networks. In old age it often shows hyaline degeneration. Melanocytes are usually found only near the surface of the muscle. The inner surface of the vascular layer of the ciliary body is lined by the continuation of the *glassy membrane* of the choroid. In the region of the ciliary body this membrane splits into three distinct lamellae.

Next to the connective tissue of the vascular layer of the ciliary body is the thin, dense *elastic lamella.* Inwardly it is followed by a dense collagenous sheet with a few fibroblasts. The inner surface of the uveal portion of the ciliary body is coated with the cuticular lamella.

The *ciliary portion of the retina* continues forward beyond the ora serrata and covers the inner surface of the ciliary body. It consists of an outer pigmented layer and of a nonpigmented inner layer and does not receive light stimuli. This deeply pigmented epithelium consists of one layer of columnar cells and continues upon the posterior surface of the iris, where it partly undergoes a muscular differentiation. The inner, colorless layer is a simple columnar epithelium. The height of its cells decreases from behind for-

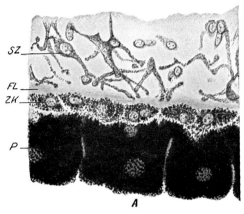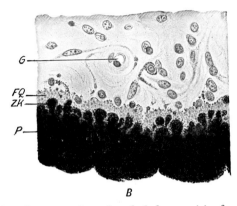

Fig. 32–11. *A,* posterior part of a radial (meridional) transection of a dark human iris, from an enucleated eyeball. *FL,* fibrillae of the dilator muscle in longitudinal section; *P,* pigment epithelium of the inner (posterior) layer of the pars iridica retinae; *SZ,* pigment containing connective tissue cells (melanophores) of the vascular layer; *ZK,* pigment containing cell bodies of the dilator muscle (outer or anterior layer of the iridial portion of the retina). *B,* tangential section of a light human iris. The fibers of the dilator muscle in cross section (*FQ*); *G,* blood vessels in the stroma. 380 ×. (After Schaffer.)

ward. Its inner surface is lined with a distinct glassy membrane—the *ciliary inner limiting membrane*—considered to be a continuation of the inner limiting membrane of the optical portion of the retina.

Toward the root of the iris, on the anterior surface of the ciliary processes, the cells of the inner epithelial layer gradually accumulate pigment granules. On the posterior surface of the iris they are as heavily pigmented as the outer layer. This is the *iridial portion of the retina.*

Iris. The posterior surface of the iris near the pupil rests upon the anterior surface of the lens; in this way the iris separates the anterior chamber from the posterior chamber. The margin of the iris connected with the ciliary body is called the *ciliary margin,* or the root of the iris. The pupil is surrounded by the *pupillary margin of the iris.* The iris diminishes in thickness toward both margins.

The anterior surface of the iris presents, besides its individually varying color, certain distinct markings. About 1.5 mm. from the pupillary margin a concentric, jagged line separates the anterior surface into a pupillary and a wider, ciliary zone. Near the pupillary and the ciliary margins the anterior surface has many irregular excavations, the *crypts,* which may extend deep into the tissue. In addition, there are oblique, irregularly arranged contraction furrows which are especially marked when the pupil is dilated.

The main mass of the iris consists of a loose, pigmented, highly vascular connective tissue and some smooth muscles. The anterior surface of the stroma is said to be lined with epithelium, which continues here from the posterior surface of the cornea. A thin layer of the stroma immediately beneath the mesenchymal epithelium, the anterior stromal sheet or lamella, is devoid of blood vessels. Farther inward is the thick vessel layer. Its posterior surface is covered with a double layer of heavily pigmented epithelium, the iridial portion of the retina.

Anterior Stromal Sheet or Lamella. This contains, in a homogeneous ground substance, a few collagenous fibers and many fibroblasts and chromatophores. The color of the iris depends on the quantity, the color and the arrangement of the pigment and on the thickness of the lamella. If this layer is thin and its cells contain but little or no pigment, the black pigment epithelium on the posterior surface, as seen through the colorless tissue, gives the iris a blue color (Fig. 32–11). An increasing amount of pigment brings about the different shades of gray and greenish hues. Large amounts of dark pigment cause the brown color of the iris. In albinos the pigment is absent or scanty, and the iris is pink because of its blood vessels.

Vessel Layer. This layer contains numer-

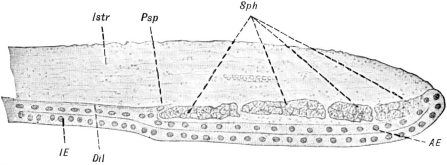

Fig. 32–12. Radial (meridional) section of pupillary border of the iris of a newborn infant. *IE*, inner epithelial layer and, *AE*, outer epithelial layer of the optic cup; *Sph*, sphincter; *Dil*, dilator of the pupil; *Psp*, spurlike process of epithelium; *Istr*, stroma of the iris. (After von Szily, from Franz.)

ous blood vessels. The spaces between them are filled with a loose connective tissue and some branched chromatophores.

Iridial Portion of the Retina. The epithelial pigment layer on the posterior surface of the iris is a direct continuation of the ciliary portion of the retina and, like it, originally consists of two layers of epithelium. The inner, nonpigmented layer of the ciliary portion becomes heavily pigmented in the iridial region, and the outer, pigmented layer becomes less pigmented. In the iris the outer, less pigmented layer differentiates into smooth muscles.

Muscles of the Iris. Being an adjustable diaphragm, the iris contains two smooth muscles which keep the membrane stretched and press it against the surface of the lens. The contraction of the circular *sphincter of the pupil* reduces the pupil. It is a thin, flat ring whose breadth changes, according to the contraction of the iris, from 0.6 to 1.2 mm. It surrounds the margin of the pupil. Its smooth muscle fibers are arranged in thin circular bundles, and on the posterior surface often course obliquely to the *dilator of the pupil.* This muscle widens the pupil and consists of radially arranged myo-epithelial elements which form a thin membrane between the vessel layer and the pigment epithelium.

The elements of the dilator at first are spindle-shaped, fibrillated cells with moderately pigmented cytoplasm. In the adult the fibrillated parts of the cells become a continuous, radially fibrillated membrane called the posterior stromal sheet or lamella. The rest of the cell bodies keep the elongated nucleus, accumulate pigment, are pushed backward, and form a layer of pigmented spindle cells (Fig. 32–11). These are only indistinctly set off from the posterior stromal lamella (*FL, FQ*), but are sharply separated from the pigment epithelium.

Numerous muscular connections can be found between the sphincter and the dilator. The innervation of both muscles, however, is quite different, although both are supplied by visceral nerve fibers. The postganglionic neurons for the dilator are located in the superior cervical ganglion and are sympathetic. Their axons pass to the gasserian ganglion, thence into the ophthalmic branch of the latter, and finally reach the dilator through the long ciliary nerves. The postganglionic neurons for the sphincter lie in the ciliary ganglion, and their axons reach the sphincter with the short ciliary nerves which also innervate the ciliary muscles; these are parasympathetic. When the eye accommodates for a near object by the contraction of the ciliary muscle, there is always a simultaneous contraction of the pupillary sphincter.

Pigment Epithelium of the Iris. The large cells of the pigment epithelium are filled with coarse, dark brown melanin granules that obscure their outlines and their nuclei. The posterior (inner) surface of the pigment layer is covered with the fine *limiting membrane of the iris,* a continuation of the inner limiting membrane of the ciliary portion of the retina.

Angle of the Iris. This circular recess at the periphery of the anterior chamber of the eye (where the posterior surface of the cornea and the anterior surface of the iris meet) plays an important role in the circulation of the intra-ocular liquid. The elements of the

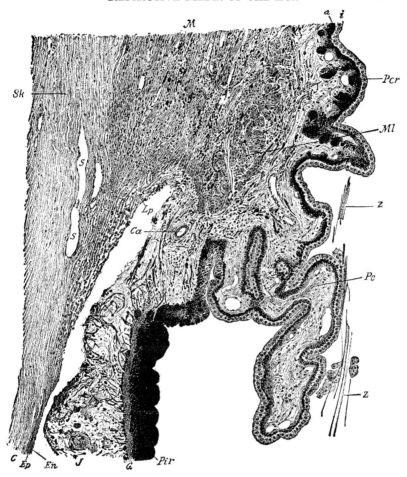

Fig. 32–13.   Meridional section of angle of the iris from an enucleated eyeball. C, innermost layers of the corneal substantia propria; Ca, major arterial ring of the iris; En, endothelium; Ep, membrane of Descemet; G, dilator of the pupil; J, stroma of the iris; Lp, pectinate ligament of the iris; M, ciliary muscle; Ml, circular fibers of the ciliary muscle; Pc, ciliary process; Pcr, ciliary portion of the retina; Pir, iridial portion of the retina; S, canal of Schlemm; Sk, innermost layers of the sclera; Z, fibers of the ciliary zonule: a, pigment epithelium of the ciliary portion of the retina; i, inner epithelial layer of the ciliary portion of the retina. 90 ×. (After Schaffer.)

sclera and of the ciliary muscle also take part in the formation of this region.

The endothelial wall of the *canal of Schlemm* at the corneoscleral junction is surrounded by loose connective tissue and is separated by connective tissue lined with mesenchymal epithelium from the anterior chamber. This meshwork is the *angle of the iris*. It extends from the edge of the membrane of Descemet to the scleral roll and to the root of the iris. Its meshes, the *spaces of Fontana,* are in direct communication with the anterior chamber. It is subdivided into a larger and coarser part, the *scleral framework* (Fig. 32–8), which is adjacent to the sclera, and into a smaller, more delicate part, connected with the iris, the *uveal framework,* or the *pectinate ligament of the iris* (Figs. 32–8, 32–13). In the human eye the meshwork of the iris angle, especially its pectinate ligament, is much less developed than in some mammals.

REFRACTIVE MEDIA OF THE EYE

The cornea and the two chambers of the eye have been described.

Lens. The lens is a transparent, round, biconvex body placed behind the pupil. Its form changes during the process of accommodation. Its outer form varies somewhat in different persons and also with age. Its diameter is from 7 mm. in a newborn up to 10 mm. in an adult. Its thickness is approximately 3.7 to 4 mm., increasing during accommodation to 4.5 mm. and more. The posterior surface or pole is more convex than the anterior, the respective radii of curvature being 6.9 and 10 mm. The index of refraction is 1.36 in the peripheral layers and 1.42 in the inner zone or nucleus. The lens weighs 0.2 gm. and is slightly yellow.

The lens is covered with a homogeneous, highly refractive *capsule,* a cuticular membrane, 11 to 18 microns thick. Beneath it and covering the anterior face is a layer of flattened hexagonal cells, the epithelium of the lens. Toward the equator these cells ap-

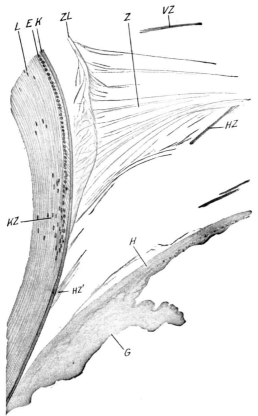

Fig. 32–14. From a meridional section of the anterior part of human eye. Attachment of the fibers of the zonula ciliaris to the equator of the lens. E, epithelium of the lens; G, vitreous body; H, membrana hyaloidea; HZ, posterior fibers of the zonule; HZ', their connection with the capsule of the lens (K); KZ, nuclear zone of the lens; L, fibers of the lens substance in longitudinal section; VZ, anterior fibers of the zonule; Z, zonule; ZL, detached outer layer of the capsule of the lens. 110 ×. (After Schaffer.)

proach a columnar form and become arranged in meridional rows. Becoming progressively elongated, the cells at the equator are transformed into *lens fibers* that constitute the tissue of the lens. In this transition or *nuclear zone* the cells have a characteristic arrangement. The epithelial cells are of prime importance for the normal metabolism of the lens. The surface of the capsule covering the posterior pole has no epithelium.

In the human lens each fiber is a six-sided prism, from 7 to 10 mm. long, 8 to 12 microns wide, and only 2 microns thick (Fig. 32–15). In the region of the nucleus the thickness may reach 5 microns. In younger fibers a firmer cortical and a semi-liquid axial part can be distinguished. With advancing age the axial part becomes increasingly solid (sclerosis). The young fibers have smooth surfaces and join one another, so that their narrow edges interdigitate. They are kept together by thin layers of a cementing substance which has the same index of refraction as the fibers themselves. This substance is considered by some to be a lubricant enabling slight movements of the fibers during accommodation. In the older fibers, in the dense, inner portion of the lens, the nucleus is absent and the outlines of the cross sections often become irregular and serrated. At the two poles of the lens where the fibers join their ends, they form a figure of a star with three or more rays (Fig. 32–9).

The lens is held in position by a system of fibers—the *ciliary zonule.* The zonule fibers (Fig. 32–14, Z, VZ, HZ) are straight, homogeneous filaments varying in thickness (up to 22 microns or more) and having many branches. They seem to arise from the epithelium of the ciliary portion of the retina. Near the ciliary crown they fuse into thicker fibers and finally form about 140 bundles. At the anterior margin of the ciliary processes they leave the surface of the ciliary body and radiate freely toward the equator of the lens. The larger ones are straight and reach the capsule in front of the equator of the lens (*anterior sheet of the zonule*). The thinner fibers assume a slightly curved course and are attached to the posterior surface of the lens (*posterior zonular sheet*). All zonular fibers break up into a multitude of fine brushlike fibers which fuse with the substance of the outermost layer of the capsule. Where the

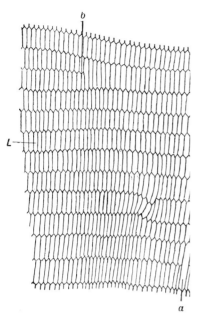

Fig. 32–15. Part of frontal section through equator of the human lens. The cross sections of the fibers are arranged in radial rows or lamellae (L): a, fiber of double width; b, branching of a radial lamella. 500 ×. (After Schaffer.)

vitreous touches the lens capsule it forms the *hyaloideocapsular ligament.*

The radii of curvature of the surfaces of the several dioptrical media of the *normal* eye, especially of the lens, and their indices of refraction are such that light rays coming from a remote point form an inverted and real image of the object in the layer of the photoreceptive cones and rods in the retina. If the object is approaching, the light rays diverge more and more and the image moves backward. A change of position of object from infinite distance to about 5 meters causes the image to shift about 60 microns backward in the retina. Since this image is still within the outer segments of the rods and cones, accommodation is not needed. For nearer distances, accommodation is necessary.

In a photographic camera the focusing of objects which move nearer to the lens is effected by moving the ground glass plate away from the lens. In the higher vertebrates and in man, the curvature of the lens is changed. When the eye is at rest the lens is kept stretched in the plane vertical to the optic axis by the ciliary zonule. When the eye has to focus a near object, the ciliary muscle, especially its meridional fibers, con-

tracts and pulls the choroid with the ciliary body forward. This relieves the tension exerted by the zonule, the lens gets thicker, and its surface, especially at the anterior pole, becomes more convex. This increases the refractive power of the lens and keeps the focus within the bacillary layer.

Vitreous Body. The vitreous body fills the space (vitreal cavity) between the lens and the retina. It adheres everywhere to the optical portion of the retina, and the connection is especially firm at the serrated margin. Farther forward it gradually recedes from the surface of the ciliary portion of the retina.

The fresh vitreous body has a gelatinous consistency, is colorless, structureless and of glasslike transparency. Its index of refraction is 1.334. When fixed, it shows a network of extremely fine fibrils with its meshes filled with clear liquid. Almost 99 per cent of the vitreous consists of water and dissolved substances.

From the papilla of the optic nerve to the posterior surface of the lens the *hyaloid canal* (Cloquet) extends through the vitreous body. It is a residue after the resorption of the embryonic hyaloid artery. It has a diameter of 1 mm. and is filled with aqueous liquid. In the living, especially in young persons, it is visible with the help of the slit lamp microscope. In the peripheral layers of the vitreous, free cells float in the liquid. They are probably hematogenous lymphoid cells.

THE RETINA

The retina is the innermost of the three coats of the eyeball and is the photoreceptor organ. It arises in early embryonic development through a bilateral evagination of the prosencephalon, the *primary optic vesicle.* Later it is transformed into the *secondary optic vesicle* (Fig. 32–30). Each optic cup remains connected with the brain by a stalk, the *future optic nerve.* In the adult this tunic consists of an outer, pigmented epithelial layer (Fig. 32–18) and an inner sheet, the *retina proper.* It contains elements similar to those of the brain, and it may be considered to be a specially differentiated part of the brain.

The *optical* or *functioning portion of the*

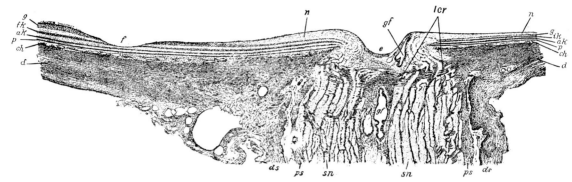

Fig. 32–16. Place of entrance of the optic nerve and the central fovea of an enucleated human eye in horizontal meridional section. *ak,* outer nuclear layer; *ch,* choroid; *d,* sclera; *ds,* dural sheath of optic nerve; *e,* physiological excavation; *f,* central fovea; *g,* layer of ganglion cells; *gf,* blood vessels; *ik,* inner nuclear layer; *lcr,* lamina cribrosa; *n,* layer of nerve fibers; *p,* pigment layer of retina; *ps,* pial sheath of the optic nerve; *sn,* bundles of fibers of the optic nerve. 17 ×. (After Schaffer.)

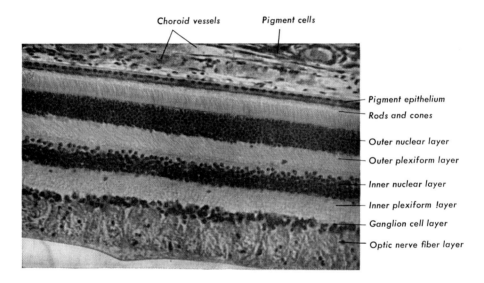

Fig. 32–17. Photomicrograph of human retina. H + E. 240 ×. (After von Herrath and Abramow.)

retina lines the inner surface of the choroid and extends from the papilla of the optic nerve to the serrated margin anteriorly (Figs. 32–1, 32–9). At the papilla, where the retina continues into the tissue of the nerve, and at the serrated margin, the retina is firmly connected with the choroid. About 2.5 mm. from the border of the optic papilla the inner surface of the retina appears excavated. This shallow, round depression is the *central fovea* (Figs. 32–1, 32–16, *f;* 32–19).

When detached from the pigment epithelium, the fresh retina is almost perfectly transparent. It has a distinctly red color due to the presence in its rod cells of *visual purple* or *rhodopsin.* Light rapidly bleaches the visual purple; in darkness the color gradually reappears. The fovea and its immediate vicinity contain yellow pigment, and are called the *macula lutea.* Large blood vessels circle above and below the central fovea, whereas only fine arteries and veins and capillaries are present in it (Fig. 32–24). In the very center of the fovea, in a territory measuring 0.5 mm. across, even the capillaries are absent, greatly increasing its transparency.

Only that portion of the image of an external object which fall upon the fovea is seen sharply. Accordingly, the eyes are moved so as to bring the object of special attention into this central part of the visual field.

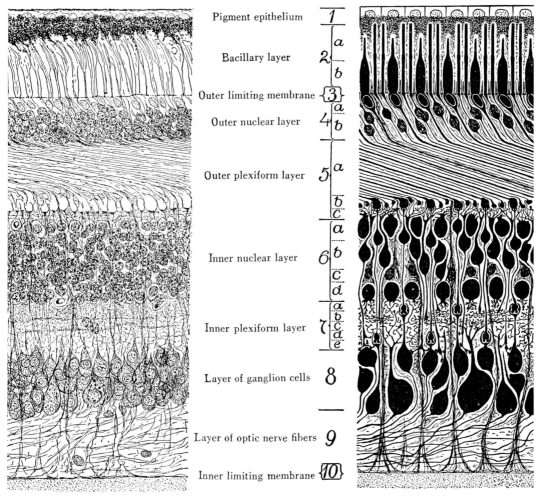

Pigment epithelium *1*

Bacillary layer *2* { a / b }

Outer limiting membrane { *3* }

Outer nuclear layer *4* { a / b }

Outer plexiform layer *5* { a / b / c }

Inner nuclear layer *6* { a / b / c / d }

Inner plexiform layer *7* { a / b / c / d / e }

Layer of ganglion cells *8*

Layer of optic nerve fibers *9*

Inner limiting membrane { *10* }

Fig. 32–18. Layers of adult human retina (region III). Left figure stained routinely, about 400 ×; the right figure is a schematic reconstruction from sections stained with Golgi's method. (Slightly modified after Polyak.)

Photoreceptors are absent from the optic papilla. This is the "blind spot" of the visual field.

Layers of Retina. In the retina, exclusive of the fovea, the papilla, and the serrated margin, ten parallel layers can be distinguished from outside inward (Fig. 32–18): (1) the pigment epithelium; (2) the layer of rods and cones (bacillary layer); (3) the outer limiting membrane; (4) the outer nuclear layer; (5) the outer plexiform layer; (6) the inner nuclear layer; (7) the inner plexiform layer; (8) the layer of ganglion cells; (9) the layer of optic nerve fibers; and (10) the inner limiting membrane. The numbers *1* to *10* correspond with those in Figures 32–18; 32–19; 32–20; 32–23; 32–25.

Regions of the Retina. The distribution of the cellular and fibrous elements varies considerably in detail from the center of the retina in the fovea to its anterior limit at the serrated margin. Thus seven circular *regions* can be distinguished (Fig. 32–19). The inner three (*I* to *III*) compose the *central area,* distinguished by the great number of ganglion cells in the eighth layer, and by the general refinement and even distribution of the structural elements, especially of the rods and cones. The most delicate elements are in the fovea (region *I*), where they are accumulated in greatest numbers. The regions outside the central area (*IV* to *VI*), including the ora serrata (*VII*), constitute the *extra-areal periphery*. Here the elements are fewer, larger, less differentiated and less evenly distributed. (Note that Roman numerals refer in text and legends to regions of the retina, while the Arabic refer to the layers.)

Pigment Epithelium. This layer consists of one row of low prismatic cells. When seen from the surface, they usually appear as fairly regular hexagons of an average diameter of 16 microns. In cross section the same cells appear as rectangles 8 microns high. The inner surface of the cells sends out thin protoplasmic processes (ten to forty to a cell) filled with pigment (fuscin), which surround the rods and cones and separate them from one another. The outer part of the protoplasm adjacent to the choroid is free of pigment and contains an oval nucleus.

With changes of illumination these pigment inclusions change their position. In an eye which has been exposed to light the rod-

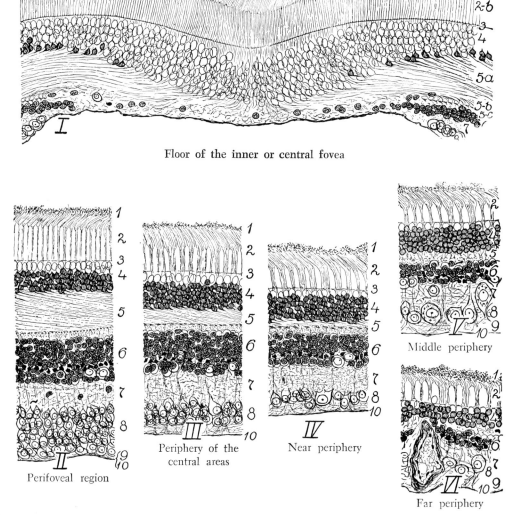

Floor of the inner or central fovea

Fig. 32–19.   Samples from various regions of the retina of a rhesus monkey. (Slightly modified after Polyak.)

shaped pigment granules move into the processes, thus providing each rod and cone with a pigment sheath. This is supposed to prevent the diffusion of light from one rod or cone to another. In an eye protected from light the pigment leaves the fringes and is massed in the cell body.

Visual Cells. These elements are the receptors of the light stimuli or photoreceptors (*2* and *4* in Figs. 32–18; 32–19; 32–20; 32–25). The light rays, before reaching them, must first penetrate most of the retina. The outer portions of the visual cells are believed to be the parts sensitive to light. There are two kinds of visual cells; (*a*) the rod cells and (*b*) the cone cells.

Rod Cells. The rod cell is a filamentous element arranged with its outer portion vertical to the surface of the retina (Fig. 32–20, *a*). This causes the regular striation of layer 2. The scleral part of the rod cell, the *rod proper*, is situated between the outer limiting membrane and the pigment epithelium, its outward third being embedded between the pigmented fringes. The vitreal end of the rod proper extends through the outer limiting membrane into layer *4*. Each rod proper consists of an outer and inner segment. The outer segment is a smooth cylinder of uniform thickness with a rounded outer end. Its substance has a peculiar brilliancy, is homogeneous in life, and is positively birefringent. The inner segment is a trifle stouter and larger than the outer segment. At its junction with the outer segment the inner rod segment contains a darkly staining "fiber apparatus" and a diplosome. With the electron microscope Sjöstrand found the outer segments of the rods in guinea pigs to be composed of double membrane disks 140 A thick and about 2μ wide. They are about 100 A apart and are connected in series by short processes. The membranes forming the disks are about 30 A thick. The center of the disk is partially hollow and about 80 A high. In the perch the rods are somewhat thicker than in the guinea pig. He also described a dense aggregation of elongate mitochondria in the outer portion of the inner segment and discovered a bundle of 16 to 18 fibrils running in one side of the outer segment and joining it to the inner segment of the rod.

As a result of his electron microscopic study of the rods and their embryogenesis in

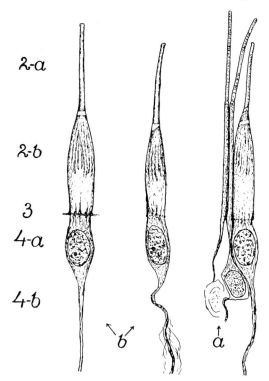

Fig. 32–20.   Rods (*a*) and cones (*b*) from an osmic acid-fixed, unstained, teased preparation of retina of a rhesus monkey (preparation of G. W. Bartelmez). Designation of layers as in Figure 32–18. Outer rod and cone segments in zone 2-*a*, inner segments in 2-*b*, rod bodies with their nuclei in zone 4-*b*, cone bodies with nuclei in 4-*a*; 3, outer limiting membrane; fiber apparatus visible in the upper portion of the inner cone segments. Some of the outer segments slightly bent. (Courtesy of S. Polyak.)

the rabbit, De Robertis believed these fibrils form an atypical cilium with its basal body in the inner segment of the rod. He also described microsomes of both vesicular (endoplasmic reticulum) and granular (RNA granules, dense granule) types.

In fishes and in birds the inner rod segment is contractile. When illuminated, it lengthens and pushes the photosensitive outer segment deeper into the pigment epithelium toward the sclera. In dim light the inner rod segment contracts, moving the outer segment closer to the outer limiting membrane and thus exposing it to more light. Little is known of the contractility of the inner rod segment in primates.

The rods are fairly uniform in appearance, although their dimensions vary somewhat

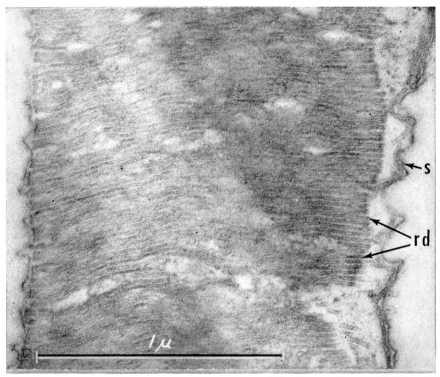

Fig. 32–21. Electron micrograph showing cross sections of double membrane rod disks (*rd*) enclosed by the thin outer membrane (*s*) of a portion of outer segment of guinea pig retinal rod in longitudinal section. Buffered osmic acid fixation. (Courtesy of F. Sjöstrand.)

from region to region. Their thickness in the central area (regions *I to III*) is 1 to 1.5 microns, gradually increasing to 2.5 or 3 microns near the ora (region *VII*). Their length decreases from approximately 60 microns in the fovea to 40 microns in the far periphery.

The rest of the rod cell is made of the *rod fiber* and the *rod body.* It extends from the lower end of the rod proper through layer 4 to layer 5-*b,* where it terminates with a tiny, round swelling, the *rod spherule,* smaller than the analogous cone pedicle. The rod fiber is a protoplasmic thread of smooth appearance and uniform thickness which does not exceed 1 micron; its length varies considerably. In the central area the course of the rod fibers assumes a slanting to horizontal position, while in the extra-areal regions it is vertical.

Along the rod fiber is the *rod body* containing a nucleus, smaller and more intensively stained than the cone nucleus, and surrounded by scant protoplasm. The rod proper with the outer fiber is the homologue of the receptive dendritic expansions of a neuron, the inner rod fiber of the emissive axis cylinder. In the central area the inner rod and cone fibers, and the corresponding portions of Müller's fibers (p. 574) which envelop them, form a thick fiber layer, the outer fiber layer of Henle (zone 5-*a*).

The rod nuclei represent the majority of the nuclei of the fourth layer (*4*) in all regions except in the fovea, where rods are few, and in its center, where they are absent.

In all rod cells, except those of a zone 3 to 4 mm. wide at the serrated margin, the rods contain visual purple. To this is due the red color of the retina during life. As there are only a few rods in the periphery of the fovea and none in its center, this area appears devoid of rhodopsin. When the retina is exposed to light, rhodopsin disintegrates, but is constantly produced anew. This regeneration occurs only as long as the connection of the rods with the pigment epithelium is preserved.

The number of rods in the human retina, according to Krause, is 130 millions.

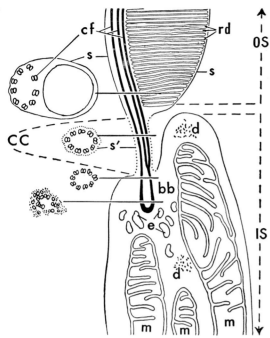

Fig. 32–22. Diagram, based on electron micrographs, of region of junction between outer and inner segments of retinal rods. The levels of the transverse sections, shown at left, are indicated on the longitudinal section at the right. The outer segment (*OS*) contains stacked rod disks (*rd*) and ciliary fibrils (*cf*) enclosed by a surface membrane (*s*). The ciliary fibrils extend into the inner segment (*IS*) where they terminate in a basal body (*bb*). A continuous surface membrane covering the connecting cilium (*cc*) between the outer and inner segments has not been clearly established, and is accordingly presented by a dotted line. In the inner segment are abundant elongate mitochondria (*m*), vesicles of endoplasmic reticulum (*e*) and dense granules (*d*). (Redrawn and modified from De Robertis.)

Cone Cells. These neurons (Fig. 32–20) are made up of essentially the same parts as the rod cells, but differ in detail. On the whole, they are bulkier. The outward portion, instead of being a slender rod, is a thick, flask-shaped structure.

The part situated outside the outer limiting membrane is the *cone,* or cone proper. It, too, is divided into two parts. The highly refractive and fragile outer segment is a long, slender cone. It rests upon the stout inner segment and tapers toward its blunt tip (the swollen tip often seen is an autolytic artefact). Sjöstrand found the outer segments of the cone to be solid disks, in the perch, in contrast to the hollow disks in the rods. The inner cone segment varies in shape and size

from place to place. In the central region and close to it, it is cylindrical, gradually becoming flask-shaped in the periphery. Like the rod, it contains a "fiber apparatus" and a diplosome. It is much more resistant to physical and chemical agents than the outer segment. There is no visual purple in the cones.

The cones vary considerably in different regions of the retina. In the central fovea the cones measure 75 microns or more in length and from 1 to 1.5 microns in thickness. Their length gradually decreases to 45 microns in the extra-areal periphery. The relative length of the outer and the inner segments is usually as three to four. In the fovea the two are approximately the same length. The lower end of the inner cone segment slips through an opening in the outer limiting membrane (3), and protrudes slightly into the fourth layer.

In teleostean fishes and amphibians the inner cone segment is contractile. It shortens in bright light and stretches in dim light or darkness. The displacement of these cones is, accordingly, opposite in direction to that of the rods. It is not certain whether human cones have the same property.

Passing the outer limiting membrane, the inner cone segment merges with its *body* containing a nucleus, which is larger and paler staining than the rod nucleus. The bodies and nuclei of the cones, as distinct from those of the rods, are placed in a single row (4-*a*) immediately beneath the outer limiting membrane. The exceptions are the cones in the outer fovea whose nuclei are accumulated in several rows (Fig. 32–19, *I*). Only here the cones have an *outer fiber.* From the body of all cones a stout, smooth *inner fiber* descends to the middle zone of the outer plexiform layer (5-*b*), where it terminates with a thick triangular or club-shaped swelling, the *cone pedicle.* Up to a dozen short, barblike filaments emanate from the base of each pedicle, except in the fovea, where there are usually none. These filamentous outgrowths spread horizontally in zone 5-*c*. The length and course of the inner cone fibers vary considerably, depending on the region, the longest (600 microns) and almost horizontally placed being those in the outer fiber layer of Henle (5-*a*) in the central area. The inner cone fibers have all the earmarks of an axis cylinder, the cone pedicle those of a telodendron of a neuron.

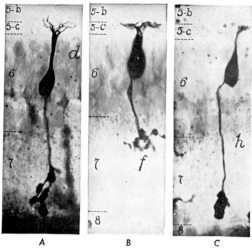

Fig. 32–23. Photomicrographs of centripetal bipolar cells: variety *d* (*A*), variety *f* (in *B*), variety *h* (in *C*). Method of Golgi. Rhesus monkey. Designation of layers as in Figure 32–18. (Courtesy of S. Polyak.)

The number of cones in the human retina is estimated at 6,000,000 to 7,000,000 (Østerberg). The ratio of the nerve fibers of the optic nerve (438,000) to the number of cones of one eye is as 1:6 or 1:7.

The relative number and distribution of the rods and cones in different vertebrates present great variations depending on the mode of life. In diurnal birds the cones are more numerous than the rods. In most diurnal reptiles there are only cones and no rods. In many nocturnal vertebrates only rods are present, although in others a few rudimentary cones can be found among numerous rods. On similar comparative data M. Schultze (1866) assumed a difference in the function of the two kinds of photoreceptors (duplicity theory).

The cones in the adult primate retina, including those of the fovea, are quite distinct from the rods. The opinion that there is more than one variety of cone cell in mammals (including primates) and that this is related to certain theories of color perception, has not been verified. The evidence indicates that the cone cells throughout the primate retina are of one variety, although they vary in detail from place to place. This is also true of the rods, though in a lesser degree.

Horizontal Cells. These cells are typical neurons whose bodies form the uppermost one or two rows of the inner nuclear layer (zone *6-a* in Figs. 32–18; 32–25). From the upper end of the body arise short dendritic twigs producing several tufts spreading in the lower zone of the outer plexiform layer (*5-c*), where each tuft comes in contact with the vitreal face of one cone pedicle. The

axis cylinder takes a horizontal course chiefly in zone *5-c,* and its terminal twigs come in contact with both rod spherules and cone pedicles. The horizontal cells, accordingly, receive impulses from a group of cone cells of one locality and transmit them to a group of rod and cone cells of another locality (Fig. 32–25, *c*).

Bipolar Cells. These neurons connect the rods and cones with the ganglion cells of the retina, and through these with the visual centers of the brain. The bipolar cells stand approximately upright with respect to the retinal layers, except in the central fovea, where their position is oblique. Their nuclei are in the sixth layer, with a few in the fifth. Each bipolar has one or several outward expansions that spread into the outer plexiform layer (5), where they synapse with the photoreceptors. With the aid of the electron microscope Sjöstrand has demonstrated the intricate manner in which the dendritic expansions of the bipolar cells penetrate the terminal swellings of the rod cells (Fig. 32–26). Similar studies of the synapses in the retina have been made by De Robertis and Franchi.

A single inward expansion of the bipolar spreads into the seventh layer, where it is synaptically related to the ganglion cells and other adjoining cells. Two groups of bipolars can be distinguished: centripetal bipolars, which transmit impulses from rods and cones to ganglion cells (Fig. 32–25, *d, e, f, h*), and centrifugal bipolars, which transmit in the opposite direction (*i*). The bipolar cells apparently play an essential role in distributing and rearranging the impulses received from the rods and cones before transmitting them to the third category of retinal neurons, the ganglion cells.

Ganglion Cells. These cells (*m, n, o, p, s* in Fig. 32–25, and layer 8 in Fig. 32–18) represent the third link, the last in the retina, of the chain of neurons that form the afferent visual pathway. These cells are larger than those of the two nuclear layers, and closely resemble neurons of the brain. The bodies are in the ganglion layer, with a few displaced into the lowermost zone of the inner nuclear layer. Their dendrites spread in the inner plexiform layer. Chromophile substance is present in all. From the body or the chief dendritic trunk of each ganglion cell arises one axis cylinder that leaves the retina and be-

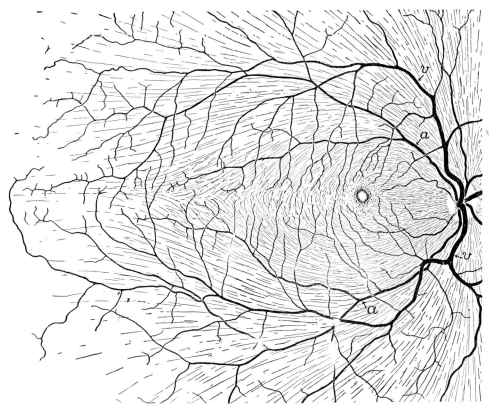

Fig. 32–24. Retina of right eye of adult rhesus monkey as seen in a total preparation. Intravital staining with methylene blue (Ehrlich). The elliptic papilla of the optic nerve is near the right side of the figure. Fine lines radiating from the papilla in all directions represent bundles of optic nerve fibers. The stippled circular area almost free from fibers is the central fovea. Within it a small white circle is the floor of the fovea; the dark ring surrounding it is the foveal slope. Note the direction of some of the foveal fibers straight to the fovea, of others more or less circling to it or around it, encircling the foveal region from above and below, and forming on the temporal side to it (left) the horizontally placed "raphe" or retinal seam. *a,* arteries; *v,* veins. Camera lucida. 8 ×. (Courtesy of S. Polyak.)

comes an optic nerve fiber terminating in the subcortical visual centers of the brain.

Optic Nerve Fibers in the Primate Retina. Because of the presence of the central fovea, the optic nerve fibers have a special course (Fig. 32–24). In general they converge radially toward the optic papilla. However, those originating in the upper temporal quadrant of the retina circle above the central area, while those originating in the lower temporal quadrant circle below the central area on their way to the papilla. They follow the larger retinal vessels fairly closely. A line connecting the fovea with the temporal circumference of the retina separates the optic nerve fibers of the upper from those of the lower temporal quadrant. This separation is preserved along the central visual pathway as far as the cortical visual center.

In primates each retina is divided into two halves along the vertical meridian passing through the center of the fovea. The fibers from the nasal half cross in the optic chiasma and pass to the optic tract of the opposite side; those from the temporal half enter the tract of the same side. Each optic tract is, therefore, composed of fibers from the temporal half of the same side and from the nasal half of the retina of the opposite eye. This arrangement remains in the visual radiation in the occipital lobes of the brain. It accounts for the blindness in the opposite halves of the two fields of view (homonymous hemianopia) when the optic tract or the visual radiation of one side is interrupted.

Supporting or Neuroglial Elements of the Retina. The retina, a modified part of the brain, contains supporting elements of neu-

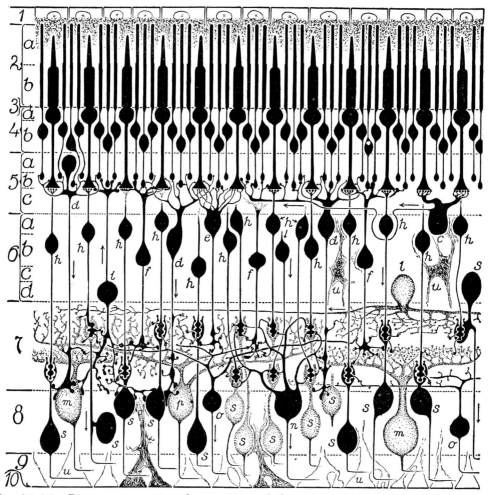

Fig. 32–25.   Diagram representing the structures of the primate retina composed from numerous Golgi-stained preparations of man, chimpanzee and macaque. The designation of layers and zones on the left side as in Figure 32–18. In the upper part the slender structures are the rod cells (*a*), the thicker ones the cone cells (*b*); *c*, horizontal cell; *d, e, f, h,* centripetal bipolar cells; *i,* centripetal bipolar cells; *l,* inner horizontal or association cell; *m, n, o, p, s,* ganglion cells; *u,* parts of the radial fibers of Müller, with their nuclei in 6, and their lower or inner ends forming the inner limiting membrane (*10*). Note the various synaptic relations between different neurons, reciprocal overlapping of expansions or its absence, the probable direction of the nervous impulses indicated by arrows, and other details. The indicated termination of the l-axon is not completely proved. The rods and the cones are not designated by letters *a* and *b* as in Figure 32–20. (After Polyak.)

roglial character. The most important are the radial fibers of Müller (*u* in Fig. 32–25). These are present throughout the central area, including the fovea, as well as in the periphery.

Their oval nuclei lie in the middle zone of the inner nuclear layer (*6-c,* Fig. 32–18). The cell body is a slender fiber or pillar which extends radially from the outer (*3*) to the inner limiting membrane (*10*). Their inner ends expand conically and form the

inner limiting membrane. In the two plexi-form layers the radial fibers give off many branches, which form a dense neuroglial net-work in whose meshes are lodged the rami-fications of the neurons described earlier.

The cell bodies of the radial fibers are beset with excavations which envelop bodies of the ganglion cells, bipolars, horizontal cells and the cone and rod cells. The bodies of the nervous elements appear to be completely enveloped in thin husks of supporting structures which perhaps serve as insulators. The rod and cone fibers are likewise encased in thin, tubelike sheaths produced by Müller's fibers.

At the limit between the outer nuclear layer and the layer of the rods and cones the radial fibers fuse and form the *outer limiting membrane*. This is pierced by numerous openings through which the rods and cones are connected with their inner parts, their bodies.

Central Area and Fovea ("Macula"). Slightly lateral to the papilla is the place of most distinct vision. This region, the *central area,* is characterized by the agglomeration of cones and other nervous elements in numbers greater than outside it and by their structural refinement and synaptic perfection. In the center of this area, the layers inward to zone 5-*a* are displaced laterally, producing a shallow depression on the vitreal surface of the retina called the *central fovea*. This permits an almost free passage of rays of light to the layer of photoreceptors, and it is here that the visual axis touches the retina.

The central fovea is a shallow bowl with its concavity toward the vitreous (Fig. 32–27). It is in the center of the central area 2 to 2.5 mm. on the temporal side of the papilla. In its center a *floor* or *fundus* can be distinguished, with the *slopes* and a *margin of the fovea*. The width of the entire foveal depression measures 1.5 mm.

In the fundus of the central fovea, the cones are most numerous and are thinner and longer than elsewhere in the retina. This formation, the *outer fovea*, contains 20,000 to 25,000 cones. This region, measuring about 400 microns across, probably corresponds to the portion of the field of view where vision is most discriminating. The *rod-free area*, where only cones are present, measures 500 to 550 microns in diameter and contains up to 30,000 cones.

Capillaries are present in the ventral layers of the foveal slopes to the very edge of the foveal floor, or 275 microns from the very center. The *avascular central territory* is almost as large as the rodless area (500 to 550 microns).

Function of the Eye. Synapses and Function of the Retina. The eye is essentially a camera obscura provided with dioptric media: the cornea with the aqueous humor and the adjustable crystalline lens are optically active. The inner surface of this dark chamber is lined by the photosensitive retina. The rays of light emanating from each point of an illuminated object which impinge on the cornea are refracted by it and converge on the lens. In the lens the rays are further refracted and focused in the photosensitive layer of the retina (2 in the figures). The sum of the foci that correspond with the points on the surface of the object seen constitutes the retinal image of this object. In relation to the object the retinal image is inverted (because of the crossing of the rays in the pupil's aperture), real (since the foci are actually on the retina and not behind or in front of it) and very much reduced in size.

Stripped of many important details, the complex story of the interneuronic relationships in the retina is as follows: In the photosensitive rods and cones, light initiates a nervous process which in turn produces nervous impulses to be forwarded along the nervous pathways to the brain. Subjectively, this is interpreted as light, colors, shapes, sizes, position and movement of the objects seen. The *synaptic mechanism* of the retina is composed of the following systems of neurons (Fig. 32–25): The rod cells (*a*) transmit impulses to two or three varieties of bipolars (*d, e-f*) and through these to all varieties of the ganglion cells (*m, n, o, p, s*). The cones (*b*), on the contrary, discharge impulses to three or four bipolar varieties (*d, e-f, h*), and through these to all varieties of ganglion cells (*m, n, o, p, s*); the cones also stimulate the horizontal cells (*c*) and thus may influence distant rods (*a*) and cones (*b*).

The rods, it is believed, are responsive to weak light stimuli, thus being adapted for seeing in dim light. They do not respond selectively to lights of different wavelengths associated with the sensation of colors. Conversely, color sensations are initiated through the stimulation of cones which are less responsive to weak "colorless" light. This makes the cones especially suitable for vision in bright light. At the third neuronal level, in the ganglion cells (*m, n, o, p, s*) since all three bipolar varieties (*d, e-f, h*) are synaptically connected with each of the several ganglion varieties—the rod and cone impulses apparently merge with one another. The fate of the impulses in the brain is unknown.

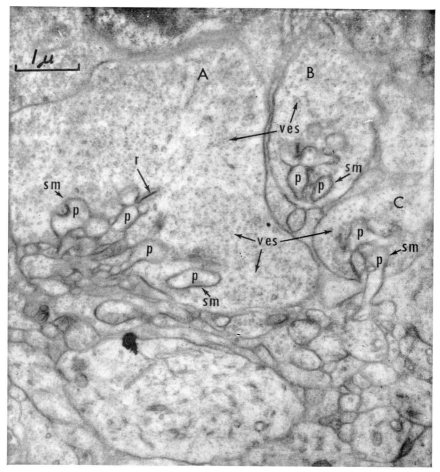

Fig. 32–26.   Electron micrograph showing synapses in the outer plexiform layer of the guinea pig retina. Branching dendritic terminals of bipolar cells (*p*) are enveloped by the cytoplasm of rod cell axon terminals (*A, B, C*) which contain characteristic synaptic vesicles (*ves*). The double membrane of the synapse (*sm*) is formed by the plasma membranes of the rod axon and the bipolar cell dendrite. A short, dense rodlet (*r*) occurs frequently. In the lower part of the picture are one large and numerous fine nerve cell processes. Buffered osmic acid fixation. (Courtesy of F. Sjöstrand.)

The synaptic relations suggest that the cones react in a more territorially restricted way than the rods. In and near the central fovea, each cone is linked to one h-bipolar, which in turn is related to a single s-ganglion cell (Fig. 9–46, *B*). This implies that the visual system here is made up of a great number of anatomical and functional units, each of which responds independently to a minute photic stimulus. This may be the structural basis for visual space perception or visual acuity.

The rods, being connected in groups to bipolars, always respond in groups, no matter

Fig. 32–27.   Diagram of the fovea. The layers are represented alternately in black and white in the right and left halves. The line dividing them is in the foveal center. Asterisks indicate the margins of the central or inner fovea (region I of the retina). The outer fovea is indicated by arrows. *Ch*, choroid membrane. The numbers of the layers correspond with those in Figure 32–18. (Slightly modified after Polyak.)

how restricted the photic stimulus may be. Thus the smallest receptive rod territory is larger than the cone territory of the same region. Such grouplike connections might well result in reinforcement of the intensity of excitation generated in the rods (Fig. 9–46, D).

In the central area the size of the receptor-conductor units corresponds roughly with that of the individual cones. This agrees with the difference in retinal acuity in different localities, the acuity being at its peak in the very center of the field of view (corresponding with the foveal center) and at first rapidly, then more slowly, decreasing toward the periphery of the field of view.

In the primate retina at least fifteen distinct varieties of neurons are present; these form at least thirty-eight kinds of synapses with one another. In the retina, in addition to photoreception, many other processes usually associated with the central nervous system, such as selection, facilitation, inhibition, summation of excitations, take place. The retina is thus essentially a *receptor-integrator* organ. (For further details see Polyak, *The Retina*, and the Symposium on "Visual Mechanisms," edited by Klüver.)

Blood Vessels of the Eye. These arise from the ophthalmic artery and can be subdivided into two groups which are almost completely independent and anastomose with each other only in the region of the entrance of the optic nerve. The first group, the *retinal system*, represented by the central artery and vein, supplies a part of the optic nerve and the retina. The second, the *ciliary system*, is destined mainly for the uveal tunic.

Lymph Spaces of the Eye. True lymph capillaries and lymph vessels are present only in the scleral conjunctiva. In the eyeball they are absent.

A mass injected into the space between the choroid and sclera penetrates along the walls of the vortex veins into the *space of Tenon*. The latter continues as the *supravaginal space* along the outer surface of the dural sheath of the optic nerve to the optic foramen. Again, it is possible to inject Tenon's space from the subarachnoid space of the brain. From the *anterior chamber* the injected liquid passes into the *posterior chamber*, and also into Schlemm's canal. All these spaces cannot, however, be regarded as belonging to the lymphatic system. The space of Tenon is more like a joint cavity and facilitates the movements of the eyeball.

The *aqueous humor* is believed to originate through secretion or transudation from the ciliary processes. This is a clear, watery fluid of slightly alkaline reaction with an index of refraction of 1.33. It contains 0.77 per cent sodium chloride, traces of urea and glucose, and practically no proteins, and

few or no wandering cells. It is much like the cerebrospinal fluid. From the posterior chamber it permeates the vitreous. It also penetrates between the lens and the iris and through the pupil into the anterior chamber. The drainage of the aqueous humor from the anterior chamber is effected mainly through the spaces of Fontana and the canal of Schlemm. The normal intra-ocular pressure (28 mm. of mercury), which causes the spherical form of the eyeball, is the resultant of the rates of transudation and of drainage of the aqueous humor. In glaucoma the intra-ocular pressure may increase considerably. Drainage through the canal of Schlemm seems doubtful, and it is possible that the liquid from the anterior chamber is resorbed by the crypts, by the blood vessels of the iris, and by the perivascular spaces of the episcleral and vortex veins.

Nerves of the Eye. These are the optic nerve, supplying the retina, and the ciliary nerves supplying the eyeball with motor, sensory and sympathetic fibers.

The *optic nerve*, an evagination of the prosencephalon, the optic vesicle, is not a peripheral nerve like the other cranial nerves, but is a tract of the central nervous system, as found in any part of the white substance. It consists of about 1200 bundles of myelinated fibers without neurolemma. The nerve fibers are kept together by the same kind of neuroglia as in the white substance of the central nervous system. On the surface of each bundle the glia forms a thin membrane which separates the nervous elements from the connective tissue. A similar layer is also found at the periphery of the optic nerve.

The meninges and the intermeningeal spaces of the brain continue upon the optic nerve. The outer sheath of the nerve is formed by the dura, which continues toward the eyeball and fuses with the sclera. The pia mater forms a connective tissue layer which is closely adherent to the surface of the nerve and fuses with the sclera at the entrance of the optic nerve. This pial layer sends connective tissue partitions with blood vessels into the nerve. Inflammatory processes can extend from the eyeball toward the meningeal spaces of the brain through the spaces between the sheaths.

The optic nerve leaves the posterior pole of the eyeball in a slightly oblique direction and continues into the entrance canal of the optic nerve. Just after leaving the eye through the openings in the lamina cribrosa, the fibers get their myelin sheaths. The central artery and the central vein reach the eyeball through the optic nerve; they penetrate the nerve on the lower side at a distance from the eyeball varying from 5 to 20 mm., usually 6 to 8 mm.

ACCESSORY ORGANS OF THE EYE

In an early stage of embryonic development the anterior segment of the eyeball projects freely on the surface. Later a circular fold of integument encircles the cornea. From its upper and lower parts the upper and lower lids grow toward each other over the surface of the cornea. In this way the conjunctival sac is formed, which protects and moistens the free surface of the eye and especially the cornea. The part lining the inner surface of the lids is the

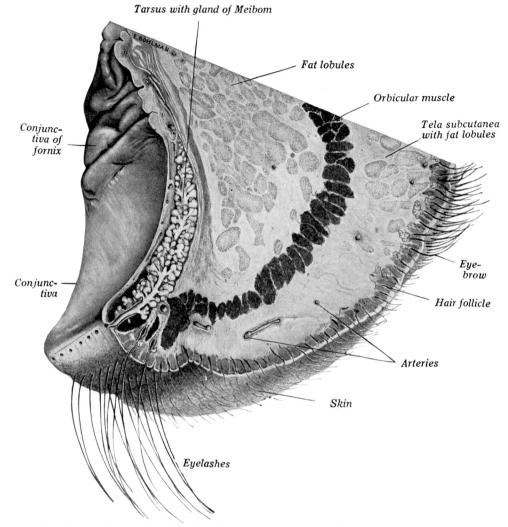

Tarsus with gland of Meibom

Fat lobules

Orbicular muscle

Tela subcutanea with fat lobules

Conjunctiva of fornix

Conjunctiva

Eyebrow

Hair follicle

Arteries

Skin

Eyelashes

Fig. 32–28.   Camera lucida drawing of a slice of the upper eyelid of a newborn infant. Stained with hematoxylin. 12 ✕. (Drawn by Miss Esther Bohlman.)

palpebral conjunctiva, that covering the eyeball is the *bulbar conjunctiva.* The reflection of the palpebral on the bulbar conjunctiva forms deep recesses between the lids and the eyeball, the superior and the inferior fornices.

Eyelids. The outermost layer is the skin. It is thin and provided with a few papillae and many small hairs with sebaceous and small sweat glands. The derma contains a varying number of pigment cells with yellow or brown granules. The loose subcutaneous layer is rich in fine elastic networks, and in Caucasians is almost completely devoid of fat. Toward the edge of the lid the derma becomes denser and has higher papillae.

The *eyelashes* are large hairs obliquely inserted in three or four rows along the edge of the lid. With their follicles they penetrate deeply into the tissue. The sebaceous glands connected with the eyelashes are small; arrector muscles are missing. The eyelashes are replaced every hundred to 150 days.

Between and behind the follicles of the eyelashes are peculiar sweat glands, the *glands of Moll.* Unlike ordinary sweat glands, the terminal portion here is generally straight or only slightly coiled. The excretory ducts open, as a rule, into the follicles. The epithelium of the terminal portions consists of an indistinct, outer myo-epithelial layer and an inner layer of pyramidal, apocrine glandular elements. The lumen is often considerably dilated, and the glandular cells are flattened. In the ducts the epithelium consists of two distinct cell layers. The nature of the secretion of these glands is not known.

The next layer inward consists of the thin, pale, striated fibers of the palpebral portion of the *ring muscle of the eye* (orbicular muscle). The part behind the follicles of the eyelashes or behind the ducts of the meibomian glands is the ciliary muscle of Riolan.

Behind the orbicular muscle is a layer of connective tissue, the palpebral fascia, a continuation of the tendon of the palpebral levator (or depressor) muscle. It contains the arterial arc (tarsal arc). In the upper part of the upper lid, strands of smooth muscle, the *superior tarsal muscle of Müller,* are attached to the edge of the tarsus. This plate of dense connective tissue forms the skeleton of the lid. In the upper lid its breadth is about 10 mm., in the lower only 5 mm. In its substance the *glands of Meibom* are embedded. They are elongated and arranged in one layer, parallel to one another and perpendicular to the length of the tarsal plate. Their openings form a single row immediately in front of the inner free edge of the lid, where the skin passes into the conjunctiva.

The meibomian glands are sebaceous, but have lobated alveolar terminal portions. They are connected by short lateral ducts with a long central excretory duct lined with stratified squamous epithelium.

The innermost layer of the lid is the *conjunctiva.* At the inner edge of the margin of the lid the epidermis continues as the narrow admarginal zone to the inner surface of the lid. Here the superficial cells become thicker, the number of layers decreases, mucous cells appear, and the epithelium assumes a stratified columnar character which is typical for the whole conjunctiva and varies only in thickness in different places. The superficial cells have a short prismatic form and are provided with a thin cuticle. Spherical goblet cells are scattered between them.

At the upper edge of the tarsus the epithelium is sometimes reduced to two cell layers, and its surface presents many irregular invaginations. Some of them are lined with mucous cells and described as glands. In the conjunctiva of the fornix the epithelium is thicker.

The lamina propria of the conjunctiva is dense connective tissue. In the region of the fornix it is loosely attached to the intra-orbital fat tissue; this permits the free motion of the eyeball in the conjunctival sac.

In the region of the corneal limbus the epithelium of the conjunctiva assumes a stratified squamous character and continues as such on the surface of the cornea. It may still contain a few scattered mucous cells.

The rudimentary *third eyelid* or *semilunar fold* (the homologue of the nictitating membrane of the lower vertebrates) is formed by the scleral conjunctiva at the inner palpebral commissure, lateral to the lacrimal caruncle. It consists of connective tissue which contains smooth muscle fibers; it is covered with conjunctival epithelium which, on the outer surface, contains many mucous cells.

Lacrimal Gland. In connection with the conjunctival space there is a system of glands, the secretion of which moistens, lubricates and flushes the surface of the eyeball and of the lids. Of these glands, only the lacrimal gland reaches a high development. It has the size and shape of an almond and is lodged beneath the conjunctiva at the lateral upper side of the eyeball. It consists of a group of separate glandular bodies and sends out six to twelve excretory ducts which open along the upper and lateral surfaces of the superior conjunctival fornix.

The lacrimal gland is of the tubulo-alveolar type.

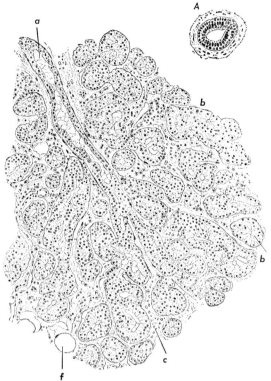

Fig. 32–29. A small lobule of human lacrimal gland. *a,* small intralobular excretory duct; *b,* terminal portions; *c,* intralobular interstitial connective tissue with blood vessels; *f,* fat cells. *A,* cross section of a larger interlobular excretory duct with pseudostratified epithelium. 112 ×. (After Schaffer.)

Its terminal portions are provided with a relatively large lumen and with irregular, saccular outpocketings. The basement membrane is lined with glandular cells resembling those of the serous salivary type. They have, however, a narrower columnar shape and contain, besides small fat droplets, large, pale secretion granules whose number changes with the volume of the cells, according to the functional conditions.

These cells are provided with secretory capillaries; between their bases and the basement membrane well-developed basket (myo-epithelial) cells are present. The smallest intralobular excretory ducts are lined with a layer of low columnar or cuboidal cells and have a few myo-epithelial cells. The larger intralobular ducts have a two-layered epithelium.

On the inner surface of the lids, especially the upper one, near the upper edge of the tarsus, a varying number of small accessory lacrimal glands—the *tarsal lacrimal glands*—are scattered.

After having washed the conjunctival cavity, the secretion of the lacrimal gland (the tears, a sterile liquid) reaches the region of the inner palpebral commissure (internal canthus). Here the two eyelids are separated by a triangular space, the *lacrimal lake,* in which the secretion accumulates temporarily. From here it passes through two tiny orifices called

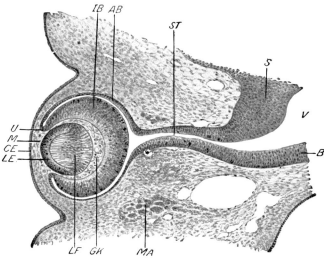

Fig. 32–30.   Primordium of eye of a mouse embryo of 8 mm. The cavity of the primary optic vesicle is reduced to a thin cleft. *AB*, outer layer of secondary optic vesicle; *B*, bottom of anterior brain vesicle; *CE*, epithelium of cornea; *GK*, vitreous body; *IB*, inner layer of secondary optic vesicle; *LE*, epithelium of the lens; *LF*, lens fibers with nuclear zone; *M*, mesenchyme; *MA*, primordium of muscle; *S*, side of anterior brain vesicle; *ST*, stalk of optic vesicle; *U*, border of the optic cup; *V*, ventricle of brain. 70 ×. (After Schaffer.)

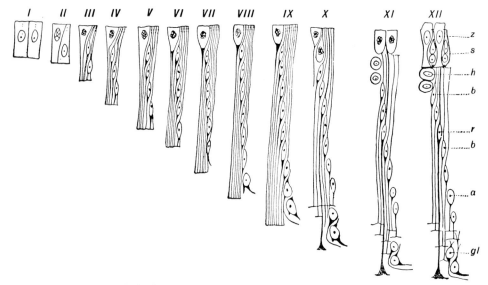

Fig. 32–31.   Diagram of the histogenesis of the retina. *I*, simple regular columnar epithelium; *II*, pseudostratified epithelium with two and, *III*, with three rows of nuclei; the number of nuclear rows increases in *IV-VII*; *VII*, the lowermost cell has developed an axon; *VIII*, the first (lower) ganglion cell has separated from the other elements; *IX*, the second ganglionic cell becomes separated; *X*, all cells except the radial fibers are separated from the inner surface; the ganglion cells and the amacrines have also severed their connections with the outer surface; *XI*, all cells except the indifferent stem cells, the visual cells and the radial fibers are separated from the outer surface; the horizontal cells also are free; *XII*, the rod cells (*s*) form a double layer between the cone cells; the cones have protoplasmic outgrowths; *z*, cone cells; *h*, horizontal cells; *r*, radial fibers; *b*, bipolars; *a*, amacrines; *gl*, ganglion cells. (After Fürst from Franz.)

lacrimal points, one on the margin of each eyelid, into the *lacrimal ducts.* The latter converge medially into the lacrimal sac, whence the *nasolacrimal duct* leads into the inferior meatus of the nose.

The wall of the excretory lacrimal passages is formed by connective tissue lined with epithelium. The epithelium of the lacrimal ducts is stratified squamous. The lacrimal sac and the nasolacrimal duct are lined with a pseudostratified, tall columnar epithelium.

From the bottom of the lacrimal lake, between the two lacrimal ducts, there bulges a small, soft mass of tissue, the *lacrimal caruncle.* The top is covered with a thick, squamous epithelium in which only the uppermost layers are flattened, although not cornified. It contains mucous cells, and gradually merges into the conjunctival epithelium. The lamina propria contains bundles of striated muscles, sweat and abortive lacrimal glands, and tiny hairs with sebaceous glands. These are the source of the whitish secretion which often collects in the region of the inner palpebral commissure.

Blood and Lymph Vessels of the Eyelids. The arteries in each lid form two archlike anastomoses, which run in front of the tarsus, one near the free margin of the lid, the other near the upper (or lower) margin of the tarsus. The palpebral conjunctiva is provided with dense, subepithelial capillary networks which can be easily studied in living condition with the aid of the slit-lamp microscope. Branches of the blood vessels in the scleral conjunctiva anastomose with the marginal blood vessels of the cornea and with the branches of the anterior ciliary arteries.

The lymphatics form dense nets in the conjunctiva behind the tarsus. In front of the latter there is another, thinner, pretarsal net. A third net can be distinguished in the skin and the subcutis. All these nets communicate with one another. The lymphatic capillaries of the scleral conjunctiva end blindly near the corneal margin.

The abundant supply of the conjunctiva with blood and lymph capillaries explains the rapid absorption of solutions introduced into the conjunctival sac.

Histogenesis of the Eye. The stalk of the optic vesicle growing out of the brain is transformed into the optic nerve; the double-walled vesicle gives rise to the retina. Where the optic vesicle touches the ectoderm, the latter forms an invagination with a greatly thickened bottom, the *primordium of the lens.* It apparently develops as the result of stimulation of the ectoderm by the optic vesicle. In amphibian larvae, after excision of the optic vesicle, the lens is not formed. The lens primordium comes to lie in the invagination of the optic vesicle. Simultaneously, mesenchyme and blood vessels grow into the choroidal fissure, which splits the lower periphery of the vesicle and continues upon the optic stalk. These vessels give rise to the hyaloid and retinal vascular systems. The opposite margins of the fissure, which received the vessels, soon grow together, and the secondary optic vesicle assumes the form of a double-walled cup, while the stalk is transformed into a solid strand, the optic nerve.

The lens primordium soon becomes detached from the ectoderm, and the space between the two is filled by the layer of mesenchyme: the primordium of the substantia propria of the cornea and of the connective tissue of the iris. The lens, surrounded by vascular mesenchyme, acquires a solid, spherical form, while the original cavity disappears. The inner, thicker sheet of the double wall of the optic cup differentiates into the *retina proper;* it remains permanently in direct continuation with the optic nerve. The outer sheet of the cup is transformed into the pigment epithelium. The surrounding mesenchyme comes into close relation with the optic cup and gives rise to the two outer tunics of the eyeball, the *uveal* and *fibrous tunics.* The structural differentiation of the retina proceeds in a way similar to that of the wall of the neural tube. It is characterized by proliferation, by shifting of the cells and by the establishment of complex synaptic relationships. The eyeball attains full size toward the end of the first decade, whereas the structure of the retina, including the central fovea, matures toward the end of the first year.

REFERENCES

Arey, L. B.: Visual Cells and Retinal Pigment, in Cowdry's Special Cytology, (2), 887, 1932, and in Penfield's Cytology and Cellular Pathology, (2), 743, 1932.

Berliner, M. L.: Biomicroscopy of the Eye. New York, Paul B. Hoeber, Inc., 1949.

De Robertis, E.: Electron microscope observations on the submicroscopic organization of the retinal rods. J. Biophys. Biochem. Cytol., 2:319, 1956.

De Robertis, E., and Franchi, C. M.: Electron microscope observations on synaptic vesicles in synapses of the retinal rods and cones. J. Biophys. Biochem. Cytol., 2:307, 1956.

Detwiler, S. R.: The eye and its structural adaptations. Amer. Scientist, 44:45, 1956.

Duke-Elder, W. S.: Textbook of Ophthalmology. The Development, Form, and Function of the Visual Apparatus. London, 1932, Vol. I.

Granit, R.: Receptors and Sensory Perception. A Discussion of Aims, Means, and Results of Electrophysiological Research into the Process of Reception. New Haven, Yale Univ. Press. 1955.

Hecht, S.: Rods, cones, and the chemical basis of vision. Physiol. Rev., 17:239, 1937.

Klüver, H. (ed.): Visual Mechanisms. Biol. Symposia, (7). Lancaster, Pa., Jaques Cattell Press, 1942.

Kolmer, W., and Lauber, H.: Haut and Sinnesorgane, 2nd part, Auge, in v. Möllendorff's Handb. d. mikroskop. Anat. (3/2), 1936.

Krause, A. C., and Sibley, J. A.: Metabolism of the retina. Arch. Ophthalmol., 36:328, 1946.

Mann, J.: The Development of the Human Eye. London, 1928. Developmental Abnormalities of the Eye. London, 1937.

Polyak, S.: The Retina. Chicago, Univ. of Chicago Press, 1941. The Vertebrate Visual System. Chicago, Univ. of Chicago Press, 1957.

Salzmann, M.: The Anatomy and Physiology of the Human Eyeball in the Normal State. Transl. by E. V. L. Brown, 1912.

Sheldon, H., and Zetterqvist, H.: An electron microscope study of the corneal epithelium in the vitamin A deficient mouse. Bull. Johns Hopkins Hosp., 98:372, 1956.

Sidman, R. L., and Wislocki, G. B.: Histochemical observations on rods and cones in retinas of vertebrates. J. Histochem. Cytochem., *2:*413, 1954.

Sjöstrand, F. S.: An electron microscope study of the retinal rods of the guinea pig eye. J. Cell. & Comp. Physiol., *33:*383, 1949. The ultrastructure of the outer segments of rods and cones of the eye as revealed by the electron microscope. J. Cell. & Comp. Physiol., *42:*15, 1953. The ultrastructure of the inner segments of the retinal rods of the guinea pig eye as revealed by electron microscopy. J. Cell. & Comp. Physiol., *42:*45, 1953.

Wald, G.: The photoreceptor process in vision. Am. J. Ophthalmol., *40:* No. 5, part II, 1955.

Walls, G. L.: The Vertebrate Eye and Its Adaptive Radiation. Bloomfield Mills, Mich., Cranbrook Press, 1943.

Wislocki, G. B., and Ladman, A. J.: The demonstration of a blood-ocular barrier in the albino rat by means of the intravitam deposition of silver. J. Biophys. Biochem. Cytol., *1:*501, 1955.

CHAPTER 33

The Ear

THE ORGAN of hearing consists of three parts. The first part, the *external ear,* receives the sound waves; the second, the *middle ear,* transmits the vibrations to the third part, the *internal ear* or labyrinth, where the sound waves elicit specific nervous impulses. These are conveyed by the acoustic nerve to the central nervous system. The internal ear also contains the vestibular organs, highly specialized end organs of the proprioceptive sense concerned chiefly with the function of equilibration.

EXTERNAL EAR

The external ear includes the auricle, the external acoustic meatus and the tympanic membrane.

Auricle. The complicated form of the auricle is due to its irregular plate of cellular elastic cartilage, 0.5 to 1 mm. thick. Its flexible perichondrium contains abundant elastic networks. The skin covering the auricle has a distinct subcutaneous layer only on the posterior surface. It carries a few small hairs with sebaceous glands, sometimes of considerable size; in old age, especially in men, large stiff hairs develop on the dorsal edge and the ear lobe. The sweat glands are scarce and small.

External Auditory Meatus. The external auditory meatus is oval in cross section and extends from the bottom of the auricle to the tympanic membrane, which separates it from the tympanic cavity. Its outer wall is formed by a continuation of the cartilage of the auricle and its inner wall by the temporal bone. The skin lining it is thin, devoid of papillae, firmly attached to the perichondrium and periosteum, and has no subcutaneous layer. The numerous hairs in the cartilaginous portion protect the meatus against the entrance of foreign bodies. In old age they enlarge considerably in the same way as those of the auricle. The sebaceous glands connected with the hair follicles are exceptionally large. In the inner, osseous portion, small hairs and sebaceous glands are found only along the upper wall.

The external meatus contains *cerumen,* a brown, waxy secretion with a bitter taste, which protects the skin from desiccation and from invasion by insects. It is a mixture of the secretion of the sebaceous and *ceruminous* glands of the skin in the meatus. These are tubular, coiled glands and are a variety of the apocrine sweat glands. The ducts of the ceruminous glands open either on the free surface of the skin or, together with the sebaceous glands, into the necks of the hair follicles.

Tympanic Membrane. The oval tympanic membrane forms a thin, semitransparent cone. One of the auditory ossicles, the *malleus,* is attached by its *manubrium* to the inner surface of the membrane and reaches its center. Two layers of collagenous bundles and fibroblasts similar to those of a tendon form the mass of the membrane. However, the flaccid part (Shrapnell's membrane) is devoid of the collagenous fibers. The fibers in the outer layer have a radial arrangement; those in the inner layer are circular. There

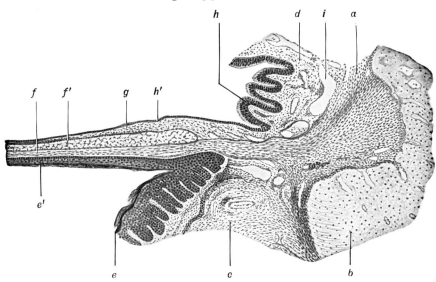

Fig. 33–1.   Cross section of edge of tympanic membrane of a child. *a,* fibrocartilaginous ring (annulus tympanicus); *b,* bone; *c,* derma with papillae; *d,* mucous membrane of tympanic cavity; *e,* epidermis of the external meatus; *e',* epidermis of the tympanic membrane; *f,* radial fibers; *f',* circular fibers of the tympanic membrane; *g,* mucosa of the tympanic membrane; *h',* its squamous epithelium; *h,* ciliated columnar epithelium of tympanic cavity; *i,* vessels. (Redrawn from von Ebner.)

are also thin networks of elastic fibers, mainly in the central part of the membrane and at its periphery. The membrane is covered by a thin layer of skin (50 to 60 microns) and is lined on its inner surface by the mucous membrane of the tympanic cavity, here only 20 to 40 microns thick. The epidermis has a thin, horny layer. Along the handle of the malleus is a layer of connective tissue, through which vessels and nerves reach the center of the membrane. The lamina propria of the mucosa consists of a few collagenous fibers and capillaries and is covered by a simple squamous epithelium.

MIDDLE EAR

The middle ear comprises the tympanic cavity and the auditory or eustachian tube.

Tympanic Cavity. The tympanic cavity is an irregular, air-containing space in the temporal bone. Its lateral wall is largely formed by the tympanic membrane, its medial wall by the lateral side of the *osseous labyrinth.* The cavity contains the ear bones (*auditory ossicles*), the tendons of the two small muscles connected with the ossicles (tensor tympani and stapedius), the chorda tympani nerve, and connective tissue trabeculae. The cavity continues into the auditory tube, which opens into the nasal part of the pharynx. The

posterior part of the tympanic cavity is connected, through the large tympanic antrum, with air-filled cavities, or "cells," in the mastoid process of the temporal bone.

The epithelium of the tympanic cavity is generally of the simple squamous type, although near the opening of the auditory tube and near the edge of the tympanic membrane, it is cuboidal or columnar and provided with cilia. The presence of glands is generally denied.

On the medial wall of the tympanic cavity, formed by the osseous labyrinth, are two "windows," the fenestrae. One of these, the *vestibular fenestra,* is an oval opening closed by the base of the stapes; this is attached to the cartilaginous edges of the opening by a circular (annular) fibroblastic ligament. This demarcates the tympanic cavity from the scala vestibuli of the cochlea. The other opening is round—the *fenestra tympanica* or *rotunda.* It is situated below and behind the oval fenestra and is closed by a fibrous membrane, the secondary tympanic membrane. It separates the tympanic cavity from the scala tympani of the cochlea.

Auditory Ossicles. These three bones—the malleus, the incus, and the stapes—extend from the tympanic membrane (to which the malleus is attached) to the oval fenestra, which is closed by the base of the stapes;

they are connected with one another by tiny articulations. They contain small cavities with vascular connective tissue. On the handle of the malleus and the base of the stapes are small patches of hyaline cartilage. The periosteum covering the ossicles fuses with the lamina propria of the mucous membrane into a thin layer of connective tissue covered by simple squamous epithelium.

Auditory or Eustachian Tube. The auditory tube has a flattened lumen (1 to 2 mm.) which in the portion nearest to the tympanic cavity is surrounded by bone. In the next part the wall is supported by a plate of hyaline cartilage. The mucous membrane lining the lumen in the bony portion has a low columnar ciliated epithelium; nearer the pharynx a taller, pseudostratified ciliated epithelium is found; at the pharyngeal opening numerous goblet cells appear. The tympanic cavity regulates the air pressure on the inner side of the tympanic membrane. By the act of swallowing, the lumen of the tube is opened for a short interval, and the pressure in the middle ear is equalized with the outside pressure.

INNER EAR OR LABYRINTH

The inner ear, called the labyrinth because of its complex structure, comprises a series of canals and cavities hollowed out of the petrous part of the temporal bone. As the layer of bone immediately surrounding the cavities is harder than the rest of the petrous portion, it is possible by careful dissection to isolate an *osseous labyrinth* from the mass of the bone. It must be kept in mind, however, that a *free* osseous labyrinth is entirely artificial. In it a central part of irregular, oval shape, the *vestibule,* can be distinguished medial to the tympanic cavity. Its wall facing the tympanic cavity contains the fenestra ovalis mentioned earlier.

Three *semicircular canals* arise from above and behind the vestibule and return to it. According to their position they are distinguished as the superior, the posterior and the lateral canals. The lateral canal is the shortest (12 to 15 mm.) and the posterior the longest (18 to 22 mm.). The lateral canals of both ears are in nearly the same plane. The superior canal of one side is approximately parallel to the posterior canal of the other.

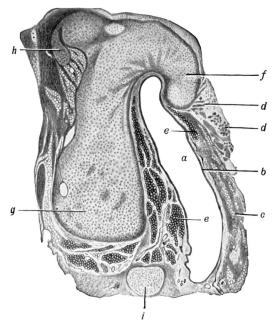

Fig. 33–2. Transection of cartilaginous portion of the auditory tube near its opening into the pharynx. *a,* lumen of the tube in dilated condition; *b,* ciliated epithelium; *c,* membranous lateral wall with fat tissue; *d,* muscle bundles; *e,* mixed glands; *f,* lateral cartilaginous plate forming hook; *g,* medial cartilaginous plate with darker spots caused by patches of elastic cartilage; *h* and *i,* accessory cartilages. 11 ×. (Redrawn from von Ebner.)

The superior and the lateral canals have dilatations, called *ampullae,* which open near each other into the upper part of the vestibule above the oval fenestra. The ampullated end of the posterior canal opens into the posterior part of the vestibule. The upper end of this canal fuses with the medial end of the superior canal to form the *crus commune,* which opens into the medial part of the vestibule. The lateral canal opens independently into the upper part of the vestibule. From the medial wall of the vestibule a thin canal extends to the posterior surface of the *pars petrosa* of the temporal bone— the *vestibular aqueduct.*

The vestibule continues into the *bony cochlea*—a spirally coiled tube which forms a conical body resembling a snail shell. It measures about 5 mm. from base to apex, with a diameter of about 9 mm. at the base.

Membranous Labyrinth. The interior of the osseous cavities is lined with endosteum and encloses a system of vesicles and canals —the membranous labyrinth. All its parts

N. ampullaris
Utriculus   superior   Ampulla membranacea superior

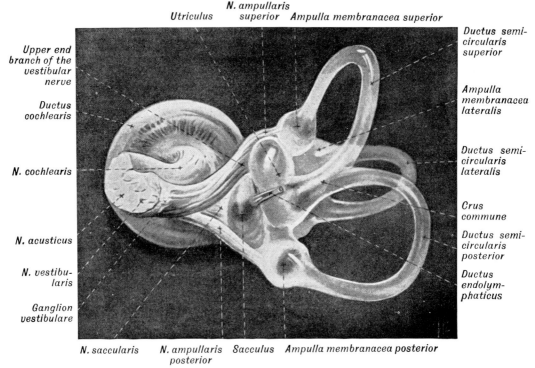

Upper end
branch of the
vestibular
nerve

Ductus
cochlearis

N. cochlearis

N. acusticus

N. vestibu-
laris

Ganglion
vestibulare

Ductus semi-
circularis
superior

Ampulla
membranacea
lateralis

Ductus semi-
circularis
lateralis

Crus
commune

Ductus semi-
circularis
posterior

Ductus
endolym-
phaticus

N. saccularis   N. ampullaris   Sacculus   Ampulla membranacea posterior
posterior

Fig. 33–3.   Right membranous labyrinth of an adult; medial and posterior aspects. 5 ✕. (After Spalteholz.)

communicate with one another and are filled with *endolymph.* The inner surface of their wall is lined with an epithelium of ectodermal origin. In some places the fibrous wall of the membranous labyrinth adheres to the periosteum of the osseous labyrinth. In general, however, it is separated from this periosteum by irregular cavities filled with *perilymph.* Thin trabeculae of connective tissue arise from the periosteum, penetrate the perilymphatic spaces, and reach the wall of the membranous labyrinth, together with the blood vessels. Thus the membranous labyrinth is suspended within the osseous labyrinth by these trabeculae. The perilymphatic spaces are homologous to the subarachnoid spaces of the meninges; the perilymph corresponds to the cerebrospinal fluid. The *cochlear aqueduct* is a channel in the osseous labyrinth filled with a meshwork like that of the arachnoid and extending from the scala tympani to the subarachnoid space.

The form and arrangement of the various parts of the membranous labyrinth generally correspond to those of the osseous labyrinth in which they are enclosed. However, the

membranous part contained in the osseous vestibule consists of two separate sacs—the *utricle* and the *saccule.*

It is relatively easy to isolate the membranous labyrinth from its osseous container. The central part is occupied by the utricle and the saccule (Fig. 33–3). The oblong *utricle* communicates by five orifices with the three membranous semicircular canals, which correspond in form and position to the osseous canals containing them. The three ampullar enlargements are much more pronounced in the membranous canals. Each ampulla has a flattened floor which forms part of the convex surface of its canal and a hemispherical roof bulging on the concave side. The superior and lateral ampullae open close to each other into the upper end of the utricle, the posterior ampulla into its lower end. The *crus commune,* formed by the superior and inferior canals, joins the middle part of the utricle near the second orifice of the lateral canal.

The roughly spherical saccule lies in front of the utricle. At the mouth of the utricle, the utricular duct and the wall form a fold, the utriculo-endolymphatic valve of Bast. The saccular duct and utricular duct, arising from their respective sacs, join to form the slender *endolymphatic duct,* which runs through the vestibular aqueduct to the posterior surface of the petrous part of the temporal bone, where it ends with an enlargement, the *endolymphatic sac.* From the lower part of the saccule the short, narrow *ductus reuniens* (Fig. 33–4) leads to the *cochlear duct.*

The wall of the membranous labyrinth becomes extremely complex in six sensory epithelial areas containing the endings of the acoustic nerve (Fig. 33–4). They are the *macula utriculi* and *macula sacculi,* the three *cristae ampullares* (one in the ampulla of each semicircular canal) and the *organ of Corti,* running along the cochlear canal.

Utricle and Saccule. The connective tissue layer of the wall of the utricle and saccule, like the other parts of the membranous labyrinth, has a finely fibrillated substance with fibroblasts and often with melanocytes. Its outer surface, the trabeculae which run through the perilymphatic spaces, and the inner surface of the periosteum, are lined with mesenchymal epithelium. The connective tissue is separated from the epithelium by a basement membrane. Except in the neuroepithelial areas, the epithelium is a layer of squamous cells, 3 to 4 microns thick and usually provided with a diplosome and a flagellum.

The spoon-shaped *macula utriculi* occupies the lateral wall of the utricle and measures 2 by 3 mm. The *macula sacculi,* occupying the medial wall of the saccule, is of similar size and is heart-shaped. The surfaces of the maculae are perpendicular to each other. The epithelium is the same in both maculae. It is 30 to 35 microns thick and consists of *supporting cells* and *hair cells.* The first are slender columnar structures containing a bundle of tonofibrils and a round nucleus at the lower end. The free surfaces, provided with cuticular plates, are interconnected by terminal bars. Under each plate lies a diplosome with a minute protruding flagellum and, farther down, a Golgi net and sometimes granular or fatty inclusions.

The *hair cells* are lodged between the supporting cells, but occupy only the upper half of the epithelial layer. They have the form of short flasks with a rounded bottom

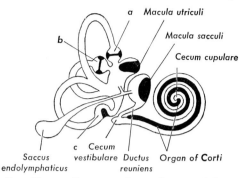

Fig. 33–4. Diagram of membranous labyrinth with neuro-epithelial areas in black. *a,* superior; *b,* lateral; *c,* posterior ampullae of respective semicircular canals. (Modified after von Ebner.)

which contains the nucleus; their free surface is covered by a round, cuticular plate, connected with the cuticles of the supporting cells. From the center of the cuticle rises a tuft of long (20 to 25 microns), nonmotile cilia, held together by a cement substance and forming a tapering brush. The diplosome sends out a flagellum which adheres to the surface of the tuft of cilia. The spaces between the supporting cells and the hair cells are filled with a semifluid substance.

The surface of the maculae is covered by the *otolithic membrane*—a thick (22 microns) layer of a gelatinous substance into which the hair tufts penetrate. Each tuft is surrounded by a narrow space filled with endolymph. Between these spaces the gelatinous substance is connected with the terminal bars of the epithelium by thin partitions. The jelly, beyond the hairs, contains a multitude of minute (3 by 5 microns) crystalline bodies, the *otoconia* or *otoliths* (Fig. 33–5, *St*). These are prisms ending in pyramids and are a mixture of calcium carbonate (aragonite) and a protein. After the calcium is dissolved, their outlines remain visible.

At the edge of the macula the hair cells end abruptly, and the supporting cells gradually pass into the simple squamous epithelium of the rest of the wall.

The connective tissue of the wall is thickened in the area of the macula and is firmly attached to the endosteum. Here the intercellular substance is especially firm, and the basement membrane is distinct. Most of the myelinated nerve fibers which supply the macula lose their myelin sheaths close to the basement membrane. The fibers pierce the

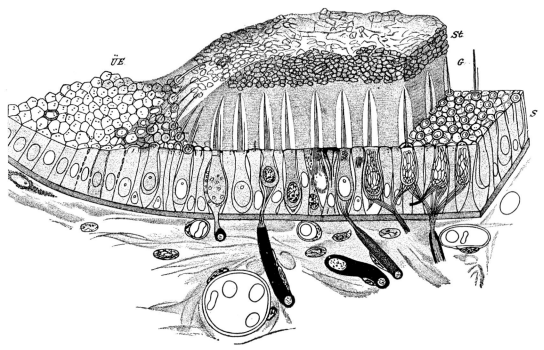

Fig. 33–5.   Plastic diagram of border region of a macula. *ÜE,* intermediate epithelium; *St,* otoconia; G, gelatinous layer; S, supporting elements. (After Kolmer.)

membrane and branch in the spaces between the epithelial cells. The terminal arborizations of the thicker fibers form basket-like nests closely surrounding the hair cells and almost reaching the free epithelial surface. The thinner fibers end with branches between the supporting cells.

Semicircular Canals. The membranous semicircular canals are slightly oval in cross section. Their convex surface is close to the periosteum, and the opening surface is surrounded by a large perilymphatic space (Fig. 33–6, *pr*) with numerous trabeculae (Fig. 33–6, *b*). The wall of the membranous canals has the same structure as that of the utricle and saccule.

In a longitudinal section of the ampulla, the *crista* appears in cross section as a rounded prominence occupying about one third of the lumen. When cut longitudinally, the crista is seen to be highest in its middle part and to slope down toward the side walls of the ampulla. Seen from the surface, the ends of the crista are rounded and edged by a crescentic area, the *planum semilunatum.* This is covered by columnar epithelium which contains inclusions and has, perhaps, a glandular function.

In the living, a gelatinous mass, in which the hairs are embedded, extends from the crista to the opposite wall of the ampulla. When fixed it becomes deformed and is the *cupula* seen in sections.

The neuro-epithelium of the human crista has much in common with that of the maculae, with similar supporting elements and hair cells. Near the surface of each hair cell a flagellum, arising from a diplosome, is continuous with what appears to be a tuft of matted cilia. In fixed preparation the crista is covered by a gelatinous cap, the cupula, which seems to rest on the hairs. The relations of the nerve fibers to the hair cells are essentially the same as in the maculae.

Cochlea. The canal of the cochlea makes two and a half spiral turns around the axis of this structure. The direction parallel to the course of the canal may be designated "spiral," a plane parallel to the axis, but not passing through it, as "tangential." The radial direction from the axis to the surface of the cochlea is called "outward." The most informative sections of the cochlea are radial ones which pass through the plane of the axis and perpendicular to the cochlear canal.

The *axis of the cochlea* is a conical pillar

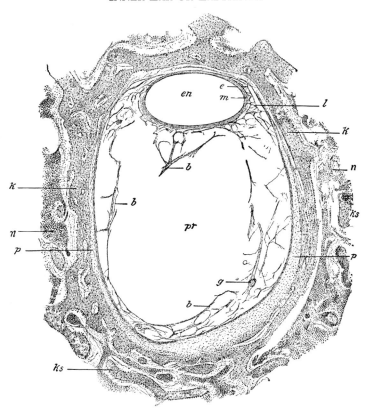

Fig. 33–6. Cross section of lateral semicircular canal of an adult man. *b*, connective tissue trabeculae in the perilymphatic space; *e*, epithelium; *en*, endolymphatic space; *g*, blood vessel; *k*, bone of the bony labyrinth; *ks*, bone trabeculae of the spongiosa; *l*, ligamentum canaliculi; *m*, membrana propria of the membranous semicircular canal; *n*, bone marrow; *p*, periosteum; *pr*, perilymphatic space. 46 ×. (After von Ebner, from Schaffer.)

of spongy bone, the *modiolus.* Its base forms the bottom of the internal acoustic meatus. Blood vessels, surrounded by connective tissue and bundles of the cochlear divisions of the acoustic nerve, penetrate through numerous openings into the bony substance of the modiolus. The nerve fibers run upward and turn outward to reach the *spiral ganglion,* which extends along the inner wall of the cochlear canal.

The lumen of the canal of the osseous cochlea (about 3 mm. in diameter) is divided along its whole course (about 35 mm. in man) into an upper and a lower section by the *spiral lamina.* Its inner zone contains bone and is called the *osseous spiral lamina* (Fig. 33–8, *Lo*). The fibrous outer zone is the *basilar membrane* (*membranous spiral lamina*) (Fig. 33–8, *Mb*). The extent of ossification is greatest in the lowest coil. At the attachment of the basilar membrane to the outer wall of the cochlea the periosteum is thickened and forms the *spiral ligament.* The *vestibular membrane* extends obliquely from the spiral lamina to the outer wall of the osseous cochlea. Thus a cross section of the osseous cochlear canal will show three cavities: the upper cavity, or *scala vestibuli,* a lower cavity, *scala tympani,* and the *ductus cochlearis,* or scala media.

The scala tympani and scala vestibuli are perilymphatic spaces whose walls have the same structure as the other perilymphatic spaces in the labyrinth. The bone is lined by a thin layer of connective tissue covered with mesenchymal epithelium. The scala vestibuli extends into and through the perilymphatic space of the vestibule and reaches the inner surface of the fenestra ovalis. At the apex of the cochlea the two scalae communicate through a small opening—the *helicotrema.*

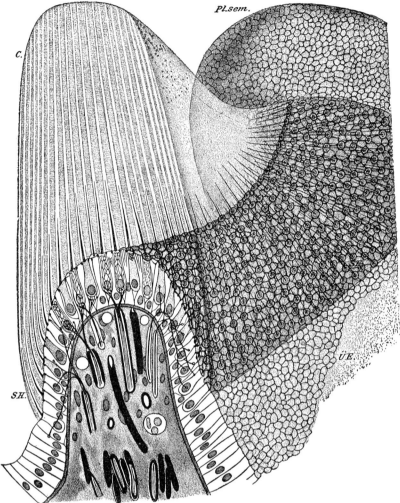

Fig. 33–7. Plastic diagram of one half of an ampulla crista as seen in a longitudinal section of a semicircular canal, passing across the crista. *SH,* hair tufts; *C,* gelatinous mass of the cupula; *ÜE,* intermediate epithelium; *Pl sem,* planum semilunatum. (After Kolmer.)

The lower, vestibular end of the cochlear duct is a small outpocketing, the *cecum vestibulare,* separated from the fenestra ovalis by the enlarged perilymphatic space. Into it opens the *canalis reuniens,* which connects it with the saccule; in adults it is almost obliterated. The upper end of the cochlear duct ends blindly with the *cecum cupulare.*

The functions of the structures in the cochlea are so imperfectly known that no consistent theory has been formulated.

Osseous Spiral Lamina and the Basilar Membrane. The spiral ganglion extends along the line of attachment of the osseous spiral lamina to the modiolus. It is lodged in an irregular cavity of the bone, the *spiral canal of the modiolus.* From the ganglion, along its whole length, bundles of nerves arise and run through radial canals in the osseous spiral lamina toward the organ of Corti.

In the inner corner of the cochlear duct, the periosteum of the upper surface of the spiral lamina bulges into the duct as the *limbus spiralis.* Its edge overhangs the *internal spiral sulcus,* with its two margins, the *vestibular* and *tympanic lips* (Fig. 33–9). The connective tissue of the limbus has a firm, intercellular substance and, especially in its deeper layers, stellate connective tissue cells. On the surface the connective tissue

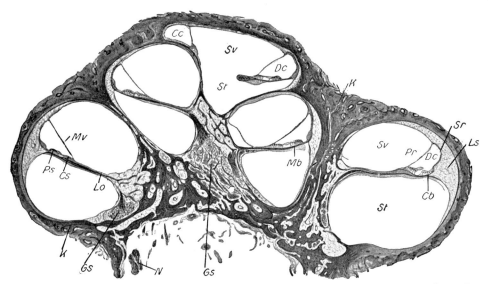

Fig. 33–8. Axial section of cochlea of a man. *Cb*, crista basilaris; *Cc*, cecum cupulare; *Cs*, crista spiralis; *Dc*, ductus cochlearis; *Gs*, ganglion spirale; *K*, bony wall of the cochlea; *Lo*, lamina spiralis ossea; *Ls*, ligamentum spirale; *Mb*, membrana basilaris; *Mv*, membrana vestibularis; *N*, cochlear nerve; *Pr*, prominentia spiralis; *Ps*, organ of Corti; *Sr*, stria vascularis; *St*, scala tympani; *Sv*, scala vestibuli. 16 ×. (After Schaffer.)

forms small ridges which protrude over the edge of the vestibular lip as the *auditory teeth of Huschke.*

The periosteum on the lower surface of the spiral osseous lamina continues outward beyond the tympanic lip of the limbus. It contains the radial bundles of myelinated fibers which come from the spiral ganglion (Fig. 33–10). In the lower coil of the cochlea, the osseous lamina extends outward as far as the tympanic lip.

A little beyond the vestibular lip, the nerve bundles enter the epithelium of the organ of Corti. In doing so, they emerge from the connective tissue (or from the bone) through a series of small radial slits, the *foramina nervosa.* When seen from above, they form a row of holes in the tympanic lip; hence the name *habenula perforata.*

The tympanic lip continues outward into the *basilar membrane* (Fig. 33–10), which is tightly stretched between it and the crest of the spiral ligament. The basilar membrane can be subdivided into the zona arcuata, extending from the foramina nervosa to the base of the external pillars, and the zona pectinata, between the external pillars and the crest of the spiral ligament.

The middle layer in both zones is formed by the *auditory strings* or *basilar fibers.* In the zona arcuata they are thin and arranged in the fashion of a net; in the zona pectinata they are thicker (1 to 2 microns), straight, and smooth, and do not branch. In fresh condition they are soft and flexible and can be isolated easily. Acetic acid dissolves them; after fixation they become hard and brittle. They are birefringent, but differ from collagenous as well as from elastic fibers. They are embedded in a small amount of ground substance. On reaching the spiral ligament, some of the strings penetrate fanlike into its tissue, while others run upward under the epithelium.

The length of the strings increases considerably from the base of the cochlea to its apex. In the beginning of the first coil they measure 64 to 128 microns, at the end of the membrane, 352 to 480 microns. The number of strings in the human basilar membrane is estimated at 24,000.

Above the middle layer with its auditory strings is a thin, homogeneous *vestibular covering layer* with a few connective tissue cells. The lower surface is lined with a delicate connective tissue, the *tympanic covering layer.* In the inner zone of this layer are blood capillaries connected with a vessel run-

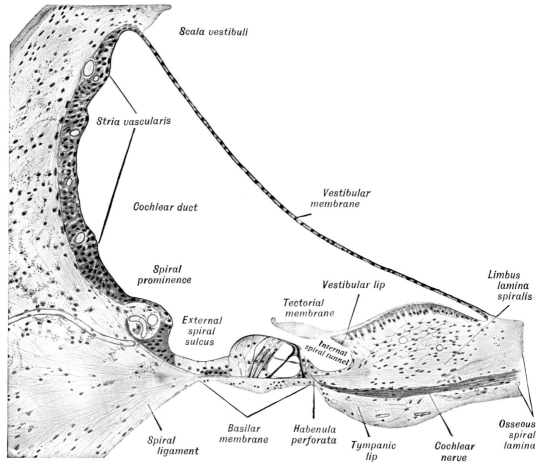

Fig. 33–9.   Radial transection of cochlear duct in the first coil of human cochlea. The separation of the
free end of the tectorial membrane from the organ of Corti is due to improper fixation. (After Held.)

ning under the tunnel of Corti. The pars
pectinata of the basilar membrane lacks blood
vessels.

The spiral ligament consists of collagenous
fibers and connective tissue cells filled with
pigment and other inclusions; it also has
numerous blood vessels. Slightly above the
attachment of the basilar membrane to the
spiral ligament, the connective tissue forms
a small ridge extending through the whole
cochlea—the *prominentia spiralis.* It contains
large capillary loops—the *vas prominens.* The
groove between the ridge and the crest of
the spiral ligament is the *external spiral
sulcus.*

The *vestibular membrane* is a thin (3
microns) connective tissue layer which in
man lacks blood vessels, but may contain
pigment cells and fine elastic networks. On
the vestibular surface it is covered with the

mesenchymal epithelium of the perilymphatic
spaces.

Epithelium of the Cochlear Duct. The
ectodermal epithelium lining the cochlear
duct presents great differences in its various
regions. The inner surface of the vestibular
membrane is covered with a simple squamous
epithelium often containing pigment. The
surface of the limbus is a mosaic of cuticular
plates belonging to epithelial cells whose
bodies are deep in the subjacent connective
tissue. They are arranged in rows along the
furrows on the limbus, between the auditory
teeth. The internal spiral sulcus is lined with
a layer of epithelial cells of medium thickness. Outwardly they are followed by the
inner border cells of the organ of Corti.

The thick epithelium covering the outer
wall of the cochlear duct extends to the
external spiral sulcus and is called the *stria*

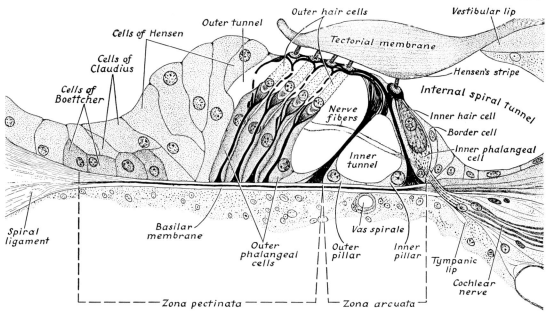

Fig. 33–10. Radial transection of the human organ of Corti, from the upper part of the first coil. (Slightly modified after Held.)

vascularis (Fig. 33–9). It is a low stratified columnar epithelium. Many of its cells send processes into the connective tissue, and some of them come in contact with the blood vessels. The abundant capillaries run for the most part in the spiral direction, forming loops which penetrate the epithelium, and sometimes accompanied by connective tissue cells.

It is believed by some that the stria vascularis secretes the endolymph of the cochlear canal and that the organ of Corti receives its nutritive materials and oxygen from the endolymph, which is probably continuously renewed. It has been reported that the endolymph has a much higher concentration of K and a lower concentration of Na than the perilymph and thus resembles intracellular ion concentration. The organ of Corti is very sensitive to lack of oxygen.

In the external spiral sulcus the epithelium is cuboidal; its cells also have processes penetrating deep into the connective tissue. Approaching the basilar membrane, the epithelium becomes more regular and continues upon the pars pectinata as the *cells of Claudius* (Fig. 33–10). In parts of the basal coil, small groups of polyhedral cells (*of Boettcher*) are scattered between the basilar membrane and the cells of Claudius.

The Organ of Corti, or the Papilla Basi-

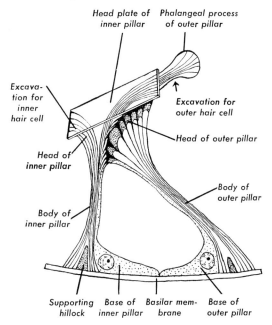

Fig. 33–11. Diagram of inner and outer pillars. (Modified after Kolmer.)

laris. The basilar membrane carries an exceedingly complex epithelial ridge—the organ of Corti, or the *papilla basilaris*. It bulges into the cochlear duct and extends throughout its length (Figs. 33–8, 33–9, 33–10). Among its elements two types may be distinguished: (1) *supporting cells* which form a rigid but flexible framework and (2) *hair cells*—neuro-epithelial receptors of the stimuli produced by the sound waves. These elements are arranged in regular, longitudinal (spiral) rows.

Supporting Cells. The several types of supporting cells have certain characteristics in common. They contain tonofibrils and are tall elements extending from the basilar membrane through the epithelium, and end as cuticular plates on the free surface of the organ of Corti. Although the cells are separated from one another by large intercellular spaces, their cuticles form a continuous membrane covering the organ. This membrane has many round holes; hence the name *reticular membrane.* These holes are filled with the round cuticular plates of the hair cells. The supporting cells include (1) inner and outer pillars, (2) inner and outer phalangeal cells, (3) border cells, (4) cells of Hensen.

Within the organ of Corti is the *inner tunnel,* a canal extending the length of the cochlea and bounded by the basilar membrane and the inner and outer pillar cells. The bodies of the pillars are separated by cleftlike spaces through which the tunnel communicates with the other intercellular cavities in the organ of Corti including the outer tunnel, the space of Nuel and the inner spiral tunnel. In all probability, the tectorial membrane is in close contact with the cells of Hensen and thus separates the cavities beneath it from the endolymph.

Inner Pillars. The inner pillars have a broad base which rests on the basilar membrane, and a cell body rising conically upward. The cytoplasm at the inner corner of the tunnel contains a round nucleus and a conical condensation surrounded by a cone of darkly staining tonofibrils. These rise into a cylindrical bundle forming the body of the pillar (2 to 3 microns thick) sheathed by a trace of protoplasm. Approaching the surface, the pillar again becomes thicker and ends with a head, covered by a rectangular cuticular plate (Fig. 33–11). Its long sides are connected with those of the neighboring inner pillars. The inner margin fits the edge of the cuticle of an inner hair cell. The outer margin overlies the cuticular plate of the outer pillars.

Outer Pillars. The outer pillars are longer than the inner ones. Their base is attached to the basilar membrane at the junction of the zona arcuata with the pectinata. Like the base of the inner pillars, it also consists of a small amount of cytoplasm surrounding a nucleus; it too continues into a long slender body with a bundle of tonofibrils (Fig. 33–11). The head of the outer pillar fits an excavation in the head of the inner pillar to which it is firmly attached. The cuticular plate projects from under the cuticle of the inner pillar and has a shovel-like shape. The cuticular plates of the outer pillars form the first row of phalanges. Into the holes between their excavated edges fit the cuticles of the first row of the outer hair cells.

The inner pillars number 5600, the outer ones 3800. On an average, three inner pillars are connected with two outer pillars.

Inner Phalangeal Cells. These cells form a row on the inner surface of the inner pillars. Their bases occupy the narrow space between the bases of the inner pillars and the foramina nervosa on the basilar membrane. The cell body contains a nucleus in its lower part, a slender bundle of tonofibrils, and ends at the surface with a small cuticular plate. The plate is elongated in the radial direction, and both its long edges are excavated; hence the name *phalanges.* The outer ends of the phalanges are connected with the cuticles of the inner pillars. Their sides, together with those of the plates of the inner pillars and of the border cells, surround the cuticular plates of the inner hair cells.

Outer Phalangeal Cells (Deiters). The three rows of outer phalangeal cells are adapted to the three rows of outer hair cells. In the second coil are four rows of each cell type. In the third coil a fifth, interrupted row of hair cells and atypical phalangeal cells is added.

The bases of the cells of Deiters rest on the basilar membrane. The cell body is prism-shaped, and through its axis runs a bundle of fibers starting in the middle of the base. The body tapers abruptly toward the surface and continues as a thin stalk formed by the fibrillar bundle. It mounts to the surface and expands into a phalanx with a semicircular excavation on each long side. Into these excavations fit the cuticles of the hair cells of the corresponding row. The phalanges of one row interdigitate with those of the next. The

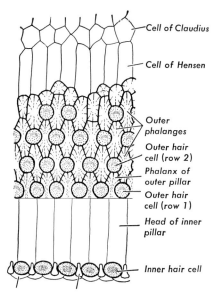

Cell of Claudius

Cell of Hensen

Outer phalanges

Outer hair cell (row 2)

Phalanx of outer pillar

Outer hair cell (row 1)

Head of inner pillar

Inner hair cell

Border cell   Inner phalanx

Fig. 33–12. Diagram of papilla spiralis viewed from above, showing cuticles of hair and supporting cells. (Modified after Retzius, Kolmer, Schaffer.)

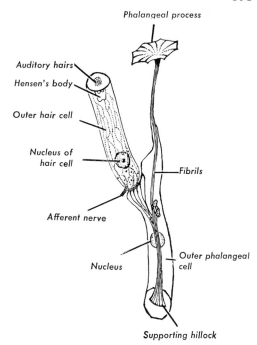

Phalangeal process

Auditory hairs

Hensen's body

Outer hair cell

Nucleus of hair cell

Fibrils

Afferent nerve

Nucleus

Outer phalangeal cell

Supporting hillock

Fig. 33–13. Diagram of supporting cells of Deiters and the associated outer hair cell. (Modified after Kolmer.)

joined phalanges of the different orders constitute the *reticular membrane* with its regular mosaic pattern and alternating rows of round openings containing the cuticles of the hair cells (Fig. 33–12). The outermost phalanges have a polygonal shape and form the outer edge of the reticular membrane.

Where the body of the outer phalangeal cell begins to taper into the thin stalk, its protoplasm lodges the lower, rounded end of a hair cell (Fig. 33–13).

In a radial section of the cochlea, the cells of Deiters are never seen in their full length, since the cell body is cut off at the level where it begins to taper. A full view of a cell of Deiters can be had only in a tangential section parallel to the axis of the modiolus. Here it is seen that the slender phalangeal process of each cell is bent toward the apex of the cochlea and that it passes three hair cells before reaching the surface and ending with its phalanx.

Whereas the basal parts of the phalangeal cells are close to one another, there are large spaces (*of Nuel*) between their processes. An especially conspicuous space is found between the outer pillars and the first row of phalangeal cells. Through the clefts between the outer pillars the spaces of Nuel communicate with the tunnel.

Border Cells. These slender elements stand in a row beside the inner hair cells (Fig. 33–10). Their narrow cuticles are also arranged in a row which forms the inner margin of the openings containing the cuticles of the inner hair cells. The basal part of these cells sends out processes which accompany the nerve fibers in the organ of Corti. Toward the inner spiral sulcus the border cells are succeeded by cells which rapidly diminish in size and pass into squamous cells.

Cells of Hensen. The cells of Deiters are succeeded in the outward direction by the tall cells of Hensen (Fig. 33–10). These are arranged in several rows, decrease rapidly in height, and pass into the *cells of Claudius.*

Hair Cells. The free surface of the hair cells, fastened in the holes of the reticular membrane, is provided with short, bristle-like outgrowths. The *inner hair cells* are arranged in a single row between the inner phalangeal and the border cells on the one hand and the inner pillars on the other (Fig. 33–10). The *outer hair cells* form three rows and are suspended between the outer pillars and the outer phalangeal cells. In the second coil a fourth, in the upper coil a fifth row of outer cells is added. All the hair cells are short cylinders with a rounded lower end containing the nucleus and with an oval cuticular plate on the free surface. Immediately under the cuticle is a modified Golgi net—the *body of Hensen.* At the lower end of the cell is a condensed protoplasmic mass with pigment granules, the *body of Retzius.* The cuticle of the inner hair cells is surmounted by forty-one to sixty-four hairs arranged in two or more straight, parallel rows in the longitudinal (spiral) direction. At the outer edge of the cuticle lies the diplosome with a minute flagellum. The hairs of the outer cells (eighty-three to one hundred hairs to a cell) form several parallel, horseshoe-shaped lines, with the convexity directed outward. The length of these hairs decreases from outside inward. The outer edge of the cuticle contains the diplosome.

Tectorial Membrane. The surface of the organ of Corti is covered by a ribbon-like, gelatinous structure, the tectorial membrane. After fixation its outer free edge is usually curled, or the whole membrane is detached from the epithelium (Figs. 33–9, 33–10). The width of the membrane increases toward the apex of the cochlea. It begins in the inner angle of the cochlear canal as a thin layer attached to the epithelial surface of the limbus. Farther outward, where the membrane overhangs the inner spiral sulcus and touches the organ of Corti, its lower surface remains even, while the upper one bulges considerably upward. Here its thickness reaches 25 microns. Passing over the organ of Corti, it again becomes thinner and is probably attached to the surface of the cells of Hensen.

The tectorial membrane is composed of a homogeneous ground substance with numerous fibrils, most conspicuous at the upper surface, where they form networks. In the deeper layers they are more or less parallel; their general direction is radial, but with a marked deviation from this plane toward the apex of the cochlea. Along the lower surface of the membrane, opposite the row of inner hair cells, the *stripe of Hensen* extends in the spiral direction. In the living condition and in well-fixed preparations the lower surface of the tectorial membrane rests upon the ends of the hairs which protrude from the hair cells.

Nerve Endings in the Organ of Corti. Except for the possible presence of vasomotor nerves in the labyrinth, the end branches of the cochlear nerve are the main nerve fibers in the cochlea. In addition, a nerve bundle (of Rasmussen) originating in the superior olive of the opposite side courses through the spiral ganglion, mainly of the first coil, but its terminations are still uncertain. Fine nerve fibers, presumably sympathetic, are intimately associated with the larger blood vessels in the modiolus and the osseous spiral lamina.

The nerve cells of the spiral ganglion are of the bipolar type; their central processes are myelinated and continue into the acoustic nerve. The peripheral, dendritic processes run through the canals of the osseous lamina and lose their myelin sheaths as they pass through the foramina nervosa on their way to the hair cells. A thin layer of myelin is also found on the surface of the cell body.

There are two kinds of nerve fibers in the organ of Corti. The first, thin and numerous, radiate from the spiral ganglion in parallel bundles to the nearest segments of the organ of Corti. Here each fiber divides into small branches which terminate with buttons attached to the surface of the hair cells. Because of their straight course they are called *direct acoustic nerve fibers* (orthoneurons of von Ebner). Each of them is stimulated by a compact group of hair cells.

Nerve fibers of the second type, usually thicker and fewer than the first, are also at first arranged radially. But after reaching the organ of Corti they turn sharply, follow a longitudinal (i.e., spiral) course and form parallel bundles beneath and between the several rows of hair cells and the supporting structures. Here they form so-called "plexuses," one beneath the inner hair cells, one in the inner tunnel, and several between the outer phalangeal cells. Because of their course these fibers are called *spiral fibers* (spironeurons of von Ebner). They, too, terminate with branches larger than in the direct fibers, each spiral fiber being related to a compact group of hair cells. The group of cells is always at a definite distance along the basilar papilla from the point where the fiber changes from the radial to the spiral course. The spiral fibers, while in the organ

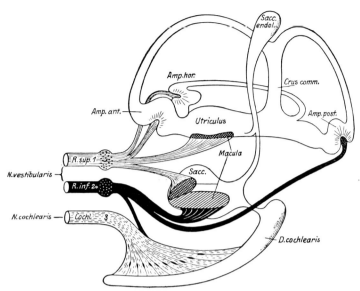

Fig. 33–14. Diagram of distribution of nerves in the membranous labyrinth of the rabbit. (After de Burlet, from Kolmer.)

of Corti, as a rule turn toward the basal coil of the cochlea.

The presence of the two varieties of acoustic nerve fibers in the organ of Corti is well established, but the interpretation of such an arrangement in terms of function is less certain. Although the relations between the peripheral receptors (hair cells) and the acoustic neurons are not as individualized as the monosynaptic relationships of the foveal cones, they are sufficiently restricted to permit the reception of localized stimuli impinging upon small segments of the cochlea. This applies to both direct and spiral fibers. The significance of the spiral fibers is unknown. Possibly, in collaboration with the groups of direct fibers, the spiral fibers serve in the reception of complex sounds, whereas the system of direct fibers alone is instrumental in the perception of simple tones.

In any event, the cochlea, like the retina, must have a receptor surface whose different points have different functional value. This view agrees with the fact that the basilar membrane is represented topically, or point for point, in the brain (Polyak, Lewi and Kobrak, Walker).

Nerves of the Labyrinth. The eighth cranial nerve supplies the sensory areas of the labyrinth. It consists of two parts of quite different functional nature and central connections—the *vestibular* and the *cochlear*

nerves. The first divides into a superior and an inferior branch. The fibers of all these nerves are the central processes (axons) of bipolar ganglionic cells which form two ganglia. Of these, the spiral or cochlear ganglion is incorporated in the cochlear nerve and located in the modiolus of the cochlea, while the vestibular ganglion belongs to the vestibular nerve and is situated in the inner auditory meatus of the temporal bone. Corresponding with the subdivision of the vestibular nerve into a superior and an inferior branch, the vestibular ganglion can also be separated into a superior and an inferior part. The peripheral branches (dendrites) of the bipolar ganglionic cells run to the sensory areas. The superior vestibular ganglion sends out four branches which supply (1) the horizontal or lateral ampulla; (2) the frontal or superior ampulla; (3) the utricular macula; and (4) a small part of the saccular macula. From the inferior vestibular ganglion three branches arise. The first supplies the larger part of the saccular macula; the second, the sagittal or posterior ampulla; the third, the smallest, joins the fibers of the cochlear nerve. This last connection needs further study.

The vestibular nerve terminates centrally in the reflex centers of the medulla oblongata and the cerebellum. Its cortical connections are unknown. The cochlear nerve also has reflex connections in the medulla oblongata and the midbrain; but most of its fibers run in the lateral lemniscus to the medial geniculate body of the thalamus and thence to the sylvian fossa of the brain center for hearing.

Blood Vessels of the Labyrinth. The labyrinthine artery is a branch of the inferior cerebellar artery. It enters the internal meatus and divides into two branches, the *vestibular artery* and the *common cochlear artery.* The latter divides into the *vestibulocochlear artery* and the *cochlear artery proper.*

The vestibular artery supplies the upper and lateral parts of the utricle and saccule and parts of the superior and lateral semicircular canals. It forms dense networks of capillaries in the region of the maculae; in the thin connective tissue layer of these structures the capillary networks are loose.

The vestibulocochlear artery supplies the lower and medial parts of the utricle and saccule, the crus commune, and the posterior semicircular canal with its vestibular branch. Its cochlear branch supplies the lowest part of the first cochlear coil.

The cochlear artery proper penetrates the cavities of the modiolus, where its branches form many zigzags and coils and run spirally to the apex; this is the so-called "spiral tract." From it, branches go to the spiral ganglion and, through the periosteum of the scala vestibuli and the spiral osseous lamina, to the inner parts of the basilar membrane. Here the capillaries are arranged in arcades in the tympanic covering layer under the tunnel and the limbus; from them arises the *vas spirale.* The vascular stria and the spiral ligament receive their blood through branches of the spiral arterial tract which run in the roof of the scala vestibuli. They do not form connections with the vessels of the basilar membrane. The lower wall of the scala tympani receives its own small arteries from the same source.

The course of the veins of the labyrinth is quite different from that of the arteries. There are three draining venous systems. In the cochlea, veins originate in the region of the prominentia spiralis and run downward and inward through the periosteum of the scala tympani to the spiral vein, which is found under the spiral ganglion. Upper and lower spiral veins, belonging to the corresponding coils of the cochlea, receive branches from the osseous spiral lamina and from the spiral ganglion. Above the spiral vein is the small vein of the spiral lamina which receives a part of the blood from the spiral lamina and from the spiral ganglion and is connected by anastomoses with the spiral vein. These cochlear veins form a plexus in the modiolus which empties the blood partly into the vena auditiva interna, which leaves the labyrinth along the labyrinthine artery, and partly into the vein of the cochlear aqueduct, which drains into the jugular vein. The veins of the vestibular apparatus and the semicircular canals empty into the veins of the vestibular and of the cochlear aqueducts.

This arrangement of the vessels in the internal ear seems to insure the best possible protection of the sound receptors from concussions caused by the pulsating waves. The arteries are arranged, for the most part, in the wall of the scala vestibuli, while the wall of the scala tympani contains the veins. The zona pectinata of the basilar membrane and the vestibular membrane are devoid of blood vessels. The course of the spiral arteries in the modiolus probably also contributes to the damping of pulsations. In certain mammals the coils of these arteries are so prominent that they suggest glomeruli.

True lymphatics are absent from the labyrinth. Instead, the excess of the tissue liquid is drained into the perilymphatic spaces, which are connected through the cochlear aqueduct with the subarachnoid spaces. A certain amount of drainage may be effected through the perivascular and perineural connective tissue sheaths.

Histophysiological Remarks. The tympanic membrane, besides protecting the middle ear, receives the sound waves and transmits them to the auditory ossicles.

Function of the Cochlea. The vibrations of the tympanic membrane are transmitted through the chain of auditory ossicles to the fenestra ovalis and hence to the perilymph filling the scala tympani. The organ of Corti is the receptor for sound stimuli. It is generally believed that the analysis of the sound waves is accomplished in the organ of Corti and that this depends upon the basilar membrane, a mechanism for *sympathetic vibration* or *resonance.* The basilar membrane may be compared to an unstressed gelatinous plate with varying resistance to displacement due to its varying width. The deformation of this membrane induced by an acoustic movement of the stapes resembles a traveling wave. Regions of observed maximum displacement change with frequency but are relatively broad. As the stimulating frequency rises the responding length of the basilar membrane becomes shorter and progressively more of the distal area becomes inactive. The associated physical deformations in the supporting and sensory cells of the organ of Corti result in nerve stimulation. The pitch discriminating ability of the ear is only partly due to this physical separation of the responding areas along the basilar membrane.

Function of the Vestibule. The nervous impulses elicited by the stimulation of the maculae and the cristae play an important role in the regulation and coordination of the movements of equilibrium and locomotion. The stimuli to the vestibular end organs

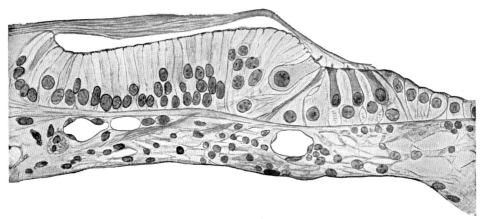

Fig. 33–15. Histogenesis of the organ of Corti in a human fetus of six months. The tectorial membrane has become detached from the large epithelial ridge and remains connected only at the periphery with the surface of the smaller ridge (the future organ of Corti); hair cells make their appearance. 311 ×. (After Kolmer.)

are angular acceleration for the semicircular canals and linear acceleration (i.e., gravity) for the maculae. These impulses exert their influence upon coordinated muscular contractions, upon muscular tonus, and upon the eyes through the brain stem and the cerebellum.

Histogenetic Remarks. *External and Middle Ears.* The tympanic cavity and the auditory tube are derivatives of the first branchial pouch. The external auditory meatus develops through an invagination of the integument directed toward the tympanic cavity. The tissue layer remaining between this invagination and the tympanic cavity becomes the tympanic membrane.

Otic Vesicle. The primordium of the labyrinth develops as a shallow groove of thickened ectoderm, dorsally to the first branchial groove, on both sides of the brain, between the myelencephalon and the metencephalon (human embryo of eight somites). The groove is invaginated into the subjacent mesenchyme and becomes the *otic vesicle.* In a human embryo of 2.8 mm. it separates through constriction from the ectoderm and is surrounded by mesenchyme. The vesicle is lined by tall, pseudostratified epithelium which secretes the endolymph filling it. From its earliest stages the otic vesicle comes into intimate contact with the large acoustic ganglion, which later divides into the vestibular and cochlear ganglia. Unequal proliferation in places in the wall of the otic vesicle transforms it into an extremely complex system of saclike and tubelike cavities. Soon after its isolation from the ectoderm, the dorsal periphery of the vesicle sends out an evagination which is the primordium of the endolymphatic duct. Then a larger dorsal part of the vesicle becomes distinct from a smaller ventral part. The first—the vestibular part—gives rise to the semicircular canals and the utricles. The second, the cochlear part, forms the saccule and the cochlea.

On the wall of the vestibular part three evaginations appear and develop into the three semicircular canals, each with an ampulla. What remains of the vestibular part is now the utricle. The cochlear part sends out a curved outpocketing—the primordium of the cochlea. It gradually gains in length, coils as it grows, and becomes separated from the saccule by a deep constriction. In a human embryo of 22 mm. the form of the labyrinth corresponds to that of the adult.

Maculae and Cristae. The maculae and cristae develop earlier than the organ of Corti. On its medial side, where the acoustic ganglion is located, the epithelium of the wall of the otic vesicle develops a thickened area, the *macula communis,* which later divides into an upper and a lower epithelial pad. The first gives rise to the macula of the utricle and to the upper and lateral cristae. A small part of the second thickening forms the crista of the posterior ampulla; the rest of the second pad divides into the macula sacculi and the primordium of the organ of Corti, which gradually extends into the growing cochlea.

In the maculae and cristae of a human embryo of 15 mm. the plumper and darker neuro-epithelial cells and the more slender supporting cells can be distinguished. In an embryo of 18.5 mm. the hair cells have developed a small tuft of hairs.

The cupula and the otolithic membrane arise in the center of the respective epithelial surfaces, when the two cell types just begin to differentiate, while at their edge the maculae or cristae are still growing. The membrane and the cupula appear first as a thin homogeneous layer on the epithelial surface. Then, new layers of jelly-like substance are added; above the hair cells free spaces remain, into which the growing hairs expand. The otoconia first arise as tiny, granular precipitates. They are believed to be secreted by the epithelium as soluble calcium salts and to diffuse into the gelatinous layer; when they reach its surface they precipitate as crystals.

Histogenesis of the Organ of Corti. The differentiation of the organ of Corti proceeds gradually from the basal coil of the growing cochlea to its apex. The epithelium extends along the basal wall of the canal as a long ridge which divides longitudinally into a large, inner ridge and a small, outer one. In the former, connective tissue penetrates the epithelium and separates it into radial rows of flask-shaped cells embedded in connective tissue, while their cuticles form a mosaic pavement on the surface. This region develops into the limbus spiralis. In the outer part of this ridge, the tall epithelial cells gradually involute, leaving a squamous epithelium which lines the internal spiral sulcus.

The small, outer ridge, the primordium of the organ of Corti, at first consists of uniform cells. Then, flask-shaped, inner and outer hair cells appear among them. The remaining elements elaborate tonofibrils and differentiate into the supporting cells. On the surface their cuticles form a continuous membrane.

The surface of both epithelial ridges is covered from the beginning by a fibrillated, jelly-like substance, the future tectorial membrane.

The connections between the sensory areas of the labyrinth and the nerve fibers of the vestibular and cochlear ganglia are established in early stages. The free ends of the fibers find their way into the thickened epithelial patches and form the endings described earlier.

Histogenesis of the Perilymphatic Space. While the otic vesicle grows and differentiates, the mesenchyme surrounding the growing labyrinth develops into a layer of cartilage, which remains separated from the epithelium by a layer of mesenchyme. This later condenses into a fibrous layer and, with the epithelium, forms the wall of the membranous labyrinth. Between the wall and the cartilaginous capsule, the mesenchyme loosens and its meshes enlarge into the perilymphatic spaces, around the membranous labyrinth. These spaces are traversed by strands of connective tissue, which connect the cartilaginous capsule with the wall of the membranous labyrinth. The mesenchyme remains dense where the epithelium forms the sensory areas. The mesenchymal cells which remain on the surface of the trabeculae and of the labyrinthine wall and perichondrium become mesenchymal epithelium.

In tadpoles of the anura, if the otic vesicle is transplanted into another area, it becomes surrounded by cartilage arising from local mesenchyme.

The cochlea receives its perilymphatic spaces, the two scalae, through extension of the perilymphatic cisterna. In embryos of 43 mm. the scala tympani appears in the region of the cochlear fenestra and the scala vestibuli at the 50-mm. stage. They gradually grow and coil with the cochlear duct, remaining attached to its upper and lower walls. At the outer periphery of the cochlear duct, as well as at its inner edge, the wall of the duct remains connected with the cartilaginous capsule. Later, ossification occurs and gives rise to the modiolus and the osseous cochlea.

REFERENCES

Alexander, G., and Marburg, O.: Handbuch der Neurologie des Ohres. Vienna, Berlin, 1921–26.

Bast, T. H.: Development of the optic capsule. I. Resorption of the cartilage in the canal portion of the optic capsule in human fetuses and its relation to the growth of the semicircular canals. Arch. Otolaryngol., *16:*19, 1932.

Bast, T. H., and Anson, B. J.: The Temporal Bone and The Ear. Springfield, Ill., Charles C Thomas, 1949.

v. Békésy, G.: Current status of theories of hearing. Science, *123:*779, 1956.

Bowen, R. E.: The cupula of the membranous labyrinth. J. Comp. Neurol., *58:*517, 1933.

Carlström, D., Engström, H., and Hjorth, S.: Electron microscopic and x-ray diffraction studies of statoconia. The Laryngoscope, *63:*1052, 1953.

Engström, H., Sjöstrand, F. S., and Wersäll, J.: The Fine Structure of the Tone Receptors of the Guinea Pig Cochlea as Revealed by the Electron Microscope. Proc. 5th International Congr. Otorhinolaryngology, Amsterdam, 1953.

Engström, H., and Wersäll, J.: Structure of the organ of Corti. Acta Otolaryngol., *43:*1 and 323, 1953.

Fernandez, C.: The innervation of the cochlea (guinea pig). The Laryngoscope, *51:*1152, 1951.

Granit, R.: Receptors and Sensory Perception. New Haven, Yale Univ. Press, 1955.

Guild, S. R.: Correlation of differences in the density of innervation of the organ of Corti with differences in acuity of hearing. Acta Otolaryngol., *15:*269, 1931; Correlations of histologic observations and the acuity of hearing. Acta Otolaryngol., *17:*207, 1932.

Hamberger, C. A., and Hydén, H.: Cytochemical changes in the cochlear ganglion caused by acoustic stimulation and trauma. Acta Otolaryngol., Suppl. 61, 1945.

Held, H.: Die Cochlea der Säugetiere, etc. In Bethe *et al.,* Handb. d. Norm. u. Pathol. Physiol., (11/1), 1926.

Kolmer, W.: Gehörorgan, in v. Möllendorff's Handb. d. mikroskop. Anat., (3/1), 250, 1927.

Lorente de Nó, R.: Études sur l'anatomie et la physiologie du labyrinthe de l'oreille et du VIIIe nerf. Trabajos (Travaux) Invest. Biol. Madrid, *24:*53, 1926; Anatomy of the Eighth Nerve. The Laryngoscope, *43:*3, 1933.

Polyak, S.: Ueber den allgemeinen Bauplan des Gehörsystems, etc. Ztschr. f. d. g. Neurol. u. Ps., *110:1,* 1927.

Polyak, S., McHugh, G., and Judd, D. K., Jr.: The Human Ear in Anatomical Transparencies. New York, 1946.

Ramón y Cajal, S.: Histologie du système nerveux. Paris, 2 vols., 1909–11.

Rasmussen, G. L.: The olivary peduncle and other fibre projections of the superior olivary complex. J. Comp. Neurol., *84:*41, 1946.

Shambaugh, G. E.: Cytology of the Internal Ear, in Cowdry's Special Cytology, (2), 927, 1932.

Tello, J. F.: Le réticule des cellules ciliées du labyrinthe chez la souris et son indépendance des terminaisons nerveuses de la VIIIe paire. Trabajos (Travaux) Invest. Biol. Madrid, *27:*151, 1931–32.

Wersäll, J.: Studies on the structure and innervation of the sensory epithelium of the cristae ampullares in the guinea pig. Acta Otolaryngol., Suppl. 126, 1956.

Wislocki, G. B., and Ladman, A. J.: Selective and histochemical staining of the otolithic membranes, cupulae and tectorial membrane of the inner ear. J. Anat., *89:*3, 1955.

Index

Numbers in *italics* represent pages containing illustrations.

Page 601